PEARSON

INDIANA

Physical Science
Concepts in Action

INDIANA Customized Teacher's Edition

Built for Indiana

- **STANDARDS** Fully aligned to the Indiana's Academic Standards for Science
- **RESOURCES** Online and editable
- **FEATURES** IN Standardized Test Prep

Wysession
Frank
Yancopoulos

About the Authors

Michael Wysession

Michael Wysession received his Ph.D. in geophysics from Northwestern University in 1991. He is an Associate Professor in Earth and Planetary Sciences at Washington University in St. Louis, Missouri. His area of specialization is using seismic waves to explore Earth's interior. Dr. Wysession is an author on more than 50 scientific publications. For his research, he was awarded a Packard Foundation Fellowship, and in 1996 was awarded a Presidential Faculty Fellowship at the White House. He also has created educational simulations to accurately show how seismic waves propagate. He currently chairs the Education & Outreach program for the Incorporated Research Institutions for Seismology (IRIS).

David Frank

David Frank completed his Ph.D. at Purdue University. For the last ten years he has been the head of the Physical Sciences Department at Ferris State University in Big Rapids, Michigan. He has taught general chemistry courses for science majors and for allied health students. With the assistance of his colleagues, he helped develop a new B.A. program in biochemistry. He has taught students in the university's Math/Science/Technology program, which enrolls gifted high school students. Recently he has worked with Michigan's "Connecting With the Learner" group, which produced a toolkit to help elementary and secondary teachers address diversity issues in the classroom.

Sophia Yancopoulos

Sophia Yancopoulos received her Ph.D. in physics from Columbia University. She has done post-doctoral research in astronomy at Yale University and in biophysics at the Mount Sinai School of Medicine. She has taught at Barnard College, Vassar College, the Stevens Institute of Technology, and Columbia University, as well as at Bronx High School of Science. She has worked on a neutrino oscillations experiment at Fermi National Laboratory, conducted experiments on acoustic modeling, and analyzed data on the extreme astrophysics of neutron stars. Currently she does research in genome evolution and works with a team of scientists at the Feinstein Institute for Medical Research trying to find a cure for a form of leukemia.

Cover, Front and Back, Bkgrnd: Tom Sanders, Aerial Focus Front Cover Insets, Left to Right: Barry Winiker, Superstock Inc.; Alexey Stiop/Shutterstock; Carroteater/Shutterstock; Jello5700/iStockphoto Back Cover Insets, Left to Right: Superstock RF/Superstock; Ablestock/GettyImages/Thinkstock; Superstock RF/Superstock; The Round Barn Theater at Amish Acres, Indiana.

Additional credits appear on page 715, which constitutes an extension of this copyright page.

ISBN-13:   978-0-13-316617-0
ISBN-10:   0-13-316617-1

1 2 3 4 5 6 7 8 9 10 V063 14 13 12 11 10

Contents in Brief

Teacher's Edition

Student Edition

Integrated Chemistry and Physics Course Overview

The overview lists Indiana's Academic Standards for Science. Use this chart to see the coverage of Indiana's Integrated Chemistry and Physics curriculum in this book. With the help of this chart, you can find solid, fully developed instruction on any standard.

SUBJECT AREA: Integrated Chemistry and Physics

The Nature of Science

Students should understand that scientific knowledge is gained from observation of natural phenomena and experimentation, by designing and conducting investigations guided by theory, and by evaluating and communicating the results of those investigations according to accepted procedures. Thus, scientific knowledge is scientists' best explanations for the data from many investigations. Further, ideas about objects in the microscopic world that we cannot directly sense are often understood in terms of concepts developed to understand objects in the macroscopic world that we can see and touch. In the science classroom student work should align with this process of science and should be guided by the following principles. These should be woven throughout the daily work that students are doing when learning the content presented in the standard indicators.

Standard	Where You'll Find It
Develop explanations based on reproducible data and observations gathered during laboratory investigations.	All labs in Student Edition
Recognize that their explanations must be based both on their data and other known information from investigations of others.	All labs in Student Edition
Clearly communicate their ideas and results of investigations verbally and in written form using tables, graphs, diagrams, and photographs.	Section: 1.4 Data Analysis: p. 24, 273, 463, All labs in Student Edition
Regularly evaluate the work of their peers and in turn have their work evaluated by their peers.	Section: 1.4
Apply standard techniques in laboratory investigations to measure physical quantities in appropriate units and convert known quantities to other units as necessary.	Section: 1.3 Quick Lab: p. 18, 79, 232, 330, 360, 424, 429, 450, 454, 476, 505, 571 Lab: p. 60–61, 92–93, 150–151, 383, 405, 438–439, 467, 525–526, 623
Use analogies and models (mathematical and physical) to simplify and represent systems that are difficult to understand or directly experience due to their size, time scale, or complexity, and recognize the limitations of analogies and models.	Sections: 1.2, 4.1, 4.2, 4.3 Science and History: p. 114–115 Quick Lab: p. 128, 173, 196, 265, 300, 304, 605, 614 Lab: p. 316–317
Focus on the development of explanatory models based on their observations during laboratory investigations.	Section: 1.1 Lab: p. 316–317
Explain that the body of scientific knowledge is organized into major theories, which are derived from and supported by the results of many experiments, and allow us to make testable predictions.	Sections: 1.2, 3.1, 4.3
Recognize that new scientific discoveries often lead to a re-evaluation of previously accepted scientific knowledge and of commonly held ideas.	Sections: 1.1, 1.2, 4.1, 4.2, 4.3, 18.1 Science and History: p. 114–115
Describe how scientific discoveries lead to the development of new technologies, and conversely how technological advances can lead to scientific discoveries through new experimental methods and equipment.	Sections: 1.1, 19.3 Concepts in Action: p. 106–107, 182–183, 253, 306–307, 522–523, 586–587, 640–641 Science and History: p. 178–179, 312–313
Explain how scientific knowledge can be used to guide decisions on environmental and social issues.	Issues in Science: p. 59, 281, 302, 513, 579, 608

Standard Code	Standard Descriptor	Where You'll Find It

Standard 1: Motion and Energy of Macroscopic Objects

Core Standard

Describe and explain the motion of macroscopic objects in terms of Newton's laws and use the concepts of kinetic and potential energy to describe motion.

ICP.1.1	Measure the motion of objects to understand the relationships between distance, velocity, and acceleration and deepen understanding through graphical analysis of the time dependence of acceleration, velocity and distance.	Sections: 11.1, 11.2, 11.3 Quick Lab: p. 330 Lab: p. 349
ICP.1.2	Describe and apply Newton's three laws of motion. By experimentation, determine the relationships among the variables in Newton's laws and how all three laws relate mass, acceleration and force as a triad of proportional variables, leading to the definitions of momentum and energy.	Sections: 11.3, 12.2, 12.3 Concepts in Action: p. 370–371 Lab: p. 383
ICP.1.3	Describe how Newton's law of universal gravitation, together with the laws of motion, explains the motions of objects on earth and of the moon, planets and stars.	Sections: 1.1, 12.1, 12.2, 12.4 Concepts in Action: p. 370–371
ICP.1.4	Describe the kinetic and potential energies of macroscopic objects, and use measurements to develop an understanding of these forms of energy.	Sections: 3.1, 15.1, 15.2 Concepts in Action: p. 460–461 Quick Lab: p. 450, 454 Lab: p. 467

Standard Code	Standard Descriptor	Where You'll Find It
Standard 2: Mechanical Energy and Propagation of Energy by Waves **Core Standard** Explain that waves transmit energy, come in two forms, transverse and longitudinal, and occur throughout nature.		
ICP.2.1	Identify properties of objects that vibrate, using Newton's laws to understand the motion. Understand that vibrating objects can give rise to mechanical waves.	Sections: 17.2, 17.4 How It Works: p. 520 Lab: p. 524–525
ICP.2.2	Identify properties of waves including frequency, wavelength, amplitude, energy, and wave speed.	Section: 17.2 Concepts in Action: p. 522–523 Quick Lab: p. 505 Math Skills: p. 506 Lab: p. 524–525
ICP.2.3	Describe how energy is propagated by waves without the transfer of mass using examples such as water waves, earthquakes, and sound waves.	Sections: 17.1, 17.2, 17.4 Concepts in Action: p. 522–533
ICP.2.4	Apply the properties of waves to wave phenomena including reflection, and refraction, as well as the transmission and loss of energy.	Sections: 17.2, 17.3, 18.3, 19.2, 19.3 Data Analysis: p. 575 Quick Lab: p. 585

Standard Code	Standard Descriptor	Where You'll Find It
Standard 3: Properties of Matter: Macroscopic as a Model for Microscopic		
Core Standard		
Understand how the energies and motions of atoms and molecules at the microscopic level can be used to understand and predict the macroscopic properties of matter of gases, liquids and solids.		
ICP.3.1	Describe how we use macroscopic properties of matter to model microscopic processes.	Sections: 3.1, 3.3, 4.1, 4.2, 4.3, 6.3, 7.5, 8.3, 8.4 Concepts in Action: p. 106–107 Lab: p. 184–185, 316–317
ICP.3.2	Study the characteristics of solids, liquids, and gases and their changes of state and interpret them in terms of a molecular model which describes their energies and motions.	Sections: 1.1, 1.3, 2.2, 3.1, 3.2, 3.3, 8.1, 8.2, 9.1, 9.2 Concepts in Action: p. 82–83 Quick Lab: p. 79, 90 Data Analysis: p. 273 Lab: p. 60–61, 92–93, 119
ICP.3.3	Understand how thermal energy (the microscopic motions of the atoms and/or molecules) is related to the macroscopic concept of temperature. Examine the differences in these concepts by measuring the temperature changes, and determining specific heat capacity, of water as it is heated or cooled.	Sections: 3.2, 3.3, 8.1, 8.2, 16.1, 16.3 Concepts in Action: p. 82–83, 484–485 Data Analysis: 273 Math Skills: p. 477 Lab: p. 493
ICP.3.4	Understand how the microscopic kinetic molecular theory, explains observations of macroscopic gas behavior in terms of temperature, volume, pressure, and the number of particles (using the mole concept).	Sections: 3.1, 3.2, 3.3 Concepts in Action: p. 82–83 Quick Lab: p. 79

Standard Code	Standard Descriptor	Where You'll Find It
Standard 4: Energy Transport **Core Standard** Describe how vibrations and waves transport energy.		
ICP.4.1	Using conservation of energy, calculate the thermal energy released or absorbed by an object and distinguish between exothermic and endothermic changes.	Section: 15.2 Math Skills: p. 458 Quick Lab: p. 454
ICP.4.2	Differentiate between conduction, convection, and radiation and identify them as types of energy transfer.	Section: 16.2 Quick Lab: p. 481
ICP.4.3	Explain that electrons can absorb energy and can release energy, and that electrons in atoms do this at specific energies.	Section: 4.3 Quick Lab: p. 117 Lab: p. 119
ICP.4.4	Describe the relationships between velocity, frequency, wavelength, and energy in electromagnetic waves. Describe the regions of the electromagnetic spectrum.	Sections: 18.1, 18.2, 18.2, 18.4 Math Skills: p. 535 Concepts in Action: p. 554–557
ICP.4.5	Understand that from diffraction we know that visible light is an electromagnetic wave.	

Standard Code	Standard Descriptor	Where You'll Find It
Standard 5: Chemical Energy, Reactions, and Bonding **Core Standard** Describe how energy is produced and absorbed in chemical reactions.		
ICP.5.1	Recognize and describe physical properties of matter and use these to differentiate between pure substances and mixtures.	Sections: 2.1, 2.2, 6.4 Concepts in Action: p. 52–53, 250–253 Quick Lab: p. 46
ICP.5.2	Use the periodic table to understand important patterns in properties of elements. Recognize that the pattern of properties of the elements correlates most closely with the configuration of the electrons in each element.	Sections: 5.1, 5.2, 5.3, 6.1, 6.2 Concepts in Action: p. 146–149 Data Analysis: p. 160 Quick Lab: p. 128, 135 Lab: p. 150–151
ICP.5.3	Understand that the atomic number is unique to each element and is the number of protons in the nucleus of the element.	Sections: 4.2, 5.2, 5.3, 6.1, 6.2
ICP.5.4	Use the concept of the mole to relate number of moles and the mass of a sample of a pure substance of known chemical composition.	Sections: 7.1, 7.2, 7.3 Quick Lab: p. 196
ICP.5.5	Using conservation principles write and balance chemical equations	Sections: 7.1, 7.2, 7.3, 8.3, 8.4, 9.1 Concepts in Action: p. 210–211 Math Skills: p. 195 Quick Lab: p. 203 Lab: p. 220–221
ICP.5.6	Identify key indicators of a chemical change and classify simple types of chemical reactions. Differentiate between covalent, ionic, hydrogen and Van der Waals bonding, and write formulas for and name compounds of each type.	Sections: 2.3, 6.1, 6.2, 6.3, 7.2, 7.3, 7.4, 7.5, 9.4 Concepts in Action: p. 210–211 Math Skills: p. 174 Quick Lab: p. 56, 203 Lab: p. 60–61, 220–221, 254–255, 285
ICP.5.7	Explain that in exothermic chemical reactions chemical energy is converted into other forms such as thermal, electrical, light, and sound energy.	Sections: 7.3, 9.4, 15.1 Concepts in Action: p. 210–211

Standard 6: Electrical Energy Propagation and Magnetism
Core Standard

Describe how the movement and transfer of changed particles results in the transfer of electrical energy.

Standard Code	Standard Descriptor	Where You'll Find It
ICP.6.1	Explain that objects that carry a net charge will exert an electric force on other objects that may be attractive or repulsive.	Sections: 4.1, 20.1 Quick Lab: p. 102
ICP.6.2	Explain that when charge is transferred from one object to another, the amount lost by one object equals the amount gained by the other, consistent with the principal of conservation of charge.	Section: 20.1
ICP.6.3	Using the example of electrolysis and its application in batteries, explain the relationship between chemical reactions and electrical energy.	Section: 8.4 Quick Lab: p. 248
ICP.6.4	Define and describe the relationships between voltage, current, resistance and power in open and closed electrical circuits.	Sections: 20.2, 20.3 Math Skills: p. 611 Quick Lab: p. 612
ICP.6.5	Describe the differences in current flow in parallel and in series circuits.	Section: 20.3
ICP.6.6	Explain that some objects, called magnets, exert magnetic forces with no direct contact.	Sections: 12.4, 21.1, 21.2 Concepts in Action: p. 338–339, 640–641 Quick Lab: p. 632 Lab: p. 648–649
ICP.6.7	Using the examples of motors and generators, explain that electrical energy can be transformed into mechanical energy and vice versa.	Sections: 15.1, 21.2, 21.3

INDIANA

Standard Code	Standard Descriptor	Where You'll Find It
Standard 7: Nuclear Energy (fission/fusion)		
Core Standard		
Describe how the stability of nuclei in terms of the binding energies of their constituent protons and neutrons explains the energy production processes of fission and fusion.		
ICP.7.1	Demonstrate how historical models and experiments supported the development of our current understanding of the atom and its nucleus.	Sections: 4.1, 4.3 Science and History: p. 114–115
ICP.7.2	Differentiate between protons, neutrons, and electrons and determine the number of these subatomic particles in each atom.	Sections: 1.1, 4.2, 10.3 Quick Lab: p. 304
ICP.7.3	Understand that the stability of nuclei depends on the numbers of neutrons and protons.	Section: 10.4 Lab: p. 316–317
ICP.7.4	Understand that fission results from large, less stable nuclei decomposing to form smaller, more stable nuclei.	Sections: 10.4, 15.1 Lab: p. 316–317
ICP.7.5	Understand that fusion results from two smaller nuclei combining to form one larger nucleus.	Sections: 10.4, 15.1
ICP.7.6	Understand that the energy radiated from the sun derives from the fusion process.	Section: 10.4
ICP.7.7	Describe the various forms of emission that are typical of radioactive decay.	Sections: 10.1, 10.2, 10.4 Concepts in Action: p. 306–307 Math Skills: p. 295
ICP.7.8	Relate the fission process to the human development and use of the fission process in war (uncontrolled) and in peace (controlled).	Section: 10.4 Science and History: p. 312–313 How It Works: p. 314

Standard Code	Standard Descriptor	Where You'll Find It
Standard 8: Society (Energy production, environment, economics) **Core Standard** Understand the impact of energy production and use on society and the environment.		
ICP.8.1	Describe how energy needs have changed throughout history and how energy needs are met in modern society.	Sections: 15.3, 21.3 Data Analysis: p. 463 How It Works: p. 465
ICP.8.2	Describe the benefits and risks of the development of non-renewable forms of energy such as coal, oil, natural gas and uranium fission sources.	Sections: 9.1, 9.3, 15.3 Concepts in Action: p. 270–271 Issues in Science: p. 281
ICP.8.3	Describe the benefits and risks of the development of renewable forms of energy such as solar energy, wind-energy, geothermal energy, fusion energy and biofuels.	Section: 15.3 Concepts in Action: p. 484–485 How It Works: p. 488
ICP.8.4	Describe how efficient use of renewable and non-renewable energy sources is essential to maintaining an acceptable environment.	Sections: 9.1, 15.3, 16.3 Concepts in Action: p. 270–271, 484–485 Issues in Science: p. 281 How It Works: p. 488
ICP.8.5	Describe how the availability of energy resources is essential to the development of an economically viable society.	Section: 15.3
ICP.8.6	Contrast the dependence on and use of energy and other natural resources in the economies of industrial nations, of developing nations and of undeveloped nations.	Sections: 15.3, 21.3
ICP.8.7	Describe the energy needs of a modern urban city, and compare and contrast these needs with those of a modern rural community.	Sections: 15.3, 21.3

Section-by-Section Correlation and Pacing Guide

This chart for *Pearson Physical Science* helps you plan your instruction time. Each chapter includes a suggested time range. The specific Indiana standards covered in each section are also provided. The Fast Track column indicates those sections and labs required to provide in-depth coverage. Those sections and labs providing supplementary information are indicated under Enrichments.

Chapters/Sections	Time	Indiana's Academic State Standards	Fast Track	Enrichments
Chapter 1 **Science Skills**	7 days			
1.1 Science Skills		ICP.3.2, ICP.7.2	■	
1.2 Using a Scientific Approach		ICP.1.3	■	
1.3 Measurement		ICP.3.2	■	
1.4 Presenting Scientific Data				▲
Chapter 2 **Properties of Matter**	6 days			
2.1 Classifying Matter		ICP.5.1	■	
2.2 Physical Properties		ICP.3.2, ICP.3.3, ICP.5.1	■	
2.3 Chemical Properties		ICP.3.2, ICP.5.6	■	
Chapter 3 **States of Matter**	6 days			
3.1 Solids, Liquids, and Gases		ICP.1.4, ICP.3.1, ICP.3.2, ICP.3.4	■	
3.2 The Gas Laws		ICP.3.2, ICP.3.3, ICP.3.4	■	
3.3 Phase Changes		ICP.3.1, ICP.3.2, ICP.3.3, ICP.3.4	■	
Chapter 4 **Atomic Structure**	6 days			
4.1 Studying Atoms		ICP.3.1, ICP.6.1, ICP.7.1	■	
4.2 The Structure of an Atom		ICP.3.1, ICP.5.3, ICP.7.2	■	
4.3 Modern Atomic Theory		ICP.3.1, ICP.3.2, ICP.4.3, ICP.7.1	■	

INDIANA

Chapters/Sections	Time	Indiana's Academic Standards for Science	Fast Track	Enrichments
Chapter 10 Nuclear Chemistry	**9 days**			
10.1 Radioactivity		ICP.7.7	■	
10.2 Rates of Nuclear Decay		ICP.7.7	■	
10.3 Artificial Transmutation		ICP.7.2, ICP.7.7		▲
10.4 Fission and Fusion		ICP.3.1, ICP.7.3, ICP.7.4, ICP.7.5, ICP.7.6, ICP.7.7, ICP.7.8	■	
Chapter 11 Motion	**6 days**			
11.1 Distance and Displacement		ICP.1.1	■	
11.2 Speed and Velocity		ICP.1.1, ICP.6.6	■	
11.3 Acceleration		ICP.1.1, ICP.1.2	■	
Chapter 12 Forces and Motion	**8 days**			
12.1 Forces		ICP.1.3	■	
12.2 Newton's First and Second Laws of Motion		ICP.1.2, ICP.1.3	■	
12.3 Newton's Third Law of Motion and Momentum		ICP.1.2	■	
12.4 Universal Forces		ICP.1.2, ICP.1.3, ICP.6.6	■	
Chapter 13 Forces in Fluids	**6 days**			
13.1 Fluid Pressure				▲
13.2 Forces and Pressure in Fluids				▲
13.3 Buoyancy				▲
Chapter 14 Work, Power, and Machines	**8 days**			
14.1 Work and Power				▲
14.2 Work and Machines				▲
14.3 Mechanical Advantage and Efficiency				▲
14.4 Gases: Simple Machines				
Chapter 15 Energy	**6 days**			
15.1 Energy and Its Forms		ICP.1.4, ICP.5.7, ICP.6.7, ICP.7.4, ICP.7.5	■	
15.2 Energy Conversion and Conservation		ICP.1.4, ICP.4.1	■	
15.3 Energy Resources		ICP.1.4, ICP.8.1, ICP.8.3, ICP.8.4, ICP.8.5, ICP.8.6, ICP.8.7	■	

Chapters/Sections	Time	Indiana's Academic Standards for Science	Fast Track	Enrichments
Chapter 16 **Thermal Energy and Heat**	**7 days**			
16.1 Thermal Energy and Matter		ICP.3.3	■	
16.2 Heat and Thermodynamics		ICP.3.3, ICP.4.2, ICP.8.3, ICP.8.4	■	
16.3 Using Heat		ICP.3.3, ICP.8.3, ICP.8.4	■	
Chapter 17 **Mechanical Waves and Sound**	**8 days**			
17.1 Mechanical Waves		ICP.2.3	■	
17.2 Properties of Mechanical Waves		ICP.2.1, ICP.2.2, ICP.2.3, ICP.2.4	■	
17.3 Behavior of Waves		ICP.2.4	■	
17.4 Sound and Hearing		ICP.2.1, ICP.2.2, ICP.2.3	■	
Chapter 18 **The Electromagnetic Spectrum and Light**	**9 days**			
18.1 Electromagnetic Waves		ICP.4.4	■	
18.2 The Electromagnetic Spectrum		ICP.4.4	■	
18.3 Behavior of Light		ICP.2.4, ICP.4.4	■	
18.4 Color		ICP.4.4		▲
18.5 Sources of Light				▲
Chapter 19 **Optics**	**8 days**			
19.1 Mirrors				▲
19.2 Lenses		ICP.2.4	■	
19.3 Optical Instruments		ICP.2.4	■	
19.4 The Eye and Vision				▲
Chapter 20 **Electricity**	**8 days**			
20.1 Electric Charge and Static Electricity		ICP.6.1, ICP.6.2	■	
20.2 Electric Current and Ohm's Law		ICP.6.4	■	
20.3 Electric Circuits		ICP.6.4, ICP.6.5	■	
20.4 Electronic Devices				▲
Chapter 21 **Magnetism**	**6 days**			
21.1 Magnets and Magnetic Fields		ICP.6.6	■	
21.2 Electromagnetism		ICP.6.6, ICP.6.7	■	
21.3 Electrical Energy Generation and Transmission		ICP.6.6, ICP.6.7, ICP.8.1, ICP.8.6, ICP.8.7	■	

Physical Science: Concepts in Action
Support Resources

- Indiana Student Edition
- Indiana ExamView® Test Bank and Assessment Suite CD-ROM
- Indiana StudentEXPRESS™ CD-ROM
- Interactive Textbook Online
- Indiana Teacher's Edition
- Success Tracker™ Online Assessment and Remediation
- Easy Planner
- Laboratory Manual
- Reading and Study Workbook, Levels A and B
- Reading and Study Workbook—Spanish
- Math Skills and Problem Solving Workbook
- Chapter and Unit Tests—English and Spanish
- Test Preparation Blackline Masters
- Test Taking Tips with Transparencies
- Transparencies
- PresentationEXPRESS™ CD-ROM
- Virtual Physical Science CD-ROM and Lab Record Sheets Workbook
- Probeware Laboratory Manual with CD-ROM
- Discovery Channel Video and DVD Field Trips
- Indiana TeacherEXPRESS™ CD-ROM
- PHSchool.com Web site

Give students the skills to succeed with strong reading support

■ Reading Focus

Introduce students to the Key Concepts, Vocabulary, and Reading Strategy in the lesson. A graphic organizer helps visual learners understand difficult-to-understand concepts.

■ Key Concepts

Clearly identified **before**, **during**, and **after** every section, Key Concepts encourage students to focus on the big ideas of science.

■ Reading Checkpoints

Reinforce students' understanding of the material just covered.

■ Section Assessments

Evaluate students' comprehension of material at the end of each section.

14.1 Work and Power

Reading Focus

Key Concepts
- Under what conditions will a force do work?
- How are work and power related?

Vocabulary
- work
- joule
- power
- watt
- horsepower

Reading Strategy
Using Visuals Before you read, preview Figures 1 to 3. Copy and complete the table below based on the work described in the caption for each figure.

WORK
- divided by time [ ]
- is less than Fd when [ ]
- is zero when [ ]

Planning a trip is hard work. First you need to make arrangements for where to stay during your visit. Next you need to buy your ticket and decide what to pack. Then you need to get to the airport or bus station. All this may seem like a lot of work. But scientists use the word work with a different meaning.

What Is Work?

Recall that a force can move an object or change the motion of an object that is already moving. **Work** is done on an object when a force moves the object. **For a force to do work on an object, the object must move and at least part of the force must act along the direction of motion.** Lifting a barbell, picking up a book from the floor, and tossing a newspaper onto a front porch are examples of work.

Work Requires Motion A force can do work by starting an object in motion or by changing the speed of a moving object. For example, when you lift a barbell as shown in Figure 1, you do work on the barbell to start it moving. Suppose the barbell is moving upwards ... in the same direction. Then the force you exert ... ork on the barbell to make it move even faster. ... o work by keeping an object in motion despite ... riction or gravity. On your trip, you might ride ... he airport. For the most part, you move at con- ... e upward force the elevator floor exerts on you ... e of gravity. Even though the force the elevator ... ot changing your motion, it does work because ... me direction as your motion.

What Is Power?

Have you ever heard the expression "Time is money?" Often people are not just concerned about getting work done; they want it done fast! And that requires power. The word power is used in many ways. People describe a storm, a country, or a concert as powerful. In baseball, power hitters hit a lot of home runs and power pitchers throw the ball at tremendous speed. But power, like work, has a very precise meaning in science.

Power is the rate of doing work. **key It** takes more power to do work at a faster rate. You can increase power by increasing the work done in a given time or by doing a given mount of work in less time. Suppose you visit relatives on your trip and decide to help out by mowing their lawn. Figure 3 shows a neighbor mowing a lawn of the same size, but with a mower that cuts a wider path through the grass. Both lawn mowers will do the same total amount of work to cut the grass, assuming they exert the same force to cut each blade of grass. But the wider mower can cut the grass in less time, so it does ... he same amount of work at a faster rate. The wider lawn mower is ... ore powerful.

Reading Checkpoint How do you calculate the work done on an ...

Section 8.4 Assessment

Reviewing Concepts
1. How is pH related to the strength of an acid?
2. What determines the degree to which an acid or base is weak or strong?
3. Are strong acids and bases good electrolytes? Explain why or why not.
4. Why is pure water neutral?
5. What does pH measure?

Critical Thinking
6. **Relating Cause and Effect** If you add another liter of water to 1 liter of a 1-molar solution of hydrochloric acid, what happens to the number of hydronium ions in solution? What happens to the concentration?

7. **Interpreting Diagrams** In the formulas on page 248, what does the symbol with the two arrows facing in opposite directions mean?
8. **Comparing and Contrasting** Would you expect oranges to work as well as lemons in making a battery? Explain your answer.

Writing in Science

Explain a Concept Write an analogy that will explain how a reaction reaches equilibrium at different points. (*Hint:* Think about various activities in your life where the balance changes.)

Solutions, Acids, and Bases **249**

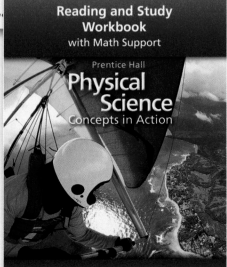

Reading and Study Workbook with Math Support

Prentice Hall

Physical Science
Concepts in Action

and with strong math support.

Math Skills

Sample Problem
You exert a vertical force of 200 newtons on a backpack to carry it upstairs, lifting the backpack a height of 3.0 meters. It takes you 10 seconds to do this work. How much power is used to lift the backpack?

1 Read and Understand
What information are you given?

Time $(t) = 10$ s
Force $(F) = 200$ N
Distance $(d) = 3.0$ m

2 Plan and Solve
What unknown are you trying to calculate?

Power $(P) = ?$

What formula contains the given quantities and the unknown?

$$Power = \frac{F \times d}{t}$$

Replace each variable with its known value.

$$Power = \frac{200\ N \times 3.0\ m}{10\ s} = 6\ W$$

3 Look Back and Check
Is your answer reasonable?

The power calculated in the previous example for lifting books is comparable to the power calculated here.

Math Practice

1. Your family is moving to a new apartment. While lifting a box 1.5 meters straight up to put it on a truck, you exert an upward force of 200 N on the box. How much work do you do on the box?

2. You lift a book from the floor to a bookshelf 1 m above the ground. How much power is used if you use an upward force of 30 N and do the work in 2 seconds?

3. It takes you 150 W of power to roll a portable basketball hoop a distance of 10 meters. If you exert a force of 150 N in the same direction as the motion, how much time does it take you to do this work?

4. You apply a horizontal force of 10 N to keep a suitcase moving at a constant speed of 0.5 m/s on flat ground. How much power is used? (*HINT*: Speed = Distance/Time)

Math Skills/Math Practice
A three-step problem-solving method, with numerous opportunities for practice at point of use, encourages students to Read and Understand, Plan and Solve, and Look Back and Check.

■ Color-coded variables
Aid student navigation and help reinforce math comprehension.

Key Formulas and Equations
Set off in boxes, Key Formulas and Equations help students easily locate and remember the skills.

rack on top of their car. How can you decide which of you has done more work?

Work Formula

$$Work = Force \times Distance$$
$$or$$
$$W = Fd$$

To calculate the amount of work done, multiply the force acting in the direction of motion by the distance that the object moves.

Data Analysis
Students analyze real-world experimental data with graphs and draw conclusions from the information. Excellent practice for state and national tests.

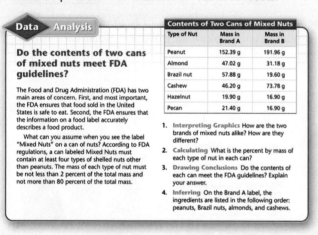

Data Analysis

Do the contents of two cans of mixed nuts meet FDA guidelines?

The Food and Drug Administration (FDA) has two main areas of concern. First, and most important, the FDA ensures that food sold in the United States is safe to eat. Second, the FDA ensures that the information on a food label accurately describes a food product.

What can you assume when you see the label "Mixed Nuts" on a can of nuts? According to FDA regulations, a can labeled Mixed Nuts must contain at least four types of shelled nuts other than peanuts. The mass of each type of nut must be not less than 2 percent of the total mass and not more than 80 percent of the total mass.

Contents of Two Cans of Mixed Nuts

Type of Nut	Mass in Brand A	Mass in Brand B
Peanut	152.39 g	191.96 g
Almond	47.02 g	31.18 g
Brazil nut	57.88 g	19.60 g
Cashew	46.20 g	73.78 g
Hazelnut	19.90 g	16.90 g
Pecan	21.40 g	16.90 g

1. **Interpreting Graphics** How are the two brands of mixed nuts alike? How are they different?

2. **Calculating** What is the percent by mass of each type of nut in each can?

3. **Drawing Conclusions** Do the contents of each can meet the FDA guidelines? Explain your answer.

4. **Inferring** On the Brand A label, the ingredients are listed in the following order: peanuts, Brazil nuts, almonds, and cashews.

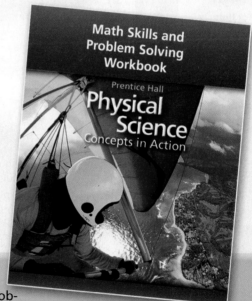

Math Skills and Problem Solving Workbook

Prentice Hall

Physical Science
Concepts in Action

Math Skills and Problem Solving Workbook
Section-based math instruction and math practice for mastering problem solving and key content.

Reading and Study Workbook, Levels A and B
Worksheets and summaries, organized around every section of the *Student Edition*, support students in mastering reading and math skills.

Reach all students
with real-world examples

We've proudly partnered with Dorling Kindersley to bring you Concepts in Action for the most vivid visual information available!

Concepts In Action

These features integrate vivid photographic illustrations with incisive text to support students in their exploration of science. The concepts can be reinforced with Discovery Channel Video Field Trips that correlate with the topics.

Research the development and use of the parachute and prepare a poster presentation of your findings. Be sure to include a development time line listing names and dates of significant contributions and advancements.

- Take a Discovery Channel Video Field Trip by watching "Air Forces."

Discovery Channel Video Field Trips

26 exciting segments support Concepts in Action topics with dramatic effect. Students will explore air pollution, solar cars, fiber optics, and more.

How It Works

From Dorling Kindersley, in-depth schematic illustrations of familiar objects—such as space suits, thermometers, and airbags—help students connect the science they learn with the science that surrounds them.

9 types of inquiry activities!

1. Inquiry Activity
2. Quick Lab
3. Exploration Lab
4. Design and Experiment Lab
5. Consumer Lab
6. Forensic Lab
7. Application Lab
8. Problem-Solving Activity
9. Data Analysis

Consumer Lab

Selecting Mirrors

In this lab, you will compare several mirrors and select the type that is best for a specific use.

Problem What mirror shape is best for magnifying images? For providing a wide view?

Materials
plane, convex, and concave mirrors;
2 metric rulers; roll of string; protractor

Skills Observing, Measuring, Comparing

Procedure

Part A: Comparing Magnification

1. Construct a data table with three rows and four columns. Label the columns Mirror, Size of Image, Magnification, and Field of View. In the column labeled Mirror, label the three rows Plane, Concave, and Convex.

Part B: Comparing Fields of View

7. Tie a string to a ruler. Hold the protractor, mirror, and free end of the string. Have a classmate hold the ruler vertically off to one side of the mirror. Position a third classmate (the observer) directly in front of and about 2 meters away from the mirror as shown.

8. Have the student holding the ruler slowly move toward the observer while keeping the string tight. The observer should look directly

Labs and Activities

Address all learning abilities. These easy-to-manage labs reinforce process skills and offer hands-on exploration of relevant and motivating topics.

and with point-of-use assessment.

Chapter Assessment and Standardized Test Prep

Check student assessment every step of the way—vital practice for test-taking success.

On the Web and CD-ROM

Program Assessment Resources

- *Indiana ExamView® Test Bank and Assessment Suite*
  - —Create and print tests in minutes from a bank of more than 2000 questions.
  - —More than 200 dynamic questions that allow you to generate new values in a question with a click of the mouse.
- *Chapter and Unit Tests—English and Spanish*
  - —Two tests for each chapter:
    Test A for average students
    Test B for basic students
  - —Two Unit Tests for each unit
- *Test Preparation Blackline Masters*
  You can evaluate student knowledge and provide test-taking practice.
- *Test Preparation Workbook*
  Students practice taking tests to improve their scores on standardized tests.

PRENTICE HALL
StudentEXPRESS™
Learn · Study · Succeed

StudentEXPRESS with Interactive Textbook provides homework, interactive assessments, and built-in activities tied to the Student Edition. Students monitor their progress at point of use with ongoing assessment, helpful hints, and instant feedback. They'll know immediately if they're on track!

Reading Comprehension: What Research Suggests

Dr. Nancy Romance • Indiana Atlantic

Q: Why are science texts often difficult for students to read and comprehend?

A: In general, science texts present complex literacy and knowledge demands on learners. They have a more technical vocabulary and a more demanding syntax and place a greater emphasis on inferential reasoning. When considering these attributes in conjunction with recent findings about students' lack of prior content knowledge and literacy skills, it becomes increasingly important for science teachers to adopt new ways of helping students interact with science texts.

Q: What does research say about how comprehension is facilitated?

A: Modern understanding of comprehension emphasizes the importance of in-depth prior knowledge and how that knowledge is organized. Studies comparing novices and experts show that the conceptual organization of experts' knowledge is very different from that of novices. For example, experts emphasize core concepts when organizing knowledge while novices focus on superficial details. To facilitate comprehension, effective teaching strategies should support and scaffold students as they build an understanding of the key concepts and concept relationships within a text unit.

Q: What strategies can teachers use to facilitate comprehension?

A: Three complementary strategies are very important in facilitating student comprehension of science texts. First, guide student interaction with the text using the built-in strategies. Second, organize the curriculum in terms of core concepts (e.g., Key Concepts in each section). Third, develop visual representations of the relationships among the key concepts and vocabulary that can be referred to during instruction. Teachers can also guide students' own construction of concept maps using these steps:

1. Select a portion of text that is the current focus of instruction.

2. Ensure students are able to read the passage fluently—present difficult vocabulary words before reading the passage.

3. Highlight text features that guide students' thinking about the concepts presented.

Dr. Nancy Romance

Dr. Nancy Romance has been a Professor of Science Education for 13 years at Florida Atlantic University. She was formerly Science Curriculum Supervisor for Broward County. She was a science classroom teacher for 12 years.

4. Guide development of a visual representation of the concept relationships.

   a. Have students identify core concepts emphasized in the passage. Write each concept on a sticky note and attach these randomly on chart paper or the chalkboard.

   b. Guide students to organize the sticky notes in a hierarchical structure, linking concepts to indicate relationships. Label the links.

5. Reread the text passage, referring to the draft concept map. Revise the map as needed.

6. Display the map for later review or expansion and have students keep a copy for study and review outside class.

7. Assign additional reading materials related to the passage and have students revise their concept map as they read.

More teaching strategies to Build Reading Literacy can be found throughout the *Teachers Edition* in the Before You Teach pages before each chapter and in the teaching suggestions for each section. These detailed examples give science teachers reading expertise.

Q: How does *Physical Science: Concepts in Action* facilitate comprehension?

A: The concept of a "considerate" text—one that provides instructional support for comprehension—has been built into the *Student Edition* through the careful design of text features.

- **Real-world applications:** An emphasis on real-world applications of the key concepts activates prior knowledge and gives students a framework for understanding new information.

- **Overall text organization:** Text structured in an outline format and key concepts highlighted in boldface type enable students to see the relationships between the big ideas and supporting details.

- **Consistent section structure:** Each section identifies Key Concepts, Critical Vocabulary, and a Reading Skill with a sample graphic organizer to help students create visual representations.

- **Frequent self-assessment:** Relevant photos and carefully constructed graphics include questions to help students recognize the thinking processes being used in learning. The Reading Checkpoints and Section Assessments let students track their comprehension.

Each of these instructional features provides a strong literacy framework for science teachers as it guides student interaction with the text. Each, in turn, also serves as a scaffold for students as they become more independent learners.

Internet Resources: Valuable Tools for High Schools

Cathy Dickerson • Humbolt County Office of Education

Connecting to the Information Superhighway

The challenge presented to education in the 1990s was to connect all classrooms to the "Information Superhighway" by the new millennium. By 2001 nearly 90% of all middle and high school classrooms in the U.S. had computers connected to the Internet, and more than 50% of students reported accessing Internet resources primarily from school. Today those percentages approach 100%, as more than 1.5 million pages are added, daily, to the World Wide Web. Our new challenge is to focus on using these vast information resources to enhance educational experiences for our students.

Over the past five years, real-time access to data collections from current scientific research has grown, free and low-cost virtual science explorations have been posted online for direct observation of scientific phenomena, and access to scientists for descriptions or clarifications of conceptual understandings has increased. Teachers who make wise use of Web resources can extend the breadth and depth of classroom learning and prepare students for academic and technical futures.

Using Web Resources

While there is a wealth of information on the Internet, scaffolding Web experiences for students can reduce the chances for misdirection and wasted time and increase the educational value of the activity. Successful scaffolding strategies used by teachers include

- Pointing students to educational Web sites or portals rather than general search engines as starting points

- Providing links to pre-selected Web resources for assignments or embedding pre-selected links in student assignments

- Selecting or designing projects and research questions that require synthesis and analysis of gathered information

Cathy Dickerson

Cathy Dickerson is currently a curriculum specialist for technology with the Humboldt County Office of Education. Cathy has been in education for 20 years, most of that time teaching science in elementary and secondary classrooms. A native of Arcata, California, she directed the SCORE Science Web site project for the California Department of Education, was recognized with a Humboldt County "Excellence in Teaching" award, served as County program manager for math and science professional development, and has presented at conferences for technology, science, and mathematics. Cathy received a master's degree in Computing and Technology for Education from Humboldt State University in 2001, a Multiple Subjects Teaching Credential from Humboldt State University in 1982, and a Bachelor of Arts degree from Stanford University in 1980.

Central to use of Internet resources in standards-based education is the need for critical evaluation of information sources. Because the Web is an open-publishing, unmoderated medium, students often find misleading and sometimes blatantly false information. Both teachers and students must be able to critically evaluate sources of information so that learners focus on materials that develop conceptual understanding rather than misleading material. To this end learners must be able to discriminate between valid, reputable sources, and those that are not.

Go Online with *Physical Science: Concepts in Action*

According to research, the most significant variable in determining the educational impact of technology-based resources is the teacher. Go Online features, in every chapter of *Physical Science: Concepts in Action*, take the guesswork and planning time out of developing meaningful Internet experiences.

Through SciLinks, the National Science Teacher's Association's topic-based Web resource service, students can access Web resources that have been reviewed by science teachers for their grade-level appropriateness and relationship to the topics under study. In addition, students can download a blackline master that guides them through a process of reviewing the Web resources and identifying the source of the information. Teachers can download background information about the specific Web resources available to use in assessing student responses.

1-800-848-9500 PHSchool.com

Other online activities at PHSchool.com include chapter labs in which students can share their data with others around the country and utilize a national data pool for making inferences and drawing conclusions. Also, students can visit *Science News*® to access current information on science topics and Planet Diary for news of the latest events affecting the global environment. In addition, students can research careers as they begin to prepare for the workplace. All this supplements self-grading assessments to help students stay on track with content standards.

Go Online activities help students develop their ability to evaluate Web resources, access the latest information, and interact with students across the country. Take advantage of all the Internet has to offer—a multitude of opportunities for students to research, experience, contribute, and learn!

Inquiry Skills

Science Process Skills

The Pearson *High School Physical Science* program provides comprehensive practice and assessment of science skills, with an emphasis on the process skills necessary for inquiry. The chart lists the skills covered in the program and cites page numbers where each skill is covered.

	Labs and Activities	Caption and Assessment Questions
Observing	37, 60, 90, 117, 119, 125, 150, 157, 167, 184, 203, 214, 220, 227, 232, 248, 254, 285, 291, 316, 330, 349, 355, 360, 389, 405, 450, 476, 481, 499, 524, 525, 531, 563, 569, 585, 593, 606, 612, 629, 637, 648	56, 70, 74, 101, 130, 138, 159, 224, 278, 420, 451, 538, 552
Inferring	18, 24, 42, 56, 60, 67, 71, 79, 90, 99, 102, 160, 191, 214, 227, 232, 233, 243, 317, 330, 349, 401, 433, 445, 476, 481, 493, 524, 525, 531, 542, 569, 599, 629, 632, 649	8, 17, 44, 51, 58, 64, 96, 103, 117, 122, 129, 143, 154, 168, 169, 196, 207, 209, 219, 224, 239, 241, 244, 258, 272, 274, 276, 280, 284, 296, 297, 301, 304, 305, 315, 320, 331, 336, 348, 361, 377, 382, 386, 391, 393, 397, 404, 417, 420, 421, 455, 459, 466, 470, 475, 490, 496, 505, 516, 528, 534, 544, 566, 573, 575, 580, 585, 592, 596, 603, 626, 636, 639, 652
Predicting	60, 61, 99, 119, 128, 157, 167, 185, 221, 248, 255, 265, 278, 327, 365, 380, 392, 411, 424, 463, 481, 542, 544, 599, 623, 632, 648, 649	44, 57, 81, 102, 122, 129, 140, 154, 164, 181, 188, 205, 224, 234, 263, 288, 297, 301, 305, 352, 362, 368, 382, 397, 408, 416, 419, 449, 470, 478, 480, 492, 496, 507, 536, 545, 549, 553, 566, 589, 596, 603, 630, 633, 639, 643, 646, 652
Measuring	26, 27, 92, 150, 254, 285, 349, 405, 438, 439, 467, 593	
Calculating	26, 42, 71, 150, 151, 196, 221, 317, 349, 377, 392, 405, 424, 429, 433, 438, 439, 454, 491, 493, 505, 542, 575, 623	18, 20, 30, 96, 109, 122, 175, 188, 198, 209, 224, 235, 239, 258, 299, 301, 320, 352, 357, 369, 376, 386, 408, 435, 442, 470, 478, 496, 528, 566, 626, 647, 652
Classifying	128, 135, 151, 203, 232, 243, 278, 445, 467	3, 6, 11, 58, 68, 96, 122, 154, 171, 177, 188, 205, 224, 237, 265, 269, 274, 280, 288, 320, 442, 487, 545
Using Tables and Graphs	24, 26, 27, 71, 92, 93, 119, 150, 160, 273, 285, 300, 349, 377, 429, 433, 454, 463, 467, 491, 623, 648, 649	23, 25, 30, 64, 85, 96, 112, 127, 134, 172, 173, 208, 215, 258, 288, 334, 352, 386, 392, 470, 496, 543, 575

Science Process Skills (continued)

	Labs and Activities	Caption and Assessment Questions
Using Models	173, 265, 291, 300, 304, 316, 317, 544, 606, 612	11, 30, 96, 166, 169, 188, 193, 219, 224, 231, 308, 382, 408, 442, 528, 538, 596
Posing Questions	1, 629	64, 118, 496
Designing Experiments	1, 99, 167, 220, 221, 493	7, 11, 30, 51, 64, 154, 224, 258, 288, 337, 352, 386, 408, 470, 507, 596, 626, 633
Formulating Hypotheses	79, 90, 117, 119, 157, 167, 220, 261, 273, 327, 355, 360, 389, 411, 499, 502	30, 122, 138, 284, 478, 496, 528, 549, 558, 562, 603, 643
Forming Operational Definitions	135, 405	288, 528
Controlling Variables	27, 473, 524, 525	78, 122, 496
Analyzing Data	18, 61, 90, 93, 196, 221, 254, 285, 300, 317, 383, 405, 429, 439, 463, 525, 563, 571, 632, 649	39, 47, 64, 143, 154, 288, 352, 470, 476, 515, 613
Drawing Conclusions	42, 61, 71, 79, 93, 102, 117, 119, 125, 151, 184, 185, 221, 227, 243, 255, 278, 285, 317, 360, 380, 401, 405, 424, 439, 445, 450, 454, 467, 493, 505, 524, 531, 542, 559, 563, 571, 593, 623, 637	55, 64, 81, 91, 96, 105, 154, 164, 181, 224, 284, 288, 392, 601, 622, 647
Communicating Results	1	386
Evaluating and Revising	46, 56, 61, 99, 285, 317, 330, 360, 389, 491, 493, 649	6, 215, 320

Inquiry Skills

Inquiry Skills (continued)

	Critical Thinking Skills	
	Labs and Activities	**Caption and Assessment Questions**
Comparing and Contrasting	18, 27, 37, 42, 46, 67, 93, 119, 128, 135, 151, 160, 173, 185, 214, 255, 411, 424, 473, 493, 502, 544, 559, 599	6, 25, 43, 58, 64, 69, 81, 96, 105, 112, 116, 118, 122, 129, 131, 138, 145, 188, 203, 224, 234, 241, 247, 249, 258, 288, 293, 310, 348, 352, 362, 373, 386, 390, 396, 408, 414, 416, 418, 442, 464, 466, 496, 501, 503, 512, 521, 545, 562, 566, 577, 578, 584, 592, 596, 622, 626, 639, 647, 652
Applying Concepts	46, 90, 185, 191, 203, 227, 304, 317, 365, 377, 383, 401, 433, 439, 450, 563, 575, 593, 623, 634	14, 20, 50, 51, 64, 74, 81, 86, 89, 91, 96, 110, 112, 122, 138, 144, 154, 169, 175, 181, 188, 194, 198, 213, 215, 224, 245, 258, 269, 274, 288, 320, 328, 337, 344, 348, 352, 362, 369, 377, 379, 386, 393, 397, 404, 408, 412, 416, 420, 426, 430, 435, 442, 447, 452, 454, 456, 457, 459, 463, 466, 470, 478, 483, 492, 496, 503, 507, 512, 521, 528, 538, 548, 549, 553, 562, 566, 573, 578, 585, 592, 596, 605, 607, 613, 619, 621, 622, 626, 637, 639, 647, 652
Interpreting Diagrams/ Photographs	21, 49, 87, 111, 137, 163, 201, 277, 314, 335, 366, 402, 434, 465, 488, 520, 560, 591, 620	4, 11, 41, 44, 77, 85, 122, 161, 169, 200, 204, 217, 258, 268, 294, 311, 358, 432, 491, 492, 503, 512, 528, 533, 540, 553, 566, 571, 572, 596, 604, 610, 631, 647
Making Judgments		6, 30, 118, 258, 288, 320, 331, 369, 386, 470, 496, 592, 626
Problem Solving		30, 154, 239, 331, 352, 566, 607, 613, 652
Using Analogies	125	73, 74, 105, 122, 154, 162, 197, 245, 275, 280, 331, 496, 622
Relating Cause and Effect	71, 160, 273, 473, 585	64, 72, 96, 105, 122, 154, 188, 249, 288, 386, 397, 431, 442, 483, 489, 509, 528, 548, 566, 603, 626, 633, 639, 647
Making Generalizations	128, 160, 261, 499	48, 96, 145, 154, 164, 188, 224, 264, 320, 426, 435, 442, 503, 511, 514, 528

Graphic Organizers

	Pages
Concept Maps and Web Diagrams	2, 7, 38, 62, 75, 94, 152, 158, 176, 186, 199, 212, 222, 256, 275, 286, 298, 318, 342, 350, 372, 384, 406, 427, 440, 446, 494, 500, 514, 526, 564, 580, 594, 624, 630, 650
Compare-and-Contrast Tables	22, 378, 468, 532, 570
Venn Diagrams	68, 206, 228, 246, 308, 550
Flowcharts	84, 113, 453, 546, 558, 642
Cycle Diagrams	486
Outlines	216, 588
Tables	14, 22, 28, 45, 54, 100, 108 (KWL), 120, 126, 130, 139, 165, 170,192, 235, 240, 262, 272, 282, 292, 303, 328, 332, 356, 363, 390, 394, 400, 412, 417, 421, 462, 474, 479, 504, 508, 539, 574, 600, 604, 609, 618, 635

Reading Strategies

Using Prior Knowledge	7, 240, 390, 514, 580, 630
Previewing	2, 14, 130, 199, 235, 262, 292, 474, 500
Predicting	170, 328, 394, 604
Building Vocabulary	45, 212, 363, 421, 446, 479, 504, 574
Identifying the Main Idea	126, 275, 462, 508, 600, 635
Identifying Cause and Effect	75, 176, 453
Comparing and Contrasting	22, 68, 206, 228, 246, 308, 378, 532, 570
Sequencing	113, 158, 486, 558, 642
Relating Text and Figures	54, 165, 356, 412, 609
Summarizing	38, 84, 100, 282, 342, 372, 400, 417, 427, 539, 618
Outlining	216, 558
Monitoring Your Understanding	108, 139, 192, 272, 303, 332, 546

Materials List

Item	Quantity	Chapter
Alcohol, isopropyl (95%)	5 mL	8.1 QL, 9 IA
Alligator clips	5	20 Lab
Alum	20 grams	6 IA
Aluminum foil	1 sheet	1 Lab, 19.3 QL
Aluminum foil strips	1	20.3 QL
Aluminum strip	1	5.2 QL, 20.2 QL
Antacid tablet	1	7 IA
Apples, ripe	1	9.3 QL
Ascorbic acid solution	50 mL	7 Lab
Bags, paper	2	4 IA
Bags, plastic (resealable)	1	5.1 QL, 7 IA
Bag, large plastic	1	10.2 QL
Baking powder	1 g	2 Lab, 8.3 QL
Baking soda	25 g	2 Lab
Balance	1	1 Lab, 5 Lab, 7 IA, 7.1 QL, 16 Lab
Ball, blue plastic-foam	1	6 Lab
Ball, black plastic-foam	1	6 Lab
Balloons, long	4	12 Lab
Balloon, small, round	1	8 IA, 12.4 QL, 16.1 QL, 17 Lab
Basketball	1	15.1 QL
Battery, 6-volt	1	20.3 QL, 21.2 QL
Battery, 9-volt	1	20 Lab
Battery clip	1	20 Lab
Beads, green	5	10 IA
	32	10.3 QL
Beads, purple	7	10 IA
	32	10.3 QL
Beaker, 25-mL	2	8 Lab
Beaker, 100-mL	1	8 Lab, 16.2 QL
Beaker, 150-mL	1	7 Lab
Beaker, 250-mL	1	1.3 QL, 6.2 QL, 7.2 QL
Beaker, 500-mL	1	3 Lab
Beverage can, empty	1	3.2 QL
Beverage, carbonated (in plastic bottle with cap)	1	8 IA
Bicycle, multispeed	1 per class	14 Lab
Bingo chips	5	4 IA
Blueberries, frozen	$\frac{1}{4}$ cup	8.3 QL

Item	Quantity	Chapter
Board, 1 meter long	1	11 IA, 14 IA, 14.3 QL
Board with 2 nails	1	14 Lab
Board, short	1	14 IA
Bolt	1	7.1 QL
Books	6	14 IA, 14.3 QL
	2	21.1 QL
Boric acid solution	5 mL	4 Lab
Bottle, plastic 2 L	1	16.1 QL
Bottle, plastic with cap	1	13.3 QL
Bread	1 slice	9.3 QL
Bubble solution	1 bottle	12.4 QL
Bubble wand	1	12.4 QL
Bucket of hot water	1	8 IA
Bulb, fluorescent	1	18.5 QL
Bulb, clear incandescent	1	18.5 QL
Bunsen burner	1	4 Lab
Calcium chloride solution	5 mL	2.3 QL, 4 Lab
Calculator, solar	1	15 IA
Can	1	13 Lab
Cardboard box	1	15.2 QL
Cardboard sheet, small	1	18 IA
Cardboard tubes	2	17 Lab
	1	19.3 QL, 21 Lab
Carbon sample	1	2 IA
Chairs with backs	2	12 Lab
Chlorine bleach solution	1–10 drops	7 Lab
Clamp	1	15 Lab, 16 Lab
Clay, modeling	1 piece	13 IA, 15.2 QL
Coin	1	12.2 QL
Container, clear plastic	2	19 IA
Copper sample	1	2 IA
Copper strips	2	8.4 QL
	1	20.2 QL
Copper(II) chloride solution	5 drops	7.4 QL
Copper(II) sulfate solution	5 mL	2.3 QL, 4 Lab
	20 mL	7.2 QL
Cornstarch, solid	25 grams	2 Lab
Cornstarch, liquid	15 mL	9.3 QL
Cotton, balls	1	9 IA
Crime scene sample	1	2 Lab

Item	Quantity	Chapter
Cups, plastic	4	8.3 QL
Cups, plastic foam	2	2.3 QL, 8.3 QL
	1	16 IA, 16 Lab
Cups, plastic foam with lid	1	16 Lab
Dominoes	20	10 Lab
Dropper pipet	2	8.3 Q
	3	8 Lab
	1	9 Lab, 11 Lab, 13.3 QL, 16.2 QL, 17 IA
Dry ice	small piece	3.3 QL
Dropper bottles	3	2 Lab
Dye bath, methyl orange	1	6 Lab
Epsom salt	20 grams	6 IA
Eraser	2	12.1 QL
Evaporating dish	1	8 Lab
Filter paper, square	1	9 IA
Flashlight	1	15 IA, 17 Lab, 20 IA
Flask, Erlenmeyer 250-mL	1	3.3 QL
Food coloring	1	16.2 QL, 17.1 QL
Food coloring, different colors	2	9 IA
Forceps	1	5 Lab, 11 Lab
Glass slide	1	20.2 QL
Gloves, leather (thick)	1 pair	14 Lab
Graduated cylinder, 10-mL	3	2.3 QL
	1	5.2 QL, 8.1 QL, 8 Lab, 11 Lab
Graduated cylinder, 25-mL	1	7.4 QL, 9 Lab
Graduated cylinder, 50-mL	1	5 Lab, 7 Lab
Graduated cylinder, 100-mL	1	1.3 QL, 3.3 QL, 7 IA, 11 Lab
	2	16 IA
Graduated cylinder, 250-mL	1	13 Lab
Graduated cylinder, 500-mL	1	16 Lab
Grip exerciser, spring loaded	1	15 Lab
Gum drops, white	7	6 Lab
Hot plate	1	3.2 QL, 3 Lab, 3.2 QL, 6 Lab, 8 Lab, 16 Lab
Hydrochloric acid solution	3 mL	8 Lab
Hydrochloric acid solution, dilute	5 mL	4 Lab, 5.2 QL

Item	Quantity	Chapter
Ice, crushed	250 mL	3 Lab
Ice cubes	12	16.1 QL
Ice water	200 mL	16 Lab
Index card	1	12.2 QL
Iodine solution	1–2 drops	2 Lab
Iodine-starch solution	50 mL	7 Lab
Iodine solution in dropper bottle	1	9.3 QL
Iron filings, small container	1	21.1 QL
Iron nail	1	20.2 QL, 21.2 QL
Juice, apple	10 mL	9 Lab
Juice, lemon	10 mL	8.3 QL
Juice, orange	10 mL	9 Lab
Juice, pineapple	10 mL	9 Lab
Knife, plastic	1	8.4 QL
Labels	2	8 Lab
Laboratory cart	1	14 IA
Lauric acid, in test tube with thermometer	1	3 Lab
Light filters, blue, green, and red	1 each color	18 IA
Light sources, blue, green, and red	1 each	18 Lab
Lead shot	1	5 Lab
Lemon, fresh-large	1	8.4 QL
Limestone sample	1	9 IA
Nuts, threaded	2	12 Lab
Magnesium	1 strip	5.2 QL
Magnet, bar	2	21 IA, 21.1 QL
	1	21 Lab
Manganese dioxide	0.1 g	7.4QL
Marbles	1	11 IA
	2	11 Lab
	3	4 IA
Marble sample	1	9 IA
Marker, fluorescent (neon)	2	4.3 QL
Markers, felt-tip (water-based ink)	1	6 .2 QL, 18 IA
Marshmallows	30	9 IA
Mass, standard 100g	1	13 Lab
Mass, standard 500 g	1	14.4 QL

Materials List (continued)

Item	Quantity	Chapter
Mass, standard 1 kg	1	14.3 QL
Meter stick	1	12 Lab, 14.4 QL, 14 Lab, 15.1 QL, 15.2 QL, 17 IA, 17.1 QL, 17 Lab, 19.1 QL
Metal rod	1	2.2 QL
Methylene blue indicator	1	9 Lab
Mirror, small	1	17 Lab, 19.1 QL
Mirror, plane	1	19 Lab
Mirror, concave	1	19 Lab
Mirror, convex	1	19 Lab
Multimeter	1	8.4 QL, 20 Lab, 21 Lab
Newspaper	1	19.1 QL
Nichrome wire loop	1	4.1 QL
Nuts	2	7.1 QL
Oil, vegetable	50 mL	18 IA
Paint pigment	1	9 IA
Paint chip strips (red, green, and blue)	3	5.1 QL
Pan	1	3.2 QL
Paper clips, Small, metal	5 / 20	4 IA / 21.2 QL
Paper, graph	1 sheet	1 Lab, 3 Lab, 5 Lab, 9.2 QL, 11 IA, 11 Lab, 15.2 QL, 15 Lab, 21 Lab
Paper, construction-black	1 sheet	6 IA, 18.2 QL, 19.3 QL
Paper, stapled stack	6 sheets	5 IA, 7.2 QL
Paper strip	1	20.2 QL
Paper towels	1 sheet	6 Lab, 13 Lab, 16.2 QL
Paper, test (chromatography)	1 strip	6.2 QL
Paper, white unlined	1 sheet / 2 sheets / 3 sheets	5 Lab, 7 IA, 21.1 QL / 10.3 QL / 18 IA
Paper, white unlined	1 large sheet	18 Lab
Pebbles	5	4 IA
Pencils, colored	1 set	18.5 QL
Pencil, glass marking	1	2.3 QL, 7.4 QL
Pencil	1	14.4 QL

Item	Quantity	Chapter
Pennies	4 / 5	4 IA / 12 IA
Periodic table	1	5 Lab, 10.3 QL
Petri dish	1	6.2 QL
Petri dishes, plastic	2	18.2 QL
pH paper	1 strip	8 Lab
Phenolphthalein indicator solution	2–5 drops	8 Lab
Pin, straight	1	19.3 QL
Plastic bottle with cap (large)	1	1.3 QL
Plastic bottle with cap (medium)	1	1.3 QL
Plastic bottle with cap (small)	1	1.3 QL
Plastic bucket	1	16.1 QL
Plastic container, large	1	3 IA
Plastic container, clear and large	1	17 IA, 17.1 QL
Plastic foam balls	1	9 IA
Paper plates, small	6	9.3 QL
Plastic plate	1	9.3 QL, 20.2 QL
Plastic tub	1	13 Lab
Platinum wire	1	7.4 QL
Potassium chloride	1 g	8.1 QL
Potassium chloride solution	5 mL	4 Lab
Potato, raw	0.1 g / 1 slice	7.4 QL / 9.3 QL
Protractor	1	19 Lab
Raisins	70	9 IA
Resistor, 100 ohms	1	20 Lab
Resistor, 1000 ohms	1	20 Lab
Resistor, 1 ohm	2	20 Lab
Resistor, 10 ohm	2	20 Lab
Ring stand	1	16 Lab
Rocks, small	5–10	23 Lab
Rope, 3-m	1	17.2 QL
Rubber band	1 / 4	14 Lab, 17 Lab / 19.3 QL
Rubber sample	1	2 IA

Item	Quantity	Chapter
Ruler, metric (30cm)	1	1 IA, 1 Lab, 2.2 QL, 4.1 QL, 5 Lab, 6.2, 3.2 QL, 7 IA, 10 Lab, 11.1 QL, 11 Lab, 12.1 QL, 15 Lab
	2	19 Lab
Salt, non-iodized	1 teaspoon	4 IA
	20 grams	6 IA
Sodium chloride solution	5 mL	4 Lab
Scalpel	1	17 Lab
Scissors	1	1 IA, 1 Lab, 2.2 QL, 5 Lab, 6 Lab, 7 IA, 12.1 QL, 17 Lab
Shampoo, clear	100 mL	11 Lab
Shoes, 3 different kinds	3	14.3 QL
Silicon piece	1	5.2 QL, 5 Lab
Soap	1 bar	6 Lab
Sodium chloride solution	5 mL	2.3 QL
Sodium hydroxide solution	3 mL	8 Lab
Spatula	5	2 Lab
	4	6 IA
Spectroscope	1	18.5 QL
Sponge	1	13 Lab
Spoon, tea	1	8.3 QL
Spot plate	2	2 Lab
	1	7 Lab
Spring scale	1	13 Lab, 14 IA, 14.3 QL, 14.4 QL
Spring scale, high capacity	1	15 Lab
Stain, methylene blue	5 mL	9 IA
Stapler	1	6.2 QL, 6 Lab
Steel bolts	10	16 Lab
Steel sample	1	2 IA
Sticky note	1	12.1 QL
Stirring rod	1	1 IA, 3 Lab, 8.1 QL,
	3	8 Lab, 9 Lab, 16 IA
Stirring rod, glass—extra long	1	11 Lab
Straw, drinking	1	12 Lab
String	3 meters	12 Lab
	20 cm	13 Lab
	50 cm	16 Lab
	1 roll	19 Lab

Item	Quantity	Chapter
Sugar	15 mL	6 IA, 9 IA
Sulfur piece	1	5.2 QL
Sunscreen	1 bottle per class	18.2 QL
Suspect's shoe sample	1	2 Lab
Switch	1	21.2 QL
Syringe and plunger	1	3 IA
Tape, masking	2, 10 cm strips	3.2 QL, 11 Lab, 12 Lab, 14.4 QL, 14 Lab, 18 Lab, 19.1 QL, 21.1 QL
Tape, measuring	1	16.1 QL, 17.2 QL
Tape, transparent (10 cm strips)	2	4.1 QL
Tape, transparent	1	17 Lab
Tennis ball	1	15.1 QL
Test circuit (9-V battery & 6-V bulb)	1	20.2 QL
Test strips, fabric	2	6 Lab
Test tube (10-mL)	2	8 Lab
Test tubes	3	2.3 QL
	4	5.2 QL, 9 Lab
	5	7.4 QL
Test tube, large	2	8.1 QL
Test-tube rack	1	2.3 QL, 5.2 QL, 7.4 QL, 8 Lab, 9 Lab
Thermometer	1	3.3 QL, 3 Lab, 8.1 QL, 16 IA
	2	16 Lab
Thermometer (liquid crystal)	1	2.2 QL
Threaded spools, 3 with different diameters	4	14 Lab
Thumbtacks, unpainted	2	20.3 QL
Tin strip	1	5 Lab
Tongs	1	3.2 QL, 6 Lab, 7.2 QL
Toothpick	1 box per class	6 Lab, 13 IA
	30	9 IA
Toy, glow-in-dark	1	4.3 QL
Toy, wind-up	1	15 IA
Tubing, glass	2	19 IA
Twine, heavy	20 cm	15 Lab
Ultraviolet lamp	1	4.3 QL

Materials List (continued)

Item	Quantity	Chapter
Vinegar, white	10 mL	2 Lab, 8.3 QL
Wallpaper, 1-cm squares	100	10.2 QL
Washers	2	7.1 QL
Wash bottle of water (distilled)	1	2 Lab, 4 Lab
Watch, or clock with a second hand	1	2.2 QL, 3 Lab, 3.2 QL, 6 Lab, 10 Lab, 11 IA, 11 Lab, 12 Lab, 17.2 QL
Watch glass, large	1	8 Lab
Water bath, boiling water	1 per class	16 Lab
Water, distilled	25 mL	8.1 QL, 8 Lab
Water, hot	50 mL	2.2 QL
Wax paper, 10-cm squares	2	17 Lab, 19.3 QL

Item	Quantity	Chapter
Weight, fishing	1	13 Lab
Window cleaner	1–10 drops	8.3 QL
Wires with stripped ends	2	20.3 QL
Wire, insulated with stripped ends, 20-cm long	1	21.2 QL
Wire, insulated with stripped ends, 1-m long	1	21.2 QL
Wood block	1	13 Lab, 20.3 QL
Wood sample	1	2 IA
Wood splints	4 1	6 IA 7.4 QL, 20.2 QL
Zinc, solid piece	1	7.2 QL
Zinc strip	1	8.4 QL

PEARSON

Physical Science

Concepts in Action

INDIANA Customized Student Edition

Wysession
Frank
Yancopoulos

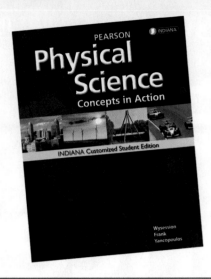

Pearson

Physical Science

Concepts in Action

Print Components
Indiana Student Edition
Indiana Teacher's Edition
Easy Planner
Laboratory Manual
Laboratory Manual, Teacher's Edition
Reading and Study Workbook, Levels A and B
Reading and Study Workbook, Levels A and B, Teacher's Editions
Chapter and Unit Tests
Transparencies
Test-Taking Tips With Transparencies
Test Preparation Blackline Masters
Math Skills and Problem Solving Workbook
Virtual Physical Science Lab Record Sheets Workbook

Technology
StudentEXPRESS CD-ROM
Indiana *ExamView*® Computer Test Bank CD-ROM
Indiana TeacherEXPRESS CD-ROM
Interactive Textbook Online
PresentationEXPRESS CD-ROM
Probeware Lab Manual With CD-ROM
Virtual Physical Science CD-ROM
Discovery Channel Field Trips Videotapes
Discovery Channel Video Field Trips DVD
Web site at PHSchool.com

Spanish Resources
Spanish Reading and Study Workbook
Spanish Chapter and Unit Tests
Spanish Section Summaries on Audio CD

Cover credits (inset photos only): **Front Left to Right:** Barry Winiker, Superstock Inc.; Alexey Stiop/Shutterstock; Carroteater/Shutterstock; Jello5700/iStockphoto; **Back Left to Right:** Superstock RF/Superstock; Ablestock/GettyImages/Thinkstock; Superstock RF/Superstock; The Round Barn Theater at Amish Acres, Indiana. Additional credits appear on page 715, which constitutes an extension of this copyright page.

ISBN-13: 978-0-13-316616-3
ISBN-10: 0-13-316616-3

1 2 3 4 5 6 7 8 9 10 V063 14 13 12 11 10

Michael Wysession

Michael Wysession received his Ph.D. in geophysics from Northwestern University in 1991. He is an Associate Professor in Earth and Planetary Sciences at Washington University in St. Louis, Missouri. His area of specialization is using seismic waves to explore Earth's interior. Dr. Wysession is an author on more than 50 scientific publications. For his research, he was awarded a Packard Foundation Fellowship, and in 1996 was awarded a Presidential Faculty Fellowship at the White House. He also has created educational simulations to accurately show how seismic waves propagate. He currently chairs the Education & Outreach program for the Incorporated Research Institutions for Seismology (IRIS).

David Frank

David Frank completed his Ph.D. at Purdue University. For the last ten years he has been the head of the Physical Sciences Department at Ferris State University in Big Rapids, Michigan. He has taught general chemistry courses for science majors and for allied health students. With the assistance of his colleagues, he helped develop a new B.A. program in biochemistry. He has taught students in the university's Math/Science/Technology program, which enrolls gifted high school students. Recently he has worked with Michigan's "Connecting With the Learner" group, which produced a toolkit to help elementary and secondary teachers address diversity issues in the classroom.

Sophia Yancopoulos

Sophia Yancopoulos received her Ph.D. in physics from Columbia University. She has done postdoctoral research in astronomy at Yale University and in biophysics at the Mount Sinai School of Medicine. She considers teaching to be a vital and exciting part of her experience, having taught at Barnard College, Vassar College, the Stevens Institute of Technology, and Columbia University, as well as at Bronx High School of Science. She has worked on a neutrino oscillations experiment at Fermi National Laboratory, conducted experiments on acoustic modeling, and analyzed data on the extreme astrophysics of neutron stars. Currently she does research in genome evolution and works with a team of scientists at the Feinstein Institute for Medical Research trying to find a cure for a form of leukemia.

Contributing Writers

Steve Miller
Science Writer
State College,
Pennsylvania

Polly Weissman
Science Writer
New York, New York

T. Griffith Jones
P.K. Yonge Developmental
  Research School
College of Education—
University of Florida
Gainesville, Florida

Contributing Writers for DK

Robert Dinwiddie
M.A. M.Sc.
Science Writer
London, England

Susan Watt
M.A. M.Sc.
Science Writer
London, England

Reading Consultant

Bonnie Armbruster, Ph.D.
Department of Curriculum
  and Instruction
University of Illinois
Champaign, Illinois

Laboratory Activity Writers

Robert W. Arts
Associate Professor of
  Physics
Pikeville College
Pikeville, Kentucky

Hasan Fakhrudin
Physics Instructor
Indiana Academy for
  Science, Mathematics,
  and Humanities
Muncie, Indiana

Yvonne Favaro
Science Teacher (retired)
Englewood Cliffs,
New Jersey

JoAnne Mowczko, Ed.D.
Science Writer
Gaithersburg, Maryland

Brian Rohrig
Science Teacher
Columbus Public Schools
Columbus, Ohio

Safety Consultant

Dr. Kenneth R. Roy
Director, Science and
  Safety
Glastonbury Public
  Schools
Glastonbury, Connecticut

Content Reviewers

Teacher Reviewers

Ann C. Andrex
James H. Blake High School
Silver Spring, Maryland

Javier Artinano
Austin Preparatory School
Reading, Massachusetts

Frederick C. Bantz
Reservoir High School
Fulton, Maryland

Dr. Louise Baxter
Bainbridge High School
Bainbridge Island,
Washington

Dale Beames
Coral Springs High School
Coral Springs, Florida

Alice C. Best
T. C. Roberson
   High School
Asheville, North Carolina

David R. Blakely
Arlington High School
Arlington, Massachusetts

Mark W. Breerwood
Cypress Springs
   High School
Cypress, Texas

Bernadine Hladik Cook
Johnstown High School
Johnstown, New York

Melissa Lynn Cook
Oakland Mills High School
Columbia, Maryland

Chris Cunningham
Capital High School
Olympia, Washington

Maryellen Duffy
Andover High School
Andover, Massachusetts

Brad Gammon
Coral Springs High School
Coral Springs, Florida

Roger Gaspar
Bishop Connolly
   High School
Fall River, Massachusetts

Paul A. Girard
Haverhill High School
Haverhill, Massachusetts

Eileen Gratkins
George N. Smith
   Junior High School
Mesa, Arizona

Roy G. Hammit
Mesa High School
Mesa, Arizona

Charles W. Kellogg, Ph.D.
Masconomet Regional
   School District
Topsfield, Massachusetts

David Kelso
Manchester High
   School Central
Manchester, New Hampshire

Jerome Leonard Kraut
Francis Lewis High School
Fresh Meadows, New York

Michelle S. Krug
Coral Springs High School
Coral Springs, Florida

Horace (Rog) Lucido
Roosevelt High School
Fresno, California

Deborah A. Maner
School for the Talented
   and Gifted
Dallas, Texas

Angie L. Matamoros, Ph.D.
ALM Consulting
Weston, Florida

Mark McCandless
The Galloway School
Atlanta, Georgia

Bruce A. Mellin
Brooks School
North Andover,
Massachusetts

Daniel R. Mullaney
Walpole High School
Walpole, Massachusetts

Noreen Paeth
Curie Metropolitan
   High School
Chicago, Illinois

Joel Palmer
Mesquite
   Independent
   School District
Mesquite, Texas

Joyce A. Reamy
Calvert Hall College
   High School
Baltimore, Maryland

Pam Rhoda
Owen High School
Black Mountain,
North Carolina

Mark Servis
DeWitt High School
DeWitt, Michigan

F. Lee Slick
Morgan Park High School
Chicago, Illinois

Deanna M. Swartzfager
Blake High School
Silver Spring, Maryland

Stephen Mark Tuccelli
Somerville Public Schools
Somerville, Massachusetts

Thomas Vaughn
Arlington High School
Arlington, Massachusetts

Renee Zimmerman
St. John's Preparatory
   School
Danvers, Massachusetts

Activity and Laboratory Field Testers

Nicholas Bernice
Northern Highlands
   Regional High School
Allendale, New Jersey

John Bingamon
Thurston High School
Redford, Michigan

Eva Brooksetta Davidson
Vance High School
Charlotte, North Carolina

Ashley P. Day
R S Central High School
Rutherfordton, North
   Carolina

Richelle Dull
ZB Vance High School
Charlotte, North Carolina

Carolyn C. Elliott
South Iredell High School
Statesville, North Carolina

Lisa Endicott
LaFollette High School
Madison, Wisconsin

Katherine M. Ewing
Sanderson High School
Raleigh, North Carolina

Lisa Freeman
Seymour High School
Seymour, Indiana

Mary Louise Freitas
Peoria High School
Peoria, Arizona

Susan J. Grabowski
Schurz High School
Chicago, Illinois

Herbert H. Gottlieb
Martin Van Buren
   High School (retired)
Queens Village, New York

Margaret A. Holzer
Chatham High School
Chatham, New Jersey

Brad Laatsch
Vance High School
Charlotte, North Carolina

Beth Meade Leavitt
Wade Hampton High School
Greenville, South Carolina

Ellen Loehman
Manzano High School
Albuquerque, New Mexico

Susan McCullen
Big Rapids High School
Big Rapids, Michigan

Amy McLaughlin
Pasadena High School
Pasadena, California

Al Pangburn
Pioneer School District
Yorkshire, New York

Richard Payne
Cobleskill–Richmondville
   Central School
Richmondville, New York

A. Marie Pool
Clinton High School
Clinton, Oklahoma

Alan Seidman
Margaretville Central School
Margaretville, New York

Tom Skaar
Ben L. Smith High School
Greensboro, North Carolina

Thomas L. Tokarski
Westchester Magnet Academy
Purchase, New York

James R. White
Southside High School
Chocowinity, North Carolina

John P. Wilbur
Caledonia-Mumford Schools
Caledonia, New York

 IN 5

Contents

Chemistry — 32

Skills and Reference Handbook   654

Labs and Activities

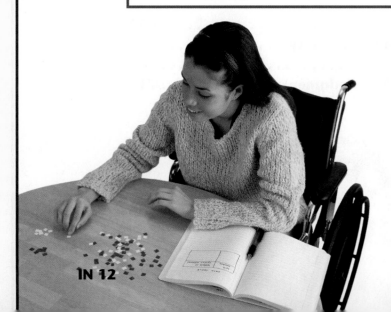

Inquiry Activity

Begin each chapter with an activity that sets a purpose for reading.

Introduce and reinforce key lesson content using simple materials.

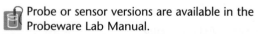 Probe or sensor versions are available in the Probeware Lab Manual.

Go Online — PHSchool.com   Share data with students from across the country at phschool.com

IN 14

Problem-Solving Activity

Apply science content in a new situation.

Math Skills

Develop math skills with sample problems and practice problems.

Data Analysis

Organize and analyze data to draw conclusions.

Features

CONCEPTS in Action

DISCOVERY CHANNEL SCHOOL

Explore science in depth with supporting Discovery Channel videos.

DK HOW It Works

Understand technology with exciting visual essays.

SCIENCE and History

Explore key developments in the history of science and technology.

issues in SCIENCE

Evaluate opposing viewpoints on current issues in science.

Careers in Science

Consider a variety of occupations that apply science.

active art

Interact with selected visuals online.

Planning Guide

SECTION OBJECTIVES	STANDARDS		ACTIVITIES and LABS
	NATIONAL	STATE	
1.1 What Is Science? pp. 2–6 🕐 1 block or 2 periods **1.1.1 Explain** how science and technology are related. **1.1.2 List** the major branches of natural science and **describe** how they overlap. **1.1.3 Describe** the main ideas of physical science.	A-1, A-2, B-1, B-2, B-4, B-5, D-4, E-2, G-1, G-2, G-3	ICP.3.2, ICP.7.2	**SE** Inquiry Activity: How Do Scientists Use Their Observations? p. 1 **L2** **TE** Teacher Demo: The Compass, p. 3 **L2**
1.2 Using a Scientific Approach, pp. 7–11 🕐 1 block or 2 periods **1.2.1 Describe** the steps in a scientific method. **1.2.2 Compare** and **contrast** facts, scientific theories, and scientific laws. **1.2.3 Explain** the importance of models in science. **1.2.4 Explain** the importance of safety in science.	A-1, A-2, E-2, F-1, G-2	ICP.1.3	**TE** Build Science Skills: Observing, p. 8 **L2** **TE** Teacher Demo: Flaps on an Airplane, p. 10 **L2**
1.3 Measurement, pp. 14–20 🕐 1 block or 2 periods **1.3.1 Perform** calculations involving scientific notation and conversion factors. **1.3.2 Identify** the metric and SI units used in science and **convert** between common metric prefixes. **1.3.3 Compare** and **contrast** accuracy and precision. **1.3.4 Relate** the Celsius, Kelvin, and Fahrenheit temperature scales.	A-1, A-2, G-2	ICP.3.2	**SE** Quick Lab: Comparing Precision, p. 18 **L2** **SE** Application Lab: Determining the Thickness of Aluminum Foil, pp. 26–27 **L2** **TE** Teacher Demo: Conversion Factor, p. 18 **L2** **LM** Investigation 1A: Evaluating Precision **L2** **LM** Investigation 1B: Measuring Volume and Temperature **L1**
1.4 Presenting Scientific Data, pp. 22–25 🕐 1 block or 2 periods **1.4.1 Organize** and **analyze** data using tables and graphs. **1.4.2 Identify** the relationship between a manipulated variable and a responding variable. **1.4.3 Explain** the importance of communicating data. **1.4.4 Discuss** the process of peer review.	A-1, A-2, E-2, G-1		

RESOURCES PRINT and TECHNOLOGY		SECTION ASSESSMENT
RSW Section 1.1 — L1		**SE** Section 1.1 Assessment, p. 6
T Chapter 1 Pretest — L2		**iT** Section 1.1
Section 1.1 — L2		
P Chapter 1 Pretest — L2		
Section 1.1 — L2		
sci_LINKS **GO** Motion — L2		
RSW Section 1.2 — L1		**SE** Section 1.2 Assessment, p. 11
DC Cracking the Case — L2		**iT** Section 1.2
T Section 1.2 — L2		
P Section 1.2 — L2		
SCIENCE NEWS **GO** Nature of science — L2		
RSW Section 1.3 — L1		**SE** Section 1.3 Assessment, p. 20
RSW Math Skill — L2		**iT** Section 1.3
MSPS Section 1.3 — L2		
T Section 1.3 — L2		
P Section 1.3 — L2		
PLANETDIARY **GO** Universal measurements — L2		
PHSchool.com **GO** Data sharing — L2		
RSW Section 1.4 — L1		**SE** Section 1.4 Assessment, p. 25
MSPS Section 1.4 — L2		**iT** Section 1.4
T Section 1.4 — L2		
P Section 1.4 — L2		
sci_LINKS **GO** Graphing — L2		

Go Online

Go online for these Internet resources.

PHSchool.com
Web Code: ccd-0010
Web Code: cca-0015

SCIENCE NEWS®
Web Code: cce-0011

NSTA SCI_LINKS
Web Code: ccn-0011
Web Code: ccn-0014

PLANETDIARY
Web Code: ccc-0013

Materials for Activities and Labs

Quantities for each group

STUDENT EDITION

Inquiry Activity, p. 1
25 mL of copper(II) chloride solution in a 50-mL beaker, scissors, metric ruler, aluminum foil, glass stirring rod

Quick Lab, p. 18
3 plastic bottles of different sizes, beaker, graduated cylinder

Application Lab, p. 26
metric ruler, aluminum foil, scissors, balance, graph paper

TEACHER'S EDITION

Teacher Demo, p. 3
compass, magnet, chalk

Build Science Skills, p. 8
low-wattage incandescent bulb, power source for the bulb

Teacher Demo, p. 10
sheet of paper

Build Science Skills, p. 12
modeling clay, at least 5 different toy cars with similar-sized tires that have different tread, cooking oil, magnifying glass

Teacher Demo, p. 18
1-lb object, 0.25-lb object, balance

Chapter Assessment

CHAPTER ASSESSMENT

SE	Chapter Assessment, pp. 29–30
CUT	Chapter 1 Test A, B
CTB	Chapter 1
iT	Chapter 1
PHSchool.com GO	Web Code: cca-0015

STANDARDIZED TEST PREP

SE	Chapter 1, p. 31
TP	Diagnose and Prescribe

Interactive Textbook with assessment at PHSchool.com

Before you teach

From the Author

Michael Wysession
Washington University

Big Ideas

The universe has rules. Science discovers these rules. Science is both a body of knowledge and a set of many different processes for revealing this knowledge. Science works by developing models of reality. Old models must continuously be unlearned to make way for new models. All students may eventually play a part in this exciting endeavor.

Space and Time The natural universe is big and old. Our universe is about 40 billion light-years in diameter (and most of it is not observable!), and is more than 13 billion years old. Our solar system (including Earth) is about 4.5 billion years old. So much is already known about our universe that its study is divided into many different branches of science. These divisions are artificial, however, as nature doesn't know physics from chemistry or biology. Much of science is interdisciplinary.

Forces and Motion Much of science involves the study of the application of forces to objects and the motions that result. Science uses standard techniques and units of measurement to study these forces and motions. Scientific observations always have limits to their accuracy and precision. Much of mathematics has been developed in order to interpret these observations.

Matter and Energy The energy of the universe was created in the initial moments of the big bang. Since then, energy has continuously converted between many different forms. Matter formed from energy during the early cooling of the universe, soon after the big bang. Common matter as we know it consists of less than 4% of the observable universe, but people are interested in it because people are made of matter.
In the current physical model, matter is made of discrete particles like quarks (and many other particles). Quarks combine to form protons and neutrons, which in turn combine with electrons to form atoms, which bond together to form the molecules of the matter of our world. This model may change, as it has many times in the past.

Science Refresher

What Is Science? 1.1

Science is a system of knowledge and methods for finding that knowledge. Technology is the application of scientific knowledge to solve a problem. A mutually beneficial relationship exists between science and technology: Technology may be developed to answer a scientific question, and science may be used to solve a technological problem.

Natural science is organized into three main branches (physical, chemistry, Earth science) that are subdivided into many overlapping areas. Approaching problems or questions from more than one direction can make them easier to understand or lead to new discoveries. It may also help scientists modify or invalidate theories. Scientific knowledge changes very rapidly, and scientists must keep up with the latest research because it can affect their own research.

Using a Scientific Approach 1.2

A scientific method is a plan for gathering information in order to solve a problem or better understand an event. Such methods allow scientists to document their procedures, observations, and findings and then share them with other scientists. As scientists share data and continue research, the body of scientific knowledge increases. Scientific theories are developed to explain observations. Scientists can also consolidate observations into scientific laws. Models can help scientists understand phenomena that are too difficult to observe directly. Models may be small-scale models or complex mathematical representations running on powerful supercomputers.

Measurement 1.3

Much of the data scientists collect can be distilled or aggregated into measurements—quantitative data. Scientific notation simplifies communication of and calculations with very large and small numbers. A standard system of measurements facilitates communication and replication of experimental results. A revised version of the metric system, the International System of Units (SI) is the standard used

Address Misconceptions

Students may think that the metric system is more accurate than the English system of units. However, accuracy and precision are related to measuring tools and methods, not the system of units. For a strategy to overcome this misconception, see **Address Misconceptions** on **page 16**.

Go Online

NSTA **PD** Links

For: Teaching methods for science skills
Visit: www.SciLinks.org/PDLinks
Web Code: ccn-0199

to make scientific measurements. SI is based on seven standard units of measure, which may be modified with prefixes (to make the units appropriate for the data collected) or combined to form derived units.

SI Base Units		
Quantity	Unit	Symbol
Length	meter	m
Mass	kilogram	kg
Temperature	kelvin	K
Time	second	s
Amount of substance	mole	mol
Electric current	ampere	A
Luminous intensity	candela	cd

Accuracy is how close a measurement is to the actual value of what is being measured. Precision is how exact a measurement is. The number of significant figures in a measurement indicates its precision.

Presenting Scientific Data 1.4

Address Misconceptions

Students may think that graphs validate data. This is false because a graph is merely a method for reporting data. (One way to validate data is to make multiple measurements, often by repeating an experiment.) For a strategy to overcome this misconception, see **Address Misconceptions** on **page 24.**

Scientific information is most useful when it is shared. Preferred formats for presenting data are clear and easy to understand. The simplest way to present data is to use data tables. The use of graphs and other visual aids can help scientists spot relationships and trends in the data.

Scientists report their experimental procedures and results (to both the scientific community and the general public) through a variety of media, literature, and events. The process of peer review allows scientists to share and debate ideas, and is crucial to the progress of science.

Build Reading Literacy

Use Prior Knowledge

Linking New Learning to Familiar Concepts

Strategy Help students construct meaning by linking new information to familiar concepts. Some references indicate that activating prior knowledge is the most important of all reading strategies. Choose a section from Chapter 1, such as pp. 2–6, to use in modeling this strategy. You may also wish to use questions such as those on p. xviii to activate prior knowledge.

Example

1. Have students turn to the pre-selected section, read the opening paragraph, and survey the headings and visuals. Ask students to recount experiences they have had with the topic, and what they already know or believe they know about each subheading. Write student responses on the board. If noticeable misconceptions arise during this discussion, begin to address them immediately.

2. Have students generate and write several questions or predictions about the topic, based on their prior knowledge.

3. Ask students to read the section with the purpose of answering their questions or confirming or refuting their predictions. Divide the section into several parts, and have students pause after each part to evaluate or revise predictions.

4. After reading, discuss with students the information learned. Discuss any new understandings that refute prior misconceptions.

5. Repeat the process for the chapter's remaining sections.

See p. 19 for a script on how to use the use prior knowledge strategy with students. For additional Build Reading Literacy strategies, see pp. 5, 7, and 22.

ASSESS PRIOR KNOWLEDGE

Use the Chapter Pretest below to assess students' prior knowledge. As needed, review these Science Concepts and Math Skills with students.

Review Science Concepts

Section 1.1 Ask students if they have encountered the terms *science* and *technology* before. Have students briefly discuss what they know about science and technology and how each is part of daily life.

Section 1.2 Have students recall situations in which steps must be done in a specific order (playing a game) and situations in which the order may be flexible (cleaning a room). Ask students how these two approaches might relate to science.

Section 1.3 Ask students if they are familiar with English and metric units of measurement. Have students list the type of quantity that each unit is used to measure.

Section 1.4 Have students recall ways in which they have organized and communicated information, for example when preparing a school report or invitations to a party.

Review Math Skills

Conversion Factors; Scientific Notation; Bar, Circle, and Line Graphs Students need to divide and multiply numbers in scientific notation, convert between measuring units, and interpret data in graphs.

Direct students to the **Math Skills** in the **Skills and Reference Handbook** at the end of the student text.

21st Century Learning
Information and Media Literacy

How does curiosity lead to scientific discoveries?

Science begins with curiosity and often ends with discovery. Go online and search for articles about a scientific discovery that you have previously read about or heard about. Identify the types of questions that drove and guided the scientists' investigation. Create a timeline or flowchart that summarizes the progress of the investigation, and present it to your class.

Indiana's Academic Standards for Science

MOTION AND ENERGY OF MACROSCOPIC OBJECTS
ICP.1.3: Describe how Newton's law of universal gravitation, together with the laws of motion, explains the motions of objects on earth and of the moon, planets and stars.

PROPERTIES OF MATTER
ICP.3.2: Study the characteristics of solids, liquids, and gases and their changes of state and interpret them in terms of a molecular model which describes their energies and motions.

NUCLEAR ENERGY (FISSION/FUSION)
ICP.7.2: Differentiate between protons, neutrons, and electrons and determine the number of these subatomic particles in each atom.

A technician tends a reactor that contains bacteria. The bacteria produce proteins that will be used in medicines.

Chapter Pretest

1. True or False: Science and technology are not related. *(False)*

2. Which of the following are areas of science? *(d)*
   a. Biology and chemistry
   b. Astronomy and geology
   c. Zoology and botany
   d. All of the above

3. Why do scientists document their observations and experiments?

(Sample answer: to remember them correctly or analyze them at a later time)

4. Which number is largest? *(a)*
   a. 1.13×10^9
   b. 3.51×10^3
   c. 5.88×10^5
   d. 7.92×10^2

5. Which unit can be used to measure volume? *(c)*
   a. m   **b.** m^2 **c.** m^3

6. Which of these units is the longest? *(c)*
   a. Meter   **b.** Centimeter
   c. Kilometer   **d.** Millimeter

7. What is the slope of a line? *(The ratio of a vertical change to the corresponding horizontal change)*

8. What types of graphs have you seen before? *(Sample answers: line, bar, and circle graphs; pictograph. Some students may also be familiar with histograms.)*

Video Field Trip

Cracking the Case

Inquiry Activity

How Do Scientists Use Their Observations?

Procedure

1. Observe the liquid that your teacher gives you. Record your observations. **CAUTION** *Do not touch or drink the liquid.*

2. Use scissors and a metric ruler to cut a 5-cm square of aluminum foil. Loosely crumple the foil and drop it into the liquid.

3. Use a stirring rod to push the foil below the surface of the liquid. Observe and record any changes that occur in the liquid and foil.

Think About It

1. **Posing Questions** Write three questions about the materials or the changes that you observed.

2. **Designing Experiments** What could you do with the same or other materials to discover an answer to one of your questions?

3. **Communicating Results** Share your proposed experiments with your classmates. What results would you expect to observe?

Science Skills **1**

Video Field Trip

Cracking the Case

Encourage students to view the Video Field Trip "Cracking the Case."

ENGAGE/EXPLORE

Inquiry Activity

How Do Scientists Use Their Observations?   **L2**

Purpose In this activity, students begin to ask specific questions that can lead to testable hypotheses.

🚩 **Address Misconceptions**

This activity can help students overcome the misconception that science consists of an unchanging body of known facts. Students observe that experiments can test hypotheses and produce new information even when the materials involved are not well-understood.

Skills Focus Observing

⏱ **Prep Time** 5 minutes

Materials 25 mL of copper(II) chloride solution in a 50-mL beaker, scissors, metric ruler, aluminum foil, glass stirring rod.

Advance Prep Prepare copper(II) chloride solution in advance. Use 50 g solid copper(II) chloride ($CuCl_2$) per 100 mL water.

Class Time 15 minutes

Safety Students should wear safety goggles, a lab apron, and plastic gloves. Students should wash their hands with warm water and soap or detergent and dispose of the used materials in a chemical waste container.

Teaching Tips
• You may need to demonstrate the use of a metric ruler.

Expected Outcome The solution will bubble and lose some of its blue color. The foil will darken, acquire rust-colored patches, and partly dissolve.

Think About It
1. Possible answers: What is the blue liquid? What other materials would make the blue liquid bubble? What made the foil change color and break up?
2. Students should describe a plan for making additional observations that would help answer one of their questions. Students may suggest repeating the activity with other materials, such as paper, rubber, or steel, instead of the aluminum foil.
3. Students should cite specific expected results such as bubbling, dissolving of the foil, or no change. **Visual**

1.1 What Is Science?

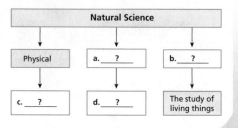

Standards: ICP.3.2, ICP.7.2

◼ FOCUS

Objectives

1.1.1 **Explain** how science and technology are related.

1.1.2 **List** the major branches of natural science and **describe** how they overlap.

1.1.3 **Describe** the main ideas of physical science.

Reading Focus

Build Vocabulary **L2**

Word-Part Analysis Tell students that many words in science consist of roots to which prefixes and/or suffixes are added. Explain that the root is the key to a word's meaning. Ask students to identify the roots in the vocabulary words and to name other words with the same root. Students may suggest *sci-, conscience; tech-, technique; phys-, physical; geo-, geography; astro-, astronaut;* and *bio-, biography.*

Reading Strategy **L2**

a. Earth and space b. Life
c. The study of nonliving things
d. The study of Earth and the universe beyond Earth

◼ INSTRUCT

Science From Curiosity

Build Science Skills **L2**

Predicting Tell students that it can be difficult to prove the existence of something invisible. Place a large candle in a jar and light it. Ask, **What do you predict will happen if the jar is covered? Explain your prediction.** *(The candle will go out once the oxygen in the jar is used up.)* Cover the jar with aluminum foil so students can check their prediction. Ask, **What invisible substances did you assume in your explanation?** *(Oxygen, carbon dioxide)* **Visual, Group**

Reading Focus

Key Concepts

- How does the process of science start and end?
- What is the relationship between science and technology?
- What are the branches of natural science?

Vocabulary

- ◆ science
- ◆ technology
- ◆ chemistry
- ◆ physics
- ◆ geology
- ◆ astronomy
- ◆ biology

Reading Strategy

Previewing Skim the section to find out what the main branches of natural science are. Copy the concept map below. As you read, complete the concept map based on what you have learned.

```
                Natural Science
        ┌──────────────┼──────────────┐
        ↓              ↓              ↓
    [Physical]     a. ___?___     b. ___?___
        ↓              ↓              ↓
    c. ___?___     d. ___?___    The study of
                                 living things
```

Figure 1 In July 1997, the six-wheeled Sojourner rover became the first robot to explore planet Mars. The next generation of Mars rovers will help scientists further study the planet's geology, geography, and climate.

Suppose you could send a robot to another planet. What kinds of experiments would you program the robot to carry out? Before you programmed the robot, you would need to figure out what information you wanted it to gather. Scientists are currently developing robots, like the one in Figure 1, that they plan to send to Mars. These robots are being designed to examine the atmosphere, rocks, gravity, and magnetic fields of the planet.

Science involves asking questions about nature and then finding ways to answer them. This process doesn't happen by itself—it is driven by the curiosity of scientists.

Science From Curiosity

Throughout history, human beings have had a strong sense of curiosity. Human curiosity led to the use of fire, the building of tools, and the development of languages. Have you ever checked what was living at the bottom of a pond? Taken off the cover of a baseball to see what was inside? Tried putting more chocolate or less in your milk to find out how much would give the best flavor? These are all examples of curiosity, and curiosity is the basis of science.

2 *Chapter 1*

Section Resources

Print
- ***Reading and Study Workbook With Math Support,*** Section 1.1
- ***Transparencies,*** Chapter Pretest and Section 1.1

Technology
- ***Interactive Textbook,*** Section 1.1
- ***Presentation Pro CD-ROM,*** Section 1.1
- ***Go Online,*** NSTA SciLinks, Motion

Science is a system of knowledge and the methods you use to find that knowledge. Part of the excitement of science is that you never know what you will find. For instance, when you flip over a rock, will you see crawling insects, a snake, or nothing at all? You won't know until you look. ◗ **Science begins with curiosity and often ends with discovery.**

Curiosity provides questions but is seldom enough to achieve scientific results. Methods such as observing and measuring provide ways to find the answers. In some experiments, observations are qualitative, or descriptive. In others, they are quantitative, or numerical. Some experiments are impossible to do, such as observing what happened at the start of the universe. Scientists cannot go back in time to observe the creation of the universe. However, they can use the evidence of the universe around them to envision how this event occurred.

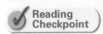 **Reading Checkpoint** *What is science?*

Science and Technology

As scientific knowledge is discovered, it can be applied in ways that improve the lives of people. **Technology** is the use of knowledge to solve practical problems. While the goal of science is to expand knowledge, the goal of technology is to apply that knowledge. Imagine living in the late 1700s, when there were no televisions, cars, antibiotics, or electricity. In a relatively small amount of time, people's lives changed dramatically. Perhaps your grandparents were born at a time when there were no televisions, and your parents were born at a time when there were no personal computers. Technology will have also changed your world dramatically by the time the generation following yours comes along.

Figure 2 illustrates the rapid evolution of the telephone, a technology invented in 1876. Within two years, the first telephone operators were connecting calls by hand. The first coin-operated phones appeared in 1889. By 1927, it was possible to make a phone call from New York to London. World War II saw the development of the first mobile telephones, which paved the way for modern cellular phones. Today, you can communicate by telephone between almost any two places in the world.

◗ **Science and technology are interdependent. Advances in one lead to advances in the other.** For example, advances in the study of physics led to the invention of the transistor. The use of transistors, in turn, led to advances in various other scientific fields, such as computer science and space science.

1876

1914

1955

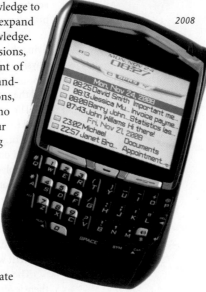

2008

Figure 2 Telephones have quickly evolved from cumbersome, expensive machines to practical, cheap tools for communicating. Classifying *How is a telephone an example of both science and technology?*

Science Skills **3**

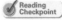

Branches of Science
Integrate Biology L2

The area of science that deals with the connections between biology and physics is biophysics. It is a very broad area that includes biomolecular systems, neural networks, immunology, evolution, and population biology. Each of these components of biophysics, as well as many others, studies how a biological response (from an organism or an ecosystem, for example) is determined by the laws of physics. Encourage students to learn about one of the areas of study within biophysics. Have students make a poster that shows how physics and biology contribute to understanding in that specialty.
Visual, Portfolio

Figure 3 Natural science covers a very broad range of knowledge. **Interpreting Diagrams** *How could you change this diagram to show how the branches of science can overlap?*

Branches of Science

The study of science is divided into social science and natural science. **Natural science is generally divided into three branches: physical science, Earth and space science, and life science.** Each of these branches can be further divided, as shown in Figure 3.

Physical science covers a broad range of study that focuses on non-living things. The two main areas of physical science are chemistry and physics. **Chemistry** is the study of the composition, structure, properties, and reactions of matter. **Physics** is the study of matter and energy and the interactions between the two through forces and motion.

The application of physics and chemistry to the study of Earth is called Earth science. The foundation of Earth science is **geology,** the study of the origin, history, and structure of Earth. Geology has traditionally focused on the study of Earth's rocks. However, modern Earth science also involves the study of systems that may include living organisms. The foundation of space science is **astronomy,** the study of the universe beyond Earth, including the sun, moon, planets, and stars.

The study of living things is known as **biology,** or life science. Biology is not only the physics and chemistry of living things, but the study of the origin and behavior of living things. Biologists study the different ways that organisms grow, survive, and reproduce.

The problem with subdividing science into different areas is that there is often overlap between them. The boundary around each area of science is not always clear. For instance, much of biology is also chemistry, while much of chemistry is also physics. And a rapidly growing area of physics is biophysics, the application of physics to biology.

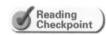 **Reading Checkpoint** *What is physical science?*

Facts and Figures

Technological Advances During the twentieth century, rapid technological changes have occurred in areas other than communications. For example, advances in transportation, especially air travel, dramatically changed society. At the beginning of the century, the Wright brothers flew a propeller-powered airplane 120 feet in 12 seconds.

On October 4, 1957, the Soviet Union launched a basketball-sized satellite called *Sputnik I* into Earth's orbit, making it the first satellite. Another milestone occurred on July 29, 1969, when Neil Armstrong and his crew flew to the moon. Armstrong was the first person to walk on the moon.

The Big Ideas of Physical Science

What are the basic rules of nature? You can read this book to find out. As a sneak preview, some of these rules are summarized here. You can think of them as the big ideas of physical science. Keep in mind that there are also unknown rules of nature that are waiting to be discovered. In fact, you can take part in the search for these unknown laws if you become a scientist. Even though scientists have already discovered a great deal about the universe, there is still much to learn.

Space and Time The universe is both very old and very big. The age of the universe is about 13,700,000,000 (13.7 billion) years. The observable universe is about 700,000,000,000,000,000,000,000,000 (700 million billion billion) meters in diameter. The diameter of Earth is "only" 12,700,000 meters. To get an idea of how big this distance is, the diameter of a giant beach ball is about 1 meter.

Matter and Change A very small amount of the universe is matter. Matter has volume and mass, and on Earth usually takes the form of a solid, liquid, or gas. All matter that you are familiar with, from plants to stars to animals to humans, is made up of building blocks called atoms. Atoms consist of even smaller building blocks called electrons, protons, and neutrons.

Forces and Motion If you push on something that is sitting still, it starts to move. If you push on something that is already moving, you will change its motion. Forces cause changes in motion. As Figure 4 shows, your world is filled with motion and forces. Calculating these forces can sometimes be very challenging. For example, on a NASA mission to Mars, the Mars Exploration Rover must blast off from Earth on a rocket with enough speed to escape Earth's gravity. The rover must then travel a great distance through space on the rocket and land delicately on a planet that is moving very rapidly around the Sun. The laws of physics allow these movements to be calculated exactly so that the NASA robots get to where scientists want them to go.

For: Links on motion
Visit: www.SciLinks.org
Web Code: ccn-0011

Figure 4 The motion of cars on a city street is captured in this time-exposure photograph. Forces govern changes in the motion of each car.

Science Skills **5**

The Big Ideas of Physical Science
Build Reading Literacy L1

Outline Refer to page **156D** in **Chapter 6**, which provides the guidelines for an outline.

This part of the section provides students with an excellent opportunity to practice outlining skills. The paragraphs are parallel in construction and each one has a subhead. Tell students to write the subheads, leaving room between each one. As students read, they can list details under each subhead.
Visual, Logical

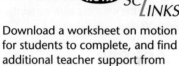

Download a worksheet on motion for students to complete, and find additional teacher support from NSTA SciLinks.

Answer to . . .

Figure 3 *By drawing dotted lines to connect related areas of science, you could show how the branches of science overlap. Another way to illustrate these overlapping relationships would be to reconfigure the branched diagram as a Venn diagram.*

Reading Checkpoint *Physical science is a branch of natural science that focuses on nonliving things. The two main areas of physical science are physics and chemistry.*

Science and Your Perspective
Use Community Resources   L2

Ask a local scientist to talk to your class about how rapidly science changes, including changes so far during the students' lifetimes. **Interpersonal**

Address Misconceptions   L2

Some students may incorrectly think that all the major discoveries in science have been made, and that current scientific work is only filling in details. Point out that science still has many unknowns, including how to cure the common cold and predict the weather with certainty. **Logical, Verbal**

3 ASSESS
Evaluate Understanding   L2

Call on students to name and describe a branch of science. They may describe a main branch or an area shown in Figure 3, or another area.

Reteach   L1

Use Figure 2 to review the relationship between science and technology. Emphasize that over time advances in technology can lead to the use of new materials and the addition of new features to machines like the telephone.

Writing in Science

Possible answers: Students might describe how areas of life science overlap with physical science.

 If your class subscribes to the Interactive Textbook, use it to review key concepts in Section 1.1.

Figure 5 Panels on a solar car convert energy from the sun into the mechanical energy of its moving parts.

Energy Energy exists in many forms. Moving objects have a kind of energy called kinetic energy. Objects moved against a force have another kind of energy called potential energy. Energy also exists in matter itself. When one form of matter changes into another form, energy is either absorbed or released. Matter itself can also be changed into energy.

Energy can be transferred from one form or object to another, but it can never be destroyed. If you push on a door and it swings open, you transfer energy from yourself to the door. Your cells are using the chemical energy stored in the food you have eaten to supply energy to your muscles, which then transfer energy to the door.

Science and Your Perspective

As you read this book, remember that science is both a process and a body of knowledge. The information in this book represents the best up-to-date models of how the universe works. However, like all models, some of these models will be rejected and replaced in the future. For instance, more moons revolving around Jupiter and Saturn will most likely be discovered as telescopes get better. It is therefore possible that by the time you read this book Saturn will be known to have more than the 62 moons currently identified. Be skeptical. Ask questions. Be aware that the scientific facts of today might change tomorrow. However, believe in the scientific process that has discovered them. And believe that you may be the one who makes the discoveries that will change scientific facts in the future.

Section 1.1 Assessment

Reviewing Concepts

1. How does the scientific process start and end?
2. How are science and technology related?
3. What are the branches of natural science?
4. Explain the advantages and disadvantages of subdividing science into many different areas.
5. Why do scientists seek to discover new laws of the universe?

Critical Thinking

6. **Evaluating** Why does the progress of science require both curiosity and methodology? Explain the role of each in scientific investigations.

7. **Making Judgments** Advances in science do not always immediately lead to advances in technology. Why are such scientific advances still valuable?
8. **Classifying** Is the study of the muscle movements in the human body an example of biology or of physics? Explain.

Writing in Science

Compare and Contrast Paragraph Write a paragraph comparing two branches of science. (*Hint:* Use an example that shows how these branches can overlap.)

1. The scientific process begins with curiosity and often ends with discovery.
2. Science and technology are interdependent. Advances in one lead to advances in the other.
3. Natural science is divided into physical science, Earth and space science, and life science.
4. Dividing science into branches makes it easier to understand such a broad subject. However, dividing science into "strict" branches neglects the fact that different areas of science frequently overlap.
5. Scientists seek to discover new laws of the universe because they are curious and wish to understand how the natural world is governed.
6. Scientific investigations are often initiated by curiosity. For example, an observed event might prompt you to ask a question. To answer that question, however, you need to use a systematic method that can provide evidence such as experimental or observational data.

7. Even if a scientific discovery does not immediately lead to advances in technology, that discovery is still useful because it adds to the overall body of scientific knowledge.
8. Both. Because muscle movements involve motion and forces, they fall under the study of physics. However, because muscle movements are specific to living things, they also fall under the study of biology.

1.2 Using a Scientific Approach

Standard: ICP.1.3

Reading Focus

Key Concepts
- What is the goal of a scientific method?
- How does a scientific law differ from a scientific theory?
- Why are scientific models useful?

Vocabulary
- scientific method
- observation
- hypothesis
- manipulated variable
- responding variable
- controlled experiment
- scientific theory
- scientific law
- model

Reading Strategy

Using Prior Knowledge Before you read, copy the web diagram below. Add to the web diagram what you already know about scientific methods. After you read, revise the diagram based on what you have learned.

If you've ever been caught in the rain without an umbrella, your first instinct was probably to start running. After all, the less time you spend in the rain, the less water there is falling down on you. So you might think that running in the rain keeps you drier than walking in the rain over a given distance. However, by running in the rain you run into more raindrops than by walking, thereby wetting more of your face, chest, and legs. Have your instincts been getting you wetter instead of keeping you drier?

You now have a question that you can try to answer with a scientific approach. Which keeps you drier in the rain—walking or running?

Scientific Methods

In order to answer questions about the world around them, scientists need to gather information. An organized plan for gathering, organizing, and communicating information is called a **scientific method.** Despite the name, a scientific method can be used by anyone, including yourself. All you need is a reason to use it. **The goal of any scientific method is to solve a problem or to better understand an observed event.**

Figure 6 To run, or not to run: that is the question. **Designing Experiments** *How can you test if running in the rain keeps you drier than walking in the rain over the same distance?*

Science Skills **7**

Section Resources

Print
- *Reading and Study Workbook With Math Support,* Section 1.2
- *Transparencies,* Section 1.2

Technology
- *Interactive Textbook,* Section 1.2
- *Presentation Pro CD-ROM,* Section 1.2
- *GoOnline,* Science News, Nature of science

Section 1.2

1 FOCUS

Objectives
1.2.1 **Describe** the steps in a scientific method.
1.2.2 **Compare** and **contrast** facts, scientific theories, and scientific laws.
1.2.3 **Explain** the importance of models in science.
1.2.4 **Explain** the importance of safety in science.

Reading Focus

Build Vocabulary   L2

Paraphrase Tell students to write the vocabulary terms on a sheet of paper and leave enough space to write the definitions. As students read, they should write the definition in their own words.

Reading Strategy   L2

a. Forming a hypothesis
b. Testing a hypothesis
c. Drawing conclusions
d. Developing a theory

2 INSTRUCT

Scientific Methods
Build Reading Literacy   L1

Sequence Refer to page **290D** in **Chapter 10,** which provides the guidelines for a sequence.

Figure 7 is a flowchart that shows the steps of a scientific method. Remind students to refer to this figure when reading about a particular step to help themselves understand how that step fits into the sequence of steps in a scientific method.
Visual

Answer to . . .

Figure 6 *Possible answer: Take two identical pieces of absorbent cloth and measure the mass of each. Give the cloths to two people to hold at arm's length during a rain storm. One person should walk a fixed distance, and the other should run the same distance. Compare the masses of the wet pieces of cloth.*

Science Skills **7**

Build Science Skills `L2`

Observing

Purpose Students observe that as the distance from a light source increases, the brightness decreases.

Materials low-wattage incandescent bulb, power source for the bulb

Class Time 10 minutes

Procedure Darken the room and turn on the bulb. Tell students that its light can be considered to be coming from a single point (a point source). Ask two or three volunteers to walk around the room and observe whether the light from the bulb is visible in all parts of the room. Be sure that volunteers observe the light's brightness at various distances from the bulb.

Expected Outcome Students will see that the bulb radiates light in all directions and that as distance from the bulb increases, the bulb's brightness decreases.
Kinesthetic, Visual, Group

Figure 7 A scientific method provides a useful strategy for solving problems.
Inferring *Is an observation required in order for you to arrive at a question? What does this tell you about the strictness of the scientific method?*

Figure 7 outlines an example of a scientific method. Each step in the method shown involves specific skills, some of which you will be learning as you read this book. It is important to note that scientific methods can vary from case to case. For example, one scientist might follow the steps shown in Figure 7 in a different order, or another might choose to skip one or more steps.

Making Observations Scientific investigations often begin with observations. An **observation** is information that you obtain through your senses. Repeatable observations are known as facts. For example, when you walk or run in the rain, you get wet. Standing in the rain leaves you much wetter than walking or running in the rain. You might combine these observations into a question: How does your speed affect how wet you get when you are caught in the rain?

Forming a Hypothesis A **hypothesis** is a proposed answer to a question. To answer the question raised by your observations about traveling in the rain, you might guess that the faster your speed, the drier you will stay in the rain. What can you do with your hypothesis? For a hypothesis to be useful, it must be testable.

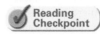 **Reading Checkpoint**   *What is a hypothesis?*

Testing a Hypothesis Scientists perform experiments to test their hypotheses. In an experiment, any factor that can change is called a variable. Suppose you do an experiment to test if speed affects how wet you get in the rain. The variables will include your speed, your size, the rate of rainfall, and the amount of water that hits you.

Your hypothesis states that one variable, speed, causes a change in another variable, the amount of water that hits you. The speed with which you walk or run is the **manipulated variable,** or the variable that causes a change in another. The amount of water that you accumulate is the **responding variable,** or the variable that changes in response to the manipulated variable. To examine the relationship between a manipulated variable and a responding variable, scientists use controlled experiments. A **controlled experiment** is an experiment in which only one variable, the manipulated variable, is deliberately changed at a time. While the responding variable is observed for changes, all other variables are kept constant, or controlled.

8   *Chapter 1*

Customize for English Language Learners

Increase Word Exposure
Ask students who are learning English to make flashcards for each step of the scientific method shown in Figure 7. Tell students to write the English words describing the steps on an index card. They should also write a brief definition in their first language on the back of each card. Students can make the flashcards as they read

the section. Then, have students shuffle their cards and place the steps of the scientific method in the correct order. Students may refer to the definition on the back of the card if they need help. Reinforce that the scientific method shown in Figure 7 is only one of many possible methods.

In 1997, two meteorologists conducted a controlled experiment to determine if moving faster keeps you drier in the rain. In the experiment, both scientists traveled 100 yards by foot in the rain. One of them walked; the other ran. By measuring the mass of their clothes before and after traveling in the rain, the scientists were able to measure how much water each had accumulated. One of the controlled variables was size—the two scientists were about the same height and build. Another was the rate of rainfall—the scientists began traveling at the same time during the same rainstorm on the same path. A third was the ability to absorb water—the scientists wore identical sets of clothes.

Drawing Conclusions The scientists' rainy-day experiment produced some convincing data. The clothes of the walking scientist accumulated 217 grams of water, while the clothes of the running scientists accumulated 130 grams of water. Based on their data, the scientists concluded that running in the rain keeps you drier than walking—about 40 percent drier, in fact. Now you have scientific evidence to support the hypothesis stated earlier.

What happens if the data do not support the hypothesis? In such a case, a scientist can revise the hypothesis or propose a new one, based on the data from the experiment. A new experiment must then be designed to test the revised or new hypothesis.

Developing a Theory Once a hypothesis has been supported in repeated experiments, scientists can begin to develop a theory. A **scientific theory** is a well-tested explanation for a set of observations or experimental results. For example, according to the kinetic theory of matter, all particles of matter are in constant motion. Kinetic theory explains a wide range of observations, such as ice melting or the pressure of a gas.

Theories are never proved. Instead, they become stronger if the facts continue to support them. However, if an existing theory fails to explain new facts and discoveries, the theory may be revised or a new theory may replace it.

Scientific Laws

After repeated observations or experiments, scientists may arrive at a scientific law. A **scientific law** is a statement that summarizes a pattern found in nature. For example, Newton's law of gravity describes how two objects attract each other by means of a gravitational force. This law has been verified over and over. However, scientists have yet to agree on a theory that explains how gravity works. **A scientific law describes an observed pattern in nature without attempting to explain it. The explanation of such a pattern is provided by a scientific theory.**

Go Online

SCIENCE NEWS®

For: Articles on the nature of science

Visit: PHSchool.com

Web Code: cce-0011

Figure 8 An environmental scientist collects a sample for a water pollution study. After analyzing the sample, the scientist can draw conclusions about how the water became polluted.

Scientific Laws
Build Science Skills `L2`

Inferring Reinforce the difference between a scientific theory and a scientific law. Ask, **How are scientific laws affected by new scientific theories?** *(Scientific laws aren't affected because new theories are new explanations of the observations. Scientific laws are descriptions of patterns in nature; they do not explain. Theories are explanations of patterns observed in nature.)* **If a scientific law were developed in one country, would it apply in a different country? Explain your answer.** *(Scientific laws apply everywhere. Scientific laws are different from legal and political laws, which apply only in specific countries.)* **Logical**

🚩 **Address Misconceptions** `L2`

Some students may incorrectly think that every hypothesis becomes a theory and then a law. Help students understand the basic definitions of these three terms. For example, tell students that a hypothesis is a reasonable idea, or reasonable guess, that is often much narrower in scope than a theory. Explain that some ideas or guesses are incorrect, incomplete, or only partially correct. Tell students that a theory is an explanation, and help them realize that some explanations are incorrect. When students thoroughly understand the definitions of these three terms, they will realize that these are not always part of a progression. **Verbal**

Go Online

SCIENCE NEWS®

Science News provides students with current information on articles on the nature of science.

Answer to . . .

Figure 7 *No, an observation is not required in order for you to be able to pose a question. This tells you that the scientific method should not be thought of as a strict sequence of steps, but rather a flexible set of guidelines for investigating a problem. The flexibility of the scientific method allows for scientists to be creative in their problem solving.*

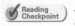 **Reading Checkpoint** *A proposed answer to a question*

Scientific Models

Scientific Models

Flaps on an Airplane L2

Purpose Students observe how models can be used.

Material sheet of paper

Procedure Tell students that the flaps on airplane wings help control how the plane flies. Point out that because you do not have an airplane in the class, you will use a model to observe how wing flaps can affect an airplane's flight. Fold the sheet of paper into a paper airplane. Throw the plane so the class sees how the plane flies without flaps. On the trailing edge of each wing, cut a flap. Bend the flaps into different positions such as both up, both down, or one up and one down. Throw the plane with different flap positions and observe how the plane flies. Ask students if they think the wing flaps on a real airplane would have the same effect.

Expected Outcome Students should see that using the paper airplane as a model for a real airplane is appropriate. With both flaps down, the plane descends; with both up, it ascends. With one flap up and the other down, the plane turns in the direction of the flap that is up.
Visual, Logical

Figure 9 Two engineers discuss a computer-aided design, or CAD, of an aircraft component.

Scientific Models

If you have ever been lost in a city, you know that a street map can help you find your location. A street map is a type of **model,** or representation, of an object or event. 🗩 **Scientific models make it easier to understand things that might be too difficult to observe directly.** For example, to understand how Earth rotates on its axis, you could look at a globe, which is a small-scale model of Earth. The computer model in Figure 9 represents the interior of an airplane. Other models help you visualize things that are too small to see, such as atoms. As long as a model lets you mentally picture what is supposed to be represented, then the model has done its job.

An example of a mental, rather than physical, model might be that comets are like giant snowballs, primarily made of ice. Scientists tested this model with observations and experiments. In 2006, a space probe collected samples from a comet. Tests on the samples confirmed that comets are made of ice, but the tests also showed that comets contain rocky material that is formed near the sun. So, a modified model of comets was adopted.

If new data show that a model is wrong, then it must either be changed or be replaced by a new model. If scientists never challenged old models, then nothing new would be learned, and we would still believe what we believed hundreds of years ago. Science works by making mistakes. The fact that newer models are continually replacing old models is a sign that new discoveries are continually occurring. As the knowledge that makes up science keeps changing, scientists develop a better and better understanding of the universe.

 Reading Checkpoint *What is a model?*

10 *Chapter 1*

Working Safely in Science

Scientists working in the field, or in a laboratory, like those in Figure 10, are trained to use safe procedures when carrying out investigations. Laboratory work may involve flames or hot plates, electricity, chemicals, hot liquids, sharp instruments, and breakable glassware.

Whenever you work in your science laboratory, it's important for you to follow safety precautions at all times. Before performing any activity in this course, study the rules in the Science Safety section of the Skills Handbook. Before you start any activity, read all the steps. Make sure that you understand the entire procedure, especially any safety precautions that must be followed.

The single most important rule for your safety is simple: Always follow your teacher's instructions and the textbook directions exactly. If you are in doubt about any step in an activity, always ask your teacher for an explanation. Because you may be in contact with chemicals you cannot see, it is essential that you wash your hands thoroughly after every scientific activity. Remember, you share responsibility for your own safety and that of your teacher and classmates.

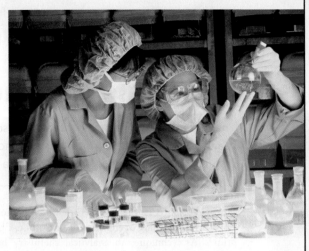

Figure 10 Safety plays an important role in science. **Interpreting Photos** *What safety measures are these scientists taking in their laboratory work?*

Section 1.2 Assessment

Reviewing Concepts

1. What is the goal of scientific methods?

2. How does a scientific law differ from a scientific theory?

3. Why are scientific models useful?

4. What are three types of variables in a controlled experiment?

5. Does every scientific method begin with an observation? Explain.

Critical Thinking

6. Classifying The scientists who tested the hypothesis on running in the rain performed only one controlled experiment that supported their hypothesis. Can their supported hypothesis be called a theory? Explain.

7. Designing Experiments Suppose you wanted to find out how running affects your pulse rate. What would your hypothesis be? Explain how you could test your hypothesis.

8. Using Models A scientific model can take the form of a physical object or a concept. List one example of each type of model. How does each one resemble what it is supposed to model?

Writing in Science

Descriptive Paragraph Write a paragraph describing two examples of pseudoscience. Use your examples to explain why pseudoscience is not actual science.

Science Skills **11**

Working Safely in Science
Use Visuals   L1

Figure 10 Emphasize that students must study the safety rules before they do lab activities. Ask, **Why are these scientists wearing goggles?** *(Because when a liquid is poured or heated, it could splash into their eyes.)* **Visual**

3 ASSESS

Evaluate Understanding   L2

Ask students to name scientific laws. If they name a theory instead of a law, help them understand why what they chose is a theory and not a law.

Reteach   L1

Use Figure 7 to review the scientific method. Point out that when scientists learn new information, they may go back to an earlier step in the method.

Writing in Science

Astrology and phrenology are two examples of pseudoscience. These activities may seem like science because they use charts to make predictions. However, they are not science because the conclusions are not based on evidence. Also, the ideas related to these topics are not tested using scientific methods.

Interactive Textbook If your class subscribes to the Interactive Textbook, use it to review key concepts in Section 1.2.

Answer to . . .

Figure 10 *They are wearing goggles, gloves, lab coats, and hair nets.*

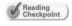 **Reading Checkpoint** *A representation of an object or event*

Section 1.2   Assessment

1. The goal of scientific methods is to solve a problem or to better understand an observed event.

2. A scientific law describes an observed pattern in nature without attempting to explain it. The explanation of such a pattern is provided by a scientific theory.

3. Scientific models make it easier to understand things that might be too difficult to observe directly.

4. Three types of variables in a controlled experiment are manipulated variables, responding variables, and controlled variables.

5. No. The order of the steps within a scientific method can vary from case to case.

6. Although the data from the meteorologists' experiment supported their hypothesis, the scope of their investigation is too narrow to be considered a theory. A scientific theory explains a broad set of observations and/or supported hypotheses—not just a single hypothesis.

7. Students will likely hypothesize that running increases one's pulse rate. Students can test their hypotheses by performing a controlled experiment in which the manipulated variable is speed (e.g., running, walking, or standing still) and the responding variable is pulse rate.

8. Possible answer: A globe, a physical model of Earth, has the same shape as Earth. The quantum mechanical model of the atom describes the behavior of electrons around the nucleus.

Forensic Science L2
Background

Forensic science is any aspect of science that relates to law. It includes methods for identifying, collecting, and analyzing evidence that may be related to a crime. At a crime scene, data is often identified and collected. Data collection may include taking fingerprints; collecting hair, blood, or tissue samples; or making plaster casts of tire prints or footprints. Depending on the nature of the crime and the crime scene, investigators may also collect samples of soil, pollen, fibers from clothing, or other materials at the crime scene. In the laboratory, technicians study and analyze the samples so that they can provide investigators with accurate information. Data analysis can shed light on what happened, where it happened, and even who might have committed the crime.

Build Science Skills L2

Analyzing Data

Purpose Students compare tire tracks to determine which ones were made by the same toy car.

Materials modeling clay, at least 5 different toy cars with similar-sized tires that have different tread, cooking oil, magnifying glass

Class Time 30 minutes

Preparation Flatten a piece of clay for each group of students. Lightly oil the tread of all the tires on the toy cars. Choose a car and roll the tire across each piece of clay to make an impression.

Safety Students who are allergic to corn or olives should wear plastic gloves and dispose of them carefully.

Procedure Tell students that they are forensic scientists and they must find out which car was at the scene of a crime based on a tire track from the scene. Give students a piece of clay with a tire track and another piece of unmarked clay. Have students use the clay to test each car's tires and, as needed, use the magnifying glass to find a match. Ask each group to write a short paragraph stating what they did and why they think they have identified the car that made the tracks.

Expected Outcome Students should correctly identify the car by the similar tire patterns. **Logical, Visual, Group**

Forensic Science

The first job of police officers at a crime scene is to seal off the area so that potential evidence is not disturbed. Such evidence will be sent to a forensic science laboratory for examination.

Forensic science is the use of scientific methods, such as fingerprint matching or the analysis of clothing fibers, to solve crimes. As techniques in analytical chemistry have become more advanced, the amount of information that can be gleaned from tiny crime-scene samples has grown. Forensic science is becoming ever more powerful as a crime-solving tool.

Criminal investigators need to use several scientific techniques. They include making observations, establishing the problem to be solved, collecting evidence and gathering information, forming hypotheses, analyzing evidence, testing hypotheses, and drawing conclusions.

The crime scene
At the scene, the investigators make observations that may shed light on the nature of the crime. The investigators establish the problem to be solved—in this case, who committed the murder?

Collecting evidence and forming a hypothesis
Forensic scientists take photographs and collect materials from the crime scene. Investigators use all of the information gathered to formulate hypotheses about how and why the crime took place.

DNA evidence can be obtained from blood stains.

12   *Chapter 1*

Analyzing the evidence
Much of the physical evidence must be analyzed in a laboratory. With a blood sample, for example, DNA is extracted and analyzed and the blood type is established.

Forensic blood sampling *Articles from a crime scene, such as the blood-stained clothing and the hatchet shown here, may match DNA to a suspect.*

Displaced objects can help determine a sequence of events.

Testing hypotheses against the evidence
Investigators now test hypotheses on who committed the crime—looking for matches in DNA, fingerprints, or clothing fibers, for example. In some cases, this testing excludes a suspect. In other cases it strengthens the case against a particular person.

Drawing conclusions
To build a convincing case against a suspect, various pieces and types of evidence may be needed. Evidence might include a fingerprint match, a piece of clothing left at the crime scene, or a connection to the murder weapon.

Documents may provide evidence for a motive.

Fibers can link a suspect to a crime scene.

Going Further

A scientific method can include the following steps: observing, posing questions, formulating a hypothesis, testing the hypothesis, and drawing conclusions. When criminal investigators arrive at a crime scene, they make observations and collect evidence. The questions they pose might include, "Who committed the crime?" or "How was the crime committed?" Investigators may then form hypotheses concerning possible suspects and the methods used to commit the crime. By analyzing the evidence obtained (e.g., fingerprint or DNA analysis), they can test their hypotheses. The results of these analyses may allow investigators to draw conclusions about the criminal's identity and methodology.
Logical

Going Further

- Describe how criminal investigators use scientific methods to solve their cases. (*Hint:* start by creating a flowchart of a scientific method. Then identify how criminal investigators carry out each step.)

- Take a Discovery Channel Video Field Trip by watching "Cracking the Case."

DISCOVERY
CHANNEL
SCHOOL™
Video Field Trip

DISCOVERY
CHANNEL
SCHOOL™
Video Field Trip
Cracking the Case

After students have viewed the Video Field Trip, ask them the following questions: **What is the main goal of forensic science?** (*To analyze clues to reconstruct past events*) **What discovery led to the use of fingerprinting in forensic science?** (*The discovery that no two people had the same fingerprints*) **What do forensic scientists look for in the pattern of a fingerprint so that they can identify who the fingerprint belongs to?** (*The tiny imperfections such as ridges that end abruptly, ridges that split, and ridges that form little dots; also where these are located with respect to one another*) **How do detectives find fingerprints on an object?** (*The old method involved spreading powder on the area. The powder adhered to traces of sweat left behind by contact with the fingers. The powder was then lifted off with transparent tape, showing the pattern. Newer methods use fluorescent powder and high intensity lasers to find prints that could otherwise be missed.*) **Name two things police detectives and forensic scientists might do to track down the identity of a car that left a suspicious tire track at a crime scene.** (*Student answers may include measure and photograph the area, make a mold of the tire track, and look for irregularities in the mold of the tire tread that are unique to that tire.*)

1 FOCUS

Objectives

1.3.1 Perform calculations involving scientific notation and conversion factors.

1.3.2 Identify the metric and SI units used in science and **convert** between common metric prefixes.

1.3.3 Compare and **contrast** accuracy and precision.

1.3.4 Relate the Celsius, Kelvin, and Fahrenheit temperature scales.

Reading Focus

Build Vocabulary   L2

LINCS Use LINCS to help students learn and review section vocabulary, including *scientific notation*: **L**ist parts that they know (*Scientific* means "related to science," and *notation* means "a system of symbols."); **I**magine a picture (Students might visualize a series of symbols written in a table.); **N**ote a sound-alike word (*Notation* is similar to *note*.); **C**onnect the terms in a sentence (*The scientist used scientific notation to communicate her results.*); **S**elf-test (quiz themselves).

Reading Strategy   L2

Possible answers may include:
a. What is SI? SI is a set of metric measuring units used by scientists.
b. What are base units? Base units are the fundamental units of SI. There are seven SI base units, including the meter, the kilogram, the kelvin, and the second.

2 INSTRUCT

Using Scientific Notation

Use Visuals   L1

Figure 11 Ask, Would it be easy to count the number of stars shown in the photo? *(No)* Why might using scientific notation be appropriate when counting the number of stars? *(The number of stars could be very large.)*
Visual, Logical

1.3 Measurement

Standard: ICP.3.2

Reading Focus

Key Concepts

- Why is scientific notation useful?
- What units do scientists use for their measurements?
- How does the precision of measurements affect the precision of scientific calculations?

Vocabulary

- scientific notation
- length
- mass
- volume
- density
- conversion factor
- precision
- significant figures
- accuracy
- thermometer

Reading Strategy

Previewing Make a table like the one below. Before you read the section, rewrite the green and blue topic headings as questions. As you read, write answers to the questions.

Measurement
Why is scientific notation useful?
a. _____?_____
b. _____?_____

Figure 11 Scientists estimate that there are more than 200 billion stars in the Milky Way galaxy. **Applying Concepts** *What is this number in scientific notation?*

14   *Chapter 1*

How old are you? How tall are you? The answers to these questions are measurements. Measurements are important in both science and everyday life. Hardly a day passes without the need for you to measure amounts of money or the passage of time. It would be difficult to imagine doing science without any measurements.

Using Scientific Notation

How many stars do you see in Figure 11? There are too many to count. Scientists often work with very large or very small numbers. For example, the speed of light is about 300,000,000 meters per second. On the other hand, an average snail has been clocked at a speed of only 0.00086 meter per second.

Instead of having to write out all the zeroes in these numbers, you can use a shortcut called scientific notation. **Scientific notation** is a way of expressing a value as the product of a number between 1 and 10 and a power of 10. For example, the number 300,000,000 written in scientific notation is 3.0×10^8. The exponent, 8, tells you that the decimal point is really 8 places to the right of the 3.

For numbers less than 1 that are written in scientific notation, the exponent is negative. For example, the number 0.00086 written in scientific notation is 8.6×10^{-4}. The negative exponent tells you how many decimals places there are to the *left* of the 8.6. **Scientific notation makes very large or very small numbers easier to work with.**

Section Resources

Print

- **Laboratory Manual,** Investigations 1A and 1B
- **Reading and Study Workbook With Math Support,** Section 1.3 and **Math Skill:** Using Scientific Notation
- **Math Skills and Problem Solving Workbook,** Section 1.3
- **Transparencies,** Section 1.3

Technology

- **Interactive Textbook,** Section 1.3
- **Presentation Pro CD-ROM,** Section 1.3
- **Go Online,** *Planet Diary,* Universal measurements; PHSchool.com, Data sharing

When multiplying numbers written in scientific notation, you multiply the numbers that appear before the multiplication signs and *add* the exponents. For example, to calculate how far light travels in 500 seconds, you multiply the speed of light by the number of seconds.

$$(3.0 \times 10^8 \text{ m/s}) \times (5.0 \times 10^2 \text{ s}) = 15 \times 10^{10} \text{ m} = 1.5 \times 10^{11} \text{ m}$$

This distance is about how far the sun is from Earth.

When dividing numbers written in scientific notation, you divide the numbers that appear before the exponential terms and *subtract* the exponents. For example, to calculate how long it takes for light from the sun to reach Earth, you would perform a division.

$$\frac{1.5 \times 10^{11} \text{ m}}{3.0 \times 10^8 \text{ m/s}} = \frac{1.5}{3.0} \times 10^{11-8} \text{ s} = 0.50 \times 10^3 \text{ s} = 5.0 \times 10^2 \text{ s}$$

For: Links on universal measurements
Visit: PHSchool.com
Web Code: ccc-0013

Math Skills

Using Scientific Notation
A rectangular parking lot has a length of 1.1×10^3 meters and a width of 2.4×10^3 meters. What is the area of the parking lot?

1 **Read and Understand**
What information are you given?

Length (l) $= 1.1 \times 10^3$ m

Width (w) $= 2.4 \times 10^3$ m

2 **Plan and Solve**
What unknown are you trying to calculate?

Area (A) $= ?$

What formula contains the given quantities and the unknown?

$A = l \times w$

Replace each variable with its known value.

$$A = l \times w = (1.1 \times 10^3 \text{ m})(2.4 \times 10^3 \text{ m})$$
$$= (1.1 \times 2.4)(10^{3+3})(\text{m} \times \text{m})$$
$$= 2.6 \times 10^6 \text{ m}^2$$

3 **Look Back and Check**
Is your answer reasonable?

Yes, the number calculated is the product of the numbers given, and the units (m^2) indicate area.

Math Practice

1. Perform the following calculations. Express your answers in scientific notation.
   a. $(7.6 \times 10^{-4} \text{ m}) \times (1.5 \times 10^7 \text{ m})$
   b. $0.00053 \div 29$

2. Calculate how far light travels in 8.64×10^4 seconds. (*Hint:* The speed of light is about 3.0×10^8 m/s.)

Science Skills **15**

Math Practice

Solutions L2
1. a. $(7.6 \times 10^{-4} \text{ m})(1.5 \times 10^7 \text{ m}) = (7.6 \times 1.5)(10^{-4+7})(\text{m} \times \text{m}) = 11 \times 10^3 \text{ m}^2 = 1.1 \times 10^4 \text{ m}^2$
1. b. $0.00053/29 = (5.3 \times 10^{-4})/(2.9 \times 10^1) = (5.3/2.9) \times 10^{(-4-1)} = 1.8 \times 10^{-5}$
2. $(3.0 \times 10^8 \text{ m/s})(8.64 \times 10^4 \text{ s}) = (3.0 \times 8.64)(10^{8+4}) \text{ m} = 26 \times 10^{12} = 2.6 \times 10^{13} \text{ m}$
(Note: This is how far light travels in one day.)
Logical

For Extra Help L1
Reinforce the concepts of adding exponents when numbers in scientific notation are multiplied and subtracting exponents when numbers in scientific notation are divided.
Logical

Direct students to the **Math Skills** in the **Skills and Reference Handbook** at the end of the student text for additional help.

Additional Problems L1
1. Perform the following calculations:
a. $1.5 \times 10^3 \text{ m} \times 1.0 \times 10^5 \text{ m}$ (*1.5 × 10⁸ m²*)
b. $4.5 \times 10^3/0.9$ (*5.0 × 10³*)
Logical, Portfolio

Go Online PLANETDIARY

Find links to additional activities and have students monitor phenomena that affect Earth and its residents.

Customize for Inclusion Students

Visually Impaired
To help visually impaired students understand the concepts of length, mass, and volume, give students common objects. Ask students to describe the objects in regard to their lengths, masses, and volumes. Help students to understand the definitions of these terms during the exercise.

Answer to . . .

Figure 11 2×10^{11}

SI Units of Measurement

Address
Misconceptions   **L2**

Some students may incorrectly think that scientists use the metric system because it is more accurate than other measurement systems. Point out to students that the units of the measurement system have little to do with accuracy. Help students overcome this misconception by measuring one object with several different centimeter- and inch-rulers. Have students record the measurements. List the metric measurements in one column on the board and the English measurements in another column. Point out that all the measurements in the metric column are similar to one another and that the measurements in the English column are also similar to one another.
Visual

Figure 12 A measurement consists of a number and a unit. One of the units used to measure temperature is the degree Celsius.

SI Units of Measurement

For a measurement to make sense, it requires both a number and a unit. For example, if you told one of your friends that you had finished a homework assignment "in five," what would your friend think? Would it be five minutes or five hours? Maybe it was a long assignment, and you actually meant five days. Or maybe you meant that you wrote five pages. You should always express measurements in numbers and units so that their meaning is clear. In Figure 12, students are measuring temperature in degrees Celsius.

Many of the units you are familiar with, such as inches, feet, and degrees Fahrenheit, are not units that are used in science. Scientists use a set of measuring units called SI, or the International System of Units. The abbreviation stands for the French name *Système International d'Unités*. SI is a revised version of the metric system, which was originally developed in France in 1791. By adhering to one system of units, scientists can readily interpret one another's measurements.

Base Units and Derived Units SI is built upon seven metric units, known as base units, which are listed in Figure 13. In SI, the base unit for **length,** or the straight-line distance between two points, is the meter (m). The base unit for **mass,** or the quantity of matter in an object or sample, is the kilogram (kg).

Additional SI units, called derived units, are made from combinations of base units. Figure 14 lists some common derived units. For example, **volume** is the amount of space taken up by an object. The volume of a rectangular box equals its length times its width times its height. Each of these dimensions can be measured in meters, so you can derive the SI unit for volume by multiplying meters by meters by meters, which gives you cubic meters (m^3).

SI Base Units		
Quantity	**Unit**	**Symbol**
Length	meter	m
Mass	kilogram	kg
Temperature	kelvin	K
Time	second	s
Amount of substance	mole	mol
Electric current	ampere	A
Luminous intensity	candela	cd

Figure 13 Seven metric base units make up the foundation of SI.

Derived Units		
Quantity	**Unit**	**Symbol**
Area	square meter	m^2
Volume	cubic meter	m^3
Density	kilograms per cubic meter	kg/m^3
Pressure	pascal ($kg/m \cdot s^2$)	Pa
Energy	joule ($kg \cdot m^2/s^2$)	J
Frequency	hertz (1/s)	Hz
Electric charge	coulomb ($A \cdot s$)	C

Figure 14 Specific combinations of SI base units yield derived units.

Facts and Figures

The Meter The meter was originally defined by the French Academy of Science in 1791. At that time, a meter was intended to be one ten-millionth part of the quadrant of Earth. This length was transferred to a platinum bar with polished ends. The bar could be measured at a specific temperature to define the length of a meter. Later measurements of Earth showed that the length of the bar was not one ten-millionth of the quadrant.

However, the meter's length was not changed. It was redefined to be the length on the bar. In 1960, the length of a meter was more precisely defined by the number of wavelengths of light, of a very precise color, emitted by krypton-86. This method was difficult to perform and was quickly replaced with the current method. Currently, a meter is defined as the distance light travels in a vacuum in $\frac{1}{299,792,458}$ second.

Figure 15 Metric prefixes allow for more convenient ways to express SI base and derived units.

SI Prefixes			
Prefix	Symbol	Meaning	Multiply Unit by
giga-	G	billion (10^9)	1,000,000,000
mega-	M	million (10^6)	1,000,000
kilo-	k	thousand (10^3)	1000
deci-	d	tenth (10^{-1})	0.1
centi-	c	hundredth (10^{-2})	0.01
milli-	m	thousandth (10^{-3})	0.001
micro-	μ	millionth (10^{-6})	0.000001
nano-	n	billionth (10^{-9})	0.000000001

Another quantity that requires a derived unit is density. **Density** is the ratio of an object's mass to its volume.

$$\text{Density} = \frac{\text{Mass}}{\text{Volume}}$$

To derive the SI unit for density, you can divide the base unit for mass by the derived unit for volume. Dividing kilograms by cubic meters yields the SI unit for density, kilograms per cubic meter (kg/m^3).

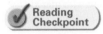 **Reading Checkpoint** *What is the SI derived unit for density?*

Metric Prefixes The metric unit for a given quantity is not always a convenient one to use. For example, the time it takes for a computer hard drive to read or write data—also known as the seek time—is in the range of thousandths of a second. A typical seek time might be 0.009 second. This can be written in a more compact way by using a metric prefix. A metric prefix indicates how many times a unit should be multiplied or divided by 10. Figure 15 shows some common metric prefixes. Using the prefix *milli-* (m), you can write 0.009 second as 9 milliseconds, or 9 ms.

$$9 \text{ ms} = \frac{9}{1000} \text{ s} = 0.009 \text{ s}$$

Note that dividing by 1000 is the same as multiplying by 0.001.

Metric prefixes can also make a unit larger. For example, a distance of 12,000 meters can also be written as 12 kilometers.

$$12 \text{ km} = 12 \times 1000 \text{ m} = 12,000 \text{ m}$$

Metric prefixes turn up in non-metric units as well. If you have used a digital camera, you may know that a megapixel is 1,000,000 pixels. A kiloton is a unit of explosive force equal to 1,000 tons of TNT.

Figure 16 A bar of gold has more mass per unit volume than a feather. **Inferring** *Which takes up more space—one kilogram of gold or one kilogram of feathers?*

Science Skills **17**

Build Science Skills L2

Inferring Have students look at Figure 15. Ask, **What factor are the metric prefixes based on?** *(10)* **How does that make it convenient for converting between units?** *(The numbers stay the same but the decimal point moves.)* **Logical, Visual**

Build Math Skills L1

Conversion Factors Give students the conversion factors 1 in = 2.54 cm and 1 ft = 30.48 cm. Divide students into pairs, and have each pair measure the lengths of at least three different objects of various sizes, such as a pencil, a desktop, and the floor of a room. Direct the pairs to calculate the measurements of each object in inches, feet, centimeters, meters, and kilometers. *(Answers will vary depending upon the objects measured.)* Ask students which conversion factors they used to make their calculations. **Kinesthetic, Logical**

Direct students to the **Math Skills** in the **Skills and Reference Handbook** at the end of the student text for additional help.

Answer to . . .

Figure 16 *Because feathers are less dense than gold, one kilogram of feathers takes up more space than one kilogram of gold.*

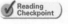 **Reading Checkpoint** *The SI derived unit for density is the kilogram per cubic meter (kg/m^3).*

Science Skills **17**

Conversion Factor `L2`

Purpose Students observe how conversion factors work.

Materials 12-in. object, 3-in. object, metric ruler

Procedure Give students the conversion factor 1 in. = 2.54 in. Measure the 12-in. object and report its length in centimeters. Tell the students the length in inches of the 3-in. object. Ask them to use the conversion factor to calculate its length in centimeters. *(7.6 cm)* Measure the object and report the length in centimeters.

Expected Outcome Students see how conversion factors convert between units of different measure. **Visual, Logical**

Comparing Precision `L2`

Objective
After completing this lab, students will be able to
- describe and distinguish accuracy and precision.
- compare the precision of measuring devices.

Skills Focus Measuring, Comparing

 Prep Time 10 minutes

Class Time 15 minutes

Safety Caution students to handle glassware carefully.

Teaching Tips
- Provide 3 different plastic bottles with labels removed, and a beaker and graduated cylinder large enough to contain the volume of each bottle.
- If necessary, use paper cups instead of plastic bottles.

Expected Outcome The graduated cylinder will provide a more precise measurement than the beaker.

Figure 17 Nutrition labels often have some measurements listed in grams and milligrams.
Calculating How many grams are in 160 milligrams?

The easiest way to convert from one unit of measurement to another is to use conversion factors. A **conversion factor** is a ratio of equivalent measurements that is used to convert a quantity expressed in one unit to another unit. Suppose you want to convert the height of Mount Everest, 8848 meters, into kilometers. Based on the prefix *kilo-*, you know that 1 kilometer is 1000 meters. This ratio gives you two possible conversion factors.

$$\frac{1 \text{ km}}{1000 \text{ m}} \qquad \frac{1000 \text{ m}}{1 \text{ km}}$$

Since you are converting from meters to kilometers, the number should get smaller. Multiplying by the conversion factor on the left yields a smaller number.

$$8848 \text{ m} \times \frac{1 \text{ km}}{1000 \text{ m}} = 8.848 \text{ km}$$

Notice that the meter units cancel, leaving you with kilometers (the larger unit).

To convert 8.848 kilometers back into meters, multiply by the conversion factor on the right. Since you are converting from kilometers to meters, the number should get larger.

$$8.848 \text{ km} \times \frac{1000 \text{ m}}{1 \text{ km}} = 8848 \text{ m}$$

In this case, the kilometer units cancel, leaving you with meters.

Comparing Precision

Materials
3 plastic bottles of different sizes, beaker, graduated cylinder

Procedure

1. Draw a data table with three rows and three columns. Label the columns Estimate, Beaker, and Graduated Cylinder.

2. Record your estimate of the volume of a plastic bottle in your data table. Then, fill the bottle with water and pour the water into the beaker. Read and record the volume of the water.

3. Pour the water from the beaker into the graduated cylinder. Read and record the volume of water.

4. Repeat Steps 2 and 3 with two other plastic bottles.

Analyze and Conclude

1. **Analyzing Data** Review your volume measurements for one of the bottles. How many significant figures does the volume measured with the beaker have? How many significant figures does the volume measured with the graduated cylinder have?

2. **Comparing and Contrasting** Which provided a more precise measurement— the beaker or the graduated cylinder?

3. **Inferring** How could you determine the accuracy of your measurements?

Analyze and Conclude
1. Answers will vary, depending on the size of the beaker and graduated cylinder. Typically, the graduated cylinder measurement will have more significant figures than the beaker measurement.
2. The graduated cylinder
3. By comparing them to measurements made with a container known to be accurate **Visual, Logical**

Limits of Measurement

Suppose you wanted to measure how much time it takes for you to eat your breakfast. Figure 18 shows two clocks you could use—an analog clock and a digital clock. The analog clock displays time to the nearest minute. The digital clock displays time to the nearest second (or one sixtieth of a minute). Which clock would you choose?

Precision The digital clock offers more precision. **Precision** is a gauge of how exact a measurement is. According to the analog clock, it might take you 5 minutes to eat your breakfast. Using the digital clock, however, you might measure 5 minutes and 15 seconds, or 5.25 minutes. The second measurement has more significant figures. **Significant figures** are all the digits that are known in a measurement, plus the last digit that is estimated. The time recorded as 5.25 minutes has three significant figures. The time recorded as 5 minutes has one significant figure. The fewer the significant figures, the less precise the measurement is.

When you make calculations with measurements, the uncertainty of the separate measurements must be correctly reflected in the final result. ● **The precision of a calculated answer is limited by the least precise measurement used in the calculation.** So if the least precise measurement in your calculation has two significant figures, then your calculated answer can have at most two significant figures.

Suppose you measure the mass of a piece of iron to be 34.73 grams on an electronic balance. You then measure the volume to be 4.42 cubic centimeters. What is the density of the iron?

$$\text{Density} = \frac{34.73 \text{ g}}{4.42 \text{ cm}^3} = 7.857466 \text{ g/cm}^3$$

Your answer should have only three significant figures because the least precise measurement, the volume, has three significant figures. Rounding your answer to three significant figures gives you a density of 7.86 grams per cubic centimeter.

Accuracy Another important quality in a measurement is its accuracy. **Accuracy** is the closeness of a measurement to the actual value of what is being measured. For example, suppose the digital clock in Figure 18 is running 15 minutes slow. Although the clock would remain precise to the nearest second, the time displayed would not be accurate.

 Reading Checkpoint *What is accuracy?*

Figure 18 A more precise time can be read from the digital clock than can be read from the analog clock. The digital clock is precise to the nearest second, while the analog clock is precise to the nearest minute.

Science Skills **19**

Facts and Figures

Measuring Time Precisely As scientific knowledge increases, so does the accuracy and precision of time measurements. In the seventeenth century, Robert Hooke developed a mechanically powered clock. It was based on Galileo's 1583 observation that each swing of a pendulum takes the same amount of time. Early pendulum clocks were much more accurate and precise than hourglasses, which may have been precise to within an hour or two.

Quartz clocks, developed in 1929, are more precise. They generally lose only one five-hundredths of a second per year. Atomic clocks measure time using the frequencies at which atoms absorb or emit light. They are the most precise clocks today. Today's cesium atomic clocks are projected to neither lose nor gain a second in 1,000,000 years. Even more precise time measurements are based on pulsars, radio pulsations from collapsed stars.

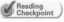
Science Skills **19**

Measuring Temperature

Use Visuals `L1`

Figure 19 Have students look at the figure. Ask, **Is any one of the three scales more accurate than the others?** *(No, they all can be used to measure temperature accurately.)* **Why do you think scientists use degrees Celsius for measuring temperature?** *(Some students may note that the range between the freezing and boiling points is 100 degrees and that like other SI units of measure, it can easily be divided into hundredths. Other students may say that it is just an agreed-upon standard.)* **Visual, Logical**

3 ASSESS

Evaluate Understanding `L2`

Ask students to write three conversion problems (with solutions) based on the prefixes used in the metric system. Have students take turns analyzing and solving the problems in class. Note that even incorrectly worded problems are useful, as students can be asked to identify and correct the errors.

Reteach `L1`

Use Figure 15 to help students understand how prefixes modify units of measurement. Give students examples such as kilogram, milliliter, and microsecond and ask students to name units that are larger and smaller.

Solutions

7. a. 3.72×10^{-11} g;
3.72×10^{-11} g $\times (\frac{1\text{ kg}}{1000\text{g}}) =$
3.72×10^{-14} kg
b. 4.5×10^{10} km;
4.5×10^{10} km $\times (\frac{1000\text{ m}}{1\text{ km}}) =$
4.5×10^{13} m
8. $V = (\pi r^2 \times l) =$
$(3.14)(6.5 \times 10^{-3} \text{ cm})^2 (1.1 \text{ cm}) =$
$(3.14)(6.5 \times 6.5)(10^{-3 \,-3})(1.1)$
$(\text{cm} \times \text{cm} \times \text{cm}) = 145.9 \times 10^{-6} \text{ cm}^3 =$
$1.5 \times 10^{-4} \text{ cm}^3$

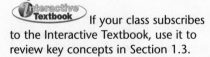 If your class subscribes to the Interactive Textbook, use it to review key concepts in Section 1.3.

Common Temperatures

	Fahrenheit (°F)	Celsius (°C)	Kelvin (K)
Water boils	212	100	373
Human body	98.6	37	310
Average room	68	20	293
Water freezes	32	0	273

Figure 19 Temperature can be expressed in degrees Fahrenheit, degrees Celsius, or kelvins.

Measuring Temperature

A **thermometer** is an instrument that measures temperature, or how hot an object is. The How It Works box on page 21 describes how a bulb thermometer measures temperature.

The two temperature scales that you are probably most familiar with are the Fahrenheit scale and the Celsius scale. On the Fahrenheit scale, water freezes at 32°F and boils at 212°F at sea level. On the Celsius (or centigrade) scale, water freezes at 0°C and boils at 100°C. A degree Celsius is almost twice as large as a degree Fahrenheit. There is also a difference of 32 degrees between the zero point of the Celsius scale and the zero point of the Fahrenheit scale. You can convert from one scale to the other by using one of the following formulas.

$$°C = \frac{5}{9}(°F - 32.0°) \qquad °F = \frac{9}{5}(°C) + 32.0°$$

The SI base unit for temperature is the kelvin (K). A temperature of 0 K, or 0 kelvin, refers to the lowest possible temperature that can be reached. In degrees Celsius, this temperature is $-273.15°C$. To convert between kelvins and degrees Celsius, use the following formula.

$$K = °C + 273$$

Figure 19 compares some common temperatures expressed in degrees Celsius, degrees Fahrenheit, and kelvins.

Section 1.3 Assessment

Reviewing Concepts

1. Why do scientists use scientific notation?
2. What system of units do scientists use for measurements?
3. How does the precision of measurements affect the precision of scientific calculations?
4. List the SI units for mass, length, and temperature.

Critical Thinking

5. **Applying Concepts** A bulb thermometer gives an indoor temperature reading of 21°C. A digital thermometer in the same room gives a reading of 20.7°C. Which device is more precise? Explain.

6. **Calculating** Convert −11°F into degrees Celsius, and then into kelvins.

Math Practice

7. Write the following measurements in scientific notation. Then convert each measurement into SI base units.
   a. 0.0000000000372 g
   b. 45,000,000,000 km
8. The liquid in a bulb thermometer falls 1.1 cm. Calculate the liquid's change in volume if the inner radius of the tube is 6.5×10^{-3} cm.

Section 1.3   Assessment

1. Scientific notation is useful because it makes very large or very small numbers easier to work with.
2. Scientists use a set of measuring units called SI.
3. The precision of a calculated answer is limited by the least precise measurement used in the calculation.

4. Kilogram (kg), meter (m), kelvin (K)
5. The digital thermometer (which yields a measurement with three significant figures) is more precise than the bulb thermometer (which yields a measurement of only two significant figures).
6. $-11°F = -24°C = 249$ K

Thermometer

A bulb thermometer consists of a sealed, narrow glass tube, called a capillary tube. It has a glass bulb at one end and is filled with colored alcohol or mercury. Because mercury is poisonous, mercury thermometers are rarely used in medicine. The thermometer works on the principle that the volume of a liquid changes when the temperature changes. When warmed, the liquid in the bulb takes up more space and moves up the capillary tube.

Interpreting Diagrams *Why is a thermometer with a narrow tube easier to read than one with a wide tube?*

Measuring temperature
Thermometers are useful scientific instruments. They can be used to measure the static temperature of a material, or to record the change in temperature of a substance being heated, as shown above.

Celsius (centigrade) temperature scale

Fahrenheit scale

Capillary tube

Colored liquid *The liquid moves up and down the capillary tube as the temperature changes.*

Bulb *The bulb contains the reservoir of liquid.*

Scale *The scale indicates the temperature according to how far up or down the capillary tube the liquid has moved.*

Wide or narrow?
The volume of a tube is calculated using the formula $V = \pi r^2 l$, where r is the radius and l is the length. For a given volume, if the radius of a tube is decreased (as in a capillary tube), the length of the liquid column increases. Any change in volume is then easier to see.

Compressed scale

Liquid rises more in a narrow tube for the same temperature change.

Liquid rises less in a wide tube for the same temperature change.

Expanded, easy-to-read scale

Thermometer [L2]

Liquid thermometers work because the liquid expands and contracts. Point out to students that all liquids do not expand at the same rate. Students may also be familiar with spiral metal thermometers found in outdoor thermometers, cooking thermometers, and thermostats. The spirals are strips made of two different metals. As the temperature changes, the two metals expand or contract differently. This expansion or contraction moves a pointer needle that points at the temperature.

Interpreting Diagrams The scale markings on a narrow-tube thermometer are further apart (and hence easier to read) than the corresponding markings on a wide-tube thermometer. It is also easier to record a temperature change on a thermometer with a narrow tube because for a given change in the thermometer liquid's volume, the narrow thermometer will show a greater change in the height of the liquid.
Logical

For Enrichment [L3]

Tell students that in the early 1600s, Galileo created a thermometer based on density. Interested students can find out more about Galileo's thermometer and create a brief report and illustration.
Portfolio

1 FOCUS

Objectives

1.4.1 **Organize** and **analyze** data using tables and graphs.

1.4.2 **Identify** the relationship between a manipulated variable and a responding variable.

1.4.3 **Explain** the importance of communicating data.

1.4.4 **Discuss** the process of peer review.

Reading Focus

Build Vocabulary L2

Paraphrase Tell students to write the vocabulary terms on a sheet of paper, leaving enough space beside each to write a definition and a mathematical formula. As students read the section, they should look for these terms. When they encounter one, they should write their own definition and a formula that illustrates the term.

Reading Strategy L2

a. A line represents variable *y* plotted vs. variable *x*. **b.** Showing how one variable responds to changes in another **c.** Scaled bars are used to represent various measurements. **d.** Comparing two sets of similar data **e.** A divided circle, with each "slice" representing a proportional fraction **f.** Showing how a part relates to the whole

2 INSTRUCT

Organizing Data
Build Reading Literacy L1

Preview Refer to page **36D** in **Chapter 2**, which provides the guidelines for a preview.

Ask students to skim Organizing Data. Tell them to pay particular attention to the figures. Ask, **Where else have you seen graphs?** (*Newspapers, television news, magazines, books, and so on*) Ask, **Why is data presented in graphs instead of in text?** (*Graphs make the data easier to read and understand.*)
Visual, Logical

1.4 Presenting Scientific Data

Reading Focus

Key Concepts
- How do scientists organize data?
- How can scientists communicate experimental data?

Vocabulary
- slope
- direct proportion
- inverse proportion

Reading Strategy

Comparing and Contrasting After you read this section, compare types of graphs by completing the table below.

Type of Graph	Description	Used For
Line	a. ___?___	b. ___?___
Bar	c. ___?___	d. ___?___
Circle	e. ___?___	f. ___?___

Much of the information you get every day comes from the news media. Newspapers, television, radio, and the Internet let you access a wealth of information about events going on in the world. But in order for news to be useful, it must be communicated. If a news reporter witnesses an event but doesn't report it, then he might as well not have seen it. If the event is reported, then it must be described in a clear, organized manner for it to be understood and appreciated. Like the news, scientific data become meaningful only when they are organized and communicated.

Organizing Data

Scientists accumulate vast amounts of data by observing events and making measurements. Interpreting these data can be a difficult task if they are not organized. **Scientists can organize their data by using data tables and graphs.** These tools make it easier to spot patterns or trends in the data that can support or disprove a hypothesis.

Data Tables The simplest way to organize data is to present them in a table. Figure 20 is a data table that shows the average annual precipitation for seven U.S. cities. The table relates two variables—a manipulated variable (location) and a responding variable (average annual precipitation).

Average Annual Precipitation for Selected U.S. Cities

City	Average Annual Precipitation (cm)
Buffalo, N.Y.	98.0
Chicago, Ill.	91.0
Colorado Springs, Colo.	41.2
Houston, Tex.	117.0
San Diego, Calif.	25.1
Tallahassee, Fla.	166.9
Tucson, Ariz.	30.5

Figure 20 Using a table is a simple way to present data visually.

22   *Chapter 1*

Section Resources

Print
- *Reading and Study Workbook With Math Support,* Section 1.4
- *Math Skills and Problem Solving Workbook,* Section 1.4
- *Transparencies,* Section 1.4

Technology
- *Interactive Textbook,* Section 1.4
- *Presentation Pro CD-ROM,* Section 1.4
- *Go Online,* NSTA SciLinks, Graphing

Mass vs. Volume of Water

Slope $= \dfrac{\text{Rise}}{\text{Run}} = \dfrac{5 \text{ g}}{5 \text{ cm}^3} = 1 \text{ g/cm}^3$

Rise = 5 g

Run = 5 cm³

Mass (g)

Volume (cm³)

Figure 21 Plotting the mass of water against the volume of water yields a straight line.
Using Graphs **What does the slope represent?**

Time to Fill a 1-gallon Pot With Water

Time (minutes)

Flow Rate (gallons per minute)

Figure 22 In an inverse proportion, the product of two variables remains constant. Each point on the graph above represents the same volume of water: 1 gallon.

Line Graphs A line graph is useful for showing changes that occur in related variables. In a line graph, the manipulated variable is generally plotted on the horizontal axis, or *x*-axis. The responding variable is plotted on the vertical axis, or *y*-axis, of the graph.

Figure 21 is a line graph that shows how the mass of water increases with volume. The data points yield a straight line. The steepness, or **slope,** of this line is the ratio of a vertical change to the corresponding horizontal change. The formula for the slope of a line is

$$\text{Slope} = \frac{\text{Rise}}{\text{Run}}$$

"Rise" represents the change in the *y*-variable. "Run" represents the corresponding change in the *x*-variable. Note that in Figure 21, because mass per unit volume is density, the slope represents the density of water.

The relationship between the mass and volume of water is an example of a direct proportion. A **direct proportion** is a relationship in which the ratio of two variables is constant. For example, suppose you have a 3-cubic-centimeter sample of water that has a mass of 3 grams. Doubling the volume of the sample to 6 cubic centimeters results in doubling the mass of the sample to 6 grams. Tripling the volume to 9 cubic centimeters results in tripling the mass to 9 grams.

Figure 22 shows how the flow rate of a water faucet affects the time required to fill a 1-gallon pot. Figure 22 illustrates an **inverse proportion,** a relationship in which the product of two variables is a constant. If you start with a flow rate of 0.5 gallon per minute, you will fill the pot in 2 minutes. If you double the flow rate to 1.0 gallon per minute, you reduce the time required to fill the pot to 1 minute, or one half of the original time.

Go Online
active art

For: Activity on plotting line graphs
Visit: PHSchool.com
Web Code: ccp-0014

Science Skills **23**

Data Analysis

Faster Than Speeding Data   L2

Answers

1. The greater the modem speed is, the shorter the upload time.

Data Transfer Rate vs. Modem Speed

2. Doubling the data transfer rate would halve the upload time.

For Extra Help   L1

Explain that modem speeds are similar to speed measurements for vehicles. For example, a car moving at 50 km/h will travel 50 km in one hour. The speed of the modems is measured in kilobits per second. If students need help constructing a line graph, refer them to the **Math Skills** in the **Skills and Reference Handbook** at the end of the student text. **Logical**

Address Misconceptions   L2

Some students may mistakenly think that graphs validate data. Point out to students that graphs are merely a method of presenting data. If necessary, work with students to graph a set of inaccurate data. For example, estimate the average daily temperatures for the past week, double them, and graph the results. Tell students that this graph is inaccurate because it is based on flawed data. Tell students that one way to validate data is to make multiple measurements. **Logical**

Use Visuals   L1

Figure 23 Ask, On the bar graph, which pairs of cities have similar annual precipitation? *(Buffalo and Chicago; San Diego and Tucson)* **Visual**

Data Analysis

Faster Than Speeding Data

A modem is a device used to send and receive data. For example, if you upload an image to a Web site, the modem in your computer converts the data of the image into a different format. The converted data are then sent through a telephone line or cable TV line. The smallest unit of data that can be read by a computer is a binary digit, or "bit." A bit is either a 0 or a 1. Computers process bits in larger units called bytes. A byte is a group of eight bits.

The table shows the data transfer rates for modems used in home computers. Data transfer rates are often measured in kilobits per second, or

Modem Speeds		
Type of Modem	Data Transfer Rate (kbps)	Upload Time for 1 MB (s)
56K dial-up	48	167
Cable (low-speed)	384	21
DSL (medium-speed)	512	16
DSL (high-speed)	768	10
Cable (high-speed)	2000	4

kbps. The time required to upload a 1-megabyte (MB) file is given for each rate listed.

1. **Using Graphs** Use the data in the table to create a line graph. Describe the relationship between data transfer rate and upload time.

2. **Inferring** How would doubling the data transfer rate affect the upload time?

Go Online
NSTA SCiLINKS

For: Links on graphing
Visit: www.SciLinks.org
Web Code: ccn-0014

Bar Graphs A bar graph is often used to compare a set of measurements, amounts, or changes. Figure 23 is a bar graph of the data from Figure 20. The bar graph makes it easy to see how the data for one city compare with the data for another.

Circle Graphs If you think of a pie cut into pieces, you have a mental model of a circle graph. A circle graph is a divided circle that shows how a part or share of something relates to the whole. Figure 24 is a circle graph that describes the composition of Earth's crust. The entire circle represents the mass of Earth's crust. Each "slice" of the circle represents a percentage of that mass corresponding to a specific substance.

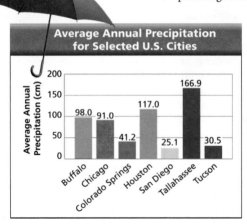

Average Annual Precipitation for Selected U.S. Cities

Buffalo 98.0, Chicago 91.0, Colorado Springs 41.2, Houston 117.0, San Diego 25.1, Tallahassee 166.9, Tucson 30.5

Figure 23 A bar graph is useful for comparing several measurements.

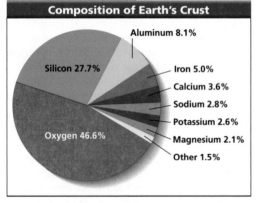

Composition of Earth's Crust

Oxygen 46.6%, Silicon 27.7%, Aluminum 8.1%, Iron 5.0%, Calcium 3.6%, Sodium 2.8%, Potassium 2.6%, Magnesium 2.1%, Other 1.5%

Figure 24 A circle graph is useful for showing how a part of something relates to the whole.

24   *Chapter 1*

Facts and Figures

Scientific Journals Thousands of scientific journals are published around the world. Some of them include articles on a broad range of topics, while others are narrowly focused. The decision that scientists make about where to publish their research depends on the nature of their results. Publishing in a well-known journal makes the research available to scientists in many different areas. Publishing in a narrowly focused journal means that the information will reach a smaller group of scientists. However, this small group includes scientists who are likely to need the information for their own research. Because it is not possible for scientists to read all the journals—or even all the journals in a single field—they must carefully choose the journals they read and the journals in which they publish their research.

Communicating Data

A crucial part of any scientific investigation is reporting the results. ⊙ **Scientists can communicate results by writing in scientific journals or speaking at conferences.** Scientists also exchange information through conversations, e-mails, and Web sites. Young scientists often present their research at science fairs like the one in Figure 25.

Different scientists may interpret the same data differently. This important notion is the basis for peer review, a process in which scientists examine other scientists' work. Not only do scientists share research with their peers, but they also invite feedback from those peers. Peer review encourages comments, suggestions, questions, and criticism from other scientists. Peer review can also help determine if data were reported accurately and honestly. Based on their peers' responses, the scientists who submitted their work for review can then reevaluate how to best interpret their data.

Figure 25 At a science fair, students communicate what knowledge they have gained by using scientific methods.

Communicating ideas and results is an important part of science. From published papers to an e-mail exchange between scientists, scientific writing must be clear and concise. Ask students to write one paragraph about the importance of written communication in science. Tell them to revise and rewrite their paragraph as needed.
Verbal, Portfolio

3 ASSESS
Evaluate
Understanding L2

Show students a graph or chart from a newspaper or similar source. Ask students to create a data table that represents the data on the graph or chart.

Reteach L1

Use Figures 21 and 22 to compare the meanings of *direct proportion* and *inverse proportion*.

Connecting Concepts

Possible answer: Scientific methods often require data to be organized and presented. For example, when making observations, you might want to organize them into a table. When testing a hypothesis, you might conduct an experiment that produces numerical data; such data must be recorded and organized in order to be useful. By presenting experimental data in a graph, you can analyze your measurements for trends that may help in evaluating your hypothesis.

Interactive Textbook If your class subscribes to the Interactive Textbook, use it to review key concepts in Section 1.4.

Section 1.4 Assessment

Reviewing Concepts

1. ⊙ How do scientists organize data?
2. ⊙ How can scientists communicate experimental results?
3. What does a given point represent on a line graph?
4. The density of copper is 8.92 g/cm³. If you plotted the mass of copper in grams versus the volume in cubic centimeters, what would the slope of the line be?

Critical Thinking

5. **Comparing and Contrasting** When would you choose a line graph to present data? When would you choose a bar graph?

6. **Using Tables and Graphs** Count the number of students in your class with blue eyes, brown eyes, and green eyes. Display these data in a table and bar graph.

Connecting Concepts

Scientific Methods Reread the description of scientific methods in Section 1.2. Then write a paragraph explaining which steps in a scientific method might require data to be organized. (*Hint:* You might use information diagrammed in Figure 7.)

Science Skills **25**

Section 1.4 Assessment

1. Scientists can organize their data by using tables and graphs.
2. Scientists can communicate results by writing in scientific journals and speaking at conferences.
3. A given point on a line graph generally represents two measurements corresponding to two related variables, one plotted on the horizontal axis and the other plotted on the vertical axis.

4. The slope would be 1.
5. A line graph is useful for showing how one variable changes with respect to another (for example, how one's distance changes with respect to time). A bar graph is useful for comparing a set of measurements (for example, how the average temperatures of various U.S. cities compare).
6. Students' graphs should show three bars representing three different groups of classmates (blue-eyed, brown-eyed, and green-eyed).

Download a worksheet on graphing for students to complete, and find additional teacher support from NSTA SciLinks.

Determining the Thickness of Aluminum Foil

Objective
After completing this activity, students will be able to
- perform conversions and calculations with metric units.
- compare the precision of measurements.

Skills Focus Measuring, Using Graphs, Calculating

Prep Time 10 minutes

Class Time 30 minutes

Safety Caution students to be careful with sharp instruments.

Teaching Tips
- Refer to Appendix B to show students how to use a balance.
- Aluminum foil is usually made of 8111 alloy aluminum, which is 98.5% aluminum, with small amounts of iron and silicon. Pure aluminum has a density of 2.70 g/cm³.
- In Step 5, remind students that there are 10 mm per cm. Therefore, there are 1000 mm³ per cm³. As a result, the density of aluminum is 0.00271 g/mm³.

Expected Outcome Precision increases with increased size of the foil square, but the estimate of thickness does not tend to increase or decrease consistently as a result.

Sample Data The average thickness of standard aluminum foil is 0.01625 mm. Manufacturers tolerate 10% variation in this thickness.

Length (mm)	Area (mm²)	Mass (g)	Volume (mm³)	Thickness (mm)
50.0	2500	0.10	36.9	0.015
100.0	10,000	0.40	148	0.015
200.0	40,000	1.60	590	0.0148

Determining the Thickness of Aluminum Foil

Many products such as aluminum foil are too thin to measure easily. However, it is important for manufacturers to know how thick they are. They wouldn't be useful if they were made too thick or too thin. In this lab, you will use the same method that manufacturers use to determine the thickness of aluminum foil.

Problem How can you determine the thickness of aluminum foil?

Materials
- metric ruler
- aluminum foil
- scissors
- balance
- graph paper

Skills Measuring, Calculating, Using Graphs

	Data Table			
Length (mm)	Area (mm²)	Mass (g)	Volume (mm³)	Thickness (mm)

Density of Alumnium = _____ g/mm³

Procedure

1. On a separate sheet of paper, make a copy of the data table shown. Include the information below the data table.

2. Cut out three squares of aluminum foil with sides of the following lengths: 50 mm, 100 mm, and 200 mm.

3. To determine the area of the 50-mm foil square, measure the length of one of its sides and then square it. Record the length and area in your data table.

4. Place the foil square on the balance to determine its mass. Record the mass of the foil square in your data table.

5. You will need the density of aluminum foil to calculate the volume of the foil square from its mass. The density of aluminum foil is 2.71 g/cm^3. Convert cm^3 to mm^3 and record the density of aluminum foil (in g/mm^3) on the line provided below your data table.

6. To determine the volume of the foil square, divide its mass by its density in g/mm^3. Record the volume in your data table.

7. To determine the thickness of the foil square, divide its volume by its area. Record this thickness in your data table.

8. Repeat Steps 3 through 7 using the 100-mm foil square.

9. Repeat Steps 3 through 7 using the 200-mm foil square.

10. Construct a graph of your data. Plot length on the horizontal axis and thickness on the vertical axis. Draw a straight line connecting all three points.

Analyze and Conclude

1. **Measuring** How many significant figures were there in your measurement of the length of each square of aluminum foil?

2. **Using Graphs** What effect, if any, did the length of the square have on your estimate of the thickness of the foil?

3. **Comparing** Which estimate of thickness was most precise? Explain your answer.

4. **Controlling Variables** What factors limited the precision of your measurements?

Go Further Aluminum is composed of small particles. Each particle has a diameter of 2.86 × 10^{-10} m. Calculate how many particles make up the thickness of the foil. Then, calculate the number of particles in the 50-mm square. Finally, determine the mass of one particle.

For: Data sharing
Visit: PHSchool.com
Web Code: ccd-0010

Analyze and Conclude

1. There were three significant figures for the 50-mm square and four for the 100- and 200-mm squares.

2. The length of the square had no effect on the estimated thickness of the foil.

3. The thickness calculated for the 200-mm square is the most precise because it has the most significant figures (three). The precision of a calculated answer is limited by the least precise measurement used in the calculation. For the 200-mm square, the least precise measurement (mass) has three significant figures. For the 50- and 100-mm squares, the least precise measurement (mass) has only two significant figures.

4. Precision was limited by the spacing of the smallest markings on the ruler, and the balance.
Logical

Go Further

Assuming that the particles (atoms) are spheres packed closely together so they are touching and arranged in orderly rows, the thickness of the foil can be expressed as a number of particles by converting the calculated thickness from units of mm to m and dividing by the diameter of a particle. This method leads to an estimated thickness of approximately 56,800 atoms for standard aluminum foil. The number of atoms in the foil can be found by dividing the volume of the foil by the volume of an atom. The mass of an aluminum atom (4.48 × 10^{-23} g) is calculated by dividing the mass of the foil by the number of atoms in the foil.
Logical

Students should see that increasing the size of the foil sample increases the precision, but not the value of the thickness measurement. Students' results will depend on their own data and the data on the site.

Study Tip

Gather Materials

Tell students to gather the materials they will need before they begin to study. Explain that students should also have available a few sheets of blank paper. As students study, they can write or sketch key ideas. Tell students that putting key ideas on paper can help them understand and remember the ideas later.

Thinking Visually

a. A fundamental unit of measurement
b. Meter
c. A unit of measurement that is formed by combining base units
d. Cubic meter (m^3)

Assessment

 If your class subscribes to the Interactive Textbook, your students can go online to access an interactive version of the Student Edition and a self-test.

Reviewing Content

1. c	**2.** d	**3.** b
4. b	**5.** c	**6.** b
7. c	**8.** b	**9.** c
10. c		

Understanding Concepts

11. Example: The study of Mars falls under the branch of space science. However, studying Mars might also involve analyzing the chemistry of substances found on Mars, which falls under physical science. If scientists search for evidence of life on Mars, then their studies might also fall under life science.
12. The goal of any scientific method is to solve a problem or to better understand an observed event.
13. Controlled experiments are useful in that they can show how one variable (the responding variable) changes with respect to another variable (the manipulated variable), while the remaining variables are controlled.
14. You might modify your hypothesis or formulate a new hypothesis based on your experimental results.

1.1 What is Science?

🌐 Key Concepts

- Science begins with curiosity and often ends with discovery.
- Science and technology are interdependent. Advances in one lead to advances in the other.
- Natural science is generally divided into three branches: physical science, Earth and space science, and life science.

Vocabulary

science, *p. 3*
technology, *p. 3*
chemistry, *p. 4*
physics, *p. 4*
geology, *p. 4*
astronomy, *p. 4*
biology, *p. 4*

1.2 Using a Scientific Approach

🌐 Key Concepts

- The goal of a scientific method is to solve a problem or to better understand an observed event.
- A scientific law describes an observed pattern in nature without attempting to explain it. The explanation of such a pattern is provided by a scientific theory.
- Scientific models make it easier to understand things that might be too difficult to observe directly.

Vocabulary

scientific method, *p. 7*
observation, *p. 8*
hypothesis, *p. 8*
manipulated variable, *p. 8*
responding variable, *p. 8*
controlled experiment, *p. 8*
scientific theory, *p. 9*
scientific law, *p. 9*
model, *p. 10*

1.3 Measurement

🌐 Key Concepts

- Scientific notation makes very large or very small numbers easier to work with.
- Scientists use a set of measuring units called SI.
- The precision of a calculation is limited by the least precise measurement used in the calculation.

Vocabulary

scientific notation, *p. 14*
length, *p. 16*
mass, *p. 16*
volume, *p. 16*
density, *p. 17*
conversion factor, *p. 18*
precision, *p. 19*
significant figures, *p. 19*
accuracy, *p. 19*
thermometer, *p. 20*

1.4 Presenting Scientific Data

🌐 Key Concepts

- Scientists can organize their data by using data tables and graphs.
- Scientists can communicate results by writing in journals or speaking at conferences.

Vocabulary

slope, *p. 23*
direct proportion, *p. 23*
inverse proportion, *p. 23*

Thinking Visually

Using Tables Use information from the chapter to complete the table below.

Type of Unit	Description	Example
Base	**a.** ?	**b.** ?
Derived	**c.** ?	**d.** ?

⏱ Chapter Resources

Print

- ***Chapter and Unit Tests,*** Chapter 1 Test A and Test B
- ***Test Prep Resources,*** Chapter 1

Technology

- ***Computer Test Bank,*** Chapter Test 1
- ***Interactive Textbook,*** Chapter 1
- ***Go Online,*** PHSchool.com, Chapter 1

Assessment

Reviewing Content

Choose the letter that best answers the question or completes the statement.

1. The application of knowledge to solve practical problems is known as
  a. science.
  b. curiosity.
  c. technology.
  d. experimentation.

2. Which is not a branch of natural science?
  a. physical science
  b. life science
  c. Earth science
  d. social science

3. What is the purpose of an experiment?
  a. to communicate data
  b. to test a hypothesis
  c. to prove a scientific law
  d. none of the above

4. A representation of an object or event is called
  a. a scientific law.
  b. a model.
  c. a hypothesis.
  d. a variable.

5. Which value is equivalent to 5×10^6?
  a. five thousand
  b. fifty thousand
  c. five million
  d. fifty million

6. What is the SI base unit of mass?
  a. gram
  b. kilogram
  c. milligram
  d. pound

7. An electric generator produces 10 megawatts. This amount is equivalent to
  a. 10,000 watts.
  b. 1,000,000 watts.
  c. 10,000,000 watts.
  d. 0.010 watt.

8. Which of the following is a ratio of equivalent measurements that is used to convert a quantity expressed in one unit to another unit?
  a. slope
  b. conversion factor
  c. derived unit
  d. density

9. When the ratio of two variables is constant, their relationship can be described as
  a. inversely proportional.
  b. interdependent.
  c. directly proportional.
  d. parallel.

10. Which of the following would best suit data that describe how a part relates to the whole?
  a. line graph
  b. bar graph
  c. circle graph
  d. scientific notation

Understanding Concepts

11. Give an example of a case where the branches of natural science appear to overlap.

12. What is the goal of a scientific method?

13. How are controlled experiments useful?

14. Suppose you perform an experiment, and the resulting data do not support your hypothesis. What is the next step you might take?

15. What are some safety precautions that you should follow when working in the laboratory?

16. What is scientific notation?

17. What are the SI base units for length and temperature?

18. How do derived units differ from base units?

19. How is the precision of a calculated result related to the precision of the measurements used in the calculation?

20. How can you convert a temperature expressed in degrees Celsius to kelvins?

21. Which of the following graphs describes a direct proportion?

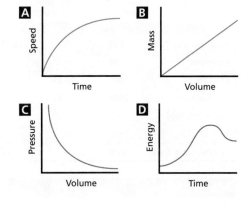

22. Why is it important for scientists to communicate their results?

Assessment (continued)

15. Some safety precautions you should follow when working in the laboratory include reading through all the steps of any activity, making sure you understand the entire procedure, following directions exactly, and asking your teacher if you're not sure about how to proceed.

16. Scientific notation is a way of expressing a value as the product of a number between 1 and 10 and a power of 10.

17. The SI base unit for length is the meter. The SI base unit for temperature is the kelvin.

18. Derived units are combinations of base units. A base unit is a fundamental unit of measurement.

19. The precision of a calculated answer is limited by the precision of the measurements used in the calculation. For example, if the least precise measurement in a calculation has three significant figures, then the calculated answer can have at most three significant figures.

20. To convert from degrees Celsius to kelvins, you can use the following formula: $K = °C + 273$

21. B

22. It is important for scientists to communicate their results so that they can share the knowledge they have gained with others, and also get feedback from other scientists.

Homework Guide

Section	Questions
1.1	1–2, 11, 33
1.2	3–4, 12–15, 23–24, 26, 31–32
1.3	5–7, 16–19, 25, 28, 30
1.4	8–10, 20–22, 27, 29

Assessment (continued)

Chapter 1

Critical Thinking

23. Some students may hypothesize that objects of greater mass fall to the ground faster than objects of lesser mass. Others may hypothesize that mass does not affect the rate at which objects fall.

24. In designing their experiments, students might suggest dropping a heavy object and a light object from the same height and measuring how long each takes to fall to the ground. (A more qualitative design might suggest releasing both objects simultaneously and observing if one reaches the ground before the other, without taking any measurements.) Height is controlled. The manipulated variable is the mass of the object. The responding variable is time.

25. 13.5 km

26. Everything drawn on a map represents a thing or place that is scaled down. For example, solid lines on the map might represent streets and highways; a green polygon on the map might represent a park; a gray square on the map might represent a building. If you plan a trip to an unfamiliar place, a map can help you by showing you how the streets are oriented. If a road forks on the map, you will see it fork as you travel on the road. If you navigate two rights and then a left on the map, you should be able to match that route to the environment you travel in.

27. Average speed = 80 km/h

Driving Distance vs. Time

Math Skills

28. 16°C; 289 K

29. The mass of the pennies is directly proportional to the number of pennies. Measuring the mass of one penny yields a ratio (i.e., grams per penny) that is constant. You can then measure the mass of all the pennies. Dividing the total mass by the mass of one penny yields the total number of pennies.

30. Between 6×10^{12} and 1.2×10^{13} stars

Critical Thinking

23. Formulating Hypotheses Suppose you want to know if objects with different masses fall to the ground at different rates. State a hypothesis about falling objects.

24. Designing Experiments Explain how you can test the hypothesis in Question 23. What will be the manipulated variable in your experiment? What will be the responding variable?

25. Calculating A triathlete enters a race in which he swims 500 meters, runs 3000 meters, and cycles 10.0 kilometers. What is the total distance of the race in kilometers?

26. Using Models Explain how a map of your town is an example of a model. How does this model help you plan a trip to an unfamiliar place?

27. Using Graphs Use the data in the table below to create a line graph. Plot distance on the vertical axis. Plot driving time on the horizontal axis. Calculate the slope of the line. If speed is the ratio of distance to time, what is the average driving speed of the trip?

Driving Distance and Time		
City	Distance From Start (km)	Driving Time From Start (h)
New York City, N.Y.	750	9.5
Cleveland, Ohio	1300	16.25
Chicago, Ill.	1900	23.25
Omaha, Nebr.	2100	26.25
Cheyenne, Wyo.	2900	36.25
Salt Lake City, Utah	3600	45
San Francisco, Calif.	4800	60

Math Skills

28. Calculating If a thermometer outside your classroom indicates a temperature of 61 degrees Fahrenheit, what is the temperature in degrees Celsius? In kelvins?

29. Problem Solving Suppose you have a large coffee can full of pennies. How can you estimate how much money the can contains without counting all the coins? (*Hint:* What is the relationship between the mass of pennies and the number of pennies?)

30. Calculating The Milky Way galaxy contains between 200 and 400 billion stars. Estimate the number of stars in a cluster of 30 galaxies similar in size to the Milky Way. Your answer should consist of a low estimate and a high estimate, both expressed in scientific notation.

Concepts in Action

31. Designing Experiments A zookeeper notices that elephants become restless shortly before an earthquake. The zookeeper forms a hypothesis that, just before an earthquake occurs, an elephant detects a sound that humans are unable to hear. How could this hypothesis be tested?

32. Making Judgments You see an advertisement on television for an over-the-counter medication that has been "scientifically proven to work." How could you find out if this claim is true?

33. Writing in Science Write a paragraph describing how advances in technology have affected your life. (*Hint:* The first sentence should state the paragraph's main idea.)

Performance-Based Assessment

Designing Experiments Grocery stores carry many brands of household detergents. Design an experiment to compare a more expensive brand of detergent with a less expensive one. Is one brand better for some purposes than the other?

For: Self-grading assessment
Visit: PHSchool.com
Web Code: cca-0015

Concepts in Action

31. The zookeeper could test his hypothesis by installing an instrument that can detect sounds that are too low or too high in frequency for humans to hear. Sounds detected by the instrument could then be compared to the elephant's behavior and the timing of earthquakes.

32. You could test the claim by finding out what has been reported or written about the medication advertised. You could do an Internet search, query the manufacturer, or query a doctor.

33. Students may describe how certain advances in technology have made their lives more convenient. For example, advances in computer technology (such as faster processors and modems) have made it easier for people to communicate, access information, study, shop, and entertain.

Standardized Test Prep for Indiana

Standardized Test Prep for Indiana

1. A 2. C 3. B
4. E 5. D 6. C

Test-Taking Tip

Calculating

Checking units is a very important part of problem solving. Keep these tips in mind when solving problems involving unit conversions:

- A conversion factor is a ratio of equivalent measurements.

- Write horizontal fractions to help keep track of conversion factors. For example, write $\frac{32\ g}{cm^3}$ as opposed to 32 g/cm^3.

- Line up conversion factors so that the unit you are converting cancels.

- If you have to square or cube a unit, make sure you square or cube the entire conversion factor.

- Make a reality check of your answer. If the units are wrong, your calculations are probably wrong. Also, verify that the numerical answer is reasonable.

Practice using these tips in Questions 2 and 4.

Choose the letter that best answers the question or completes the statement.

1. In a controlled experiment,
- (A) there are multiple responding variables.
- (B) the responding variable is kept constant.
- (C) the manipulated variable is kept constant.
- (D) the responding variable is deliberately changed.
- (E) only one variable at a time is deliberately changed.

2. The speed of an object indicates how far it travels in a given amount of time. If an electron travels 2.42×10^8 meters in 2.00 seconds, what is the speed of this electron in cm/s?
- (A) 1.21×10^8 cm/s
- (B) 4.84×10^8 cm/s
- (C) 1.21×10^{10} cm/s
- (D) 2.42×10^{10} cm/s
- (E) 4.84×10^{10} cm/s

3. A doctor measures the temperature of a patient to be 101°F. What is this temperature in kelvins?
- (A) 38.3 K
- (B) 73.8 K
- (C) 214 K
- (D) 311 K
- (E) 346 K

4. The density of seawater is 1.024×10^3 kg/m^3. What is the density of seawater in g/cm^3?
- (A) 102.4 g/cm^3
- (B) 1.024×10^{-6} g/cm^3
- (C) 1.024 g/cm^3
- (D) 3.072×10^3 g/cm^3
- (E) 1.024×10^9 g/cm^3

5. A student conducts an experiment by dropping a basketball and a box of cereal of the same weight from the top of a building. The student measures the time it takes for each object to strike the ground. What was the student's hypothesis?

- (A) A basketball weighs more than cereal.
- (B) Curved objects travel through the air faster than flat objects.
- (C) Heavier objects travel through the air faster than lighter objects.
- (D) Gravity pulls on objects of the same weight with the same force.
- (E) Heavier objects strike the ground with a greater force than lighter objects.

6. If two variables are directly proportional, then
- (A) an increase in one variable causes a decrease in the other variable.
- (B) the product of the two variables is constant.
- (C) the ratio of the two variables is constant.
- (D) neither variable is the controlled variable.
- (E) both variables are constant.

 Standards Guide

Question	Standards
2	ICP.7.2
5	ICP.1.3

Performance-Based Assessment

Students may think of different ways to evaluate/measure the responding variable (how effectively a detergent cleans) in their experiments. Another important aspect of the experimental design is how to make the stains a controlled variable, for in order for a comparison of two cleaning agents to be exact, they must be tested on uniformly stained surfaces.

Your students can independently test their knowledge of the chapter and print out their test results for your files.

CHEMISTRY

The Interactive Textbook, found both online and on CD-ROM, includes the following materials.

Activities and Labs

Worksheets for each activity and lab are available as PDF files with clickable safety symbols.

Colorful Visuals

All art and relevant photographs from the Student Edition can be accessed in the Interactive Textbook.

Self Assessment

Provides additional assessment opportunities and questions:
- Interactive Reading Checkpoint questions
- Interactive Figure caption questions
- Chapter Pretests with hints
- Printable Chapter Assessments
- Standardized Test Prep

My Notes

Students can enter answers for questions or make notes about what they are learning.

References

Provides a drop-down menu of resources:
- Skills and Reference Handbook
- Glossary

Careers

Information on science careers is available through the Career page on www.PHSchool.com.

Fireworks Display in ▶ Sydney, Australia
When fireworks explode, they produce colorful displays of light.

32

Chemistry

Focus on the BIG Ideas

Chemistry is the study of the composition, structure, properties, and reactions of matter. Matter that always has exactly the same composition is classified as a substance. Elements are the simplest substances. The smallest particle of an element is an atom.

There are only about 100 elements. In the modern periodic table, elements are arranged by increasing atomic number (number of protons). Based on their chemical and physical properties, elements are classified as metals, nonmetals, and metalloids.

Unlike physical changes, chemical changes involve a change in the composition of matter. During a reaction, chemical bonds in the reactants are broken and chemical bonds in the products are formed. Mass is conserved in chemical reactions.

Nuclear changes (such as radioactivity) involve the conversion of atoms of one element to atoms of another. During nuclear reactions, mass can be created or destroyed, and it is the total sum of mass and energy that is conserved.

For students, the PHSchool.com Web site contains interactive data-sharing labs, interactive self-assessments, and science-related links. The PHSchool.com Web site also provides teachers with curriculum support, reference links, a way to create state-specific lesson plans, and instructions on how to create a Web page.

NSTA SciLinks provides student worksheets for specific topics with additional teacher support.

Chemistry   33

Use the following videos to help students understand the concepts in each chapter.

Chapter 1 Science Skills
Cracking the Case
Describes how forensic scientists analyze evidence left at the scene of a crime.

Chapter 2 Properties of Matter
Fresh-Squeezed Water
Shows and discusses equipment that is used to distill seawater into fresh water.

Chapter 3 States of Matter
Up, Up, and Away
Features hot-air balloons and discusses how they ascend and descend.

Chapter 4 Atomic Structure
Go For Gold
Discusses how some properties of gold are related to the structure of gold and how the surface of gold can be viewed with an electron microscope.

Chapter 5 The Periodic Table
You Are What You Eat
Discusses what scientists can learn from studying mummies, including finding clues to what they ate.

Chapter 6 Chemical Bonds
Good Conduct
Shows how silicon is refined and processed into chips and discusses how doping silicon increases its conductivity.

Chapter 7 Chemical Reactions
Taming the Flames
Shows how firefighters use a combination of chemistry and courage to put out wildfires.

Chapter 8 Solutions, Acids, and Bases
Suspended in Blood
Explains how the red blood cells, white blood cells, and platelets in your blood play a crucial role in keeping your body healthy.

Chapter 9 Carbon Chemistry
Clean Energy
Provides a closer look at fuel cells, a clean-energy technology that may power the cars of the future.

Chapter 10 Nuclear Chemistry
Nuclear Medicine
Explains how nuclear radiation and radioisotopes are used in the detection and treatment of many cancers.

Go Online
SCIENCE NEWS®

Students can find current information about specific discoveries in science from *Science News*.

Go Online
PLANETDIARY

Planet Diary contains current geological, astronomical, meteorological, and environmental news from around the world. Additional information and activities are included in the Phenomena Backgrounders.

Careers in Chemistry

The educational requirements for the chemistry-related careers on these two pages range from a high-school diploma to a master's degree.

Toxicologist

Connection to Chapter 5
Characteristics Good at written and oral communications, detail-oriented, computer literate
Preparation Courses in biology, human anatomy and physiology, environmental science
Employers Government agencies (USFDA and EPA), pharmaceutical companies, universities

Forensic Chemist

Connection to Chapter 2
Characteristics Curious, analytical, accurate record keeper, impartial, detail-oriented, capable of preparing evidence for presentation in court as well as testifying as an expert witness
Preparation Courses in biology, physics, English composition, metallurgy. Some states require several years of forensic laboratory experience.
Employers Local, state, and federal governments, universities, forensic laboratories, hospitals

Food Science Technician

Connection to Chapter 4
Characteristics Good at written and oral communications, analytical, able to work independently or as part of a team, computer literate
Preparation Courses in chemistry, biochemistry, microbiology, food engineering, basic business principles, statistics
Employers United States Food and Drug Administration (FDA), food processing industry, universities

Careers in Chemistry

What do the people on these pages have in common? They all use chemistry on the job. From toxicologists to firefighters, there are many exciting chemistry careers to choose from.

Toxicologist
Toxicologists determine the effects natural and synthetic chemicals may have on people, other organisms, and the environment. Toxicologists conduct experiments to find out whether certain chemicals are dangerous or safe to use. They also determine how much of a given chemical could be harmful.
Educational requirements Four-year bachelor of science degree, majoring in chemistry

Food Science Technician
Food science technicians help to ensure that the food you eat is healthful, safe, and flavorful. They use their knowledge of chemistry to develop new or better ways of preserving, processing, packaging, and storing foods. Some food service technicians analyze food content to determine levels of vitamins, fat, carbohydrates, or protein.
Educational requirements Four-year college degree, majoring in chemistry

Forensic Chemist
Forensic chemists help law enforcement officials solve crimes. At a crime scene, a forensic chemist carefully gathers all the physical evidence and brings it back to the laboratory for analysis and identification. Physical evidence may include fibers, paints, glass, and stains.
Educational requirements Master's degree in chemistry

34

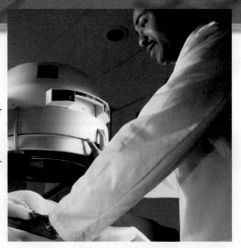

Nuclear Medicine Technologist

Nuclear medicine technologists apply their knowledge of nuclear chemistry to help diagnose diseases and disorders. They prepare and administer radioactive substances and use radiation detection devices to trace these substances in the body. Nuclear medicine technologists work directly with patients and closely with nuclear medicine physicians.

Educational requirements Two-year community or junior college degree, or a one-year certificate in nuclear medicine technology

Firefighter

Firefighters are highly trained professionals who respond to fires, hazardous chemical spills, and medical emergencies. When responding to a fire or spill, firefighters have to know what effects different chemicals have in different situations.

Educational requirements High-school diploma

Pharmacist

A pharmacist dispenses drugs prescribed by physicians and dentists and gives information to patients about the drugs and their uses. Pharmacists understand the uses, effects, and composition of drugs, including their chemical properties and biological side effects.

Educational requirements Two years of college, four-year college of pharmacy program, internship, and passage of a state board examination

For: Career links
Visit: PHSchool.com
Web Code: ccb-1000

Nuclear Medicine Technologist

Connection to Chapter 10
Characteristics Good at written and oral communications, computer literate
Preparation Courses in human anatomy and physiology, physics, mathematics, medical technology, medical ethics, CPR certification, equipment certification
Employers Medical centers and hospitals, independent imaging centers, research centers

Firefighter

Connection to Chapter 7
Characteristics Demonstrate physical dexterity and strength, be mentally alert and a team player
Preparation 18–31 years of age, have corrected 20/20 vision, score well on the examination given by local governments. Many fire departments now require an Emergency Medical Technician (EMT) certificate as a condition of employment.
Employers Local, state, and federal governments

Pharmacist

Connection to Chapter 8
Characteristics Accurate record keeper, good at written and oral communications, conscientious, detail-oriented, desire to help others
Preparation Courses in mathematics, biology, and physics
Employers Hospitals and medical centers, independent pharmacies, drug companies, universities

Career Teaching Strategy

You can have students find out more about chemistry-related careers by looking for information in the library or on the Internet. Students can then construct a table that lists the position, describes the nature of the work, educational and training requirements, employment outlook, working conditions, and other necessary information.

Planning Guide

SECTION OBJECTIVES	STANDARDS		ACTIVITIES and LABS
	NATIONAL	STATE	
2.1 Classifying Matter, pp. 38–44 🕐 1 block or 2 periods **2.1.1 Classify** pure substances as elements or compounds. **2.1.2 Describe** the characteristics of an element and the symbols used to identify elements. **2.1.3 Describe** the characteristics of a compound. **2.1.4 Distinguish** pure substances from mixtures. **2.1.5 Classify** mixtures as heterogeneous or homogeneous. **2.1.6 Classify** mixtures as solutions, suspensions, or colloids.	A-1, A-2, G-1, G-2, G-3	ICP5.1	**SE** Inquiry Activity: What Properties Could You Use to Describe Materials? p. 37　**L2** **TE** Teacher Demo: Transmission Versus Scattering, p. 43　**L2**
2.2 Physical Properties, pp. 45–51 🕐 1 block or 2 periods **2.2.1 Describe** physical properties of matter. **2.2.2 Identify** substances based on their physical properties. **2.2.3 Describe** how properties are used to choose materials. **2.2.4 Describe** methods used to separate mixtures. **2.2.5 Describe** evidence that indicates a physical change is taking place.	A-1, A-2, B-2, E-2, F-1	ICP3.2, ICP3.3, ICP5.1	**SE** Quick Lab: Comparing Heat Conductors, p. 46　**L2** **TE** Teacher Demo: Comparing Melting Points, p. 48　**L2** **TE** Build Science Skills: Applying Concepts, p. 50　**L2** **LM** Investigation 2B: Determining the Densities of Liquids　**L1**
2.3 Chemical Properties, pp. 54–58 🕐 1 block or 2 periods **2.3.1 Describe** chemical properties of matter. **2.3.2 Describe** clues that indicate that a chemical change is taking place. **2.3.3 Distinguish** chemical changes from physical changes.	A-1, A-2, B-3	ICP5.6, ICP3.2	**SE** Quick Lab: Identifying a Chemical Change, p. 56　**L2** **SE** Forensics Lab: Using Properties to Identify Materials, pp. 60–61　**L2** **TE** Teacher Demo: Oxygen Is Needed, p. 55　**L2** **LM** Investigation 2A: Recognizing Chemical and Physical Changes　**L2**

RESOURCES
PRINT and TECHNOLOGY

RSW Section 2.1 **L1**

MSPS Section 2.1 **L2**

T Chapter 2 Pretest **L2**

Section 2.1 **L2**

P Chapter 2 Pretest **L2**

Section 2.1 **L2**

SC/LINKS GO Mixtures **L2**

RSW Section 2.2 **L1**

RSW Math Skill **L2**

DC Fresh-Squeezed Water **L2**

T Section 2.2 **L2**

P Section 2.2 **L2**

SCIENCE NEWS GO Properties of matter **L2**

RSW Section 2.3 **L1**

T Section 2.3 **L2**

P Section 2.3 **L2**

SC/LINKS GO Chemical and physical changes **L2**

SECTION
ASSESSMENT

SE Section 2.1 Assessment, p. 44

iT Section 2.1

SE Section 2.2 Assessment, p. 51

iT Section 2.2

SE Section 2.3 Assessment, p. 58

iT Section 2.3

Go Online

Go online for these Internet resources.

PHSchool.com
Web Code: cca-1020
Web Code: cch-1020

NSTA SC/LINKS
Web Code: ccn-1021
Web Code: ccn-1023

SCIENCE NEWS
Web Code: cce-1022

Materials for Activities and Labs

Quantities for each group

STUDENT EDITION

Inquiry Activity, p. 37
rubber band, copper wire, steel paper clip, wooden toothpick, graphite pencil filler

Quick Lab, p. 46
2 plastic foam cups, scissors, metric ruler, metal rod, wooden rod, 2 liquid crystal thermometers, hot water, clock or watch with second hand

Quick Lab, p. 56
3 test tubes; test-tube rack; glass-marking pencil; 3 10-mL graduated cylinders; solutions of copper sulfate, calcium chloride, and sodium chloride

Forensics Lab, pp. 60–61
2 spot plates, glass-marking pencil, 5 laboratory spatulas, cornstarch, baking soda, baking powder, wash bottle of water, vinegar, iodine solution, sample from crime scene, sample from suspect's shoe

TEACHER'S EDITION

Teacher Demo, p. 43
2 beakers, water, iodine solution, table salt, stirring rods, milk, fish tank, flashlight, white paper

Teacher Demo, p. 48
water, ethanol, foam cups, freezer, large beaker, thermometer

Build Science Skills, p. 50
a mixture of salt, sand, and iron filings; beaker; magnet; plastic bag; water; funnel; filter paper

Build Science Skills, p. 52
tap water, bottled water, distilled water

Teacher Demo, p. 55
2 small candles, matches, large beaker

Chapter Assessment

CHAPTER ASSESSMENT

SE Chapter Assessment, pp. 63–64
CUT Chapter 2 Test A, B
CTB Chapter 2
iT Chapter 2
PHSchool.com GO
Web Code: cca-1020

STANDARDIZED TEST PREP

SE Chapter 2, p. 65
TP Diagnose and Prescribe

Interactive Textbook with assessment at PHSchool.com

Before you teach

From the Author

David Frank
Ferris State University

Big Ideas

Chemistry, at its heart, is the study of matter, although the focus of the study can vary among composition, structure, properties, and reactions. In this chapter, students will be introduced to matter through a discussion of properties that students can observe. In later chapters, students will study theories that explain the properties of matter, including the kinetic theory and the atomic theory.

Matter and Change In Section 2.1, students learn how the composition of a material can be used to classify the material as a pure substance or a mixture, and how the distribution of materials within a mixture can be used to classify the mixture as homogeneous or heterogeneous.

In this text, *material* is used to describe a particular type of matter, pure substance or mixture. The term *substance* is synonymous with *pure substance*. Thus, *substance* is used to refer to only elements and compounds.

In Sections 2.2 and 2.3, students are introduced to some properties that can be used to describe materials. Terms such as *viscosity* and *malleability* may be unfamiliar, but students should be familiar with the behaviors that they describe from such experiences as pouring ketchup or bending a paper clip. In Sections 2.2 and 2.3, students also begin to distinguish physical from chemical changes.

Take the opportunity to show students the relationships among different topics. For example, air is primarily a mixture of oxygen and nitrogen, while water is a compound of oxygen and hydrogen. A physical change occurs when oxygen and nitrogen are mixed. A difference in boiling points can be used to separate the mixture. A chemical change occurs when oxygen and hydrogen react and form water. A difference in physical properties cannot be used to separate water into its component elements.

Because Chapter 2 is an introductory chapter, many of the topics introduced in this chapter will be addressed in greater detail in later chapters: melting and boiling in Chapter 3, atoms in Chapter 4, elements in Chapter 5, chemical changes in Chapter 7, and solutions in Chapter 8.

Chemistry Refresher

Classifying Matter 2.1

The system for classifying matter presented in Section 2.1 is the first of many classification systems students will encounter in the chemistry unit. Students will also study solids, liquids, and gases; metals, nonmetals, and metalloids; acids, bases, and salts; and classes of organic compounds, as well as radioactive and non-radioactive isotopes. In Section 2.1, substances are classified as pure substances or mixtures. The key difference between pure substances and mixtures is uniformity of composition. The composition of a pure substance is constant. The composition of a mixture can vary widely.

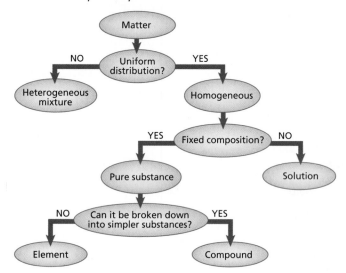

The key difference between heterogeneous mixtures and homogeneous mixtures is uniformity of distribution. Chemists agree that solutions are homogeneous mixtures. But they do not always agree on the classification of suspensions and colloids. Some classify suspensions and colloids as heterogeneous mixtures. Some classify colloids as homogeneous mixtures. Some say that a colloid falls somewhere between a solution and a suspension.

Properties of Solutions, Colloids, and Suspensions

Property	Solution	Colloid	Suspension
Particle type	ions, atoms, small molecules	large molecules or particles	large particles or aggregates
Particle size (approximate)	0.1–1 nm	1–100 nm	100 nm and larger
Effect of light	no scattering	scattering	scattering
Effect of gravity	does not separate	does not separate	separates into layers
Filtration	cannot separate	cannot separate	can separate
Uniformity	homogeneous	borderline	heterogeneous

For: Teaching methods for properties of matter
Visit: www.SciLinks.org/PDLinks
Web Code: ccn-0299

Criteria used to distinguish among types of mixtures are helpful but not 100% definitive. For example, the particles in a colloid are supposed to remain dispersed, but many people classify dust and paint as colloids even though dust can settle out of the air and paint sometimes needs to be stirred. Also, a solution is supposed to be transparent, but that description would not fit a concentrated solution of iodine in alcohol.

Address Misconceptions

All of the particles in mixtures and solutions are similar in size. If this were true, mixtures could not be separated by filtration. For a strategy to overcome this misconception, see **Address Misconceptions** on **page 50.**

Classifying Properties 2.2 and 2.3

Students may focus on properties related to a specific sample (mass, volume, and shape) rather than properties that depend on the type of material used in the object. The terms used to describe these two classes of properties are extrinsic and intrinsic, respectively. This chapter focuses on intrinsic physical and chemical properties. Intrinsic properties such as viscosity, malleability, and density do not vary with the size of the sample.

It can be difficult to classify some properties as chemical or physical. An argument can be made that taste and smell are chemical properties because their detection depends on interactions between chemicals and sensory receptors in the mouth and nose. A substance dissolving in a solvent may be classified as a physical change or a chemical change depending on whether the substance dissociates (table salt), disperses (sucrose), or ionizes (hydrogen chloride) as it dissolves. (These processes are described in Section 8.1.)

Address Misconceptions

There is no distinction between chemical and physical changes. However, comparing the properties of substances before and after a change can indicate whether the change is physical or chemical. For a strategy to overcome this misconception, see **Address Misconceptions** on **page 58.**

Build Reading Literacy

Preview

Skim Ahead to Understand Text Organization

Strategy Get an advance idea of how the text is organized and activate prior knowledge. This prereading strategy involves skimming the titles, headings, visuals, and boldfaced text. Like checking a roadmap before beginning a trip, previewing helps the reader to recall familiar material and to prepare to learn new material. Before students begin to read, select a portion of Chapter 2 for them to preview, such as pp. 38–44.

Example

1. Ask students to look at the chapter title, section titles, and heads. Tell them to notice whether the terms and concepts mentioned are familiar or unfamiliar.
2. Have students look at the Reading Focus for the specific section to be previewed.
3. Ask students to compare the key concepts and the boldfaced statements in the section.
4. Have students look at the visuals in the section and (where possible) relate each to a specific heading.
5. You may wish to have students prepare a study guide using the headings, key concept questions, and vocabulary as categories in a chart showing the section organization. Have students read the selected pages in depth, filling in the chart with details as they read.

See p. 54 for a script on how to use the preview strategy with students. For additional Build Reading Literacy strategies, see pp. 41 and 48.

ASSESS PRIOR KNOWLEDGE

Use the Chapter Pretest below to assess students' prior knowledge. As needed, review these Science Concepts with students.

Review Science Concepts

Section 2.1 Review different kinds of quantities to be measured, such as temperature, volume, and mass, and the units used to describe each quantity.

Section 2.2 Encourage students to recall what derived units are. For example, review how to use mass and volume to calculate density.

Section 2.3 Have students review the definition of chemistry. Also review with students the types of topics that chemists study.

CHAPTER

2 Properties of Matter

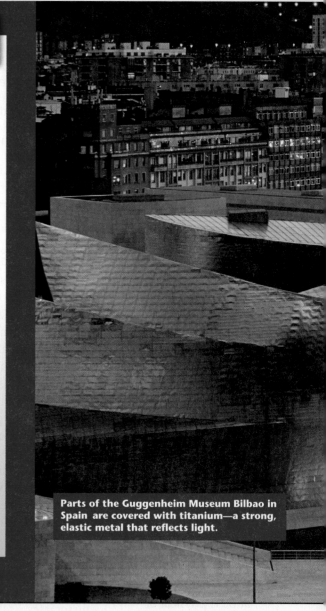

21st Century Learning
Economic Literacy

What factors influence the cost of metal?

Pots and pans, beverage cans, jewelry, the change in your pocket—these are just a few examples of everyday objects around you that are made of metal. Some metals, due to their properties, are more valuable than others. Select a particular metal and research its properties, uses, and price history. Digitally record a podcast that describes the metal, its current price per unit mass (or weight), and how its price has changed over the years.

Indiana's Academic Standards for Science

PROPERTIES OF MATTER
ICP.3.2: Study the characteristics of solids, liquids, and gases and their changes of state and interpret them in terms of a molecular model which describes their energies and motions; **ICP.3.3:** Understand how thermal energy (the microscopic motions of the atoms and/or molecules) is related to the macroscopic concept of temperature.

CHEMICAL ENERGY, REACTIONS, AND BONDING
ICP.5.1: Recognize and describe physical properties of matter and use these to differentiate between pure substances and mixtures; **ICP.5.6:** Identify key indicators of a chemical change and classify simple types of chemical reactions.

Parts of the Guggenheim Museum Bilbao in Spain are covered with titanium—a strong, elastic metal that reflects light.

36 *Chapter 2*

Chapter Pretest

1. What instrument would you use to measure temperature? *(A thermometer)*

2. Which of the following is a unit of volume? *(d)*
   a. Gram
   b. Atmosphere
   c. Meter
   d. Liter

3. What characteristic of matter can you measure using a graduated cylinder? *(Volume)*

4. The sides of a cube are 2 cm by 2 cm. What is the volume of the cube? *($8 \ cm^3$)*

5. What additional quantity would you need to calculate the density of the cube described in Question 4? *(The cube's mass)*

6. Which of the following topics is not studied in chemistry? *(d)*
   a. Composition of matter
   b. Reactions of substances
   c. Properties of materials
   d. Motion of large objects

Chapter Preview

DISCOVERY SCHOOL

Video Field Trip

Fresh-Squeezed Water

Inquiry Activity

What Properties Could You Use to Describe Materials?

Procedure

1. Your teacher will provide you with samples of rubber, copper, steel, wood, and carbon. On a sheet of paper, list the materials, leaving room to write your description of each.

2. Determine and record the properties or characteristics of the materials by touching, manipulating, smelling, and looking at them.

Think About It

1. **Comparing and Contrasting** List one or more properties of each material that can be used to distinguish it from the others.

2. **Observing** Write a description of one of the materials that could be used to clearly identify it.

Properties of Matter **37**

DISCOVERY CHANNEL SCHOOL

Video Field Trip

Fresh-Squeezed Water

Encourage students to view the Video Field Trip "Fresh-Squeezed Water."

ENGAGE/EXPLORE

Inquiry Activity

What Properties Could You Use to Describe Materials? L2

Purpose In this activity, students begin to identify various properties of matter that can be used to describe materials.

⚑ Address Misconceptions

Students may confuse the properties of objects with the properties of materials. Show students plastic and metal paper clips. Point out that the shape of an object is not a property of a material, but the ability to be shaped can be.

Skills Focus Classifying

 Prep Time 10 minutes

Materials rubber band, copper wire, steel paper clip, wooden toothpick, graphite pencil filler

Advance Prep You may use other objects containing the five materials, or objects made of different materials, but each material in the set must have a distinguishing property.

Class Time 10 minutes

Teaching Tips

• Identify the materials for the students (rubber band, copper wire, steel paper clip, wooden toothpick, and graphite pencil filler).

• Ask students leading questions such as "Is the material rigid or flexible?" "Is the material easily torn or broken?" and "Is the material easily stretched?"

• Some students may be more successful at this activity if you provide blank tables (with columns labeled Material and Observations) in which to record their observations.

Expected Outcome Students should observe a set of properties for each material and identify properties that can distinguish the materials.

Think About It

1. Possible distinguishing properties are rubber's elasticity, copper's color, steel's shininess, wood's brittleness, and graphite's slipperiness.

2. A possible answer for copper is a reddish solid that is flexible enough to be shaped into a narrow wire, which can be bent.

Visual, Kinesthetic

① FOCUS

Objectives

2.1.1 **Classify** pure substances as elements or compounds.

2.1.2 **Describe** the characteristics of an element and the symbols used to identify elements.

2.1.3 **Describe** the characteristics of a compound.

2.1.4 **Distinguish** pure substances from mixtures.

2.1.5 **Classify** mixtures as heterogeneous or homogeneous.

2.1.6 **Classify** mixtures as solutions, suspensions, or colloids.

Build Vocabulary `L2`

Paraphrasing To help students understand the definitions of vocabulary terms, you may replace less familiar words in a definition with a more familiar word or phrase. For example, you can replace *distributed* in the definition of a homogeneous mixture with "spread out," or *shattering* in the definition of malleability with "breaking into pieces."

Reading Strategy `L2`

a. Substance **b.** Compound
c. and d. Homogeneous mixture or heterogeneous mixture

② INSTRUCT

Address Misconceptions `L2`

Some students may associate the term *material* exclusively with solids because they can see and hold solid materials. They may have difficulty recognizing that liquids and gases are also matter. Challenge this misconception by pointing to the Materials list for the lab on p. 60 and asking students to identify the liquids.
Verbal

2.1 Classifying Matter

Standard: ICP.5.1

Reading Focus

Key Concepts

- Why are elements and compounds classified as pure substances?
- How do mixtures differ from pure substances?
- What is the main difference among solutions, suspensions, and colloids?

Vocabulary

- ◆ pure substance
- ◆ element
- ◆ atom
- ◆ compound
- ◆ heterogeneous mixture
- ◆ homogeneous mixture
- ◆ solution
- ◆ suspension
- ◆ colloid

Reading Strategy

Summarizing Copy the diagram below. As you read, complete the classification of matter.

Matter
 → a.___?___ → Element, b.___?___
 → Mixture → c.___?___, d.___?___

Each piece of clothing sold has a care label, which lists recommended cleaning methods for the clothing. For a sweater, the instructions might say to machine wash the sweater using a gentle cycle, and then tumble dry at a low temperature. They might say to hand wash the sweater in cold water and lay the sweater flat to dry. The label might even say, "Dry clean only."

Why is it necessary to put care instructions on a label? The same cleaning method will not work for all materials. For example, a shirt made from 100 percent cotton may need to be ironed after washing. But a shirt made from a cotton and polyester blend may come out of the dryer wrinkle free. A wool jacket often needs to be dry cleaned because wool can shrink when washed in water.

The tendency to wrinkle when washed is a property of cotton. The tendency not to wrinkle when washed is a property of polyester. The tendency to shrink when washed is a property of wool. Cotton, wool, and polyester have different properties because they have different compositions. The word *composition* comes from a Latin word meaning "a putting together," or the combining of parts into a whole. Based on their compositions, materials can be divided into pure substances and mixtures.

Figure 1 You can use the care labels on clothing to sort laundry into batches for cleaning. The care label shown is for a wool sweater that needs to be dry cleaned or washed by hand.

Section Resources

Print

- ● *Reading and Study Workbook With Math Support,* Section 2.1
- ● *Math Skills and Problem Solving Workbook,* Section 2.1
- ● *Transparencies,* Chapter Pretest and Section 2.1

Technology

- ● *Interactive Textbook,* Section 2.1
- ● *Presentation Pro CD-ROM,* Chapter Pretest and Section 2.1
- ● *Go Online,* NSTA SciLinks, Mixtures

Pure Substances

Matter that always has exactly the same composition is classified as a **pure substance,** or simply a substance. Table salt and table sugar are two examples of pure substances. Every pinch of salt tastes equally salty. Every spoonful of sugar tastes equally sweet. ⬤ **Every sample of a given substance has the same properties because a substance has a fixed, uniform composition.** Substances can be classified into two categories—elements and compounds.

Elements

Although there are millions of known substances, there are only about 100 elements. An **element** is a substance that cannot be broken down into simpler substances. Imagine cutting a copper wire into smaller and smaller pieces. Eventually you would end up with extremely tiny particles called copper atoms. An **atom** is the smallest particle of an element. ⬤ **An element has a fixed composition because it contains only one type of atom.**

No two elements contain the same type of atom. In Chapter 4, you will find out more about atoms, including how the atoms of one element differ from the atoms of every other element.

Examples of Elements At room temperature (20°C, or 68°F), most elements are solids, including the elements aluminum and carbon. You have seen aluminum foil used to wrap food. Most soft drink cans are made from aluminum. Carbon is the main element in the marks you make with a pencil on a piece of paper. Some elements are gases at room temperature. The elements oxygen and nitrogen are the main gases in the air you breathe. Only two elements are liquids at room temperature, bromine and mercury, both of which are extremely poisonous. Figure 2 shows four elements and their symbols.

Figure 2 Aluminum, carbon, and gold are elements that you can see in common objects, such as cans, pencils, and rings. Mixtures containing iodine are used to prevent and treat infections. **Analyzing Data** *Which of these elements has a symbol that is not related to its name in English?*

Iodine (I)

Aluminum (Al)

Gold (Au)

Carbon (C)

Properties of Matter **39**

Pure Substances
FYI

Samples of pure substances almost always contain impurities, some that are unintentional, some intentional. For example, table salt is not pure sodium chloride. It contains between 0.006% and 0.01% potassium iodide.

Elements
FYI

Sometimes an atom is defined as "the smallest particle of an element that has the properties of the element." However, an atom of copper has none of the properties associated with bulk copper, such as malleability, ductility, or density.

Build Science Skills   L2

Observing Have students look at the elements in Figure 2. Ask, **What are some characteristics of the elements in Figure 2?** (*Gold is yellow and shiny. Aluminum is gray and shiny. Carbon is dull and black. Iodine is a dark purple solid.*) Follow up on their observations by asking students to hypothesize about why the iodine sample is in a closed container. (*At room temperature, iodine evaporates and forms a purple gas, which is visible in the container. The gas is poisonous.*) **Visual**

Customize for English Language Learners

Sharing Experiences
Encourage multilingual students to describe what a particular element is called in their native language. This exercise will be most useful for those elements that have been

known for centuries or millennia. (Examples include carbon, mercury, sulfur, iron, copper, tin, zinc, silver, gold, and lead.) Use this information as a springboard for discussing the element names given in the text.

Answer to . . .

Figure 2 *Gold*

Integrate
Language Arts
L2

Have students research and explain the origin of element symbols (other than Au) that are not abbreviations for element names in English. Examples include silver (Ag), lead (Pb), tin (Sn), antimony (Sb), and mercury (Hg).
Verbal, Portfolio

Compounds
FYI

When the terms *element, atom, compound,* and *molecule* are defined in an introductory section, the definition of a molecule is often both too broad and too narrow. Molecules are not the smallest particle of all compounds, and many elements exist in nature as molecules. For this reason, in this text, the formal definition of molecule does not appear until Chapter 6, the chapter on bonding, where it can be defined accurately. (The term *molecule* is introduced informally in Section 3.3 when water molecules are described.)

Silicon

Oxygen

Figure 3 Elements have different properties than their compounds. Silicon is a gray solid and oxygen is a colorless gas, which can be stored in a metal tank. Silicon and oxygen combine to form silicon dioxide—a colorless, transparent solid found in most grains of sand.

Silicon dioxide

Symbols for Elements

In 1813, Jöns Berzelius, a Swedish chemist, suggested that chemists use symbols to represent elements. Many of the symbols he assigned to elements are still used. Each symbol has either one or two letters. The first letter is always capitalized. If there is a second letter, it is not capitalized.

It is easy to see why C and Al are used to represent carbon and aluminum. But why does gold have the symbol Au? The symbols that Berzelius chose were based on the Latin names of the elements. The Latin name for gold is *aurum.*

The symbols allow scientists who speak different languages to communicate without confusion. For example, nitrogen is known as *azote* in France, as *stickstoff* in Germany, and as *nitrógeno* in Mexico. But scientists who speak English, French, German, and Spanish all agree that the symbol for the element nitrogen is N.

Sometimes an element's name contains a clue to its properties. For example, the name hydrogen comes from the Greek words *hydro* and *genes,* meaning "water" and "forming."

Compounds

Water is composed of the elements hydrogen and oxygen. When electricity passes through water, bubbles of oxygen and hydrogen gas form and rise to the surface of the water. If the gases are collected in a container and a flame is brought near the mixture, the hydrogen and oxygen react and form water. Water is classified as a compound. A **compound** is a substance that is made from two or more simpler substances and can be broken down into those simpler substances. The simpler substances are either elements or other compounds.

The properties of a compound differ from those of the substances from which it is made. For example, oxygen and hydrogen are gases at room temperature, but water is a liquid. Hydrogen can fuel a fire, and oxygen can keep a fire burning, but water does not burn or help other substances to burn. In fact, water is one of the substances commonly used to put out fires.

Figure 3 shows another example of how properties change when elements join and form compounds. Silicon dioxide is a compound found in most light-colored grains of sand. It is a colorless, transparent solid. Yet, silicon dioxide is made from a colorless gas (oxygen) and a gray solid (silicon). Silicon is used to make chips for computers.

A compound always contains two or more elements joined in a fixed proportion. For example, in silicon dioxide, there are always two oxygen atoms for each silicon atom. (*Di-* means "two.") In water, there are always two hydrogen atoms for each oxygen atom.

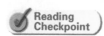 **Reading Checkpoint** *What happens if electricity passes through water?*

Facts and Figures

Electrolysis of Water Early chemists were able to use heat to break down many compounds into their constituent elements. Because water cannot be decomposed by this method, water was classified as an element until chemists were able to use electric current to break down water into hydrogen and oxygen. (The decomposition of water into hydrogen and oxygen will not occur unless ions are added to the water because there are not enough ions in pure water to conduct an electric current.)

Figure 4 The ingredients shown are used to make one kind of salsa, which is an example of a heterogeneous mixture.

Salsa

- 4 or 5 plum tomatoes
- 3–5 fresh Serrano chili peppers
- 12 sprigs of cilantro
- large garlic clove
- small white onion
- 1½ teaspoons fresh lime juice
- ¾ teaspoon salt

Mixtures

Suppose you are making salsa using the ingredients shown in Figure 4. You have a choice. You can use exactly the amounts listed in the recipe, or you can adjust the ingredients according to your own taste. You might have to prepare the recipe a few times before deciding if you have just the right amount of each ingredient.

Mixtures tend to retain some of the properties of their individual substances. But the properties of a mixture are less constant than the properties of a substance. **The properties of a mixture can vary because the composition of a mixture is not fixed.** The type of pepper and the quantity of pepper used in a salsa recipe determine the "hotness" of a batch of salsa. Chili peppers contain a compound called capsaicin (kap SAY uh sin) that can cause a burning sensation in your mouth. The amount of capsaicin varies among types of peppers. Cayenne peppers, for example, contain more capsaicin than do jalapeño peppers.

No matter how well you stir a batch of salsa, the ingredients will not be evenly distributed. There may, for example, be more onion in one portion of the salsa than another. Mixtures can be classified by how well the parts of the mixture are distributed throughout the mixture.

Heterogeneous Mixtures If you look at a handful of sand from a beach, the sand appears to be all the same material. However, if you use a hand lens, you will notice that the sample of sand is not the same throughout. Figure 5 shows that grains of sand vary in size. Also, some grains are light in color and some are dark. Sand is an example of a heterogeneous mixture. Heterogeneous (het uh roh GEE nee us) comes from the Greek words *hetero* and *genus*, meaning "different" and "kind." In a **heterogeneous mixture,** the parts of the mixture are noticeably different from one another.

Figure 5 Sand is a heterogeneous mixture. The spoon is stainless steel, which is a homogeneous mixture.
Interpreting Photographs
Explain how viewing sand through a hand lens helps show that sand is a heterogeneous mixture.

Properties of Matter **41**

Do the Contents of Two Cans of Mixed Nuts Meet FDA Regulations? **L2**

Answers

1. Both brands contain the same six types of nuts, but the amount of each type of nut varies.

2. There are 344.79 g in Brand A and 350.32 g in Brand B. The percents by mass in Brand A are: 44.2% peanuts, 13.64% almonds, 16.79% Brazil nuts, 13.4% cashews, 5.77% hazelnuts, and 6.21% pecans. The percents by mass in Brand B are: 54.8% peanuts, 8.90% almonds, 5.59% Brazil nuts, 21.06% cashews, 4.82% hazelnuts, and 4.82% pecans.

3. Yes. Both brands contain more than four types of nuts other than peanuts. The percent of each nut by mass is within the 2% to 80% range.

4. The ingredients are listed in order by total mass. The ingredient with the largest total mass is listed first.

For Extra Help **L1**

Have students answer Question 3 by calculating 2% and 80% of each total mass and checking to see if any of the masses fall outside that range.
Logical

Solutions, Suspensions, and Colloids
FYI

Many alloys are not true solutions. Sterling silver, a mixture of silver and copper, is an example. Silver and copper are completely soluble in all proportions when molten. However, solid sterling silver is a two-phase alloy with pockets of silver and pockets of a 71.9% silver and 28.1% copper mixture.

Download a worksheet on mixtures for students to complete, and find additional teacher support from NSTA SciLinks.

Data Analysis

Do the Contents of Two Cans of Mixed Nuts Meet FDA Regulations?

The Food and Drug Administration (FDA) has two main areas of concern about food. First, and most important, the FDA ensures that food sold in the United States is safe to eat. Second, the FDA ensures that the information on a food label accurately describes a food product.

What can you assume when you see the label "mixed nuts" on a can of nuts? According to the FDA regulations, a can labeled *mixed nuts* must contain at least four types of shelled nuts other than peanuts. The mass of each type of nut must be not less than 2 percent of the total mass and not more than 80 percent of the total mass.

Contents of Two Cans of Mixed Nuts		
Type of Nut	Mass in Brand A	Mass in Brand B
Peanut	152.39 g	191.96 g
Almond	47.02 g	31.18 g
Brazil nut	57.88 g	19.60 g
Cashew	46.20 g	73.78 g
Hazelnut	19.90 g	16.90 g
Pecan	21.40 g	16.90 g

1. **Comparing and Contrasting** How are the two brands of mixed nuts alike? How are they different?

2. **Calculating** What is the percent by mass of each type of nut in each can?

3. **Drawing Conclusions** Do the contents of each can meet the FDA regulations? Explain.

4. **Inferring** On the Brand A label, the nuts are listed in this order: peanuts, Brazil nuts, almonds, cashews, pecans, and hazelnuts. What do you think determines the order?

For: Links on mixtures
Visit: www.SciLinks.org
Web Code: ccn-1021

Homogeneous Mixtures If you collect water from both the shallow end and the deep end of a swimming pool, the water samples will appear the same. The water in a swimming pool is a homogeneous (hoh moh GEE nee us) mixture of water and substances that dissolve in water. In a **homogeneous mixture,** the substances are so evenly distributed that it is difficult to distinguish one substance in the mixture from another. A homogeneous mixture appears to contain only one substance. The serving spoon in Figure 5 is made of stainless steel—a homogeneous mixture of iron, chromium, and nickel.

Solutions, Suspensions, and Colloids

It isn't always easy to tell a homogeneous mixture from a heterogeneous mixture. You may need to observe the properties of a mixture before you decide. The size of the particles in a mixture has an effect on the properties of the mixture. **Based on the size of its largest particles, a mixture can be classified as a solution, a suspension, or a colloid.**

Solutions If you place a spoonful of sugar in a glass of hot water and stir, the sugar dissolves in the water. The result is a homogeneous mixture of sugar and water. When substances dissolve and form a homogeneous mixture, the mixture that forms is called a **solution.** The windshield wiper fluid in Figure 6 is a solution. So is tap water.

Facts and Figures

Regulatory Agencies Responsibility for protecting the food supply is shared among the FDA, the Department of Agriculture, and the EPA, which regulates pesticides. Food that is adulterated or mislabeled may be voluntarily destroyed or recalled, or seized by court order. The FDA is responsible for establishing standards for identity, quality, and fill of container. If standards have been set for a product, such as mixed nuts, the product must comply with those standards. Food labels must include a statement of identity (usual or common name), the net quantity of the contents, the name and place of business of the supplier, and a list of ingredients in descending order by mass. The goal is to have honest and informative labels.

Figure 6 The liquids shown represent three categories of mixtures. **A** Windshield wiper fluid is a solution. **B** Muddy water collected from a swamp is a suspension. **C** Milk is a colloid.
Comparing and Contrasting Based on appearance, how are a solution and a colloid similar?

Liquid solutions are easy to recognize. They do not separate into distinct layers over time. If you pour a liquid solution through a filter, none of the substances in the solution are trapped in the filter. You can see through solutions that are liquids because light passes through them without being scattered in all directions. These three properties of liquid solutions can be traced to the size of the particles in a solution. The particles in a solution are too small to settle out of the solution, be trapped by a filter, or scatter light.

Suspensions Have you ever seen the instruction "Shake well before using" on a bottle? This instruction is a clue that the material in the bottle is a suspension. A **suspension** is a heterogeneous mixture that separates into layers over time. For example, if you shake up a container of sand and water, the sand mixes with the water and forms a suspension. Over time, the suspended particles of sand settle to the bottom of the container.

You could use a filter to separate the sand from the water. The water would pass through the filter, but the sand would remain in the filter paper. Suspended particles settle out of a mixture or are trapped by a filter because they are larger than the particles in a solution. The worker in Figure 7 is using a mask to filter out particles of plastic foam that are suspended in air. Because larger particles can scatter light in all directions, suspensions are cloudy.

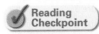 *What happens to suspended particles over time?*

Figure 7 When a surfboard is sanded, particles of plastic become suspended in air. The worker wears a mask to keep from breathing in the particles.

Properties of Matter **43**

Transmission Versus Scattering L2

Purpose Students observe light pass through different mixtures.

Materials 2 beakers, water, iodine solution, table salt, stirring rods, milk, fish tank, flashlight, white paper

Procedure Demonstrate that a solution can have color and still transmit light. Fill two beakers halfway with water. Add a small amount of iodine solution to one beaker and stir. Add table salt to the second beaker. Ask students to describe the color of each mixture and state whether it is clear. Demonstrate transmission of light versus scattering. Fill the tank with water. Turn off the lights. Shine a flashlight through the tank so that it lights up the white paper placed behind the tank. Add some milk to the water and stir. Shine the light through the tank again. (These behaviors of light are discussed in detail in Section 18.3.)

Expected Outcome Although the salt solution is colorless and the iodine solution is colored, both transmit light. Light passes through the water in the tank and makes a bright spot on the paper. With milk added, the light is scattered so that the spot is much less distinct.
Visual

Use Visuals L1

Figure 7 To emphasize that suspended particles settle out over time, ask, **What will happen to the particles of plastic suspended in the air?** *(The particles will eventually settle out.)* Discuss with students the dangers of inhaling suspended particles. Ask, **How does a mask prevent the worker from inhaling particles of plastic?** *(The particles in suspensions can be separated by filtration. The mask is a filter.)*
Visual

> **Answer to . . .**
>
> **Figure 6** *The solution and the colloid both appear homogeneous.*
>
> 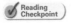 *Suspended particles settle out of a mixture.*

Build Science Skills L3

Classifying Have interested students research categories of colloids such as gels, foams, aerosols, and emulsions. Have students find out how scientists distinguish different types of colloids. Have them identify household examples of each type.
Visual, Portfolio

3 ASSESS

Evaluate Understanding L2

Have students make a game of concentration using the terms in the chapter and their definitions. Have groups of students write each term on separate index cards and the definition of each term on a second set of index cards. To play the game, students should shuffle all the cards together and then lay them face down in a grid. Each student takes turns flipping over two index cards. If the cards match, the student can remove the cards from the grid. If the cards do not match, the student places the cards face down. After all of the cards are gone, the student who has removed the most cards wins the match.

Reteach L1

Use Figure 6 as a visual aid to summarize the key differences among different types of mixtures.

Writing in Science

Students should specify which ingredients are required for the cereal to qualify for a particular label and suggest a range for ingredients such as dried fruit or nuts. (Students could choose another edible mixture, such as canned vegetable soup.)

Interactive Textbook If your class subscribes to the Interactive Textbook, use it to review key concepts in Section 2.1.

Figure 8 The photograph shows how water droplets in fog scatter the light from high beams. The drawing compares the areas lit by high beams and low beams. *Interpreting Diagrams Which beams normally make a larger area of a road visible?*

Colloids Milk is a mixture of substances including water, sugar, proteins, and fats. When fresh cow's milk is allowed to stand, a layer of cream rises to the top. This layer contains much of the fat in the milk. In the milk you buy at the store, the cream does not form a separate layer. The milk has been processed so that the fat remains dispersed throughout the milk. The result is homogenized milk, which is a colloid.

A **colloid** contains some particles that are intermediate in size between the small particles in a solution and the larger particles in a suspension. Like solutions, colloids do not separate into layers. You cannot use a filter to separate the parts of a colloid.

Fog is a colloid of water droplets in air. Figure 8 shows how fog affects which headlights a driver uses. Automobiles have headlights with low beams for normal driving conditions and high beams for roads that are poorly lit. With the high beams, a driver can see a bend in the road or an obstacle sooner. But the high beams are not useful on a foggy night because the water droplets scatter light back toward the driver and reduce visibility. With the low beams, much less light is scattered. The scattering of light is a property that can be used to distinguish colloids and suspensions from solutions.

Section 2.1 Assessment

Reviewing Concepts

1. Why does every sample of a given substance have the same properties?
2. Explain why the composition of an element is fixed.
3. Describe the composition of a compound.
4. Why can the properties of a mixture vary?
5. On what basis can mixtures be classified as solutions, suspensions, or colloids?

Critical Thinking

6. **Predicting** If you added salt instead of sugar to a pitcher of lemonade, how would this change the properties of the lemonade?

7. **Interpreting Visuals** Explain why silicon dioxide cannot be the only compound in the sample of sand shown in Figure 5.
8. **Inferring** Fresh milk is a suspension. After fresh milk is homogenized, it is a colloid. What happens to the size of the drops of fat in milk when milk is homogenized?

Writing in Science

Writing Instructions Pick a cereal that is an obvious mixture. Write rules that could be used to control the cereal's composition. Use the FDA rules for mixed nuts as a model.

Section 2.1 Assessment

1. A pure substance has a fixed composition.
2. An element contains only one kind of atom.
3. Compounds contain two or more elements joined in a fixed proportion.
4. Because the composition of a mixture is not fixed
5. Mixtures can be classified as solutions, suspensions, or colloids based on the size of their largest particles.

6. The lemonade would taste salty instead of sweet.
7. Silicon dioxide is colorless. There must be at least one other compound in the sample to account for the dark-colored grains.
8. Large drops are broken down into smaller drops, which can remain dispersed throughout the milk.

Answer to . . .

Figure 8 *High beams*

2.2 Physical Properties

Standards: ICP.3.2, ICP.3.3, ICP.5.1

Reading Focus

Key Concepts
- What are some examples of physical properties?
- How can knowing the physical properties of matter be useful?
- What processes are used to separate mixtures?

Vocabulary
- physical property
- viscosity
- conductivity
- malleability
- melting point
- boiling point
- filtration
- distillation
- physical change

Reading Strategy
Building Vocabulary Copy the table. As you read, write a definition for each property.

Physical Property	Definition
Viscosity	a.___?___
Malleability	b.___?___
Melting point	c.___?___

If there are pitchers of ice water and lemonade on a picnic table, how do you know which liquid is in each pitcher? It's easy! The lemonade is yellow. Lemonade also has a tart taste that is hard to miss. A yellow color and a tart taste are two properties of lemonade.

Examples of Physical Properties

A **physical property** is any characteristic of a material that can be observed or measured without changing the composition of the substances in the material. Viscosity, conductivity, malleability, hardness, melting point, boiling point, and density are examples of physical properties.

Viscosity Suppose you knock over an open bottle of vinegar and an open jar of honey at exactly the same time. In the time it takes for the vinegar bottle to empty, the honey will scarcely start to flow. The tendency of a liquid to keep from flowing—its resistance to flowing—is called its **viscosity**. The greater the viscosity, the slower the liquid moves. Thick liquids, such as corn syrup and the honey in Figure 9, have a high viscosity. Thin liquids, such as vinegar, have a low viscosity.

The viscosity of a liquid usually decreases when it is heated. For example, a spoonful of cooking oil will spread more quickly across the bottom of a heated frying pan than across the bottom of a cold pan.

Why is the viscosity of a liquid important? Consider the motor oil used to keep the parts of an automobile engine from wearing away as they move past one another. The motor oil must not be too thick in cold weather or too thin in hot weather.

Figure 9 The object in the photograph is called a honey dipper. Honey is an example of a liquid with a high viscosity.

Properties of Matter **45**

Section Resources

Print
- *Laboratory Manual*, Investigation 2B
- *Reading and Study Workbook With Math Support*, Section 2.2 and **Math Skill:** Melting and Boiling Points
- *Transparencies*, Section 2.2

Technology
- *Interactive Textbook*, Section 2.2
- *Presentation Pro CD-ROM*, Section 2.2
- *Go Online*, *Science News*, Properties of matter

---

1 FOCUS

Objectives
2.2.1 Describe physical properties of matter.
2.2.2 Identify substances based on their physical properties.
2.2.3 Describe how properties are used to choose materials.
2.2.4 Describe methods used to separate mixtures.
2.2.5 Describe evidence that indicates a physical change is taking place.

Reading Focus

Build Vocabulary

LINCS Have students use the LINCS strategy to learn and review the terms *viscosity, conductivity,* and *malleability.* In LINCS exercises, the students **L**ist what they know about each term, **I**magine a picture that describes the word or phrase, **N**ote a reminding "sound-alike" word (such as *visible, train conductor,* and *mallet*), **C**onnect the terms to the sound-alike word by making up a short story, and then perform a brief **S**elf-test.

Reading Strategy

a. The tendency of a liquid to resist flowing **b.** The ability of a solid to be hammered without shattering **c.** The temperature at which a substance changes from a solid to liquid

2 INSTRUCT

Examples of Physical Properties
FYI

The text mentions that lemonade can be identified by its taste. Remind students that taste should never be used to identify an unknown substance and that no substances, known or unknown, should ever be ingested in a lab.

Quick Lab

Comparing Heat Conductors

Objective
After completing this activity, students will be able to
• distinguish a material that is a good conductor of heat from a material that is a poor conductor of heat.

Skills Focus Observing, Inferring

 Prep Time 10 minutes

Advance Prep
Acquire wood and metal rods of similar length from the metal or woodworking classroom, a crafts shop, or a home repair shop. Liquid crystal thermometers may be purchased at a pet or aquarium supply store. You may want to cut the cups and attach the thermometers to the rods in advance to save class time. Thermometers can be attached to the rods with their own adhesive backing or taped on. Heat enough water to fill each foam cup about 3/4 full.

Class Time 20 minutes

Safety
Remind students to handle the setup carefully to prevent burns after the hot water is added.

Teaching Tips
• You may need to provide tape to attach thermometers to the rods.
• Construct a blank data table on the board, an overhead transparency, or a computer and have each group enter its data in this table. All data can then be pooled and averaged for greater accuracy.

Expected Outcome
Metal will conduct heat faster than wood.

Analyze and Conclude
1. Metal is a better conductor. Students should cite the differences in temperature over time as evidence.
2. Metal is not the best choice for this purpose. Because metals are good conductors, the contents of the cup will cool quickly as heat is transferred to the surroundings.
3. Depending on what rods are used, possible sources of error are different lengths, different diameters, and different densities of the materials.
Kinesthetic, Logical

Quick Lab

Comparing Heat Conductors

Liquid crystal thermometer
Metal rod
Wooden rod
Foam cups

Materials
2 plastic foam cups, scissors, metric ruler, metal rod, wooden rod, 2 liquid crystal thermometers, hot water, clock or watch with second hand

Procedure

1. Make a data table with a column for time and a column to record the temperature of each rod.
2. Cut 3 cm off the top of one cup. Turn the cup upside down. Use the metal rod to make two holes about 3 cm apart in the bottom.
3. Attach a thermometer to each rod as shown.
4. Insert both rods so they will just touch the bottom of the second cup. Lay the cup with the rods on the table. Do not touch the rods and thermometers during the experiment.
5. Ask your teacher to add hot water to the intact cup until it is about three fourths full.
6. Hold the cup with the hot water firmly as you place the cup with the rods on top of it. **CAUTION** *Be careful not to overturn the cup.*
7. Observe and record the temperatures every minute for five minutes.

Analyze and Conclude
1. **Comparing and Contrasting** Is metal or wood a better conductor of heat? Explain.
2. **Applying Concepts** Is a metal cup a good container for keeping a drink hot for as long as possible? Give a reason for your answer.
3. **Evaluating** Describe any variables, other than the type of material, that were not controlled in this lab.

Figure 10 Because gold is both malleable and beautiful, it is often used to make jewelry. These ancient gold medallions were made to form a necklace.

Conductivity Which spoon should you choose for stirring a pot of soup heating on the stove—a metal spoon or a wooden spoon? If one end of a metal object is heated, the other end will soon feel hot. A material's ability to allow heat to flow is called **conductivity.**

Materials that have a high conductivity, such as metals, are called conductors. If a material is a good conductor of heat, it is usually also a good conductor of electricity. Wood is not a good conductor of heat. You can stir hot soup with a wooden spoon without worrying about burning your hand because the wooden spoon stays cool to the touch.

Malleability The ancient gold objects in Figure 10 were found in a tomb in Greece. A goldsmith made the medallions by tapping gold with a small hammer and punch. Gold can be shaped in this way because it is malleable. **Malleability** (mal ee uh BIL uh tee) is the ability of a solid to be hammered without shattering. Most metals are malleable. By contrast, an ice cube breaks into small pieces when struck with a hammer. So does ordinary glass when hit by a fast-moving object such as a baseball. Solids that shatter when struck are brittle.

 Reading Checkpoint *Why would a cook use a wooden spoon to stir hot soup?*

Customize for Inclusion Students

Visually Impaired
Provide students who have visual impairments with samples of two different nontoxic solids that have approximately the same mass. By handling the samples, students can infer their relative densities from their volumes.

Provide samples of materials with a range of hardness. Have students do scratch tests to determine an order of hardness. Students should be able to feel any indentations on the surfaces of the softer materials.

Hardness One way to compare the hardness of two materials is to see which of the materials can scratch the other. The blade of a typical kitchen knife, for example, can scratch a copper sheet because stainless steel is harder than copper. The stainless steel in a knife blade is a hard solid that can be shaped into a sharp cutting edge. The material used to sharpen the blade must be harder than stainless steel. Diamond is the hardest known material. Some of the grinding wheels used to sharpen steel contain small grains of diamond. The man in Figure 11 is carving a canoe from a soft wood—Western red cedar.

Melting and Boiling Points If you leave a tray of ice cubes on your kitchen counter, the ice cubes will melt. The temperature at which a substance changes from solid to liquid is its **melting point.** For water, this change normally occurs at 0°C. If you heat water to cook pasta at sea level, the water will start to boil at 100°C. The temperature at which a substance boils is its **boiling point.** Figure 12 shows the melting point and the boiling point for some substances.

Density Density can be used to test the purity of a substance. Recall that density is the ratio of the mass of a substance to its volume. At room temperature, silver has a density of 10.5 g/cm³. If a coin has a density of 9.9 g/cm³ at room temperature, either the coin is not made from silver or the coin contains substances in addition to silver.

Density can be used to test the purity of methanol. Methanol is a fuel burned in some racing motorcycles. The American Motorcycle Association (AMA) requires racers to use fuel that is at least 99.65 percent pure. Race officials may collect a sample of fuel and measure its temperature and density. Then they compare the measured density to the expected density of methanol at that temperature. These spot checks keep racers from adding substances to the fuel that will give them an unfair advantage in a race.

Figure 11 This Tlingit carver is using an adze to carve a canoe from Western red cedar. Red cedar is a relatively soft wood.

Melting and Boiling Points of Some Substances

Substance	Melting Point	Boiling Point
Hydrogen	−259.3°C	−252.9°C
Nitrogen	−210.0°C	−195.8°C
Ammonia	−77.7°C	−33.3°C
Octane (found in gasoline)	−56.8°C	125.6°C
Water	0.0°C	100.0°C
Acetic acid (found in vinegar)	16.6°C	117.9°C
Table salt	800.7°C	1465°C
Gold	1064.2°C	2856°C

Figure 12 The table lists the melting points and boiling points for several substances.
Analyzing Data *Which of these substances are liquids at room temperature (20°C, or 68°F)?*

Using Physical Properties
Build Reading Literacy L1

Outline Refer to page **156D** in **Chapter 6**, which provides the guidelines for an outline.

Have students read pp. 48–50 and gather information on identifying, choosing, and separating substances based on their physical properties. Then, have students use the headings as major divisions in an outline. Have students refer to their outlines when answering the questions in the Section 2.2 Assessment.
Visual

Teacher > Demo

Comparing Melting Points L2

Purpose Students observe the differences in melting points of two substances.

Materials water, ethanol, foam cups, freezer, large beaker, thermometer

Procedure Tell students that you will demonstrate that the melting points of two substances differ. The night before, place a foam cup filled with water and a second foam cup filled with ethanol in the freezer. During class, pull both cups out of the freezer. Have students note that the water is frozen, but the ethanol is not. Remove the ice from the cup and add it to the large beaker. Add a small amount of water and allow the ice to begin melting. While the temperature of the ice water is leveling off, have a volunteer measure the temperature of the ethanol. Compare that temperature to the temperature of the ice water.

Expected Outcome Because most freezers do not cool to temperatures below the melting point of ethanol, –114.7°C, the ethanol will remain a liquid. After some of the ice has melted, the temperature of the solid-liquid system will stop decreasing and level off. This is the melting point of water, 0°C. The temperature of the chilled ethanol is below 0°C.
Visual

Using Physical Properties

People use data about physical properties to solve many different types of problems. ⊂⊃ **Physical properties are used to identify a material, to choose a material for a specific purpose, or to separate the substances in a mixture.**

Using Properties to Identify Materials The steps used to identify a material are similar to the steps used to test for purity. The first step is to decide which properties to test. The second step is to do tests on a sample of the unknown. The final step is to compare the results with the data reported for known materials.

The identification of a material can be a crucial step in solving a crime. A detective collects red paint chips from the scene of a hit-and-run accident. He asks a chemist at the crime lab to use the chips to identify the model of the missing vehicle. Because paint is a mixture of substances, the chemist can do tests that distinguish one type of red paint from another. The technician compares the data she collects to an FBI database. The database contains information about the paints used on different makes and models of cars. Once the detective knows the make and model, he uses a database of registered owners to create a list of possible suspects.

Using Properties to Choose Materials Properties determine which materials are chosen for which uses. For example, you wouldn't want shoelaces made from wood. Shoelaces must be flexible, that is, they must be able to bend without breaking. They must also be durable, that is, they must be able to withstand repeated use. Laces in hiking boots like those in Figure 13 are usually nylon or leather.

People don't consider just one property when choosing a material for a particular application. They look at a set of properties. For example, the How It Works box on page 49 explains how the properties of wax are used when clay molds are made for casting metal sculptures.

Figure 13 Shoelaces for hiking boots are sometimes made from leather. So are some belts and shoes. **Making Generalizations** *What properties of leather would make it a suitable material for all three types of objects?*

48 Chapter 2

Facts and Figures

Identifying Substances Sometimes a single property is not sufficient to positively identify a substance. Iron, nickel, and cobalt, which are often found together in nature, look quite similar. The density of iron is 7.87 g/cm³. The density of nickel is 8.90 g/cm³. The density of cobalt is 8.86 g/cm³. Measurements of mass made on the type of balance found in most school labs would be precise enough to distinguish iron from cobalt or nickel, but not precise enough to distinguish cobalt from nickel.

Making a Sculpture

A process called lost-wax casting is used to make metal sculptures. Different stages of the process depend on physical properties of wax, clay, and metal. Wax can be carved and molded. Clay becomes brittle when baked at a high temperature. When melted, most metals form homogeneous mixtures, which can be poured into molds.

Interpreting Diagrams *Why is it important that wax has a low melting point?*

Preparing clay molds
This artist from Nepal in southern Asia is preparing molds for lost-wax casting. She is applying layers of clay to a wax model.

1 Wax model A wax model of the sculpture is built up around a clay core. Wax is used because it is soft enough for carving fine details, but hard enough to retain its shape at room temperature.

Wax model

Cast metal sculpture

Molten metal poured into mold

Layers of clay applied to the wax model

Clay core

Wax model

Melting wax

Broken clay

2 Clay mold Clay is applied to the wax model in layers of increasing coarseness, and left to dry. The inner, finer layers capture every detail of the sculpture in a smooth mold. The outer, coarser layers (clay mixed with sand) provide strength.

3 Melting wax The clay-covered wax model is then baked in a kiln. Because wax has a low melting point, the wax model melts away inside the clay, leaving a hardened shell mold. This clay mold is then used to make the final sculpture.

4 Molten metal Molten (liquid) metal is poured into the clay mold and left to cool and harden. For this sculpture of an African head, a mixture of copper, zinc, and lead was used.

5 Metal sculpture When the metal has cooled, the clay shell is broken open to reveal the finished metal sculpture.

Properties of Matter **49**

DK HOW It Works

Making a Sculpture L2

There are a number of variations to the method described in the text. For example, sometimes there is no clay core. The lost-wax method of casting can also be used to make replicas of existing sculptures.

Many other molding and casting techniques also take advantage of the physical properties of different substances to maximize the quality of the final product. For example, the properties of some types of rubber make them ideal materials for molds. Rubber molds are flexible enough that the cast can be pulled out without breaking the mold, yet strong enough to preserve fine details in the final product. Because of their durability, rubber molds can be reused many times.

Interpreting Diagrams The wax must melt away when the model is heated in a kiln.
Logical

For Enrichment L3

Because an imprint made in wet sand will hold its shape, filling the imprint with melted wax or wet plaster will produce a cast of the object pressed into the sand. This sculpting technique is called a sand mold. Have students find out about sand molds and use them to make candles or plaster casts of their footprints or handprints.
Visual, Portfolio

Use Community Resources L2

Arrange for a sculptor or jewelry maker to visit the class. Have the artist describe the molding and casting techniques he or she uses. Before the visit, have students prepare questions about how the artist chooses materials based on their physical properties.
Interpersonal

Answer to . . .
Figure 13 *Flexibility and durability*

Using Properties to Separate Mixtures
Build Science Skills L2

Applying Concepts

Purpose In this activity, students use properties to separate the components of a mixture.

Materials a mixture of table salt, sand, and iron filings; beaker; magnet; plastic bag; water; funnel; filter paper

Class Time 20 minutes

Procedure Encourage students to consider properties that can be used to separate each material from the other two materials in the mixture. Then, have students design a procedure to complete the separation.

Expected Outcome Students can colleet the iron filings using a magnet covered with a plastic bag. They can add water to the mixture to dissolve the salt. They can use a filter to collect the sand. Students can collect the salt by letting the water evaporate for a few days.
Visual, Portfolio

Address Misconceptions L2

Students may think that all the particles in mixtures are similar in size. This is true for solutions and colloids, but not for suspensions. Challenge this misconception by displaying common devices used to filter mixtures (such as a sieve, a colander, and a coffee filter) and discussing the mixtures these devices are used to separate. The size of the holes in a filter determines whether filtration can be used to separate a suspension. Hole size also determines whether all the particles in a colloid pass through the filter or all the particles are trapped in the filter. Either way, the end result is that the colloid is not separated by filtration.
Verbal

Science News provides students with current information on properties of matter.

Figure 14 These Americorps students are looking for artifacts at the San Diego Presidio—a fort that was built in 1769. As the students sift dirt through a screen, small objects buried in the dirt collect on the screen. Applying Concepts *How could changing the size of the holes in a screen change the number of objects found?*

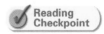

For: Articles on properties of matter
Visit: PHSchool.com
Web Code: cce-1022

Using Properties to Separate Mixtures

Some properties can be used to separate mixtures. 🌐 **Filtration and distillation are two common separation methods.**

Filtration One way to make a pot of tea is to pour hot water over loose tea leaves. Some compounds in the tea leaves, such as caffeine, dissolve in the water. You can separate the hot tea from the loose leaves by pouring the mixture through a strainer. Using a strainer is a type of filtration. **Filtration** is a process that separates materials based on the size of their particles. Particles of the compounds that dissolve are small enough to pass through the strainer, but the tea leaves themselves are too large to pass through the strainer. The drip method of brewing coffee also uses a filter to separate the brewed coffee from the coffee grounds.

The students in Figure 14 are using a wire screen to locate small objects buried in the sand at an archaeological site. Particles of dirt are small enough to pass through the holes in the screen, but objects such as broken bits of pottery are too large to pass through the screen.

Distillation How can you separate the parts of a solution when all the particles in a solution are small enough to pass through a filter? Sometimes distillation can work. **Distillation** is a process that separates the substances in a solution based on their boiling points.

One practical use of distillation is to provide fresh water for submarines. Most submarines can store only enough fresh water to last about ten days. Each submarine has equipment that can convert seawater into fresh water. The water is heated until it changes from a liquid to a gas. The gas is cooled until it changes back to a liquid, which is collected in a separate container. Boiling can separate fresh water from seawater because water has a much lower boiling point than the compounds dissolved in seawater. These compounds are left behind in the original container.

✓ **Reading Checkpoint** *How can loose tea leaves be removed from a pot of brewed tea?*

Facts and Figures

Tea Tea contains compounds called polyphenols, which are often referred to as tannins. There are health claims made for both black and green tea. The health claims made for green tea are related to the concentration of polyphenols. During the processing of black tea, most of the polyphenols are oxidized. Oxidation of polyphenols is limited during the processing of green tea. (The tea dumped into Boston harbor on December 16, 1773, was green tea, which outsold black tea in the Colonies.)

Recognizing Physical Changes

The change of water from a liquid to a gas during boiling is a physical change. A **physical change** occurs when some of the properties of a material change, but the substances in the material remain the same. For example, if you slowly heat butter in a pan, it changes from a solid to a liquid, but the substances in the butter do not change. Two other examples of physical changes are crumpling a piece of paper and slicing a tomato. Crumpling and slicing are actions that change the size and shape of a material, but not its composition.

Some physical changes can be reversed. You can freeze water, melt the ice that forms, and then freeze the water again. You can use an iron to remove the wrinkles from a cotton shirt. You can braid hair, unbraid the hair, and then braid it again. Some physical changes cannot be reversed. You would not expect to reconstruct a whole tomato from tomato slices or to replace the peel on a peeled orange. Figure 15 shows one physical change that can be reversed and one that cannot be reversed.

Figure 15 Braiding hair and cutting hair are examples of physical changes. Braiding is a reversible change. Cutting cannot be reversed.

Section 2.2 Assessment

Reviewing Concepts

1. 🌐 List seven examples of physical properties.
2. 🌐 Describe three uses of physical properties.
3. 🌐 Name two processes that are used to separate mixtures.
4. When you describe a liquid as thick, are you saying that it has a high or a low viscosity?
5. Explain why sharpening a pencil is an example of a physical change.
6. What allows a mixture to be separated by distillation?

Critical Thinking

7. **Designing Experiments** How could you find out whether copper is harder or softer than the plastic used in a plastic cup?

8. **Inferring** Why would you expect the materials used to make pot holders to be poor conductors of heat?
9. **Applying Concepts** Silicon dioxide is a solid at room temperature and methanol is a liquid. Which substance has the higher melting point?

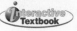

Organizing Data In what order are the substances arranged in Figure 12? Use what you studied about organizing data in Section 1.4 to explain why this order is useful. Explain why you might choose a different order if you had similar data for 500 substances.

FYI

If butter heated in a pan begins to brown, this is a sign that a chemical change is starting to occur. Students are asked to compare the possible changes to heated butter in Question 5 of the Section 2.3 Assessment.

3 ASSESS

Evaluate Understanding · L2

Tell students that a layer of fat rises to the top in a pot of chicken soup. Ask, **How can the cook remove the fat?** *(Skim the fat from the surface or freeze the soup and remove the solid fat layer.)*

Reteach · L1

Use the How It Works feature on p. 49 to review with students the importance of examining physical properties when choosing a material. Discuss why the physical properties of wax, clay, and metal determine what roles they play in the making of a sculpture.

Connecting Concepts

The substances are ordered from lowest to highest melting point, which groups them into gases, liquids, and solids at room temperature. With a larger database, alphabetical order would be more useful for retrieving the data.

Interactive Textbook

If your class subscribes to the Interactive Textbook, use it to review key concepts in Section 2.2.

Section 2.2 Assessment

1. Students may list hardness, viscosity, conductivity, density, malleability, melting point, and boiling point. Students may also list color, taste, flexibility, and durability.
2. Identify materials, choose a material for a specific purpose, or separate the substances in a mixture
3. Filtration and distillation
4. A thick liquid has a high viscosity.
5. The shape and size of the pencil change, but the composition of the pencil remains the same.
6. A difference in boiling points allows mixtures to be separated by distillation.
7. By scratching the cup with an object made of copper
8. Pot holders are designed to prevent the transfer of heat from a cooking utensil.
9. Silicon dioxide

Answer to . . .

Figure 14 *With smaller holes, more objects would collect on the screen.*

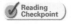 Reading Checkpoint · *Loose tea leaves can be removed by filtration.*

Getting a Fresh Start

Background

Aeration is of great importance during waste-water treatment because of the organic compounds in sewage. Aeration is also important when the water source is groundwater because of the likely concentration of dissolved carbonates. Water that contains dissolved calcium and magnesium compounds is called hard water because deposits of these salts can accumulate in water and lessen the effectiveness of soap. Water softeners replace calcium and magnesium compounds with sodium compounds, which do not cause the same problems.

Build Science Skills

Observing

Purpose Students observe that water can taste different depending on its source and on its purity.

Materials tap water, bottled water, distilled water

Class Time 10 minutes

Procedure Have students taste samples of tap water, bottled water, and distilled water. Have them describe any differences or similarities they taste.

Safety Use only water that is intended for consumption.

Expected Outcome Students will be able to observe that the taste that they associate with water is due to substances dissolved in the water, and not to the water itself.

Kinesthetic, Visual

Getting a Fresh Start

Water found in nature is never 100 percent pure. There are always substances dissolved in the water. Some of these substances, as well as bacteria and particles of dirt, must be removed before the water is fit to drink.

1 Coarse filter A screen prevents large items such as leaves from entering the water treatment plant.

Reservoir

Coarse filter screen

Aeration tank

Outlet tower

2 Aeration During aeration, air may be bubbled into the water or water may be sprayed into the air. Aeration removes substances from water, such as iron compounds, that give water an unpleasant taste.

Alum (aluminum sulfate) added

Colloid forms.

Layer of lumps

Cleaned water spills over into a trough.

3 Forming a colloid Alum is added to the mixing tank. Alum causes small particles in the water to form a type of colloid called a gel. Most of the bacteria in the water are trapped in the gel.

4 Sedimentation In the sedimentation tank, large lumps slowly settle to the bottom of the tank from where they can be removed.

Sedimentation tank

Water from the ground
About half of the drinking water in the United States comes from natural underground sources. Although this groundwater is filtered as it passes through rocks and sand, it sometimes contains high levels of dissolved minerals or chemical pollutants. So groundwater is purified using a modified version of surface water filtration.

6 Carbon filter The water is sometimes passed through a carbon filter. This filter removes tiny amounts of dissolved impurities, and improves the water's taste and color.

5 Sand and gravel filter
Next, the water trickles through sand and gravel filter beds, which trap the remaining suspended particles. Because the filter beds can become clogged, they are washed every 24 hours.

Water storage tank

Water softener added

Fluorine compound added

Chlorine added

Carbon filter

Gravel layer

Sand layer

Filtered water

7 Additives
The fluorine compound prevents tooth decay and the chlorine kills bacteria. The water softener removes some magnesium and calcium compounds.

8 Storage Finally, the water is held in storage tanks before passing into the public water supply.

Going Further

- Some people use a system to purify water at home. Research and write about one of these systems. What is the system designed to do? Compare the method used to the processes that occur at a water purification plant.
- Take a Discovery Channel Video Field Trip by watching "Fresh-Squeezed Water."

DISCOVERY CHANNEL **SCHOOL** Video Field Trip

Going Further

Most home water purification systems use activated charcoal (AC) filters or reverse osmosis (RO). Neither system removes all contaminants. Activated charcoal is an extremely porous solid with a large surface area on which substances are absorbed. Activated charcoal is effective for removing volatile organic compounds, pesticides, some metals, and chlorine. Sometimes bacteria grow on the filter. The surface of the activated charcoal may become saturated and ineffective before the consumer replaces the filter.

During reverse osmosis, normal household water pressure forces water through a semipermeable membrane. Reverse osmosis is useful for removing lead and other transition metals, asbestos, and many dissolved organic compounds. Reverse osmosis is a slow, wasteful process that uses three to nine gallons per gallon of purified water. (Some people use RO systems in their fish tanks.)

In parts of the world without municipal treatment plants, UV light is used to kill waterborne pathogens.
Verbal

DISCOVERY CHANNEL **SCHOOL** **Video Field Trip**

Fresh-Squeezed Water

After students have viewed the Video Field Trip, ask them the following questions: **Why did the people on Catalina Island need to convert seawater to fresh water?** *(They were running out of drinkable water.)* **What is a semipermeable membrane?** *(A semipermeable membrane is a* material that has microscopic holes to allow water to pass through while blocking salts and viruses.)* **What is reverse osmosis?** *(During reverse osmosis, water under high pressure passes through a semipermeable membrane, which removes dissolved salts and other unwanted substances.)* **Why is NASA also interested in desalination methods?** *(Being able to recycle the water on board a spacecraft reduces the amount and the weight of water that must accompany the astronauts on their voyages.)*

1 FOCUS

Objectives

2.3.1 Describe chemical properties of matter.

2.3.2 Describe clues that indicate that a chemical change is taking place.

2.3.3 Distinguish chemical changes from physical changes.

Reading Focus

Build Vocabulary L2

Word-Part Analysis Have students look up the words *flammable, inflammable,* and *nonflammable.* Have them find two meanings of the prefix *in-* to explain why the terms are confusing. Ask them to consider why it is very important to know what each term means. *(Inflammable and flammable are synonyms. The prefix in- can mean "not," or "into" as in "burst into flames." It is important to use the correct meanings when writing or interpreting fire safety warnings.)*

Reading Strategy L2

a. Copper roof changing color from red to green when exposed to moist air
b. Formation of carbon dioxide gas when vinegar is added to baking soda
c. Formation of cottage cheese curds when acid is added to milk

2 INSTRUCT

Observing Chemical Properties

Build Reading Literacy L1

Preview Refer to page **36D** in this chapter, which provides the guidelines for previewing.

Before they read the section, have students skim the headings, visuals, and boldfaced material to preview how the text is organized.
Visual

FYI

If the combustion of paraffin is not complete, carbon monoxide will form. Combustion as a type of reaction is addressed in Chapter 7. Combustion of fossil fuels is discussed in Chapter 9.

2.3 Chemical Properties

Standard: ICP.5.6

Reading Focus

Key Concepts

- When can chemical properties be observed?
- What observations might indicate that a chemical change has occurred?
- What is the difference between chemical and physical changes?

Vocabulary

- chemical property
- flammability
- reactivity
- chemical change
- precipitate

Reading Strategy

Relating Text and Visuals Copy the table. Find examples of the clues for recognizing chemical changes in Figures 19 and 20.

Clue	Example
Change in color	a. ___?___
Production of gas	b. ___?___
Formation of precipitate	c. ___?___

Figure 16 When candles burn, new substances form. The ability to burn is a chemical property.

How would you describe candles like the ones in Figure 16? You might describe their color or their hardness. Or, you might observe that the candles float on water, and conclude that the density of candle wax is less than that of water. Color, hardness, and density are physical properties. But there is something else about the candles that may seem even more obvious to you: the fact that the candles are burning. The ability to burn is not a physical property because you cannot observe burning without changing the composition of the material that is burning. As a candle burns, new substances form.

Observing Chemical Properties

Most candles are made from paraffin, which is a mixture of compounds containing carbon and hydrogen. As a candle burns, the compounds combine with oxygen in the air to form water and carbon dioxide. (Carbon dioxide is the gas that gives a carbonated beverage its fizz.) The ability to burn is a chemical property. A **chemical property** is any ability to produce a change in the composition of matter. **Chemical properties can be observed only when the substances in a sample of matter are changing into different substances.** Flammability and reactivity are two examples of chemical properties.

Flammability Materials that burn can be used as fuel. Sometimes, people use burning newspapers to start a fire in a fireplace. Gasoline is the fuel burned in most automobiles. The chemical property that paper and gasoline share is their flammability. **Flammability** is a material's ability to burn in the presence of oxygen.

Section Resources

Print
- *Laboratory Manual,* Investigation 2A
- *Reading and Study Workbook With Math Support,* Section 2.3
- *Transparencies,* Section 2.3

Technology
- *Interactive Textbook,* Section 2.3
- *Presentation Pro CD-ROM,* Section 2.3
- *Go Online,* NSTA SciLinks, Chemical and physical changes

Sometimes flammability is not a desirable property. For example, there are laws that regulate the flammability of fabrics. The fabrics used in children's sleepwear must have a low flammability. These fabrics are described as flame-resistant because they are difficult to ignite. If they do ignite, they burn slowly.

Reactivity The property that describes how readily a substance combines chemically with other substances is **reactivity.** Nitrogen and oxygen are the main gases in air. Oxygen is a highly reactive element. Nitrogen has an extremely low reactivity.

Oxygen reacts easily with most other elements. Figure 17 shows the rust that forms when oxygen reacts with iron and water. Rust is a brittle, reddish-brown compound. A rusty chain or bolt is more likely to break than a new chain or bolt because rust is weaker than iron. Because iron is highly reactive, you would not choose iron to make decorative objects, such as jewelry or coins.

Many uses of nitrogen depend on its low reactivity. For example, seawater is often stored in steel tanks located below the lowest deck of a ship. The seawater helps to keep the ship stable in the water. Over time, rust forms in the tanks because iron in the steel reacts with oxygen dissolved in the water. Researchers in Japan have developed a way to reduce the amount of rust produced. They pump nitrogen gas into the tanks, and the nitrogen displaces the dissolved oxygen.

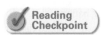 **Reading Checkpoint** *Which element is more reactive—oxygen or nitrogen?*

For: Links on chemical and physical changes
Visit: www.SciLinks.org
Web Code: ccn-1023

Figure 17 This automobile must have been exposed to air and water for many years. **Drawing Conclusions** *What evidence is there that parts of the automobile contained iron?*

Properties of Matter **55**

Recognizing Chemical Changes

Identifying a Chemical Change L2

Objective
After completing this activity, students will be able to
• recognize evidence of a chemical change.

Skills Focus Observing, Drawing Conclusions

 Prep Time 20 minutes

Advance Prep To prepare 1-M solutions of calcium chloride, sodium chloride, and copper sulfate, dissolve 1 mole of each salt (111.0 g $CaCl_2$; 58.5 g NaCl; or 249.69 g $CuSO_4 \cdot 5H_2O$) in approximately 800 mL of distilled or deionized water in a 1-L volumetric flask. Once a salt has dissolved, add enough water to make a 1000-mL solution. Stir the solution. Provide each group with 25 mL of each solution in a wash bottle, which is the easiest container for students to handle. Be sure to label each container with its contents.

Class Time 20 minutes

Safety Remind students to wash their hands thoroughly at the end of the lab, to be careful when handling glassware, and to dispose properly of chemical wastes.

Teaching Tips
• Review how to pour a liquid from a graduated cylinder and accurately read the volume.

Expected Outcome A precipitate of calcium sulfate will form in test tube A. The other two combinations will show no evidence of a chemical change.

Analyze and Conclude
1. Formation of a precipitate indicated that a chemical change occurred in test tube A.
2. No, formation of a precipitate is evidence for a chemical change, but it is not conclusive.
Visual, Logical

≡Quick › Lab

Identifying a Chemical Change

Materials
3 test tubes; test-tube rack; glass-marking pencil; 3 10-mL graduated cylinders; solutions of copper sulfate, calcium chloride, and sodium chloride

Procedure

1. Construct a data table with columns labeled Test Tube, Contents, and Observations.

2. Label the test tubes A, B, and C.

3. Pour 5 mL of copper sulfate solution into test tube A. Pour 5 mL of calcium chloride solution into test tube B. Pour 5 mL of sodium chloride solution into test tube C. **CAUTION** *Do not allow the solutions to touch your skin. They may cause irritation.*

4. Add 5 mL of calcium chloride solution to test tube A. Add 5 mL of sodium chloride solution to test tube B. Add 5 mL of copper sulfate solution to test tube C.

5. Examine the test tubes for evidence of a chemical change. Record your observations.

6. Pour the contents of the test tubes into the sink. Rinse out the test tubes and flush the contents down the drain. **CAUTION** *Wash your hands thoroughly with soap or detergent before leaving the laboratory.*

Analyze and Conclude

1. **Inferring** In which test tube(s) did a chemical change occur? Explain your answer.

2. **Evaluating** Can you be sure that a chemical change occurred? Explain your answer.

Figure 18 As a banana ripens, chemical changes cause the peel to change color from green to yellow. In a banana that is overly ripe, different chemical changes cause the peel to turn brown. *Observing Based on your experience, what other properties of a banana change as it ripens?*

Recognizing Chemical Changes

Figure 18 shows what happens to banana peels as bananas ripen. The color change in a banana peel is caused by chemical changes that are taking place in the cells of the banana. A **chemical change** occurs when a substance reacts and forms one or more new substances. Chemical changes occur when a cake bakes in an oven, leaves on trees change color, and food is digested in your stomach.

How can you recognize a chemical change? You have to look for clues. For example, when food spoils, it often gives off an unpleasant odor. **Three common types of evidence for a chemical change are a change in color, the production of a gas, and the formation of a precipitate.**

⌐ Facts and Figures

Banana Science There are four stages of banana development: growth, maturation, ripening, and senescence. During ripening, bananas produce increased amounts of ethylene gas, which triggers chemical changes. The peel changes color and becomes more permeable, the pulp softens, starches break down into sugar, and compounds responsible for flavor and aroma are produced. Once ripening begins, the process cannot be stopped. Ripening occurs whether the banana is attached or detached from the parent plant.

A Change in Color Over time, a shiny silver bracelet that is exposed to air will darken. As a match burns, it shrivels up and turns black. The new copper roof and the old copper roof in Figure 19 have different colors. In each of these examples, a change in color is a clue that a chemical change has produced at least one new substance.

Production of a Gas Figure 20A shows what happens when you mix vinegar with baking soda. Bubbles of carbon dioxide form immediately. A similar chemical change happens when you use baking powder as an ingredient in a cake recipe. Baking powder is a mixture of baking soda and one or more acids that react when wet. As the cake bakes, the bubbles of carbon dioxide expand and cause the cake to rise.

Formation of a Precipitate Another chemical change you can observe in the kitchen is the curdling of milk. If you add lemon juice or vinegar to milk, small bits of white solid will separate from the liquid. Any solid that forms and separates from a liquid mixture is called a **precipitate.** When an acid is added to milk, proteins in the milk undergo a chemical change that alters their structure, causing them to stick together in clumps. They form the precipitate shown in Figure 20B.

 Reading Checkpoint *What happens when you add vinegar to baking soda?*

Figure 19 When copper is exposed to moist air, it forms a thin coating called a patina. A new copper roof has a reddish color. The green patina on an old copper roof is a mixture of copper compounds.
Predicting **Would a patina form faster in a rainy climate or in a dry climate?**

Figure 20 The formation of a gas or a precipitate can be a clue to chemical change. **A** Carbon dioxide gas forms when vinegar is mixed with baking soda. **B** The curds in cottage cheese form when an acid is added to milk.

Facts and Figures

Acids in Action When acid is added to milk, one of the proteins in milk (casein) coagulates. The milk may thicken (as in buttermilk or yogurt) or separate into solid curds and liquid whey (as in cottage cheese). This process is called curdling. Acids may be added directly to the milk or produced by bacteria. Adding rennin (a coagulating enzyme) produces larger curds.

Single-action baking powder contains three dry ingredients: an acid (e.g., cream of tartar), a base (e.g., baking soda), and filler (e.g., cornstarch). When water is added, the acid and base react. Double-action baking powders contain two acids, one that reacts faster than the other. Recipes that use baking soda have another ingredient that provides the acid.

Use Visuals L1

Figure 20 Emphasize that the best way to determine if a chemical change is taking place is to compare materials before and after the reaction. Ask, **Describe baking soda and vinegar before they are mixed.** *(Baking soda is a white solid, and vinegar is a clear solution.)* **What clue indicates that a chemical change is taking place?** *(There is production of a gas.)* **When you see no obvious clues to a chemical change, can you be certain that a chemical change has not occurred?** *(No)* **Visual**

Answer to . . .

Figure 18 *Students may say that the banana becomes softer and that its odor increases.*

Figure 19 *In a rainy climate*

 Reading Checkpoint *Bubbles of carbon dioxide form.*

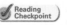

Is a Change Chemical or Physical?

Address Misconceptions L2

Students often have trouble distinguishing chemical from physical changes. Explain that the composition of *some* substances must change during a chemical change, but the composition of *all* substances must remain the same during a physical change.
Verbal

FYI

The release of heat or light is sometimes listed as a clue for a chemical change, but energy changes occur with both physical and chemical changes. Exothermic and endothermic changes are discussed in Sections 3.3 (Phase Changes) and 7.3 (Energy Changes in Reactions).

3 ASSESS

Evaluate Understanding L2

Have students list three clues that indicate that a chemical change is taking place and give an example of each. Then, have them exchange their work with a partner and discuss examples of physical changes that also exhibit these clues.

Reteach L1

Use Figures 18, 19, and 20 to review the clues that indicate that a chemical change is taking place.

Connecting C Concepts

Students might argue that observation and experimentation are the key steps in a scientific method for determining whether a change is physical or chemical.

Interactive Textbook If your class subscribes to the Interactive Textbook, use it to review key concepts in Section 2.3.

Figure 21 A blacksmith uses a hammer to shape a horseshoe that has been heated. Although the color of the iron horseshoe changes, no chemical change is occurring. **Inferring** *Other than color, what physical property of iron is affected by heating?*

Is a Change Chemical or Physical?

It is not always easy to distinguish a chemical change from a physical change. Even if you observe a color change, a gas, or a precipitate, you cannot be sure that a chemical change has taken place. When the iron horseshoe in Figure 21 is heated, its color changes from gray to red. Despite this change in color, the iron is still iron. When water boils on a stove, the bubbles of gas that rise to the surface are still water.

Before you decide whether or not a chemical change has occurred, ask yourself this question: Are different substances present after the change takes place? If not, then the change is physical, not chemical. **When matter undergoes a chemical change, the composition of the matter changes. When matter undergoes a physical change, the composition of the matter remains the same.**

Section 2.3 Assessment

Reviewing Concepts

1. Under what conditions can chemical properties be observed?
2. List three common types of evidence for a chemical change.
3. How do chemical changes differ from physical changes?
4. Explain why the rusting of an iron bar decreases the strength of the bar.
5. A pat of butter melts and then burns in a hot frying pan. Which of these changes is physical and which is chemical?

Critical Thinking

6. **Comparing and Contrasting** Compare the properties of a raw egg to those of a hard-boiled egg.

7. **Classifying** If you spill household bleach on denim jeans, you will observe that the area of the spill no longer has a blue color. Is this change chemical or physical? Give a reason for your answer.
8. **Inferring** Gold and platinum are often used to make jewelry. What can you infer about the reactivity of these elements?

Connecting C Concepts

Scientific Methods Section 1.2 listed typical steps scientists use. Which steps might you use to decide whether a change is physical or chemical? Explain.

58 Chapter 2

Section 2.3 Assessment

1. When the substances in a sample of matter are changing into different substances
2. A change in color, the production of a gas, or the formation of a precipitate
3. A chemical change produces new substances. A physical change produces no new substances.
4. When iron rusts, the compound that forms is brittle.

5. Melting is a physical change. Burning is a chemical change.
6. The raw egg is a viscous liquid. The egg white is cloudy and the yolk is orange. The hard-boiled egg is a soft solid. The egg white is opaque and the yolk is yellow.
7. Because the bleach has caused the denim to change color, the change is likely to be a chemical change.
8. Because jewelry is designed to last a long time, the reactivity of gold and platinum must be relatively low.

Answer to . . .

Figure 21 *Malleability increases.*

What Should Be Done With Arsenic-Treated Wood?

Termites are among the organisms that attack untreated wood. In 1950, United States suppliers of lumber began to treat wood with a mixture of copper, chromium, and arsenic (CCA). The mixture slows the damage to wood by poisoning the attacking organisms. Outdoor structures such as decks and porches were made from CCA-treated wood. By 2002, more than 95 percent of treated lumber sold for use outdoors contained CCA.

Arsenic is a poison that has been linked with certain types of cancer. Arsenic can be absorbed through the skin or ingested in water or food. Consumers were especially concerned about children touching CCA-treated wood and then placing their unwashed fingers in their mouths. Some consumers asked the Environmental Protection Agency (EPA) to ban the use of CCA. In 2002, the chemical and home-improvement industries agreed to stop producing CCA-treated wood for home use.

The Viewpoints

Old CCA-Treated Wood Does Not Need to Be Removed

The EPA did not recommend tearing down existing structures made from CCA-treated wood. A panel of Florida doctors reported that they found no studies linking cancer in children and exposure to CCA-treated wood. They concluded that the amount of arsenic that children could absorb from treated wood is small compared to the amount of arsenic that occurs naturally in soil.

There are risks associated with disposing of treated wood. Burning arsenic-treated wood produces ash with high levels of arsenic. The ash would poison a person who inhaled, ingested, or touched it. The only acceptable method of disposal is in landfills, which are rapidly filling. Also, arsenic from landfills can end up in groundwater.

Old CCA-Treated Wood Needs to Be Removed

A report produced by one state's Department of Environmental Protection concluded that there is a serious risk for children exposed to arsenic from treated wood. The level of arsenic remains high for 20 years in CCA-treated wood. The useful life of most treated wood products is about 20 years.

An area of CCA-treated wood the size of a four-year-old's hand contains about 120 times the amount of arsenic allowed in a 6-ounce glass of water. (The EPA limit for arsenic in drinking water is 10 parts per billion.) Rainwater penetrates wood and dissolves arsenic. The arsenic ends up on the surface of the wood or in the soil near the wood.

Research and Decide

1. **Defining the Issue** In your own words, describe the issue that needs to be resolved about existing structures made from CCA-treated wood.

2. **Analyzing the Viewpoints** List three arguments of those who don't think that existing structures made from CCA-treated wood need to be removed. List three arguments of those who want to remove existing structures made from CCA-treated wood.

3. **Forming Your Opinion** Should existing structures built from CCA-treated wood be removed? Which argument did you find most convincing?

For: More on this issue
Visit: PHSchool.com
Web Code: cch-1020

What Should Be Done With Arsenic-Treated Wood? L2

Background
Woods that are naturally resistant to attack, such as cedar and redwood, tend to be more expensive than timber treated with CCA. Alternatives to waterborne preservatives such as CCA included creosote and pentachloro-phenol, or penta. Creosote is a smelly mixture of chemicals distilled from coal tar. Railroads began to treat railroad ties with creosote in 1889. Penta was generally applied in a 5% solution of petroleum solvents. Its use became limited after the price of oil rose in the 1970s. Because there are health risks associated with both penta and creosote, their use has been restricted since 1986.

After students answer Question 3, ask, **What evidence did the opponents and supporters of CCA removal have that you do not have? Explain how that evidence might have influenced your opinion.** *(The viewpoints as presented were based on opposing interpretations of scientific studies. Being able to see the actual data might have influenced their opinions.)*

Have students further research the issues related to this topic.

Answers
1. Are structures built from CCA-treated wood enough of a health hazard for children that the structures should be removed?
2. **Old CCA-Treated Wood Does Not Need to Be Removed:** The EPA has not recommended removal of the structures. No studies link cancer in children and exposure to CCA-treated wood. There are serious risks associated with disposal of the wood.

Old CCA-Treated Wood Needs to Be Removed: The level of arsenic remains high over the lifetime of the wood. The level of arsenic in the wood is much higher than the level allowed in water. Rain causes arsenic to collect on the surface of the wood or in soil.
3. Students should provide a reason for their decision.

Using Properties to Identify Materials

Objective

After completing this activity, students will be able to

• identify simple chemical changes.
• identify an unknown sample by comparing its properties to those of known materials.

Skills Focus Observing, Inferring, Predicting

Prep Time 10 minutes

Advance Prep Set out small, labeled containers of each of the materials to be tested for each group. Provide dropper bottles of water, vinegar, and iodine solution for each group. If you need to prepare iodine solution, mix 1 mL of concentrated tincture of iodine with 50 mL of water. Use baking powder for the crime scene sample and baking soda for the suspect's shoe sample.

Class Time 45 minutes

Safety Make sure that students wear aprons, goggles, and plastic disposable gloves throughout the lab. Caution students about the proper handling of the iodine solution because it is poisonous and can stain skin and clothing. Rinse iodine spills with water.

Questioning Strategies

Ask students: **What observations could indicate that a chemical change has taken place?** (The release of a gas, the formation of a precipitate, or a color change can indicate that a chemical change has taken place.) **Which test distinguishes baking soda from baking powder?** (Addition of iodine solution causes bubbling with baking powder, but not with baking soda.) **How could you use data from this lab to help you identify the unknown samples?** (By comparing the test results of the known samples with the test results of the unknown samples) **Why do you need to use different wells for each material?** (To avoid contamination of materials being tested)

Forensics Lab

Using Properties to Identify Materials

Forensic chemists test the physical and chemical properties of materials found at a crime scene. They also do similar tests on the materials found on a suspect's skin or clothing. These materials are often complex mixtures, such as soil, which contain many substances. In this lab, you will compare the properties of three known materials with two samples of "evidence." These samples represent evidence from a crime scene and evidence from a suspect's shoe. Although your materials and equipment are less complex than those used by forensic chemists, your overall method will be similar to the methods they use.

Problem Can the properties of materials that appear similar be used to tell them apart?

Materials

• 2 spot plates
• glass-marking pencil
• 5 laboratory spatulas
• cornstarch
• baking soda
• baking powder
• wash bottle of water
• vinegar
• iodine solution
• sample from crime scene
• sample from suspect's shoe

Skills Observing, Inferring, Predicting

Procedure

Part A: Properties of Known Substances

1. On a separate sheet of paper, copy the data table shown.

2. Use a glass-marking pencil to label 15 wells A through O on the spot plates. Make a mark next to each well, not in the well.

3. Use a spatula to place a small amount of cornstarch in wells A, B, and C. Record any physical properties of the cornstarch that you observe.

4. Use a clean spatula to place a small amount of baking soda in wells D, E, and F. Record any physical properties of baking soda you observe.

5. Using a clean spatula, place a small amount of baking powder in wells G, H, and I. Record any physical properties of baking powder you observe.

6. Fill wells A, D, and G with water. Record any changes you observe.

Data Table				
Sample	Description	Result of Adding Water	Result of Adding Vinegar	Result of Adding Iodine
Cornstarch				
Baking soda				
Baking powder				
Crime scene sample				
Sample from suspect's shoe				

Sample Data Table

Sample	Description	Result of Adding Water	Result of Adding Vinegar	Result of Adding Iodine
Cornstarch	white powder	no change	no change	blue-black
Baking soda	white powder	dissolves	bubbles	no change
Baking powder	white powder	partly dissolves, bubbles	bubbles	bubbles
Crime scene sample	white powder	partly dissolves, bubbles	bubbles	bubbles
Sample from suspect's shoe	white powder	dissolves	bubbles	bubbles

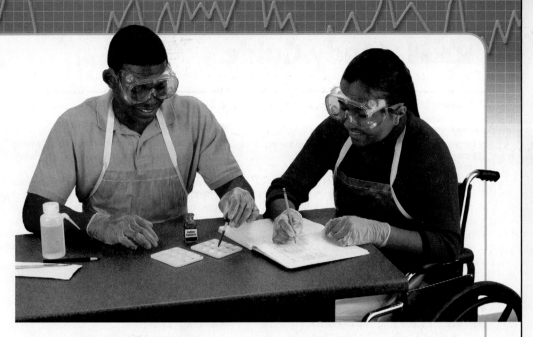

Go Further

Check students' proposed procedures for safety before permitting them to carry out their experiments. Samples can be placed on a can lid with safely smoothed edges for heating over a Bunsen burner or hot plate. Cornstarch will visibly char when heated. The other materials will not undergo any visible changes. **Kinesthetic, Logical**

7. Fill wells B, E, and H with vinegar. Record any changes you observe.

8. Add one drop of iodine solution to wells C, F, and I. Record any changes you observe. **CAUTION** *Iodine solution is corrosive and poisonous. It can stain skin and clothing. Rinse any iodine spills with water.*

Part B: Properties of Unknown Substances

9. **Predicting** Look at the sample from the crime scene and the sample from the suspect's shoe. Based on your observations, predict whether testing will show that the samples are identical. Record your prediction.

10. Use a clean spatula to place a small amount of the sample from the crime scene in wells J, K, and L. Record any physical properties of the sample that you observe.

11. Use a clean laboratory spatula to place a small amount of the sample from the suspect's shoe in wells M, N, and O. Record any physical properties of the sample that you observe.

12. Fill wells J and M with water. Record your observations.

13. Fill wells K and N with vinegar. Record your observations.

14. Add one drop of iodine solution to wells L and O. Record your observations.

15. Rinse all materials off the spot plates and flush them down the drain with at least ten times as much water. Dispose of your plastic gloves as directed by your teacher. **CAUTION** *Wash your hands thoroughly with soap or detergent before leaving the laboratory.*

Analyze and Conclude

1. **Analyzing Data** Were you able to use the ability to dissolve in water to distinguish all three materials? Explain.

2. **Drawing Conclusions** Are the samples from the suspect and from the crime scene identical?

3. **Evaluating and Revising** Did the data you collected support your prediction? Explain your answer.

Go Further Design an experiment to determine the effect of heating on the materials you tested in this lab. With your teacher's approval and supervision, carry out your experiment and use the data you collect to identify a sample of an unknown material.

Analyze and Conclude
1. The ability to dissolve in water distinguished cornstarch from baking soda and baking powder, but not baking soda from baking powder.
2. The results did not indicate that the sample from the crime scene (baking powder) has the same properties as the sample from the suspect's shoe (baking soda).

3. Yes or no (depending on the prediction made). Students should use evidence from the water and iodine solution tests to support their answers.
Visual, Logical

Study Tip

Structure Study Time

A good way to begin to study for a test is to figure out what topics will be covered and to what extent they will appear on the test. Tell students that they should structure their study time by studying each topic for an amount of time proportionate to its coverage in class or in the textbook. They should set time goals for themselves and take small breaks as a reward for accomplishing each goal.

Thinking Visually

a. Chemical change
b. Boiling, freezing, crumpling, slicing, braiding, or cutting
c. Burning

2.1 Classifying Matter

Key Concepts

- Every sample of a given substance has the same properties because a substance has a fixed, uniform composition.
- An element has a fixed composition because it contains only one type of atom.
- A compound always contains two or more elements joined in a fixed proportion.
- The properties of a mixture can vary because the composition of a mixture is not fixed.
- Based on the size of its largest particles, a mixture can be classified as a solution, a suspension, or a colloid.

Vocabulary

pure substance, *p. 39*
element, *p. 39*
atom, *p. 39*
compound, *p. 40*
heterogeneous mixture, *p. 41*
homogeneous mixture, *p. 42*
solution, *p. 42*
suspension, *p. 43*
colloid, *p. 44*

2.2 Physical Properties

Key Concepts

- Viscosity, conductivity, malleability, hardness, melting point, boiling point, and density are examples of physical properties.
- Physical properties are used to identify a material, to choose a material for a specific purpose, or to separate the substances in a mixture.
- Filtration and distillation are two common separation methods.

Vocabulary

physical property, *p. 45*
viscosity, *p. 45*
conductivity, *p. 46*
malleability, *p. 46*
melting point, *p. 47*
boiling point, *p. 47*
filtration, *p. 50*
distillation, *p. 50*
physical change, *p. 51*

2.3 Chemical Properties

Key Concepts

- Chemical properties can be observed only when the substances in a sample of matter are changing into different substances.
- Three common types of evidence for a chemical change are a change in color, the production of a gas, and the formation of a precipitate.
- When matter undergoes a chemical change, the composition of the matter changes. When matter undergoes a physical change, the composition of the matter remains the same.

Vocabulary

chemical property, *p. 54*
flammability, *p. 54*
reactivity, *p. 55*
chemical change, *p. 56*
precipitate, *p. 57*

Thinking Visually

Concept Map Use information from the chapter to complete the concept map below.

 ## Chapter Resources

Print
- ***Chapter and Unit Tests,*** Chapter 2 Test A and Test B
- ***Test Prep Resources,*** Chapter 2

Technology
- ***Computer Test Bank,*** Chapter Test 2
- ***Interactive Textbook,*** Chapter 2
- ***Go Online,*** PHSchool.com, Chapter 2

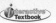
Reviewing Content

Choose the letter that best answers the question or completes the statement.

1. Which of these substances is not an element?
  a. water   **b.** hydrogen
  c. aluminum   **d.** iron

2. Tap water is
  a. an element.   **b.** a compound.
  c. a substance.   **d.** a mixture.

3. When a homemade oil-and-vinegar salad dressing is left standing, it separates into layers. The salad dressing is a
  a. solution.   **b.** suspension.
  c. colloid.   **d.** compound.

4. Which of the following is not an example of a physical property?
  a. density   **b.** flammability
  c. hardness   **d.** melting point

5. Which material is a poor conductor of heat?
  a. iron   **b.** silver
  c. wood   **d.** copper

6. A material that can be hit without shattering is
  a. viscous.   **b.** flammable.
  c. malleable.   **d.** hard.

7. At room temperature, a substance with a melting point of 40°C is a
  a. solid.   **b.** liquid.
  c. gas.   **d.** mixture.

8. Which action involves a chemical change?
  a. making ice cubes
  b. adding sugar to tea
  c. cutting wrapping paper
  d. baking a cake

9. A substance that has little tendency to change into other substances is said to have low
  a. reactivity.   **b.** density.
  c. viscosity.   **d.** conductivity.

10. Formation of a precipitate is usually evidence of
  a. the separation of a mixture.
  b. a chemical change.
  c. the formation of a mixture.
  d. a physical change.

Understanding Concepts

11. Explain why the properties of a pure substance do not vary from sample to sample.

12. What is the difference between an element and a compound?

13. How does the composition of a mixture of hydrogen and oxygen differ from the composition of a compound containing hydrogen and oxygen?

14. Suppose all the grains in a sample of sand were exactly the same size. Could the sample still be a heterogeneous mixture? Explain your answer.

15. What allows a mixture to be separated by filtration?

16. Explain why viscosity is classified as a physical property.

17. Based on these pieces of pottery found in Grand Canyon National Park, would you describe pottery as a malleable or brittle material?

18. A sample of copper can be drawn into a thin wire. Is this property of copper a physical property or a chemical property? Explain.

19. Name one physical property and one chemical property of wood.

20. Why is breaking down a compound into its elements considered a chemical change?

21. List one physical change and one chemical change that occur when a candle burns.

22. Suppose you need to identify the material in an object without changing the object in any way. Should you use physical or chemical properties to identify the material? Explain your choice.

Properties of Matter **63**

Assessment

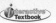 If your class subscribes to the Interactive Textbook, your students can go online to access an interactive version of the Student Edition and a self-test.

Reviewing Content

1. a   2. d   3. b
4. b   5. c   6. c
7. a   8. d   9. a
10. b

Understanding Concepts

11. The properties of a substance are constant because the composition of a substance does not vary.

12. A compound can be broken down into simpler substances, but an element cannot.

13. The relative proportions of hydrogen and oxygen in the mixture can vary. The relative proportions of hydrogen and oxygen in the compound cannot vary.

14. Grains with identical sizes could contain different substances (which would be suggested by grains having different colors).

15. Some particles in the mixture are much larger than other particles in the mixture.

16. The viscosity of a substance can be determined without changing the substance into a different substance.

17. Pottery is brittle.

18. It is a physical property because the composition of copper does not change as its shape changes.

19. Students are likely to say that wood is a poor conductor of heat (physical) and wood is flammable (chemical).

20. Because a compound and its elements are different substances, a chemical change has taken place.

21. Students are likely to say that the melting of wax is a physical change and the burning of wax is a chemical change.

22. You should use physical properties because in order to determine chemical properties, you must change the material in the object.

 Homework Guide

Section	Questions
2.1	1–3, 11–15, 23, 24
2.2	4–7, 16–18, 25–29, 31, 35
2.3	8–10, 19–22, 30, 32–34

Critical Thinking

23. No. The properties of a compound do not necessarily match the properties of the elements from which the compound is formed.

24. Possible questions: "Is the air dusty?" and "Does the air contain water droplets?"

25. Mass and volume are properties that vary from sample to sample of a substance.

26. No. Although the density of the solid matches the density of one of the substances in the table, isopropyl alcohol is a liquid at room temperature, not a solid.

27. No. Gold is too dense to float on water.

28. No. It is possible for two different substances to have the same density or for a mixture to have the same density of a substance.

29. You could measure the density of the bracelet and compare that value to the known density of pure gold.

30. You would have observed two common clues for a chemical change— a color change and the formation of a precipitate.

Concepts in Action

31. The syrup has a greater viscosity than the sap because it contains much less water, which has a low viscosity.

32. You can infer that hair is flammable.

33. Nitrogen has a low reactivity compared to oxygen.

34. The paint prevents the iron from coming in contact with oxygen and water. If the paint flakes off, the iron will start to rust.

35. The cheesecloth acts as a filter. The lemon juice can pass through, but the seeds cannot.

Go Online
PHSchool.com

Your students can independently test their knowledge of the chapter and print out their test results for your files.

Critical Thinking

23. Applying Concepts Ammonia is a compound of hydrogen and nitrogen that dissolves easily in water. Can you conclude that hydrogen and nitrogen dissolve in water? Explain your answer.

24. Posing Questions What information would you need to know about a sample of air before you could classify the sample as a solution, suspension, or colloid?

25. Applying Concepts Explain why you cannot use mass or volume alone to identify substances.

Use the table to answer questions 26 and 27.

Melting Points and Densities of Some Substances

Substance	Melting Point	Density
Aluminum	660.3°C	2.70 g/cm³
Table salt	800.7°C	2.17 g/cm³
Isopropyl alcohol	−89.5°C	0.78 g/cm³
Bromine	−7.2°C	3.10 g/cm³
Water	0.0°C	1.00 g/cm³
Gold	1064.2°C	19.3 g/cm³

26. Analyzing Data You have a solid with a density of 0.78 g/cm³. Is it possible that this solid is one of the substances listed in the table? Explain.

27. Using Tables A solid, rectangular block of material floats on water. Is it possible that the block is pure gold? Explain your answer.

28. Drawing Conclusions At room temperature, two white solids have the same density. With just this information, is it possible to conclude that the two solids are the same material? Explain.

29. Designing Experiments How could you use density to show that a gold bracelet contains elements other than gold?

30. Inferring Suppose you mix two colorless liquids together and a green solid settles to the bottom of the container. Explain why you might be confident that a chemical change has taken place.

Concepts in Action

31. Comparing and Contrasting The photo shows maple sap being collected in a bucket. The sap is about 97% water and 3% sugar with traces of other compounds. Cans of 100% pure maple syrup contain about 34% water and 66% sugar. Which would have the greater viscosity—the maple sap or the maple syrup? Give a reason for your answer.

32. Inferring One of the general safety instructions for working in a laboratory is to tie back long hair, especially when using a lab burner. From this instruction, what can you infer about the flammability of hair?

33. Applying Concepts Why might valuable documents be stored in pure nitrogen instead of in air? Recall that air is a mixture of gases, including nitrogen and oxygen.

34. Relating Cause and Effect Explain why painting an iron railing can slow down the rate at which the railing rusts.

35. Writing in Science Cheesecloth is a type of cotton cloth used by cooks. Write a paragraph explaining why a cook might wrap a lemon wedge in cheesecloth before squeezing juice from the lemon. What process for separating mixtures is the cook using?

Performance-Based Assessment

Writing in a Journal Keep a journal for a day. List five physical changes and five chemical changes that you observe. Be sure to describe why you think each change is physical or chemical.

Go Online
PHSchool.com

For: Self-grading assessment
Visit: PHSchool.com
Web Code: cca-1020

Performance-Based Assessment

Ask students to identify the criteria they used to classify the changes. Students may observe some events that will not be easy to classify. For example, a student might conclude that a chemical reaction occurs when a soft drink can is opened, because bubbles appear.

Test-Taking Tip

Using Models

For some test questions, you will be asked to decide what a visual model represents. Look at the model below. Notice that there are two types of particles shown and notice how the particles are distributed. Use what you observe to decide which answer is the best choice.

What type of matter does the model represent?
(A) a solution
(B) a colloid
(C) a suspension
(D) an element
(E) a homogeneous mixture

(Answer: C)

Choose the letter that best answers the question or completes the statement.

1. All pure substances
   (A) contain only one type of atom.
   (B) can be broken down into simpler substances.
   (C) cannot be broken down into simpler substances.
   (D) have a fixed composition.
   (E) have a variable composition.

2. Which property can be used to separate a mixture by distillation?
   (A) melting point
   (B) boiling point
   (C) density
   (D) viscosity
   (E) conductivity

3. During which of these events does a chemical change occur?
   (A) Ice cubes melt.
   (B) A pot of water boils.
   (C) A heated iron bar turns red.
   (D) A paper clip is bent.
   (E) A cake rises in the oven.

4. You can be certain that a change is a chemical change if
   (A) the change cannot be reversed.
   (B) new substances form.
   (C) bubbles are produced.
   (D) a precipitate forms.
   (E) there is a color change.

Use the drawings to answer Questions 5 and 6.

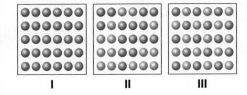

I   II   III

5. Which of the drawings could represent a homogeneous mixture?
   (A) drawing I
   (B) drawing II
   (C) drawing III
   (D) drawings I and III
   (E) drawings II and III

6. Which of the drawings could represent an element?
   (A) drawing I
   (B) drawing II
   (C) drawing III
   (D) drawings I and III
   (E) drawings II and III

 Standards Guide

Question	Standards
1	ICP.5.1
2	ICP.5.1
3	ICP.5.6
4	ICP.5.6
5	ICP.5.1

Planning Guide

SECTION OBJECTIVES	STANDARDS		ACTIVITIES and LABS
	NATIONAL	STATE	
3.1 Solids, Liquids, and Gases, pp. 68–74 🕐 1 block or 2 periods **3.1.1 Describe** the five states of matter. **3.1.2 Classify** materials as solids, liquids, or gases. **3.1.3 Explain** the behavior of gases, liquids, and solids, using kinetic theory.	A-1, B-2, B-5, F-5, G-1, G-2, G-3	ICP.1.4, ICP.3.1, ICP.3.2, ICP.3.4	**SE** Inquiry Activity: How Easy Is It to Compress Air and Water? p. 67 **L2** **TE** Teacher Demo: Comparing Liquid Volume, p. 69 **L2** **TE** Teacher Demo: Detecting the Motion of a Gas, p. 72 **L2** **LM** Investigation 3B: Measuring Spaces Between Particles of Matter **L1**
3.2 The Gas Laws, pp. 75–81 🕐 1 block or 2 periods **3.2.1 Define** pressure and gas pressure. **3.2.2 Identify** factors that affect gas pressure. **3.2.3 Predict** changes in gas pressure due to changes in temperature, volume, and number of particles. **3.2.4 Explain** Charles's law, Boyle's law, and the combined gas law. **3.2.5 Apply** gas laws to solve problems involving gases.	A-1, A-2, B-2, B-4, B-5, G-1, G-2, G-3	ICP.3.2, ICP.3.3, ICP.3.4	**SE** Quick Lab: Observing the Effect of Temperature on Gas Pressure, p. 79 **L2** **TE** Build Science Skills: Observing, p. 75 **L2** **TE** Teacher Demo: Changing Volume of a Balloon, p. 76 **L2**
3.3 Phase Changes, pp. 84–91 🕐 1 block or 2 periods **3.3.1 Describe** phase changes. **3.3.2 Explain** how temperature can be used to recognize a phase change. **3.3.3 Explain** what happens to the motion, arrangement, and average kinetic energy of water molecules during phase changes. **3.3.4 Describe** each of the six phase changes. **3.3.5 Identify** phase changes as endothermic or exothermic.	A-1, A-2, B-2, B-5	ICP.3.1, ICP.3.2, ICP.3.3, ICP.3.4	**SE** Quick Lab: Observing Phase Changes, p. 90 **L2** **SE** Exploration Lab: Investigating Changes in Temperature During Heating of Solids, pp. 92–93 **L2** **TE** Teacher Demo: Energy Transfer, p. 86 **L2** **LM** Investigation 3A: Performing a Fractional Distillation **L2**

RESOURCES PRINT and TECHNOLOGY	SECTION ASSESSMENT
RSW Section 3.1 **L1**	**SE** Section 3.1 Assessment, p. 74
MSPS Section 3.1 **L2**	
T Chapter 3 Pretest **L2**	**iT** Section 3.1
Section 3.1 **L2**	
P Chapter 3 Pretest **L2**	
Section 3.1 **L2**	
GO Kinetic theory **L2**	
RSW Section 3.2 **L1**	**SE** Section 3.2 Assessment, p. 81
RSW Math Skill **L2**	
MSPS Section 3.2 **L2**	**iT** Section 3.2
DC Up, Up, and Away **L2**	
T Section 3.2 **L2**	
P Section 3.2 **L2**	
GO Properties of matter **L2**	
PLM Lab 1: Investigating Changes in Temperature During Heating of Solids **L2**	**SE** Section 3.3 Assessment, p. 91
RSW Section 3.3 **L1**	**iT** Section 3.3
T Section 3.3 **L2**	
P Section 3.3 **L2**	
GO Phases of matter **L2**	
PHSchool.com GO Data sharing **L2**	

Go Online

Go online for these Internet resources.

PHSchool.com
Web Code: ccd-1030
Web Code: cca-1030

SCiLINKS
Web Code: ccn-1031
Web Code: ccn-1033

SCIENCE NEWS®
Web Code: cce-1032

Materials for Activities and Labs

Quantities for each group

STUDENT EDITION

Inquiry Activity, p. 67
syringe (sealed at narrow end), water

Quick Lab, p. 79
pan, metric ruler, empty beverage can, masking tape, hot plate, clock, tongs

Quick Lab, p. 90
250-mL Erlenmeyer flask, graduated cylinder, thermometer, dry ice

Exploration Lab, pp. 92–93
500-mL beaker, crushed ice, thermometer, hot plate, clock with second hand, test tube of lauric acid with thermometer, glass stirring rod, graph paper

TEACHER'S EDITION

Teacher Demo, p. 69
3 glass jars or bottles with lids, each having a noticeably different diameter but about the same volume; graduated cylinder; water

Teacher Demo, p. 72
spray can of air freshener, 3 stopwatches

Build Science Skills, p. 75
clay, CD case, textbook

Teacher Demo, p. 76
inflated balloons, refrigerator, warm place

Build Science Skills, p. 82
plastic bag (dry cleaner or thin garbage bag), string, hair dryers

Teacher Demo, p. 86
tray of ice cubes

Chapter Assessment

CHAPTER ASSESSMENT

SE Chapter Assessment, pp. 95–96
CUT Chapter 3 Test A, B
CTB Chapter 3
iT Chapter 3
PHSchool.com GO Web Code: cca-1030

STANDARDIZED TEST PREP

SE Chapter 3, p. 97
TP Diagnose and Prescribe

Interactive Textbook with assessment at PHSchool.com

Before you teach

From the Author

David Frank
Ferris State University

Big Ideas

On Earth, matter is readily observed in three states: gas, liquid, and solid. The kinetic theory is used to explain the behavior of these states of matter, including what occurs within a sample of a substance as the substance changes from one state to another. The forces of attraction that hold solids and liquids together are also a key factor.

Matter and Change In Section 3.3, students build on knowledge from Chapter 2. They should realize that phase changes are physical changes because composition does not change during a phase change. You may need to stress that the molecules in ice, liquid water, and water vapor are identical. Only their arrangement is different. Because water is used as an example throughout the section, be sure that students do not assume that all substances have exactly the same properties as water. For example, substances that are normally gases at room temperature must have boiling points below 20°C.

Forces and Motion To understand the general properties of solids, liquids, and gases, students must envision the constant motion of atoms and molecules. To further understand gases, students need to know that gas pressure in an enclosed container is caused by particles colliding with the walls of their container. Section 3.2 focuses on the variables that affect the pressure of gases: temperature, volume, and number of particles. The section is organized so that you have options for presenting the relationships between the variables—qualitative descriptions of the factors that affect gas pressure, graphs of Charles's and Boyle's laws, and mathematical expressions.

Energy Energy is transferred between a system and its surroundings during a phase change. Students learn that the energy absorbed by material can overcome forces of attraction between particles in the material or increase the average kinetic energy of the particles.

Chemistry Refresher

States of Matter and Kinetic Theory 3.1

Solid, liquid, and gas are the common states of matter on Earth. However, almost all the matter in the observable universe exists as plasma. Plasma is formed when a gas is heated to temperatures near 10,000°C. At these temperatures, electrons can be lost during collisions between atoms or stripped by ionizing radiation. Because it contains mobile electrons, plasma can conduct an electric current. On Earth, plasma occurs mainly in lightning discharges and fluorescent lights. Not every substance can exist in every state. For example, some compounds that are solids at room temperature—e.g., mercury(II) oxide or sodium iodate—will decompose before they melt or boil.

Solids such as rubber, asphalt, and glasses are classified as amorphous solids because they lack the orderly internal structure found in crystalline solids. With the data supplied by improved instruments, scientists now know that glasses contain regions where the arrangement of particles is orderly.

The kinetic theory applies the laws of mechanics to individual atoms or molecules. It explains the physical properties of matter in terms of the motion of the particles. Two major contributors to the theory were James Joule (Count Rumford) and James Clerk Maxwell. The theory works best for gases (because the effect of attractive forces is minimal), but it can be applied to liquids and solids.

Address Misconceptions

Students may think that particles in gases have more kinetic energy than particles in liquids or solids. They are confusing how freely particles move with their speed of motion. For a strategy to overcome this misconception see **Address Misconceptions** *on* **page 73.**

The Gas Laws 3.2

Four variables are used to describe the behavior of a gas: temperature (T), pressure (P), volume (V), and amount. The amount of a gas is usually expressed as the number of moles (n). In 1662, Robert Boyle investigated the relationship between the volume and pressure of a gas. Using a J-shaped tube, Boyle measured gas pressure (indicated by the height of mercury) and gas volume at a constant temperature. His conclusions are now known as Boyle's law: $P_1 V_1 = P_2 V_2$.

Go Online
NSTA / PD LINKS

For: Teaching methods for states of matter
Visit: www.SciLinks.org/PDLinks
Web Code: ccn-0399

In 1787, Jacques Charles made a graph of volume versus temperature in degrees Celsius for a gas at constant pressure. The graph showed that volume increased as temperature increased, but it did not represent a direct relationship because the straight line did not pass through the (0, 0) point. When the line on the graph was extended beyond the data, the line crossed the x-axis at −273.15°C. This value is 0 K on the temperature scale developed by Lord Kelvin (William Thompson). As shown on the graph below, when Charles's data is plotted using kelvins instead of degrees Celsius, there is a direct relationship between the variables and Charles's law can be stated as $V_1/T_1 = V_2/T_2$.

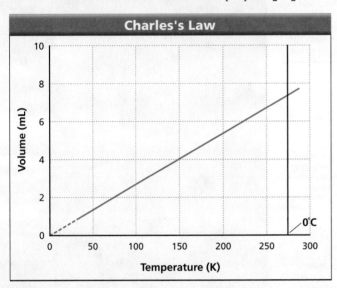

Charles's Law

Volume (mL) vs. Temperature (K)

0°C

Phase Changes 3.3

A phase change involves the transfer of energy between a system and its surroundings. As a substance changes from a solid to a liquid to a gas, the degree of order in the system increases. When a phase change is from a more-ordered to a less-ordered state, energy must be absorbed by the system to overcome attractive forces. When the change is to a more-ordered state, energy is released by the system to the surroundings.

Build Reading Literacy

Predict

Previewing to Predict Content

Strategy Help students activate their prior knowledge about a topic and become actively engaged in reading. The process of making and confirming predictions also helps students correct their own misconceptions. Before students begin, have them focus on one topic in Chapter 3, such as the introductory paragraph on p. 68 and Describing the States of Matter on pp. 68–70.

Example
1. Introduce students to the topic by having them read the heading and subheadings.
2. Ask students what they think they will learn about the topic.
3. Have a student read aloud the first Key Concept under Reading Focus at the top of the page.
4. Have another student read aloud the Comparing and Contrasting instructions in the Reading Strategy.
5. Based on what they've read so far, ask students to predict the content of the section. Write their predictions on the board.
6. Have a student read aloud the boldfaced key statement on p. 68. Then, have other students read aloud the boldfaced terms on p. 69.
7. Discuss with students the predictions on the board. Allow them to revise the predictions if they wish.
8. Have students read through the section independently. Afterwards, ask which of their predictions were confirmed. Point out that there's nothing wrong with making an incorrect prediction. Predicting can help readers learn more about a topic.

See p. 77 for a script on how to use the predicting strategy with students. For additional Build Reading Literacy strategies, see pp. 69 and 85.

Address Misconceptions

Some students think that gases, such as those in air, do not have mass. But the particles in air must have mass to exert pressure. For a strategy to overcome this misconception see **Address Misconceptions** on **page 79.**

Boyle's law relates pressure and volume. Charles's law relates temperature and volume. In 1808, Joseph Gay-Lussac proposed the law that relates temperature and pressure: There is a direct relationship between the pressure of a gas and its kelvin temperature. The combined gas law describes all three laws, but it doesn't account for moles of a gas. Because gas pressure is due to the collision of particles, the number of particles in a sample of gas is key, not the type of particles. Amedeo Avogadro first stated this important idea as a hypothesis in 1811: Equal volumes of gases at the same temperature and pressure contain the same number of particles. The equation that relates all four variables—V, T, P, and n—is the ideal gas equation $PV = nRT$, where the ideal gas constant R equals 8.314 kPa·L/mol·K.

ASSESS PRIOR KNOWLEDGE

Use the Chapter Pretest below to assess students' prior knowledge. As needed, review these Science Concepts and Math Skills with students.

Review Science Concepts

Section 3.1 Review density, pure substances, homogeneous mixtures, and heterogeneous mixtures with students. Students may refer to the graphic organizer they completed in Section 2.1.

Section 3.2 Encourage students to review scientific methods, including forming and testing hypotheses. Discuss how developing a hypothesis is an important step in a scientific method.

Section 3.3 Have students review SI units for temperature and volume.

Review Math Skills

Formulas and Equations Students will need to know how to write equations and solve them for unknowns in order to solve problems involving gas laws.

Direct students to the **Math Skills** in the **Skills and Reference Handbook** at the end of the student text.

CHAPTER

3 States of Matter

When temperatures rise in the spring, the ice begins to melt on Bow Lake at Banff National Park in Alberta, Canada.

21st Century Learning
Creativity and Intellectual Curiosity

What can you find out about plasma or Bose-Einstein condensates?

You are probably familiar with three common states of matter—solid, liquid, and gas. But scientists also recognize two states of matter that are more rare: plasma and Bose-Einstein condensate. Choose one of these for a research project. Find out how scientists define this particular state of matter and under what conditions it forms. Present your research to the class by posting on your class blog or wiki.

 Indiana's Academic Standards for Science

PROPERTIES OF MATTER
ICP.3.1: Describe how we use macroscopic properties of matter to model microscopic processes; ICP.3.2: Study the characteristics of solids, liquids, and gases and their changes of state and interpret them in terms of a molecular model which describes their energies and motions; ICP.3.3: Understand how thermal energy (the microscopic motions of the atoms and/or molecules) is related to the macroscopic concept of temperature. Examine the differences in these concepts by measuring the temperature changes of water as it is heated or cooled; ICP.3.4: Understand how the microscopic kinetic molecular theory, explains observations of macroscopic gas behavior in terms of temperature, volume, pressure, and the number of particles (using the mole concept).

MOTION AND ENERGY OF MACROSCOPIC OBJECTS
ICP.1.4: Describe the kinetic and potential energies of macroscopic objects, and use measurements to develop an understanding of these forms of energy.

66 Chapter 3

Chapter Pretest

1. What is the density of a sample whose mass is 12.02 g and whose volume is 6.01 mL? *(2.00 g/mL)*

2. Which of the following is an element? *(c)*
  a. Sand   **b.** Water
  c. Gold   **d.** Sugar

3. Differentiate heterogeneous from homogeneous mixtures. *(Heterogeneous mixture: parts are noticeably different; homogeneous mixture: parts are difficult to distinguish)*

4. Which of the following is not a step in a scientific method? *(b)*
  a. Developing a procedure to test a hypothesis
  b. Drawing a conclusion without any supporting evidence
  c. Forming a testable hypothesis
  d. Making observations

5. Identify tools needed to measure temperature and length. *(Thermometer and ruler)*

6. True or False: All of the following units are SI units: meter, pound, and kelvin. *(False)*

7. Density, mass, and volume are related by the equation *density = mass/volume.* What equation would you use to find volume if you knew the density and mass? *(volume = mass/density)*

8. Bromine boils at a temperature of 58.63°C. What is this temperature in kelvins? *(331.78 K)*

Chapter Preview

3.1 Solids, Liquids, and Gases

3.2 The Gas Laws

3.3 Phase Changes

Discovery CHANNEL SCHOOL

Video Field Trip

Up, Up, and Away

Inquiry Activity

How Easy Is It to Compress Air and Water?

Procedure

1. Insert a plunger into a syringe that is sealed at the narrow end. Push the plunger into the syringe as far as you can. Use the marks on the side of the syringe to read the volume of the air inside the syringe. Record this volume.

2. Remove the plunger. Fill the syringe with water by holding it under water in a large plastic container of water. **CAUTION** *Wipe up any spilled water right away to avoid slips and falls.*

3. While holding the syringe over the container, repeat Step 1. Record the volume of the water.

Think About It

1. **Comparing and Contrasting** Which was harder to compress, the air or the water? (To compress means to squeeze into a smaller volume.)

2. **Inferring** Based on your answer to Question 1, in which material are the particles closer together, in air or in water? Explain your answer.

States of Matter **67**

Video Field Trip

Up, Up, and Away

Encourage students to view the Video Field Trip "Up, Up, and Away."

Inquiry Activity

How Easy Is It to Compress Air and Water? L2

Purpose In this activity, students will infer that gases are more easily compressed than liquids because there is more space between the particles in a gas than between the particles in a liquid.

Skills Focus Comparing

Prep Time 5 minutes

Materials syringe (sealed at narrow end), water

Advance Prep Obtain syringes from a scientific supply company. Remove the needles and seal the tip of each syringe by removing the plunger and dropping some nonwater-soluble glue into the head of the syringe.

Class Time 15 minutes

Safety Students should wear safety goggles and lab aprons.

Teaching Tips

- To keep track of the syringes, number them with an indelible marker before distributing them to students. As you distribute, record the syringe number and student's name. When you retrieve the syringes, check against the list.

- Demonstrate the proper handling of the syringe and plunger. Show students how to correctly read the markings on the syringes.

- Separate the plungers from the syringes before distributing them.

- Separate the plungers from the syringes, rinse them with distilled water, and allow them to air-dry before storing them.

Expected Outcome The plunger will be pushed farther into the air-filled syringe than into the water-filled syringe.

Think About It

1. The water was harder to compress.

2. The particles are closer together in water. Air can be compressed more easily than water because there is more space between the particles in air.

Visual, Logical

1 FOCUS

Objectives

3.1.1 Describe the five states of matter.

3.1.2 Classify materials as solids, liquids, or gases.

3.1.3 Explain the behavior of gases, liquids, and solids, using kinetic theory.

Reading Focus

Build Vocabulary `L2`

Word Origins Explain to students that a Flemish chemist, Jan Baptista van Helmont (1577–1644), coined the word *gas*. Its origin is the Greek word *khaos*. Point out that the English word *chaos* refers to a disordered state. Relate this definition to the relative disorder of gases.

Reading Strategy `L2`

a. Definite shape b. Definite volume
c. Variable shape d. Variable volume

2 INSTRUCT

Describing the States of Matter

Use Visuals `L1`

Figure 1 Have students look at the magnified portion. Ask, **Why is the air bubble above the liquid in the tube?** *(Air is less dense than the liquid.)* **When might the tube in the middle of the level be used?** *(To see whether a shelf or counter is perfectly horizontal)* **When might the tube on the right be used?** *(To see whether a wall or doorframe is perfectly vertical)* If possible, bring in levels for students to observe and use. **Visual**

3.1 Solids, Liquids, and Gases

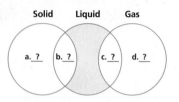

Standards: ICP.1.4, ICP.3.1, ICP.3.2, ICP.3.4

Reading Focus

Key Concepts

- How can shape and volume be used to classify materials?
- How can kinetic theory and forces of attraction be used to explain the behavior of gases, liquids, and solids?

Vocabulary

- ◆ solid
- ◆ liquid
- ◆ gas
- ◆ kinetic energy

Reading Strategy

Comparing and Contrasting Copy the diagram. As you read, replace each letter with one of these phrases: *definite volume, definite shape, variable volume,* or *variable shape.*

Do you recognize the object in Figure 1? It is a carpenter's level. A level can be used to see whether a surface is perfectly horizontal. The level has one or more transparent tubes inside a metal or wooden frame. Inside each tube is a clear liquid, such as alcohol, and an air bubble. When a carpenter places the level on a surface that is perfectly horizontal, the air bubble stays in the middle of the horizontal tube. The bubble moves to the high end of the tube if the surface is slanted.

The metal, alcohol, and air in a carpenter's level represent three states of matter. At room temperature, most metals are solids, alcohol is a liquid, and air is a gas. In this chapter, you will learn why the appearance and behavior of solids, liquids, and gases are different.

Describing the States of Matter

If you were asked to classify some materials as solids, liquids, or gases, you would probably find the task fairly easy. But could you describe what method you used to classify the materials? You might notice that some materials have a definite shape and volume and some materials do not. ☞ **Materials can be classified as solids, liquids, or gases based on whether their shapes and volumes are definite or variable.** Shape and volume are clues to how the particles within a material are arranged.

Figure 1 Carpenters use a level to find out if a surface is perfectly horizontal. In the level shown, three clear plastic tubes are set into an aluminum frame. Each tube contains a liquid and a gas. **Classifying** *What property could you use to distinguish the liquid or gas from the solids in a level?*

68 Chapter 3

Section Resources

Print

- **Laboratory Manual,** Investigation 3B
- **Reading and Study Workbook With Math Support,** Section 3.1
- **Math Skills and Problem Solving Workbook,** Section 3.1
- **Transparencies,** Chapter Pretest and Section 3.1

Technology

- **Interactive Textbook,** Section 3.1
- **Presentation Pro CD-ROM,** Chapter Pretest and Section 3.1
- **Go Online,** NSTA SciLinks, Kinetic theory

Solids Think about these familiar objects: a pencil, a quarter, a book, and a cafeteria tray. What do these four objects have in common? They all have a recognizable shape and they all take up a certain amount of space. The materials in these objects are all in the solid state. **Solid** is the state of matter in which materials have a definite shape and a definite volume.

The term *definite* means that the shape and volume of a pencil won't change as you move the pencil from a desk drawer to a pencil case to a backpack. Changing the container doesn't change the shape or volume of a solid. However, the term *definite* doesn't mean that the shape or volume can never change. After all, you can change the shape of a pencil by sharpening it. You can change the shape of a copper wire by bending the wire.

Figure 2 shows the arrangement of atoms in a copper wire. The copper atoms are packed close together and are arranged in a regular pattern. Almost all solids have some type of orderly arrangement of particles at the atomic level.

Figure 2 Samples of solid copper have definite volume. Copper atoms are packed close together in an orderly arrangement.

Liquids How good are you at estimating whether the juice remaining in an almost-empty bottle will fit in a glass? If your estimate is not accurate, you will run out of space in the glass before you run out of juice in the bottle.

Appearances can be deceiving. Imagine a narrow glass and a wide bottle side by side. Each contains exactly 350 milliliters of juice (about three quarters of a pint). There will seem to be more juice in the glass because the juice rises almost to the rim of the glass. There will seem to be less juice in the bottle because the juice forms a shallow layer. What can you learn about liquids from this comparison?

A liquid always has the same shape as its container and can be poured from one container to another. **Liquid** is the state of matter in which a material has a definite volume but not a definite shape.

Mercury exists as a liquid at room temperature. The drawing in Figure 3 shows the arrangement of atoms in liquid mercury. Compare this arrangement to the arrangement of copper atoms in Figure 2. The mercury atoms are close together but their arrangement is more random than the arrangement of atoms in copper.

Figure 3 At room temperature, mercury is a liquid. Drops of mercury on a flat, clean surface have a round shape. Mercury in a container has the same shape as its container. Comparing and Contrasting *Compare the arrangement of atoms in copper and mercury.*

States of Matter **69**

Comparing Liquid Volume L2

Purpose Students observe that it is difficult to compare the volume of liquids in different containers because liquids take the shape of their containers.

Materials 3 glass jars or bottles with lids, each having a noticeably different diameter but about the same volume; graduated cylinder; water

Advance Prep Before class, use a graduated cylinder to add the same amount of water to each of the three containers. Pick a volume that will almost fill the narrowest container. To avoid evaporation, replace the lids on the containers.

Procedure Have students predict which container has the largest volume of water. Have volunteers use graduated cylinders to measure the amount of water in each container.

Expected Outcome If students' predictions are influenced by the height of the liquids in the containers, they will predict that the container with the narrowest diameter has the greatest volume.
Visual

Build Reading Literacy L1

Relate Text and Visuals Refer to page 190D in **Chapter 7**, which provides the guidelines for relating text and visuals.

Have students compare the drawings of a solid and a liquid in Figures 2 and 3 to the definitions for these states of matter.
Visual, Portfolio

Customize for English Language Learners

Think-Pair-Share
Have students work in pairs to make a table describing solids, liquids, and gases. Remind students that they need to include in their descriptions information about shape, volume, and the arrangement of particles. An example of such a table would have Solids, Liquids, and Gases as column heads and Shape, Volume, and Arrangement of Particles as row heads. Students should title their tables States of Matter. Suggest that students list common examples of each state. Strengthen language skills by having students present their tables to the class.

Answer to . . .

Figure 1 *The liquid and gas have variable shapes.*

Figure 3 *In both copper and mercury, the atoms are close together, but the arrangement of atoms in mercury is less orderly (more random).*

Figure 4 To help students distinguish a visual model of atoms from actual atoms, point out that the pink spheres represent helium atoms in a balloon. Ask, **Do the size and color of the spheres represent the actual size and color of helium atoms?** *(No, helium atoms are too small to see and helium is a colorless gas.)* Tell students that the actual distance between helium atoms in a balloon is about 10 times the diameter of a helium atom. Have students consider why illustrations cannot accurately represent such distances. **Visual, Logical**

FYI

In this chapter, plasma is not defined as an ionized gas because students are not introduced to ions until Chapter 6.

Gases If you were asked to name a gas, what would you say? Air, which is a mixture of gases, is probably the most obvious example. You might also mention natural gas, which is used as a fuel for heating homes. **Gas** is the state of matter in which a material has neither a definite shape nor a definite volume. (The adjective form of the word *gas* is *gaseous* (GAS e us), as in *gaseous state*.) A gas takes the shape and volume of its container.

The balloons in Figure 4 are filled with helium, a colorless gas that is less dense than air. Two of the balloons are teardrop-shaped and two are disk-shaped. The "shape" of the helium in a balloon is the same as the shape of the balloon itself. The volume of the helium in a balloon is equal to the volume of the balloon.

The helium atoms in a balloon are not arranged in a regular pattern, as shown in the drawing in Figure 4. They are at random locations throughout the balloon. There is more space between two helium atoms in a balloon than between two neighboring atoms in solid copper or liquid mercury.

Because of the space among helium atoms, a large amount of helium can be compressed into a metal cylinder. When helium flows from the cylinder into a balloon, the helium atoms spread out. If 200 balloons are filled from a single cylinder, the total volume of the balloons will be much larger than the volume of the cylinder.

Other States of Matter On Earth, almost all matter exists in a solid, liquid, or gaseous state. But ninety-nine percent of all the matter that can be observed in the universe exists in a state that is not as common on Earth. At extremely high temperatures, such as those found on the sun or other stars, matter exists as plasma. You will read more about the properties of plasmas in Chapter 10.

In the 1920s Satyendra Bose, a physicist from India, wrote a paper about the behavior of light. After Albert Einstein read the paper, he realized that the behavior described could apply to matter under certain conditions. Einstein made a bold prediction. He predicted that a fifth state of matter would exist at extremely low temperatures. At temperatures near −273°C, groups of atoms would behave as though they were a single particle. In 1995, scientists produced this fifth state of matter, which is called a Bose-Einstein condensate (or BEC). It behaved as Einstein had predicted decades before.

Figure 4 Helium gas takes the volume and shape of its container. **Observing** *Describe the shape of the helium in the blue balloon.*

 Reading Checkpoint *How can atoms behave at temperatures near −273°C?*

Facts and Figures

Bose-Einstein Condensate In 1995, physicists at the University of Colorado at Boulder were the first to produce a BEC. The team of scientists, which included Eric Cornell and Carl Wieman, used lasers and magnets to cool about 2000 rubidium atoms to 20 billionths of a degree above absolute zero (−273.15°C). The rubidium atoms formed a tiny, almost stationary ball, which looked like a cherry pit with a diameter of 20 microns.

In 1997, Steven Chu, William Phillips, and Claude Cohen-Tannnoudji shared the Nobel Prize for Physics for their independent work using lasers to cool atoms. In 1985, Chu and his team had produced "optical molasses," an effect in which the movement of atoms was about one kilometers per hour instead of the expected 4000 kilometers per hour. At that speed the temperature of the sample was close to absolute zero.

Why Was Mercury Used in Thermometers?

Until recently, mercury thermometers were used in homes and schools. When a thermometer broke, people were exposed to mercury. When broken thermometers were thrown away, they ended up in landfills. Mercury is a toxic substance that can harm humans and other organisms. Schools no longer use mercury thermometers and people are encouraged to replace their fever thermometers.

So why did people continue to use mercury thermometers long after they knew the dangers of mercury? Look at the data table. It lists some densities over a temperature range from 0°C to 150°C. The temperatures are given at 30-degree intervals.

1. **Using Tables** How does the density of mercury change as the temperature increases?

2. **Relating Cause and Effect** How does a change in density affect the volume of a mercury sample?

Density of Mercury		
Temperature (°C)	Density (g/mL)	Volume of One Gram (mL)
0	13.60	0.07356
30	13.52	0.07396
60	13.45	0.07436
90	13.38	0.07476
120	13.30	0.07517
150	13.23	0.07558

3. **Calculating** If a thermometer contained a gram of mercury, how much would the volume of the mercury change when the temperature rose from 0°C to 30°C? From 30°C to 60°C? From 60°C to 90°C? From 90°C to 120°C?

4. **Drawing Conclusions** Why was mercury a better choice than water for the liquid in a thermometer? (*Hint:* Between 0°C and 30°C, the volume of a gram of water changes by 0.0042 mL. Between 30°C and 60°C, the volume changes by 0.0127 mL. Between 60°C and 90°C, the volume changes by 0.0188 mL.)

5. **Inferring** Why is the mercury in a thermometer stored in a narrow tube?

Kinetic Theory

Why, under ordinary conditions, is copper a solid, mercury a liquid, and helium a gas? To begin to answer that question, you need to know something about kinetic energy. An object that is moving has kinetic energy. The word *kinetic* comes from a Greek word meaning "to move." **Kinetic energy** is the energy an object has due to its motion.

The faster an object moves, the greater its kinetic energy is. A ball thrown at 85 miles (137 kilometers) per hour by the pitcher in Figure 5 has more kinetic energy than a ball thrown at 78 miles (125 kilometers) per hour. When a baseball is thrown, a batter can see that it is moving. But the batter cannot see that there is also motion occurring within the baseball. According to the kinetic theory of matter, particles inside the solid baseball are moving. Particles in the air that the baseball travels through are moving too.

The kinetic theory of matter says that all particles of matter are in constant motion. The theory was developed in the mid-1800s to explain the behavior of gases. It can also help to explain the behavior of liquids and solids.

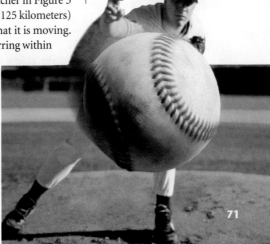

Figure 5 The kinetic energy of a baseball depends on the speed at which the pitcher throws the ball.

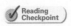

71

Facts and Figures

Mercury Thermometer Daniel Fahrenheit invented the alcohol thermometer in 1709 and the mercury thermometer in 1714. He chose mercury because it remains a liquid over a wider range of temperatures than does water. The expansion rate of mercury is fairly uniform, mercury does not adhere to glass, and its color makes it easy to read.

Inhalation of mercury vapor can damage the nervous system and the respiratory system.

To prevent mercury vapor from being inhaled when thermometers break, the Environmental Protection Agency, along with state and local agencies, has encouraged consumers to replace mercury fever thermometers. Alternatives to mercury thermometers include digital thermometers that use a change in the resistance in a thermoresistor and thermometers with sensors that detect infrared radiation.

Explaining the Behavior of Gases

Detecting the Motion of a Gas **L2**

Purpose Students infer that particles in gases are in constant motion.

Materials spray can of air freshener, 3 stopwatches

Procedure Spray the air freshener at a distant corner of the room. Have students located in various parts of the room time how long it takes before they smell the gas. (The mist from the spray will evaporate.) Ask students to explain the results.

Expected Outcome Students will detect odor several moments after the air freshener is sprayed. Students should explain that they could smell the air freshener because the particles in a gas are in constant, random motion. That motion carried particles from the corner of the room to the students' locations.
Kinesthetic, Logical

Use Visuals **L1**

Figures 6 and 7 Have students compare the models of collisions shown in Figures 6 and 7. Ask, **How are the paths of billiard balls and helium atoms the same?** (The paths of both are straight lines.) **How is the motion of billiard balls different from the motion of helium atoms?** (The motion of billiard balls is not constant or random.) **What is a weakness of the model of helium atoms shown in Figure 7?** (There are only two atoms to represent the billions of atoms that would be in such a jar.)
Visual

Figure 6 This photograph of billiard balls was taken just after the cue struck the white ball, which began to move. The white ball moved in a straight line until it collided with the dark blue ball. The collision caused the dark blue ball to start moving. The motion of billiard balls can be compared to the motion of particles in a gas.

Figure 7 A helium atom travels in a straight line until it collides with another helium atom or the side of its container.
Relating Cause and Effect *What can happen to the kinetic energy of two helium atoms when the atoms collide?*

Explaining the Behavior of Gases

You can compare the motion of the particles in a gas to the movement of balls during a game of billiards. When a cue strikes a billiard ball, as shown in Figure 6, the ball moves in a straight line until it strikes the side of the billiard table or another ball. When a moving ball strikes a ball at rest, the first ball slows down and the second ball begins to move. Kinetic energy is transferred during those collisions.

Motion in Gases Unlike billiard balls, the particles in a gas are never at rest. At room temperature, the average speed of the particles in a sample of gas is about 1600 kilometers per hour. The use of the term *average* is a clue that not all particles are moving at the same speed. Some are moving faster than the average speed and some are moving slower than the average speed.

Figure 7 shows the possible paths of two helium atoms in a container of helium gas. Notice that each atom moves in a straight line until it collides with the other atom or with a wall of the container. During a collision, one atom may lose kinetic energy and slow down while the other atom gains kinetic energy and speeds up. However, the total kinetic energy of the atoms remains the same.

The diagram in Figure 7 does not accurately compare the volumes of the atoms and the container. The volume of a helium atom is extremely small compared to the volume of its container. If there were a billion times a trillion helium atoms in a liter bottle, there would still be a large amount of space in the bottle.

Between collisions, why doesn't one particle in a gas affect the other particles in the gas? ◗ **There are forces of attraction among the particles in all matter.** If the particles are apart and moving fast, as in a gas, the attractions are too weak to have an effect. Under ordinary conditions, scientists can ignore the forces of attraction in a gas.

Facts and Figures

Mean Free Path The distance a particle of gas travels between collisions is called its mean free path. This distance varies with temperature and pressure. At 1 atmosphere of pressure and 25°C, the mean free path for a hydrogen molecule is 12.6×10^{-8} meters. For a nitrogen molecule, it is 6.76×10^{-8} meters. At 1 atmosphere of pressure and 25°C, a hydrogen molecule will collide with another molecule about 7.1×10^{11} times per second, while a nitrogen molecule will collide with another molecule about 1.42×10^{10} times per second. The shorter the mean free path is, the greater the number of collisions per second.

Kinetic Theory of Gases The kinetic theory explains the general properties of a gas. ☝ **The constant motion of particles in a gas allows a gas to fill a container of any shape or size.** Think about air in a tire. The walls of the tire keep the air contained. What if there is a hole in the tire? Because the particles in the air are in constant motion, some of the particles would travel to the hole and move out of the tire. The kinetic theory as applied to gases has three main points.

- Particles in a gas are in constant, random motion.

- The motion of one particle is unaffected by the motion of other particles unless the particles collide.

- Forces of attraction among particles in a gas can be ignored under ordinary conditions.

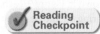 *Describe the motion of particles in a gas.*

Explaining the Behavior of Liquids

The particles in liquids also have kinetic energy. So why does a liquid such as mercury have a definite volume at room temperature instead of expanding to fill its container? The average speed of a mercury atom is much slower than the average speed of a helium atom at the same temperature. A mercury atom has about 50 times the mass of a helium atom. This greater mass is only partly responsible for the slower speed. What other factor is responsible?

The particles in a liquid are more closely packed than the particles in a gas. Therefore, attractions between the particles in a liquid do affect the movement of the particles. A mercury atom in liquid mercury is like a student in the crowded hallway in Figure 8. The student's path may be blocked by students moving in the other direction. The student's ability to move is affected by interactions with other students.

In a liquid, there is a kind of tug of war between the constant motion of particles and the attractions among particles. This tug of war explains the general behavior of liquids. ☝ **A liquid takes the shape of its container because particles in a liquid can flow to new locations. The volume of a liquid is constant because forces of attraction keep the particles close together.** Because forces of attraction limit the motion of particles in a liquid, the particles in a liquid cannot spread out and fill a container.

For: Links on kinetic theory
Visit: www.SciLinks.org
Web Code: ccn-1031

For: Activity on mercury in the enviroment
Visit: PHSchool.com
Web Code: ccc-1031

Figure 8 Particles in a liquid behave like students moving through a crowded hallway.

Explaining the Behavior of Liquids
Build Science Skills [L2]

Using Analogies Have students think of analogies for the motion of particles in a liquid other than the analogy shown in Figure 8. Possible answers include dancers on a dance floor or bumper cars at an amusement park. Be sure students understand that the objects representing particles in the analogy should be in a confined space.
Logical

Address Misconceptions [L2]

Students may think that the particles in gases have more kinetic energy than the particles in liquids or solids. Students are confusing an increase in the ability of particles to move freely with an increase in average speed. Challenge this misconception by explaining that the particles in all substances at a given temperature have, on average, similar amounts of kinetic energy. Ask, **Why don't particles in a solid move as freely as particles in a gas at room temperature?** *(Strong forces of attraction among particles in the solid keep the particles vibrating around fixed locations within the solid.)*
Logical

Download a worksheet on kinetic theory for students to complete, and find additional teacher support from NSTA SciLinks.

Find links to additional activities and have students monitor phenomena that affect Earth and its residents.

Answer to . . .

Figure 7 *One atom may gain kinetic energy and speed up while the other atom loses kinetic energy and slows down.*

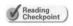 *Particles in a gas are in constant, random motion.*

Explaining the Behavior of Solids
Build Science Skills `L2`

Using Models Fill a clear plastic box or tray with enough marbles to fill the bottom of the box. Gently move the box back and forth. Ask, **What state of matter does this model represent?** *(Solid)* **How are the particles in a solid like the marbles in this model?** *(Both the marbles and the particles in a solid are in fixed locations. They can only move back and forth.)* The marbles do not move until the box is shaken. **How well does this part of the model represent the behavior of particles in a solid?** *(Not well, because particles in a solid are constantly moving.)*
Visual

3 ASSESS

Evaluate Understanding `L2`

Have each student write a paragraph explaining how kinetic theory can be used to explain the general characteristics of solids, liquids, and gases.

Reteach `L1`

Review the properties of solids, liquids, and gases. Use Figure 1 to encourage students to think of practical applications in which the state of matter is important. For example, molten metals can be shaped in a mold, but a metal must be solid to be shaped by hammering.

Connecting ⊂ Concepts

In a liquid, there is a tug of war between the motion of the particles and attractions among particles. With liquids at the same temperature, the deciding factor would be the strength of the attractive forces. An increase in these forces would decrease a liquid's ability to flow and increase its viscosity.

Interactive Textbook If your class subscribes to the Interactive Textbook, use it to review key concepts in Section 3.1.

Answer to . . .

Figure 9 *People remain in the same seats, but the positions of their bodies change.*

Figure 9 These photographs of an audience in a movie theater were taken at different times on the same day. The behavior of the audience can be compared to the behavior of particles in a solid. **Observing** *What stayed the same and what changed between the photographs?*

Explaining the Behavior of Solids

You might compare the particles in a solid to a polite audience in a movie theater. While the movie is running, people stay in their seats. Although people move around in their seats, as shown in Figure 9, each person remains in essentially the same location during the movie. They have "fixed" locations in a total volume that does not change.

⊂ **Solids have a definite volume and shape because particles in a solid vibrate around fixed locations.** Vibration is a repetitive back-and-forth motion. Look back at the orderly arrangement of copper atoms in Figure 2. Strong attractions among the copper atoms restrict their motion and keep each atom in a fixed location relative to its neighbors. Each atom vibrates around its location but it does not exchange places with a neighboring atom.

Section 3.1 Assessment

Reviewing Concepts

1. ⊂ How are shape and volume used to classify solids, liquids, and gases?

2. ⊂ What does the kinetic theory say about the motion of atoms?

3. ⊂ How is a gas able to fill a container of any size or shape?

4. ⊂ Use kinetic theory and attractive forces to explain why a liquid has a definite volume and a shape that can vary.

5. ⊂ Explain why a solid has a definite shape and volume.

6. How does the arrangement of atoms in most solids differ from the arrangement of atoms in a liquid?

Critical Thinking

7. **Using Analogies** Explain how the behavior of popcorn in a popcorn popper can be used as an analogy for the motion of gas particles.

8. **Applying Concepts** A hazardous chemical is leaking from a tank truck. Rescue workers need to evacuate people who live near the accident. Why are more people likely to be affected if the chemical is a gas, rather than a liquid?

Connecting ⊂ Concepts

Viscosity Review the description of viscosity in Section 2.2. Use the tug of war between forces of attraction and kinetic energy to explain differences in viscosity among liquids at the same temperature.

Section 3.1 Assessment

1. Materials can be classified as solids, liquids, or gases based on whether their shapes and volumes are definite or variable.

2. All particles of matter are in constant motion.

3. The constant motion of gas particles allows a gas to fill a container of any shape and size.

4. Particles in a liquid can flow to new locations, but forces of attraction keep the particles close together.

5. The particles in a solid vibrate around fixed locations.

6. The atoms in most solids have a more orderly arrangement than the atoms in liquids, which are not restricted to fixed locations.

7. While popping occurs, the motion of the individual popcorn kernels is random and fairly continuous.

8. The particles of a gas have greater freedom of movement and will reach a wider area more quickly.

3.2 The Gas Laws

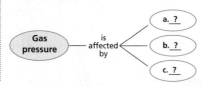

Standards: ICP.3.2, ICP.3.3, ICP.3.4

Reading Focus

Key Concepts
- What causes gas pressure in a closed container?
- What factors affect gas pressure?
- How are the temperature, volume, and pressure of a gas related?

Vocabulary
- pressure
- absolute zero
- Charles's law
- Boyle's law

Reading Strategy
Identifying Cause and Effect Copy the diagram. As you read, identify the variables that affect gas pressure.

Gas pressure — is affected by → a. ? / b. ? / c. ?

---

1 FOCUS

Objectives

3.2.1 Define pressure and gas pressure.

3.2.2 Identify factors that affect gas pressure.

3.2.3 Predict changes in gas pressure due to changes in temperature, volume, and number of particles.

3.2.4 Explain Charles's law, Boyle's law, and the combined gas law.

3.2.5 Apply gas laws to solve problems involving gases.

Reading Focus

Build Vocabulary

Paraphrase Replace less familiar words in a definition with more familiar words or phrases.

Reading Strategy

a. Temperature b. Volume c. Number of particles

The woman in Figure 10 is taking a deep breath. This action helps reduce her breathing rate and increase the volume of air she inhales. When you inhale, the volume of your chest cavity increases and air moves into your lungs. When you exhale, the volume of your chest cavity decreases and air is pushed out of your lungs.

After you read this section, you will understand how changing the volume of your chest cavity causes air to move into and out of your lungs. Changes in the volume, the temperature, the pressure, and the number of particles have predictable effects on the behavior of a gas.

Figure 10 Taking a deep breath increases the volume of your chest cavity, which causes air to move into your lungs.

Pressure

At many hockey rinks, a layer of shatterproof glass keeps the puck away from the spectators. The force with which the puck hits the glass depends on the speed of the puck. The faster the puck is traveling, the greater the force is. The smaller the area of impact is, the greater the pressure produced. **Pressure** is the result of a force distributed over an area. If the edge of the puck hits the glass, it exerts more pressure than if the face of the puck hits the glass at the same speed.

The SI unit of pressure is derived from SI units for force and area. Force is measured in newtons (N) and area in square meters (m^2). When a force in newtons is divided by an area in square meters, the unit of pressure is newtons per square meter (N/m^2). The SI unit for pressure, the pascal (Pa), is shorthand for newtons per square meter. One pascal is a small amount of pressure. Scientists often express larger amounts of pressure in kilopascals. One kilopascal (kPa) is equal to 1000 pascals.

States of Matter **75**

2 INSTRUCT

Pressure
Build Science Skills

Observing

Purpose Show the effect of area on pressure.

Materials clay, CD case, textbook

Advance Prep Prepare two flattened pieces of clay 3 cm thick.

Procedure Put the broad side of the CD case on a piece of clay with the book on top. After about 30 seconds, carefully remove the book and case. Then, put the case on the other piece of clay, narrow side down. Balance the book on the case for 30 seconds. (Place your hands on either side of the book as a precaution.) Remove the book and case. Ask, **How do the depths of the imprints compare?** *(The imprint is deeper when the case is placed on its edge.)* **What caused this difference?** *(Because the weight of the book was applied to a smaller area, the pressure was greater.)*

Expected Outcome When the same force is applied to a smaller area, the depth of the imprint increases.
Visual

Section Resources

Print
- *Reading and Study Workbook With Math Support,* Section 3.2 and **Math Skill:** The Combined Gas Law
- *Math Skills and Problem Solving Workbook,* Section 3.2
- *Transparencies,* Section 3.2

Technology
- *Interactive Textbook,* Section 3.2
- *Presentation Pro CD-ROM,* Section 3.2
- *Go Online,* Science News, Properties of matter

Factors that Affect Gas Pressure

Changing Volume of a Balloon `L2`

Purpose Students observe the effect of temperature on the volume of a balloon.

Materials inflated balloons, refrigerator, warm place

Advance Prep One day ahead, inflate a balloon for each class. Place the balloons in a refrigerator overnight.

Procedure At the beginning of class, bring out a balloon and tell students where it has been. Ask, **Do you predict that the volume of the balloon will increase, decrease, or stay the same after the balloon has been in a warm place?** *(Increase)* Place the balloon in a warm place until shortly before the end of class. Make sure the balloon has room to expand, and that the temperature does not exceed 42°C. Ask, **What happened to the volume of the gas inside the balloon?** *(It increased.)* Explain that as temperature increases, the particles move faster, on average, which increases the pressure of the gas inside the balloon. The increased pressure causes the balloon to expand.

Expected Outcome The balloon's volume will increase as the temperature increases.
Visual, Logical

Use Visuals `L1`

Figure 11 Bring in a pressure gauge like the one in the photo. (The gauge measures how much the air pressure in the tire exceeds atmospheric pressure.) Have a volunteer note the units of pressure on the gauge. *(Pounds per square inch)* Explain that in the United States, pressure is not always measured in SI units. Ask, **Have you seen any other units used for pressure?** *(Students may have seen barometric pressure reported in inches of mercury.)* **Why is data from experiments measured and reported in SI units?** *(Scientists must use standard units so that their data can be shared with and tested by scientists in all countries.)*
Logical, Visual

An object does not need to be as large as a hockey puck to exert pressure when it collides with another object. Recall that the helium atoms in a balloon are constantly moving. The pressure produced by a single helium atom colliding with a wall is extremely small. However, there are more than 10^{22} helium atoms in a small balloon. When so many particles collide with the walls of a container at the same time, they produce a measurable pressure.

● **Collisions between particles of a gas and the walls of the container cause the pressure in a closed container of gas.** The more frequent the collisions, the greater the pressure of the gas is. The speed of the particles and their mass also affect the pressure.

Reading Checkpoint *How does the frequency of collisions affect the pressure of a gas?*

Figure 11 The firefighter is using a pressure gauge to check the air pressure in a tire on a firetruck. If the tires on the truck have a 44.5-inch diameter, the pressure on a front tire should be about 125 pounds per square inch (psi).

Factors That Affect Gas Pressure

Think again about the collisions that produce gas pressure. What changes might affect the pressure of a gas in a container? The particles in the gas could move faster or slower. The gas could be moved into a larger or smaller container. You could add gas or remove gas from the container. ● **Factors that affect the pressure of an enclosed gas are its temperature, its volume, and the number of its particles.**

Temperature Suppose you are about to go on a long drive. The driver suspects that the air pressure in the automobile tires might be low. You check the pressure in each tire, using a pressure gauge like the one in Figure 11. You find that the measurements are well within the automobile manufacturer's guidelines. If you checked the tire pressures again after a few hours on the highway, would you be surprised to find that the pressure in the tires had increased?

The constant motion of tires on the highway causes the tires and the air in the tires to warm up. As the temperature rises, the average kinetic energy of the particles in the air increases. With increased kinetic energy, the particles move faster and collide more often with the inner walls of the tires. The faster-moving particles also hit the walls with greater force. The increase in the number of collisions along with the increase in the force of the collisions causes an increase in the pressure of the air in the tires. ● **Raising the temperature of a gas will increase its pressure if the volume of the gas and the number of particles are constant.**

Customize for Inclusion Students

Visually Impaired
Have students with visual impairments observe different air pressures in a bicycle tire. Bring a bicycle tire and a pump with a built-in gauge. Let out all of the air in the tire. Attach the pump to the inner tube valve. Read the pressure on the gauge and allow students to feel that the tire is completely flat. Pump up the tire to a third of the maximum recommended pressure (marked on the tire). Read the pressure on the gauge and allow students to feel the tire again. Pump up the tire to the maximum recommended pressure and allow students to repeat the observation. Discuss with students how the quantity of air in the tire affects the firmness of the tire.

Inhaling

Diaphragm contracts. Rib cage is lifted up and out.

Exhaling

Diaphragm relaxes. Rib cage moves down and in.

Lungs
Rib cage
Diaphragm

Volume Imagine that you have a plastic bottle that appears empty. If you twist the cap onto the bottle and then squeeze the bottle, what will happen? At first, the plastic will give a little, reducing the volume of the bottle. But soon you will feel pressure from inside the bottle resisting your efforts to further reduce the volume. The pressure you feel is a result of the increased pressure of the air trapped inside the bottle. As the volume is decreased, particles of trapped air collide more often with the walls of the bottle. **Reducing the volume of a gas increases its pressure if the temperature of the gas and the number of particles are constant.**

Figure 12 shows how the relationship between volume and pressure explains what happens when you breathe. As you inhale, a muscle called the diaphragm (DY uh fram) contracts. The contraction causes your chest cavity to expand. This temporary increase in volume allows the particles in air to spread out, which lowers the pressure inside the chest cavity. Because the pressure of the air outside your body is now greater than the pressure inside your chest, air rushes into your lungs.

When you exhale, your diaphragm relaxes and the volume of your chest cavity decreases. The particles in the air are squeezed into a smaller volume and the pressure inside your lungs increases. Because the pressure of the air inside your chest is now greater than the pressure of the air outside your body, air is forced out of your lungs.

Number of Particles You can probably predict what will happen to the pressure when you add more gas to a container. Think about a tire. Once the tire is inflated, its volume is fairly constant. So adding more air will increase the pressure inside the tire. The more particles there are in the same volume, the greater the number of collisions and the greater the pressure. At some point the rubber from which the tire is made will not be strong enough to withstand the increased pressure and the tire will burst. **Increasing the number of particles will increase the pressure of a gas if the temperature and the volume are constant.**

Figure 12 Movement of a muscle called the diaphragm changes the volume of your chest cavity. The volume increases when you inhale and decreases when you exhale.
Interpreting Diagrams *How does the movement of your rib cage affect the volume of your chest cavity?*

For: Articles on properties of matter
Visit: PHSchool.com
Web Code: cce-1032

Build Reading Literacy [L1]

Predict Refer to page **66D** in this chapter, which provides the guidelines for predicting.

List on the board examples of volume, temperature, and number of particles increasing or decreasing. Tell students to predict how each change will affect gas pressure in a closed container. Ask students to use the number of particle collisions to explain their predictions. As students provide their predictions and explanations, write the correct effect on pressure and the correct explanation on the board.
Logical, Portfolio

Go Online
SCIENCE NEWS

Science News provides students with current information on properties of matter.

Facts and Figures

Fainting Couches During the Victorian era, well-to-do households often had fainting couches. The tightly laced, whalebone corsets women wore restricted their ability to breathe deeply. As a result, they had low levels of oxygen in their blood, causing them to faint, or swoon. Today, Victorian fainting couches can be seen in historic houses or museums. Antique fainting couches and reproductions are available in some furniture and antique stores.

Answer to . . .

Figure 12 *The volume increases as the rib cage is lifted up and out. The volume decreases as the rib cage moves down and in.*

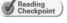 Reading Checkpoint *The more frequent the collisions, the greater the pressure of the gas is.*

Charles's Law
Build Science Skills
L2

Using Tables and Graphs Have students analyze Figure 13. Have students look first at the graph for Charles's law. Point out the straight line with the positive slope. Ask, **What relationship does this line describe?** *(It describes a direct relationship between volume and temperature: As temperature increases, volume also increases.)* Ask, **Why is part of the line solid and part dashed?** *(The solid line represents actual data, while the dotted line is the extension of the collected data toward the zero point for volume.)* Have students refer to the Boyle's Law graph. Ask, **What happens to pressure as volume increases?** *(As volume increases, pressure decreases.)* **Visual, Logical**

Build Math Skills
L1

Line Graphs Students are likely to need help understanding why Charles's law does not apply when temperatures are expressed in degrees Celsius. Have students find the point on the graph where the temperature is 0°C and ask them to estimate the volume at that temperature. Then, tell them that the straight line must pass through (0, 0) for the responding variable to be directly proportional to the manipulated variable. **Logical, Portfolio**

Direct students to the **Math Skills** in the **Skills and Reference Handbook** at the end of the student text for additional help.

Figure 13 These graphs compare the effects of temperature and volume on the pressure of a gas. Charles's law describes the direct relationship between the temperature and the volume. Boyle's law describes the inverse relationship between the volume and the pressure.
Controlling Variables *For each graph, name the manipulated variable and the responding variable.*

Charles's Law

During his lifetime, the French physicist Jacques Charles (1746–1823) was known for his inventions, including the hydrogen balloon. Today, Charles is best known for his investigations of the behavior of gases. Charles collected data on the relationship between the temperature and volume of gases. When he graphed the data, the graph was a straight line, as shown in Figure 13. The graph shows that the volume of a gas increases at the same rate as the temperature of the gas.

Charles extended the line on his graph beyond the measured data to see what the temperature would have to be to produce a volume of 0 L. The temperature at the point where the line crossed the *x*-axis was −273.15°C. This temperature is equal to 0 K on the Kelvin temperature scale. A temperature of 0 K is called **absolute zero.** No scientist has produced a temperature of absolute zero in a laboratory, but some have come extremely close. As a gas cools to temperatures near 0 K, the gas changes to a liquid, a solid, or sometimes a Bose-Einstein condensate.

Charles's law states that the volume of a gas is directly proportional to its temperature in kelvins if the pressure and the number of particles of the gas are constant. Charles's law can be written as a mathematical expression in which T_1 and V_1 represent the temperature and volume of a gas before a change occurs. T_2 and V_2 represent the temperature and volume after a change occurs.

Charles's Law

$$\frac{V_1}{T_1} = \frac{V_2}{T_2}$$

The temperatures must be expressed in kelvins. If temperatures in degrees Celsius are used in the expression, the volume will not be directly proportional to the temperature.

78 *Chapter 3*

Facts and Figures

Absolute Zero Based on the decrease in the volume of a gas as it cooled, scientists hypothesized that if an ideal gas were cooled to absolute zero (0 K on the Kelvin temperature scale or −273.15 on the Celsius scale), its volume would be zero. However, as actual gases are cooled, they reach temperatures at which they change to liquids or solids.

Theoretically, all motion of particles in matter should cease at absolute zero. But according to quantum mechanics, a substance will contain some energy of motion, regardless of its temperature. For that reason, substances cannot be cooled to absolute zero. However, Bose-Einstein condensates produced in laboratories exist at temperatures very close to absolute zero.

Boyle's Law

Robert Boyle, who was born in Ireland in 1627, was the first to describe the relationship between the pressure and volume of a gas. The graph in Figure 13 shows what happens when the volume of a cylinder containing a set amount of gas is decreased. What happens when the volume of the cylinder is reduced from 2.0 liters to 1.0 liter? The pressure of the gas in the cylinder doubles from 50 kilopascals to 100 kilopascals.

Boyle's Law

$$P_1V_1 = P_2V_2$$

Boyle's law states that the volume of a gas is inversely proportional to its pressure if the temperature and the number of particles are constant. Boyle's law can be expressed mathematically. P_1 and V_1 represent the pressure and volume of a gas before a change occurs. P_2 and V_2 represent the pressure and volume of a gas after a change occurs.

 Reading Checkpoint *How is Boyle's law expressed mathematically?*

Observing the Effect of Temperature on Gas Pressure

Materials
pan, metric ruler, empty beverage can, masking tape, hot plate, clock, tongs

Procedure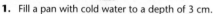

1. Fill a pan with cold water to a depth of 3 cm.
2. Use masking tape to cover half the opening of the can. **CAUTION** *Do not cover the entire opening with tape.*
3. Place the can on the hot plate and turn the hot plate to a high setting. Heat the can for 5 minutes and then turn off the hot plate.
4. Use tongs to remove the can from the hot plate and place it upside down in the pan of water as shown. The opening should be below the surface of the water. Observe the can as it cools.

Analyze and Conclude

1. **Inferring** How did the temperature of the air inside the can change when you heated the can? How did it change when you put the can in the water?
2. **Drawing Conclusions** What happened to the pressure of the air inside the can when you put the can in the cold water?
3. **Inferring** Did the air pressure outside the can change during the experiment?
4. **Formulating Hypotheses** What caused the change you observed in Step 4?

Boyle's Law

 Quick Lab

Observing the Effect of Temperature on Gas Pressure **L2**

Objective
After completing this activity, students will be able to
• predict the effect of temperature on the pressure of a gas.

Address Misconceptions

This lab helps dispel the misconception that a gas does not have mass. Explain that air pressure is the result of particles in air colliding with the can. The force of the collisions (and pressure) depends on the mass and speed of the particles.

Skills Focus Inferring

Prep Time 10 minutes

Materials pan, metric ruler, empty beverage can, masking tape, hot plate, clock, tongs

Advance Prep Ask students to contribute clean, empty beverage cans. Use dissecting pans, cake pans, or plastic dishpans.

Class Time 20 minutes

Safety Caution students not to touch the hot plate or the can once the hot plate has been turned on.

Expected Outcome The can will crack or collapse within one minute after being placed in cold water.

Analyze and Conclude
1. The temperature increased when the can was heated and decreased when it was placed in cold water.
2. The pressure decreased.
3. The air pressure outside the can did not change.
4. As the gas inside the can cooled, its pressure decreased until it could no longer offset the outside air pressure.

Answer to . . .

Figure 13 *For Charles's law, the manipulated variable is temperature and the responding variable is volume. For Boyle's law, the manipulated variable is volume and the responding variable is pressure.*

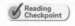 **Reading Checkpoint** $P_1V_1 = P_2V_2$

Build Math Skills

Formulas and Equations A gas has a pressure of 200 kPa in a 0.5-L container. Use Boyle's law to determine the pressure of the gas in a 2.0 container. *(50 kPa)*
Logical

Direct students to the **Math Skills** in the **Skills and Reference Handbook** at the end of the student text for additional help.

The Combined Gas Law

Integrate Math L2

Have students show how the combined gas law can be used to derive Boyle's and Charles's laws. If temperature is constant, the temperature cancels out to reveal Boyle's law $P_1V_1 = P_2V_2$. Similarly, if volume remains constant, Charles's law of $P_1/T_1 = P_2/V_2$ is derived. **Logical**

Solutions L2

1. $V_2 = (P_1V_1/P_2) =$
(50 kPa)(5.0 L)/125 kPa = 2.0 L
2. $T_2 = (P_2T_1/P_1) =$
(825 kPa)(273 K)/388 kPa = 580 K
3. $T_2 = (V_2T_1/V_1) =$
(0.285 L)(283 K)/0.250 L =
323 K or 50°C **Logical**

For Extra Help L1

Remind students that before they solve a specific problem, they should determine which variable is not changing and remove that variable from the combined gas law. Then, they need to identify which of the variables is the unknown—V_2, T_2, or P_2—and rearrange the equation to solve for that variable. If students are having trouble rearranging the equation, provide students with the six possible forms of the equation.
Logical

Additional Problems

1. A gas is stored at constant volume at a pressure of 137 kPa at 274 K. If the temperature rises to 296 K, what is the pressure? *(148 kPa)*
2. At constant temperature, the volume of a gas at 1000 kPa is changed from 100 L to 10 L. What is the new pressure? *(10,000 kPa)* **Logical**

The Combined Gas Law

The relationships described by Boyle's law and Charles's law can be described by a single law. The combined gas law describes the relationship among the temperature, volume, and pressure of a gas when the number of particles is constant.

> **Combined Gas Law**
> $$\frac{P_1V_1}{T_1} = \frac{P_2V_2}{T_2}$$

The combined gas law is used to solve many problems involving gases.

The Combined Gas Law

A cylinder that contains air at a pressure of 100 kPa has a volume of 0.75 L. The pressure is increased to 300 kPa. The temperature does not change. Find the new volume of air.

① Read and Understand
What information are you given?

$P_1 = 100\text{ kPa}$ $P_2 = 300\text{ kPa}$ $V_1 = 0.75\text{ L}$

② Plan and Solve
What unknown are you trying to calculate?

V_2

What expression can you use?

$$\frac{P_1V_1}{T_1} = \frac{P_2V_2}{T_2}$$

Cancel out the variable that does not change and rearrange the expression to solve for V_2.

$$P_1V_1 = P_2V_2 \qquad V_2 = \frac{P_1V_1}{P_2}$$

Replace each variable with its known value.

$$V_2 = 100\text{ kPa} \times \frac{0.75\text{ L}}{300\text{ kPa}} = 0.25\text{ L}$$

③ Look Back and Check
Is your answer reasonable?

Volume should decrease as pressure increases. The pressure tripled from 100 kPa to 300 kPa. The answer, 0.25 L, is one third the original volume, 0.75 L.

1. A gas has a volume of 5.0 L at a pressure of 50 kPa. What happens to the volume when the pressure is increased to 125 kPa? The temperature does not change.

2. Gas stored in a tank at 273 K has a pressure of 388 kPa. The safe limit for the pressure is 825 kPa. At what temperature will the gas reach this pressure?

3. At 10°C, the gas in a cylinder has a volume of 0.250 L. The gas is allowed to expand to 0.285 L. What must the final temperature be for the pressure to remain constant? (*Hint:* Convert from degrees Celsius to kelvins using the expression °C + 273 = K.)

Facts and Figures

Weather Balloons Large weather balloons are made of natural or synthetic rubber. They are filled with either helium or hydrogen. As the balloon expands, the thickness of the rubber decreases from about 0.051 mm to 0.0025 mm at the altitude when the balloon bursts. A balloon that is about 2 m in diameter at launch will be about 6 m in diameter after it expands. Balloons are launched twice a day at sites around the world.

Attached to the weather balloon is a radiosonde, an instrument that measures pressure, temperature, and relative humidity. Because the radiosonde can be reconditioned and used again, a parachute and mailing bag are also attached to the weather balloon. (The photograph in Figure 14 was taken at the National Weather Station in Maryland.)

It is harder for scientists to do a controlled experiment when they are studying events that occur in natural settings. Scientists need laws like the combined gas law to deal with situations in which multiple variables are changing. Balloons like the one in Figure 14 are used by scientists to gather data about Earth's atmosphere. The balloon is filled with hydrogen or helium. It carries a package of weather instruments up into the atmosphere. The instruments measure temperature, pressure, and water content at different levels in the atmosphere.

What will happen to the volume of the weather balloon as it rises through the atmosphere? Both pressure and temperature decrease as the altitude increases in Earth's atmosphere. A decrease in external pressure should cause the balloon to expand to a larger volume. A decrease in temperature should cause the balloon to contract to a smaller volume. Whether the balloon actually expands or contracts depends on the size of the changes in pressure and temperature.

Figure 14 These scientists are releasing a weather balloon into the atmosphere. The balloon is designed to burst when it reaches an altitude of about 27,400 meters. Drawing Conclusions *What happens to the pressure inside a weather balloon as it rises?*

Section 3.2 Assessment

Reviewing Concepts

1. 💬 How is the gas pressure produced in a closed container of gas?
2. 💬 What three factors affect gas pressure?
3. 💬 How does increasing the temperature affect the pressure of a contained gas?
4. 💬 What happens to the pressure of a gas if its volume is reduced?
5. 💬 How does increasing the number of particles of a contained gas affect its pressure?

Critical Thinking

6. **Predicting** What happens to the pressure in a tire if air is slowly leaking out of the tire? Explain your answer.
7. **Comparing and Contrasting** What do Boyle's law and Charles's law have in common? How are they different?

8. **Applying Concepts** Some liquid products are sold in aerosol cans. Gas is stored in a can under pressure and is used to propel the liquid out of the can. Explain why an aerosol can should never be thrown into a fireplace or incinerator.

Math **Practice**

9. Two liters of hydrogen gas are stored at a pressure of 100 kPa. If the temperature does not change, what will the volume of the gas be when the pressure is decreased to 25 kPa?
10. You know that a gas in a sealed container has a pressure of 111 kPa at 23°C. What will the pressure be if the temperature rises to 475°C?

States of Matter **81**

Use Visuals   L1

Figure 14 The balloon will burst when it reaches an altitude of about 27,400 m. Ask, **What variables change as the balloon rises? How do they change?** *(Temperature and pressure both decrease.)* **How does each change affect the volume of the balloon?** *(Decreasing atmospheric pressure causes the balloon to expand. Decreasing temperature causes the balloon to shrink.)* **Visual, Logical**

3 ASSESS

Evaluate Understanding   L2

Have students look at the mathematical presentations of Charles's law on p. 78 and Boyle's law on p. 79 and describe the relationships in their own words.

Reteach   L1

Write Charles's law and Boyle's law on the board. Have students quiz each other about the behavior of the responding variable when another variable increases or decreases.

Math **Practice**

Solutions

9. $V_2 = (P_1V_1/P_2) =$ (100 kPa)(2.0 L)/25 kPa = 8.0 L
10. $P_2 = (P_1T_2/T_1) =$ (111 kPa)(748 K)/296 K = 280 kPa

Interactive Textbook If your class subscribes to the Interactive Textbook, use it to review key concepts in Section 3.2.

Answer to . . .

Figure 14 *The pressure increases.*

Section 3.2   Assessment

1. Collisions between particles of a gas and the walls of the container cause the pressure in a closed container of gas.
2. Temperature, volume, and number of particles
3. Raising the temperature will increase the pressure if volume and number of particles are constant.

4. If the volume is reduced, the pressure of a gas increases if temperature and number of particles are constant.
5. Increasing the number of particles will increase the pressure if temperature and volume are constant.
6. Because the number of particles of air is reduced from the leak, the pressure will slowly decrease.

7. Both laws describe a relationship between two variables that affect a gas when other variables are constant. Charles's law shows how the volume of a gas is directly proportional to its temperature in kelvins. Boyle's law shows how the volume of a gas is inversely proportional to its pressure.
8. At a high temperature, the pressure in the gas might increase to the point where the can would explode.

CONCEPTS
— in Action —

Riding on Air
Background

On August 27, 1783, Jacques Charles released his first hydrogen-filled balloon, which was about 4 m in diameter. He prepared the hydrogen by pouring sulfuric acid over scrap iron. Charles also made improvements to hot-air balloons, including a valve line that allowed operators to release gas from the balloon and a wicker basket (a nacelle), which was attached to the balloon by ropes. The first publication of Charles's work was by Joseph Gay-Lussac, who referred to Charles's work in an 1802 paper. Gay-Lussac also did ballooning. His altitude record of 7016 m (4.3 miles) stood for almost 50 years.

Build Science Skills

Observing

Purpose Students will observe that heating air causes it to expand and become less dense.

Materials plastic bag (dry cleaner or thin garbage bag), string, hair dryers

Class Time 20 minutes

Procedure Organize students into groups of two or three. Have students tie a string around the closed end of the plastic bag and place evenly spaced paper clips around the open end as weights. Tell students to hold the open end of the plastic bag over the hair dryer (set on high) and let the bag fill with hot air. The plastic bag begins to rise as it fills with hot air. When the students feel the bag begin to rise, have them release the bag. Ask, **What causes the bag to rise?** (*The heated air inside the bag is less dense than the air outside the bag.*) **Use what happened to the plastic bag to explain how a hot-air balloon works.** (*A hot-air balloon rises because air in the balloon is heated.*)

Expected Outcome When the air inside the bag is heated, the bag begins to rise.
Visual, Group

CONCEPTS in Action

Riding on Air

Warm air is less dense than cold air. So if enough warm air is confined to a lightweight container, the container can rise through the surrounding colder air. This is the principle that allows a hot-air balloon to get off and stay off the ground.

When air is heated, the particles in the air gain energy and move faster on average. The particles also move farther apart, so a given volume of hot air contains fewer particles and has less mass than the same volume of cold air. This difference in density produces an upward force. In a hot-air balloon, the force is very small, equivalent to lifting about one tenth of a gram for each liter of air. A large volume of air is needed to support the mass of the balloon and any passengers. That is why hot-air balloons need to be large.

To heat the air, the pilot burns propane gas, which is stored under pressure in tanks. The bottom of the balloon's envelope (the skirt) is treated so that it is not flammable.

As the balloon nears the chosen altitude, the pilot turns the burner off so that the balloon will stop rising. The pilot maintains the altitude of the balloon by turning the burner on and off and by opening a valve at the top of the balloon to let hot air escape.

The horizontal movement of the balloon is much harder to control. The wind speed and wind direction vary at different altitudes. The pilot uses the burner and the valve to change the altitude of the balloon and take advantage of favorable winds. A hot-air balloon cannot land at the same spot from which it took off. The ground crew must drive to the landing site to collect the balloon and the passengers.

Taking Off and Landing

Launching and piloting a hot-air balloon is an activity that takes skill and patience.

1 The crew uses fans to fill the envelope with cold air.

2 Gas burners are switched on to heat the air and inflate the balloon, which begins to rise.

3 Once up, the pilot maintains altitude by occasionally turning on the burner for a few seconds.

4 To lose altitude, the pilot opens a valve at the top of the envelope to let out some hot air.

Valve

Burner

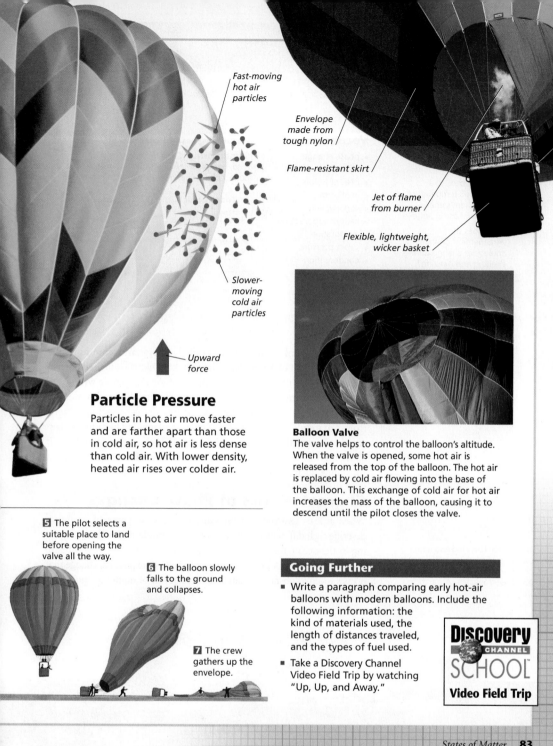

Fast-moving hot air particles

Envelope made from tough nylon

Flame-resistant skirt

Jet of flame from burner

Flexible, lightweight, wicker basket

Slower-moving cold air particles

Upward force

Particle Pressure

Particles in hot air move faster and are farther apart than those in cold air, so hot air is less dense than cold air. With lower density, heated air rises over colder air.

Balloon Valve
The valve helps to control the balloon's altitude. When the valve is opened, some hot air is released from the top of the balloon. The hot air is replaced by cold air flowing into the base of the balloon. This exchange of cold air for hot air increases the mass of the balloon, causing it to descend until the pilot closes the valve.

5 The pilot selects a suitable place to land before opening the valve all the way.

6 The balloon slowly falls to the ground and collapses.

7 The crew gathers up the envelope.

Going Further

- Write a paragraph comparing early hot-air balloons with modern balloons. Include the following information: the kind of materials used, the length of distances traveled, and the types of fuel used.
- Take a Discovery Channel Video Field Trip by watching "Up, Up, and Away."

DISCOVERY CHANNEL SCHOOL
Video Field Trip

Going Further

The Montgolfier hot-air balloon that first carried human passengers had an envelope made of cotton and paper coated with alum to reduce flammability. The fuel used was straw. The balloon flew from the center of Paris to the outskirts (a distance of about 9 kilometers) in 25 minutes on November 21, 1783. (Hot-air balloons were soon eclipsed by helium balloons or hydrogen balloons.) Modern passenger hot-air balloons were developed in the United States in the 1960s. Their envelopes are made of nylon and they use propane fuel. Hot-air balloons generally stay aloft for about an hour. (For long distance flights, balloonists generally use combination helium and hot-air balloons called Rozier balloons after Pilâtre de Rozier, a passenger on the first "manned" flight.)
Verbal

DISCOVERY CHANNEL SCHOOL

Video Field Trip
Up, Up, and Away

After students have viewed the Video Field Trip, ask them the following questions: **What gases have commonly been used in balloons that carry passengers?** *(Hot air, helium, and hydrogen)* **Why do the particles of a gas inside a balloon fill the entire balloon?** *(A gas has no particular size or shape and expands to fill the volume available.)* **What**

causes a hot-air balloon to lift off and rise from a surface? *(Hot air inside the balloon is less dense than the cooler, denser air outside the balloon. The difference in density results in an upward force.)* In 1931, Auguste Piccard, a Swiss physicist and educator, built a balloon that could rise a distance of 16 miles. **Why did Piccard design the balloon so that it could become airborne when it was only partially filled?** *(Piccard knew the gas inside the balloon would continue to expand as the balloon floated up to greater heights because*

the outside air pressure decreased as the balloon rose.) In Piccard's balloon, the pressure in the cabin was controlled as it is in planes that travel at great heights above Earth's surface. Air pressure in the cabin is kept higher than atmospheric pressure. **Why must the air pressure inside the cabin be controlled?** *(Atmospheric pressure decreases with altitude until it no longer can sustain respiration.)*

1 FOCUS

Objectives

3.3.1 Describe phase changes.

3.3.2 Explain how temperature can be used to recognize a phase change.

3.3.3 Explain what happens to the motion, arrangement, and average kinetic energy of water molecules during phase changes.

3.3.4 Describe each of the six phase changes.

3.3.5 Identify phase changes as endothermic or exothermic.

Reading Focus

Build Vocabulary **L2**

Word-Part Analysis List on the board the following word parts and meanings: *-ion,* "the act of" or "the result of an action"; *-ic,* "related to or characterized by"; *endo-,* "inside"; *exo-,* "outside"; *therm,* "heat"; *-ize,* "to become." Have students identify these word parts in the vocabulary terms. Discuss the terms' meanings with students.

Reading Strategy **L2**

a. Liquid **b.** Liquid **c.** Gas **d.** Liquid **e.** Gas **f.** Gas

2 INSTRUCT

Characteristics of Phase Changes

Use Visuals **L1**

Figure 15 Note that water is one of the few substances that exist naturally as a solid, liquid, and gas under ordinary conditions. Have students look at the figure and read the caption. Ask, **Which two phases of water are visible in the photograph?** *(Solid and liquid)* **Where would the third phase most likely be found?** *(In the air)*
Visual, Logical

3.3 Phase Changes

Standards: ICP.3.1, ICP.3.2, ICP.3.3, ICP.3.4

Reading Focus

Key Concepts

- What are six common phase changes?
- What happens to a substance's temperature and a system's energy during a phase change?
- How does the arrangement of water molecules change during melting and freezing?
- How are evaporation and boiling different?

Vocabulary

- phase change
- endothermic
- heat of fusion
- exothermic
- vaporization
- heat of vaporization
- evaporation
- vapor pressure
- condensation
- sublimation
- deposition

Reading Strategy

Summarizing Copy the diagram. As you read, complete the description of energy flow during phase changes.

Endothermic

| Solid | → | Liquid |

| b._?_ | → | c._?_ |

| Solid | → | e._?_ |

Exothermic

| a._?_ | → | Solid |

| Gas | → | d._?_ |

| f._?_ | → | Solid |

Massive chunks of frozen water called icebergs are a common sight off the continent of Antarctica. A large iceberg like the one in Figure 15 contains enough fresh water to supply millions of people with water for a year. During the summer in southern Australia, fresh water is a scarce resource. People have proposed towing icebergs to Australia from Antarctica. The plan has not been implemented because the trip could take months to complete and much of the iceberg would melt along the way. In this section, you will find out what happens when a substance, such as water, changes from one state to another.

Characteristics of Phase Changes

When at least two states of the same substance are present, scientists describe each different state as a phase. For example, if an iceberg is floating in the ocean, there are two phases of water present—a solid phase and a liquid phase. A **phase change** is the reversible physical change that occurs when a substance changes from one state of matter to another.

Figure 15 The solid and liquid phases of water are visible in this photograph of an iceberg in the Amundsen Sea near Antarctica.

 Section Resources

Print
- *Laboratory Manual,* Investigation 3A
- *Reading and Study Workbook With Math Support,* Section 3.3
- *Transparencies,* Section 3.3

Technology
- *Probeware Lab Manual,* Lab 1
- *Interactive Textbook,* Section 3.3
- *Presentation Pro CD-ROM,* Section 3.3
- *Go Online,* NSTA SciLinks, Phases of matter; PHSchool.com, Data sharing

In Figure 16, a state of matter is listed at each corner of the triangle. Each arrow in the diagram represents a different phase change. Each pair of arrows represents a set of reversible changes. For example, the arrow starting at the solid phase and ending at the liquid phase represents melting. The arrow starting at the liquid phase and ending at the solid phase represents freezing.

◖ Melting, freezing, vaporization, condensation, sublimation, and deposition are six common phase changes. All phase changes share certain characteristics related to energy and temperature.

Temperature and Phase Changes
One way to recognize a phase change is by measuring the temperature of a substance as it is heated or cooled. ◖ The temperature of a substance does not change during a phase change.

Naphthalene (NAF thuh leen) is a compound that is sometimes used in mothballs. Figure 17 is a graph of the data collected when a solid piece of naphthalene is slowly heated. Temperature readings are taken at regular intervals. At first the temperature rises as the solid naphthalene warms up. But at 80°C, the temperature of the naphthalene stops rising. The temperature remains at 80°C, which is the melting point of naphthalene, until melting is complete.

If liquid naphthalene is placed in an ice-water bath, the temperature of the liquid will drop until it reaches 80°C. It will remain at 80°C until all the liquid freezes. The temperature at which the substance freezes—its freezing point—is identical to the temperature at which it melts. The freezing and melting points of naphthalene are both 80°C.

If naphthalene is heated after it has completely melted, its temperature begins to rise again. The temperature keeps rising until it reaches 218°C, which is the boiling point of naphthalene. Until boiling is complete, the temperature remains at 218°C.

Figure 16 This diagram lists six physical changes that can occur among the solid, liquid, and gaseous phases of a substance. *Interpreting Diagrams* *Explain why the changes are grouped into the pairs shown on the diagram.*

For: Links on phase diagrams
Visit: www.SciLinks.org
Web Code: ccn-1030

Heating Curve for Naphthalene

Figure 17 This graph shows what happens to the temperature of a solid sample of naphthalene as the sample is slowly heated. *Using Graphs* *What happened to the temperature in the interval between four and seven minutes?*

States of Matter **85**

Integrate Biology

One of the main causes of frost damage in crops is ice-nucleating bacteria. These bacteria provide a nucleus around which ice can form. When ice forms on plants, it pierces their cell walls and causes the cells to desiccate, or dry out because water escapes from the cells. Have students search the Internet for information on ice-nucleating bacteria. Have students present what they learn in a pamphlet that offers suggestions on how to prevent frost damage from bacteria.
Verbal

Teacher > Demo

Energy Transfer

Purpose Students observe that the phase change from ice to water is endothermic.

Materials tray of ice cubes

Procedure Place a tray of ice cubes on a counter at the beginning of class. As the ice begins to melt, ask students where the energy to melt the ice comes from.

Expected Outcome Students will observe that the ice melts. They will infer that the energy to melt the ice comes from the air and the counter because these materials are warmer than the ice.
Visual

Figure 18 This ice sculpture of a dog sled was carved at a winter fair in Fairbanks, Alaska. The ice sculpture will start to melt if the temperature rises above 0°C or sunlight shines directly on the ice.

Energy absorbed

Energy released

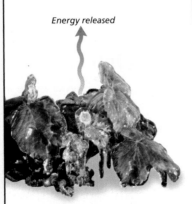

Figure 19 Energy released as ice forms on these strawberry plants keeps the plants from freezing at temperatures slightly below 0°C. Applying Concepts *Explain why a farmer would need to keep spraying the plants with water while the temperature remains below freezing.*

Energy and Phase Changes During a phase change, energy is transferred between a substance and its surroundings. The direction of the transfer depends on the type of phase change. ⬤ **Energy is either absorbed or released during a phase change.**

The ice sculpture in Figure 18 isn't going to last forever. When the temperature of the air rises above 0°C or when sunlight shines directly on the ice, an ice sculpture begins to melt. Melting is an example of an endothermic change. During an **endothermic** change, the system absorbs energy from its surroundings.

The amount of energy absorbed depends on the substance. For example, one gram of ice absorbs 334 joules (J) of energy as it melts. This amount of energy is the **heat of fusion** for water. Fusion is another term for melting. The heat of fusion varies from substance to substance.

One gram of water releases 334 joules of energy to its surroundings as it freezes, the same amount of energy that is absorbed when one gram of ice melts. Farmers use this release of energy to protect their crops. When farmers expect temperatures to drop slightly below 0°C, they spray the crops with water as shown in Figure 19. As water freezes, it releases heat. The flow of heat slows the drop in temperature and helps protect the crops from damage. Freezing is an example of an exothermic change. During an **exothermic** change, the system releases energy to its surroundings.

An understanding of phase changes can be useful in many situations. The How It Works box explains how the design of an ice rink in Utah allows the manager of the rink to control the hardness of the ice.

Reading Checkpoint   *How much energy does one gram of ice absorb as it melts?*

Facts and Figures

Preventing Frost Damage For a frost control system to work, a farmer needs to start the sprinklers just before the temperature at ground level reaches 0°C. Placing a shallow pan of water in the lowest part of the field is an easy way to monitor the temperature. As soon as ice begins to form around the edge of the pan, the sprinklers should be turned on. The sprinklers should stay on until the temperature rises enough to start melting the ice.

This method of frost control is effective for strawberry plants down to about −6.6°C. When strawberries are in bloom, sprinklers are best started at 1.1°C. Blueberries with open blooms are safe from damage at temperatures as low as 0°C. Because of the cost of installation and operation, frost control systems are generally used for crops that can demand high unit prices, such as oranges, strawberries, Blueberries, and asparagus.

Custom-Tailored Ice

At the Utah Olympic Oval the hardness of the ice can be controlled. The ice must be cold and hard for long speed-skating races, where the length of a skater's glide is important. For shorter races, the skaters need more traction, so the ice is made a little warmer and softer.

Interpreting Diagrams *What is the purpose of the sand layer?*

Speed Skater
This skater is racing at the Utah Olympic Oval, one of the world's most technically advanced ice rinks.

Lubricant

Paint layer with markings

Paint layer with logos

Paint layer with background color

A **Skating surface** The surface is built up from thin layers of ice to a depth of less than 2 cm. The ice can be as cold as −8°C. The temperature and the hardness of the ice are controlled by tiny changes to the temperature of the underlying concrete layer.

B **Chilled concrete slab** The temperature is controlled by cold salt water, which is pumped through pipes embedded in the slab. The salt water remains liquid because its freezing point is lower than that of pure water.

C **Insulating layers** These layers prevent heat from rising up into the concrete slab from the warmer sand layer underneath.

D **Sand layer** To prevent the gravel layer from freezing, which could damage the rink structure, the sand layer is kept at a temperature above 0°C.

E **Gravel layer** This layer provides the foundation for the rink.

Ice layers
The skating surface is formed with as many as 24 layers of ice and paint. Warm water is used for the top layers because it contains less dissolved air, and can produce a denser, harder, frozen surface.

States of Matter **87**

DK HOW It Works

Custom-Tailored Ice L2

Skaters traveling at speeds up to 80 km/h will be slowed by a surface that is not smooth, level, and uniformly hard. The conditions of the ice at the Utah Olympic Oval, which was constructed for the 2000 Winter Olympics, can be changed overnight. For sprinters, the ice is softer so that their traction, or ability to grip the ice, is greater. A harder surface allows long-distance skaters to glide more easily across the ice.

Controlling the indoor climate is also important in maintaining the ice surface. The Utah Olympic Oval has two air-filtering systems and a dehumidifier that can reduce humidity to 3%. The air temperature varies only 3°C from the ice to the ceiling. Controlling the conditions above and below the ice allows for precise control of the ice surface.

Interpreting Diagrams The sand layer prevents the gravel layer from freezing and damaging the rink structure.
Visual, Logical

For Enrichment L3

Have students research playing surfaces used in other sports, such as football, tennis, and golf. Explain that different surfaces affect an athlete's performance. Students could compare the advantages and disadvantages of artificial turf and grass football fields; or cement, clay, and grass tennis courts. They could also find out how the length of grass affects shots at different locations on a golf course.
Logical

Answer to . . .

Figure 19 *Until the temperature rises above freezing, the farmer must continue to provide energy to keep the plants from freezing.*

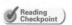
Reading Checkpoint *334 joules*

Melting and Freezing
Use Visuals   L1

Figure 20 Keeping food cool requires the transfer of energy. Ask, **What change occurs in the evaporator? Is this change exothermic or endothermic?** *(Liquid to gas; the change is endothermic because energy is absorbed from the food compartment)* **What change occurs in the condenser? Is this change exothermic or endothermic?** *(Gas is liquid; the change is exothermic because energy is released to the surroundings)*
Visual

FYI

Refrigeration is also discussed in Chapter 16, where the focus is on the need for work to be done for heat to flow from an area of lower temperature to an area at higher temperature. In this chapter, the focus is on the endothermic and exothermic phase changes.

Vaporization and Condensation
Use Community Resources   L2

Invite an appliance repairperson to come to the class and speak about compounds used in air conditioner and refrigerator cooling coils. Suggest that the speaker describe the types of compounds used, how the compounds have changed over time, and whether there are any problems with the replacement compounds.
Interpersonal

Download a worksheet on phases of matter for students to complete, and find additional teacher support from NSTA SciLinks.

For: Links on phases of matter
Visit: www.SciLinks.org
Web Code: ccn-1033

Figure 20 In a refrigerator, a pair of phase changes keep the food cold. Energy from inside the food compartment is used to change a liquid to a gas in the evaporator. This energy is released when the compressed gas changes back to a liquid in the condenser.

Evaporator

Energy removed from food compartment

Condenser

Compressor

Energy released to surroundings

Melting and Freezing

In water, hydrogen and oxygen atoms are combined in small units called molecules. Each water molecule contains two hydrogen atoms and one oxygen atom. ◖▶ **The arrangement of molecules in water becomes less orderly as water melts and more orderly as water freezes.**

Melting In ice, attractions between water molecules keep the molecules in fixed positions. When ice cubes are removed from a freezer and placed in an empty glass, heat flows from the air to the ice. As the ice gains energy, the molecules vibrate more quickly. At the melting point of water, 0°C, some molecules gain enough energy to overcome the attractions and move from their fixed positions. When all the molecules have enough energy to move, melting is complete. Any energy gained by the water after the phase change increases the average kinetic energy of the molecules, and the temperature rises.

Freezing When liquid water is placed in a freezer, energy flows from the water to the air in the freezer, and the water cools down. As the average kinetic energy of its molecules decreases, they move more slowly. At the freezing point of water, some molecules move slowly enough for the attractions between molecules to have an effect. When all the molecules have been drawn into an orderly arrangement, freezing is complete. Any energy removed from the ice after the phase change decreases the average kinetic energy of the molecules, and the temperature of the ice drops.

Often, people think of cold temperatures when they hear the term *freezing*. But substances that are solids at room temperature can freeze at temperatures that are quite high. For example, silicon freezes at 1412°C (2574°F). As a comparison, you can bake cookies at 177°C (350°F).

Vaporization and Condensation

Figure 20 shows how food cools and stays cold in a refrigerator. The process depends on a substance that changes from a liquid to a gas to a liquid over and over again. During these phase changes, energy flows from the inside of the refrigerator to the outside.

The phase change in which a substance changes from a liquid into a gas is **vaporization.** Vaporization is an endothermic process. That is, a substance must absorb energy in order to change from a liquid to a gas. One gram of water gains 2258 joules of energy when it vaporizes at 100°C. This amount of energy is the **heat of vaporization** for water. The heat of vaporization varies from substance to substance.

Facts and Figures

Chlorofluorocarbons Under the Clean Air Act, which became effective in November of 1995, it became illegal to release into the air compounds that harm Earth's ozone layer. Chlorofluorocarbons (CFCs) are among the banned substances. CFCs were used as refrigerants in cooling devices, such as refrigerators and air conditioners.

Because CFCs do not dissolve easily in water and are generally not very reactive, they tend to stay in the atmosphere once they are released. In the lower atmosphere, their presence causes few problems. However, these compounds move into the stratosphere where they are exposed to high energy radiation. This radiation causes the CFCs to react and release chlorine atoms. These chlorine atoms react with oxygen to form chlorine monoxide, which causes the ozone to decompose into oxygen. Hydrogen fluorocarbons (HFCs) have replaced CFCs in many cooling devices.

Scientists distinguish two vaporization processes—boiling and evaporation. ● **Evaporation takes place at the surface of a liquid and occurs at temperatures below the boiling point.**

Evaporation If you go outside after a rain shower on a sunny, warm day, you may notice puddles of water. If you return to the same location after a few hours, the puddles may be gone. This disappearance of the puddles is due to evaporation. **Evaporation** is the process that changes a substance from a liquid to a gas at temperatures below the substance's boiling point.

Figure 21 shows what is happening as water evaporates from a small, shallow container. Some molecules near the surface are moving fast enough to escape the liquid and become water vapor. (A vapor is the gaseous phase of a substance that is normally a solid or liquid at room temperature.) The greater the surface area of the container, the faster the water evaporates.

What happens if the water is in a closed container? As the water evaporates, water vapor collects above the liquid. The pressure caused by the collisions of this vapor and the walls of the container is called **vapor pressure.** The vapor pressure of water increases as the temperature increases. At higher temperatures, more water molecules have enough kinetic energy to overcome the attractions of other molecules in the liquid.

Figure 21 Evaporation takes place at the surface of a liquid.

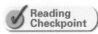 **Reading Checkpoint** *How does the surface area of a liquid affect the rate of evaporation?*

Boiling As you heat a pot of water, both the temperature and the vapor pressure of the water increase. When the vapor pressure becomes equal to atmospheric pressure, the water boils. The temperature at which this happens is the boiling point of water.

The kinetic theory explains what happens when water boils. As the temperature increases, water molecules move faster and faster. When the temperature reaches 100°C, some molecules below the surface of the liquid have enough kinetic energy to overcome the attraction of neighboring molecules. Figure 22 shows that bubbles of water vapor form within the liquid. Because water vapor is less dense than liquid water, the bubbles quickly rise to the surface. When they reach the surface, the bubbles burst and release water vapor into the air.

Figure 22 Boiling takes place throughout a liquid. Applying Concepts *Explain why the temperature of water does not rise during boiling.*

89

Quick Lab

Observing Phase Changes L2

Objective
After completing this lab, students will be able to
- identify examples of condensation and sublimation.

Skills Focus Observing

 Prep Time 15 minutes

Advance Prep Obtain dry ice from a local supplier or from a scientific supply house, ice cream wholesaler, or compressed gas dealer. Do not store dry ice in an airtight container. Leave a window open in your car if you have dry ice in the car. Use a hammer to carefully break the dry ice into pea-sized pieces.

Class Time 20 minutes

Safety Do not handle dry ice with bare hands. It damages skin tissue on contact. Wear safety goggles, a lab apron, and leather gloves when handling dry ice. Use forceps to dispense a pea-sized piece of dry ice into each flask. Caution students not to touch dry ice and to use care when handling glassware to avoid breakage. Provide only nonmercury thermometers.

Teaching Tips
- Do this lab after students have studied sublimation.
- If students are having trouble with Question 2, ask at what temperature water boils. If they are having trouble with Question 4, remind them that water vapor exists above the liquid.

Expected Outcome When dry ice is added to water, vigorous bubbling begins and a fog appears above the liquid.

For Enrichment L3
Challenge students to propose a way to have solid, liquid, and gaseous water together in the same test tube. One way is to place ice in liquid water in a closed container. Water vapor will collect above the surface of the water.
Visual, Logical

 Quick Lab

Observing Phase Changes

Materials
250-mL Erlenmeyer flask, graduated cylinder, thermometer, dry ice

Procedure
1. Pour 150 milliliters of water into a 250-mL Erlenmeyer flask. Place a thermometer in the flask. **CAUTION** *Wipe up any spilled water right away to avoid slips and falls.*
2. Observe what happens after your teacher adds a small piece of dry ice to the flask. (Dry ice is solid carbon dioxide.) **CAUTION** *Dry ice can damage skin on contact. Do not touch the dry ice.*
3. Record the temperature of the water just after the dry ice is added and again after it is no longer visible.

Analyze and Conclude
1. **Observing** What happened when the dry ice was added to the water?
2. **Analyzing Data** Did adding the dry ice cause the water to boil? Explain your answer.
3. **Inferring** What was the source of the bubbles in the water?
4. **Formulating Hypotheses** What caused a cloud to form above the flask?
5. **Applying Concepts** What phase changes occurred in the flask?

Figure 23 Water vapor from the air condensed into drops of liquid water on these blades of grass.

The boiling point of a substance depends on the atmospheric pressure. The normal boiling point of water at sea level is 100°C. At higher elevations, the atmospheric pressure is lower. Do you know that Denver, Colorado, is called the mile-high city? This nickname is based on Denver's location at one mile above sea level. In Denver, the vapor pressure of water will equal atmospheric pressure at temperatures below 100°C. The boiling point of water in Denver can be as low as 95°C. Food does not cook as quickly at 95°C as it does at 100°C. Pasta takes longer to cook in Denver than in New Orleans, Louisiana, a city that is located near sea level.

Condensation Have you ever come out of a shower to find your bathroom mirror clouded over? The "cloud" on the mirror is caused by water vapor that cooled as it came in contact with the mirror. The water vapor transferred heat to the mirror and condensed into liquid water. **Condensation** is the phase change in which a substance changes from a gas or vapor to a liquid. This process is also responsible for the morning dew on the blades of grass in Figure 23. Condensation is an exothermic process.

Analyze and Conclude
1. Bubbles formed in the water, and a fog formed above the water. The temperature of the water decreased.
2. No, because the water was not at 100°C when bubbles appeared.
3. Carbon dioxide gas from the dry ice

4. Cold carbon dioxide gas chilled the air above the water, causing water vapor to condense into tiny liquid droplets.
5. Sublimation of carbon dioxide and condensation of water occurred. Students may also mention vaporization of water.
Logical, Kinesthetic

Sublimation and Deposition

Directors of concerts and plays sometimes use dry ice to create a fog-like special effect. Dry ice is the common name for the solid form of carbon dioxide. At room temperature, dry ice can directly change from a solid to a colorless gas. **Sublimation** is the phase change in which a substance changes from a solid to a gas or vapor without changing to a liquid first. Sublimation is an endothermic change. As dry ice sublimes, the cold carbon dioxide vapor causes water vapor in the air to condense and form clouds.

Where does the name dry ice come from? Solid carbon dioxide does not form a liquid as its temperature rises. Suppose 100 steaks are shipped from Omaha, Nebraska, to a supermarket in Miami, Florida. The steaks will spoil unless they are kept cold during the trip. If regular ice is used, water collects in the shipping container as the ice melts. If the steaks are shipped in dry ice, the container and the steaks stay dry during the journey. Figure 24 shows another use of dry ice.

When a gas or vapor changes directly into a solid without first changing to a liquid, the phase change is called **deposition.** This exothermic phase change is the reverse of sublimation. Deposition causes frost to form on windows. When water vapor in the air comes in contact with cold window glass, the water vapor loses enough kinetic energy to change directly from a gas to a solid.

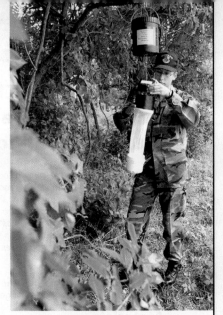

Figure 24 A technician at Tinker Air Force Base in Oklahoma hangs a mosquito trap. The trap is baited with dry ice because mosquitoes are attracted to carbon dioxide.

Section 3.3 Assessment

Reviewing Concepts

1. ⬤ Name six common phase changes.
2. ⬤ What happens to the temperature of a substance during a phase change?
3. ⬤ How does the energy of a system change during a phase change?
4. ⬤ What happens to the arrangement of water molecules as water melts and freezes?
5. ⬤ What is the difference between evaporation and boiling?
6. Explain why sublimation and deposition are classified as physical changes.

Critical Thinking

7. **Applying Concepts** How can the mass of a pile of snow decrease on a sunny day when the air temperature does not rise above 0°C?

8. **Drawing Conclusions** At room temperature, table salt is a solid and acetone is a liquid. Acetone is the main ingredient in nail polish remover. What conclusion can you draw about the melting points of these materials?

Writing in Science

Steps in a Process Write a paragraph describing three steps that must occur for a water molecule to start on the surface of hot bath water and end up on the surface of a bathroom mirror. Note whether the phase changes that take place during the process are endothermic or exothermic. (*Hint:* Use words such as *first, next,* and *finally* to show the order of events.)

Sublimation and Deposition

Use Visuals L1

Figure 24 Have students examine Figure 24. Explain that the trap was hung as part of a study of West Nile virus, a mosquito-borne disease. Mosquitoes acquire the virus from infected birds and then transmit the virus to other animals and humans. Mosquitoes are collected and sent to a laboratory for identification by species and gender. Samples of similar female mosquitoes are blended and their RNA is analyzed for West Nile virus. Ask, **Why is dry ice used to bait the mosquito trap rather than gaseous carbon dioxide?** (*The large amount of carbon dioxide stored in dry ice is released slowly over time rather than all at once.*) **Logical**

3 ASSESSMENT

Evaluate Understanding L2

Have students write the six terms that describe phase changes. Next to each term, students should describe the type of change. For example, for *melting*, students would indicate that the phase change is from a solid to a liquid. Tell students to include arrows pointing up to identify exothermic changes and arrows pointing down to identify exothermic changes.

Reteach L1

Use Figure 16 to review the six phase changes described in this section. Ask, **What do the phase changes with red arrows have in common?** (*They are all exothermic processes.*) **What do the phase changes with blue arrows have in common?** (*They are all endothermic processes.*)

Writing in Science

First, the water molecule on the surface of the bath water evaporates—an endothermic change. Next, random motion of the molecule carries it to the surface of the mirror. Finally, the molecule condenses on the mirror—an exothermic change.

Interactive Textbook If your class subscribes to the Interactive Textbook, use it to review key concepts in Section 3.3.

Section 3.3 Assessment

1. Melting, freezing, vaporization, condensation, sublimation, and deposition
2. The temperature of a substance does not change during a phase change.
3. Energy is either released or absorbed during a phase change.
4. The arrangement of molecules becomes less orderly as water melts and more orderly as water freezes.
5. Evaporation takes place at the surface of a liquid and occurs at temperatures below the boiling point.
6. A substance's identity does not change during sublimation or deposition.
7. When snow absorbs energy from sunlight, it either melts or sublimes.
8. Table salt must have a melting point above room temperature, and acetone must have a melting point below room temperature.

Investigating Changes in Temperature During Heating of Solids L2

Objective

After completing this activity, students will be able to

- explain the constant temperature of a substance that is undergoing a phase change.

 Address Misconceptions

Students might think the temperature should keep increasing as the ice melts. Ask them to predict the shape of the melting curve. After performing the lab, ask students to compare their predictions to the actual curves.

Skills Focus Measuring, Using Tables and Graphs

Prep Time 30 minutes

Advance Prep Buy crushed ice or crush it by placing ice cubes into a plastic bag and hitting them with a mallet while wearing goggles. Pour granular lauric acid into the test tubes and insert a thermometer into each test tube. Rather than discarding the lauric acid after the first class, leave the thermometers in the test tubes and allow the test tubes to cool to room temperature. The thermometers will be embedded in the solidified lauric acid.

Class Time 45 minutes

Safety Provide only nonmercury thermometers. Position hot plates away from the edges of tables. Place power cords behind the hot plates, where they are not likely to become entangled with arms or clothing. Once a hot plate is turned on, students should not touch it.

Teaching Tips

- Emphasize the importance of making an accurate measurement of the initial temperature of the ice.
- You may wish to save time by having some students perform Part A of the lab and others perform Part B. Students can then exchange data before making their graphs.
- To help students construct their graphs, show a sample graph on an overhead transparency. Include the grids for the horizontal and vertical axes, but not the data.
- You may wish to postpone the graphing of the results of Part A (Step 7) to the end of the lab, after all data have been collected.

Investigating Changes in Temperature During Heating of Solids

Lauric acid is a solid that is found in coconuts and processed foods that are made with coconut oil. Lauric acid is also used to make some soaps and cosmetics. In this lab, you will measure the temperature of ice and of lauric acid as these solids are heated and melt. You will graph the data you collect and compare the heating curves for ice and lauric acid.

Problem
What happens to the temperature of a substance during a phase change?

Materials
- 500-mL beaker
- crushed ice
- thermometer
- hot plate
- clock with second hand
- test tube of lauric acid with thermometer
- glass stirring rod
- graph paper

For the probeware version of this lab, see the Probeware Lab Manual, Lab 1.

Skills
Measuring, Using Graphs

Procedure

Part A: Heating Ice

1. On a sheet of paper, make a copy of the data table shown. Start with 11 blank rows, but leave space below your data table to add more rows, if necessary.

2. Fill a 500-mL beaker halfway with crushed ice. **CAUTION** *Use care when handling glassware to avoid breakage. Wipe up any spilled ice right away to avoid slips and falls.*

3. Place the beaker on a hot plate. Don't turn the hot plate on yet. Insert a thermometer into the ice. Because it takes several seconds for the thermometer to adjust to the temperature of its surroundings, wait 20 seconds and then measure the temperature of the ice. Record this temperature next to the 0 minutes entry in your data table.

4. Turn the hot plate to a low setting. **CAUTION** *Be careful not to touch the hot plate because contact with the hot plate could cause a burn.*

5. Observe and record the temperature at one-minute intervals until all the ice has changed to liquid water. Circle the temperature at which you first observe liquid water and the temperature at which all the ice has changed to liquid water.

Data Table		
Time (minutes)	Temperature of Water (°C)	Temperature of Lauric Acid (°C)
0		
1		

 Probeware Lab Manual Versions of this lab for use with probeware available from Pasco, Texas Instruments, and Vernier are in the Probeware Manual.

6. After all the ice has melted, make five more measurements of the temperature at one-minute intervals. Turn off the hot plate.

7. Graph your data with time on the horizontal axis and temperature on the vertical axis.

Part B: Heating Lauric Acid

8. Empty the water from the beaker into the sink. Fill the beaker halfway with cool tap water.

9. Place a test tube containing lauric acid and a thermometer into the beaker. If necessary, add or remove water from the beaker so that the surface of the water is above the surface of the lauric acid but below the opening of the test tube.

10. Place the beaker on the hot plate. After 20 seconds, measure the temperature of the lauric acid. Record this temperature next to the 0 minutes entry in your data table.

11. Repeat Steps 4 through 7 using the lauric acid instead of the ice. To keep the temperature the same throughout the water bath, use the glass stirring rod to stir the water after you take each temperature measurement.

Analyze and Conclude

1. **Using Graphs** Describe the shape of your graph for ice.

2. **Analyzing Data** What happened to the temperature of the ice-water mixture during the phase change?

3. **Drawing Conclusions** What happened to the energy that was transferred from the hot plate to the ice during the phase change?

4. **Comparing and Contrasting** Compare the shapes of the graphs for ice and for lauric acid. Compare the melting points of ice and lauric acid.

For: Data sharing
Visit: PHSchool.com
Web Code: ccd-1030

States of Matter **93**

Expected Outcome In Part A, if the readings are taken quickly enough, the first few temperature readings may be below 0°C. The temperature readings should remain at 0°C until all the ice has melted. The temperature should begin to rise once the ice has melted. Heating solid lauric acid raises its temperature to its melting point of 43.2°C. The temperature will begin to rise again after the lauric acid has melted.

Sample Data

Typical Melting Curves

Analyze and Conclude

1. The graph rises quickly to 0°C and remains horizontal at that temperature for a number of minutes. Then, it begins to rise again.

2. The temperature remained constant until the phase change was completed.

3. At first, the energy absorbed by the ice was used to overcome the forces of attraction holding water molecules in fixed positions. After all of the ice had melted, the energy absorbed increased the kinetic energy of the molecules in the liquid water.

4. The two graphs had similar shapes. However, ice melted at 0°C and lauric acid melted at about 43°C.

Logical

Have students pool and compare their data with students nationwide by visiting the Prentice Hall Web site at www.PHSchool.com.

Study Guide

Study Tip

Study With a Partner
On occasion, study with a friend. Quiz each other, compare notes from class lectures, go over homework answers, and discuss concepts that you need help with understanding.

Thinking Visually

a. and b. Condensation, freezing
c. Endothermic
d. Vaporization

Assessment

Interactive Textbook If your class subscribes to the Interactive Textbook, your students can go online to access an interactive version of the Student Edition and a self-test.

Reviewing Content

1. b   2. c   3. c
4. b   5. a   6. d
7. c   8. b   9. c
10. a

3.1 Solids, Liquids, and Gases

Key Concepts

- Materials can be classified as solids, liquids, or gases based on whether their shapes and volumes are definite or variable.
- The kinetic theory of matter states that all particles of matter are in constant motion.
- There are forces of attraction among the particles in all matter.
- The constant motion of particles in a gas allows a gas to fill a container of any shape or size.
- A liquid takes the shape of its container because particles in a liquid can flow to new locations. The volume of a liquid is constant because forces of attraction keep the particles close together.
- Solids have a definite volume and shape because particles in a solid vibrate around fixed locations.

Vocabulary

solid, *p. 69;* liquid, *p. 69;* gas, *p. 70;* kinetic energy, *p. 71*

3.2 The Gas Laws

Key Concepts

- Collisions between particles of a gas and the walls of the container cause the pressure in a closed container of gas.
- Factors that affect the pressure of an enclosed gas are its temperature, its volume, and the number of its particles.
- Raising the temperature of a gas will increase its pressure if the volume of the gas and the number of particles are constant.
- Reducing the volume of a gas increases its pressure if the temperature of the gas and the number of particles are constant.
- Increasing the number of particles will increase the pressure of a gas if the temperature and the volume are constant.
- The combined gas law can be expressed as

$$\frac{P_1 V_1}{T_1} = \frac{P_2 V_2}{T_2}$$

Vocabulary

pressure, *p. 75;* absolute zero, *p. 78;* Charles's law, *p. 78;* Boyle's law, *p. 79*

3.3 Phase Changes

Key Concepts

- Melting, freezing, vaporization, condensation, sublimation, and deposition are six common phase changes.
- The temperature of a substance does not change during a phase change.
- Energy is either absorbed or released during a phase change.
- The arrangement of molecules in water becomes less orderly as water melts, and more orderly as water freezes.
- Evaporation takes place at the surface of a liquid and occurs at temperatures below the boiling point.

Vocabulary

phase change, *p. 84;* endothermic, *p. 86;* heat of fusion, *p. 86;* exothermic, *p. 86;* vaporization, *p. 88;* heat of vaporization, *p. 88;* evaporation, *p. 89;* vapor pressure, *p. 89;* condensation, *p. 90;* sublimation, *p. 91;* deposition, *p. 91;*

Thinking Visually

Web Diagram Use information from the chapter to complete the web diagram on phase changes.

 Chapter Resources

Print
- *Chapter and Unit Tests,* Chapter 3 Test A and Test B
- *Test Prep Resources,* Chapter 3 *Transparencies,* Section 3.1

Technology
- *Computer Test Bank,* Chapter Test 3
- *Interactive Textbook,* Section 3.1
- *Go Online,* PHSchool.com, Chapter 3

Reviewing Content

Choose the letter that best answers the question or completes the statement.

1. Which state of matter has a definite volume but a variable shape?
 a. solid
 b. liquid
 c. gas
 d. vapor

2. In which state(s) of matter can materials take the shape of their containers?
 a. solid and liquid
 b. solid and gas
 c. liquid and gas
 d. liquid only

3. Which statement is true about the atoms in helium gas?
 a. They travel in circular paths.
 b. They have strong attractions to one another.
 c. They are not closely packed.
 d. They are arranged in an orderly pattern.

4. If the speed of an object increases, its kinetic energy
 a. decreases.
 b. increases.
 c. stays the same.
 d. is unpredictable.

5. The SI unit of pressure is the
 a. pascal.
 b. newton.
 c. square meter.
 d. psi.

6. Increasing which variable would decrease the pressure of a contained gas?
 a. temperature
 b. number of particles
 c. boiling point
 d. volume

7. Boyle's law relates pressure and
 a. temperature.
 b. number of particles.
 c. volume.
 d. mass.

8. Which of the following changes is exothermic?
 a. evaporation
 b. freezing
 c. boiling
 d. sublimation

9. The phase change that is the reverse of vaporization is
 a. freezing.
 b. melting.
 c. condensation.
 d. evaporation.

10. Which of these phase changes does NOT involve changing a liquid into a gas?
 a. sublimation
 b. vaporization
 c. evaporation
 d. boiling

Understanding Concepts

11. Provide an example of each of the three states of matter that exist at room temperature.

12. Compare and contrast liquid water and ice in terms of how definite their shapes and volumes are.

13. What three assumptions about particles in a gas are made by the kinetic theory?

14. Using the kinetic theory, explain why a liquid has a definite volume but a gas does not.

15. How do the way that atoms are arranged in liquid mercury and solid copper affect the movement of mercury and copper atoms?

16. Using the kinetic theory, explain what causes gas pressure.

17. What three factors affect the pressure of a gas in a closed container?

18. If a piston moves downward in a cylinder, what happens to the volume and pressure of the gas in the cylinder? The temperature remains constant.

19. What happens to the speed of the particles inside an air-filled balloon if the temperature of the balloon increases?

20. Using the kinetic theory, explain why the pressure of a gas increases when its temperature increases.

21. How are the pressure and volume of a gas related?

22. How does an endothermic phase change differ from an exothermic phase change?

23. Compare the vapor pressure of water at 10°C with its vapor pressure at 50°C.

24. Explain why water has a different boiling point at an elevation of 3000 meters than it does at sea level.

States of Matter **95**

Understanding Concepts

11. Examples might include solid copper, liquid water, and the helium inside a balloon as a gas.
12. Both liquid water and ice have a definite volume. Ice has a definite shape, but liquid water does not.
13. The particles are in constant, random motion. The motion of one particle is unaffected by the motion of other particles unless the particles collide. Under ordinary conditions, forces of attraction between particles can be ignored.
14. The attractions between the particles in a liquid are strong enough to keep the particles close together. Without any significant attractions between particles in a gas, the particles are free to expand into any volume that is available.
15. The atoms in copper vibrate around fixed positions. The atoms in mercury can flow past one another.
16. Gas pressure is caused by collisions of atoms with their containers.
17. Temperature, volume, and the number of particles
18. The volume decreases and the pressure increases.
19. The particles in the air move faster, on average, when the temperature increases because they have more kinetic energy.
20. When the temperature of a gas increases, the particles have greater kinetic energy, on average, and move faster. Thus, atoms hit the walls of the container more often and with greater force, causing the pressure to increase.
21. The volume of a gas is inversely proportional to its pressure.
22. During an endothermic phase change, energy is absorbed by the system. During an exothermic phase change, energy is released by the system.
23. The vapor pressure of water is greater at 50°C than it is at 10°C.
24. Water boils when its vapor pressure becomes equal to atmospheric pressure. At 3000 m, the atmospheric pressure is lower than it is at sea level. Thus, vapor pressure equals atmospheric pressure at a lower temperature, and water boils at a lower temperature.

 Homework Guide

Section	Questions
3.1	1–4, 11–16, 33
3.2	5–7, 17–21, 27–28, 30–32, 35–36
3.2	8–10, 22–26, 29, 34, 37

Critical Thinking

25. A balloon that is flexible will shrink. This observed change is not a phase change because helium is a gas before and after the change.

26. (a) Water melts and freezes at the same temperature. (b) Melting is an endothermic process. Freezing is an exothermic process.

27. Graph A

28. Graph A

29. Graph C

Math Skills

30. $P_1/P_2 = T_1/T_2$ or $P_1/T_1 = P_2/T_2$

31. 371 kPa

32. 1.8 L

Concepts in Action

33. There is almost no attraction between particles in a gas. They will quickly spread throughout the building. Because particles in a liquid strongly attract one another, they remain close together and don't spread throughout the building (unless the water quantity is large and there is no drain).

34. Because energy is being added but no increase in temperature occurs, a phase change is occurring in the can.

35. A decrease in pressure causes an increase in volume. A decrease in temperature causes a decrease in volume. Because the volume of the balloon increases, the decrease in pressure must affect the balloon more than the decrease in temperature.

36. The pressure increases.

37. Heating causes the water to vaporize. With continued heating, the pressure of the vapor increases because the volume of the confined vapor is constant. Eventually, the increased pressure causes the kernel to burst open.

Your students can independently test their knowledge of the chapter and print out their test results for your files.

Critical Thinking

25. Classifying If you take a helium balloon from inside a warm house to outside on a snowy day, what will happen to the balloon? Could you classify this change as a phase change? Explain your answer.

26. Comparing and Contrasting Compare the melting and freezing of water in terms of (a) the temperature at which these processes take place and (b) how energy is involved in these processes.

Use the graphs to answer Questions 27–29.

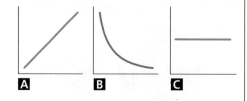

27. Using Graphs Which graph represents what happens to the pressure in a tire as air is added to the tire? Assume the temperature of the gas is constant.

28. Using Graphs Which graph represents what happens to the pressure in an aerosol can if the can is heated?

29. Applying Concepts Which graph represents temperature versus time during a phase change?

Math Skills

30. Making Generalizations The pressure of a gas is directly proportional to its temperature in kelvins. Using P_1, P_2, T_1, and T_2, write a mathematical equation that expresses this relationship.

31. Calculating An automobile tire has a pressure of 325 kPa when the temperature is 10°C. If the temperature of the tire rises to 50°C and its volume is constant, what is the new pressure?

32. Calculating A gas sample occupies 4.2 L at a pressure of 101 kPa. What volume will it occupy if the pressure is increased to 235 kPa?

Concepts in Action

33. Using Models If there is a gas leak in the basement of a building, you will soon notice an odor throughout the house. However, if there is a water leak in the basement, you will need to go to the basement to detect the leak. Use the kinetic theory to explain the differences.

34. Inferring A student examines a thermometer placed in a can containing a substance that is being heated. The temperature remains the same for several minutes, and then it starts to rise. Without looking in the can, how does the student know what is occurring in the can?

35. Relating Cause and Effect In Earth's atmosphere, pressure and temperature both decrease as altitude increases. Weather balloons expand as they rise. Which has more effect on the weather balloon, the decrease in pressure or the decrease in temperature? Explain your answer.

36. Drawing Conclusions In a car engine, air and gasoline vapors are mixed in a cylinder. A piston is pushed into the cylinder before a spark ignites the mixture of gases. When the piston is pushed into the cylinder, what happens to the pressure of the gases in the cylinder?

37. Writing in Science Unpopped popcorn kernels contain a small amount of water. Use what you know about vaporization and how gases behave to explain why popcorn pops when it is heated.

Performance-Based Assessment

Making a Poster The gas laws have many practical applications in cooking. Make a poster, including diagrams, that shows how two factors that affect gases affect cooking. Examples might include explaining why cakes rise while baking or why some recipes specify high-altitude temperatures and cooking times.

For: Self-grading assessment
Visit: PHSchool.com
Web Code: cca-1030

Performance-Based Assessment

Possible poster topics: Gas bubbles formed in cake batter increase in volume when the batter is heated, causing the cake to rise. Cake mixes often have instructions for baking at higher altitudes because the boiling point of water decreases at higher elevations. In a pressure cooker, the volume of air is constant. Heating the air increases both its temperature and pressure, and the food cooks in a shorter amount of time.

Standardized Test Prep for Indiana

Test-Taking Tip

Watch For Qualifiers
The words *best* and *least* are examples of qualifiers. If a question contains a qualifier, more than one answer will contain correct information. However, only one answer will be complete and correct for the question asked. Look at the question below. Eliminate any answers that are clearly incorrect. Then choose the remaining answer that offers the best explanation for the question asked.

Choose the *best* explanation for why one particle in a gas does not affect other particles in a gas unless the particles collide.
(A) Particles in a gas are constantly moving.
(B) All the particles in a gas have the same kinetic energy.
(C) There are no forces of attraction among particles in a gas.
(D) There are billions of particles in a small sample of a gas.
(E) Particles in a gas are relatively far apart.

(Answer: E)

Choose the letter that best answers the question or completes the statement.

1. A material can be classified as a liquid if
   (A) it has a definite shape and a definite volume.
   (B) it has a definite shape and a variable volume.
   (C) it has a variable shape and a definite volume.
   (D) it has a variable shape and a variable volume.
   (E) its particles vibrate around fixed locations.

2. Which statement *best* explains what must take place for water to boil?
   (A) The water releases energy to its surroundings.
   (B) Bubbles rise to the surface of the water.
   (C) The vapor pressure of the water becomes equal to atmospheric pressure.
   (D) Molecules at the surface of the water overcome the attractions of neighboring molecules.
   (E) The temperature of the water increases.

3. Condensation is the phase change in which a substance changes from
   (A) a solid to a gas.
   (B) a solid to a liquid.
   (C) a liquid to a solid.
   (D) a liquid to a gas.
   (E) a gas to a liquid.

4. Which of these statements about an enclosed gas is true? (Assume all quantities are constant except the two variables described in each statement.)
   (A) Raising the temperature of a gas will increase its pressure.
   (B) Increasing the volume of a gas will increase its pressure.
   (C) Reducing the number of particles of a gas will increase its pressure.
   (D) The volume of a gas is inversely proportional to its temperature in kelvins.
   (E) The volume of a gas is directly proportional to its pressure.

Use the illustration to answer Question 5. Assume that the number of particles of gas in container A equals the number of particles of gas in container B.

1.0 L   0.5 L
A   B

5. If the temperature is constant, the pressure in container B is
   (A) one half the pressure in container A.
   (B) twice the pressure in container A.
   (C) equal to the pressure in container A.
   (D) five times the pressure in container A.
   (E) one fifth the pressure in container A.

6. During an endothermic phase change,
   (A) the temperature of a substance rises.
   (B) the temperature of a substance decreases.
   (C) energy is transferred from a substance to its surroundings.
   (D) a substance absorbs energy from its surroundings.
   (E) there is no transfer of energy.

States of Matter **97**

 ### Standards Guide

Question	Standards
1	ICP.3.2
2	ICP.3.3
3	ICP.3.2
4	ICP.3.4
5	ICP.3.4
6	ICP.4.1

Planning Guide

SECTION OBJECTIVES	STANDARDS		ACTIVITIES and LABS
	NATIONAL	STATE	
4.1 Studying Atoms, pp. 100–105 ⏱ 1 block or 2 periods **4.1.1 Describe** ancient Greek models of matter. **4.1.2 List** the main points of Dalton's atomic theory and **describe** his evidence for the existence of atoms. **4.1.3 Explain** how Thomson and Rutherford used data from experiments to produce their atomic models.	A-1, A-2, B-1, B-2, B-6, E-2, G-1, G-2, G-3	ICP.3.1, ICP.6.1, ICP.7.1	**SE** Inquiry Activity: How Can You Study Objects That Are Not Visible? p. 99 **L2** **SE** Quick Lab: Investigating Charged Objects, p. 102 **L2** **TE** Teacher Demo: Comparing Atomic Models, p. 104 **L2**
4.2 The Structure of an Atom, pp. 108–112 ⏱ 1 block or 2 periods **4.2.1 Identify** three subatomic particles and **compare** their properties. **4.2.2 Distinguish** the atomic number of an element from the mass number of an isotope, and use these numbers to **describe** the structure of atoms.	A-1, B-1, B-2, E-1, G-1, G-2, G-3	ICP.3.1, ICP.5.3, ICP.7.2	**TE** Teacher Demo: Particles and Numbers, p. 110 **L2**
4.3 Modern Atomic Theory, pp. 113–118 ⏱ 1 block or 2 periods **4.3.1 Describe** Bohr's model of the atom and the evidence for energy levels. **4.3.2 Explain** how the electron cloud model represents the behavior and locations of electrons in atoms. **4.3.3 Distinguish** the ground state from excited states of an atom based on electron configurations.	A-1, A-2, B-1, B-2, G-1, G-2, G-3	ICP.3.1, ICP.3.2, ICP.4.3, ICP.7.1	**SE** Quick Lab: Comparing Excited States, p. 117 **L2** **SE** Forensics Lab: Using Flame Tests, p. 119 **L2** **TE** Teacher Demo: Electron Cloud Model, p. 116 **L2** **LM** Investigation 4A: Constructing a Model of an Atom **L2** **LM** Investigation 4B: Modeling an Electron Cloud **L1**

RESOURCES
PRINT and TECHNOLOGY

RSW	Section 4.1	**L1**
DC	Go For Gold	**L2**
T	Chapter 4 Pretest	**L2**
	Section 4.1	**L2**
P	Chapter 4 Pretest	**L2**
	Section 4.1	**L2**
GO	Atomic theory	**L2**

RSW	Section 4.2	**L1**
RSW Math Skill		**L2**
T	Section 4.2	**L2**
P	Section 4.2	**L2**
GO	Atomic chemistry	**L2**

RSW	Section 4.3	**L1**
T	Section 4.3	**L2**
P	Section 4.3	**L2**
GO	Energy levels	**L2**

SECTION ASSESSMENT

SE Section 4.1 Assessment, p. 105

iT Section 4.1

SE Section 4.2 Assessment, p. 112

iT Section 4.2

SE Section 4.3 Assessment, p. 118

iT Section 4.3

Go Online

Go online for these Internet resources.

PHSchool.com
Web Code: cca-1040

NSTA SCiLINKS
Web Code: ccn-1041
Web Code: ccn-1043

SCIENCE NEWS®
Web Code: cce-1042

Materials for Activities and Labs

Quantities for each group

STUDENT EDITION

Inquiry Activity, p. 99
2 sealed, brown paper bags

Quick Lab, p. 102
transparent tape, metric ruler, scissors

Quick Lab, p. 117
fluorescent ("neon") markers, glow-in-the-dark toy, ultraviolet (UV) lamp

Forensics Lab, p. 119
solutions of calcium chloride, boric acid, potassium chloride, copper(II) sulfate, sodium chloride, and an unknown; Bunsen burner; nichrome wire loop; dilute solution of hydrochloric acid; wash bottle with distilled water

TEACHER'S EDITION

Teacher Demo, p. 104
3 clear, round bowls; flavored gelatin mix; canned blueberries; maraschino cherries

Build Science Skills, p. 106
modeling clay, plastic knives

Teacher Demo, p. 110
overhead projector, red and green gummy candies

Teacher Demo, p. 116
small, round balloon; large, round balloon; 10 beads with 4-mm diameter; 5 beads with 2-mm diameter

Chapter Assessment

CHAPTER ASSESSMENT

SE Chapter Assessment, pp. 121–122
CUT Chapter 4 Test A, B
CTB Chapter 4
iT Chapter 4
PHSchool.com GO
Web Code: cca-1040

STANDARDIZED TEST PREP

SE Chapter 4, p. 123
TP Diagnose and Prescribe

Interactive Textbook with assessment at PHSchool.com

Before you teach

From the Author

David Frank
Ferris State University

Big Ideas

Once students have some understanding of the properties that are used to describe and classify matter, they need theories to explain why matter behaves in predictable ways. In Chapter 3, students used kinetic theory to explain the behavior of solids, liquids, and gases. The atomic theory presented in Chapter 4 will be used in Chapters 6 and 7 to explain bonding and chemical reactions.

Matter and Change In the nineteenth and early twentieth centuries, scientists refined models of the atom based on strong indirect evidence. Section 4.1 describes some of the methods scientists used to gather evidence about atomic structure. You can use Section 4.1 to help students understand the relationship between scientific laws (which summarize observed patterns in nature) and theories (which explain these observed patterns). Dalton's atomic theory is a case in point. In his theory, Dalton described properties of atoms that could explain the law of conservation of mass and the law of definite proportions.

Some people think that a theory must be discarded if evidence is discovered that contradicts the theory. More often, a theory is revised to account for new evidence. For example, the discovery of isotopes disproved Dalton's assumption that every atom of an element had the same mass. Subsequently, the atomic theory was revised to state that every atom of an element has the same number of protons, but not necessarily the same number of neutrons.

Forces and Motion The idea that oppositely charged particles attract and that similarly charged particles repel is a fundamental concept in science. The attraction of particles to a positive plate in Thomson's experiment demonstrated the negative charge of these particles (electrons). The repulsion of positively charged alpha particles in the gold foil experiment demonstrated that the nucleus of an atom has a positive charge.

Chemistry Refresher

Ancient Models of Atoms 4.1

Democritus of Abdera thought that the shapes and sizes of the atoms in a material determined the properties of the material. Atoms were seen as constantly moving in space, sometimes colliding and forming groups. Later, Aristotle gained authority for his idea that all substances were built up from only four elements because his proposals fit with the existing worldview throughout the Middle Ages. Much of alchemy was based on the theory that elements could be transformed into other elements through the qualities they possessed in common.

Evidence for Dalton's Theory 4.1

In 1802, John Dalton proposed the law of partial pressures of gases: A gas in a mixture of gases contributes the same pressure it would produce if it were the only gas in a container. In 1803, Dalton proposed the law of definite proportions, which states that elements form compounds in certain fixed ratios. Dalton's work with gas pressure and with the composition of compounds led him to consider the fundamental nature of matter. He presented his atomic theory in a series of lectures in 1807.

Dalton's Symbols for Some Elements

Symbol	Chemical Name	Symbol	Chemical Name
⊙	Hydrogen	●	Carbon
⊕	Azote (Nitrogen)	○	Oxygen

Subatomic Particles 4.1 and 4.2

J.J. Thomson studied the flow of current through gases in a sealed tube. He used a magnet to deflect the cathode rays. He could not use an electric field because the passage of the rays through the tube caused the gas to become a conductor. The conducting gas screened the particles in the rays from the effect of the external electric field. When Thomson removed almost all the gas from the tube, the effect of the field could be seen.

Address Misconceptions

Many students think that isotopes are different from "ordinary" or "regular" atoms. However, isotopes are atoms of an element that have differing nuclear compositions. For a strategy to overcome this misconception, see **Address Misconceptions** on **page 112.**

In 1909, Ernest Rutherford (who had worked with Thomson) asked Ernest Marsden (an undergraduate student from New Zealand) to find out whether any alpha particles were scattered by more than a few degrees as they passed through foil. Marsden used a sheet of gold foil that was only 0.00004 (4×10^{-5}) cm thick. After World War I, Rutherford experimented with bombarding nitrogen atoms with alpha particles. Some of the nitrogen atoms released hydrogen nuclei and transmuted into oxygen atoms. He concluded that these nuclei were released from the nitrogen nuclei and that they were fundamental particles. He is usually credited with naming these particles protons, after the Greek word *protos*, meaning "first." Although Rutherford predicted the existence of neutrons in 1920, it was his research assistant, James Chadwick, who provided the supporting evidence.

Electrons and Energy Levels 4.3

🚩 Address Misconceptions

Students may think that electrons travel around the nucleus in fixed orbits, like planets orbiting the sun. However, the exact path or location of an electron cannot be determined. For a strategy to overcome this misconception, see **Address Misconceptions** on **page 114.**

In a staircase, the distance between steps is (ideally) constant from step to step. In an atom, the difference in energy between energy levels is not constant. It decreases as the quantum number of the energy level (*n*) increases. The specific amount of energy that is absorbed or released when an electron moves between energy levels is called a *quantum* of energy. When the energy absorbed or released by an atom is light energy, the quanta are called *photons*.

Go Online PD LINKS
NSTA

For: Teaching methods for atomic structure
Visit: www.SciLinks.org/PDLinks
Web Code: ccn-0499

Build Reading Literacy

Identify Main Idea/Details

Locating Topic Sentences in Paragraphs

Strategy Help students understand and remember the most important information about a topic. This strategy can be applied to short segments of text, such as a single paragraph or a subsection, to find the main idea and details that support the topic. Assign students a short passage to read, such as The Gold Foil Experiment on p. 104.

Example

1. Tell students that many paragraphs have a topic sentence that expresses the paragraph's main idea. Topic sentences are often the first or second sentence in the paragraph. Sometimes, however, they are the last sentence, or even a sentence in the middle of the paragraph.
2. Then, explain that the rest of the paragraph contains details, or additional facts and examples about the main idea.
3. Direct students' attention to a paragraph with a clearly stated topic sentence, and ask students which sentence best states the main idea of the paragraph.
4. Next, help students find sentences with details that explain more about the main idea.
5. Have students organize the main idea and details visually in a web format.
6. Have students work in pairs to identify the main idea and details in another passage and organize them in a web.

See p. 110 for a script on how to use the identify main ideas/details strategy with students. For additional Build Reading Literacy strategies, see pp. 103 and 113.

Photon Emission as a Result of Energy Level Transitions

ASSESS PRIOR KNOWLEDGE

Use the Chapter Pretest below to assess students' prior knowledge. As needed, review these Science Concepts and Math Skills with students.

Review Science Concepts

Section 4.1 Encourage students to recall that compounds have fixed compositions. Remind students that an atom is the smallest particle of an element.

Section 4.2 Have students review the terms *mass, volume,* and *density* and the units used for each.

Section 4.3 Review two things that can happen when matter absorbs energy.

Review Math Skills

Scientific Notation Students will need to know how to use scientific notation to understand values for certain properties of subatomic particles.

Direct students to the **Math Skills** in the **Skills and Reference Handbook** at the end of the student text.

21st Century Learning

Problem Identification, Formulation, and Solution

What are subatomic particles?

Atoms are too small to be seen, but scientists have learned much about their structure. Atoms are made of even smaller particles called subatomic particles. Make a slide-show presentation that describes the structure of an atom. Your presentation should include information about the size, mass, charge, and location of each type of subatomic particle. Show your presentation in class or post it to your class blog.

 Indiana's Academic Standards for Science

ENERGY TRANSPORT
ICP.4.3: Explain that electrons can absorb energy and can release energy, and that electrons in atoms do this at specific energies.

CHEMICAL ENERGY, REACTIONS, AND BONDING
ICP.5.3: Understand that the atomic number is unique to each element and is the number of protons in the nucleus of the element.

ELECTRICAL ENERGY PROPAGATION AND MAGNETISM
ICP.6.1: Explain that objects that carry a net charge will exert an electric force on other objects that may be attractive or repulsive.

NUCLEAR ENERGY (FISSION/FUSION)
ICP.7.1: Demonstrate how historical models and experiments supported the development of our current understanding of the atom and its nucleus;
ICP.7.2: Differentiate between protons, neutrons, and electrons and determine the number of these subatomic particles in each atom.

Also covered: ICP.3.1, ICP.3.2

These images of carbon were magnified as much as 20 million times. Color was added to the images to highlight features.

Chapter Pretest

1. True or False: Compounds have fixed compositions. *(True)*

2. What is an atom? *(An atom is the smallest particle of an element.)*

3. Which of the following units is a unit of mass? *(c)*
  a. mL   **b.** °C
  c. g   **d.** cm

4. Volume is *(c)*
  a. the straight-line distance between two points.
  b. the quantity of matter in an object.
  c. the amount of space taken up by an object.
  d. a representation of an object or event.

5. What is density? *(Density is the ratio of the mass of a substance to its volume.)*

6. Which two of the following events can take place when a liquid absorbs energy? *(a and d)*
  a. The average kinetic energy of the particles in the liquid increases.
  b. The temperature decreases.
  c. The liquid freezes.
  d. The liquid changes to a gas.

Chapter Preview

DISCOVERY
SCHOOL

Video Field Trip

Go For Gold

Inquiry Activity

How Can You Study Objects That Are Not Visible?

Procedure

1. Make and record observations about the contents of two sealed bags. Use your senses of touch, smell, and hearing to help you make your observations.

2. **Predicting** Based on your observations, make a prediction about what objects could be in each bag. Decide whether there is a single object or more than one object in each bag.

3. Your teacher will list on the chalkboard all of the predictions from the class.

Think About It

1. **Inferring** What evidence did you use to predict what objects were in the bags and how many objects were in the bags?

2. **Evaluating and Revising** Record one of the predictions listed that fits your observations as well as or better than your own prediction.

3. **Designing Experiments** Propose an experiment that would test the prediction.

Atomic Structure **99**

DISCOVERY
SCHOOL

Video Field Trip

Go For Gold

Encourage students to view the Video Field Trip "Go For Gold."

ENGAGE/EXPLORE

Inquiry Activity

How Can You Study Objects That Are Not Visible?

Purpose In this activity, students make inferences based on their observations and conclude that indirect evidence must be used to study the structure of objects that are too small to see.

Skills Focus Observing, Inferring

 Prep Time 5 minutes

Materials 2 sealed, brown paper bags

Advance Prep Place a single type of small object in each bag. Possible objects that can be identified by properties other than sight are lemon slices (odor), pennies (shape), rubber bands (elasticity), sandpaper squares (texture), and bells (sound). Use a letter code to identify the object in each bag. Seal the bags before distributing them to students.

Class Time 10 minutes

Teaching Tips

• Use more than two types of objects so each group of students does not have an identical set.

• To model the study of atoms, ask students not to open the bags at the end of the activity.

• Ask students how they could apply what they have learned in this activity to the study of atoms, which are too small to see.

Expected Outcome Students should recognize that detailed observations can reveal information about objects and events that cannot be observed directly.

Think About It

1. Acceptable student answers may include sound, texture, hardness, smell, and how objects move inside the bags.

2. Students may choose a prediction that they did not record in Step 2 if this prediction is a better fit for the evidence they list for Question 1.

3. Answers should include a practical test that would clearly support or contradict the prediction chosen in Question 2.

Logical

1 FOCUS

Objectives

4.1.1 **Describe** ancient Greek models of matter.

4.1.2 **List** the main points of Dalton's atomic theory and **describe** his evidence for the existence of atoms.

4.1.3 **Explain** how Thomson and Rutherford used data from experiments to produce their atomic models.

Reading Focus

Build Vocabulary   `L2`

Latin Plural Forms Explain that the word *nucleus* comes from a Latin word meaning "kernel." Explain that a kernel is a grain or seed. Ask students to discuss how the definition of the term *nucleus* relates to its Latin origin. (*Like the kernel of a nut, the nucleus is a small, massive center of the atom.*) Remind students that the plural of the word *nucleus* is *nuclei*.

Reading Strategy   `L2`

a. Dalton **b.** Indivisible, solid spheres
c. Thomson **d.** Negative charges evenly scattered through a positively charged mass of matter (plum pudding model)
e. Deflection of alpha particles passing through gold foil

2 INSTRUCT

Ancient Greek Models of Atoms

Use Visuals   `L1`

Figure 1 Have students examine the diagram in Figure 1 that lists the qualities of each of Aristotle's four elements. Ask, **What qualities did Aristotle use to describe air?** (*Air is a combination of hot and wet.*) **What element was a combination of dry and cold?** (*Earth*) **Is "wet and cold" an accurate description of water?** (*Wet describes water, but water isn't always cold.*)
Visual

4.1 Studying Atoms

Reading Focus

Key Concepts

- What was Dalton's theory of the structure of matter?
- What contributions did Thomson and Rutherford make to the development of atomic theory?

Vocabulary

- nucleus

Reading Strategy

Summarizing Copy the table. As you read, complete the table about atomic models.

Scientist	Evidence	Model
a. ___?___	Ratio of masses in compounds	b. ___?___
c. ___?___	Deflected beam	d. ___?___
Rutherford	e. ___?___	Positive, dense nucleus

Studying the structure of atoms is a little like studying wind. Because you cannot see air, you must use indirect evidence to tell the direction of the wind. You might notice which way fallen leaves move as they are pushed by the wind, and infer that the leaves and wind are moving in the same direction.

Atoms pose a similar problem because they are extremely small. Even with a microscope, scientists cannot see the structure of an atom. In this chapter, you will find out how John Dalton, J. J. Thomson, Ernest Rutherford, Niels Bohr, and other scientists used evidence from experiments to develop models of atoms.

Ancient Greek Models of Atoms

If you cut a piece of aluminum foil in half, you have two smaller pieces of the same shiny, flexible substance. You could cut the pieces again and again. Can you keep dividing the aluminum into smaller pieces? Greek philosophers debated a similar question about 2500 years ago.

The philosopher Democritus believed that all matter consisted of extremely small particles that could not be divided. He called these particles *atoms* from the Greek word *atomos*, which means "uncut" or "indivisible." He thought there were different types of atoms with specific sets of properties. The atoms in liquids, for example, were round and smooth, but the atoms in solids were rough and prickly.

Aristotle did not think there was a limit to the number of times matter could be divided. Figure 1 shows the model Aristotle used to describe matter. For many centuries, most people accepted Aristotle's views on the structure of matter. But by the 1800s, scientists had enough data from experiments to support an atomic model of matter.

Figure 1 Aristotle thought that all substances were built up from only four elements—earth, air, fire, and water. These elements were a combination of four qualities—hot, cold, dry, and wet. Fire was a combination of hot and dry. Water was a combination of cold and wet.

Section Resources

Print
- ***Reading and Study Workbook With Math Support,*** Section 4.1
- ***Transparencies,*** Chapter Pretest and Section 4.1

Technology
- ***Interactive Textbook,*** Section 4.1
- ***Presentation Pro CD-ROM,*** Chapter Pretest and Section 4.1
- ***Go Online,*** NSTA SciLinks, Atomic theory

Dalton's Atomic Theory

John Dalton was born in England in 1766. He was a teacher who spent his spare time doing scientific experiments. Because of his interest in predicting the weather, Dalton studied the behavior of gases in air. Based on the way gases exert pressure, Dalton correctly concluded that a gas consists of individual particles.

Evidence for Atoms Dalton gathered evidence for the existence of atoms by measuring the masses of elements that combine when compounds form. He noticed that all compounds have something in common. No matter how large or small the sample, the ratio of the masses of the elements in the compound is always the same. In other words, compounds have a fixed composition.

For example, when magnesium burns, as shown in Figure 2, it combines with oxygen. The product of this change is a white solid called magnesium oxide. A 100-gram sample of magnesium combines with 65.8 grams of oxygen. A 10-gram sample of magnesium combines with 6.58 grams of oxygen. The ratio of the mass of magnesium to the mass of oxygen is constant in magnesium oxide.

Dalton's Theory Dalton developed a theory to explain why the elements in a compound always join in the same way. **Dalton proposed the theory that all matter is made up of individual particles called atoms, which cannot be divided.** The main points of Dalton's theory are as follows.

- All elements are composed of atoms.
- All atoms of the same element have the same mass, and atoms of different elements have different masses.
- Compounds contain atoms of more than one element.
- In a particular compound, atoms of different elements always combine in the same way.

In the model of atoms based on Dalton's theory, the elements are pictured as solid spheres like those in Figure 3. Each type of atom is represented by a tiny, solid sphere with a different mass.

Recall that a theory must explain the data from many experiments. Because Dalton's atomic theory met that goal, the theory became widely accepted. Over time, scientists found that not all of Dalton's ideas about atoms were completely correct. But this did not cause later scientists to discard the atomic theory. Instead, they revised the theory to take into account new discoveries.

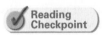 **Reading Checkpoint** *What did Dalton notice that all compounds have in common?*

Figure 2 Magnesium reacts with oxygen to form the compound magnesium oxide. The ratio of magnesium to oxygen, by mass, in magnesium oxide is always about 3 : 2. **Observing** *What color is magnesium oxide?*

Figure 3 Dalton made these wooden spheres to represent the atoms of different elements.

Build Science Skills L2

Evaluating As students read Chapter 4, have them evaluate what portions of Dalton's model were accurate and what portions needed to be revised. *(Dalton did not discuss subatomic particles, which are smaller components of atoms. Atoms of the same element can have different masses.)*
Logical

 Address Misconceptions L2

Many students have trouble differentiating compounds from mixtures. Remind students that Dalton noticed that the ratio of masses of elements in a compound is always the same. Compounds are distinguished from mixtures and solutions by their fixed compositions. Have students recall examples of mixtures and describe how their compositions can vary.
Verbal

Use Visuals L1

Figure 3 Have students examine the wooden spheres shown in Figure 3. Ask, **Why do you think there are holes in Dalton's wooden spheres?** *(One acceptable answer is that Dalton used the holes in the spheres to connect spheres together to construct models of compounds.)*
Visual, Logical

FYI

Not every scientist was convinced that Dalton had the physical evidence to support the assumption that elements are composed of indivisible particles called atoms. William Whewell (1784–1868) argued that particles could combine in fixed proportions in compounds, but still not be indivisible.

Customize for English Language Learners

Using Visual Aids
Have students draw simple illustrations for the models of atoms according to Dalton, Thompson, and Rutherford. Have them describe each model to a partner using the illustrations as a visual aid. Then, have each pair of students discuss the similarities and differences among the three models.

Answer to . . .

Figure 2 *White*

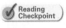 **Reading Checkpoint** *Dalton noticed that the ratio of masses of elements in a compound is always the same.*

Thomson's Model of the Atom

Investigating Charged Objects   L2

Objective
After completing this activity, students will be able to
• explain that like charges repel and unlike charges attract.

Skills Focus Observing, Drawing Conclusions, Formulating Hypotheses

Prep Time 5 minutes

Class Time 10 minutes

Expected Outcome Students will discover that the two pieces of tape are attracted to one another after they are pulled apart and then brought near one another.

Analyze and Conclude
1. The two pieces of tape have opposite charges because they attract when brought close together.
2. Possible answers include clothes that cling together when removed from a dryer, and the charge that builds up when a person walks across a carpet (which is demonstrated by the spark that occurs when the person touches a doorknob).
Kinesthetic, Logical

FYI

If you do not want to present all the experimental evidence for the atomic theory, be sure students understand attraction and repulsion of charged particles and Rutherford's nucleus model of the atom.

�Quick⟩Lab

Investigating Charged Objects

Materials
transparent tape, metric ruler, scissors

Procedure ✂

1. Cut two 10-cm pieces of tape. Fold over 1 cm of tape at one end of each piece of tape to form a "handle."

2. Hold the pieces of tape by their folded ends so that they are hanging straight down. Then, without letting the pieces of tape touch, slowly bring their sticky sides close together. Record your observations.

3. Place one piece of tape on a clean surface with the sticky side facing down.

Sticky sides down

4. Place the second piece, sticky side down, directly over the first piece, as shown. Press down firmly so the pieces stick together.

5. Remove the joined strips from the table. Slowly peel the strips apart.

6. Bring the separated strips close together without touching. Record your observations.

Analyze and Conclude

1. **Drawing Conclusions** What can you conclude about the charges on the two pieces of tape after they are separated?

2. **Inferring** What other objects have you observed that became charged?

Figure 4 Amber is the hardened form of a sticky, viscous liquid that protects trees from insects and disease. If amber is rubbed with wool, it becomes charged and can attract a feather. **Predicting** *What will happen to the feather if the amber loses its charge?*

Thomson's Model of the Atom

When some materials are rubbed, they gain the ability to attract or repel other materials. Glass and the amber in Figure 4 have this property. Based on their behavior, such materials are said to have either a positive or a negative electric charge. Objects with like charges repel, or push apart. Objects with opposite charges attract, or pull together.

Some charged particles can flow from one location to another. A flow of charged particles is called an electric current. When you turn on an appliance such as a hair dryer, a current flows from the wall socket through the appliance. Joseph John Thomson (1856–1940), better known as J. J. Thomson, used an electric current to learn more about atoms.

Thomson's Experiments Thomson used a device like the one shown in Figure 5A. At the center of the device is a sealed glass tube from which most of the air has been removed. There is a metal disk at each end of the tube. Wires connect the metal disks to a source of electric current. When the current is turned on, one disk becomes negatively charged and the other disk becomes positively charged. A glowing beam appears in the space between the disks.

Thomson hypothesized that the beam was a stream of charged particles that interacted with the air in the tube and caused the air to glow. In one experiment Thomson did to test his hypothesis, he placed a pair of charged metal plates on either side of the glass tube, as shown in Figure 5B. The plates caused the beam to deflect, or bend, from its straight path. Thomson observed that the beam was repelled by the negatively charged plate and attracted by the positively charged plate.

102 *Chapter 4*

⌐ Facts and Figures

Charge People have known for thousands of years that amber can attract other materials after it has been rubbed with fur. Plato even refers to these attractive powers of amber in one of his dialogues.

The labels *positive* and *negative* were arbitrarily assigned by Benjamin Franklin during his studies of electric charge and electric current. (He also was the first to use the terms *battery* and *conductor*.)

A

Sealed tube filled with gas at low pressure

Glowing beam

Metal disk

–

+

Metal disk

Source of electric current

B

Positive plate

–

+

Negative plate

Metal disk

Source of electric current

Figure 5 Thomson used a sealed tube of gas in his experiments. **A** When the current was on, the disks became charged and a glowing beam appeared in the tube. **B** The beam bent toward a positively charged plate placed outside the tube.
Inferring **What was the charge on the particles in the beam?**

Evidence for Subatomic Particles Thomson concluded that the particles in the beam had a negative charge because they were attracted to the positive plate. He hypothesized that the particles came from inside atoms. He had two pieces of evidence to support his hypothesis. No matter what metal Thomson used for the disk, the particles produced were identical. The particles had about $\frac{1}{2000}$ the mass of a hydrogen atom, the lightest atom.

Thomson's discovery changed how scientists thought about atoms. Before his experiments, the accepted model of the atom was a solid ball of matter that could not be divided into smaller parts. ⬥ **Thomson's experiments provided the first evidence that atoms are made of even smaller particles.** Thomson revised Dalton's model to account for these subatomic particles.

Thomson's Model An atom is neutral, meaning it has neither a negative nor a positive charge. How can an atom contain negative particles and still be neutral? There must be some positive charge in the atom. In Thomson's model of the atom, the negative charges were evenly scattered throughout an atom filled with a positively charged mass of matter. The model is called the "plum pudding" model, after a traditional English dessert.

You might prefer to think of Thomson's model as the "chocolate chip ice cream" model. Think of the chocolate chips in Figure 6 as the negative particles and the vanilla ice cream as the positively charged mass of matter. When the chocolate chips are spread evenly throughout the ice cream, their "negative charges" balance out the "positive charge" of the vanilla ice cream.

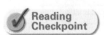 **Reading Checkpoint** *How do objects with the same charge behave when they come close to one another?*

Figure 6 A scoop of chocolate chip ice cream can represent Thomson's model of the atom. The chips represent negatively charged particles, which are spread evenly through a mass of positively charged matter—the vanilla ice cream.

Atomic Structure **103**

FYI

Thomson used the speed of an electron, its angle of deflection, and the strength of the current to determine the charge-to-mass ratio of an electron. Robert Milliken determined the actual mass of an electron through his oil-drop experiment.

The current that flows through an appliance is an alternating current. The current Thomson used in his experiment was a direct current. Not all movement of charge is a current. Charge can flow to or from a balloon (or between a hand and a doorknob). With a current, charge must flow continuously (at least until the circuit is interrupted). The concepts of electric charge and current are addressed in depth in Chapter 20.

Use Community Resources `L2`

Have a physics or chemistry professor visit the class and demonstrate Thomson's experiment using a cathode ray tube. Encourage students to think of questions to ask about how the experiment demonstrates the properties of electrons.
Interpersonal, Visual

Build Reading Literacy `L1`

Compare and Contrast Refer to page **226D** in **Chapter 8**, which provides the guidelines for comparing and contrasting.

Have students read about the different atomic models described in Section 4.1. Then, have students create a chart that compares and contrasts each model.
Logical

Answer to . . .

Figure 4 *The feather will no longer be attracted to the amber and will drop to the ground.*

Figure 5 *Negative*

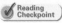 **Reading Checkpoint** *Objects with the same charge repel.*

Rutherford's Atomic Theory

FYI

Based on Figure 7, students might conclude that Marsden used a circular screen. The screen in the diagram represents multiple positions of a smaller screen that was moved from one position to another while data was collected. Alpha particles will be identified as helium nuclei in Chapter 10.

Comparing Atomic Models **L2**

Purpose Students will compare different atomic models.

Materials 3 clear, round bowls; flavored gelatin mix; canned blueberries; maraschino cherries

Procedure The day before, prepare the flavored gelatin mix. Divide the liquid gelatin evenly into the three bowls. Chill slightly. Drain the blueberries and add them to one of the bowls so that they are distributed as evenly as possible in the nearly gelled mix. Return the bowls to the refrigerator. Right before class, place a cherry in the center of the third bowl. Have students discuss which atomic models are represented by each bowl of gelatin.

Expected Outcome The gelatin alone represents Dalton's atomic model. The gelatin with blueberries represents Thomson's "plum-pudding" atomic model, with the berries representing electrons. The gelatin with the cherry represents Rutherford's atomic model.
Visual, Logical

Rutherford's Atomic Theory

When you try something new, you may have expectations about the outcome. Does the outcome always meet your expectations or are you sometimes surprised? Scientists can also be surprised by the results of their experiments, but unexpected results can lead to important discoveries. This is what happened to Ernest Rutherford (1871–1937).

Rutherford's Hypothesis In 1899, Ernest Rutherford discovered that uranium emits fast-moving particles that have a positive charge. He named them alpha particles. In 1909, Rutherford asked one of his students, Ernest Marsden, to find out what happens to alpha particles when they pass through a thin sheet of gold.

Recall that in Thomson's model of the atom, the mass and positive charge are evenly spread throughout an atom. Based on this model, Rutherford hypothesized that the mass and charge at any location in the gold would be too small to change the path of an alpha particle. He predicted that most particles would travel in a straight path from their source to a screen that lit up when struck. Those few that did not pass straight through would be deflected only slightly.

The Gold Foil Experiment Marsden used the equipment shown in Figure 7. He aimed a narrow beam of alpha particles at the gold. The screen around the gold was made of a material that produced a flash of light when struck by a fast-moving alpha particle. By observing the flash, Marsden could figure out the path of an alpha particle after it passed through the gold.

Some of the locations of the flashes on the screen did not support Rutherford's prediction. More particles were deflected than he expected. About one out of every 20,000 was deflected by more than 90 degrees. Some of the alpha particles behaved as though they had struck an object and bounced straight back.

Figure 7 The path of an alpha particle can be detected by the location of a flash on a screen. Rutherford expected the paths of the positively charged alpha particles that were aimed at the thin gold foil to be affected only slightly by the gold atoms. But more particles were deflected than expected and some particles bounced straight back.

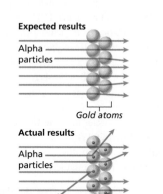

Facts and Figures

In His Own Words In a lecture Rutherford gave at Cambridge in 1936, he recalled his reaction when Geiger told him about alpha particles being scattered backward by the gold foil. Rutherford described his reaction. "It was almost as incredible as if you fired a 15-inch shell at a piece of tissue paper and it came back and hit you."

Discovery of the Nucleus The alpha particles whose paths were deflected must have come close to another charged object. The closer they came, the greater the deflection was. But many alpha particles passed through the gold without being deflected. From these results, Rutherford concluded that the positive charge of an atom is not evenly spread throughout the atom. It is concentrated in a very small, central area that Rutherford called the nucleus. The **nucleus** is a dense, positively charged mass located in the center of the atom. (The plural of *nucleus* is *nuclei*.)

Because Thomson's model no longer explained all the evidence, Rutherford proposed a new model. ⬤ According to Rutherford's model, all of an atom's positive charge is concentrated in its nucleus. The alpha particles whose paths were deflected by more than 90 degrees came very close to a nucleus. The alpha particles whose paths were not bent moved through the space surrounding the nuclei without coming very close to any nucleus.

Figure 8 shows the inside of the Astrodome, a domed stadium in Houston, Texas. The roof of the stadium rises to a height of 202 feet above the center of the field. If an atom had the same volume as the stadium, its nucleus would have the volume of a marble. The total volume of an atom is about a trillion (10^{12}) times the volume of its nucleus.

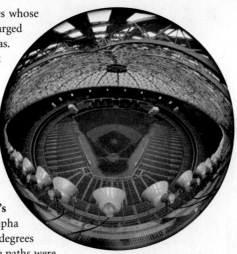

Figure 8 The Houston Astrodome occupies more than nine acres and seats 60,000 people. If the stadium were a model for an atom, a marble could represent its nucleus. *Using Analogies In the model, where would the marble have to be located in the stadium to represent the nucleus?*

Section 4.1 Assessment

Reviewing Concepts

1. ⬤ What theory did Dalton propose about the structure of matter?

2. ⬤ What evidence did J. J. Thomson provide about the structure of an atom?

3. ⬤ What did Rutherford discover about the structure of an atom?

4. What evidence did Thomson have that his glowing beam contained negative particles?

5. Why was Dalton's model of the atom changed after Thomson's experiment?

Critical Thinking

6. **Comparing and Contrasting** Explain why scientists accepted Dalton's atomic theory but not the idea of an atom proposed by the Greek philosophers.

7. **Drawing Conclusions** If you observed a beam of particles being bent toward a negatively charged plate, what might you conclude?

8. **Relating Cause and Effect** In the Rutherford experiment, why weren't all the alpha particles deflected?

Writing in Science

Writing to Persuade Imagine you live in ancient Greece. Assume all you know about matter is what you can observe with your five senses. You have heard the views of both Democritus and Aristotle about matter. Write a paragraph supporting one of their views.

Section 4.1 Assessment

1. All matter is composed of individual particles called atoms, which cannot be divided.
2. Thomson provided the first evidence that atoms are made from even smaller particles.
3. All of the positive charge of an atom is concentrated in its nucleus.
4. The beam was attracted to a positively charged plate and repelled by a negatively charged plate.

5. Dalton assumed atoms were solid, indivisible particles. Thomson had evidence that smaller particles existed inside atoms.
6. Dalton had data from experiments to support his theory, whereas the Greeks did not have data.
7. The particles have a positive charge.
8. The nucleus is small compared with the atom as a whole. Very few of the alpha particles came close enough to a gold nucleus to be deflected.

Build Science Skills `L2`

Using Models Have students model the gold foil experiment by shooting marbles across the floor at an arrangement of widely spaced, small objects—such as beads that are glued to a flat surface—and recording the angle of the marbles that are deflected. Discuss the results of their experiment in light of Marsden's findings.
Kinesthetic, Interpersonal

Integrate Biology `L2`

Cells in most living organisms have a central structure called a nucleus. This organelle contains the cell's genetic, or hereditary, material. Ask, **How are an atom's nucleus and a cell's nucleus similar?** *(They are both central structures of a basic unit.)*
Logical

3 ASSESS

Evaluate Understanding `L2`

Ask groups of students to summarize Dalton's, Thompson's, and Rutherford's atomic theories. Have them come up with simple word phrases or mnemonic devices to help them easily distinguish among the three theories. For example, **D**ogs **S**ort **S**ocks = **D**alton's **S**olid **S**phere; **T**urtles **P**lay **P**ing-pong = **T**homson's **P**lum **P**udding; and **R**ats **P**oke **N**oodles = **R**utherford's **P**ositive **N**ucleus.

Reteach `L1`

Use the Science and History time line on p. 114 to present and discuss a summary of the three models.

Writing in Science

Students might argue that the properties Democritus assigned to atoms match observed properties of matter, such as smoothness and roughness. Students might argue that the properties Aristotle assigned to elements serve a similar purpose, and his system also seems to account for changes between types of matter.

 Interactive Textbook If your class subscribes to the Interactive Textbook, use it to review key concepts in Section 4.1.

Answer to . . .

Figure 8 *The marble would have to be located in the center of the stadium.*

Small-Scale Construction `L2`
Background

The diameter of one of the silicon gears is 50 microns (50,000 nanometers). Despite their relative sizes on the page, the silicon gear is much larger than the model of nanogears. (The atomic radius of a carbon atom is only 770 nanometers.)

In 1959, Richard Feynman suggested the possibility of nanometer-scale construction when he said, "The principles of physics, as far as I can see, do not speak against the possibility of maneuvering things atom by atom."

The uses for small-scale construction are potentially very diverse, though currently they are very limited. Biologists already use nanotechnology to make tiny labels for use in diagnostic and pharmaceutical research. Such molecular labels can be injected or absorbed in one part of the body and then traced as they travel throughout the body. One company has even made a sunscreen with nanometer-sized particles that scatter harmful light rays while transmitting visible light, which makes the cream clear instead of white.

Build Science Skills `L2`

Using Models

Purpose Students will explore the difference between top-down and bottom-up methods of construction.

ACTIVITY

Materials modeling clay, plastic knives

Class Time 10 minutes

Procedure Have students use the top-down method to construct a model of a gear like the one shown in the dust mite photo. Consider bringing in samples of gears for students to observe. Then, have students use the bottom-up method to construct a model of the stick figure shown in the feature.

Expected Outcome Students will make a gear by starting with a lump of clay and then removing clay to shape the gear (a top-down construction method). They will make a stick figure by joining small pieces of clay together (a bottom-up method of construction).
Kinesthetic, Visual

Small-Scale Construction

Some scientists and engineers think of atoms and molecules as construction materials for building very small objects.

The field of science called nanotechnology is named for a unit of measurement—the nanometer. A billion nanometers (10^9 nm) can fit in one meter. The diameter of a human hair is about 80,000 nm. Scientists and engineers who use nanometers as measuring units are building miniature versions of objects such as motors.

There are two general methods for building any object. You can start with more material than you need and shape the object by removing matter or you can build up the object from smaller pieces. When you shape your nails with an emery board, you are using a top-down construction method. When you see "some assembly required" on the side of a box, the manufacturer expects you to use a bottom-up method of construction.

Dust mite

Silicon gear assembly

Building from the top down
Gears are toothed disks that are designed to fit together so that the motion of one gear controls the motion of another. These silicon gears are among the smallest objects ever made from the top down.

Building from the bottom up
With a scanning tunneling microscope, it is possible to move individual atoms or molecules. This figure, made of linked carbon monoxide molecules, is just five nanometers (0.000005 mm) tall. In 1990, scientists built this figure to demonstrate bottom-up construction methods.

Futuristic model of a nanorobot performing surgery in a blood vessel.

Going Further

Possible uses include bar codes that attach to molecules and are used to monitor biological processes, devices that deliver drugs to specific locations in the body at specific times, and self-assembling products. One overall challenge is the construction of interfaces between humans and tiny devices.
Verbal, Visual

The future of nanotechnology
Potential applications for nanotechnology include medical diagnostic tools and atomic-level electronic devices that assemble themselves. If such devices prove successful, perhaps someday the surgical robot will be built.

Sheet of carbon atoms rolled into a tube

Ring of carbon atoms with hydrogen atoms attached

Nanogears
This image of nanogears was produced with a computer program designed to make models of molecules. Hollow tubes (nanotubes) made from sheets of carbon atoms do exist. So do the rings containing carbon and hydrogen atoms, which are used for the "teeth" of the gears. But researchers need to figure out how to get the "teeth" to attach to the tubes.

Going Further

- Research proposed uses of nanotechnology. Make a poster describing one proposed use. Explain the advantage of using small objects in this application. What problems must be solved before the application can be used?
- Take a Discovery Channel Video Field Trip by watching "Go For Gold."

DISCOVERY CHANNEL SCHOOL
Video Field Trip

Atomic Structure **107**

DISCOVERY CHANNEL SCHOOL

Video Field Trip
Go For Gold

After students have viewed the Video Field Trip, ask them the following questions: **What did the ancient Egyptians know about how gold reacts with air?** *(They realized that gold does not react easily with air and does not corrode like many other metals.)* **Name a practical reason why temple roofs were often covered with gold in countries with hot climates.** *(Because gold is an excellent reflector of sunlight, it kept the interiors cooler than they would have been otherwise.)* **How do the properties of gold make it useful on space missions?** *(Gold is often used to coat space vehicles in order to reflect the intense sunlight. A thin layer of gold on the goggles used by astronauts reduces the intensity of light reaching the astronauts' eyes.)* **How can the arrangement of atoms on the surface of gold be observed?** *(Electron microscopes are designed to trace the arrangement of particles on a surface through the up-and-down movement of a probe tip.)*

1 FOCUS

Objectives

4.2.1 **Identify** three subatomic particles and **compare** their properties.

4.2.2 **Distinguish** the atomic number of an element from the mass number of an isotope, and use these numbers to **describe** the structure of atoms.

Reading Focus

Build Vocabulary L2

Word-Part Analysis Have students look up the term *isotope* in a dictionary that provides word prefixes. Have them use the prefix *iso-* to help them understand the term. *(The prefix iso-means "same." Isotopes of an element have the same atomic number, but different numbers of neutrons.)*

Reading Strategy L2

Most students will know that atoms are the "building blocks" of matter, and some may know that atoms contain subatomic particles. Students may say that they want to learn more about the structure of atoms.

2 INSTRUCT

Properties of Subatomic Particles
Use Visuals L1

Figure 9 Have students examine the photo and the caption that describes it in Figure 9. Suggest some familiar objects that have a mass of 5 kg, such as a 12-pack of 16-ounce beverage containers. Ask, **If a proton's mass was 10 tons and an electron's mass was 5 kg, what mass would represent the mass of a neutron?** *(10 tons)* **Logical**

FYI

Different books use different conventions for symbols for subatomic particles. For example, some texts use only the letters *e, p,* and *n*. Others include a superscript zero on the *n* to indicate the lack of charge. Electrons, protons, and neutrons are not the only subatomic particles. Quarks will be discussed in Chapter 10.

4.2 The Structure of an Atom

  Standards: ICP.3.1, ICP.5.3, ICP.7.2

Reading Focus

Key Concepts
- What are three subatomic particles?
- What properties can be used to compare protons, electrons, and neutrons?
- How are atoms of one element different from atoms of other elements?
- What is the difference between two isotopes of the same element?

Vocabulary
- proton
- electron
- neutron
- atomic number
- mass number
- isotopes

Reading Strategy
Monitoring Your Understanding Before you read, copy the table. List what you know about atoms and what you would like to learn. After you read, list what you have learned.

What I Know About Atoms	What I Would Like to Learn	What I Have Learned

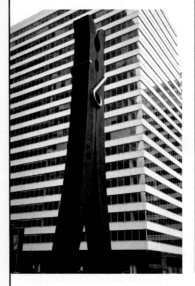

Figure 9 This 45-foot-tall steel sculpture of a clothespin is in Philadelphia, Pennsylvania. Claes Oldenburg made the clothespin in 1976 from 10 tons of steel. If a proton had a mass of 10 tons, then an electron would have a mass of about 5 kilograms.

Beams like the ones Thomson produced create the images on many television screens. When a beam sweeps across the screen, spots on the screen light up in the same way the screen in the gold-foil experiment lit up when struck by an alpha particle. In a color television, there are three beams, one for each primary color of light—red, green, and blue. The particles in these beams are subatomic particles.

Properties of Subatomic Particles

By 1920, Rutherford had seen evidence for the existence of two subatomic particles and had predicted the existence of a third particle. **Protons, electrons, and neutrons are subatomic particles.**

Protons Based on experiments with elements other than gold, Rutherford concluded that the amount of positive charge varies among elements. Each nucleus must contain at least one particle with a positive charge. Rutherford called these particles protons. A **proton** is a positively charged subatomic particle that is found in the nucleus of an atom. Each proton is assigned a charge of 1+. Some nuclei contain more than 100 protons.

Electrons The particles that Thomson detected were later named electrons. *Electron* comes from a Greek word meaning "amber." An **electron** is a negatively charged subatomic particle that is found in the space outside the nucleus. Each electron has a charge of 1−.

108   *Chapter 4*

Section Resources

Print
- **Reading and Study Workbook With Math Support,** Section 4.2 and **Math Skill:** Electrons and Orbitals
- **Transparencies,** Section 4.2

Technology
- **Interactive Textbook,** Section 4.2
- **Presentation Pro CD-ROM,** Section 4.2
- **Go Online,** Science News, Atomic chemistry

Properties of Subatomic Particles

Particle	Symbol	Relative Charge	Relative Mass (proton = 1)	Actual Mass (g)	Model
Electron	e⁻	1−	$\frac{1}{1836}$	9.11×10^{-28}	
Proton	p+	1+	1	1.674×10^{-24}	
Neutron	n	0	1	1.675×10^{-24}	

Figure 10 This table lists the symbol, the relative charge, the relative mass, and the actual mass of an electron, a proton, and a neutron. The Model column shows the colors used in this book to represent the subatomic particles. **Calculating** *What is the difference in actual mass between a proton and a neutron?*

Neutrons In 1932, the English physicist James Chadwick designed an experiment to show that neutrons exist. Chadwick concluded that the particles he produced were neutral because a charged object did not deflect their paths. A **neutron** is a neutral subatomic particle that is found in the nucleus of an atom. It has a mass almost exactly equal to that of a proton.

Comparing Subatomic Particles

Figure 10 summarizes some properties of protons, electrons, and neutrons. **Protons, electrons, and neutrons can be distinguished by mass, charge, and location in an atom.** Protons and neutrons have almost the same mass. But the data in Figure 10 show that it would take about 2000 electrons to equal the mass of one proton. Electrons have a charge that is equal in size to, but the opposite of, the charge of a proton. Neutrons have no charge. Protons and neutrons are found in the nucleus, but electrons are found in the space outside the nucleus.

Go Online
SCIENCE NEWS®

For: Articles on atomic chemistry
Visit: PHSchool.com
Web Code: cce-1042

 Problem-Solving Activity

Designing an Atomic Exhibit

You work as a volunteer at the local science museum. You are asked to design an exhibit that compares the size of a lithium atom to the size of its nucleus. A lithium atom has a diameter of about 3×10^2 picometers. The nucleus of a lithium atom has a diameter of about 5×10^{-3} picometers. There are a trillion (10^{12}) picometers in a meter.

Defining the Problem State the problem in your own words. What decisions will you need to make before you can proceed?

Organizing Information How many times larger is the lithium atom than its nucleus? Find several objects that could represent the nucleus in your exhibit and measure their diameters.

Creating a Solution Pick one of the objects you measured to represent the nucleus in your atomic exhibit. Figure out how far away from the object you would have to place a marker so that people could visualize the relative sizes of the atom and the nucleus.

Presenting Your Plan Write a proposal to present to the committee that approves projects. Tell them where you would place the nucleus and where you would have to place the marker. Be prepared to explain why your exhibit needs the space you are requesting.

Atomic Structure **109**

Atomic Number and Mass Number

FYI

The atomic mass unit will be introduced in Section 5.2, when atomic masses listed in the periodic table are discussed. The force that binds protons and neutrons together in the nucleus is called the strong nuclear force and is addressed in Chapter 10, as is the effect of the size of a nucleus on its stability.

Particles and Numbers **L2**

Purpose Students will observe the relationship between number of protons, number of neutrons, atomic number, and mass number.

Materials overhead projector, red and green gummy candies

Procedure Explain that the green candies represent neutrons and the red candies represent protons. Model a lithium-7 nucleus by placing a group of three red candies and four green candies on the overhead. Ask students to count the number of candies (particles) to determine the mass number of the lithium atom. Then, remove (subtract) the green candies (neutrons) to get the atomic number. Perform a similar demonstration with oxygen-16 (eight protons and eight neutrons) and boron-11 (five protons and six neutrons).

Expected Outcome Students should gain a familiarity with determining mass numbers and atomic numbers.
Visual

Build Reading Literacy **L1**

Identify Main Idea/Details Refer to page 98D in this chapter, which provides the guidelines for identifying main ideas and details.

Have students read Atomic Number and Mass Number on p. 110. Ask them to identify the main idea of each paragraph. Point out that the main idea is usually within the first or second sentence of a paragraph. Encourage students to include this exercise in the notes they use to study.
Verbal

Figure 11 Each element has a different atomic number. **A** The atomic number of sulfur (S) is 16. **B** The atomic number of iron (Fe) is 26. **C** The atomic number of silver (Ag) is 47.
Applying Concepts *How many protons are there in each atom of sulfur, iron, and silver?*

Everything scientists know about the nucleus and subatomic particles is based on how the particles behave. Scientists still do not have an instrument that can show the inside of an atom. But they do have microscopes that can show how atoms are arranged on the surface of a material. The How It Works box on page 111 describes one of those microscopes.

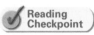 **Reading Checkpoint** *Which scientist demonstrated the existence of neutrons?*

Atomic Number and Mass Number

Dalton predicted that the atoms of any element are different from the atoms of all other elements. With the discovery of subatomic particles, scientists were able to describe those differences.

Atomic Number The atoms of any given element always have the same number of protons. For example, there is one proton in the nucleus of each and every hydrogen atom. Therefore, hydrogen is assigned the atomic number 1. The **atomic number** of an element equals the number of protons in an atom of that element.

Hydrogen atoms are the only atoms with a single proton. **Atoms of different elements have different numbers of protons.** The sulfur shown in Figure 11A is assigned atomic number 16 because a sulfur atom has 16 protons. You can use atomic numbers to refer to elements, like names and symbols, because each element has a unique atomic number.

Each positive charge in an atom is balanced by a negative charge because atoms are neutral. So the atomic number of an element also equals the number of electrons in an atom. Each hydrogen atom has one electron. Each sulfur atom has 16.

Mass Number The atomic number tells you the number of protons in an atom's nucleus. It does not give you any information about the number of neutrons in an atom. For that information, you need to know the atom's mass number. The **mass number** of an atom is the sum of the protons and neutrons in the nucleus of that atom. An atom of aluminum with 13 protons and 14 neutrons has a mass number of 27. If you know the atomic number and the mass number of an atom, you can find the number of neutrons by subtracting.

Number of Neutrons

Number of neutrons = Mass number − Atomic number

Scanning Tunneling Microscope

A probe is moved back and forth across the surface of a sample. When electrons jump, or tunnel, across the gap between the sample and the probe, an electric current is produced. A computer uses data about changes in the probe's position to produce an image of the sample's surface. **Interpreting Diagrams** *How is the distance between the probe tip and the sample kept constant?*

Scanning tunneling microscope
Modern scanning tunneling microscopes produce images of metal samples or biological specimens such as DNA.

A **Scanning probe**
As the probe is moved over the sample, current flows between the probe tip and the sample. The processor holds the tip at a constant distance from the sample by keeping the electric current constant. Thus, changes in the vertical position of the probe will follow the contours of the sample's surface.

Electrical signal from processor

Electrical signal from probe

B **Processor**
The processor sends, receives, and records information about the movement of the probe.

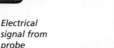

Scanning device *This device raises and lowers the probe.*

Electron flow
Electrons flow across a gap of about one nanometer (0.000001 mm) between the probe tip and the sample, producing an electric current.

Gold sample

C **Computer** A computer assembles a map of the sample's surface, using data received from the processor. Color was added to the image shown on the computer screen.

Probe tip *The tip of the probe is only one or two atoms in width.*

DK HOW It Works

Scanning Tunneling Microscope **L2**

The scanning tunneling microscope (STM) is used to obtain high-resolution images of solid surfaces. This technology allows scientists and researchers to view a three-dimensional profile of a surface, which can give information about surface textures and crystal structure. STM data is initially displayed as a black and white image that is colorized to highlight different features.

In 1986, Gerd Binnig of Germany and Heinrich Rohrer of Switzerland shared the Nobel Prize in Physics with Germany's Ernst Ruska for designing the scanning tunneling microscope.

Interpreting Diagrams The processor maintains a constant electric current between the probe tip and the sample, which keeps the distance between the tip and sample constant.
Logical

For Enrichment **L3**

Encourage students to explore the use of scanning tunneling microscopes in research on surface textures, crystal structure, or molecular shape. Have them present their findings to the class in the form of a poster.
Visual

Facts and Figures

Coining Terms The English physician William Gilbert (1544–1603) introduced the term *electric*, which is based on the Greek word for amber. (William Gilbert was the personal physician to Queen Elizabeth I and a pioneer in the study of magnetism. A unit of magnetic force is named for him.) Credit for naming the electron goes to G. Johnstone Stoney, an Irish physicist who suggested the name in 1891.

Answer to . . .

Figure 11 *There are 16 protons in a sulfur atom, 26 in an iron atom, and 47 in a silver atom.*

 Reading Checkpoint *James Chadwick*

Isotopes
Build Science Skills   L2

Calculating Uranium-238 has a mass number of 238 with 146 neutrons in the nucleus. Uranium-235 has 143 neutrons in the nucleus. Ask, **What is the atomic number of uranium?** (92)
Logical

Address Misconceptions   L2

Many students think that isotopes are different from "ordinary" or "regular" atoms. To challenge this misconception, have students read the text on this page and examine the data presented in Figure 12. Ask, **How are the compositions of heavy water and ordinary water similar?** *(Both contain hydrogen and oxygen atoms.)* **What type of hydrogen atoms does ordinary water contain?** *(Hydrogen-1 atoms)* **What type of hydrogen atoms does heavy water contain?** *(Hydrogen-2 atoms)* **Compare the properties of heavy water and ordinary water.** *(They have different melting points, boiling points, and densities.)*
Logical

3 ASSESS

Evaluate Understanding   L2

Have students write three review questions for this section. Students should then break into groups of three or four and ask each other their questions.

Reteach   L1

Revisit Figure 10 to review the differences among protons, neutrons, and electrons.

Connecting C Concepts

Students might say that "type of atom" refers to the atomic number of the atom or to the number of protons in the atom.

Interactive Textbook If your class subscribes to the Interactive Textbook, use it to review key concepts in Section 4.2.

Answer to . . .

Figure 12 *3.81°C*

Comparing Ordinary Water and Heavy Water		
Property	Ordinary Water	Heavy Water
Melting point	0.00°C	3.81°C
Boiling point	100.00°C	101.42°C
Density (at 25°C)	0.99701 g/cm³	1.1044 g/cm³

Figure 12 Heavy water contains hydrogen-2 atoms, which have twice the mass of hydrogen-1 atoms. **Using Tables** *At what temperature would a sample of heavy water freeze?*

Isotopes

In Dalton's atomic theory, all the atoms of a given element are identical. Every atom of a given element *does* have the same number of protons and electrons. But every atom of a given element *does not* have the same number of neutrons. **Isotopes** are atoms of the same element that have different numbers of neutrons and different mass numbers. **Isotopes of an element have the same atomic number but different mass numbers because they have different numbers of neutrons.**

For example, every atom of oxygen has 8 protons. Some oxygen atoms have 8 neutrons and a mass number of 16. Some oxygen atoms have 9 neutrons and a mass number of 17. Some oxygen atoms have 10 neutrons and a mass number of 18. When it is important to distinguish one oxygen isotope from another, the isotopes are referred to as oxygen-16, oxygen-17, and oxygen-18. All three oxygen isotopes can react with hydrogen to form water or combine with iron to form rust.

With most elements, it is hard to notice any differences in the physical or chemical properties of their isotopes. Hydrogen is an exception. Hydrogen-1 has no neutrons. (Almost all hydrogen is hydrogen-1.) Hydrogen-2 has one neutron, and hydrogen-3 has two neutrons. Because a hydrogen-1 atom has only one proton, adding a neutron doubles its mass. Water that contains hydrogen-2 atoms in place of hydrogen-1 atoms is called heavy water. Figure 12 compares some physical properties of ordinary water and heavy water.

Section 4.2 Assessment

Reviewing Concepts

1. Name three subatomic particles.
2. Name three properties you could use to distinguish a proton from an electron.
3. Which characteristic of an atom always varies among atoms of different elements?
4. How are the isotopes of an element different from one another?
5. What do neutrons and protons have in common? How are they different?
6. How can atoms be neutral if they contain charged particles?
7. What is the difference between atoms of oxygen-16 and oxygen-17?

Critical Thinking

8. **Comparing and Contrasting** What property do protons and electrons have that neutrons do not?
9. **Applying Concepts** Explain why it isn't possible for an atom to have a mass number of 10 and an atomic number of 12.

Connecting C Concepts

Elements In Section 2.1, you were told that elements contain only one type of atom. How would you define "type of atom" to account for the existence of isotopes?

Section 4.2   Assessment

1. Proton, electron, and neutron
2. Mass, charge, and location in an atom
3. The atoms of any element have a different number of protons than the atoms of all other elements.
4. Isotopes of an element have the same atomic number but different mass numbers because they have different numbers of neutrons.
5. Protons and neutrons have almost the same mass and are both located in the nucleus of the atom. Protons are charged particles. Neutrons are neutral particles.
6. The positive charge of the protons in the nucleus is balanced by the negative charge of the electrons.
7. Each oxygen-17 atom has one more neutron than each oxygen-16 atom.
8. Protons and electrons are charged particles. Neutrons have no charge.
9. An atom with an atomic number of 12 has 12 protons. Because the mass number is the sum of the protons and neutrons, the mass number would need to be at least 12.

4.3 Modern Atomic Theory

Standards: ICP.3.1, ICP.4.3, ICP.7.1

Reading Focus

Key Concepts
- What can happen to electrons when atoms gain or lose energy?
- What model do scientists use to describe how electrons behave in atoms?
- What is the most stable configuration of electrons in an atom?

Vocabulary
- energy levels
- electron cloud
- orbital
- electron configuration
- ground state

Reading Strategy
Sequencing Copy the flowchart. After you read, complete the description of how a gain or loss of energy affects atoms.

Electrons and Energy Levels

a. ___?___ → [Excited state] → b. ___?___ → [Emits energy]

Have you ever wondered what produces the different colors in a fireworks display? Why does one explosion produce red light and another explosion produce green light? The people who make fireworks know that certain compounds will produce certain colors of light when they are heated. For example, compounds containing the element strontium produce red light when they are heated. Compounds containing barium produce green light.

You have seen two things that can happen when atoms absorb energy—an increase in kinetic energy or a phase change. But there is another possibility. The energy may be temporarily absorbed by the atom and then emitted as light. The colors in a fireworks display are a clue to how electrons are arranged in atoms.

Bohr's Model of the Atom

You may have seen diagrams of an atom that look like a solar system with planets revolving around a sun. These diagrams are based on a model of the atom that was developed by Niels Bohr (1885–1962), a Danish physicist who worked for a while with Rutherford. Bohr agreed with Rutherford's model of a nucleus surrounded by a large volume of space. But Bohr's model did something that Rutherford's model did not do. It focused on the electrons. A description of the arrangement of electrons in an atom is the centerpiece of the modern atomic model.

Figure 13 Fireworks are often displayed above the Lincoln Memorial in Washington, D.C. The red light was produced by a strontium compound.

Atomic Structure **113**

Section Resources

Print
- *Laboratory Manual*, Investigations 4A and 4B
- *Reading and Study Workbook With Math Support*, Section 4.3
- *Transparencies*, Section 4.3

Technology
- *Interactive Textbook*, Section 4.3
- *Presentation Pro CD-ROM*, Section 4.3
- *Go Online*, NSTA SciLinks, Energy levels

---

1 FOCUS

Objectives
4.3.1 Describe Bohr's model of the atom and the evidence for energy levels.
4.3.2 Explain how the electron cloud model represents the behavior and locations of electrons in atoms.
4.3.3 Distinguish the ground state from excited states of an atom based on electron configurations.

Reading Focus

Build Vocabulary

LINCS Have students use the LINCS strategy to learn the terms *energy levels, electron cloud, orbital, electron configuration,* and *ground state.* In LINCS exercises, students **L**ist what they know about each term, **I**magine a picture that describes the term, **N**ote a reminding "sound-alike" word, **C**onnect the terms to the sound-alike word by making up a short story, and then perform a brief **S**elf-test.

Reading Strategy

a. Electron moves to higher energy level.
b. Electron moves to lower energy level.

2 INSTRUCT

Bohr's Model of the Atom
Build Reading Literacy

Relate Text and Visuals Refer to page **190D** in **Chapter 7**, which provides the guidelines for relating text and visuals.

Have students read Bohr's Model of the Atom on pp. 113–116. Then, have students examine the diagram of Bohr's model in the time line on p. 115. Ask, **What do the circles around the nucleus represent?** *(They represent energy levels.)* **Visual**

Address Misconceptions L2

Students may think that electrons travel around the nucleus in fixed orbits, like planets orbiting the sun. Challenge this misconception by having students compare Bohr's model and the electron cloud model. Explain that Bohr's model correctly introduced the concept of energy levels, but energy levels cannot be used to describe the actual location of an electron. The electron cloud model can be used to model the probability that an electron is in a certain location. The exact speed and location of a single electron cannot be determined.
Verbal

FYI

The usefulness of Bohr's model was limited. The model could be used to describe the behavior of the single electron in a hydrogen atom quite accurately. However, this model could not be applied to atoms with multiple electrons.

Integrate Space Science L2

Planets in the solar system travel in fixed orbits around the sun. Because most of the orbits are nearly circular, the difference between the distance to the sun when a planet is closest and when it is farthest away is not great (given the magnitude of distances in space). Pluto is an exception. Its orbit is so elliptical that there are times during Pluto's journey around the sun (249 Earth days) when it is closer to the sun than Neptune is. This switch in order of proximity to the sun lasts 20 years. It last happened between 1979 and 1999. Have students research when it will happen again.
Logical

Energy Levels In Bohr's model, electrons move with constant speed in fixed orbits around the nucleus, like planets around a sun. Each electron in an atom has a specific amount of energy. If an atom gains or loses energy, the energy of an electron can change. The possible energies that electrons in an atom can have are called **energy levels.**

To understand energy levels, picture them as steps in a staircase. As you move up or down the staircase, you can measure how your position changes by counting the number of steps you take. You might take one step up, or you might jump two steps down. Whether you are going up or down, you can move only in whole-step increments. Just as you cannot stand between steps on a staircase, an electron cannot exist between energy levels.

DK SCIENCE and History

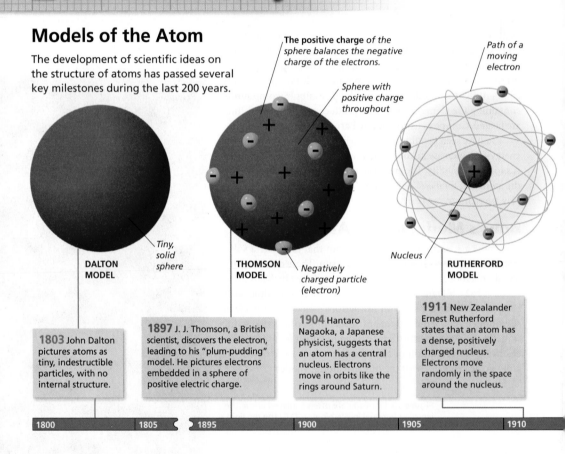

Models of the Atom

The development of scientific ideas on the structure of atoms has passed several key milestones during the last 200 years.

The positive charge of the sphere balances the negative charge of the electrons.

Sphere with positive charge throughout

Path of a moving electron

Tiny, solid sphere

DALTON MODEL

THOMSON MODEL

Negatively charged particle (electron)

Nucleus

RUTHERFORD MODEL

1803 John Dalton pictures atoms as tiny, indestructible particles, with no internal structure.

1897 J. J. Thomson, a British scientist, discovers the electron, leading to his "plum-pudding" model. He pictures electrons embedded in a sphere of positive electric charge.

1904 Hantaro Nagaoka, a Japanese physicist, suggests that an atom has a central nucleus. Electrons move in orbits like the rings around Saturn.

1911 New Zealander Ernest Rutherford states that an atom has a dense, positively charged nucleus. Electrons move randomly in the space around the nucleus.

| 1800 | 1805 | 1895 | 1900 | 1905 | 1910 |

114 *Chapter 4*

Customize for English Language Learners

Think-Pair-Share
Have students work in pairs to think of structures that can serve as analogies for energy levels. Examples include rungs of a ladder, guitar frets, and the series of holes on a belt or shoe strap. Note, however, that in all of these models, the intervals are equal, which is not true of the intervals between energy levels. Provide pictures of dressers that have drawers of different sizes or bookshelves that have adjustable shelves, which might better model the intervals of energy levels. Strengthen discussion skills by having students share their examples with the class.

The landing at the bottom of the staircase is like the lowest energy level in an atom. Each step up represents a higher energy level. The distance between two steps represents the difference in energy between two energy levels. To continue the analogy, there would need to be a different staircase for each element because no two elements have the same set of energy levels.

👉 **An electron in an atom can move from one energy level to another when the atom gains or loses energy.** An electron may move up two energy levels if it gains the right amount of energy. An electron in a higher energy level may move down two energy levels if it loses the right amount of energy. The size of the jump between energy levels determines the amount of energy gained or lost.

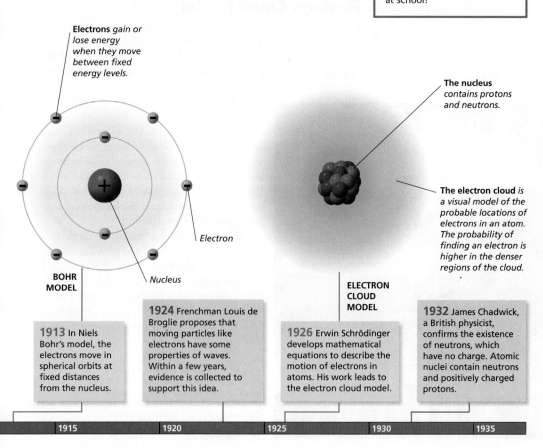

Electrons *gain or lose energy when they move between fixed energy levels.*

The nucleus *contains protons and neutrons.*

Electron

The electron cloud *is a visual model of the probable locations of electrons in an atom. The probability of finding an electron is higher in the denser regions of the cloud.*

BOHR MODEL

Nucleus

ELECTRON CLOUD MODEL

1913 In Niels Bohr's model, the electrons move in spherical orbits at fixed distances from the nucleus.

1924 Frenchman Louis de Broglie proposes that moving particles like electrons have some properties of waves. Within a few years, evidence is collected to support this idea.

1926 Erwin Schrödinger develops mathematical equations to describe the motion of electrons in atoms. His work leads to the electron cloud model.

1932 James Chadwick, a British physicist, confirms the existence of neutrons, which have no charge. Atomic nuclei contain neutrons and positively charged protons.

| 1915 | 1920 | 1925 | 1930 | 1935 |

Atomic Structure **115**

Facts and Figures

De Broglie and Schrödinger In 1924, Louis de Broglie, a French graduate student, derived an equation that describes the wavelength of a moving particle. Using de Broglie's equation, an electron has a wavelength of about 2×10^{-10} cm. In 1926, Erwin Schrödinger, an Austrian physicist, wrote a mathematical equation to describe the location and energy of the electron in a hydrogen atom. When the equation is solved (using advanced calculus), it produces a series of wave functions that describe the behavior of electrons. The quantum mechanical model of atoms is based on these wave functions. Atomic physicists define an orbital as the space-dependent part of the Schrödinger wave function of an electron in an atom or molecule.

that

...kills **L2**

...Have students examine ...n Figure 14. Ask, **How are ...ill blades similar to an ...n cloud?** *(You cannot be sure at ...specific moment where the windmill ...ades or electrons are located. However, the central part of the blades and the nucleus of an atom are in fixed locations.)* **What other examples can you think of that could model the concept of an electron cloud?** *(Acceptable answers include a ceiling fan, or moths flying around a light bulb.)* **Visual**

Teacher Demo

Electron Cloud Model **L2**

Purpose Students will use a model to describe the probable position of electrons.

Materials small, round balloon; large, round balloon; 10 beads with 4-mm diameter; 5 beads with 2-mm diameter

Procedure Put the 4-mm beads into the small balloon. Tell students that the small balloon represents the nucleus of a boron atom (five neutrons, five protons). Put the 2-mm beads into the large balloon. Explain that the beads represent electrons and the balloon represents the electron cloud. Slightly inflate the small balloon and push it completely into the large balloon. Inflate the large balloon and tie the end. Agitate the balloon so that the small beads are in constant motion.

Expected Outcome The precise location of a bead at a specific time is unknown, but the probability that it is in the large balloon is quite high. **Kinesthetic**

Download a worksheet on energy levels for students to complete, and find additional teacher support from NSTA SciLinks.

For: Links on energy levels
Visit: www.SciLinks.org
Web Code: ccn-1043

Evidence for Energy Levels What evidence is there that electrons can move from one energy level to another? Scientists can measure the energy gained when electrons absorb energy and move to a higher energy level. They can measure the energy released when the electron returns to a lower energy level.

The movement of electrons between energy levels explains the light you see when fireworks explode. Light is a form of energy. Heat produced by the explosion causes some electrons to move to higher energy levels. When those electrons move back to lower energy levels, they emit energy. Some of that energy is released as visible light. Because no two elements have the same set of energy levels, different elements emit different colors of light.

Reading Checkpoint *What determines the amount of energy gained or lost when an electron moves between energy levels?*

Electron Cloud Model

Like earlier models, Bohr's model was improved as scientists made further discoveries. Bohr was correct in assigning energy levels to electrons. But he was incorrect in assuming that electrons moved like planets in a solar system. Today, scientists know that electrons move in a less predictable way.

Scientists must deal with probability when trying to predict the locations and motions of electrons in atoms. An **electron cloud** is a visual model of the most likely locations for electrons in an atom. The cloud is denser at those locations where the probability of finding an electron is high. **Scientists use the electron cloud model to describe the possible locations of electrons around the nucleus.**

Figure 14 provides an analogy for an electron cloud. When the blades of a windmill are at rest, you can count the number of blades. When they are moving, the blades spin so fast that you see only a blur. You know that the blades are located somewhere in the blur, but at any specific moment in time you can't be exactly sure where each blade is located.

Figure 14 When the blades of a windmill are at rest, you can see their locations. When the blades are spinning, you see only a blur that is similar to a drawing of an electron cloud. **Comparing and Contrasting** *Describe one difference between the motion of windmill blades and the motion of an electron.*

116 *Chapter 4*

Facts and Figures

Emission and Absorption Spectra When the energy gained or lost by an atom is light energy, each frequency (or wavelength) of light corresponds to a movement of an electron between two energy levels in the atom. An element can be identified by the frequencies of light that are absorbed or emitted by its atoms because no two elements have the same set of energy levels. For example, the element helium was discovered on the sun in 1868 before it was discovered on Earth. The spectrum of light emitted by gases on the surface of the sun contained a yellow line that did not match a known element.

Comparing Excited States

Materials
fluorescent ("neon") markers, glow-in-the-dark toy, ultraviolet (UV) lamp

Procedure

1. Use the fluorescent markers to draw a picture on a piece of paper.

2. With the room darkened, observe your drawing under a UV lamp. **CAUTION** *Do not look directly at the light.* Remove the drawing from under the UV light and observe it again. Record your observations.

3. Observe the glow-in-the-dark toy under the UV light. Remove the toy from the light and observe it again. Record your observations.

Analyze and Conclude

1. **Observing** How did the glow of the toy differ from the glow of your drawing?

2. **Formulating Hypotheses** Use the concepts of ground and excited states to explain how UV light caused your drawing and the toy to glow.

3. **Drawing Conclusions** In which object, your drawing or the toy, do the atoms have excited states that are more stable, or less likely to change? Explain your answer.

Atomic Orbitals

The electron cloud represents all the orbitals in an atom. An **orbital** is a region of space around the nucleus where an electron is likely to be found. To understand the concept of an orbital, imagine a map of your school. Suppose you mark your exact location with a dot once every 10 minutes over a period of one week. The places you visit the most—such as your classrooms, the cafeteria, and the area near your locker—would have the highest concentration of dots. The places you visit the least would have the lowest concentration of dots.

The dots on your map are a model of your "orbital." They describe your most likely locations. There are some locations in your orbital that you may not visit every week—such as the principal's office or the auditorium. These locations may not be represented by a dot on your map. Despite such omissions, the dots on your map are a good model of how you usually behave in your orbital. **An electron cloud is a good approximation of how electrons behave in their orbitals.**

The level in which an electron has the least energy—the lowest energy level—has only one orbital. Higher energy levels have more than one orbital. Figure 15 shows the number of orbitals in the first four energy levels of an atom. Notice that the maximum number of electrons in an energy level is twice the number of orbitals. Each orbital can contain two electrons at most.

Figure 15 The table lists the number of orbitals in the first four energy levels of an atom. It also lists the maximum number of electrons in each energy level. *Inferring* **How many electrons can be in each orbital?**

Energy Levels, Orbitals, and Electrons		
Energy Level	Number of Orbitals	Maximum Number of Electrons
1	1	2
2	4	8
3	9	18
4	16	32

FYI

According to the quantum mechanical model, an orbital is the mathematical function that describes the behavior of an electron in space.

Comparing Excited States
L2

Objective
After completing this activity, students will be able to
- explain how UV light causes objects to glow.
- use the persistence of light to compare excited states.

Skills Focus
Observing, Formulating Hypotheses

Prep Time 5 minutes

Class Time 15 minutes

Safety Check the MSDS for the markers to make sure that they are low in VOCs (volatile organic compounds). Students should not look directly at UV light, which is harmful to the eyes. Demonstrate safe use of the UV lamps before allowing students to use them.

Teaching Tips
- Do this lab only after you teach ground state and excited states.

Expected Outcome Fluorescent ink will emit brilliant visible light under UV light. This fluorescence will instantly cease when the UV light is removed. Phosphorescent (glow-in-the-dark) objects will continue to emit visible light even after the UV light is removed.

Analyze and Conclude
1. The toy still glowed after the UV light was removed. The drawing did not.
2. The drawing and the toy absorbed energy from the UV light. When electrons moved to higher energy levels, the atoms were in an excited state. When electrons returned to lower energy levels, energy was released as visible light.
3. The fact that the toy's glow persisted suggests that the excited state of atoms in the toy was more stable than the excited state of atoms in the drawing.

Visual, Kinesthetic

Answer to . . .

Figure 14 *The windmill blades have a single, set path, and the blades stop moving when the wind stops blowing.*

Figure 15 *Two*

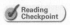 Reading Checkpoint *The size of the jump between energy levels*

Electron Configurations

Use Visuals   L1

Figure 16 Extend the analogy of the gymnast on the balance beam by having students consider a gymnast doing an entire routine on equipment such as a balance beam, a pommel horse, parallel bars, or uneven bars. **In the analogy, when is the configuration of the gymnast like an atom in an excited state?** *(When the gymnast is in a precarious position, such as when the gymnast is not in direct contact with the equipment)* **In the analogy, when is the gymnast most like an atom in its ground state?** *(The gymnast is in her most stable position when she is standing on the floor.)*
Logical

3 ASSESS

Evaluate Understanding   L2

Have students draw and label a diagram that represents Bohr's model of an atom. Then, have students explain how the electron cloud model differs from Bohr's model.

Reteach   L1

Use the diagrams on p. 115 in the Science and History feature to review Bohr's model, energy levels, and electron clouds.

 Writing in Science

The shelves in a bookcase can represent energy levels in an atom. If students know about potential energy, they may compare what happens to the energy of a book as it is moved between shelves to the difference in energy between electrons in different energy levels.

Interactive Textbook If your class subscribes to the Interactive Textbook, use it to review key concepts in Section 4.3.

Figure 16 A gymnast on a balance beam is like an atom in an excited state—not very stable.

Electron Configurations

How are the seats in your classroom arranged? Are they lined up neatly in rows, or are they grouped in clusters? A configuration is an arrangement of objects in a given space. Some configurations are more stable than others, meaning that they are less likely to change. The position of the gymnast on the balance beam in Figure 16 is not very stable because the beam is only 10 centimeters wide.

An **electron configuration** is the arrangement of electrons in the orbitals of an atom. **The most stable electron configuration is the one in which the electrons are in orbitals with the lowest possible energies.** When all the electrons in an atom have the lowest possible energies, the atom is said to be in its **ground state.**

For example, lithium is a silvery-white metal with an atomic number of 3, which means that a lithium atom has three electrons. In the ground state, two of the lithium electrons are in the orbital of the first energy level. The third electron is in an orbital of the second energy level.

If a lithium atom absorbs enough energy, one of its electrons can move to an orbital with a higher energy. This configuration is referred to as an excited state. An excited state is less stable than the ground state. Eventually, the electron that was promoted to a higher energy level loses energy, and the atom returns to the ground state. Helium, neon, argon, krypton, and xenon atoms returning from excited states to the ground state emit the light you see in "neon" lights.

Section 4.3 Assessment

Reviewing Concepts

1. When is an electron in an atom likely to move from one energy level to another?
2. What model do scientists use to describe how electrons move around the nucleus?
3. Describe the most stable configuration of the electrons in an atom.
4. What did Bohr contribute to modern atomic theory?
5. What does an electron cloud represent?

Critical Thinking

6. **Comparing and Contrasting** A boron atom has two electrons in the first energy level and three in the second energy level. Compare the relative energies of the electrons in these two energy levels.

7. **Making Judgments** Was Rutherford's model of an atom incorrect or incomplete? Explain your answer.
8. **Posing Questions** Apply what you know about charged particles to the modern model of the atom. Is there anything about the behavior of electrons in atoms that is unexpected? Explain your answer.

Writing in Science

Describing Energy Levels Use a bookcase as an analogy for the energy levels in an atom. Use the analogy to write a paragraph about electrons and energy levels. (*Hint:* Reread the staircase analogy on pages 114 and 115.)

118 *Chapter 4*

1. Electrons are likely to move from one energy level to another when atoms gain or lose energy.
2. The electron cloud model
3. The most stable configuration is the one in which the electrons are in orbitals with the lowest possible energy.
4. Bohr contributed the idea that electrons have energy levels with specific amounts of energy.

5. An electron cloud represents the most probable locations of an electron in an atom.
6. The electrons in the second energy level will have more energy than the electrons in the first energy level.
7. Rutherford's description of an atom was correct, but incomplete. It did not provide as much information about the behavior of the electrons as later models.
8. Students may ask why the negatively charged electrons are not drawn into the nucleus by the positively charged protons.

Using Flame Tests

Forensic scientists use various approaches to distinguish different substances. In this lab, you will observe the flame colors of several substances and use the data to determine the identity of an unknown substance.

Problem How can the color of a flame be used to distinguish substances?

Materials

- solutions of calcium chloride, boric acid, potassium chloride, copper(II) sulfate, sodium chloride, and an unknown
- Bunsen burner
- nichrome wire loop
- dilute solution of hydrochloric acid
- wash bottle with distilled water

Skills Observing, Predicting, Using Data Tables

Procedure

Part A: Observing Flame Colors

1. Make a copy of the data table shown.

Data Table	
Solution	Flame Color
Calcium chloride	
Potassium chloride	
Boric acid	
Copper(II) sulfate	
Sodium chloride	
Unknown	
Identity of Unknown	

2. Light the Bunsen burner. **CAUTION** *Put on safety goggles and a lab apron. Tie back loose hair and clothing before working with a flame.*

3. Dip the wire loop into the calcium chloride solution and then place the loop in the flame as shown. Observe and record the color of the flame.

4. Clean the loop by dipping it into hydrochloric acid. Then, while holding the loop over a sink, rinse away the acid with distilled water. **CAUTION** *Keep hydrochloric acid away from your skin and clothing. Do not breathe in its vapor.*

5. Repeat Steps 3 and 4 with each of the other solutions. Be careful not to transfer any solution from one container to another. **CAUTION** *These chemicals are poisonous. Do not let them get on your skin.*

Part B: Examining an Unknown Solution

6. Obtain the unknown solution from your teacher.

7. Repeat Steps 3 and 4 using the unknown solution. Compare your observations with the other data you recorded to identify the unknown. **CAUTION** *Wash your hands thoroughly before leaving the laboratory.*

Analyze and Conclude

1. **Comparing and Contrasting** Is there a relationship between the color of the flame and the color of the solution?

2. **Formulating Hypotheses** How do these substances produce light of different colors?

3. **Drawing Conclusions** A forensic scientist does a flame test on a substance that was found at a crime scene. What might the scientist conclude if the flame turns green?

Go Further There is another test that you can use to distinguish elements by color. With your teacher supervising, dip a wire loop in borax. Heat the loop in a flame until the borax melts. Remove the loop from the flame and let the borax cool. It will form a clear glass bead. Dip the bead in a tiny sample of solid copper sulfate and return the loop to the flame for a few seconds. Remove the loop and observe the color of the bead as it cools.

Analyze and Conclude
1. There is no relationship between flame color and solution color.
2. When the compounds are placed in the flame, atoms absorb energy and electrons move to higher energy levels. As these electrons move back to lower energy levels, they release energy as visible light. The color of light produced depends on the difference in energy between two specific energy levels in an atom.
3. The green flame indicates that the substance may contain copper, barium, or boron.
Visual, Logical

Using Flame Tests   L2

Objective
After completing this activity, students will be able to
- observe that different substances produce different colors when placed in a flame.

Skills Focus **Observing, Predicting, Using Data Tables, Drawing Conclusions**

Prep Time 20 minutes

Advance Prep Provide each lab group with a sample of each solution and unknown in a small, labeled container with a lid. Film canisters work well and they can be obtained free of charge from any photo shop. Prepare solutions that are about 0.1 M. Provide 0.1 M HCl in a glass container.

Class Time 40 minutes

Safety Students need to wear safety goggles and lab aprons. Review proper use of the Bunsen burner and appropriate safety precautions for using flames. Make sure long hair is tied back and loose clothing is not worn. Some of the substances are extremely toxic if ingested. Make sure students wash their hands thoroughly before leaving the laboratory.

Teaching Tips
- Demonstrate proper technique for performing flame tests and cleaning the wire loop between samples. Stress the importance of not contaminating one sample with another.
- Have students test the sodium chloride solution last because it can remain on the loop and make it difficult to see the other colors.
- Stress the importance of recording specific colors, for example, "fire-engine red" instead of simply "red."

Expected Outcome Students should be able to make accurate observations of flame colors and use them to identify their unknown solutions.

Sample Data
The following flame colors are characteristic: calcium: orange; potassium: violet; boron: light-green; copper: green; sodium: yellow-orange.

Go Further

The copper-glass bead will change from green to blue as it cools.
Kinesthetic, Visual

Study Guide

Study Tip

Organize New Information
Tell students to organize the key information from the chapter into one comprehensive document. They should consider creating an outline, a chart, a set of flashcards, a time line, or a concept map to help them visualize the relationships. For example, they might wish to organize all of the information in this chapter on an annotated time line. They could include drawings that illustrate each atomic model. They could also label the drawings with vocabulary terms and their definitions.

Thinking Visually

a. p^+
b. $1-$
c. 0
d. 1
e. 1

Study Guide

4.1 Studying Atoms

Key Concepts

- Dalton proposed the theory that all matter is made up of individual particles called atoms, which cannot be divided.
- Thomson's experiments provided the first evidence that atoms are made of even smaller particles.
- According to Rutherford's model, all of an atom's positive charge is concentrated in its nucleus.

Vocabulary
nucleus, *p. 105*

4.2 The Structure of an Atom

Key Concepts

- Protons, electrons. and neutrons are subatomic particles.
- Protons, electrons, and neutrons can be distinguished by mass, charge, and location in an atom.
- Atoms of different elements have different numbers of protons.
- Isotopes of an element have the same atomic number but different mass numbers because they have different numbers of neutrons.

Vocabulary
proton, *p. 108*
electron, *p. 108*
neutron, *p. 109*
atomic number, *p. 110*
mass number, *p. 110*
isotopes, *p. 112*

120 *Chapter 4*

4.3 Modern Atomic Theory

Key Concepts

- An electron in an atom can move from one energy level to another when the atom gains or loses energy.
- Scientists use the electron cloud model to describe the possible locations of electrons around the nucleus.
- An electron cloud is a good approximation of how electrons behave in their orbitals.
- The most stable electron configuration is the one in which the electrons are in orbitals with the lowest possible energies.

Vocabulary
energy levels, *p. 114*
electron cloud, *p. 116*
orbital, *p. 117*
electron configuration, *p. 118*
ground state, *p. 118*

Thinking Visually

Table of Properties Use information from the chapter to complete the table below.

Particle	Proton	Electron	Neutron
Symbol	a. ?	e^-	n
Relative charge	1+	b. ?	c. ?
Relative mass	d. ?	$\frac{1}{1836}$	e. ?

 Chapter Resources

Print
- ***Chapter and Unit Tests,*** Chapter 4 Test A and Test B
- ***Test Prep Resources,*** Chapter 4

Technology
- ***Computer Test Bank,*** Chapter Test 4
- ***Interactive Textbook,*** Chapter 4
- ***Go Online,*** PHSchool.com, Chapter 4

Assessment

 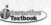
Reviewing Content

Choose the letter that best answers the question or completes the statement.

1. One of the first people to state that matter is made up of atoms was
   a. Democritus.   b. Aristotle.
   c. Dalton.   d. Rutherford.

2. Dalton's model of an atom is best described as
   a. a solar system.   b. a solid sphere.
   c. a plum pudding.   d. an electron cloud.

3. Who provided the first evidence that atoms contain subatomic particles?
   a. Dalton   b. Rutherford
   c. Thomson   d. Bohr

4. Almost all the mass of an atom is located in its
   a. protons.   b. electrons.
   c. electron cloud. d. nucleus.

5. An electron is a particle with
   a. a negative charge, found in the nucleus.
   b. a positive charge, found in the nucleus.
   c. no charge, found outside the nucleus.
   d. a negative charge, found outside the nucleus.

6. Which particle is the least massive?
   a. proton   b. electron
   c. neutron   d. nucleus

7. All atoms of an element have the same
   a. mass number.   b. number of isotopes.
   c. atomic number. d. number of neutrons.

8. The number of neutrons in an atom equals the
   a. mass number minus atomic number.
   b. atomic number plus number of electrons.
   c. mass number plus atomic number.
   d. atomic number minus mass number.

9. The atomic number of sulfur is 16. How many electrons are there in an atom of sulfur-34?
   a. 16   b. 34
   c. 18   d. 50

10. Atoms emit energy as light when
    a. electrons move to a higher energy level.
    b. electrons move to a lower energy level.
    c. protons move to a higher energy level.
    d. protons move to a lower energy level.

Understanding Concepts

11. Why must indirect evidence be used to study the structure of atoms?

12. What evidence convinced Dalton that elements must be made of individual particles called atoms?

13. In Thomson's experiment, why was the glowing beam repelled by a negatively charged plate?

14. What evidence supported Thomson's hypothesis that the negative particles he observed came from inside atoms?

15. Compare the mass and volume of the nucleus to the total mass and volume of an atom.

16. Compare the relative masses of protons, neutrons, and electrons in an atom.

17. What is the difference between the atomic number of an atom and its mass number?

18. If the atomic number of an atom is 11, how many electrons does the atom have? Explain.

19. If an atom has an atomic number of 6 and a mass number of 14, how many protons, electrons, and neutrons are in the atom?

20. What part of Dalton's theory was modified after the discovery of isotopes?

21. Which isotope of oxygen is represented by the drawing—oxygen-16, oxygen-17, or oxygen-18? Assume that all the protons and neutrons in the nucleus are visible in the drawing. Give a reason for your answer.

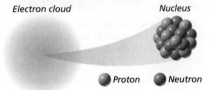

Electron cloud   *Nucleus*

● *Proton*   ● *Neutron*

22. What is the main difference between Bohr's model of the atom and the atomic theory that is currently accepted?

23. What does it mean to say that an atom is in an excited state?

Homework Guide

Section	Questions
4.1	1–2, 11–14, 24–25, 34
4.2	3–9, 15–21, 26–33, 37
4.3	10, 22–23, 35–36

Assessment

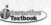 If your class subscribes to the Interactive Textbook, your students can go online to access an interactive version of the Student Edition and a self-test.

Reviewing Content

1. a	2. b	3. c
4. d	5. d	6. b
7. c	8. a	9. a
10. b		

Understanding Concepts

11. Atoms are too small to observe directly.

12. The ratio of the mass of elements in a compound is always the same.

13. The beam contained negatively charged particles, and like charges repel.

14. The particles were much less massive than the lightest known atom. The same particles were produced no matter which metal was used as the origin of the particles.

15. Almost all of the mass of an atom is located in the nucleus. The volume of the nucleus is much smaller than the volume of the atom as a whole.

16. Protons and neutrons have almost the same mass, which is about 2000 times greater than the mass of an electron.

17. The atomic number represents the number of protons or electrons in the atom. The mass number represents the number of protons and neutrons.

18. Because an atom must be neutral, it has 11 electrons to balance the charge on the 11 protons.

19. Six protons, six electrons, eight neutrons

20. All atoms of an element are identical.

21. Oxygen-17 because there are eight protons and nine neutrons

22. Bohr assumed that electrons traveled in orbits around the nucleus. Current atomic theory assumes that electrons do not travel in fixed paths.

23. One or more of the electrons in an atom have moved from the ground state to an orbital with a higher energy.

Critical Thinking

24. There are no external charged plates in setup A.

25. Because neutrons have no charge, the charged plates would not deflect the beam.

26. Carbon-14

27. A neutral particle is more difficult to detect than a charged particle because charged plates do not deflect its path.

28. The atom would have a negative charge, and atoms are neutral.

29. They are atoms of different elements because they have different numbers of protons. All atoms of a given element have the same number of protons.

Math Skills

30. 31 neutrons; 26 electrons

31. 19 protons, 19 electrons, 20 neutrons

32. Two protons and two neutrons

Concepts in Action

33. Iron-59 is different from other isotopes of iron because it contains 33 neutrons. It is the same as other isotopes because they all contain 26 protons.

34. Possible choices for the top-down analogy include a stone sculpture, a clay pot, or a carved wooden object, such as a totem pole. Choices for the bottom-up analogy include a brick wall, a bead necklace, a tile floor, or a patchwork quilt.

35. You cannot be certain because elements other than barium also may produce a green color.

36. Each element used in neon lights produces a distinctive color when its atoms are excited. If there are multiple colors, there must be multiple elements present.

37. With a scanning tunneling microscope, scientists can gather previously unavailable data about atoms, such as how atoms are arranged on the surface of materials. An electron microscope could not be developed until scientists knew that electrons existed.

PHSchool.com

Your students can independently test their knowledge of the chapter and print out their test results for your files.

Critical Thinking

24. Controlling Variables Look at the drawing of the experimental setup in Figure 5A. Explain how the setup is a control for the setup in Figure 5B.

25. Predicting How would the results of Thomson's experiment change if the beam were a stream of neutrons instead of a stream of electrons?

26. Interpreting Diagrams The atomic number of carbon is 6. The atomic number of nitrogen is 7. The atomic number of oxygen is 8. Name the isotope represented by the drawing.

Electron cloud   *Nucleus*

● Proton   ● Neutron

27. Hypothesizing Why were the proton and electron discovered before the neutron?

28. Applying Concepts Explain why a neutral atom cannot have one proton, one neutron, and two electrons.

29. Classifying The nucleus of an atom contains six neutrons and six protons. The nucleus of a second atom contains six neutrons and five protons. Are they atoms of different elements or isotopes of the same element? Explain your answer.

Math Skills

30. Calculating The atomic number for iron is 26. How many neutrons are in the nucleus of an iron atom with a mass number of 57? How many electrons does the iron atom have?

31. Applying Concepts If a potassium atom has an atomic number of 19 and a mass number of 39, how many protons, electrons, and neutrons are in the atom?

32. Applying Concepts A helium-4 atom has twice as many protons as a hydrogen atom. How many protons and how many neutrons are in the nucleus of a helium-4 atom?

Concepts in Action

33. Comparing and Contrasting The compound in blood that carries oxygen to cells throughout the body contains iron. Iron has an atomic number of 26. Iron-59 is used to diagnose disorders in the blood. How is iron-59 different from all other isotopes of iron? How is it the same?

34. Using Analogies Scientists working in the field of nanotechnology use either a top-down or bottom-up approach to construct tiny objects. Give an example of a visible structure that was made using the bottom-up approach and one that was made using the top-down approach.

35. Inferring If you see a green color when fireworks explode, can you be certain that the fireworks contained a barium compound? Give a reason for your answer.

36. Relating Cause and Effect Brightly colored neon lights consist of tubes filled with a gas. When an electric current passes through the tubes, different colors are emitted. Why might you conclude that the tubes in a multicolored display contain more than one element?

37. Writing in Science Better technology leads to an increase in scientific knowledge. An increase in knowledge allows for the invention of new technology. Write a paragraph discussing these statements. Use a scanning tunneling microscope as your example.

Performance-Based Assessment

Preparing a Survey Write ten questions you could ask to find out what people know about the modern model of an atom. Figure out the best order for the questions to test someone's knowledge fairly. Be prepared to explain your choices.

Go Online
PHSchool.com

For: Self-grading assessment
Visit: PHSchool.com
Web Code: cca-1040

Performance-Based Assessment

Students should ask at least one question about the overall structure of an atom, the properties of subatomic particles, and the behavior of electrons. Students should be able to explain the order they have chosen.

Standardized Test Prep for Indiana

Using Data Tables

When presented with a question that is related to a data table, read the title of the table to see what type of data it contains. Then look at the headings of the columns and rows to see how the data are organized. The table below lists properties for subatomic particles. There is a row for each particle and a column for each property. Read the question to find out which data you will need to answer the question. In this case, you will need the data on relative charge.

Properties of Subatomic Particles

Particle	Symbol	Relative Charge	Relative Mass (proton = 1)
Electron	e^-	1–	$\dfrac{1}{1836}$
Proton	p^+	1+	1
Neutron	n	0	1

Which of the following statements is true?
(A) The charge on a proton is larger than the charge on an electron.
(B) The charge on a proton is smaller than the charge on an electron.
(C) The charge on a proton is identical to the charge on an electron
(D) The charge on a proton is equal in size but opposite to the charge on an electron.
(E) A proton is a neutral particle.

(Answer: D)

Choose the letter that best answers the question or completes the statement.

1. J. J. Thomson demonstrated that electrons
(A) have a negative electric charge.
(B) have a positive electric charge.
(C) are repelled by a positively charged object.
(D) are attracted to a negatively charged object.
(E) do not have an electric charge.

2. According to Dalton's atomic theory, an atom is
(A) made of smaller particles.
(B) a particle with a positive charge.
(C) the smallest particle of an element.
(D) in constant motion.
(E) a particle with a negative charge.

3. Electrons in the first energy level of an atom
(A) have no energy.
(B) have the lowest possible energy.
(C) have the highest possible energy.
(D) are in an excited state.
(E) are in an unstable state.

4. Most alpha particles pass through a thin layer of gold without deflection because gold atoms
(A) are filled with positively charged matter.
(B) have no overall charge.
(C) have a negatively charged nucleus.
(D) do not have a nucleus.
(E) have a dense nucleus surrounded by space.

Use the data table to answer Question 5.

Comparison of Oxygen Isotopes

Property	Oxygen-16	Oxygen-18
Protons	8	8
Neutrons	8	10
Electrons	8	8
Percentage in nature	99.757	0.205

5. What is the mass number of oxygen-18?
(A) 8
(B) 10
(C) 16
(D) 18
(E) 0.205

6. An electron configuration describes
(A) regions of space around the nucleus of an atom.
(B) possible energies that an electron can have.
(C) the arrangement of electrons in an atom.
(D) the emission of light from an excited atom.
(E) the number of possible orbitals in an atom.

 Standards Guide

Question	Standards
2	ICP.7.1
4	ICP.7.1
5	ICP.7.2
6	ICP.7.2

Atomic Structure **123**

Planning Guide

SECTION OBJECTIVES	STANDARDS		ACTIVITIES and LABS
	NATIONAL	STATE	
5.1 Organizing the Elements, pp. 126–129 🕐 1 block or 2 periods **5.1.1 Describe** how Mendeleev arranged the elements in his table. **5.1.2 Explain** how the predictions Mendeleev made and the discovery of new elements demonstrated the usefulness of his periodic table.	A-1, A-2, B-2, G-1, G-2, G-3	ICP.5.2	**SE** Inquiry Activity: How Much Data Do You Need to Identify a Pattern? p. 125 **L2** **SE** Quick Lab: Making a Model of a Periodic Table, p. 128 **L2**
5.2 Modern Periodic Table, pp. 130–138 🕐 1 block or 2 periods **5.2.1 Describe** the arrangement of elements in the modern periodic table. **5.2.2 Explain** how the atomic mass of an element is determined and how atomic mass units are defined. **5.2.3 Identify** general properties of metals, nonmetals, and metalloids. **5.2.4 Describe** how properties of elements change across a period in the periodic table.	A-1, A-2, B-1, B-2	ICP.5.2, ICP.5.3	**SE** Quick Lab: Defining a Metal, p. 135 **L2** **SE** Exploration Lab: Predicting the Density of an Element, pp. 150–151 **L2** **TE** Teacher Demo: Period 3 Properties, p. 138 **L2** **LM** Investigation 5A: Analyzing Patterns in the Periodic Table **L2**
5.3 Representative Groups, pp. 139–145 🕐 1 block or 2 periods **5.3.1 Relate** the number of valence electrons to groups in the periodic table and to properties of elements in those groups. **5.3.2 Predict** the reactivity of some elements based on their locations within a group. **5.3.3 Identify** some properties of common A group elements.	B-1, B-2, B-3, C-1, C-5, F-1, F-3, F-5	ICP.5.2, ICP.5.3	**LM** Investigation 5B: Comparing Chemical Properties **L1**

RESOURCES
PRINT and TECHNOLOGY

RSW Section 5.1 **L1**

T Chapter 5 Pretest **L2**
Section 5.1 **L2**

P Chapter 5 Pretest **L2**
Section 5.1 **L2**

NSTA *SCiLINKS* **GO** Periodic table **L2**

PLM Lab 2: Predicting the Density of an Element **L2**

RSW Section 5.2 **L1**

RSW Math Skill **L2**

T Section 5.2 **L2**

P Section 5.2 **L2**

NSTA *SCiLINKS* **GO** Periodic law **L2**

RSW Section 5.3 **L1**

Discovery SCHOOL **DC** You Are What You Eat **L2**

T Section 5.3 **L2**

P Section 5.3 **L2**

SCIENCE NEWS **GO** Elements **L2**

SECTION ASSESSMENT

SE Section 5.1 Assessment, p. 129

iT Section 5.1

SE Section 5.2 Assessment, p. 138

iT Section 5.2

SE Section 5.3 Assessment, p. 145

iT Section 5.3

Go Online

Go online for these Internet resources.

PHSchool.com
Web Code: cca-1050

SCIENCE NEWS
Web Code: cce-1053

NSTA *SCiLINKS*
Web Code: ccn-1051
Web Code: ccn-1052

Materials for Activities and Labs

Quantities for each group

STUDENT EDITION

Inquiry Activity, p. 125
stapled stack of paper with familiar phrases (some letters replaced with squares)

Quick Lab, p. 128
resealable plastic sandwich bag, different colored paint chip strips

Quick Lab, p. 135
forceps; magnesium; test tubes; test-tube rack; graduated cylinder; 20 mL 2 M HCl; small pieces of sulfur, aluminum, and silicon

Exploration Lab, pp. 150–151
unlined white paper, scissors, metric ruler, balance, forceps, silicon, tin, lead shot, 50-mL graduated cylinder, graph paper, periodic table

TEACHER'S EDITION

Teacher Demo, p. 138
6-volt battery, flashlight bulb with holder, 3 pieces of insulated wire with the ends stripped, 2.5-cm aluminum strip, small silicon chip, 2.5-cm piece of sulfur

Build Science Skills, p. 147
empty containers of fortified food products such as milk, juice, salt, and bread

Chapter Assessment

CHAPTER ASSESSMENT

SE Chapter Assessment, pp. 153–154
CUT Chapter 5 Test A, B
CTB Chapter 5
iT Chapter 5
PHSchool.com GO
Web Code: cca-1050

STANDARDIZED TEST PREP

SE Chapter 5, p. 155
TP Diagnose and Prescribe

Interactive Textbook with assessment at PHSchool.com

Before you teach

From the Author

David Frank
Ferris State University

Big Ideas

The arrangement of elements by atomic number produces a periodic table that reflects the underlying structure of atoms. Elements in a group have similar properties because they have the same number of valence electrons. Thus, the organization of the periodic table demonstrates the usefulness of the atomic theory taught in Chapter 4.

Matter and Change Mendeleev couldn't organize his table by atomic number because the subatomic structure of elements wasn't known in 1869. Instead, he arranged elements by atomic mass. Sometimes he had to violate this organizing principle by placing an element with a larger atomic mass before one with a smaller atomic mass so that elements with similar properties ended up in the same group. Because Mendeleev recognized that the periodic table was based on an actual pattern in nature, he had the confidence to leave blank spaces in his table when the known properties of elements didn't match those of the next available group. He even predicted properties for some missing elements. When germanium and gallium were discovered, their properties were a close match for the properties predicted for eka-silicon and eka-aluminum, which helped demonstrate the predictive power of the periodic law.

In Sections 5.2 and 5.3, specific elements are used to illustrate general trends. Some students may be overwhelmed by the amount of information provided. It is most important for students to know the general properties and locations of metals, nonmetals, and metalloids. Help them focus on the general properties of representative groups (for example, halogens are the most reactive nonmetals) rather than on the individual properties of fluorine, chlorine, and iodine.

Energy Although aluminum is the most abundant metal in Earth's crust, it was not commonly used until the late 1800s. Charles Hall developed an electrolytic process to recover the pure metal from its bauxite ore. Because this process is energy-intensive, recycling of aluminum helps conserve energy.

Chemistry Refresher

Organizing the Elements 5.1

After Lavoisier classified elements into metals, nonmetals, gases and earths in 1789, there were many attempts to find a rational system for organizing the elements. In 1829, Johann Döbereiner proposed a law of triads. A triad is a group of similar elements in which the properties of the middle element fall midway between the properties of the lighter and heavier elements as shown here for the atomic masses of alkali metals. Notice that the atomic mass of sodium (22.990) is close to the arithmetic mean of the atomic masses of lithium and potassium: $(6.941 + 39.098)/2 = 23.02$.

Element	Symbol	Atomic Mass
Lithium	Li	6.941
Sodium	Na	22.990
Potassium	K	39.098

In 1865, John Newlands arranged elements into seven columns in order of increasing atomic mass. The arrangement was inspired by the notes in a Western musical scale. Many modern chemists credit Newlands with the concept of periodicity, which he described in his law of octaves. However, he was not able to develop a useful system from his concept. In 1865, William Odling revised Newlands's system and produced a table that was similar to the one developed by Mendeleev. However, Odling did not explain the relationships shown in his table. In 1870, the German chemist Lothar Meyer published a plot of atomic volume vs. atomic mass, which showed a series of waves with sharp peaks at the beginning of each new period. Meyer is sometimes credited with an independent discovery of the periodic table. When Mendeleev prepared his table, he was not aware of the work of Newlands, Odling, or Meyer.

Address Misconceptions

Students may think that advances in science are always achieved by scientists working alone. They may not realize that most advances are the result of contributions by many scientists. For a strategy to overcome this misconception, see **Address Misconceptions** *on* **page 129.**

CHAPTER 5

Assessment

 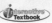
Reviewing Content

Choose the letter that best answers the question or completes the statement.

1. Mendeleev arranged the elements in his periodic table in order of
   a. atomic number.   b. number of electrons.
   c. mass.   d. number of neutrons.

2. Mendeleev's decision to leave gaps in his periodic table was supported by the discovery of
   a. electrons.   b. protons.
   c. argon.   d. gallium.

3. In a modern periodic table, elements are arranged in order of
   a. atomic number.   b. number of isotopes.
   c. atomic mass.   d. number of neutrons.

4. How many periods does the periodic table have?
   a. 18   b. 7
   c. 9   d. 8

5. An atomic mass unit is
   a. one twelfth the mass of a carbon-12 atom.
   b. the mass of a carbon-12 atom.
   c. the mass of a neutron.
   d. the mass of a proton.

6. An element that is shiny and conducts electric current is likely to be a
   a. gas.   b. metal.
   c. metalloid.   d. nonmetal.

7. Copper is an example of
   a. an alkali metal.   b. an alkaline earth metal.
   c. a nonmetal.   d. a transition metal.

8. Elements that have the same number of valence electrons are
   a. in the same period.
   b. in the same group.
   c. called noble gases.
   d. called transition metals.

9. The most reactive metals are the
   a. transition metals. b. alkaline earth metals.
   c. alkali metals.   d. metalloids.

10. Which elements are all gases at room temperature?
    a. Group 1A   b. Period 3
    c. Group 7A   d. Group 8A

Understanding Concepts

11. What information did Mendeleev have about the elements he organized into a periodic table?

12. How did Mendeleev know where to leave the spaces in his table?

13. Why is the table of the elements shown in Figure 7 called a periodic table?

14. Why does the number of elements vary from period to period?

15. Explain how the atomic mass of an element is affected by the distribution of its isotopes in nature.

16. List three ways that the elements in the periodic table can be classified.

17. In general, what happens to the reactivity of elements in groups labeled A as atomic numbers increase across a period?

18. Why don't the elements within an A group in the periodic table have identical properties?

19. Why was it difficult to discover the noble gases?

Use this portion of the periodic table to answer Questions 20–23.

14	15	16	17
Si	**P**	**S**	**Cl**
Silicon	Phosphorus	Sulfur	Chlorine
28.086	30.974	32.06	35.453
32	33	34	35
Ge	**As**	**Se**	**Br**
Germanium	Arsenic	Selenium	Bromine
72.59	74.922	78.96	79.904

20. How many of the elements shown are metals? How many are nonmetals? How many are metalloids?

21. Which element is a liquid at room temperature and which is a gas at room temperature?

22. Which of the two halogens shown is more reactive? Give a reason for your answer.

23. Does selenium have more in common with sulfur or bromine? Explain your answer.

The Periodic Table **153**

Homework Guide

Section	Questions
5.1	1–2, 11–12
5.2	3–7, 13–17, 20–21, 23–25, 38
5.3	8–10, 18–19, 22, 26–37, 39–40

Assessment

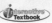 If your class subscribes to the Interactive Textbook, your students can go online to access an interactive version of the Student Edition and a self-test.

Reviewing Content

1. c   2. d   3. a
4. b   5. a   6. b
7. d   8. b   9. c
10. d

Understanding Concepts

11. Mendeleev knew their relative masses and properties.
12. Mendeleev placed elements in the groups where they logically belonged based on their properties.
13. The table is called a periodic table because the properties of the elements repeat at regular intervals from row to row.
14. The number of elements per period varies because the number of available orbitals increases as the energy level increases.
15. An atomic mass is a weighted average of the atomic masses of an element's isotopes. The distribution of the isotopes determines how much each isotope affects the weighted average.
16. Elements can be classified by their state at room temperature; by whether they exist in nature; and by whether they are metals, nonmetals, or metalloids.
17. Across a period from left to right, metals become less reactive and nonmetals become more reactive, excluding the elements in Group 8A.
18. Elements in the same A group do not have identical properties because their valence electrons are in different energy levels.
19. The noble gases were difficult to discover because they are colorless, odorless, and very rarely react.
20. 0 metals, 5 nonmetals, and 3 metalloids
21. Bromine is a liquid and chlorine is a gas.
22. Chlorine is more reactive than bromine because the reactivity of nonmetals increases from the bottom to the top of a group.
23. Selenium has more in common with sulfur because they are in the same group and have the same number of valence electrons.

Critical Thinking

24. There is not enough data for the solid because solids at room temperature can be metals, nonmetals, or metalloids. There is enough data for the gas because there are no gaseous metals or metalloids at room temperature.
25. Boron, with an atomic mass of 10.81
26. Three
27. Cesium is an extremely reactive metal; argon is an extremely unreactive nonmetal.
28. Halogens are always found in nature in compounds because halogens are highly reactive nonmetals.
29. Silicon
30. You would choose fluorine because it is much more likely to react than nitrogen is.
31. Elements X and Y are in Group 1 (1A) and Element Z is in Group 17 (7A).
32. Elements Y and Z are gases; element X is a solid.
33. Element Y is hydrogen, because hydrogen is the only gas in Group 1.

Concepts in Action

34. The beaker might shatter.
35. Students are likely to say nitrogen and phosphorus.
36. An element that is helpful in small quantities may be harmful when present in larger quantities. For example, trace amounts of selenium help maintain the immune system, but larger amounts can cause nerve damage.
37. The books would not fall apart if stored in a noble-gas atmosphere.
38. There is a repeating pattern of days and months on a calendar. However, Tuesdays do not necessarily have a different set of properties from Thursdays and there are no trends among Tuesdays equivalent to the trends in atomic mass or reactivity within a group in the periodic table.
39. Magnesium is required to produce chlorophyll, the green pigment in plants.
40. The essays should contain accurate information and make a reasonable argument for the value of the element.

Critical Thinking

24. **Classifying** If you know that an element is a solid at room temperature, do you have enough data to classify the element as a metal, metalloid, or nonmetal? If you know that the element is a gas at room temperature, do you have enough data? Explain your answers.

25. **Applying Concepts** An element on the periodic table has two naturally occurring isotopes. One isotope has an atomic mass of about 10 amu. The other isotope has an atomic mass of about 11 amu. What is the name of this element?

26. **Predicting** How many valence electrons would an element with atomic number 113 have?

27. **Applying Concepts** Why are samples of the alkali metal cesium usually stored in argon gas?

28. **Applying Concepts** Why are halogens found in nature only in compounds?

29. **Applying Concepts** Which element on the periodic table has chemical properties that are most similar to those of carbon?

30. **Designing Experiments** If you were trying to make a compound of the noble gas xenon, would you use nitrogen or fluorine? Explain your choice.

Use the table to answer Questions 31–33.

Properties of Elements X, Y, and Z

Element	Melting Point	Boiling Point	Valence Electrons
X	97.80°C	883°C	1
Y	−259.34°C	−252.87°C	1
Z	−101.5°C	−34.04°C	7

31. **Analyzing Data** In general, where would you find Elements X, Y, and Z on the periodic table?

32. **Classifying** Describe the state of each element at room temperature based on its melting and boiling points.

33. **Drawing Conclusions** Use your answers to Questions 31 and 32 to identify element Y. Explain your reasoning.

Concepts in Action

34. **Predicting** What might happen to a heated beaker made from glass that does not contain boron if the beaker were placed in a pan of ice water?

35. **Inferring** Based on the content of most fertilizers, name two elements other than carbon that are found in compounds in plants.

36. **Making Generalizations** Explain how the amount of a trace element an organism is exposed to affects the element's ability to help or harm an organism. Use the example of selenium. (*Hint:* Refer to the discussion on page 149.)

37. **Problem Solving** Sometimes old books fall apart when they are stored in air. Use what you know about the reactivity of elements to propose a way that old books could be kept from falling apart.

38. **Using Analogies** Explain how a calendar is similar to a periodic table and how it is different.

39. **Relating Cause and Effect** When corn plants have yellow leaves, it is a sign that the plants lack an essential element. Which element must be added to the soil to produce leaves with a healthy green color?

40. **Writing in Science** You write for a newsletter that has a feature called Element of the Month. It is your turn to write the feature. Pick an element that you think is worthy of attention. Write a brief essay and suggest a photo to be used with your feature.

Performance-Based Assessment

Design Your Own Periodic Table Make a version of the periodic table that presents the information provided in Figure 7 in a different, but useful, way.

For: Self-grading assessment
Visit: PHSchool.com
Web Code: cca-1050

Performance-Based Assessment

Students should be able to give reasons for their designs.

Your students can independently test their knowledge of the chapter and print out their test results for your files.

Standardized Test Prep for Indiana

1. B   2. C   3. A
4. C   5. B   6. D
7. E

Standards Guide

Question	Standards
1	ICP.5.2
2	ICP.5.2
3	ICP.5.2
4	ICP.5.2
5	ICP.5.2

Test-Taking Tip

Narrowing the Choices

If after reading all the answer choices you are not sure which one is correct, eliminate those answers that you know are wrong. In the question below, first eliminate the answers that require a whole number. Then focus on the remaining choices.

6
C
Carbon
12.011

The number 12.011 is the

(A) atomic number for carbon.
(B) mass number for carbon.
(C) atomic mass of carbon-12.
(D) average atomic mass of carbon.
(E) percentage of carbon-12 in nature.

(Answer: D)

Choose the letter that best answers the question or completes the statement.

1. Which elements are as reactive as alkali metals?
  (A) alkaline earth metals
  (B) halogens
  (C) noble gases
  (D) transition metals
  (E) metalloids

2. How many valence electrons do atoms of oxygen and sulfur have?
  (A) 2
  (B) 4
  (C) 6
  (D) 8
  (E) 10

3. Moving across a period from left to right,
  (A) elements become less metallic.
  (B) elements become more metallic.
  (C) elements become more reactive.
  (D) elements become less reactive.
  (E) elements have fewer valence electrons.

4. Which statement *best* describes nonmetals?
  (A) Nonmetals are good conductors of heat and electric current.
  (B) Nonmetals are brittle solids.
  (C) Many general properties of nonmetals are opposite to those of metals.
  (D) Nonmetals are located on the left side of the periodic table.
  (E) All nonmetals are extremely reactive.

Use this portion of the periodic table to answer Questions 5–7.

13	14	15
Al	**Si**	**P**
Aluminum	Silicon	Phosphorus
26.982	28.086	30.974
31	32	33
Ga	**Ge**	**As**
Gallium	Germanium	Arsenic
69.72	72.59	74.922

5. Which list of elements contains only metalloids?
  (A) aluminum and gallium
  (B) silicon and germanium
  (C) phosphorus and arsenic
  (D) aluminum, silicon, and phosphorus
  (E) gallium, germanium, and arsenic

6. Which elements did Mendeleev leave spaces for in his first periodic table?
  (A) aluminum and phosphorus
  (B) aluminum and germanium
  (C) silicon and arsenic
  (D) gallium and germanium
  (E) gallium and aluminum

7. Which of the elements are among the most abundant in Earth's crust?
  (A) silicon and phosphorus
  (B) aluminum and phosphorus
  (C) phosphorus and arsenic
  (D) gallium and arsenic
  (E) aluminum and silicon

The Periodic Table **155**

Planning Guide

| SECTION OBJECTIVES | STANDARDS | | ACTIVITIES and LABS |
	NATIONAL	STATE	
6.1 Ionic Bonding, pp. 158–164 🕐 1 block or 2 periods **6.1.1 Recognize** stable electron configurations. **6.1.2 Predict** an element's chemical properties using number of valence electrons and electron dot diagrams. **6.1.3 Describe** how an ionic bond forms and how ionization energy affects the process. **6.1.4 Predict** the composition of an ionic compound from its chemical formula. **6.1.5 Relate** the properties of ionic compounds to the structure of crystal lattices.	A-1, B-1, B-2, G-1	ICP.5.2, ICP.5.3, ICP.5.6	**SE** Inquiry Activity: What Can the Shape of a Material Tell You About the Material? p. 157 **L2**
6.2 Covalent Bonding, pp. 165–169 🕐 1 block or 2 periods **6.2.1 Describe** how covalent bonds form and the attractions that keep atoms together in molecules. **6.2.2 Compare** polar and nonpolar bonds, and **demonstrate** how polar bonds affect the polarity of a molecule. **6.2.3 Compare** the attractions between polar and nonpolar molecules.	A-1, A-2, B-2	ICP.3.1, ICP.5.2, ICP.5.3, ICP.5.4, ICP.5.6	**SE** Quick Lab: Analyzing Inks, p. 167 **L2** **SE** Consumer Lab: Improving the Dyeing of Nonpolar Fabrics, pp. 184–185 **L2** **TE** Teacher Demo: Modeling Overall Polarity, p. 168 **L2** **TE** Teacher Demo: Surface Tension, p. 169 **L2** **LM** Investigation 6B: Comparing Ionic and Covalent Compounds **L1**
6.3 Naming Compounds and Writing Formulas, pp. 170–175 🕐 1 block or 2 periods **6.3.1 Recognize** and **describe** binary ionic compounds, metals with multiple ions, and polyatomic ions. **6.3.2 Name** and **determine** chemical formulas for ionic and molecular compounds.	A-1, A-2, B-2, G-2	ICP.5.6	**SE** Quick Lab: Modeling Molecules, p. 173 **L2** **LM** Investigation 6A: Playing the Ionic Compounds Card Game **L2**
6.4 The Structure of Metals, pp. 176–181 🕐 1 block or 2 periods **6.4.1 Describe** the structure and strength of bonds in metals. **6.4.2 Relate** the properties of metals to their structure. **6.4.3 Define** an alloy and **demonstrate** how the composition of an alloy affects its properties.	A-1, A-2, B-2, B-6, E-2, G-1, G-2, G-3	ICP.5.1, ICP.3.1	**TE** Teacher Demo: Comparing Bond Types, p. 177 **L2** **TE** Teacher Demo: Bronze and Brass Tones, p. 180 **L2**

RESOURCES PRINT and TECHNOLOGY		SECTION ASSESSMENT
RSW Section 6.1	**L1**	**SE** Section 6.1 Assessment, p. 164
MSPS Section 6.1	**L2**	
T Chapter 6 Pretest	**L2**	**iT** Section 6.1
Section 6.1	**L2**	
P Chapter 6 Pretest	**L2**	
Section 6.1	**L2**	
SC_INKS_ **GO** Ionic bonds	**L2**	
RSW Section 6.2	**L1**	**SE** Section 6.2 Assessment, p. 169
T Section 6.2	**L2**	
P Section 6.2	**L2**	**iT** Section 6.2
SC_INKS_ **GO** Covalent bonding	**L2**	
RSW Section 6.3	**L1**	**SE** Section 6.3 Assessment, p. 175
RSW Math Skill	**L2**	
MSPS Section 6.3	**L2**	**iT** Section 6.3
T Section 6.3	**L2**	
P Section 6.3	**L2**	
SC_INKS_ **GO** Chemical formulas	**L2**	
RSW Section 6.4	**L1**	**SE** Section 6.4 Assessment, p. 181
DC Good Conduct	**L2**	
T Section 6.4	**L2**	**iT** Section 6.4
P Section 6.4	**L2**	
SCIENCE NEWS **GO** Metals	**L2**	

Go Online

Go online for these Internet resources.

PHSchool.com
Web Code: cca-1060

SCIENCE NEWS
Web Code: cce-1064

 SC_INKS_
Web Code: ccn-1061
Web Code: ccn-1062
Web Code: ccn-1063

Materials for Activities and Labs

Quantities for each group

STUDENT EDITION

Inquiry Activity, p. 157
4 wood splints or small lab spatulas, sodium chloride, black construction paper, hand lens, alum, Epsom salts, sucrose

Quick Lab, p. 167
test paper, metric ruler, felt-tip markers, stapler, beaker, alcohol-water mixture, Petri dish

Quick Lab, p. 173
blue plastic-foam ball, black plastic-foam ball, 7 white gumdrops, toothpicks

Consumer Lab, pp. 184–185
tongs, 2 fabric test strips, hot dye bath containing methyl orange, clock or watch, paper towels, scissors, soap, hot iron(II) sulfate solution

TEACHER'S EDITION

Teacher Demo, p. 168
molecular model kit, 4 12-inch pieces of string or yarn, tape, overhead projector

Teacher Demo, p. 169
200-mL beaker, water, sewing needle, tweezers, dropper pipet

Teacher Demo, p. 177
salt lick (or rock salt), copper wire, hammer, goggles

Teacher Demo, p. 180
brass bell, bronze bell

Build Science Skills, p. 182
access to a library or the Internet, notepad for data collection

Chapter Assessment

CHAPTER ASSESSMENT

SE	Chapter Assessment, pp. 187–188
CUT	Chapter 6 Test A, B
CTB	Chapter 6
iT	Chapter 6
PHSchool.com GO	
Web Code: cca-1060	

STANDARDIZED TEST PREP

SE	Chapter 6, p. 189
TP	Diagnose and Prescribe

Interactive Textbook with assessment at PHSchool.com

Before you teach

From the Author

David Frank
Ferris State University

Big Ideas

The overriding theme of Chapter 6 is the principle that when the highest occupied energy level of an atom is filled with electrons, that atom tends to be stable. Except for elements in the first row of the periodic table, it takes eight electrons to fill the highest occupied energy level. For this reason, the principle is sometimes referred to as the octet rule. Because atoms of noble gases have an octet of valence electrons, these elements are extremely unlikely to react. Other elements must form bonds to achieve stable electron configurations.

Matter and Change Help students connect types of bonds to differences in properties among classes of substances. A good example is electrical conductivity. Covalent compounds do not conduct an electric current because their fundamental particles are neutral molecules with covalent bonds. Ionic compounds don't conduct in the solid state because their charged particles (ions) are fixed in position, but they do conduct as liquids because the ions are then free to move. Metals conduct even in the solid state due to their mobile electrons.

Forces and Motion Forces of attraction are the key to bond formation. Ionic bonds form because cations and anions attract one another. Covalent bonds form because the (positive) nuclei of two atoms are attracted to their shared electrons. Metallic bonds form because cations are attracted to a pool of shared valence electrons.

Energy The tendency for ionization energy to decrease from top to bottom within a group is related to another trend within groups—the increasing size of atomic radii. Valence electrons are shielded from the positive nucleus by all the nonvalence electrons. In larger atoms, such as cesium (Cs), there are more nonvalence electrons than in a smaller atom such as sodium (Na). So it takes less energy to remove an electron from cesium than from sodium. Ionization energy is important for explaining the behavior of metals. The ability to attract electrons is important for explaining the behavior for nonmetals.

Chemistry Refresher

Bond Strength in Ionic Compounds 6.1

An ionic compound forms when electrons are transferred from metal atoms to nonmetal atoms. The ions that form are in a three-dimensional array called a crystal lattice. Within the lattice, there are strong attractions between an ion and neighboring ions of opposite charge. The strength of the bonds depends on the arrangement of the ions, their sizes, and their charges. Crystals are classified by the angles at which the faces (sides) of the

Address Misconceptions

Objects become positively charged because they gain protons. However, electrons are the only subatomic particles that can be transferred during a chemical change. For a strategy to overcome this misconception, see **Address Misconceptions** on **page 159.**

crystal meet and by how many of the edges on a face are of equal length. Most binary ionic compounds, such as sodium chloride, have cube-shaped crystals. In a cubic crystal, all of the edges on a face are of equal length and all the faces meet at a 90° angle. A unit cell (like the one shown below) is the smallest unit of a crystal that shows the arrangement of ions. For a given arrangement, the bond strength increases as the charges on the ions increase and as the distance between ions decreases (with smaller ionic radii).

$= Na^+$

$= Cl^-$

Sodium Chloride Unit Cell

Electronegativity and Bond Types 6.2

Electronegativity is a quantity that describes an atom's ability to attract the electrons within a bond. Values for electronegativity are often based on values for ionization energy and electron affinity. Ionization energy is a measure of an atom's ability to lose electrons. Electron affinity is a measure of an atom's ability to gain electrons.

Go Online

PD LINKS

NSTA

For: Teaching methods for chemical bonds
Visit: www.SciLinks.org/PDLinks
Web Code: ccn-0699

Differences in electronegativity are used to predict the type of bond that will form between atoms of two elements. As the difference in electronegativity increases, the bond becomes more polar until the electrons are transferred and an ionic bond forms.

Electronegativity Values for Selected Elements

Li 1.0	Be 1.5	B 2.0	C 2.5	N 3.0	O 3.5	F 4.0
Na 0.9	Mg 1.2	Al 1.5	Si 1.8	P 2.1	S 2.5	Cl 3.0
K 0.8	Ca 1.0	Ga 1.6	Ge 1.8	As 2.0	Se 2.4	Br 2.8

Naming Compounds 6.3

The preferred method for naming ionic compounds of metals that have variable charge is the Stock system, which uses Roman numerals to represent the charge on the ion. However, an older system that uses a root word combined with different suffixes still persists for metals that have only two charges. In this older system, the suffix -*ous* is used for the ion with the lesser charge and the suffix -*ic* is used for the ion with the greater charge. Thus, an iron(II) ion is a ferrous ion and an iron(III) ion is a ferric ion. The older system does not indicate the actual charge on the ion.

Metallic Bonding 6.4

Address Misconceptions

Many students think that particles in solids cannot move. However, in all solids, particles constantly vibrate about a fixed position. For a strategy to overcome this misconception, see **Address Misconceptions** on **page 177**.

The valence electrons in a metal are often referred to as a "sea of electrons" because of their mobility. In general, the strength of a metallic bond increases with the number of valence electrons. A metal's melting point increases with bond strength. However, melting points for transition metals peak at Group 6B even though the number of valence electrons is still increasing across the period. According to quantum theory, valence electrons in metals are in a band of overlapping atomic orbitals. Properties of metals depend on electrons moving from lower to higher energy orbitals when energy is absorbed. The configuration in Group 6B metals is ideal because all the lower energy orbitals are filled while all the higher energy orbitals are unoccupied.

Build Reading Literacy

Outline

Understanding Text Structure
Strategy Help students focus on the text and not simply skim it. Outlining is a good strategy to apply to an entire section, if it is not excessively long, using the headings as major divisions. Outlining is best applied to sections in which the headings are parallel, and in which there are main headings and subheadings. Before you begin, choose a section for students to read and outline, such as Section 6.1, pp. 158–164.

Example
1. Before students read, have them preview the section's title and headings. Demonstrate and display how to make a skeleton outline for the section. Have students list the section title at the top level, the main headings as major divisions, and the sub-headings at the next level.

  I. Section Title
  A. Main Heading
    1. Subheading
      a. detail
      b. detail
      c. detail

2. Have students copy the skeleton outline as they read, filling in details under each main heading and subheading of the outline.
3. Tell students not to outline sections that focus on the details of cycles or processes. Students can represent these by diagrams and flowcharts rather than outlining.
4. After reading, have students review the entire section and their outlines to make sure they have included all vocabulary definitions and key concepts as main ideas or details under the appropriate levels of their outlines.

See p. 171 for a script on how to use the outline strategy with students. For additional Build Reading Literacy strategies, see pp. 161, 166, and 179.

ASSESS PRIOR KNOWLEDGE

Use the Chapter Pretest below to assess students' prior knowledge. As needed, review these Science Concepts and Math Skills with students.

Review Science Concepts

Sections 6.1 and 6.2 Review the structure of atoms. Remind students that a particle with a negative charge will attract a particle with a positive charge. Encourage students to recall what they have learned about valence electrons and electron configurations. Students should be familiar with the organization of the periodic table.

Section 6.3 Review the locations of elements in the periodic table.

Section 6.4 Have students review the general properties of metals. Review the difference in composition between a substance and a mixture.

Review Math Skills

Ratios and Proportions Students will need to understand ratios and proportions in order to determine chemical formulas.

Direct students to the **Math Skills** in the **Skills and Reference Handbook** at the end of the student text.

CHAPTER
6 Chemical Bonds

21st Century Learning
Self Direction

How can compounds be shown with electron dot diagrams?

Elements that do not have complete sets of valence electrons tend to react. In certain cases, the reaction involves the transfer of electrons between atoms. You can describe this process by using electron dot diagrams. Use the animation tools in presentation software to illustrate the formation of two different ionic compounds. Each animation should show how the transfer of one or more electrons between atoms results in the formation of the compound.

 Indiana's Academic Standards for Science

CHEMICAL ENERGY, REACTIONS, AND BONDING
ICP.5.1: Recognize and describe physical properties of matter and use these to differentiate between pure substances and mixtures; **ICP.5.2:** Use the periodic table to understand important patterns in properties of elements. Recognize that the pattern of properties of the elements correlates most closely with the configuration of the electrons in each element; **ICP.5.3:** Understand that the atomic number is unique to each element and is the number of protons in the nucleus of the element; **ICP.5.4:** Use the concept of the mole to relate number of moles and the mass of a sample of a pure substance of known chemical composition; **ICP.5.6:** Identify key indicators of a chemical change and classify simple types of chemical reactions. Differentiate between covalent, ionic, hydrogen and Van der Waals bonding, and write formulas for and name compounds of each type.

PROPERTIES OF MATTER
ICP.3.1: Describe how we use macroscopic properties of matter to model microscopic processes.

The calcium carbonate in shells and the silicon dioxide in sand are examples of compounds with different types of bonds.

Chapter Pretest

1. Describe the structure of atoms. *(An atom consists of a dense, positively charged nucleus containing protons and neutrons, surrounded by space in which negatively charged electrons move.)*
2. True or False: Objects with opposite charges attract one another. *(True)*
3. What are valence electrons? *(Electrons in the highest occupied energy level of an atom)*

4. Which group in the periodic table contains elements that hardly react at all? *(The noble gases)*
5. Where on the periodic table are nonmetals generally found? *(The right side)*
6. How do the compositions of mixtures differ from those of substances? *(The composition of a mixture can vary. The composition of a substance is fixed.)*

7. What property is being described when someone says that a solid is easily hammered into sheets? *(b)*
  a. Conductivity
  b. Malleability
  c. Melting point
  d. Density

Chapter Preview

Discovery SCHOOL

Video Field Trip

Good Conduct

ENGAGE/EXPLORE

Inquiry > Activity

What Can the Shape of a Material Tell You About the Material?   L2

Purpose In this activity, students begin to recognize that the shape of pieces of a compound could be related to its structure at the atomic level.

Skills Focus Observing, Comparing and Contrasting

 Prep Time 10 minutes

Materials 4 wood splints or small lab spatulas, sodium chloride, black construction paper, hand lens, alum, Epsom salts, sucrose

Class Time 15 minutes

Safety Students should wear safety goggles, lab aprons, and disposable plastic gloves.

Teaching Tips
- Point out that if all the samples of a substance have a similar shape, the shape may be a property of the substance.
- Encourage students to think about the spatial arrangement of the particles in a substance.

Expected Outcome Each substance forms crystals with a particular and different shape.

Think About It

1. Sodium chloride crystals are cubes. Alum crystals are small and irregular "cuboids" shaped like a cube that is missing part of a side. Crystals of Epsom salts look like cylinders with one or both ends pointed. Sucrose crystals may appear oblong with slightly slanted ends.
2. Although the samples have distinctive shapes, the shapes are not sufficiently distinct to help a person identify each substance. (Many crystals have the same general shape.)
3. Students may hypothesize that the arrangement of particles at the atomic level might be responsible for the different crystal shapes.

Visual, Logical

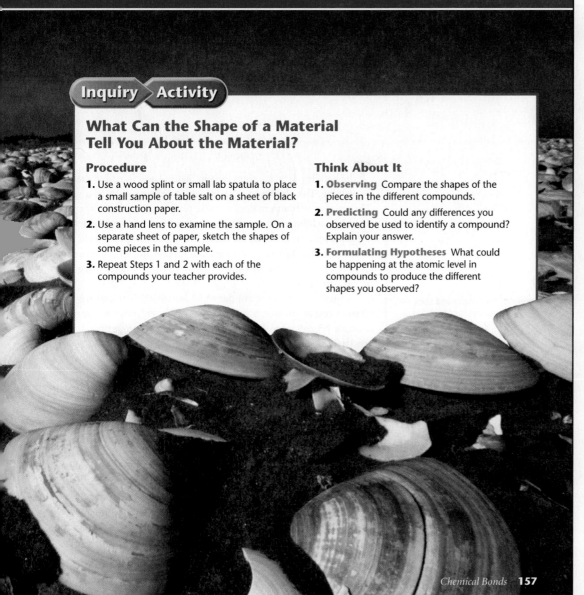

Inquiry > Activity

What Can the Shape of a Material Tell You About the Material?

Procedure

1. Use a wood splint or small lab spatula to place a small sample of table salt on a sheet of black construction paper.

2. Use a hand lens to examine the sample. On a separate sheet of paper, sketch the shapes of some pieces in the sample.

3. Repeat Steps 1 and 2 with each of the compounds your teacher provides.

Think About It

1. **Observing** Compare the shapes of the pieces in the different compounds.

2. **Predicting** Could any differences you observed be used to identify a compound? Explain your answer.

3. **Formulating Hypotheses** What could be happening at the atomic level in compounds to produce the different shapes you observed?

Chemical Bonds **157**

Discovery SCHOOL

Video Field Trip

Good Conduct

Encourage students to view the Video Field Trip "Good Conduct."

1 FOCUS

Objectives

6.1.1 Recognize stable electron configurations.

6.1.2 Predict an element's chemical properties using number of valence electrons and electron dot diagrams.

6.1.3 Describe how an ionic bond forms and how ionization energy affects the process.

6.1.4 Predict the composition of an ionic compound from its chemical formula.

6.1.5 Relate the properties of ionic compounds to the structure of crystal lattices.

Reading Focus

Build Vocabulary   L2

Word Forms Have students think of word forms related to *crystals* such as *crystalline* and *crystallize*. Have them discuss ways people commonly use these words—and the word *crystal*—and compare those usages to the way *crystals* is defined in Section 6.1.

Reading Strategy   L2

a. Form a cation **b.** Form an anion

2 INSTRUCT

Stable Electron Configurations
Integrate Social Studies   L2

In 1902, G.N. Lewis proposed "the theory of the cubical atom." He illustrated his theory with drawings of cubes with valence electrons placed at their corners. In his classic 1916 paper, "The Atom and the Molecule," Lewis simplified his diagrams by using dots to represent electrons and a symbol to represent the kernel of an atom.

Recreate the cube models for lithium and beryllium on the board or overhead projector. (Draw cubes with one and two corners circled, respectively.) Explain that each circle represents a valence electron. Then, have students refer to Figure 2 and draw their own cube models for boron, carbon, nitrogen, oxygen, and fluorine.
Logical, Visual

6.1 Ionic Bonding

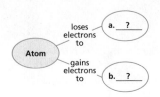

Standards: ICP.5.2, ICP.5.3, ICP.5.6

Reading Focus

Key Concepts

- When is an atom unlikely to react?
- What is one way in which elements can achieve stable electron configurations?
- How does the structure of an ionic compound affect its properties?

Vocabulary

- electron dot diagram
- ion
- anion
- cation
- chemical bond
- ionic bond
- chemical formula
- crystals

Reading Strategy

Sequencing Copy the concept map. As you read, complete the concept map to show what happens to atoms during ionic bonding.

```
                    loses
                  electrons      a.   ?
                     to
        Atom
                    gains
                  electrons      b.   ?
                     to
```

The handle of the titanium mug in Figure 1 was joined to the body by welding. The pieces were heated until their surfaces fused together. The welding of titanium does not take place in air. At the temperature at which welding occurs, titanium becomes hot enough to react with oxygen in the air, forming an oxide. The oxide makes the weld more brittle and likely to break. Because titanium does not react with a noble gas such as argon, the welding of titanium usually takes place in an argon atmosphere.

Argon's name is a reminder of its inactivity. It comes from the Greek word *argos*, which means "idle" or "inert." Why is argon very inactive yet oxygen is highly reactive? Chemical properties, such as reactivity, depend on an element's electron configuration.

Stable Electron Configurations

The highest occupied energy level of a noble gas atom is filled. **When the highest occupied energy level of an atom is filled with electrons, the atom is stable and not likely to react.** The noble gases have stable electron configurations with eight valence electrons (or two in the case of helium).

The chemical properties of an element depend on the number of valence electrons. Therefore, it is useful to have a model of atoms that focuses only on valence electrons. The models in Figure 2 are electron dot diagrams. An **electron dot diagram** is a model of an atom in which each dot represents a valence electron. The symbol in the center represents the nucleus and all the other electrons in the atom.

Figure 1 The handle and body of this titanium mug were welded together in an argon atmosphere. If titanium is allowed to react with oxygen in air, the compound that forms makes the weld more brittle and more likely to break.

158 *Chapter 6*

Section Resources

Print

- **Reading and Study Workbook With Math Support,** Section 6.1
- **Math Skills and Problem Solving Workbook,** Section 6.1
- **Transparencies,** Chapter Pretest and Section 6.1

Technology

- **Interactive Textbook,** Section 6.1
- **Presentation Pro CD-ROM,** Chapter Pretest and Section 6.1
- **Go Online,** NSTA SciLinks, Ionic bonds

Go Online
NSTA

For: Teaching methods for the
Visit: www.SciLinks.org/PDLinks
Web Code: ccn-0599

Metalloids 5.2

Many periodic tables use a diagonal line to divide the metallic and nonmetallic regions of the periodic table. Elements that lie close to the line are described as having properties intermediate to those of metals and nonmetals. Because these borderline elements look like metals, they are often referred to as metalloids even though they do not exhibit all the general properties of metals. There is not universal agreement on which elements to classify as metalloids. Polonium is often classified as a metal and astatine is sometimes classified as a nonmetal. (The classification of metalloids presents similar issues as the classification of colloids—the intermediate category between solutions and suspensions.)

Diagonal Relationships 5.3

Using the first element in a group to refer to the group as a whole, as in The Boron Family, can be misleading because there can be significant differences between the properties of the first element and the properties of the rest of the group. Sometimes the first element has more in common with the second element of the neighboring group than with the second element in its own group. These cross-group relationships are called diagonal relationships. They exist between lithium and magnesium, beryllium and aluminum, and boron and silicon.

Lithium and magnesium can serve as an example. Lithium is the only alkali metal to react with nitrogen in air to form a nitride. Magnesium reacts with nitrogen in air, too. Lithium carbonate and lithium hydroxide decompose when heated. So do magnesium carbonate and magnesium hydroxide. Carbonates and hydroxides of the other alkali metals are stable when heated. Many lithium compounds are less soluble in water than comparable compounds of other alkali metals. The lithium compounds are similar in solubility to magnesium compounds. Similarities between the chemistry of lithium and magnesium are mainly attributed to the similar sizes of their atoms and ions. (See the table of atomic and ionic radii in the Data Analysis on page 160.)

Build Reading Literacy

KWL (Know-Want-Learned)

What I Know/Want to Know/Learned
Strategy To help students access prior knowledge, set a purpose for reading, recall what has been read, and link new information to prior knowledge. The KWL strategy has students create and complete a three-column chart similar to the one below. As students read, they complete the Learned column.

Know	Want to Know	Learned

Finally, students categorize information they learned in a box titled Information I Expect to Use.

Information I Expect to Use

Assign a section in Chapter 5, such as Classes of Elements, pp. 135–136, for students to read. Before they begin, have them create and complete the first two columns of the KWL chart.

Example
1. Draw a three-column KWL chart on the board for students to copy.
2. Have students complete the Know column with facts, examples, and other information they already know about the topic.
3. Tell students to complete the Want to Know column with questions about the topic that they want answers to. Students may scan the section to help them generate questions.
4. Have students read the section to learn more about the topic and determine answers to their questions. As they read, have them note answers in the Learned column, along with other facts, examples, and details they learned.
5. Below their KWL chart, have students draw an Information I Expect to Use box. Have them review the information in the Learned column and use it to complete the box with the useful categories of information.

See p. 144 for a script on how to use the KWL strategy with students. For additional Build Reading Literacy strategies, see pp. 126, 131, 136, and 143.

...he Chapter Pretest below to assess
...dents' prior knowledge. As needed,
...view these Science Concepts with
students.

Review Science Concepts

Section 5.1 Have students recall how symbols are used to represent elements. Have them list examples of physical and chemical properties. Review three clues for recognizing a chemical change (a color change, production of a gas, formation of a precipitate).

Section 5.2 Ask students to recall that the atomic number of an element is the number of protons in an atom of the element and that each element has a different atomic number. Review the concept of isotopes and remind students that isotopes of an element have different numbers of neutrons.

Section 5.3 Have students review energy levels in preparation for a discussion of valence electrons. Ask students what they recall about the reactivity of elements such as oxygen and nitrogen.

5 The Periodic Table

21st Century Learning

Critical Thinking and Systems Thinking

What are periodic trends and why are they important?

The periodic table lists important information about the elements. This information is communicated in the text entries within the table and also in the arrangement of the table's rows and columns. After you have learned how to read the periodic table, create a Web page that explains periodic trends. Include both a graphic description and a written description of each trend. Your finished Web page should serve as a useful reference for someone wanting to find the information quickly.

Indiana's Academic Standards for Science

CHEMICAL ENERGY, REACTIONS, AND BONDING

ICP.5.2: Use the periodic table to understand important patterns in properties of elements. Recognize that the pattern of properties of the elements correlates most closely with the configuration of the electrons in each element; **ICP.5.3:** Understand that the atomic number is unique to each element and is the number of protons in the nucleus of the element.

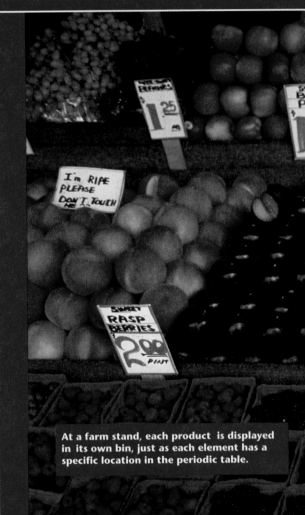

At a farm stand, each product is displayed in its own bin, just as each element has a specific location in the periodic table.

Chapter Pretest

1. Which of the following is a symbol for an element? *(b)*
a. Aluminum
b. Al
c. al
d. AL

2. Is flammability a physical property or a chemical property? *(A chemical property)*

3. What happens to the composition of matter during a physical change? *(It remains the same.)*

4. What does the atomic number of an element represent? *(The number of protons in an atom of the element)*

5. Isotopes of an element have different numbers of *(a)*
a. neutrons. b. electrons.
c. protons.   d. nuclei.

6. True or False: Electrons in atoms occupy orbitals in energy levels. *(True)*

7. Which element is more reactive, oxygen or nitrogen? *(Oxygen)*

Chapter Preview

DISCOVERY SCHOOL

Video Field Trip

You Are What You Eat

Inquiry › Activity

How Much Data Do You Need to Identify a Pattern?

Procedure

1. Your teacher will give you a stapled stack of paper. Look at the squares on the top sheet of paper. Try to figure out what familiar phrase you would see if all the squares were filled in. Record your prediction on the sheet.

2. Remove the top sheet and look at the second sheet. Again, try to figure out what letters belong in the squares. Record your prediction.

3. Continue this process until you have looked at all the sheets in the stack.

Think About It

1. **Observing** How did the information on the sheets change as you moved from the top to the bottom of the stack?

2. **Drawing Conclusions** How did the number of letters provided affect your ability to predict the phrase?

3. **Using Analogies** Describe another situation in which having more data makes it easier to recognize a pattern.

The Periodic Table **125**

DISCOVERY SCHOOL

Video Field Trip

You Are What You Eat

Encourage students to view the Video Field Trip "You Are What You Eat."

ENGAGE/E...

Inquiry › Activity

How Much Data Do You Need to Identify a Pattern?

Purpose In this activity, students identify a relationship between the amount of data available and the ability to recognize a pattern.

Skills Focus Predicting, Evaluating and Revising

Prep Time 15 minutes

Materials stapled stack of papers

Advance Prep Select a phrase that will be familiar to students. Draw a series of boxes on a sheet of paper to represent the letters of the phrase, leaving spaces between words. Make five copies of this sheet. Fill in two or three letters on the first copy. Add a few letters to each subsequent copy. Plan for two or three blanks on the fifth sheet. Give each student or group a stapled stack arranged in order of completeness with the least complete copy on top.

Class Time 10 minutes

Teaching Tips

• Before distributing the stacks, explain to students that they should not look ahead in the stack. For the activity to be successful, they must work with only one sheet at a time.

Expected Outcome Students' predictions will become increasingly accurate as they progress through the stack.

Think About It

1. There was more information.
2. Increasing the number of letters made it easier to predict the phrase.
3. In the suggested situations, the data must be limited to start. (If students are having trouble thinking of an example, ask what they can tell about a movie from a trailer or about a novel after reading one page.) **Logical**

For Enrichment L3

Use a numerical example to reinforce the need for enough data to reveal a pattern. Ask students to predict the next number in the sequence 3, 5, and 7. *(9)* Then say that the next number is 11. Ask what property the numbers 3, 5, 7, and 11 have in common. *(They are prime numbers.)* **Visual, Logical**

Standard: ICP.5.2

(left margin teacher notes)

Describe how Mendeleev arranged the elements in his table.

.2 **Explain** how the predictions Mendeleev made and the discovery of new elements demonstrated the usefulness of his periodic table.

Reading Focus

Build Vocabulary   L2

Word Forms Use the word *periodical* to help students understand the meaning of *periodic*. Explain that a periodical is published at regular intervals (weekly, monthly, or quarterly).

Reading Strategy   L2

a. Mendeleev arranged the elements in order of increasing mass so that elements with similar properties were in the same column. **b.** Mendeleev used the properties of existing elements to predict properties of undiscovered elements. **c.** The close match between Mendeleev's predictions and the actual properties of new elements showed how useful his periodic table could be.

2 INSTRUCT

The Search for Order
Build Reading Literacy   L1

Sequence Refer to **page 290D** in **Chapter 10**, which provides the guidelines for a sequence.

Have students create a flowchart showing the sequence of events described in the last two paragraphs on page 126. Ask, **Based on your sequence, what happened after Lavoisier grouped the known elements into four categories?** *(Scientists looked for different ways to classify the elements.)*
Verbal, Portfolio

(main body)

Figure 1 Older movies in video stores are placed into categories such as Drama or Comedy.

In a video store, the latest movies are usually placed on the shelves in alphabetical order. Older movies are grouped into categories such as Action or Comedy. The manager has to choose a set of categories and then place each movie in the most appropriate location.

Scientists faced a similar challenge when they looked for a logical way to organize the elements. They had to decide what categories to use and where to place each element. An organized table of the elements is one of the most useful tools in chemistry. The placement of elements on the table reveals the link between the atomic structure of elements and their properties.

The Search for Order

Until 1750, scientists had identified only 17 elements. These were mainly metals, such as copper and iron. The rate of discovery increased rapidly as chemists began to investigate materials in a systematic way. As the number of known elements grew, so did the need to organize them into groups based on their properties.

In 1789, French chemist Antoine Lavoisier (la VWAH zee ay) grouped the known elements into categories he called metals, nonmetals, gases, and earths. For the next 80 years, scientists looked for different ways to classify the elements. But none of their systems provided an organizing principle that worked for all the known elements. A Russian chemist and teacher, Dmitri Mendeleev (Duh MEE tree Men duh LAY uff), would discover such a principle.

126 *Chapter 5*

Section Resources

Mendeleev's Periodic Table

In the 1860s, Mendeleev was working on a textbook to use with his chemistry students. Because he needed to describe 63 elements, Mendeleev was looking for the best way to organize the information. He found a way to approach the problem while playing his favorite card game, a version of solitaire. In this game, the player sorts a deck of cards by suit and value. To finish the game, the player must end up with four columns, as shown in Figure 2. Each column contains cards of a single suit arranged in order by value.

Mendeleev's Proposal Mendeleev's strategy for organizing the elements was modeled on the card game. Mendeleev made a "deck of cards" of the elements. On each card, he listed an element's name, mass, and properties. He paid special attention to how each element behaved in reactions with oxygen and hydrogen. When Mendeleev lined up the cards in order of increasing mass, a pattern emerged. The key was to break the elements into rows, as shown in Figure 3.

⚫ **Mendeleev arranged the elements into rows in order of increasing mass so that elements with similar properties were in the same column.** The final arrangement was similar to a winning arrangement in solitaire, except that the columns were organized by properties instead of suits. Within a column, the masses increased from top to bottom. Mendeleev's chart was a periodic table. A **periodic table** is an arrangement of elements in columns, based on a set of properties that repeat from row to row.

Figure 2 A deck of cards can be divided into four suits—diamonds, spades, hearts, and clubs. In one version of solitaire, a player must produce an arrangement in which each suit is ordered from ace to king. This arrangement is a model for Mendeleev's periodic table.

Figure 3 This is a copy of a table that Mendeleev published in 1872. He placed the elements in groups based on the compounds they formed with oxygen or hydrogen. **Using Tables** *How many elements did Mendeleev place in Group II?*

Group I	Group II	Group III	Group IV	Group V	Group VI	Group VII	Group VIII
H = 1							
Li = 7	Be = 9.4	B = 11	C = 12	N = 14	O = 16	F = 19	
Na = 23	Mg = 24	Al = 27.3	Si = 28	P = 31	S = 32	Cl = 35.5	Fe = 56, Co = 59,
K = 39	Ca = 40	— = 44	Ti = 48	V = 51	Cr = 52	Mn = 55	Ni = 59, Cu = 63.
(Cu = 63)	Zn = 65	— = 68	— = 72	As = 75	Se = 78	Br = 80	
Rb = 85	Sr = 87	Yt = 88	Zr = 90	Nb = 94	Mo = 96	— = 100	Ru = 104, Rh = 104, Pd = 106, Ag = 108.
(Ag = 108)	Cd = 112	In = 113	Sn = 118	Sb = 122	Te = 125	I = 127	
Cs = 133	Ba = 137	Di = 138	Ce = 140				
(—)	—	—	—	Ta = 182	W = 184	—	Os = 195, Ir = 197,
—	—	Er = 178	La = 180				Pt = 198, Au = 199.
(Au = 199)	Hg = 200	Tl = 204	Pb = 207	Bi = 208			
—	—	—	Th = 231	—	U = 240		

The Periodic Table **127**

Integrate So...
Lavoisier based his ...
elements on a vast an...
data. He used Boyle's d...
element as a substance t...
cannot separate into simpl...
Most of the elements Lavoisi...
were elements, but his list did i...
heat, light, and five oxides that s...
had not been able to decompose.
Have students consider what it mean...
to "discover" an element by having
them research and compare discovery
dates for elements with the dates those
elements were first isolated. (For
example, beryllium was discovered
in 1797, but it was not isolated
until 1828.)
Verbal, Interpersonal

Mendeleev's Periodic Table
Use Visuals `L1`

Figure 3 Ask, **How is the table organized?** *(Elements are arranged in order of increasing mass.)* **What do the long dashes represent?** *(They represent undiscovered elements.)* **Why are masses listed with some of the dashes, but not with all of them?** *(Mendeleev was able to predict properties for some unknown elements based on the properties of neighboring elements.)*
Visual, Logical

FYI

In Section 5.1, the term *mass* is used as a shorthand for *atomic mass* because atomic mass is not defined until Section 5.2. Mendeleev was comparing the relative atomic masses of the elements. Mendeleev attended the first international chemistry congress in Karlsruhe in 1860. During that meeting, chemists agreed on a standard method for calculating atomic masses.

Customize for Inclusion Students

Learning Disabled
To reinforce the meaning of the word *periodic*, ask students to think of periodic activities in their own lives. Make a class list of these activities. Organize the list by time interval: daily, weekly, monthly, yearly, and so on. For example, students may have a weekly music lesson or a dance recital every six months. They celebrate a birthday once a year. You may also want to encourage students to think of periodic events that occur less frequently than once a year, for example, the Olympics or presidential elections.

Answer to . . .

Figure 3 *Mendeleev placed eight elements in Group II.*

Model
...iodic Table **L2**

...ve

...completing this activity, students
...be able to

...organize items in an array based on
properties.
• predict where an additional item
would fit in an incomplete array.

Skills Focus Classifying, Inferring,
Observing

 Prep Time 20 minutes

Materials resealable plastic sandwich
bag, different colored paint chip strips

Advance Prep For each group, collect
4 strips with distinctly different colors.
Make sure the color chips are about the
same size after you cut off any printing
number codes used to identify the
shades. Remove one chip from each set.
Place each set of chips in a bag.

Class Time 20 minutes

Expected Outcome Students are
likely to organize chips of the same color
in columns based on the intensity of the
shades so that the pattern of colors
repeats across the rows.

Analyze and Conclude
1. Students are likely to choose color
and shade.
2. Color or intensity of shade repeats
across each row.
3. Students should describe the
color and approximate shade of the
missing chip.
4. Both processes involve selecting
properties to organize related items in
a repeating pattern and predicting the
properties of missing items. However,
unlike the periodic table, the order of
the columns in the color array can be
arbitrary. **Visual, Logical**

 Quick **Lab**

Making a Model of a Periodic Table

Materials

plastic bag containing color chips

Procedure

1. Remove the color chips from the bag and
place them on a flat surface, color side up.

2. Identify a property that you can use to divide
the chips into groups. Then, identify a second
property that you can use to order the chips
from top to bottom within a group.

3. Use the properties you chose to arrange the
chips into a table with rows and columns.
Your teacher deliberately left out a chip from
each bag. Decide where to leave a gap in your
table for the missing chip.

Analyze and Conclude

1. **Classifying** What property did you use to
divide the color chips into groups? What
property did you use to arrange the chips
within a group from top to bottom?

2. **Making Generalizations** What pattern
repeats across each row of your table?

3. **Predicting** Based on its location on your
table, describe the missing chip.

4. **Comparing and Contrasting** Compare
the process you used to construct your table
to the process Mendeleev used to make his
table. Describe similarities and differences.

Mendeleev's Prediction Mendeleev could not make a complete table of the elements because many elements had not yet been
discovered. He had to leave spaces in his table for those elements. For
example, Mendeleev placed bromine (Br) in Group VII because
bromine and chlorine (Cl) have similar properties. This placement left
four spaces in row 4 between zinc (Zn) and bromine. Mendeleev had
only two elements, arsenic and selenium, to fill those spaces, based on
their masses. He placed arsenic and selenium in the columns where
they fit best and left gaps in the columns labeled Groups III and IV.

Mendeleev was not the first to arrange elements in a periodic table.
He was not even the first to leave spaces in a periodic table for missing
elements. But he was able to offer the best explanation for how the properties of an element were related to its location in his table.

An excellent test for the correctness of a scientific model, such as
Mendeleev's table, is whether the model can be used to make accurate
predictions. Mendeleev was confident that the gaps in his table would be
filled by new elements. He used the properties of elements located near
the blank spaces in his table to predict properties for undiscovered elements. Some scientists didn't accept these predictions. Others used the
predictions to help in their search for undiscovered elements.

For: Links to periodic table
Visit: www.SciLinks.org
Web Code: ccn-1051

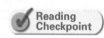 **Reading Checkpoint** *Why did Mendeleev place bromine in Group VII of his periodic table?*

Go Online
NSTA sci**LINKS**

Download a worksheet on the
periodic table for students to
complete, and find additional
teacher support from NSTA
SciLinks.

Facts and Figures

Recognizing a Pattern Actions Mendeleev
took while developing his table show that he
realized the table represented a fundamental
pattern in nature. First, he left gaps in the
table for undiscovered elements. Second, he
sometimes ignored accepted knowledge. For
example, Berzelius had reported a formula of

Be_2O_3 for beryllium oxide, which (if true) would
mean that beryllium belonged in the third
column. But, Mendeleev used beryllium to fill a
space in the second column. Third, Mendeleev
did not place all elements in order by atomic
mass. He placed tellurium before iodine even
though tellurium has a larger atomic mass.

Evidence Supporting Mendeleev's Table

Mendeleev named missing elements after elements in the same group. He gave the name eka-aluminum to the element that belonged one space below aluminum on the table. (*Eka* is a Sanskrit word meaning "one.") Mendeleev predicted that eka-aluminum would be a soft metal with a low melting point and a density of 5.9 g/cm^3.

In 1875, a French chemist discovered a new element. He named the element gallium (Ga) in honor of France. (The Latin name for France is *Gallia*.) Gallium is a soft metal with a melting point of 29.7°C and a density of 5.91 g/cm^3. Figure 4 shows a sample of gallium and a traffic signal that uses gallium compounds.

The properties of gallium are remarkably similar to the predicted properties of eka-aluminum. Scientists concluded that gallium and eka-aluminum are the same element. **The close match between Mendeleev's predictions and the actual properties of new elements showed how useful his periodic table could be.** The discovery of scandium (Sc) in 1879 and the discovery of germanium (Ge) in 1886 provided more evidence. With the periodic table, chemists could do more than predict the properties of new elements. They could explain the chemical behavior of different groups of elements.

Figure 4 Gallium was discovered in 1875. Heat from a person's hand can melt gallium. In some traffic signals, there are tiny light emitting diodes (LEDs) that contain a compound of gallium. **Comparing and Contrasting** *How does the melting point of gallium (29.7°C) compare to room temperature (about 25°C)?*

Section 5.1 Assessment

Reviewing Concepts
1. Describe how Mendeleev organized the elements into rows and columns in his periodic table.
2. How did the discovery of new elements such as gallium demonstrate the usefulness of Mendeleev's table?
3. Scientists before Mendeleev had proposed ways to organize the elements. Why were Mendeleev's efforts more successful?
4. What characteristic of solitaire did Mendeleev use as a model for his periodic table?
5. Why did Mendeleev leave spaces in his table?
6. In general, how can a scientist test the correctness of a scientific model?

Critical Thinking
7. **Inferring** Explain why it would not have been possible for a scientist in 1750 to develop a table like Mendeleev's.
8. **Predicting** How was Mendeleev able to predict the properties of elements that had not yet been discovered?

Writing to Persuade Write a paragraph about Mendeleev's periodic table. Use the paragraph to convince a reader that the periodic table is extremely useful to scientists. (*Hint:* Use specific facts to support your argument.)

Address Misconception

Students may think that [...] science are always achieve[...] working alone. They shoul[...] most advances are the result [...] scientists working on different [...] a problem. To help students over[...] this misconception, have them rese[...] the Nobel Laureates in Chemistry and [...] note how many times the prize was shared. Students could also look at the lists of authors in scientific journals.
Logical

FYI

The initial value reported for the density of gallium was 4.7 g/cm^3, but additional tests showed it to be 5.9 g/cm^3.

3 ASSESS

Evaluate Understanding   L2

Assign each student to one of the four pages in Section 5.1. Have students write a review question related to the content of their assigned page. Invite students to take turns posing their questions to the class. Continue until everyone has had a turn, or until the questions become repetitive.

Reteach   L1

Use Figure 3 to review Mendeleev's strategy for arranging the elements into rows and columns to form a periodic table.

Writing in Science

The paragraph should include information on how Mendeleev organized his table, why he left gaps in the table, the predictions he made based on the table, and how the discovery of gallium demonstrated the usefulness of the table.

Interactive Textbook If your class subscribes to the Interactive Textbook, use it to review key concepts in Section 5.1

Section 5.1   Assessment

1. Mendeleev arranged the elements in rows in order of increasing mass so that elements with similar properties were in the same column.
2. The close match between Mendeleev's predictions and the actual properties of new elements showed how useful his periodic table could be.
3. Mendeleev provided an organizing principle that worked for all of the known elements.
4. In solitaire, cards are arranged into categories called suits and ordered by value.
5. In order to place elements with similar properties in the same column, Mendeleev needed to leave spaces for undiscovered elements.
6. The scientist tests whether the model can be used to make accurate predictions.
7. With only 17 known elements to work with, the scientist would not have had enough data.
8. Mendeleev based his predictions on the properties of nearby elements and other elements in the same column.

Answer to . . .

Figure 4 *The melting point of gallium is slightly higher than room temperature.*

Reading Checkpoint *Mendeleev placed bromine in Group VII because bromine and chlorine have similar properties.*

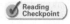

The Periodic Table **129**

5.2 The Modern Periodic Table

 Standards: ICP.5.2, ICP.5.3

(Left margin objectives)

Describe the arrangement of elements in the modern periodic table.

.2 **Explain** how the atomic mass of an element is determined and how atomic mass units are defined.

5.2.3 **Identify** general properties of metals, nonmetals, and metalloids.

5.2.4 **Describe** how properties of elements change across a period in the periodic table.

Figure 5 shows a synthesizer keyboard with labels for the notes that correspond to the white keys. If you strike the key labeled middle C and then play the white keys in order from left to right, you will hear the familiar do-re-mi-fa-sol-la-ti scale. The next white note is a C that is an octave above middle C. An octave is the interval between any two notes with the same name. (The prefix *octa-* means "eight.") Because the scale repeats at regular eight-note intervals, the scale is an example of a periodic pattern.

The sounds of musical notes that are separated by an octave are related, but they are not identical. In a similar way, elements in the same column of the periodic table are related because their properties repeat at regular intervals. But elements in different rows are not identical. You can use the modern periodic table of elements to classify elements and to compare their properties.

Figure 5 On this synthesizer keyboard, there is a repeating pattern of notes. The eight-note interval between any two notes with the same name is an octave. **Observing** *How many octaves are visible on the keyboard?*

A B C D E F G A B C D E F G A B C D E

The Periodic Law

Mendeleev developed his periodic table before the discovery of protons. He did not know that all atoms of an element have the same number of protons. He did not know that atoms of two different elements could not have the same number of protons. ⊖ **In the modern periodic table, elements are arranged by increasing atomic number (number of protons).** Figure 6 shows one way the known elements can be arranged in order by increasing atomic number.

Periods Each row in the table of elements in Figure 6 is a **period.** Period 1 has 2 elements. Periods 2 and 3 have 8 elements. Periods 4 and 5 have 18 elements. Period 6 has 32 elements. The number of elements per period varies because the number of available orbitals increases from energy level to energy level.

To understand the structure of the table, think about what happens as the atomic number increases. The first energy level has only one orbital. The one electron in a hydrogen atom and the two electrons in a helium atom can fit in this orbital. But one of the three electrons in a lithium atom must be in the second energy level. That is why lithium is the first element in Period 2. Sodium, the first element in Period 3, has one electron in its third energy level. Potassium, the first element in Period 4, has one electron in its fourth energy level. This pattern applies to all the elements in the first column on the table.

Groups Each column on the periodic table is called a **group.** The elements within a group have similar properties. ⊖ **Properties of elements repeat in a predictable way when atomic numbers are used to arrange elements into groups.** The elements in a group have similar electron configurations. An element's electron configuration determines its chemical properties. Therefore, members of a group in the periodic table have similar chemical properties. This pattern of repeating properties is the **periodic law.**

Look at Figure 7 on pages 132 and 133. There are 18 groups in this periodic table. Some elements from Periods 6 and 7 have been placed below Period 7 so that the table is more compact.

Figure 6 This diagram shows one way to display a periodic table of the elements. There are 7 rows, or periods, in the table. There are 32 columns, or groups, in the table.
Comparing and Contrasting *Compare the numbers of elements in Periods 1, 3, and 5.*

For: Links on periodic law
Visit: www.SciLinks.org
Web Code: ccn-1052

---

② INSTRU

The Periodic
Build Reading Lite

Preview Refer to **page 36**
Chapter 2, which provides the
lines for using a preview strategy

Have students preview the section
(pp. 130–138), focusing their attent
on headings, visuals, and boldfaced
material. Ask, **Based on your preview,
which figure in the section contains
the most information?** *(Figure 7 on
pp. 132–133)* **Based on your preview,
name three classes of elements.**
(Metals, nonmetals, and metalloids)
Visual, Verbal

Build Science Skills **L2**

Using Tables and Graphs Use the
data in Figure 7 to show the advantage
of arranging elements by atomic number
instead of atomic mass. Make a large
graph with atomic number on the
horizontal axis and atomic mass on the
vertical axis for elements 1 through 20.
Draw straight lines between the points.
Ask, **What does the graph show about
the general relationship between
atomic number and atomic mass?** *(As
the atomic number increases, so does the
atomic mass.)* **Are there any points on
the graph that do not follow the pattern?** *(Yes, the atomic mass of element 18,
argon, is greater than the atomic mass of
element 19, potassium.)* Point out that
arranging the elements strictly by
increasing atomic mass would result in
some elements with unlike properties
being grouped together.
Visual, Logical

Download a worksheet on the
periodic law for students to
complete, and find additional
teacher support from NSTA SciLinks.

Answer to . . .

Figure 5 *3 octaves*

Figure 6 *There are 2 elements in
Period 1, 8 in Period 3, and 18 in
Period 5.*

L1

...n by having students
...layouts in Figures 6 and 7.
...**is the major difference in
...uts?** (Some elements from
...6 and 7 have been placed below
...able.) **How are the layouts alike?**
...ements are arranged in order by atomic
...umber. Elements with similar properties
are in the same group and properties
repeat in a predictable way from period to
period.) Return to Figure 7 when atomic
masses are discussed on p. 134, and
when ways to classify elements on the
periodic table are introduced on p. 135.
(The table shows two classification
systems: the 1–18 numbering system
approved by the International Union
of Pure and Applied Chemistry (IUPAC),
and a system in which two sets of
groups numbered 1–8 are distinguished
by A and B labels. Unless students ask,
you may want to let students wonder
about the A and B classification system,
which will be addressed in the introduction to Section 5.3.)
Visual, Logical

FYI

Placement of the lanthanides and
actinides below the main body of the
table also serves to emphasize the
similarities among these elements
related to their electron configurations.

Periodic Table of the Elements

Figure 7 In a modern periodic table of the elements, elements are arranged in order of increasing atomic number.

Lanthanide Series

Actinide Series

Go **O**nline
active art

For: Activity on the periodic table
Visit: PHSchool.com
Web Code: ccp-1052

Atomic number — 6
Element symbol — C
Element name — Carbon
Atomic mass — 12.011

							18 8A
		13 3A	14 4A	15 5A	16 6A	17 7A	2 He Helium 4.0026
		5 B Boron 10.81	6 C Carbon 12.011	7 N Nitrogen 14.007	8 O Oxygen 15.999	9 F Fluorine 18.998	10 Ne Neon 20.179
10	11 1B	12 2B / 13 Al Aluminum 26.982	14 Si Silicon 28.086	15 P Phosphorus 30.974	16 S Sulfur 32.06	17 Cl Chlorine 35.453	18 Ar Argon 39.948

28 Ni Nickel 58.71	29 Cu Copper 63.546	30 Zn Zinc 65.38	31 Ga Gallium 69.72	32 Ge Germanium 72.59	33 As Arsenic 74.922	34 Se Selenium 78.96	35 Br Bromine 79.904	36 Kr Krypton 83.80
46 Pd Palladium 106.4	47 Ag Silver 107.87	48 Cd Cadmium 112.41	49 In Indium 114.82	50 Sn Tin 118.69	51 Sb Antimony 121.75	52 Te Tellurium 127.60	53 I Iodine 126.90	54 Xe Xenon 131.30
78 Pt Platinum 195.09	79 Au Gold 196.97	80 Hg Mercury 200.59	81 Tl Thallium 204.37	82 Pb Lead 207.2	83 Bi Bismuth 208.98	84 Po Polonium (209)	85 At Astatine (210)	86 Rn Radon (222)
110 Ds Darmstadtium (269)	111 Rg Roentgenium (272)	112 Cn Copernicium (277)	113 *Uut Ununtrium (284)	114 *Uuq Ununquadium (289)	115 *Uup Ununpentium (288)	116 *Uuh Ununhexium (293)		118 *Uuo Ununoctium (299)

*Name not officially assigned

| 63 Eu Europium 151.96 | 64 Gd Gadolinium 157.25 | 65 Tb Terbium 158.93 | 66 Dy Dysprosium 162.50 | 67 Ho Holmium 164.93 | 68 Er Erbium 167.26 | 69 Tm Thulium 168.93 | 70 Yb Ytterbium 173.04 |
| 95 Am Americium (243) | 96 Cm Curium (247) | 97 Bk Berkelium (247) | 98 Cf Californium (251) | 99 Es Einsteinium (252) | 100 Fm Fermium (257) | 101 Md Mendelevium (258) | 102 No Nobelium (259) |

The Periodic Table **133**

Go **O**nline
active art

For: Activity on the periodic table
Visit: PHSchool.com
Web Code: ccp-1052

Students can learn more about the elements by interacting with a clickable periodic table online.

(continued)

Mass

dress
onceptions **L2**

...s may not realize that all atoms of ...ment are isotopes. In other words, ...ents may think that there is one ...egular" atom and several variations called isotopes. Explain that a sample of an element found in nature contains a mixture of the different isotopes of that element. The symbols on the periodic table represent "average" atoms of elements. In fact, atoms with the atomic masses listed on the table do not exist. For example, there are no carbon atoms with an atomic mass of 12.011 amu. This value is a weighted average of the atomic masses of stable carbon isotopes. The value is close to the assigned value for carbon-12 because about 99% of a carbon sample is carbon-12 atoms.
Verbal, Logical

FYI

An atomic mass given in parentheses in Figure 7 is the mass number of the longest-lived isotope of an element that has no stable isotopes and for which the abundance of isotopes in nature shows great variability (or a complete absence in the case of technetium or promethium). Technetium and promethium have been detected in the spectra of stars.

Atomic number	17
Element symbol	Cl
Element name	Chlorine
Atomic mass	35.453

Figure 8 This box provides four pieces of information about the element chlorine: its symbol, its name, its atomic number, and its atomic mass.

Distribution of Chlorine Isotopes in Nature

Isotope	Percentage	Atomic Mass
Chlorine-35	75.78%	34.969
Chlorine-37	24.22%	36.966

Figure 9 This table shows the distribution and atomic masses for the two natural isotopes of chlorine. Using Tables *Which isotope occurs more often in nature?*

Atomic Mass

There are four pieces of information for each element in Figure 7: the name of the element, its symbol, its atomic number and its atomic mass. **Atomic mass is a value that depends on the distribution of an element's isotopes in nature and the masses of those isotopes.** You will use atomic masses when you study chemical reactions in Chapter 7.

Atomic Mass Units The mass of an atom in grams is extremely small and not very useful because the samples of matter that scientists work with contain trillions of atoms. In order to have a convenient way to compare the masses of atoms, scientists chose one isotope to serve as a standard. Recall that each isotope of an element has a different number of neutrons in the nuclei of its atoms. So the atoms of two isotopes have different masses.

Scientists assigned 12 atomic mass units to the carbon-12 atom, which has 6 protons and 6 neutrons. An **atomic mass unit** (amu) is defined as one twelfth the mass of a carbon-12 atom.

Isotopes of Chlorine In nature, most elements exist as a mixture of two or more isotopes. Figure 8 shows that the element chlorine has the symbol Cl, atomic number 17, and an atomic mass of 35.453 atomic mass units. (The unit for atomic mass is not listed in the periodic table, but it is understood to be the amu.) Where does the number 35.453 come from? There are two natural isotopes of chlorine, chlorine-35 and chlorine-37. An atom of chlorine-35 has 17 protons and 18 neutrons. An atom of chlorine-37 has 17 protons and 20 neutrons. So the mass of an atom of chlorine-37 is greater than the mass of an atom of chlorine-35.

Weighted Averages Your teacher may use a weighted average to determine your grade. In a weighted average, some values are more important than other values. For example, test scores may count more heavily toward your final grade than grades on quizzes or grades on homework assignments.

Figure 9 lists the atomic masses for two naturally occurring chlorine isotopes. If you add the atomic masses of the isotopes and divide by 2, you get 35.967, not 35.453. The value of the atomic mass for chlorine in the periodic table is a weighted average. The isotope that occurs in nature about 75% of the time (chlorine-35) contributes three times as much to the average as the isotope that occurs in nature about 25% of the time (chlorine-37).

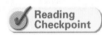 Reading Checkpoint **What is an atomic mass unit?**

Facts and Figures

Atomic Mass Units From the mid-1800s to 1960, oxygen was the standard for atomic masses. (Oxygen was likely chosen because it forms compounds with many elements.) After the discovery of isotopes, physicists and chemists began to use different standards. Physicists assigned the value 16.000 amu exclusively to oxygen-16. Other oxygen isotopes had different values. Chemists continued to use 16.000 amu as the average for all oxygen atoms. Although the differences between the standards were small, the situation was potentially confusing.

In 1961, chemists and physicists agreed on a unified standard based on the carbon-12 isotope, which is assigned a value of 12.000 amu. (Although the SI abbreviation for atomic mass unit was changed to u for unified when scientists adopted the unified atomic mass unit, the amu notation is still widely used.)

Classes of Elements

The periodic table in Figure 7 presents three different ways to classify elements. First, elements are classified as solids, liquids, or gases, based on their states at room temperature. The symbols for solids are black. The symbols for liquids are purple. The symbols for gases are red.

Second, elements are divided into those that occur naturally and those that do not. All but two elements with atomic numbers 1 through 92 occur on Earth. Elements with atomic numbers of 93 and higher do not occur naturally. The symbols for these elements are white. In Chapter 10, you will find out how elements that do not occur in nature are produced.

The third classification system puts elements into categories based on their general properties. ● **Elements are classified as metals, nonmetals, and metalloids.** In the periodic table, metals are located on the left, nonmetals are on the right, and metalloids are in between.

Metals The majority of the elements on the periodic table are classified as metals. In Figure 7, they are represented by blue boxes. **Metals** are elements that are good conductors of electric current and heat. Except for mercury, metals are solids at room temperature. Most metals are malleable. Many metals are ductile; that is, they can be drawn into thin wires.

Some metals are extremely reactive and some do not react easily. One way to demonstrate this difference is to compare the behavior of gold and the behavior of magnesium when these metals are exposed to the oxygen in air. Gold remains shiny because it does not react with the oxygen. Magnesium reacts with the oxygen and quickly dulls. Figure 10A shows one magnesium coil that is dull and one that is shiny. Figure 10B shows one use for a metal with a shiny surface.

Figure 10 Magnesium and aluminum are typical metals. **A** When magnesium reacts with oxygen, a dull layer forms on its surface. The layer can be removed to reveal magnesium's shiny surface. **B** Many telescope mirrors are coated with aluminum to produce a surface that reflects light extremely well.

≡Quick Lab

Defining a Metal
Procedure

1. Use forceps to put a piece of magnesium into a test tube in a test tube rack. Using a graduated cylinder, add 5 mL of hydrochloric acid to the test tube. **CAUTION** *Wear plastic gloves because the acid can burn skin or clothing.* Record your observations.

2. Repeat Step 1 with sulfur, aluminum, and silicon.

Analyze and Conclude

1. **Classifying** Based on their locations in the periodic table, classify the four elements as metals, metalloids, or nonmetals.

2. **Comparing and Contrasting** Compare the behavior of the metals with the acid to the behavior of the other elements with the acid.

3. **Forming Operational Definitions** Use your observations to write a definition of a metal.

Classes of E[...]

≡Quick Lab

Defining a Metal

Objective
After completing this activity, stud[...] will be able to
• use a chemical property to distingu[...] metals.

Skills Focus Forming Operational Definitions

⏱ **Prep Time** 20 minutes

Materials forceps; magnesium; test tubes; test-tube rack; graduated cylinder; 20 mL 2 M HCl; small pieces of sulfur, aluminum, and silicon

Advance Prep Prepare 1 L of 2 M HCl: add 200 mL of 10 M HCl to a 1-L volumetric flask containing 750 mL of water and swirl gently to mix. Add water to bring the volume to 1 L. **CAUTION** *Wear safety goggles, a lab apron, and neoprene gloves.* Use concentrated HCl in a fume hood or other well-ventilated area. Never add water to acid.
Polish the magnesium lightly with steel wool to remove any magnesium oxide.

Class Time 20 minutes

Safety Remind students to use care in adding the acid and to rinse any acid off skin or clothing with water. **CAUTION** *The reaction of Mg in HCl will make the test tube hot.* Keep spill-control materials (baking soda or citric acid) nearby to clean up spills. Repeat as necessary to remove all acid contamination. Elemental sulfur may emit H_2S when dispersed in HCl. Test the sulfur beforehand in a fume hood or other well-ventilated area. Supply silicon as chips, not in powdered form, which is flammable. Neutralize the acid solutions with baking soda and wash them down the drain with excess water.

Teaching Tips
• Caution students not to get fingerprints on the Mg and Al samples.
• The complete reaction of Al and HCl will require more than 45 minutes. However, the results after 15 minutes will indicate how the materials react.

Expected Outcome

Element	Observation
Magnesium	Bubbles, test tube becomes hot, reaction complete in about 30 seconds, final solution clear.
Sulfur	No visible reaction
Aluminum	Slight bubbling in 5 minutes, test tube becomes warm after about 15 minutes, final mixture slightly cloudy with powdery gray precipitate.
Silicon	No visible reaction

Analyze and Conclude
1. Aluminum and magnesium are metals. Sulfur is a nonmetal and silicon is a metalloid.
2. Only the metals react with the acid.
3. A metal is a substance that reacts with HCl.
Logical

Answer to . . .

Figure 9 *Chlorine-35*

✓ Reading Checkpoint *One-twelfth the mass of a carbon-12 atom*

...ork under fluorescent
...nd a lot of time viewing
...r screen sometimes choose
...es. Athletes participating in
...peed winter sports often use pink
...s because they help to increase
...ntrast and depth perception when
...he available light is limited. Gray lenses
are very common; they reduce the
amount of light without changing its
color. Have students research situations
in which lenses with colors other than
pink are used.
Verbal, Portfolio

Build Reading Literacy **L1**

Summarize Refer to **page 598D** in **Chapter 20**, which provides the guidelines for summarizing.

Have students write a summary of the text on pp. 135–136. Summaries should include information about each of the vocabulary terms on these pages. Ask, **Based on your summary, which class of elements has properties that fall between the properties of two other classes of elements?** *(Metalloids)*
Verbal, Portfolio

FYI

The important role metalloids play as semiconductors is addressed in Chapter 6.

Figure 11 A compound of erbium (Er) and oxygen is used to tint glass pink.

Figure 12 Toothpaste contains a compound that helps to protect teeth from tooth decay. The compound is formed from the nonmetal fluorine and the metal sodium.

The metals in groups 3 through 12 are called transition metals. **Transition metals** are elements that form a bridge between the elements on the left and right sides of the table. Transition elements, such as copper and silver, were among the first elements discovered. One property of many transition metals is their ability to form compounds with distinctive colors. The How It Works box on page 137 describes the use of transition elements in the production of colored glass.

Some transition elements have more properties in common than elements in other groups. This is especially true of elements in the lanthanide and actinide series. These elements are so similar that chemists in the 1800s had difficulty separating them when they were found mixed together in nature. A compound of erbium and oxygen was used to tint the lenses shown in Figure 11.

Nonmetals In Figure 7, nonmetals are represented by yellow boxes. As their name implies, nonmetals generally have properties opposite to those of metals. **Nonmetals** are elements that are poor conductors of heat and electric current. Because nonmetals have low boiling points, many nonmetals are gases at room temperature. In fact, all the gases in the periodic table are nonmetals. The nonmetals that are solids at room temperature tend to be brittle. If they are hit with a hammer, they shatter or crumble.

Nonmetals vary as much in their chemical properties as they do in their physical properties. Some nonmetals are extremely reactive, some hardly react at all, and some fall somewhere in between. Fluorine in Group 17 is the most reactive nonmetal. It even forms compounds with some gases in Group 18, which are the least reactive elements in the table. The toothpaste in Figure 12 contains a compound of the nonmetal fluorine and the metal sodium. This compound helps to protect your teeth against decay.

Metalloids In the periodic table in Figure 7, metalloids are represented by green boxes. **Metalloids** are elements with properties that fall between those of metals and nonmetals. For example, metals are good conductors of electric current and nonmetals are poor conductors of electric current. A metalloid's ability to conduct electric current varies with temperature. Pure silicon (Si) and germanium (Ge) are good insulators at low temperatures and good conductors at high temperatures.

Reading Checkpoint *Which type of metals tend to form compounds with distinctive colors?*

136 *Chapter 5*

Facts and Figures

Fluoride in Toothpaste According to FDA regulations, toothpaste can contain sodium fluoride, sodium monofluorophosphate, or stannous fluoride at concentrations of 850 to 1150 ppm total fluorine. A package of toothpaste sold commercially cannot contain more than 276 mg of fluorine. Because too much fluoride can have adverse affects on health, people should rinse away excess toothpaste. There must be a warning on toothpaste packages to keep the product out of the reach of children under 6 years of age. Young children need to be supervised when they brush their teeth until they have learned how to minimize ingestion of the toothpaste.

Making Glass

For more than 4500 years, people have made glass from sand. The float-glass process shown below is used to make large sheets of glass for windows, while molds are used to make glass bottles. **Interpreting Diagrams** *How is air used in making glass bottles?*

Colored glass
Metallic elements are mixed with the raw ingredients to produce colored glass. Iron or chromium is added for green, copper or gold for red, and cobalt for blue.

Cullet (waste glass)
Lime (calcium oxide)
Sand (silicon dioxide)
Soda ash (sodium carbonate)

1 Adding the raw ingredients Sand, lime, and soda ash are poured into the furnace and heated to 1500°C (2730°F). Recycled waste glass, called cullet, is also added, to reduce the cost of raw materials.

2 Heating in the furnace The furnace heats the ingredients, producing liquid glass at 1100°C (2010°F). Rollers move the hot and molten glass to the next stage.

3 Liquid glass The glass is floated over a bath of melted tin. The glass emerges at 600°C (1110°F) as a continuous sheet with the same thickness throughout.

Furnace

Rollers

Melted tin *Floating the glass on liquid tin produces a glass surface that is as smooth as the surface of the liquid tin.*

4 Cooling the glass The glass is cooled slowly in a temperature-controlled oven to keep it from cracking.

Making bottles
Mass-produced glass bottles are made by adding hot glass to a mold and shaping the glass with air at high pressure.

Air pushes the glass to the bottom of the mold, where the neck of the bottle will form.

Hot glass is placed in the mold.

Mold sealed

Oven

Glass cutter

Air tube

Air blown through the air tube forces the liquid glass to assume the shape of the bottle mold.

5 Cutting the glass A diamond-tipped cutter is used to cut the cooled glass.

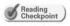

The Periodic Table **137**

DK HOW It V

Making Glass

Float-glass plants are among buildings in the world. Giant b the raw materials for making gla roof ventilators and stacks release intense heat needed to produce the liquid glass. The glassmaking operation is continuous, with the fires burning constantly. Often a glass plant will produce various tints of glass that are used in different applications.

Interpreting Diagrams Air at high pressure is used to force the liquid glass to take the shape of the mold.
Visual, Verbal

For Enrichment   L3

Interested students can research and report on the work of glassblowers and compare their techniques for shaping glass with the molding process that is described on p. 137. Have students use the library to find books, magazine articles, and videos to help in their research.
Verbal, Portfolio

FYI

Tell students that showing the raw ingredients of glass as four equal segments of a pie is not meant to reflect their actual percentages in the mixture. Adding soda ash saves energy because sodium carbonate lowers the melting temperature of the mixture. Running the glass over rollers instead of the molten tin produces an uneven surface.

Answer to . . .

Reading Checkpoint   *Transition metals*

The Periodic Table 137

| Sodium | Magnesium | Aluminum | Silicon | Phosphorus | Sulfur | Chlorine | Argon |

riod 3 Properties L2

Purpose Students observe differences in electrical conductivity among three Period 3 elements.

Materials 6-volt battery, flashlight bulb with holder, 3 pieces of insulated wire with the ends stripped, 2.5-cm aluminum strip, small silicon chip, 2.5-cm piece of sulfur

Advance Prep Use the battery, flashlight bulb with holder, and the wires to make an open circuit.

Procedure Touch the free ends of the two wires to each end of the aluminum strip. Have students observe the bulb. Repeat for silicon and sulfur.

Expected Outcome The material used to complete the circuit determines the brightness of the light. For aluminum, the bulb is bright; for silicon, the bulb is dim; for sulfur, the bulb does not light. Students should conclude that the Period 3 elements become less metallic from left to right across the period.
Visual, Logical

3 ASSESS

Evaluate Understanding L2
Ask students to identify the general properties of metals, nonmetals, and metalloids.

Reteach L1

Use Figure 13 to illustrate how the properties of elements change from left to right across a period in the periodic table.

 Writing in Science

Student answers should reflect the fact that all the isotopes of an atom occupy the same place on the periodic table, despite their different mass numbers.

Interactive Textbook If your class subscribes to the Interactive Textbook, use it to review key concepts in Section 5.2.

Answer to . . .

Figure 13 *Chlorine*

Figure 13 From left to right across Period 3, there are three metals (Na, Mg, and Al), one metalloid (Si), and four nonmetals (P, S, Cl, and Ar). Many light bulbs are filled with argon gas.
Observing *Which other element in Period 3 is a gas?*

Variation Across a Period

The properties within a period change in a similar way from left to right across the table, except for Period 1. **Across a period from left to right, the elements become less metallic and more nonmetallic in their properties.** The most reactive metals are on the left side of the table. The most reactive nonmetals are on the right in Group 17. The Period 3 elements shown in Figure 13 provide an example of this trend.

There are three metals, a metalloid, and four nonmetals in Period 3. If you were unwise enough to hold a piece of sodium in your hand, it would react quickly and violently with the water on your moist skin. But magnesium will not react with water unless the water is hot. Aluminum does not react with water, but it does react with oxygen.

Silicon is the least reactive element in Period 3 (except for argon). Under ordinary conditions, phosphorus and sulfur do not react with water, but they do react with oxygen. They also react with chlorine, which is a highly reactive nonmetal. Chlorine must be handled with as much care as sodium. Argon hardly reacts at all.

Section 5.2 Assessment

Reviewing Concepts

1. What determines the order of the elements in the modern periodic table?

2. Describe the periodic law.

3. What two factors determine the atomic mass of an element?

4. Name three categories that are used to classify the elements in the periodic table.

5. What major change occurs as you move from left to right across the periodic table?

Critical Thinking

6. **Formulating Hypotheses** The atomic mass of iodine (I) is less than the atomic mass of tellurium (Te). But an iodine atom has one more proton than a tellurium atom. Explain how this situation is possible.

7. **Applying Concepts** Explain how you know that no new element with an atomic number less than 100 will be discovered.

8. **Comparing and Contrasting** Compare the reactions with water of the elements sodium and magnesium.

Writing in Science

Explanatory Paragraph The word *isotope* comes from the Greek words *isos,* meaning "equal," and *topos,* meaning "place." Write a paragraph explaining how the isotopes chlorine-35 and chlorine-37 occupy the same place in the periodic table.

138 *Chapter 5*

Section 5.2   Assessment

1. In the modern periodic table, elements are arranged by increasing atomic number.
2. Properties of elements repeat in a predictable way when atomic numbers are used to arrange elements into groups.
3. Atomic mass is a value that depends on the distribution of an element's isotopes in nature and the masses of those isotopes.
4. Metals, nonmetals, and metalloids
5. The elements become less metallic and more nonmetallic in their properties.

6. Answers may include that the tellurium isotopes that are most abundant have many neutrons in their nuclei or that all tellurium atoms have more neutrons than iodine atoms.
7. The atomic number of an element corresponds to the number of protons in the element's atoms. The atomic number must be a whole number. All the places between 1 and 100 are already filled with existing elements.
8. Sodium reacts quickly and violently with water at room temperature. Magnesium will not react unless the water is hot.

5.3 Representative Groups

Standards: ICP.5.2, ICP.5.3

Reading Focus

Key Concepts
- Why do the elements in a group have similar properties?
- What are some properties of the A groups in the periodic table?

Vocabulary
- valence electron
- alkali metals
- alkaline earth metals
- halogens
- noble gases

Reading Strategy
Monitoring Your Understanding Copy the table below. As you read, record an important fact about each element listed.

Element	Important Fact
Magnesium	a. _____?_____
Aluminum	b. _____?_____
Chlorine	c. _____?_____

Why is hydrogen located on the left side of the periodic table with the active metals? It is a nonmetal gas that seems to have more in common with the nonmetals in Group 17. Hydrogen's location is related to its electron configuration, not its properties.

Valence Electrons

Did you wonder why there are two numbering schemes on the periodic table in Figure 7? When the A groups are numbered from 1 through 8, they provide a useful reminder about the electron configurations of the elements in those groups. The number of an A group matches the number of valence electrons in an electron configuration for an element in that group. A **valence electron** is an electron that is in the highest occupied energy level of an atom. These electrons play a key role in chemical reactions. Properties vary across a period because the number of valence electrons increases from left to right.

👉 **Elements in a group have similar properties because they have the same number of valence electrons.** These properties will not be identical because the valence electrons are in different energy levels. Valence electrons explain the location of hydrogen. Because hydrogen has a single valence electron, it is grouped with other elements, such as lithium, that have only one valence electron.

Figure 14 Because hydrogen is flammable, it can be used as a fuel in automobiles like this one. An engine that burns hydrogen has a key advantage over an engine that burns gasoline. Only water is produced when hydrogen burns.

139

Section Resources

Print
- *Laboratory Manual,* Investigation 5B
- *Reading and Study Workbook With Math Support,* Section 5.3
- *Transparencies,* Section 5.3

Technology
- *Interactive Textbook,* Section 5.3
- *Presentation Pro CD-ROM,* Section 5.3
- *Go Online,* Science News, Elements

li Metals

L1

Ask students to study the
tos and the column of elements
re 15. Ask, **What properties of
m are shown in the photos?**
dium is a soft solid at room tempera-
ure with a metallic luster when first
exposed to air. Sodium is extremely
reactive and it reacts violently with water
to form hydrogen gas.) Point out to
students that the reactivity of the alkali
metals increases from the top of the
group to the bottom. Ask, **Which alkali
metals are less reactive than cesium
but more reactive than lithium?**
(Sodium, potassium, and rubidium)
Visual, Logical

Build Science Skills

L2

Communicating Results Explain to
students that Robert Bunsen and Gustav
Kirchoff discovered cesium in 1840 and
rubidium in 1841 by burning the substances and observing the color of the
flames. Have students research the origin
of the terms cesium and rubidium. Have
students explain why these names are
appropriate. (Cesium comes from the Latin
word caesium, which means "heavenly
blue." Rubidium comes from the Latin
word rubidus, which means "dark red."
The names describe the colors of light
emitted when the elements are burned.)
Logical

FYI

Francium has been described as the
most unstable element among the first
103 elements. Its longest-lived isotope,
francium-223, has a half-life of only 22
minutes. The estimate is that there is
only about one ounce of francium on
Earth at any moment.

Science News provides students
with current information on
elements.

Figure 15 The element sodium is an alkali
metal **A** Unlike most metals, sodium is soft
enough to cut with a knife. **B** When sodium
reacts with water, enough energy is released
to ignite the hydrogen that is produced.
Predicting *What happens when potassium
comes in contact with water?*

Group 1A

3	**Li** Lithium
11	**Na** Sodium
19	**K** Potassium
37	**Rb** Rubidium
55	**Cs** Cesium
87	**Fr** Francium

For: Articles on elements
Visit: PHSchool.com
Web Code: cce-1053

The Alkali Metals

The elements in Group 1A are called **alkali metals.** These metals have
a single valence electron and are extremely reactive. Because they are
so reactive, alkali metals are found in nature only in compounds. The
most familiar of these compounds is table salt—a compound of
sodium and chlorine (sodium chloride). Sodium chloride can be
obtained through the evaporation of seawater or from large salt
deposits on the surface of Earth or underground.

Not all the elements in a group are equally reactive. Sodium is more
reactive than lithium, potassium is more reactive than sodium, and
rubidium is more reactive than potassium. **The reactivity of alkali
metals increases from the top of Group 1A to the bottom.**

Sodium is about as hard as cold butter and can be cut with a sharp
knife, as shown in Figure 15A. Sodium melts at about 98°C and has a
lower density than water. A piece of sodium may be able to float on
water, but Figure 15B shows that it won't be there for long. The sodium
reacts violently with water and releases enough energy to ignite the
hydrogen gas that is produced. Sodium and potassium are stored
under oil to keep them from reacting with the oxygen and water vapor
in air. Cesium is so reactive that it reacts with water at temperatures as
low as −115°C. Cesium is usually stored in a sealed glass tube containing argon gas.

Reading Checkpoint *How many valence electrons does an alkali
metal have?*

Customize for English Language Learners

Compare/Contrast Chart
After students have read about Groups 1A and
2A, create a chart on the board with the title
Alkali Metals vs. Alkaline Earth Metals. Separate
the chart into two columns labeled Similarities
and Differences. Ask for student responses
to help you fill in the chart. After all correct
answers have been recorded, keep the chart
displayed as a reference for students.

The Alkaline Earth Metals

The elements in Group 2A are called **alkaline earth metals**. All alkaline earth metals have two valence electrons. Metals in Group 2A are harder than metals in Group 1A. The melting point of magnesium is 650°C, which is much higher than the melting point of sodium—98°C.

👁 **Differences in reactivity among the alkaline earth metals are shown by the ways they react with water.** Calcium, strontium, and barium react easily with cold water. Magnesium will react with hot water, but no change appears to occur when beryllium is added to water. Magnesium and calcium have essential biological functions and they provide materials used in construction and transportation.

Magnesium Magnesium plays a key role in the process that uses sunlight to produce sugar in plants like the one in Figure 16. The compound at the center of this process is chlorophyll (KLAWR uh fil), and at the center of chlorophyll is magnesium. A mixture of magnesium and other metals can be as strong as steel, but much lighter. Reducing overall mass without sacrificing strength is an important consideration in transportation. The frames of bicycles and backpacks often contain magnesium.

Calcium Your body needs calcium to keep your bones and teeth strong. Calcium carbonate—a compound of calcium, carbon, and oxygen—is the main ingredient in chalk, limestone, coral, and the pearl in Figure 16. Your toothpaste may contain the compound calcium carbonate because this hard substance can polish your teeth. The plaster cast in Figure 16 contains calcium sulfate, which is a compound of calcium, sulfur, and oxygen.

Group 2A

4
Be
Beryllium

12
Mg
Magnesium

20
Ca
Calcium

38
Sr
Strontium

56
Ba
Barium

88
Ra
Radium

Figure 16 Chlorophyll molecules in spinach contain magnesium. An oyster shell and a pearl are both made from calcium carbonate. A plaster cast contains the compound calcium sulfate.

Spinach plant

Oyster shell with pearl

The Periodic Table **141**

FYI

The mineral gypsum is heated to produce a white powdery substance called plaster of Paris. When water is added to plaster of Paris, heat is released as the plaster quickly hardens. During the process, the plaster expands by about 0.3–0.6%. A plaster cast is often replaced by a sturdier, more lightweight fiberglass cast after the swelling around an injury subsides.

Egyptians used plaster to join blocks of stone in pyramids. Romans made plaster casts of Greek statues. In the 1700s, wooden houses in Paris were often covered in plaster to protect against fire. This measure was taken in response to the destruction of London by fire in 1666.

Answer to . . .

Figure 15 *When potassium reacts with water, enough energy is released to ignite the hydrogen that is produced.*

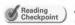 Reading Checkpoint   *An alkali metal has one valence electron.*

Boron Family

Community Resources   L2

Invite a representative from a community recycling program or a commercial recycler to speak to your class about the importance of recycling materials such as aluminum. Have students ask questions about the kinds of materials that are recycled and how the recycling process is different for each of them. They may also ask how recycling has changed over the past 10 years and what changes are expected in the future.
Interpersonal, Portfolio

The Carbon Family
Integrate Math   L2

Tell students that silicon dioxide is the most abundant substance in Earth's crust. It is, of course, a compound of the elements silicon and oxygen. Point out to students that only eight elements make up 98.5% of Earth's crust: oxygen (46.6%), silicon (27.7%), aluminum (8.1%), iron (5.0%), calcium (3.6%), sodium (2.8%), potassium (2.6%), and magnesium (2.1%). Have students work in pairs to create a circle graph that shows this data. Remind students that they may need to combine some elements under a category labeled Other. If students need help constructing a circle graph, you may want to refer them to the **Math Skills** in the **Skills and Reference Handbook** at the end of the student text.
Visual, Logical

The Boron Family

Group 3A contains the metalloid boron, the well-known metal aluminum, and three less familiar metals (gallium, indium, and thallium). All these elements have three valence electrons.

◉ **Aluminum is the most abundant metal in Earth's crust.** It is often found combined with oxygen in a mineral called bauxite (BAWKS eyet). Aluminum is less reactive than sodium and magnesium. It is strong, lightweight, malleable, and a good conductor of electric current.

More than 10 percent of the aluminum produced is used as packaging. Some aluminum is used in window screens, window frames, and gutters. Parts of cars and airplanes are also made from aluminum. People are encouraged to recycle aluminum because the energy needed to purify recycled aluminum is only about 5 percent of the energy needed to extract aluminum from bauxite.

A compound of boron, silicon, and oxygen is used to make a type of glass that does not shatter easily when it undergoes a rapid change in temperature. Glass that contains boron is used to make laboratory glassware, such as the flasks in Figure 17. It is also used in cookware that can go directly from the oven to the refrigerator.

Figure 17 These students are using flasks made from glass that contains boron. This type of glass does not shatter as easily as glass without boron.

Group 3A
5 **B** Boron
13 **Al** Aluminum
31 **Ga** Gallium
49 **In** Indium
81 **Tl** Thallium

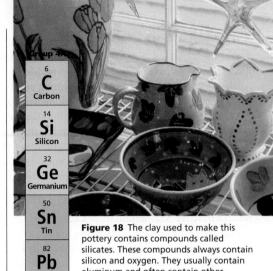

Group 4A
6 **C** Carbon
14 **Si** Silicon
32 **Ge** Germanium
50 **Sn** Tin
82 **Pb** Lead

Figure 18 The clay used to make this pottery contains compounds called silicates. These compounds always contain silicon and oxygen. They usually contain aluminum and often contain other elements such as iron.

The Carbon Family

Group 4A contains a nonmetal (carbon), two metalloids (silicon and germanium), and two metals (tin and lead). Each of these elements has four valence electrons. Notice that the metallic nature of the elements increases from top to bottom within the group. In keeping with this trend, germanium is a better conductor of electric current than silicon.

Life on Earth would not exist without carbon. ◉ **Except for water, most of the compounds in your body contain carbon.** Reactions that occur in the cells of your body are controlled by carbon compounds. Carbon and its compounds are discussed in Chapter 9, Carbon Chemistry.

Silicon is the second most abundant element in Earth's crust. It is found as silicon dioxide in quartz rocks, sand, and glass. The clay used to produce the pottery in Figure 18 contains silicon compounds called silicates. Silicon carbide, a compound of silicon and carbon, is extremely hard. Saw blades tipped with silicon carbide last many times longer than ordinary steel blades.

✓ **Reading Checkpoint**   *Which Group 3A element is a nonmetal?*

The Nitrogen Family

Group 5A contains two nonmetals (nitrogen and phosphorus), two metalloids (arsenic and antimony), and one metal (bismuth). Like the groups on either side of it, Group 5A includes elements with a wide range of physical properties. Nitrogen is a nonmetal gas, phosphorus is a solid nonmetal, and bismuth is a dense metal. Despite their differences, all the elements in Group 5A have five valence electrons. Nitrogen and phosphorus are the most important elements in Group 5A.

When air is cooled, the oxygen condenses before the nitrogen because nitrogen has a lower boiling point than oxygen. Much of the nitrogen obtained from air is used to produce fertilizers, like the three shown in Figure 19. **Besides nitrogen, fertilizers often contain phosphorus.** Your body uses compounds containing nitrogen and phosphorus to control reactions and release energy from food.

Phosphorus exists as an element in several forms with different properties. White phosphorus is so reactive that it bursts into flame when it is in contact with oxygen. Red phosphorus is less reactive and is used to make matches ignite.

Figure 19 The composition of a fertilizer varies with its intended use. The numbers on the bags of fertilizer are, from left to right, the relative amounts of nitrogen, phosphorus, and potassium.
Analyzing Data **Which type of fertilizer contains the most phosphorus?**

Group 5A
7 **N** Nitrogen
15 **P** Phosphorus
33 **As** Arsenic
51 **Sb** Antimony
83 **Bi** Bismuth

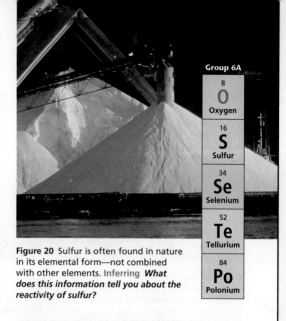

Group 6A
8 **O** Oxygen
16 **S** Sulfur
34 **Se** Selenium
52 **Te** Tellurium
84 **Po** Polonium

Figure 20 Sulfur is often found in nature in its elemental form—not combined with other elements. *Inferring* **What does this information tell you about the reactivity of sulfur?**

The Oxygen Family

Group 6A has three nonmetals (oxygen, sulfur, and selenium), and two metalloids (tellurium and polonium). All the elements in Group 6A have six valence electrons.

Oxygen is the most abundant element in Earth's crust. Complex forms of life need oxygen to stay alive because oxygen is used to release the energy stored in food. Oxygen can be stored as a liquid under pressure in oxygen tanks. There must be no sparks or flames near an oxygen tank because materials that are flammable burn easily in pure oxygen.

Ozone is another form of the element oxygen. At ground level, ozone can irritate your eyes and lungs. At upper levels of the atmosphere, ozone absorbs harmful radiation emitted by the sun.

Sulfur was one of the first elements to be discovered because it is found in large natural deposits like the one in Figure 20. The main use of sulfur is in the production of sulfuric acid, a compound of sulfur, hydrogen, and oxygen. More sulfuric acid is produced in the United States than any other chemical. About 65 percent of the sulfuric acid produced is used to make fertilizers.

The Periodic Table **143**

The Nitrogen Fam
Build Reading Literacy

Identify Main Idea/Details Re
page 98D in **Chapter 4**, which pro
the guidelines for identifying main id
and details.

Guide students in applying this strategy to the text on page 143. Tell students to look for the main idea of each paragraph and then list one or two supporting details. If the paragraph has no topic sentence, have students list two important facts from the paragraph.
Verbal, Portfolio

FYI

Of the 18 elements essential for plant growth, nitrogen, phosphorus, and potassium are most likely to be lacking. The numbers on the fertilizer packages shown in Figure 19 represent percent N, percent P_2O_5, and percent K_2O. (In the past, oxides were often used as standards for chemical comparisons.) Nitrogen and phosphorus are often present as nitrates and phosphates.

The Oxygen Family

Address Misconceptions **L2**

Students may think that the air they breathe is pure oxygen. Challenge this misconception by reminding students that air is a mixture of gases. Air is 78% nitrogen and 21% oxygen. Have students research what gases make up the remaining 1% of air. *(Answers should include carbon dioxide, water vapor, argon, and other noble gases.)*
Logical

Facts and Figures

Phosphorus The element phosphorus has 10 forms, which are usually grouped as white, red, and black phosphorus for simplicity. The white phosphorus forms are the least stable.

In 1680, Robert Boyle demonstrated that phosphorus ignited by friction could be used to light wooden splints that had been dipped in sulfur. There are two types of matches. In a strike-anywhere match, all of the required ingredients (often phosphorus sulfide and potassium chlorate) are in the match head. In a safety match, the ingredients are divided between the match head and a rough striking surface on the side of the matchbox. A safety match can be lit only when the tip is drawn across the striking surface, which contains phosphorus sulfide.

Answer to . . .

Figure 19 *Tomato food*

Figure 20 *Sulfur is not highly reactive under ordinary conditions.*

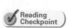 Reading Checkpoint *Carbon*

L Refer to **page 124D** in this hapter, which provides the guidelines or KWL (Know/Want to Know/Learned).

Teach this independent study skill as a whole-class exercise. **1.** Draw a three-column KWL chart on the board for students to copy. **2.** Have students complete the Know column with facts, examples, and other information that they already know about the Group 7A elements (the halogens). **3.** Tell students to complete the Want to Know column with questions about the halogens. **4.** Have students read p. 144 to learn more about the halogens. As they read, have them note answers to their questions in the Learned column, along with other facts, examples, and details they learned. **5.** Have students draw an Information I Expect to Use box below their KWL chart. Have them review the information in the Learned column and categorize the useful information in the box.
Verbal

Figure 21 At room temperature, chlorine is a gas, bromine is a liquid, and iodine is a solid. Halogens react easily with metals, such as the iron in steel wool. At a swimming pool, the chlorine content must be tested frequently. **Applying Concepts** *What process causes iodine vapor to collect in a flask of solid iodine?*

Chlorine reacting with steel wool

The Halogens

The elements in Group 7A are called **halogens.** Each halogen has seven valence electrons. Figure 21 shows the range of physical properties among the halogens. Fluorine and chlorine are gases, bromine is a liquid that evaporates quickly, and iodine is a solid that sublimes. **Despite their physical differences, the halogens have similar chemical properties.** They are highly reactive nonmetals, with fluorine being the most reactive and chlorine a close second. Halogens react easily with most metals. Figure 21 shows what happens when heated steel wool is plunged into chlorine.

Recall that a fluorine compound is used to prevent tooth decay. If you use pans with a nonstick coating to make omelets or muffins, you have seen another use of a fluorine compound. Have you ever noticed a sharp smell when adding bleach to a load of clothes? The smell comes from a small amount of chlorine gas that is released from a chlorine compound in the bleach. Chlorine is also used to kill bacteria in drinking water and swimming pools. The woman in Figure 21 is testing the level of chlorine in a swimming pool.

Your body needs iodine to keep your thyroid gland working properly. This gland controls the speed at which reactions occur in your body. Seafood is a good source of iodine. At a time when fresh fish was not available in all parts of the United States, people began to add iodine compounds to table salt. Salt that contains such compounds is called iodized salt.

144 *Chapter 5*

Facts and Figures

Halogens The name astatine comes from the Greek *astatos*, meaning "unstable." Astatine is a radioactive element whose most stable isotope, At-210, has a half-life of only 8.1 h. Astatine is the most metallic of the halogens. It is usually classified as a metalloid, but is sometimes regarded as a nonmetal.

Because of its rarity and instability, astatine has no practical uses.

Both bromine and iodine are volatile. Iodine comes from the Greek *ioeides,* meaning "violet colored." It is named for the color of iodine vapor, not the color of its solid crystals, which are dark gray.

The Noble Gases

The elements in Group 8A are called **noble gases.** Helium has two valence electrons. Each of the other noble gases has eight valence electrons. 👁 **The noble gases are colorless and odorless and extremely unreactive.** In Chapter 6, you will study the relationship between the electron configurations of the noble gases and their low reactivity.

It is not easy to discover a colorless, odorless gas. It is even harder if the gas rarely reacts. Scientists discovered argon when they noticed that the density of nitrogen collected from air did not match the density of nitrogen formed during chemical changes. In time, the scientists figured out that the "impurity" in atmospheric nitrogen was an unknown element.

An element that does not react easily with other elements can be very useful. For example, during one stage in the process of making computer chips, pure silicon is heated in a furnace at 1480°C. At this temperature, silicon reacts with both oxygen and nitrogen. So the heating must take place in an argon atmosphere.

Some light bulbs are filled with argon because the glowing filament in the bulb will not react with argon as it would react with oxygen. Using argon increases the number of hours the bulb can be lit before it burns out. All the noble gases except radon are used in "neon" lights like those shown in Figure 22.

Group 8A

2 **He** Helium
10 **Ne** Neon
18 **Ar** Argon
36 **Kr** Krypton
54 **Xe** Xenon
86 **Rn** Radon

Figure 22 When electric current passes through noble gases, they emit different colors. Helium emits pink, neon emits orange-red, argon emits lavender, krypton emits white, and xenon emits blue.

Section 5.3 Assessment

Reviewing Concepts

1. 👁 Explain why elements in a group have similar properties.
2. 👁 What is the relationship between an alkali metal's location in Group 1A and its reactivity?
3. 👁 What element exists in almost every compound in your body?
4. 👁 Which Group 5A elements are found in fertilizer?
5. 👁 Which group of elements is the least reactive?
6. Why is hydrogen located in a group with reactive metals?
7. What biological function requires magnesium?
8. Why is aluminum recycled?
9. What is the main use of sulfur?
10. Why is chlorine added to drinking water?

Critical Thinking

11. **Comparing and Contrasting** In which class of elements is there a greater range of properties, the metals or the nonmetals? Give an example to support your answer.
12. **Making Generalizations** What happens to the reactivity of nonmetals within a group from the top of the group to the bottom?

Connecting Concepts

Using Physical Properties In Section 2.2, three ways to use physical properties are discussed. Find one example in Section 5.3 that illustrates each use. If necessary, reread pages 48 and 50.

The Periodic Table **145**

The Noble Gases
Build Science Skills

Inferring Hold up an incandescent light bulb and tell students that the filament in the light bulb is made of tungsten, which emits light when it is heated to a high temperature. Explain that a light bulb with a tungsten filament contains small amounts of gases, such as argon, that do not react easily. Ask, **Why isn't air used in the light bulb?** (*The heated filament would burn in air, which contains oxygen.*) **Visual, Logical**

3 ASSESS

Evaluate Understanding   L2

Write the names of A group elements discussed in Section 3.3 on separate index cards. Distribute one card to each pair of students and have them add the following information to the card: chemical symbol, atomic number, group number and group name, number of valence electrons, physical state at room temperature, class of element (metal, nonmetal, or metalloid), and one or two properties of the element.

Reteach   L1

Use the segments of the periodic table that appear throughout the section to review each A group. Emphasize how the metallic properties of elements increase from top to bottom within a group and how the number of valence electrons changes from left to right across the periodic table.

Connecting Concepts

Examples of Identifying Materials: Distinguish halogens by their states and colors at room temperature.

Examples of Choosing Materials: Using hard calcium carbonate to polish teeth; using argon to increase the life of a light bulb.

Examples of Separating Materials: Sodium chloride from seawater by evaporation; nitrogen from oxygen based on their boiling points.

 Interactive Textbook If your class subscribes to the Interactive Textbook, use it to review key concepts in Section 5.3.

Answer to . . .
Figure 21 *Sublimation*

The Periodic Table   145

Section 5.3   Assessment

1. They have similar properties because they have the same number of valence electrons.
2. The reactivity of alkali metals increases from the top of Group 1A to the bottom.
3. Carbon
4. Nitrogen and phosphorus
5. The noble gases (Group 8A)
6. Hydrogen is placed with other elements that have a single valence electron.
7. The process that uses sunlight to produce sugar in plants

8. The energy needed to purify recycled aluminum is only about 5% of the energy needed to extract aluminum from bauxite.
9. To produce sulfuric acid
10. Chlorine is added to drinking water to kill bacteria.
11. Accept all answers that are supported by reasonable arguments. Students may choose nonmetals and say that they display a greater range of physical properties and reactivity.
12. The reactivity of nonmetals decreases from the top to the bottom of a group.

ONCEPTS
in Action

**emental
riends and Foes** `L2`

Background

All packaged and processed food sold in the United States displays a label with nutritional information. The label is designed to be easy to read and to enable consumers to quickly find the information they need to make appropriate food choices.

The label contains a Daily Value percentage (%DV) for calorie-containing nutrients such as fats and carbohydrates, as well as for cholesterol, vitamins, and minerals. For vitamins and minerals, the %DV is based on the Reference Daily Intake (RDI) values established by the U.S. Food and Drug Administration.

On current food labeling, the %DV for vitamins and minerals is the percentage of RDI available in a single serving. For example, the RDI for magnesium is 400 milligrams. If a single serving of a certain brand of cereal contains 40 milligrams of magnesium, the %DV for magnesium is listed as 10%.

It is likely that the number of elements classified as essential will grow along with advancements in understanding of nutrition and the human body. For example, nickel is an essential element in some species, but has not yet been determined to be essential in humans.

Elemental Friends and Foes

Some elements are essential for your health, and some are extremely harmful. You need to obtain the right amounts of the twenty-five essential elements through a balanced diet, and to reduce your exposure to the harmful elements.

Eating a variety of foods helps to ensure that all the elements needed by your body are available. The required elements can be classified as major, lesser, or trace elements. An element is classified based on its percentage by mass in the body.

The six major elements are hydrogen, oxygen, carbon, nitrogen, phosphorus, and calcium. These six major elements account for almost 99 percent of your body mass. Nearly every compound in your body contains carbon and hydrogen, and many contain oxygen too. The compounds that control all the chemical changes that take place in cells contain nitrogen. Calcium is essential for healthy bones and teeth. Phosphorus is found in your DNA and in the molecules that transfer energy within cells.

The lesser elements are iron, potassium, zinc, sodium, sulfur, chlorine, and magnesium. For each lesser element, there is a recommended amount that needs to be taken in daily. These amounts vary from 15 milligrams for zinc to 400 milligrams for magnesium. Lesser elements help your body build tissues and maintain other cell processes. For example, nerves and muscles require magnesium to function properly.

The trace elements are vanadium, chromium, molybdenum, manganese, cobalt, copper, boron, tin, silicon, selenium, fluorine, and iodine. The quantities required are tiny, but trace elements perform important functions. For example, red blood cells would not mature without cobalt.

Essential Elements of the Human Body

- Major elements (approximately 98.6 percent of total)
- Lesser elements (approximately 1.4 percent of total)
- Trace elements (less than 0.01 percent of total)
- Nonessential elements

Essential elements

The 25 elements essential to the human body are generally ingested as part of compounds found in food. The roles and functions of a few of these elements are shown here.

PASTA

Oxygen
This is the most abundant element in your body. The most important function of oxygen is to help release the energy stored in foods. You absorb oxygen from the air you breathe.

WATER

Carbon
Carbon is the second most common element in the human body. It is essential to life, because it is present in almost every compound in the body. If a food contains carbohydrates, proteins, or fats, it contains carbon compounds.

Hydrogen
Hydrogen is found in foods and in water, which accounts for more than 60 percent of body mass. Chemical reactions in cells take place in water.

Iron
Iron is a very important trace element because it is part of hemoglobin. This compound transports oxygen through the blood to every cell in the body. Meat, fish, and leafy green vegetables, such as spinach, are good sources of iron.

SPINACH

Iodine
Iodine is required in small amounts for the production of thyroxine by the thyroid gland. Thyroxine controls the rate of all chemical processes in the body. Fresh fish is a good source of iodine.

RED SNAPPER

GRAPES

Vanadium
Vanadium can help control blood sugar levels. It also plays an important role in the formation of bones and teeth. Vanadium can be found in black peppercorns.

Potassium
Potassium is essential to muscle and nerve function, and helps keep the body's fluids in balance. It also stimulates the kidneys to remove body wastes. Potassium can be found in fruit and dairy products.

BLACK PEPPERCORNS

CHEESES

Drawing Conclusions

Purpose Students identify elements whose compounds are used to fortify foods.

Materials empty containers of fortified food products such as milk, juice, salt, and bread

Class Time 15 minutes

Procedure Explain that sometimes compounds of essential elements are added to foods so that people will have a sufficient amount of these elements in their diets. Tell students that to *fortify* means to enrich or increase the nutrient value of food. Pass the empty containers around. Have students look at the labels. Ask, **Which essential elements have been added to the foods?** *(Answers may include calcium, iron, and iodine.)* **Why are these elements essential?** *(Students' answers should include information from pp. 146 and 147.)*

Expected Outcome Students discover that compounds of calcium, iron, and iodine are likely to be added when food is fortified.
Logical, Visual

(continued)

Build Science Skills L2

Making Judgments Assign as a research topic one of the harmful elements—mercury, lead, or arsenic—to each student. Have students use the Internet or the library to find two or three recent newspaper or magazine articles related to the harmful effects of exposure to the element. Ask students to write a paragraph summarizing each article, and then write a paragraph explaining whether or not they think that more steps should be taken to protect people from exposure to the element.

Have a class discussion or debate in which students present their research findings and their viewpoints. Ask, **What are the harmful effects of the element you researched?** *(Sample answer: Exposure to lead can damage the central nervous system, kidneys, and digestive system.)* **What precautions for the use of this element are currently in place?** *(Sample answer: Lead is no longer allowed as a gasoline additive; regulations prohibit renting an apartment or house with peeling and flaking lead paint to families with young children; and lead levels in drinking water have been reduced.)* **Are these precautions sufficient? Explain your answer.** *(Sample answer: Yes, because these regulations have helped significantly reduce the number of children suffering from lead exposure. According to the Centers for Disease Control, this number decreased about 80% between the late 1970s and mid-1990s. An EPA document dated December 2002 reports that in 1978 nearly three to four million children were affected. In the 1990s, the number declined to about 890,000.)*
Interpersonal, Group

Harmful Elements

Some elements should be avoided completely. These foes include metals, such as lead and mercury, and the metalloid arsenic. Harmful elements may enter the body in water, air, or food. Inside the body, nonessential elements may compete with essential elements and disrupt cell functions. Large amounts of harmful elements can stress the body's normal methods for eliminating toxins. Harmful elements can build up in body tissues.

For decades lead was used in paint and in gasoline to improve engine performance. These products are now lead free. The use of mercury in thermometers has been reduced and arsenic compounds are no longer used in pesticides.

Many trace elements are only helpful if ingested in the small recommended amounts. Larger quantities of most trace elements can be harmful, as can larger-than-required amounts of lesser elements, such as sodium.

82 Pb Lead
Lead Too much lead in the bloodstream can lead to organ damage and learning difficulties, especially in young children. For this reason, the use of lead-based paint was banned in 1978. Children may still be a risk if they live in an older house with layers of peeling paint.

80 Hg Mercury
Mercury Mercury is used in numerous industrial processes, but it is toxic and can damage the brain and nervous system. For this reason it should be handled with great care. It is particularly important to avoid inhaling mercury vapor.

33 As Arsenic
Arsenic Arsenic has been known as a poison for centuries, yet compounds of arsenic were used to treat some diseases before the discovery of penicillin. Arsenic compounds are no longer used to protect crops from insect pests or to preserve wood. Drinking water can absorb arsenic as it flows over rocks. But the amount of arsenic in drinking water is limited by law to less than 50 micrograms in each liter of water.

Arsenic pesticide

148 *Chapter 5*

Too much of a good thing

Many of the elements found in your body are needed in only very small amounts. Too much can often be harmful. The Food and Drug Administration provides guidelines on the safe daily quantities to take through food or supplements.

BEEF

Zinc
This trace element can be found in almost every cell of your body. Among other things, it helps to support a healthy immune system. Beef is a good source of zinc, but no more than 40 milligrams of zinc should be taken daily. Too much zinc can cause anemia by reducing iron uptake.

Sodium
It is hard to avoid sodium in your diet because table salt contains a sodium compound (sodium chloride). Everybody needs some sodium each day to maintain water balance and nerve function. But too much sodium (more than 3 grams daily) can cause high blood pressure.

TABLE SALT

Selenium
This trace element helps to maintain a healthy immune system. Brazil nuts are a good source of selenium, as are fruits and vegetables. While selenium supplements may be useful for some people, no more than 400 micrograms should be taken daily. Too much selenium can cause nerve damage.

BRAZIL NUTS

Going Further

- Choose a trace element other than vanadium, selenium, or iodine. Find out which foods are good sources of the element. Write a paragraph explaining how your diet meets or could be adjusted to meet your need for this element.

- Take a Discovery Channel Video Field Trip by watching "You Are What You Eat."

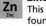

DISCOVERY CHANNEL **SCHOOL** Video Field Trip

The Periodic Table **149**

DISCOVERY CHANNEL **SCHOOL** Video Field Trip

You Are What You Eat

After students have viewed the Video Field Trip, ask them the following questions: **How did some ancient civilizations preserve their dead?** *(By embalming, or using preservatives)* **What are two types of information that scientists discover by examining mummies?** *(Student answers may include age, gender, diet, and cause of death.)* **What evidence led forensic scientists to suspect Tutankhamen, also known as King Tut, might**

not have died from natural causes? *(X-rays showed bone damage to his skull probably caused by a blow to his head.)* **List features that scientists found in the bones of mummies in Chile.** *(Student answers may include bone deformation around the ear, bones with significant nitrogen deposits, and strong and healthy teeth.)* **What do forensic scientists suspect to be the causes of the features found in these mummies?** *(Fishing in cold waters could have caused the growth around the ears. Nitrogen deposits in their bones could have been caused by a diet rich in seafood. A diet of fish could explain the strong, healthy teeth.)*

icting the Density
an Element

Objective

After completing this activity, students will be able to
- state that density increases from the top to the bottom within a group in the periodic table.
- evaluate predictions of physical properties based on the periodic table.

Skills Focus Measuring, Predicting, Analyzing Data, Using Graphs and Tables

Prep Time 20 minutes

Advance Prep Place each of the elements into a separate small, labeled container. Select sample sizes that will fit in the available graduated cylinders.

Class Time 40 minutes

Safety Make sure that students wear safety goggles, disposable plastic gloves, and lab aprons and wash their hands before leaving the laboratory. Caution students about the proper handling of chemicals. If you cut pieces of tin for students to use, be sure to file the edges smooth. Do not discard lead.

Teaching Tips
- Review the proper techniques for accurate use of the balance. Also remind students to read volumes in a graduated cylinder at eye level and at the bottom of the meniscus.

Questioning Strategies
Ask, **Why is it necessary to subtract the mass of the weighing paper from the total mass of the weighing paper and the sample?** *(To obtain the mass of the sample)* **Why is it necessary to subtract the volume of water from the total volume of water and sample when determining the volume of the silicon, tin, and lead?** *(To obtain the volume of each sample)*

Expected Outcome The elements' densities increase from the top to the bottom of Group 4A, but not in a simple linear manner.

 Exploration Lab

Predicting the Density of an Element

Density is a useful property for identifying and classifying elements. In this lab, you will determine the densities of three elements in Group 4A—silicon, tin, and lead. Then you will use your data to predict the density of another element in Group 4A—germanium.

Problem Can the densities of elements within a group be used to help predict the density of another element in the group?

Materials

- unlined white paper
- scissors
- metric ruler
- balance
- forceps
- silicon
- tin
- lead shot
- 50-mL graduated cylinder
- graph paper
- periodic table

 For the probeware version of this lab, see the Probeware Lab Manual, Lab 2.

Skills Measuring, Observing, Using Graphs, Calculating

Procedure

Part A: Measuring Mass

1. On a sheet of paper, make a copy of the data table shown.
2. Cut out three 10-cm × 10-cm pieces of paper from a sheet of unlined white paper. Label one piece of paper Silicon, the second Tin, and the third Lead. Find the mass of each piece of paper and record it in your data table.

3. Using forceps, place the silicon onto the paper labeled Silicon, as shown. Find the mass of the silicon and the paper. Record this mass in your data table. Then, subtract the mass of the paper from the mass of the silicon and paper. Record the mass of silicon in your data table. Set the paper containing the silicon aside for now.

4. Repeat Step 3 to find the masses of tin and lead.

Part B: Measuring Volume

5. Place 25 mL of water in the graduated cylinder. Measure the volume of the water to the nearest 0.1 mL. Record the volume (in cm³) in your data table. (*Hint:* 1 mL = 1 cm³)

6. Tilt the graduated cylinder and carefully pour the silicon from the paper into the graduated cylinder, as shown on page 151. Make sure that the silicon is completely covered by the water. Measure and record the volume of the water and silicon in your data table. Then, subtract the volume of water from the volume of the water and silicon. Record the result in your data table.

7. Repeat Steps 5 and 6 to find the volumes of tin and lead.

Data Table							
Element	Mass of Paper (g)	Mass of Paper and Element (g)	Mass of Element (g)	Volume of Water (cm³)	Volume of Water and Element (cm³)	Volume of Element (cm³)	Density of Element (g/cm³)
Silicon							
Tin							
Lead							

 Probeware Lab Manual Versions of this lab for use with Probeware available from Pasco, Texas Instruments, and Vernier are in the Probeware Manual.

Sample Data Table

Element	Density (g/cm³)
Silicon	2.4
Tin	7.1
Lead	11.3
Germanium	4.6 (from student graph)

Analyze and Conclude
1. Silicon, tin, and lead
2. A typical student estimate for t[..]
density of germanium is 4.6 g/cm[..]
which is a rough approximation of t[..]
actual value of 5.3 g/cm^3.
3. Student estimates are likely to be
approximately 16% lower than the
actual value.
4. From silicon to lead, the density of
the elements increases.
Logical

Go Further

Students will discover that there also is
a relationship, though slight, between
position in the periodic table and other
physical properties such as melting
points and boiling points.
Visual, Logical

Part C: Calculating Density

8. To calculate the density of silicon, divide its mass by its volume.

$$\text{Density} = \frac{\text{Mass}}{\text{Volume}}$$

Record the density of silicon in your data table.

9. Repeat Step 8 to find the densities of tin and lead.

10. Make a line graph that shows the relationship between the densities of silicon, tin, and lead and the periods in which they are located in the periodic table. Place the number of the period (from 1 to 7) on the horizontal axis and the density (in g/cm^3) on the vertical axis. Draw a straight line that comes as close as possible to all three points.

11. Germanium is in Period 4. To estimate the density of germanium, draw a dotted vertical line from the 4 on the horizontal axis to the solid line. Then, draw a dotted horizontal line from the solid line to the vertical axis. Read and record the density of germanium.

12. Wash your hands with warm water and soap before you leave the laboratory.

Analyze and Conclude

1. **Classifying** List lead, silicon, and tin in order of increasing density.

2. **Comparing and Contrasting** How does your estimate of the density of germanium compare with the actual density of germanium, which is 5.3 g/cm^3?

3. **Calculating** Use the formula for percent error (PE) to calculate a percent error for your estimate of the density of germanium.

$$PE = \frac{\text{Estimated value} - \text{Accepted value}}{\text{Accepted value}} \times 100$$

4. **Drawing Conclusions** How does the density of the elements change from silicon to lead in Group 4A?

Go Further Use reference books or sites on the Internet to research properties of Group 4A elements. Construct a graph that shows how another property, such as melting point or boiling point, varies among the Group 4A elements you explored. Determine whether knowing the values for three of the elements would allow you to accurately predict a value for the fourth element.

CHAPTER
5

Study Guide

Study Tip

Organize Information
Tell students that organizing information will help them remember it more easily. Suggest that students write key information from the chapter on index cards or large self-stick notes and use them to create large concept maps.

Thinking Visually

a. Metalloids
b. Nonmetals
c. Liquids

5.1 Organizing the Elements

Key Concepts

- Mendeleev arranged the elements into rows in order of increasing mass so that elements with similar properties were in the same column.

- The close match between Mendeleev's predictions and the actual properties of new elements showed how useful his periodic table could be.

Vocabulary

periodic table, *p. 127*

5.2 The Modern Periodic Table

Key Concepts

- In the modern periodic table, elements are arranged by increasing atomic number (number of protons). Each row on the table is a period. Each column is a group.

- Properties of elements repeat in a predictable way when atomic numbers are used to arrange elements into groups.

- Atomic mass is a value that depends on the distribution of an element's isotopes in nature and the masses of those isotopes.

- Elements are classified as metals, nonmetals, and metalloids. Metals are elements that are good conductors of electric current and heat. Nonmetals are poor conductors of electric current and heat. Metalloids are elements with properties that fall between those of metals and nonmetals.

- Across a period from left to right, the elements become less metallic and more nonmetallic in their properties.

Vocabulary

period, *p. 131*
group, *p. 131*
periodic law, *p. 131*
atomic mass unit (amu), *p. 134*
metals, *p. 135*
transition metals, *p. 136*
nonmetals, *p. 136*
metalloids, *p. 136*

5.3 Representative Groups

Key Concepts

- Elements in a group have similar properties because they have the same number of valence electrons.

- The alkali earth metals in Group 1A are extremely reactive. The reactivity of these metals increases from the top of the group to the bottom.

- Differences in reactivity among the alkaline earth metals in Group 2A are shown by the ways they react with water.

- Group 3A contains the most abundant metal in Earth's crust—aluminum. The energy needed to recycle aluminum is 5 percent of the energy needed to extract aluminum from bauxite.

- Group 4A contains the nonmetal carbon. Most compounds in your body contain carbon. Carbon compounds control reactions that occur in cells.

- Fertilizers usually contain the Group 5A elements nitrogen and phosphorus.

- Oxygen, in Group 6A, is the most abundant element in Earth's crust.

- Despite their physical differences, the halogens in Group 7A are all highly reactive nonmetals.

- The noble gases, in Group 8A, are colorless and odorless and extremely unreactive.

Vocabulary

valence electron, *p. 139*
alkali metals, *p. 140*
alkaline earth metals, *p. 141*
halogens, *p. 144*
noble gases, *p. 145*

Thinking Visually

Web Diagram Use information from the chapter to complete the web diagram below. The web relates states of matter at room temperature to categories of elements.

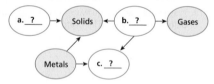

Chapter Resources

Print
- ***Chapter and Unit Tests,*** Chapter 5 Test A and Test B
- ***Test Prep Resources,*** Chapter 5

Technology
- ***Computer Test Bank,*** Chapter Test 5
- ***Interactive Textbook,*** Chapter 5
- ***Go Online,*** PHSchool.com, Chapter 5

Electron Dot Diagrams for Some Group A Elements							
Group							
1A	2A	3A	4A	5A	6A	7A	8A
H·							He:
Li·	·Be·	·B·	·C·	·N·	·O·	:F·	:Ne:
Na·	·Mg·	·Al·	·Si·	·P·	·S·	:Cl·	:Ar:
K·	·Ca·	·Ga·	·Ge·	·As·	·Se·	:Br·	:Kr:

Figure 2 In an electron dot diagram, each dot represents a valence electron. **Observing** *How many valence electrons do sodium and chlorine have?*

Ionic Bonds

Elements that do not have complete sets of valence electrons tend to react. By reacting, they achieve electron configurations similar to those of noble gases. ⊙ **Some elements achieve stable electron configurations through the transfer of electrons between atoms.**

Transfer of Electrons Look at the electron dot diagram for chlorine in Figure 2. A chlorine atom has one electron fewer than an argon atom. If the chlorine atom were to gain a valence electron, it would have the same stable electron arrangement as argon. Look at the electron dot diagram for sodium. A sodium atom has one more electron than a neon atom. If a sodium atom were to lose this electron, its highest occupied energy level would have eight electrons. It would then have the same stable electron arrangement as neon.

What happens at the atomic level when sodium reacts with chlorine? An electron is transferred from each sodium atom to a chlorine atom. Each atom ends up with a more stable electron arrangement than it had before the transfer.

$$ \text{Na}· \; + \; ·\ddot{\underset{··}{\text{Cl}}}: \; \longrightarrow \; \text{Na}^+ \; :\ddot{\underset{··}{\text{Cl}}}:^- $$

Formation of Ions When an atom gains or loses an electron, the number of protons is no longer equal to the number of electrons. The charge on the atom is not balanced and the atom is not neutral. An atom that has a net positive or negative electric charge is called an **ion.** The charge on an ion is represented by a plus or a minus sign. Notice the plus sign next to the symbol for sodium and the minus sign next to the symbol for chlorine.

For: Links on ionic bonds
Visit: www.SciLinks.org
Web Code: ccn-1061

Chemical Bonds **159**

What Determines the Size of an Atom or Ion? L2

Answers

1. Within a period, the atomic radius decreases as the atomic number increases.

2. Within these groups, the atomic radius increases as the atomic number increases.

3. When the next higher energy level is occupied, there is a significant increase in the atomic radius.

4. The ionic radius for potassium is much smaller than its atomic radius. The ionic radius for bromine is much larger than its atomic radius.

5. With the loss of valence electrons, the radius decreases. With the addition of valence electrons, the radius increases.

6. An energy level that was occupied is no longer occupied and the size decreases.

For Extra Help L1

Explain that attractions between protons and electrons largely determine the atomic radius of a specific atom.
Verbal

FYI

Because an electron cloud does not have an outer edge, the radius for elements that form diatomic molecules is calculated by measuring the distance between the two nuclei in the molecule and dividing by two.

Data Analysis

What Determines the Size of an Atom or Ion?

Scientists use atomic radii to compare the sizes of atoms of different elements. Remember from mathematics that the radius of a sphere is the distance from the center of the sphere to its outer edge. The radius is half the diameter of the sphere. Because atomic radii are extremely small, these distances are expressed in units called picometers (pm). As a comparison, there are one billion (10^9) picometers in a millimeter.

The table shows the atomic radius and ionic radius for six metals and six nonmetals. You will use the data to relate the size of an element's atoms to the element's location on the periodic table. You also will use the data to compare the sizes of atoms and their ions.

1. **Using Tables** Within a period, what happens to the atomic radius as the atomic number of the elements increases?

2. **Using Tables** Within Groups 1A, 2A, 6A, and 7A, what happens to the atomic radius of elements as the atomic number increases?

Atomic and Ionic Radii

1A	2A	6A	7A
152	112	66	64
Li	Be	O	F
1+ 60	2+ 31	2– 140	1– 136
186	160	103	99
Na	Mg	S	Cl
1+ 95	2+ 65	2– 184	1– 181
227	197	117	114
K	Ca	Se	Br
1+ 133	2+ 99	2– 198	1– 195

Atomic radius / Ionic radius

3. **Inferring** How does adding an occupied energy level affect the atomic radius? (*Hint:* Lithium is a Period 2 element and sodium is a Period 3 element.)

4. **Comparing and Contrasting** Compare the atomic and ionic radii for potassium (K), and for bromine (Br).

5. **Making Generalizations** What happens to the radius of an atom when the atom loses electrons? When the atom gains electrons?

6. **Relating Cause and Effect** Explain the difference in size between a metal atom and its cation.

The ion that forms when a chlorine atom gains an electron has 17 protons and 18 electrons. This ion has a charge of 1– because it has one extra electron. The symbol for the ion is written Cl^{1-}, or Cl^- for short. An ion with a negative charge is an **anion** (AN eye un). Anions like the Cl^- ion are named by using part of the element name plus the suffix *–ide*. Thus, Cl^- is called a *chloride* ion.

A sodium ion has 11 protons and 10 electrons. Because it has one extra proton, the sodium ion has a charge of 1+. The symbol for the ion is written Na^{1+}, or Na^+ for short. An ion with a positive charge is a **cation** (KAT eye un). Naming a cation is easy. You just use the element name, as in the *sodium* ion.

Formation of Ionic Bonds Remember that a particle with a negative charge will attract a particle with a positive charge. When an anion and a cation are close together, a chemical bond forms between them. A **chemical bond** is the force that holds atoms or ions together as a unit. An **ionic bond** is the force that holds cations and anions together. An ionic bond forms when electrons are transferred from one atom to another.

160 *Chapter 6*

Facts and Figures

Atomic and Ionic Radii The radius of an atom decreases from left to right across a period because valence electrons are shielded from the nucleus by electrons in lower energy levels. The amount of positive nuclear charge experienced by valence electrons is mainly determined by the difference in charge between the nucleus and the inner (or core) electrons. Because the number of core electrons does not change across a period, as the number of protons increases the charge experienced by valence electrons increases and the atomic radius decreases.

The radius of an anion is larger than the radius of its corresponding atom. Adding electrons to the highest occupied energy level increases the repulsions among electrons. The increase in repulsions causes the electrons to spread out more in space.

Ionization Energy An electron can move to a higher energy level when an atom absorbs energy. Cations form when electrons gain enough energy to escape from atoms. The energy allows electrons to overcome the attraction of the protons in the nucleus. The amount of energy used to remove an electron is called ionization energy. It varies from element to element. The lower the ionization energy, the easier it is to remove an electron from an atom.

Figure 3 shows two trends for ionization energy. Ionization energies tend to increase from left to right across a period. It takes more energy to remove an electron from a nonmetal than from a metal in the same period. Ionization energies tend to decrease from the top of a group to the bottom. In Group 1A, potassium has a lower ionization energy than sodium. So it is easier to remove an electron from potassium than from sodium, and potassium is more reactive than sodium.

Generally increases →
↕ Generally decreases
Trends in Ionization Energy

Figure 3 Ionization energies generally increase from left to right across a period.
Interpreting Diagrams *What is the trend for ionization energy within a group?*

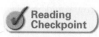
Reading Checkpoint *What is ionization energy?*

Ionic Compounds

Compounds that contain ionic bonds are ionic compounds, which can be represented by chemical formulas. A **chemical formula** is a notation that shows what elements a compound contains and the ratio of the atoms or ions of these elements in the compound. The chemical formula for sodium chloride is NaCl. From the formula, you can tell that there is one sodium ion for each chloride ion in sodium chloride.

Based on the diagram in Figure 4, what would the formula for magnesium chloride be? A magnesium atom cannot reach a stable electron configuration by reacting with just one chlorine atom. It must transfer electrons to two chlorine atoms. After the transfer, the charge on the magnesium ion is 2+ and its symbol is Mg^{2+}. The formula for the compound is $MgCl_2$. The 2 written to the right and slightly below the symbol for chlorine is a subscript. Subscripts are used to show the relative numbers of atoms of the elements present. If there is only one atom of an element in the formula, no subscript is needed.

Figure 4 Magnesium chloride forms when magnesium atoms transfer electrons to chlorine atoms. Magnesium chloride is used to control dust that is stirred up by traffic on unpaved roads.

Chemical Bonds **161**

Integrate Earth Science L2

Geologists use a system to classify minerals similar to the one used by chemists to classify compounds. Ask students to use the library or Internet to find photographs of minerals that have cubic crystals (like sodium chloride) or hexagonal crystals (like ruby). Some students may also want to find examples of tetragonal, monoclinic, triclinic, and orthorhombic crystals.
Visual

Use Visuals L1

Figure 5 Have students examine Figure 5. Ask, **How are sodium ions represented in the figure?** *(Sodium ions are represented by the smaller, orange spheres.)* **How are chloride ions represented in the figure?** *(Chloride ions are represented by the larger, green spheres.)* **What do you notice about the pattern of the locations of positive and negative ions in the diagram?** *(No two neighboring ions have the same charge.)* **What similarity do you notice between the diagram and the photograph of sodium chloride crystals?** *(The structures in both the diagram and the photograph have a cubic shape.)*
Visual

Build Science Skills L2

Applying Concepts Help students understand the structure of a crystal lattice by encouraging them to think of three-dimensional analogies for lattices, such as scaffolding on a building or cups and saucers stacked on a tray in a restaurant.
Visual, Logical

Figure 5 The structure and shape of a crystal are related. **A** In a sodium chloride crystal, each ion is surrounded by six oppositely charged ions. **B** Sodium chloride crystals are shaped like cubes.

Crystal Lattices A chemical formula for an ionic compound tells you the ratio of the ions in the compound. But it does not tell you how the ions are arranged in the compound. If you looked at a sample of sodium chloride with a hand lens or microscope, you would be able to see that the pieces of salt are shaped like cubes. This shape is a clue to how the sodium and chloride ions are arranged in the compound.

Figure 5A shows that the ions in sodium chloride are arranged in an orderly, three-dimensional structure. Each chloride ion is surrounded by six sodium ions and each sodium ion is surrounded by six chloride ions. Each ion is attracted to all the neighboring ions with an opposite charge. This set of attractions keeps the ions in fixed positions in a rigid framework, or lattice. The repeating pattern of ions in the lattice is like the repeating pattern of designs on the wallpaper in Figure 6.

Solids whose particles are arranged in a lattice structure are called **crystals.** Compare the cubic shape of the sodium chloride crystals in Figure 5B to the arrangement of ions in Figure 5A. The shape of an ionic crystal depends on the arrangement of ions in its lattice. In turn, the arrangement of the ions depends on the ratio of ions and their relative sizes. Crystals are classified into groups based on the shape of their crystals. Crystals of ruby have a six-sided, hexagonal shape. The How It Works box on page 163 describes one way to make rubies.

Reading Checkpoint *What shape are sodium chloride crystals?*

Figure 6 This wallpaper displays a repeating pattern of flower and fruit designs. Using Analogies *How is this arrangement of designs similar to the arrangement of ions in a crystal?*

Facts and Figures

Crystal Systems Crystals are classified into seven different crystal systems, which are described by geometric figures with six faces. The figures are distinguished by the angles at which the faces meet and by how many edges on a face are equal in length. Cubic: three equal edges, three 90° angles; tetragonal: two equal edges, three 90° angles; orthorhombic: no equal edges, three 90° angles; monoclinic: no equal edges, two 90° angles; triclinic: no equal edges, no 90° angles; hexagonal: two equal edges, two 90° angles, one 120° angle; rhombohedral: three equal edges, two 90° angles.

Synthetic Rubies

Rubies are mainly aluminum oxide, which is white. The substitution of a small percentage of chromium ions for aluminum ions gives rubies their distinctive red color. Because natural rubies are rare, rubies are often manufactured. **Interpreting Diagrams** *What substances are in the mixture used to make rubies?*

SYNTHETIC RUBY BOULE

HEXAGONAL CRYSTAL STRUCTURE

NATURAL RUBY

Synthetic ruby
A synthetic ruby boule has a hexagonal crystal structure identical to the natural ruby gemstone. Its shape is determined by the arrangement of ions in the crystal.

Making synthetic rubies
One way of making synthetic rubies is called the pulled-growth method. It was invented by Polish scientist Jan Czochralski (1885–1953).

Aluminum and chromium oxides

Rotating rod

Melt

Ruby forming

Seed crystal

Ruby boule

Heater

Crucible

Furnace vessel

1 **Seed crystal** Aluminum oxide and chromium(VI) oxide are melted. A tiny piece of ruby, called a seed crystal, is attached to a rod and placed above the molten mixture (melt).

2 **Lowering into the melt** The rod is lowered until the seed crystal touches the melt. The rod is slowly lifted, and ions in the melt begin to attach themselves to the seed crystal to form a ruby.

3 **Forming a boule** As the rod is lifted higher, an oblong-shaped crystal called a boule grows from the end. Once cooled, the boule can be cut into different shapes.

Chemical Bonds **163**

Synthetic Rubies **L2**

Another technique used to create synthetic rubies was first used in 1902. It is called the Verneuil flame-fusion process. It differs from the more expensive Czochralski pulled-growth process described in the text in that the mixture of aluminum and chromium oxides is heated in open air with a flame instead of melted in a crucible.

The mineral corundum consists of aluminum oxide mixed with chromium, iron, or other mineral impurities. The color of a corundum crystal depends on the type and amount of impurities. Crystals of red corundum are called rubies, while crystals of other colors are called sapphires. In addition to the familiar use of synthetic rubies in jewelry, some lasers use synthetic rubies to produce light of a specific frequency.

Interpreting Diagrams Oxides of aluminum and chromium
Visual

For Enrichment **L3**

Interested students can make a poster presentation for the class explaining other methods for synthesizing gemstones. Some common methods besides the flame-fusion and pulled-growth methods include the flux-growth method, the solution-growth process, and horizontal crystallization.
Visual, Portfolio

Answer to . . .

Figure 6 *The pattern of design elements in the wallpaper repeats the way the arrangement of ions repeats in a crystal lattice.*

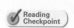 Reading Checkpoint *They are cubes.*

FYI

Real crystals are not perfect. Sites in a lattice may be vacant, sites may be occupied by impurities, and occupied sites may be squeezed in between regular sites in the lattice (an interstitial defect). In an ionic compound, a cation vacancy is balanced by a nearby anion vacancy or by an interstitial cation (which maintains an overall balance of charge). Crystal defects are largely responsible for how crystals fracture under stress.

Use Visuals **L1**

Figure 7 Have students compare the before-and-after diagrams. Ask, **When the hammer hits the crystal, what happens to the positions of the ions?** *(Ions with similar charge are pushed near one another.)* **How do objects with the same charge behave?** *(They repel.)* **Visual**

3 ASSESS

Evaluate Understanding **L2**

Have students describe the formation of anions, cations, and ionic bonds.

Reteach **L1**

Use the diagram at the bottom of p. 161 to review the formation of cations, anions, and ionic bonds.

Connecting C Concepts

Potassium is more reactive than calcium because the amount of energy needed to remove a single valence electron from a potassium atom is much smaller than the amount of energy needed to remove two valence electrons from a calcium atom.

Interactive Textbook If your class subscribes to the Interactive Textbook, use it to review key concepts in Section 6.1.

Hammer strikes crystal.

Ionic crystal shatters when struck.

Figure 7 When an ionic crystal is struck, ions are moved from their fixed positions. Ions with the same charge repel one another and the crystal shatters.

Properties of Ionic Compounds The properties of sodium chloride are typical of an ionic compound. It has a high melting point (801°C). In its solid state, sodium chloride is a poor conductor of electric current. But when melted, it is a good conductor of electric current. Sodium chloride crystals shatter when struck with a hammer. ◉ **The properties of an ionic compound can be explained by the strong attractions among ions within a crystal lattice.**

Recall that the arrangement of particles in a substance is the result of two opposing factors. The first factor is the attractions among particles in the substance. The second factor is the kinetic energy of the particles. The stronger the attractions among the particles, the more kinetic energy the particles must have before they can separate.

For an electric current to flow, charged particles must be able to move from one location to another. The ions in a solid crystal lattice have fixed positions. However, when the solid melts, the lattice breaks apart and the ions are free to flow. Melted, or molten, sodium chloride is an excellent conductor of electric current.

Rock salt contains large crystals of sodium chloride. If you tapped a crystal of rock salt sharply with a hammer, it would shatter into many smaller crystals. Figure 7 shows what happens to the positions of the ions when the crystal is struck. Negative ions are pushed into positions near negative ions, and positive ions are pushed into positions near positive ions. Ions with the same charge repel one another and cause the crystal to shatter.

Section 6.1 Assessment

Reviewing Concepts

1. ◉ When is an atom least likely to react?
2. ◉ Describe one way an element can achieve a stable electron configuration.
3. ◉ What characteristic of ionic bonds can be used to explain the properties of ionic compounds?
4. Use ionization energy to explain why metals lose electrons more easily than nonmetals.
5. Why is a rock salt crystal likely to shatter when struck?

Critical Thinking

6. **Making Generalizations** What will the ratio of ions be in any compound formed from a Group 1A metal and a Group 7A nonmetal? Explain your answer.

7. **Drawing Conclusions** Why do ionic compounds include at least one metal?

8. **Predicting** Based on their chemical formulas, which of these compounds is not likely to be an ionic compound: KBr, SO_2, or $FeCl_3$? Explain your answer.

Connecting C Concepts

Reactivity of Metals Use what you know about how ionic bonds form to explain the difference in reactivity between potassium and calcium. If necessary, reread the description of Group 1A and Group 2A properties in Section 5.3.

Section 6.1 Assessment

1. When the highest occupied energy level of an atom is filled with electrons
2. Through the transfer of electrons between atoms
3. The strong attractions among ions within a crystal lattice
4. Metals have lower ionization energies than nonmetals. The lower the ionization energy, the easier it is to remove an electron from an atom.

5. When ions with the same charge are pushed close together, they repel one another.
6. The ratio will be one to one because a Group 1A metal loses one electron and a Group 7A nonmetal gains one electron to achieve a stable electron configuration.
7. One element in an ionic compound must form cations, but nonmetals tend to form anions.
8. SO_2 because sulfur and oxygen are both nonmetals and unlikely to form cations

6.2 Covalent Bonding

Standards: ICP.3.1, ICP.5.2, ICP.5.3, ICP.5.4, ICP.5.6

Reading Focus

Key Concepts
- How are atoms held together in a covalent bond?
- What happens when atoms don't share electrons equally?
- What factors determine whether a molecule is polar?
- How do attractions between polar molecules compare to attractions between nonpolar molecules?

Vocabulary
- covalent bond
- molecule
- polar covalent bond

Reading Strategy
Relating Text and Visuals Copy the table. As you read, look closely at Figure 9. Complete the table by describing each type of model shown.

Model	Description
Electron dot	a. _____?_____
Structural formula	b. _____?_____
Space-filling	c. _____?_____
Electron cloud	d. _____?_____

Plants absorb water through their roots from soil or from a solution containing nutrients, as in Figure 8. Carbon dioxide from the air enters the plants through small openings in their leaves. The plants use the energy from sunlight to convert water and carbon dioxide into a sugar. Energy is stored in the chemical bonds of the sugar.

The elements in sugar are carbon, oxygen, and hydrogen. All three are nonmetals, which have relatively high ionization energies. A transfer of electrons does not tend to occur between nonmetal atoms. So, how are two nonmetals able to form bonds?

Covalent Bonds

You and a friend are participating in a treasure hunt. The rules state that the first person to find all eight items on a list will win a 21-speed bicycle. After about an hour, you have found six of the items on the list and your friend has found the other two. You and your friend have incomplete sets of items. But if you are willing to share your items with your friend, together you will have a complete set of items and qualify for the prize. Of course, you will have to be willing to share the bicycle, too. When nonmetals join together, they display a similar sharing strategy.

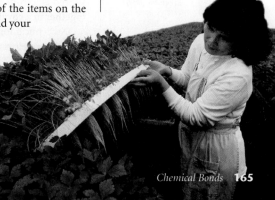

Figure 8 When plants are grown in water instead of soil, you can see their roots. Plants absorb water through their roots and carbon dioxide through small openings in their leaves.

Chemical Bonds **165**

Section Resources

Print
- *Laboratory Manual,* Investigation 6B
- *Reading and Study Workbook With Math Support,* Section 6.2
- *Transparencies,* Section 6.2

Technology
- *Interactive Textbook,* Section 6.2
- *Presentation Pro CD-ROM,* Section 6.2
- *Go Online,* NSTA SciLinks, Covalent bonding

Section 6.2

1 FOCUS

Objectives
6.2.1 Describe how covalent bonds form and the attractions that keep atoms together in molecules.

6.2.2 Compare polar and nonpolar bonds, and **demonstrate** how polar bonds affect the polarity of a molecule.

6.2.3 Compare the attractions between polar and nonpolar molecules.

Reading Focus

Build Vocabulary L2

Concept Map Have students construct a concept map using the terms *atoms, molecules, ions, covalent bonds, ionic bonds, polar, nonpolar,* and *electrons.* Instruct students to place the terms in ovals and connect the ovals with lines on which linking words are placed. Students should place the main concept (Chemical Bonding) at the top or the center. As the distance from the main concept increases, the content should become more specific.

Reading Strategy L2
a. Dots represent valence electrons. **b.** A line represents a pair of shared valence electrons. **c.** Three-dimensional spheres represent atoms. **d.** Electron clouds represent atoms.

2 INSTRUCT

Covalent Bonds

Address Misconceptions L2

Many students do not differentiate among atoms, ions, and molecules in their sketches of particle models. Challenge this misconception by asking students to make drawings to represent an atom, a molecule, and an ion. Students should draw a single sphere for an atom, at least two spheres joined in some way for a molecule, and one sphere with either a plus or a minus charge for an ion.
Visual

Use Visuals L1

Figure 10 Have students examine Figure 10. Ask, **Why are the atoms in the models of diatomic molecules not complete spheres?** *(The space-filling models show that orbitals of atoms overlap when they form covalent bonds.)* Have students compare the space-filling models in Figure 10 to the data on atomic radii in the Data Analysis on p. 160. Ask, **Why are the spheres in the models of fluorine, chlorine, and bromine different sizes?** *(The different sizes of spheres model the different atomic radii of the atoms.)* **Logical**

Build Reading Literacy L1

Visualize Refer to page 354D in **Chapter 12**, which provides the guidelines for visualizing.

After students have read about ionic and covalent bonds and the difference between polar and nonpolar bonds, encourage students to draw diagrams that demonstrate the differences between three types of bonding: nonpolar covalent, polar covalent, and ionic.
Visual, Portfolio

FYI

Not all nonmetal elements exist as molecules. Of those that do, not all form diatomic molecules. Molecules of crystalline sulfur contain eight sulfur atoms, S_8. Molecules of white phosphorus contain four phosphorus atoms, P_4.

Based on the octet rule, a molecule of ozone, O_3, should contain one double bond and one single coordinate covalent bond (a bond in which one of the atoms donates an unshared pair of electrons). However, the measured bond lengths for the two bonds in an ozone molecule are identical. The bonds are hybrids—not strictly single bonds or double bonds.

Figure 9 As a space shuttle lifts off, it leaves a water vapor trail. A reaction of hydrogen and oxygen produces the water.
Using Models **How is the bond between hydrogen atoms represented in each model of a hydrogen molecule?**

Fluorine (F_2)

Nitrogen (N_2)

Chlorine (Cl_2)

Bromine (Br_2)

Iodine (I_2)

Figure 10 These space-filling models represent diatomic molecules of five elements.
Using Models **How many atoms are in a diatomic molecule?**

166 *Chapter 6*

Sharing Electrons A hydrogen atom has one electron. If it had two electrons, it would have the same electron configuration as a helium atom. Two hydrogen atoms can achieve a stable electron configuration by sharing their electrons and forming a covalent bond. A **covalent bond** is a chemical bond in which two atoms share a pair of valence electrons. When two atoms share one pair of electrons, the bond is called a single bond.

Figure 9 shows four different ways to represent a covalent bond. In the electron dot model, the bond is shown by a pair of dots in the space between the symbols for the hydrogen atoms. In the structural formula, the pair of dots is replaced by a line. The electron cloud model and the space-filling model show that orbitals of atoms overlap when a covalent bond forms.

Molecules of Elements Two hydrogen atoms bonded together form a unit called a molecule. A **molecule** is a neutral group of atoms that are joined together by one or more covalent bonds. The hydrogen molecule is neutral because it contains two protons (one from each atom) and two electrons (one from each atom). What keeps the hydrogen atoms together in the molecule? ⬤ **The attractions between the shared electrons and the protons in each nucleus hold the atoms together in a covalent bond.**

A chemical formula can be used to describe the molecules of an element as well as a compound. The element hydrogen has the chemical formula H_2. The subscript 2 indicates that there are two atoms in a molecule of hydrogen.

Many nonmetal elements exist as diatomic molecules. *Diatomic* means "two atoms." Four of the models in Figure 10 are of halogens. A halogen atom has seven valence electrons. If two halogen atoms share a valence electron from each atom, both atoms have eight valence electrons.

Customize for English Language Learners

Think-Pair-Share
Have students work in pairs to think of situations that serve as analogies for ionic and covalent bonding. For example, if a jeweler lends an expensive piece of jewelry to a presenter at an awards show, a guard will accompany the presenter and stay as close as possible. This is similar to an ionic bond, in which a cation stays close to an anion to which it donates an electron. By contrast, students reading from one copy of the same book are like two atoms sharing a pair of electrons in a covalent bond. Strengthen discussion skills by having students share analogies with the class.

Analyzing Inks

Materials

test paper, metric ruler, felt-tip markers, stapler, beaker, alcohol-water mixture, Petri dish

Procedure

Pencil line

2 cm   5 cm   8 cm   11 cm   1.5 cm

1. Place the test paper on a clean surface. Use the ruler to draw the pencil line shown in the drawing. Use your markers to place color dots at the locations shown in the drawing.

2. With the ink marks on the outside, staple the two ends of the paper together to form a tube.

3. Pour the alcohol-water mixture into the beaker to a depth of 0.5 cm. Stand the paper in the beaker so that the dots are at the bottom. The paper should not touch the sides of the beaker. Invert the Petri dish over the beaker.

4. When the mixture reaches the top of the paper, remove the paper from the beaker. Unstaple the paper and lay it flat. Make a drawing of the results with each colored area labeled.

Analyze and Conclude

1. **Observing** Which markers contained inks that were mixtures of colored substances?

2. **Formulating Hypotheses** How did some molecules in the ink move up the paper?

3. **Predicting** Assume that molecules in the test paper are more polar than molecules in the alcohol-water mixture. Would you expect the most polar molecules in ink to stick tightly to the paper or to move with the liquid? Explain.

4. **Designing Experiments** How could the procedure from this lab be used to identify a black ink whose composition is unknown?

Multiple Covalent Bonds Nitrogen has five valence electrons. If two nitrogen atoms shared a pair of electrons, each one would have only six valence electrons. If they shared two pairs of electrons, each atom would have only seven valence electrons. When the atoms in a nitrogen molecule (N_2) share three pairs of electrons, each atom has eight valence electrons. Each pair of shared electrons is represented by a long dash in the structural formula $N \equiv N$. When two atoms share three pairs of electrons, the bond is called a triple bond. When two atoms share two pairs of electrons, the bond is called a double bond.

 What does the subscript 2 in the formula for a hydrogen molecule indicate?

Unequal Sharing of Electrons

In general, elements on the right of the periodic table have a greater attraction for electrons than elements on the left have (except for noble gases). In general, elements at the top of a group have a greater attraction for electrons than elements at the bottom of a group have. Fluorine is on the far right and is at the top of its group. It has the strongest attraction for electrons and is the most reactive nonmetal.

For: Links on covalent bonding
Visit: www.SciLinks.org
Web Code: ccn-1062

Chemical Bonds **167**

Unequal Sharing of Electrons

Analyzing Inks   **L2**

Objective
After completing this activity, students will be able to
• explain how differences in polarity can be used to separate the components of a solution.

Skills Focus Observing, Inferring

 Prep Time 10 minutes

Advance Prep Provide each group with an 8-cm × 16-cm piece of test (chromatography) paper. The alcohol-water mixture is 70% isopropyl alcohol in water.

Class Time 20 minutes

Safety Provide only markers containing water-based inks or inks that are low in volatile organic compounds (VOCs). Make sure that there are no flames in the laboratory when alcohol is in use.

Teaching Tips
• Have students do this lab after they study polar molecules and attractions between molecules.
• Tell students not to touch the test paper with their bare hands because oil naturally present on their fingers will interfere with the results. They should wear plastic gloves.

Expected Outcome Most inks will contain more than one pigment.

Download a worksheet on covalent bonding for students to complete, and find additional teacher support from NSTA SciLinks.

Analyze and Conclude

1. In general, darker inks (such as brown or black) contain two or more red, blue, and yellow pigments.

2. Molecules that dissolved easily in the alcohol-water mixture moved up the paper with the mixture.

3. The most polar molecules would be found near the bottom of the paper because they are more strongly attracted to the paper than to the alcohol-water mixture.

4. If an unknown black ink produces a color pattern similar to one of the known inks, they are likely to be identical.
Visual, Logical

Answer to . . .

Figure 9 *A pair of dots, a line, overlapping spheres, and overlapping electron clouds*

Figure 10 *Two*

The subscript 2 shows that there are two atoms in a hydrogen molecule.

Teacher > Demo

Modeling Overall Polarity L2

Purpose Students examine a model for molecular polarity.

Materials molecular model kit, 4 12-inch pieces of string or yarn, tape, overhead projector

Procedure Show students ball-and-stick models of a carbon dioxide molecule and a water molecule. Have them compare the linear shape of CO_2 with the bent shape of H_2O. Tie or tape one piece of string onto each of the oxygen atoms of the CO_2 model and onto each of the hydrogen atoms of the H_2O model. Place the CO_2 model on the overhead and demonstrate the effect of pulling the strings gently in opposite directions. Explain that this represents the canceling effect of opposing polar bonds (dipoles). Place the H_2O model on the overhead and demonstrate the effect of pulling the strings gently away from the oxygen atom in the direction of the bond angles. Explain that this represents the additive effect of polar bonds that are at an angle.

Expected Outcome The CO_2 model will stay in one place. The H_2O model will move in the direction of the hydrogen atoms.
Visual

Build Science Skills L2

Using Models Show students a ball-and-stick molecular model of ammonia, NH_3. Ask students to predict whether the molecule is polar or nonpolar and to give a reason for their choice. *(Ammonia is a polar molecule because its three bonds are oriented to one side of the central nitrogen atom. The polar bonds do not cancel out.)* Now show students a molecular model of sulfur trioxide, SO_3. Ask students to predict whether this molecule is polar or nonpolar and to explain their reasoning. *(Sulfur trioxide is a nonpolar molecule because its three bonds are oriented symmetrically in a plane around the central sulfur atom. The polar bonds cancel each other out.)*
Logical, Visual

Figure 11 Shared electrons in a hydrogen chloride molecule spend less time near the hydrogen atom than near the chlorine atom. *Inferring* **Which element has a greater attraction for electrons—hydrogen or chlorine?**

HCl

CO₂

H₂O

Figure 12 In a carbon dioxide (CO_2) molecule, the polar bonds between the carbon atom and the oxygen atoms cancel out because the molecule is linear. In a water (H_2O) molecule, the polar bonds between the oxygen atom and the hydrogen atoms do not cancel out because the molecule is bent.

168 Chapter 6

Polar Covalent Bonds In a molecule of an element, the atoms that form covalent bonds have the same ability to attract an electron. Shared electrons are attracted equally to the nuclei of both atoms. In a molecule of a compound, electrons may not be shared equally.

Figure 11 shows models of the molecule that forms when hydrogen reacts with chlorine. A chlorine atom has a greater attraction for electrons than a hydrogen atom does. In a hydrogen chloride molecule, the shared electrons spend more time near the chlorine atom than near the hydrogen atom. A covalent bond in which electrons are not shared equally is called a **polar covalent bond.** (One meaning of the term *polar* is "opposite in character, nature, or direction.")

When atoms form a polar covalent bond, the atom with the greater attraction for electrons has a partial negative charge. The other atom has a partial positive charge. The symbols $\delta-$ and $\delta+$ are used to show which atom has which charge. (δ is the lowercase version of the Greek letter delta.)

Polar and Nonpolar Molecules Can you assume that a molecule that contains a polar covalent bond is polar? If a molecule has only two atoms, it will be polar. But, when molecules have more than two atoms, the answer is not as obvious. The type of atoms in a molecule and its shape are factors that determine whether a molecule is polar or nonpolar.

Compare the models of carbon dioxide and water in Figure 12. In carbon dioxide, there are double bonds between each oxygen atom and the central carbon atom. Because oxygen has a greater attraction for electrons than carbon does, each double bond is polar. However, the molecule is linear: all three atoms are lined up in a row. The carbon-oxygen double bonds are directly opposite each other. There is an equal pull on the electrons from opposite directions. The pulls cancel out and the molecule as a whole is nonpolar.

There are two single bonds in a water molecule. The bonds are polar because oxygen has a greater attraction for electrons than hydrogen does. Because the water molecule has a bent shape rather than a linear shape, the polar bonds do not cancel out. The two hydrogen atoms are located on the same side of the molecule, opposite the oxygen atom. The oxygen side of the molecule has a partial negative charge. The hydrogen side of the molecule has a partial positive charge.

168 Chapter 6

Facts and Figures

Surface Tension Refer back to the discussion in Section 3.3 about the effect of intermolecular attractions on the evaporation of water. Hydrogen bonds explain other properties of water, including its high surface tension.

Because molecules on the surface are drawn inward by attractions from molecules beneath the surface, surface area is reduced. Surface tension explains why water drops bead up on a clean, waxed surface.

Attraction Between Molecules

In a molecular compound, there are forces of attraction between molecules. These attractions are not as strong as ionic or covalent bonds, but they are strong enough to hold molecules together in a liquid or solid. 🔵 **Attractions between polar molecules are stronger than attractions between nonpolar molecules.**

Water molecules are similar in mass to methane (CH_4) molecules. Yet, methane boils at $-161.5°C$ and water boils at $100°C$ because methane molecules are nonpolar and water molecules are polar. Each dashed line in Figure 13 represents an attraction between a partially positive hydrogen atom in one water molecule and a partially negative oxygen atom in another. Molecules on the surface of a water sample are attracted to molecules that lie below the surface and are pulled toward the center of the sample. These attractions increase the energy required for water molecules to evaporate. They raise the temperature at which vapor pressure equals atmospheric pressure—the boiling point.

Attractions among nonpolar molecules are weaker than attractions among polar molecules, but they do exist. After all, carbon dioxide can exist as solid dry ice. Attractions among nonpolar molecules explain why nitrogen can be stored as a liquid at low temperatures and high pressures. Because electrons are constantly in motion, there are times when one part of a nitrogen molecule has a small positive charge and one part has a small negative charge. At those times, one nitrogen molecule can be weakly attracted to another nitrogen molecule.

Figure 13 Each dashed line in the drawing represents an attraction between a hydrogen atom and an oxygen atom.
Interpreting Diagrams *In a water molecule, which atom has a partial negative charge? Which has a partial positive charge?*

Section 6.2 Assessment

Reviewing Concepts

1. 🔵 What attractions hold atoms together in a covalent bond?

2. 🔵 What happens to the charge on atoms when they form a polar covalent bond?

3. 🔵 Name the two factors that determine whether a molecule is polar.

4. 🔵 Compare the strength of attractions between polar molecules to the strength of attractions between nonpolar molecules.

5. What is a molecule?

Critical Thinking

6. **Applying Concepts** Which of these elements does not bond to form molecules: oxygen, chlorine, neon, or sulfur?

7. **Inferring** Why is the boiling point of water higher than the boiling point of chlorine?

8. **Using Diagrams** Based on their electron dot diagrams, what is the formula for the covalently bonded compound of nitrogen and hydrogen?

Connecting C Concepts

Viscosity Review the description of the physical property viscosity in Section 2.2. Then write a paragraph explaining how attractions between molecules might affect the viscosity of a liquid.

Chemical Bonds **169**

Section 6.2 Assessment

1. The attractions between the shared electrons and the protons in each nucleus hold the atoms together in a covalent bond.
2. When atoms form a polar covalent bond, the atom with the greater attraction for electrons has a partial negative charge. The other atom has a partial positive charge.
3. The type of atoms in a molecule and its shape are factors that determine whether a molecule is polar or nonpolar.
4. Attractions between polar molecules are stronger than attractions between nonpolar molecules.
5. A neutral group of atoms that are joined together by one or more covalent bonds
6. Neon
7. Attractions between polar water molecules are stronger than attractions between nonpolar chlorine molecules.
8. NH_3

Attraction Between Molecules

Teacher Demo

Surface Tension L2

Purpose Students observe how surface tension can support a needle.

Materials 200-mL beaker, water, sewing needle, tweezers, dropper pipet

Procedure Fill the beaker with water. Using tweezers, gently place the needle on the water's surface so that surface tension supports it. Remove the needle, and place it in the water vertically so that it sinks. Pour the water out and collect the needle.

Expected Outcome Surface tension supports the needle.
Logical, Visual

3 ASSESS

Evaluate Understanding L2

Have students make a chart that compares and contrasts polar covalent bonds and nonpolar covalent bonds. Be sure students discuss the bonding atoms' attractions for electrons, partial charges, and attractions between molecules.

Reteach L1

Use Figures 11, 12, and 13 as visual aids while reviewing polar covalent bonds, nonpolar and polar molecules, and attractions between molecules.

Connecting C Concepts

A greater attraction between molecules is likely to produce an increase in viscosity because the attractions would act in opposition to the motion of the molecules and reduce their ability to flow.

 Interactive Textbook If your class subscribes to the Interactive Textbook, use it to review key concepts in Section 6.2.

Answer to . . .

Figure 11 *Chlorine*

Figure 13 *The oxygen atom has a partial negative charge. The hydrogen atoms have partial positive charges.*

Chemical Bonds **169**

6.3 Naming Compounds and Writing Formulas

1 FOCUS

Objectives

6.3.1 **Recognize** and **describe** binary ionic compounds, metals with multiple ions, and polyatomic ions.

6.3.2 **Name** and **determine** chemical formulas for ionic and molecular compounds.

Reading Focus

Build Vocabulary **L2**

Word-Part Analysis Ask students what words they know that have the prefix *poly-*. (*Polygon, polysyllabic, polyglot, polytechnic,* and *polygraph*) Give a definition of the prefix. (*Poly-* means "many.") Have students predict the meaning of the term *polyatomic ion*. (*A polyatomic ion is a covalently bonded group of atoms that has a positive or negative charge and acts as a unit.*)

Reading Strategy **L2**

a. and b. Students should assume that any particle described as an ion has a charge. If they know the meaning of *poly-*, they may conclude that the ion contains three or more atoms.

2 INSTRUCT

Integrate Language Arts **L2**

The production of lime through the decomposition of limestone (or any form of calcium carbonate) has been known for millennia, which is why there is a word for lime in many ancient languages. In Latin, this word is *calx*, which is the source for the name calcium. Have students research the origin of the phrase "in the limelight." (*Drummond developed limelight first as an aid to surveying. When lime was heated in a hydrogen-oxygen flame, it produced a bright, white light. In 1825, a light that Drummond placed on top of a hill in Belfast could be seen in Donegal about 105 km (66 miles) away. Limelight was first used in a theater in 1856, when a lens was placed in front of the limelight to produce a spotlight.*)
Logical

Reading Focus

Key Concepts

- What information do the name and formula of an ionic compound provide?
- What information do the name and formula of a molecular compound provide?

Vocabulary

- polyatomic ion

Reading Strategy

Predicting Copy the table. Before you read, predict the meaning of the term *polyatomic ion*. After you read, if your prediction was incorrect, revise your definition.

Vocabulary Term	Before You Read	After You Read
Polyatomic ion	a. ___?___	b. ___?___

Thomas Drummond was a Scottish surveyor and inventor. Around 1826, he discovered that a white solid called lime emits a bright light when heated to a high temperature. This discovery was extremely useful in the era before electric lighting. Limelight was used to produce a light that could be focused on a single spot on a stage. It also was used to produce lighthouse beams that could be seen from a great distance.

People have used mixtures of lime and water for centuries to white-wash houses and fences. The flowerpots in Figure 14 were coated with a lime wash to which paint pigments were added. Other names for lime are quicklime and unslaked lime. Having two or more names for a compound can be confusing. Also, names like lime or quicklime don't tell you much about the composition of a compound.

Chemists use a system for naming compounds that is based on rules established by the International Union of Pure and Applied Chemistry (IUPAC). In this system, the chemical name for lime is calcium oxide and its chemical formula is CaO. This formula tells you that there is a one-to-one ratio of calcium ions to oxide ions in calcium oxide. The formula of a compound serves as a reminder of the composition of the compound.

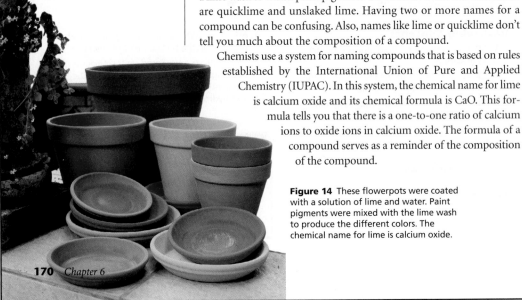

Figure 14 These flowerpots were coated with a solution of lime and water. Paint pigments were mixed with the lime wash to produce the different colors. The chemical name for lime is calcium oxide.

170 *Chapter 6*

Section Resources

Print
- *Laboratory Manual,* Investigation 6A
- *Reading and Study Workbook With Math Support,* Section 6.3 and **Math Skill:** Writing Formulas for Ionic Compounds
- *Math Skills and Problem Solving Workbook,* Section 6.3
- *Transparencies,* Section 6.3

Technology
- *Interactive Textbook,* Section 6.3
- *Presentation Pro CD-ROM,* Section 6.3
- *Go Online,* NSTA SciLinks, Chemical formulas

Describing Ionic Compounds

Both of the objects in Figure 15 are coated with compounds of copper and oxygen. Based on the two colors of the coatings, copper and oxygen must form at least two compounds. One name cannot describe all the compounds of copper and oxygen. There must be at least two names to distinguish red copper oxide from black copper oxide. **The name of an ionic compound must distinguish the compound from other ionic compounds containing the same elements. The formula of an ionic compound describes the ratio of the ions in the compound.**

Binary Ionic Compounds A compound made from only two elements is a binary compound. (The Latin prefix *bi-* means "two," as in bicycle or bisect.) Naming binary ionic compounds, such as sodium chloride and cadmium iodide, is easy. The names have a predictable pattern: the name of the cation followed by the name of the anion. Remember that the name for the cation is the name of the metal without any change: sodium atom and sodium ion. The name for the anion uses part of the name of the nonmetal with the suffix *–ide*: iodine atom and iodide ion. Figure 16 shows the names and charges for eight common anions.

Figure 15 The brass vase on the left is coated with an oxide of copper that is red. Most of the surface of the plate on the right is coated with an oxide of copper that is black.
Classifying *How can you be sure that the oxides of copper are different compounds?*

Figure 16 The table lists the element names, ion names, symbols, and charges for eight anions. The name of an anion is formed by adding the suffix *–ide* to the stem of the name of the nonmetal.

Common Anions			
Element Name	Ion Name	Ion Symbol	Ion Charge
Fluorine	Fluoride	F^-	1–
Chlorine	Chloride	Cl^-	1–
Bromine	Bromide	Br^-	1–
Iodine	Iodide	I^-	1–
Oxygen	Oxide	O^{2-}	2–
Sulfur	Sulfide	S^{2-}	2–
Nitrogen	Nitride	N^{3-}	3–
Phosphorus	Phosphide	P^{3-}	3–

Chemical Bonds **171**

Use Visuals ᴸ¹

Figure 18 Have students compare the two models of an ammonium ion. Have them discuss the advantages of each type of model. *(Both models show the number and types of atom in the ion. The electron dot diagram shows the valence electrons. The space-filling model shows the relative sizes of the atoms and how they are arranged in space.)* Point out that the brackets in the electron dot diagram indicate that the group of atoms as a whole, not any specific atom, has a positive charge. Ask, **What is the charge on an ammonium ion?** *(1+)* **How many covalent bonds are in an ammonium ion?** *(Four)* **How many valence electrons are involved in the bonds in the ammonium ion?** *(Eight)* **Visual**

FYI

Paint is a mixture of nonvolatile ingredients (the pigment and the binder) that are dispersed in a volatile liquid. A pigment is a substance that provides the color.

Some Metal Cations			
Ion Name	Ion Symbol	Ion Name	Ion Symbol
Copper(I)	Cu^+	Chromium(II)	Cr^{2+}
Copper(II)	Cu^{2+}	Chromium(III)	Cr^{3+}
Iron(II)	Fe^{2+}	Titanium(II)	Ti^{2+}
Iron(III)	Fe^{3+}	Titanium(III)	Ti^{3+}
Lead(II)	Pb^{2+}	Titanium(IV)	Ti^{4+}
Lead(IV)	Pb^{4+}	Mercury(II)	Hg^{2+}

Figure 17 Many paint pigments contain compounds of transition metals. These metals often form more than one type of ion. The ion names must contain a Roman numeral. **Using Tables** *How is the Roman numeral in the name related to the charge on the ion?*

Ammonium ion
(NH_4^+)

Figure 18 The atoms in an ammonium ion are joined by covalent bonds. The ion loses a valence electron as it forms. This loss leaves only 10 electrons to balance the charge on 11 protons.

Metals With Multiple Ions The alkali metals, alkaline earth metals, and aluminum form ions with positive charges equal to the group number. For example, the symbol for a potassium ion is K^+, the symbol for a calcium ion is Ca^{2+}, and the symbol for an aluminum ion is Al^{3+}.

Many transition metals form more than one type of ion. Notice the two copper ions listed in Figure 17, a copper(I) ion with a 1+ charge and a copper(II) ion with a 2+ charge. When a metal forms more than one ion, the name of the ion contains a Roman numeral to indicate the charge on the ion. These ion names can distinguish red copper(I) oxide from black copper(II) oxide. The formula for "copper one oxide" is Cu_2O because it takes two Cu^{1+} ions to balance the charge on an O^{2-} ion. The formula for "copper two oxide" is CuO because it takes only one Cu^{2+} ion to balance the charge on an O^{2-} ion.

Polyatomic Ions The electron dot diagram in Figure 18 describes a group of atoms that includes one nitrogen and four hydrogen atoms. It is called an ammonium ion. The atoms are joined by covalent bonds. Why does the group have a positive charge? The nitrogen atom has seven protons, and each hydrogen atom has one proton—eleven in total. But the group has only ten electrons to balance the charge on the protons—eight valence electrons and nitrogen's two inner electrons.

A covalently bonded group of atoms that has a positive or negative charge and acts as a unit is a **polyatomic ion.** The prefix *poly-* means "many." Most simple polyatomic ions are anions. Figure 19 lists the names and formulas for some polyatomic ions. Sometimes there are parentheses in a formula that includes polyatomic ions. For example, the formula for iron(III) hydroxide is $Fe(OH)_3$. The subscript 3 indicates that there are three hydroxide ions for each iron(III) ion.

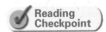
Reading Checkpoint *When are Roman numerals used in compound names?*

Modeling Molecules

Materials
blue plastic-foam ball, black plastic-foam ball, 7 white gumdrops, toothpicks

Procedure

1. To make a model of an ammonia molecule (NH_3), insert a toothpick in each of 3 gumdrops. The gumdrops represent hydrogen atoms and the toothpicks represent bonds.

2. An ammonia molecule is like a pyramid with the nitrogen at the top and the hydrogen atoms at the corners of the base. Insert the toothpicks in the blue foam ball (nitrogen) so that each gumdrop is the same distance from the ball.

3. The hydrogen atoms in a methane molecule (CH_4) are equally spaced around the carbon. Use the black ball to make a model of methane.

Analyze and Conclude

1. **Comparing and Contrasting** Compare the shapes of the methane and ammonia molecules.

2. **Using Models** Why is carbon in the center of the methane molecule?

Writing Formulas for Ionic Compounds If you know the name of an ionic compound, you can write its formula. Place the symbol of the cation first, followed by the symbol of the anion. Use subscripts to show the ratio of the ions in the compound. Because all compounds are neutral, the total charges on the cations and anions must add up to zero.

Suppose an atom that gains two electrons, such as sulfur, reacts with an atom that loses one electron, such as sodium. There must be two sodium ions (Na^+) for each sulfide ion (S^{2-}). The formula for sodium sulfide is Na_2S. The $2-$ charge on one sulfide ion is balanced by the $1+$ charges on two sodium ions.

Some Polyatomic Ions			
Name	**Formula**	**Name**	**Formula**
Ammonium	NH_4^+	Acetate	$C_2H_3O_2^-$
Hydroxide	OH^-	Peroxide	O_2^{2-}
Nitrate	NO_3^-	Permanganate	MnO_4^-
Sulfate	SO_4^{2-}	Hydrogen sulfate	HSO_4^-
Carbonate	CO_3^{2-}	Hydrogen carbonate	HCO_3^-
Phosphate	PO_4^{3-}	Hydrogen phosphate	HPO_4^{2-}
Chromate	CrO_4^{2-}	Dichromate	$Cr_2O_7^{2-}$
Silicate	SiO_3^{2-}	Hypochlorite	OCl^-

Figure 19 This table lists the names and formulas of some polyatomic ions. Except for the ammonium ion, all the ions listed are anions. Using Tables *Which element is found in all the anions whose names end in -ate?*

Modeling Molecules   L2

Objective
After completing this activity, students will be able to
• use physical models to compare the shapes of molecules.

Skills Focus Using Models

 Prep Time 10 minutes

Advance Prep Plastic-foam balls are available from craft supply stores. If black and blue foam balls are not available, wrap other foam balls in colored foil, glue colored tissue paper around them, or spray-paint them to match the colors used in this book to represent atoms of carbon and nitrogen.

Class Time 20 minutes

Safety Tell students not to eat the gumdrops or anything else in the laboratory.

Expected Outcome Students will make tetrahedral (pyramidal) models of methane molecules.

Analyze and Conclude
1. The methane molecule is a tetrahedron (equal-sided triangular pyramid) and the ammonia molecule has a triangular shape.
2. The carbon atom is in the center because each of the four hydrogen atoms must bond to one carbon atom. **Visual, Kinesthetic**

Build Science Skills   L2

Inferring Molecules of NH_3 and NF_3 have the same shape, but bonds in NH_3 are shorter than bonds in NF_3. In other words, the hydrogen atoms are closer to the nitrogen atom in an ammonia molecule than the fluorine atoms are to the nitrogen atom in nitrogen trifluoride. Ask, **What does this data imply about the relative sizes of hydrogen and fluorine atoms?** *(The data confirms that a hydrogen atom has a smaller atomic radius than does a nitrogen atom.)* **Logical**

Answer to . . .

Figure 17 *The Roman numeral is equal to the charge on the ion.*

Figure 19 *Oxygen*

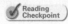 *When the metal in the compound can form more than one type of ion*

Build Math Skills L1

Positive and Negative Numbers

Remind students that the charges in an ionic compound must cancel each other. Ask, **How many atoms of a halogen would combine with one atom of an alkaline earth metal? Why?** *(Two atoms; the alkaline earth metal atom loses two electrons but each halogen atom needs only one electron to become stable.)* **Logical**

Direct students to the **Math Skills** in the **Skills and Reference Handbook** at the end of the student text for additional help.

Solutions L2

1. It takes one calcium ion with a charge of 2+ to balance one oxide ion with a charge of 2−. The formula is CaO.

2. Two copper(I) ions, each with a charge of 1+, balance one sulfide ion with a charge of 2−. The formula is Cu_2S.

3. Two sodium ions, each with a charge of 1+, balance one sulfate ion with a charge of 2−. The formula is Na_2SO_4.

4. In the formula, Na represents the sodium ion and OH represents the hydroxide ion. The name of the compound is sodium hydroxide. **Logical**

For Extra Help L1

Make sure the first step students take is to find the symbols and charges on the ions. Then, check that they are able to balance the charges.
Logical

Additional Problems

1. Write the formula for lithium oxide. *(Li_2O)*
2. Write the formula for iron(III) oxide. *(Fe_2O_3)*
Logical

Describing Molecular Compounds

FYI

There are two exceptions to the general rule for naming molecular compounds. Hydrogen is treated as though it were positioned between Group 5A and Group 6A, and oxygen is treated as though it were positioned after chlorine but before fluorine.

Math Practice

1. Write the formula for the compound calcium oxide.
2. Write the formula for the compound copper(I) sulfide.
3. Write the formula for the compound sodium sulfate.
4. What is the name of the compound whose formula is NaOH?

Go Online

For: Links on chemical formulas
Visit: www.SciLinks.org
Web Code: ccn-1063

Math Skills

Writing Formulas for Ionic Compounds

What is the formula for the ionic compound calcium chloride?

1 Read and Understand
What information are you given?

The name of the compound is calcium chloride.

2 Plan and Solve
List the symbols and charges for the cation and anion.

Ca with a charge of 2+ and Cl with a charge of 1−

Determine the ratio of ions in the compound.

It takes two 1− charges to balance the 2+ charge. There will be two chloride ions for each calcium ion.

Write the formula for calcium chloride.

$CaCl_2$

3 Look Back and Check
Is your answer reasonable?

Each calcium atom loses two electrons and each chlorine atom gains one electron. So there should be a 1-to-2 ratio of calcium ions to chloride ions.

Describing Molecular Compounds

Like ionic compounds, molecular compounds have names that identify specific compounds, and formulas that match those names. With molecular compounds, the focus is on the composition of molecules. **The name and formula of a molecular compound describe the type and number of atoms in a molecule of the compound.**

Naming Molecular Compounds The general rule is that the most metallic element appears first in the name. These elements are farther to the left in the periodic table. If both elements are in the same group, the more metallic element is closer to the bottom of the group. The name of the second element is changed to end in the suffix *-ide*, as in carbon dioxide.

Download a worksheet on chemical formulas for students to complete, and find additional teacher support from NSTA SciLinks.

Two compounds that contain nitrogen and oxygen have the formulas N_2O_4 and NO_2. The names of these two compounds reflect the actual number of atoms of nitrogen and oxygen in a molecule of each compound. You can use the Greek prefixes in Figure 20 to describe the number of nitrogen and oxygen atoms in each molecule.

In an N_2O_4 molecule, there are two nitrogen atoms and four oxygen atoms. The Greek prefixes for two and four are *di-* and *tetra-*. The name for the compound with the formula N_2O_4 is dinitrogen tetraoxide. In an NO_2 molecule, there are one nitrogen atom and two oxygen atoms. The Greek prefixes for one and two are *mono-* and *di-*. So a name for the compound with the formula NO_2 is mononitrogen dioxide. However, the prefix *mono-* often is not used for the first element in the name. A more common name for the compound with the formula NO_2 is nitrogen dioxide.

Writing Molecular Formulas Writing the formula for a molecular compound is easy. Write the symbols for the elements in the order the elements appear in the name. The prefixes indicate the number of atoms of each element in the molecule. The prefixes appear as subscripts in the formulas. If there is no prefix for an element in the name, there is only one atom of that element in the molecule.

What is the formula for diphosphorus tetrafluoride? Because the compound is molecular, look for elements on the right side of the periodic table. Phosphorus has the symbol P. Fluorine has the symbol F. *Di-* indicates two phosphorus atoms and *tetra-* indicates four fluorine atoms. The formula for the compound is P_2F_4.

Prefixes For Naming Compounds

Number of Atoms	Prefix
1	mono-
2	di-
3	tri-
4	tetra-
5	penta-
6	hexa-
7	hepta-
8	octa-
9	nona-
10	deca-

Figure 20 These Greek prefixes are used to name molecular compounds. The prefix *octa-* means "eight," as in the eight tentacles of an octopus.

Section 6.3 Assessment

Reviewing Concepts

1. What does the formula of an ionic compound describe?
2. What do the name and formula of a molecular compound describe?
3. What suffix is used to indicate an anion?
4. Why are Roman numerals used in the names of compounds that contain transition metals?
5. What is a polyatomic ion?

Critical Thinking

6. **Applying Concepts** How is it possible for two different ionic compounds to contain the same elements?

7. **Calculating** How many potassium ions are needed to bond with a phosphate ion?

Math Practice

8. What are the names of these ionic compounds: LiCl, BaO, Na_3N, and $PbSO_4$?
9. Name the molecular compounds with these formulas: P_2O_5 and CO.
10. What is the formula for the ionic compound formed from potassium and sulfur?

Chemical Bonds **175**

1 FOCUS

Objectives

6.4.1 Describe the structure and strength of bonds in metals.
6.4.2 Relate the properties of metals to their structure.
6.4.3 Define an alloy and **demonstrate** how the composition of an alloy affects its properties.

Reading Focus

Build Vocabulary **L2**

Vocabulary Knowledge Rating Chart Have students construct a chart with four columns labeled Term, Can Define It/Use It, Heard It/Seen It, and Don't Know. Have students copy the terms *metallic bond, metal lattice, alloy,* and *metallurgy* into the first column and rate their term knowledge by putting a check in one of the other columns. Ask how many students actually know each term. Have them share their knowledge. To provide a purpose for reading, ask focused questions to help students predict text content based on each term. After students have read the section, have them rate their knowledge again.

Reading Strategy **L2**

a. and b. Conductivity or malleability

2 INSTRUCT

Metallic Bonds

Integrate Social Studies **L2**

In the first light bulbs, air was removed from the light bulb to prevent combustion as the filament heated up. This solution was not ideal because atoms can sublime from the hot filament at very low pressures. With almost no air, atoms of the vaporized filament have uninterrupted paths to the inner walls of the bulb where they are deposited. The modern light bulb uses an argon atmosphere and a tungsten filament. This prolongs the life of the bulb because collisions between tungsten atoms and argon atoms can redirect tungsten atoms back toward the filament. Have interested students research the search for an effective filament. Students can present their findings in a poster or other visual display.
Visual

6.4 The Structure of Metals

Standard: ICP.5.1

Reading Focus

Key Concepts

- What are the forces that give a metal its structure as a solid?
- How do metallic bonds produce some of the typical properties of metals?
- How are the properties of alloys controlled?

Vocabulary

- metallic bond
- alloy

Reading Strategy

Relating Cause and Effect Copy the concept map. As you read, complete the map to relate the structure of metals to their properties.

```
                          a. ?
Mobile          produce
electrons
                          b. ?
```

Figure 21 This photograph of the tungsten filament from a light bulb was taken with a scanning electron microscope. Color was added to the photo. The filament is magnified more than 100 times. The diameter of the wire is about 15 μm, or 0.0015 cm.

Light bulbs are easy to ignore unless a bulb burns out and you are searching for a replacement in the dark. But in the decades just before the year 1900, light bulbs were an exciting new technology. One challenge for researchers was to find the best material for the filaments in light bulbs. The substance had to be ductile enough to be drawn into a narrow wire. It could not melt at the temperatures produced when an electric current passes through a narrow wire. It had to have a low vapor pressure so that particles on the surface were not easily removed by sublimation.

The substance the researchers found was tungsten (W), a metal whose name means "heavy stone" in Swedish. Figure 21 shows a magnified view of the narrow coils in a tungsten filament. Tungsten has the highest melting point of any metal—3410°C—and it has the lowest vapor pressure. The properties of a metal are related to bonds within the metal.

Metallic Bonds

Metal atoms achieve stable electron configurations by losing electrons. But what happens if there are no nonmetal atoms available to accept the electrons? There is a way for metal atoms to lose and gain electrons at the same time. In a metal, valence electrons are free to move among the atoms. In effect, the metal atoms become cations surrounded by a pool of shared electrons. A **metallic bond** is the attraction between a metal cation and the shared electrons that surround it.

Section Resources

Print
- **Reading and Study Workbook With Math Support,** Section 6.4
- **Transparencies,** Section 6.4

Technology
- **Interactive Textbook,** Section 6.4
- **Presentation Pro CD-ROM,** Section 6.4
- **Go Online,** Science News, Metals

Hammer strikes metal.

Metal changes shape but does not break.

 The cations in a metal form a lattice that is held in place by strong metallic bonds between the cations and the surrounding valence electrons. Although the electrons are moving among the atoms, the total number of electrons does not change. So, overall, the metal is neutral.

The metallic bonds in some metals are stronger than in other metals. The more valence electrons an atom can contribute to the shared pool, the stronger the metallic bonds will be. The bonds in an alkali metal are relatively weak because alkali metals contribute only a single valence electron. The result is that alkali metals, such as sodium, are soft enough to cut with a knife and have relatively low melting points. Sodium melts at 97.8°C. Transition metals, such as tungsten, have more valence electrons to contribute and, therefore, are harder and have higher melting points. Recall that tungsten melts at 3410°C.

Explaining Properties of Metals

The structure within a metal affects the properties of metals. The mobility of electrons within a metal lattice explains some of the properties of metals. The ability to conduct an electric current and malleability are two important properties of metals.

Recall that a flow of charged particles is an electric current. A metal has a built-in supply of charged particles that can flow from one location to another—the pool of shared electrons. An electric current can be carried through a metal by the free flow of the shared electrons.

The lattice in a metal is flexible compared to the rigid lattice in an ionic compound. Figure 22 is a model of what happens when someone strikes a metal with a hammer. The metal ions shift their positions and the shape of the metal changes. But the metal does not shatter because ions are still held together by the metallic bonds between the ions and the electrons. Metallic bonds also explain why metals, such as tungsten and copper, can be drawn into thin wires without breaking.

Reading Checkpoint *What two important properties of metals can be explained by their structure?*

Figure 22 In a metal, cations are surrounded by shared valence electrons. If a metal is struck, the ions move to new positions, but the ions are still surrounded by electrons. Classifying *What property of metals is displayed when a hammer strikes a metal?*

Chemical Bonds **177**

Alloys

Use Community Resources `L2`

Arrange for your class to visit the workshop of a jewelry maker, metalworker, blacksmith, or welder. Have students observe the types of equipment used to work with different metals. Ask questions regarding the artisan's choice of materials for different projects. Ask about the use of different alloys in metallurgy.
Interpersonal

FYI

There are different categories of alloys: true solutions, heterogeneous mixtures with two phases (a pure element and a compound), or intermetallic compounds with definite compositions.

DK SCIENCE and History

Milestones in Metallurgy `L2`

Ask students to choose one of the significant events in metallurgy history described in the time line. Have them do research in the library or on the Internet to find out more about the materials, applications, and people involved in their chosen topic. Have them present their findings to the class. Be sure that part of their presentation focuses on the specific properties of metals and alloys.
Verbal

(Writing) in Science

Henry Ford saw an automobile part made from vanadium steel when a French racer crashed at a European race meeting in 1905. He was impressed with the strength and low weight of the steel. American foundries did not have furnaces that could achieve the temperature required to produce the alloy. Ford found a small steel company in Ohio that was willing to experiment with the process and produce the alloy exclusively for Ford.
Verbal

Alloys

A friend shows you a beautiful ring that she says is made from pure gold. Your friend is lucky to have such a valuable object. The purity of gold is expressed in units called karats. Gold that is 100 percent pure is labeled 24-karat gold. Gold jewelry that has a 12-karat label is only 50 percent gold. Jewelry that has an 18-karat label is 75 percent gold.

The surface of an object made from pure gold can easily be worn away by contact with other objects or dented because gold is a soft metal. When silver, copper, nickel, or zinc is mixed with gold, the gold is harder and more resistant to wear. These gold mixtures are alloys. An **alloy** is a mixture of two or more elements, at least one of which is a metal. Alloys have the characteristic properties of metals.

DK SCIENCE and History

Milestones in Metallurgy

The science of metallurgy includes ways to extract metals from ores, refine metals, and use metals. Described here are some advances in metallurgy since 1850.

Hot gas flame *The flame from a burning gas melts the surfaces where two metal parts will join.*

BESSEMER CONVERTER

Vanadium steel *This alloy becomes popular in car manufacturing because it is lightweight and strong.*

Gas torch

GAS WELDING

1856 Henry Bessemer develops an efficient process for producing steel by blowing air through molten iron.

1886 Charles Hall and Paul Héroult independently develop a method for using electricity to obtain aluminum from aluminum oxide.

1908 Henry Ford uses vanadium steel (an alloy of iron with carbon and vanadium) extensively in his Model T Fords.

1914 The start of World War I leads to the wide-scale use of welding techniques, such as gas welding with acetylene, for ship building.

| 1850 | 1880 | 1910 |

178 Chapter 6

Copper Alloys The first important alloy was bronze, whose name is associated with an important era in history—the Bronze Age. Metalworkers in Thailand may have been the first to make bronze. But people in other locations probably thought they were the first to make bronze. News didn't travel quickly in that era.

Metalworkers might have noticed that the metal they extracted by heating deposits of copper was not always the same. The difference in properties could be traced to the presence of tin. In its simplest form, bronze contains only copper and tin, which are relatively soft metals. Mixed together in bronze, the metals are much harder and stronger than either metal alone. 🌐 **Scientists can design alloys with specific properties by varying the types and amounts of elements in an alloy.**

Writing in Science

Cause-Effect Paragraph
Write a paragraph about Henry Ford's decision to use vanadium steel for automobile parts. Where did Ford first see parts made from vanadium steel? What properties of this type of steel impressed Ford? Did Ford need to overcome any problems before going ahead with his plan?

Build Reading Literacy L1

Compare and Contrast Refer to page 226D in Chapter 8, which provides the guidelines for comparing and contrasting.

Have students read the passage on copper alloys. Then, have students construct a chart that does the following: 1. Identify two copper alloys described in the text. 2. Make a list of properties the alloys have in common. 3. Make a list of properties that differ between the two alloys.
Visual

Steel-framed structure *The Empire State Building is supported by a framework of steel columns and beams that weigh 60,000 tons.*

Metal parts, *such as the gears in this gold watch, are made by applying heat and pressure to powdered metal in a mold.*

Superalloys containing rhenium are used in jet engines.

EMPIRE STATE BUILDING

1931 The 102-story Empire State Building in New York City is completed. Skyscrapers would be impossible without steel-framed construction.

METAL PARTS FROM POWDER

1942 Making small, complex parts from metal powders is less wasteful than machining. World War II spurs advances in iron powder metallurgy.

1991 New alloys containing rhenium are introduced. These superalloys are capable of retaining their strength at very high temperatures.

1940   1970   2000

Chemical Bonds **179**

Facts and Figures

Bronze Bronze jewelry found in graves beneath the town of Ban Chiang in northeast Thailand has been dated to 3600 B.C., but this date is controversial. If correct, the site predates sites in Mesopotamia by several hundred years. Some copper alloys that contain little tin but are similar in color to bronze are labeled as bronzes to take advantage of the reputation of bronze as a hard, durable material.

Teacher ⟩ Demo

Bronze and Brass Tones ⬛L2

Purpose Students observe the difference in tone between a brass bell and a bronze bell.

Materials brass bell, bronze bell

Procedure Allow students to examine each bell to see if they appear different in color or shininess. Ring each bell and allow students to note the difference in tone.

Expected Outcome In general, brass is shinier than bronze. A brass bell will have a duller tone that does not last as long as the clear, loud tone of a bronze bell. (Bell bronze contains about 80% copper and 20% tin, which is just the right composition to produce a hard, resonant material.)
Visual, Musical

Build Science Skills ⬛L2

Applying Concepts After students read about copper alloys, present the following problem to the class. **Imagine that you are going to make a wind chime in shop class as a gift. You have two choices of metals to use, brass or bronze. Which do you choose?**
Explain your answer. *(Some students may choose brass because it is shinier and easier to shape into forms than bronze. Others may choose bronze because it has a clearer, louder tone and weathers better than brass.)*
Intrapersonal

Go Online
SCIENCE NEWS®

Science News provides students with current information on metals.

Figure 23 This ancient statue of horses from Venice, Italy, and this modern French horn are both made from copper alloys. The statue is made from bronze, an alloy of copper and tin. The French horn is made from brass, an alloy of copper and zinc.

Go Online
SCIENCE NEWS®

For: Articles on metals
Visit: PHSchool.com
Web Code: cce-1064

Bronze is hard and durable enough to be used for propellers on ships and for statues, such as the statue of horses in Figure 23. A bronze bell has a clear, loud tone that lasts for several seconds.

A brass bell has a duller tone that dies away quickly. Brass is another alloy of copper that has been known for centuries. In its simplest form, brass contains only copper and zinc. Although both bronze and brass are alloys of copper, they have distinctly different properties. Brass is softer than bronze and is easier to shape into forms such as the French horn in Figure 23. Brass is shinier than bronze but is likely to weather more quickly.

Steel Alloys The 1900s could be called the Age of Steel because of the skyscrapers, automobiles, and ships that were built from steel during the 1900s. Steel is an alloy of iron that contains small quantities of carbon, ranging from less than 0.2 percent to about 3 percent by mass. The smaller carbon atoms fit in the spaces between the larger iron atoms in the lattice. The carbon atoms form bonds with neighboring iron atoms. These bonds make the lattice harder and stronger than a lattice that contains only iron.

The properties of any particular type of steel depend on which elements other than iron and carbon are used and how much of those elements are included. Stainless steels contain more than 10 percent chromium by mass, but almost no carbon. Stainless steels are durable because chromium forms an oxide that protects the steel from rusting. But stainless steel is more brittle than steels that contain more carbon. The steel cables in the bridge in Figure 24 have to be strong enough to resist forces that might stretch the cables or cause them to break. The steel used contains sulfur, manganese, phosphorus, silicon, and 0.81 percent carbon.

Facts and Figures

Bronze Horses The origin of the gilded bronze horses of St. Mark's is unclear. The sculptures are not similar in style to other Greek or Roman sculptures of horses. Nor are they similar in composition. From chemical analyses, art historians know that the bronze is 98% copper, 1% tin, and 1% lead, which is an unusually high percent of copper. Art historians do know that the horses were cast in pieces that were welded together. The pieces were made using the lost wax method described in Chapter 2.

The horses can be traced from a triumphal arch in Rome to one in Constantinople. They were taken from Constantinople to Venice in 1204 (where they were placed on a balcony of the cathedral), then to Paris in 1797, and then back to Venice in 1815. For protection from air pollution, the horses are now stored inside the cathedral. A copy appears on the balcony.

Figure 24 The Golden Gate Bridge is a landmark in San Francisco, California. Its cables, towers, and deck contain steel. The steel in the cables needs to resist forces that pull on the cables. The steel in the towers needs to resist the compression forces caused by the weight of the cables, the deck, and the vehicles that travel across the bridge.
Drawing Conclusions *Would the steel used for the cables and the steel used for the towers have the same composition? Give a reason for your answer.*

Other Alloys Airplane parts are made of many different alloys that are suited to particular purposes. The body of a plane is large and needs to be made from a lightweight material. Pure aluminum is lighter than most metals, but it bends and dents too easily. If a small amount of copper or manganese is added to aluminum, the result is a stronger material that is still lighter than steel.

For certain aircraft parts, even lighter materials are needed. Alloys of aluminum and magnesium are used for these parts. Magnesium is much less dense than most metals used to build structures. However, pure magnesium is soft enough to cut with a knife, and it burns in air. An aluminum-magnesium alloy keeps the advantages of magnesium without the disadvantages.

Section 6.4 Assessment

Reviewing Concepts
1. What holds metal ions together in a metal lattice?
2. What characteristic of a metallic bond explains some of the properties of metals?
3. How can scientists design alloys with specific properties?
4. Explain why the metallic bonds in some metals are stronger than the bonds in other metals.
5. Why are metals good conductors of electric current?
6. How does adding carbon to steel make the steel harder and stronger?

Critical Thinking
7. **Predicting** Which element has a higher melting point, potassium in Group 1A or calcium in Group 1B? Give a reason for your answer.
8. **Applying Concepts** Can two different elements form a metallic bond together?

Compare-Contrast Paragraph Write a paragraph comparing the properties of ionic compounds and alloys. Relate their properties to the structure of their lattices.

Chemical Bonds **181**

Section 6.4 Assessment

1. Metal ions are held together by the strong metallic bonds between the cations and the surrounding valence electrons.
2. The mobility of electrons within a metal lattice explains some of the properties of metals.
3. Scientists can design alloys with specific properties by varying the types and amounts of elements in an alloy.
4. The more valence electrons a metal can contribute, the stronger the bonds will be.
5. The valence electrons are free to move because they are not attached to a specific metal ion.
6. The smaller carbon atoms fit into spaces between the iron atoms and form bonds with neighboring iron atoms, which makes the lattice harder and stronger.
7. Calcium has a higher melting point because it contributes twice as many electrons to the metallic bonds.
8. Yes, alloys usually are mixtures of elements with metallic bonds.

Integrate Materials Science   L2

The properties of an alloy that are determined by its composition include malleability, ductility, hardness, corrosion resistance, tensile strength (the ability to resist being pulled apart), shear strength (the ability to resist opposing forces that are not acting in a straight line), compressive strength (the ability to withstand pressures acting on a given plane), and elasticity (the ability to return to its original size and shape). Ask, **What properties of steel make it useful for the cables and towers of the Golden Gate Bridge?** *(Its high tensile strength makes steel a useful material for the cables, and its high compressive strength makes it a useful material for the towers.)* **Logical**

3 ASSESS

Evaluate Understanding   L2

Have students write the names of the following elements on index cards: copper, gold, silver, nickel, zinc, tin, iron, carbon, and aluminum. On the other side of the cards, have students write common uses for these elements. (For example, alloys of aluminum and copper are used to make airplane parts.)

Reteach   L1

Use Figure 22 to review how the structure within a metal affects the properties of a metal.

In the rigid network of a crystal lattice, the charged particles are not free to flow unless the solid melts. When struck, the crystal shatters because ions with the same charge shift position in the lattice and repel. Thus, ionic solids are brittle and are poor conductors. In a metal lattice, the electrons are free to move and conduct a current. The lattice is malleable when struck because if a cation moves it is still surrounded by particles with an opposite charge.

Interactive Textbook If your class subscribes to the Interactive Textbook, use it to review key concepts in Section 6.4.

***

Answer to . . .

Figure 24 *The compositions would probably be different because the forces acting on the cables and towers are different—tensile versus compressive, respectively.*

CONCEPTS
in Action

Chipping In

Background

The silicon crystal shown in the photo is called an ingot. Pure silicon ingots can be produced by the Czochralski pulled-growth method described on p. 163. Wafers cut from the ingot can be ground, polished, cleaned, etched, doped with elements such as phosphorus and boron, and sliced with a diamond saw to produce microchips.

Build Science Skills

Applying Concepts

Purpose Students observe the importance of transistors in their lives.

Materials access to a library or the Internet, notepad for data collection

Class Time 20–30 minutes of research, one day of data collection, 20 minutes of class discussion

Procedure Have students use the library or the Internet to come up with a list of electronic devices that contain transistors. Have students record every time they use a device that contains a transistor, and the type of device. Have students compare their data in a class discussion.

Expected Outcome Devices that contain transistors include alarm clocks, watches, refrigerators, microwave ovens, washers, dryers, calculators, computers, radios, CD players, televisions, VCRs, DVD players, and video game consoles.
Intrapersonal, Kinesthetic

Chipping In

Tasks done by computers that filled an entire room in the 1950s are now done by devices the size of a credit card. This miniaturization in the electronics industry is due to semiconductors.

Semiconductors are solid substances, such as silicon, that have poor electrical conductivity at ordinary temperatures. Silicon has four valence electrons. In pure silicon, each atom forms single bonds with four other atoms. This arrangement leaves no electrons free to move through the silicon. The conductivity of silicon is greatly improved by adding small amounts of other elements to silicon, a process called doping.

Doping
An element with five valence electrons, such as phosphorus, can be added to silicon. After a phosphorus atom bonds with four atoms, there is an extra electron that is free to move. Silicon doped with phosphorus is called *n*-type silicon because electrons have a negative charge. An element with three valence electrons, such as boron, can be added to silicon. Adding boron leaves holes to which electrons can move from neighboring atoms. Because the lack of an electron has the effect of a positive charge, silicon with boron is called *p*-type silicon.

Silicon wafer

Silicon crystal

Wafers and chips
Silicon crystals are cut into wafer-thin slices. Each wafer can be made into hundreds of silicon chips.

Pure Silicon

Silicon with boron

Silicon with phosphorus

182

Vacuum tube
Glass vacuum tubes used in early computers were fragile and took up space.

Integrated circuit on a silicon chip

Computer chip
In 1974, the first computer microchip contained 6000 transistors. Today, more than 40 million transistors can be placed on a single computer chip.

Diode
In a diode, a layer of *p*-type silicon is joined to a layer of *n*-type silicon. When the leads on a diode are correctly connected in a circuit, electrons flow toward the junction between the two types of silicon. Electrons from the *n*-type silicon fill holes in the *p*-type silicon. In devices that use batteries, a diode can keep electrons from flowing if the batteries are not inserted correctly. Some diodes emit light when the circuit is complete.

Transistor
In a transistor, there are three layers of doped silicon. There is a layer of *p*-type silicon sandwiched between two layers of *n*-type silicon or a layer of *n*-type silicon between two layers of p-type silicon. Transistors are used to amplify current. A small current applied to the central layer of a transistor can produce a larger current.

Going Further

Transistors were developed to solve a problem with long distance telephone service. Until the 1950s, AT&T used vacuum tubes to amplify signals as they were transferred from one switch box to the next. Vacuum tubes were unreliable, used a lot of power, and produced a lot of heat.

After World War II, a team at Bell Laboratories in New Jersey (John Bardeen, Walter Brattain, and William Shockley) developed the transistor. In 1956, they shared the Nobel Prize in Physics. A transistor is a thin three-layer sandwich with a *p*-type semiconductor in the outer layers and an *n*-type in the middle (PNP), or an *n*-type semiconductor on opposite sides of a *p*-type (NPN).

Because transistors are so much smaller than vacuum tubes, devices such as radios, televisions, and computers were reduced in size when vacuum tubes were replaced with transistors.
Verbal

Going Further

- Research and write about the development of transistors. Why were researchers looking for a replacement for vacuum tubes? How did replacing vacuum tubes with transistors affect the size of radios and computers?

- Take a Discovery Channel Video Field Trip by watching "Good Conduct."

DISCOVERY CHANNEL SCHOOL
Video Field Trip

Chemical Bonds **183**

DISCOVERY CHANNEL SCHOOL

Video Field Trip
Good Conduct

After students have viewed the Video Field Trip, ask them the following questions: **What is the main element in computer chips?** *(Silicon)* **What is the purpose of the seed crystal that is lowered into the rotating vat of molten silicon?** *(The atoms in the seed crystal form a lattice. As the molten silicon cools, silicon atoms*

follow this pattern as they form a much larger silicon crystal.) **Why is pure silicon a poor conductor of electric current?** *(After each silicon atom forms four bonds with neighboring atoms, there are no free electrons to conduct electric current.)* **What happens when a boron atom is substituted in the lattice?** *(Boron has only three valence electrons, so holes [or the absence of an electron] are left to which electrons from neighboring atoms can move as they conduct electric current.)* **What happens**

when a phosphorus atom is substituted in the lattice? *(A phosphorus atom has five valence electrons, so there is an extra electron that can freely move and conduct electric current.)* **How can the ability of pure silicon to conduct current at room temperature be increased?** *(Impurities, called dopants, can be added to increase the number of electrons or holes available to conduct an electric current.)*

Improving the Dyeing of Nonpolar Fabrics

Improving the Dyeing of Nonpolar Fabrics

Objective

After completing this activity, students will be able to

- relate the ability of fabrics to absorb and retain dyes to the polar or nonpolar character of their fibers.

Skills Focus Observing

 Prep Time 40 minutes

Advance Prep Wear plastic gloves, a lab apron, and a dust mask when preparing the solutions. To prepare methyl orange dye solution, add 2.1 g Na_2SO_4 and 6–9 drops concentrated H_2SO_4 to 450 mL of water. Then, add 1.50 g methyl orange powder to the solution. Stir the solution. To prepare iron(II) sulfate solution, add 12.6 g $FeSO_4 \cdot H_2O$ to 450 mL water. Stir the solution. Place the solutions in 1-L beakers on hot plates and heat them in advance to near boiling. Arrange hot plates with the two solutions at several lab stations. Test fabrics that consist of a repeating pattern of wool, polyester, nylon, cotton, and various other natural and synthetic fibers may be obtained from a commercial fabric company. You may also make up your own test strips from fabric remnants.

Class Time 45 minutes, if different lab groups perform Parts A and B simultaneously. Alternatively, the work can be done by all groups over the course of two days.

Safety Review the safety information on the MSDS for methyl orange and iron(II) sulfate with students. Make sure students wear their goggles, gloves, and lab aprons at all times during the investigation. Emphasize the importance of protective clothing for this investigation. Any spills should be wiped up promptly to avoid slips and falls. The hot plates and furniture should be placed so that students will not bump into them as they move around. Do not use flames to heat the solutions. Advise students to wear old clothes suitable for painting on the day of this investigation. Stains from methyl orange may be permanent.

Most natural fibers, such as cotton and wool, consist of large molecules that have regions with a partial positive or partial negative charge. These polar molecules have a strong attraction for dyes that contain either polar molecules or ions.

The molecules in some manufactured fibers, such as nylon, are nonpolar molecules. These synthetic fibers are difficult to dye. Molecules of other synthetic fibers, such as polyester and rayon, have only a few polar regions. As you might suspect, polyester and rayon have intermediate attractions for dyes. In this lab, you will investigate a process for improving a fiber's ability to absorb and retain dye.

Problem

How can you increase the dye-holding capacity of nonpolar fibers?

Materials

- tongs
- 2 fabric test strips
- hot dye bath containing methyl orange
- clock or watch
- paper towels
- scissors
- soap
- hot iron(II) sulfate solution

Skills Observing, Drawing Conclusions

Procedure

Part A: Dyeing Without Treatment

1. On a sheet of paper, copy the data table shown.

2. Use the tongs to immerse a fabric test strip in the methyl orange dye bath. **CAUTION** *The dye bath is hot. Do not touch the glass. The dye will stain skin and clothing.*

3. After 7 minutes, remove the strip from the dye bath. Allow as much of the dye solution as possible to drip back into the bath as shown on page 185. Rinse off the excess dye with water in the sink.

4. Place the strip on a paper towel to dry. Be careful to avoid splashes when transferring the strip between the dye bath and paper towel. Record your observations in your data table.

5. After the fabric strip is dry, test it for colorfastness, or the ability to hold dye. Cut the strip in half lengthwise and wash one half of the strip in the sink with soap and water.

Data Table		
Dye Treatment	Dyeing of Fibers	Colorfastness of Fibers
Methyl orange		
Iron sulfate and methyl orange		

6. Allow the washed half-strip to dry and then compare the washed half to the unwashed half. Record your observations in your data table. Staple the half-strips to a sheet of paper and label each half-strip to indicate how you treated it.

Part B: Dyeing With Treatment

7. Use the tongs to place the second fabric strip in the iron(II) sulfate solution for 25 minutes. Then use tongs to lift the strip and allow it to drain into the iron(II) sulfate solution. Wring the strip as dry as possible over the solution. **CAUTION** *The strip will be hot. Allow it to cool before touching it. Wear plastic gloves.*

8. Repeat Steps 2, 3, and 4 using the strip that you treated with iron(II) sulfate.

9. To test the strip for colorfastness, repeat Steps 5 and 6.

10. Clean up your work area and wash your hands thoroughly with warm water and soap before leaving the laboratory.

Analyze and Conclude

1. **Comparing and Contrasting** How did the color of the untreated strip compare with the color of the treated strip?

2. **Comparing and Contrasting** How did the colorfastness of the untreated strip compare to the colorfastness of the treated strip?

3. **Applying Concepts** Silk blouses and shirts can be purchased in many intense colors. Why do you think silk is able to hold a variety of intense dyes?

4. **Drawing Conclusions** How does iron(II) sulfate affect the ability of a fabric to absorb dyes? (*Hint:* What kind of compound is iron(II) sulfate?)

5. **Predicting** A care label might say *Wash in cold water only.* What might happen to the color of a piece of clothing with this label if you washed the clothing in hot water?

Teaching Tips
• Explain the role of ionic and polar regions in the dyeing process. In Part A, students perform direct dyeing, which involves the ionic sites of the dye molecules attaching to ionic sites in the fabric. In Part B, ionic sites are introduced into the synthetic fibers so that more dye can bond to the fibers.
• Identify the different fibers in the fabric test strips for students.
• Make sure that the dye and iron(II) sulfate baths stay close to the boiling point, but do not let them boil, as they may spatter.

Expected Outcome Natural fibers absorb dye more easily and are more colorfast than synthetic fibers. Iron(II) sulfate treatment improves the dyeing and colorfastness of synthetic fibers.

Analyze and Conclude
1. Treatment increased the intensity of the colors for synthetic fibers.
2. In general, treatment improved colorfastness, especially in synthetic fabrics.
3. Silk is a natural fiber. Like most natural fibers, it has many polar regions that allow the dye to attach to the fibers.
4. Iron(II) sulfate is an ionic compound. Treatment with this compound adds ionic sites to the fabric, increasing its ability to bind dyes.
5. The hot water would remove more dye than would cold water, and the colors would run.
Visual, Kinesthetic

Sample Data Table

Dye Treatment	Dyeing of Fibers	Colorfastness of Fibers
Methyl orange	Intensity of color varies; wool is strongest, synthetics weakest.	Wool and cotton are colorfast; synthetic fibers are not.
Iron sulfate and methyl orange	Intensity of color varies, but increase in intensity is strongest in synthetics.	All fibers are colorfast.

Study Tip

Plan Ahead

Tell students to examine their schedules at least a week before the test. They should figure out how much time they will have available to study. Then, they should divide up that time and plan when they are going to study each topic covered on the test. They should review the most important topics first. That way, they can cut the time allotted for reviewing less important topics if they have less time for studying than expected.

Thinking Visually

a. Polar covalent bond
b. Nonpolar covalent bond

6.1 Ionic Bonding

Key Concepts

- When the highest occupied energy level of an atom is filled with electrons, the atom is stable and not likely to react.
- Some elements achieve stable electron configurations through the transfer of electrons between atoms. An ionic bond forms when electrons are transferred from one atom to another.
- The properties of an ionic compound can be explained by the strong attractions among ions within a crystal lattice.

Vocabulary

electron dot diagram, *p. 158*
ion, *p. 159*
anion, *p. 160*
cation, *p. 160*
chemical bond, *p. 160*
ionic bond, *p. 160*
chemical formula, *p. 161*
crystals, *p. 162*

6.2 Covalent Bonding

Key Concepts

- The attractions between the shared electrons and the protons in each nucleus hold the atoms together in a covalent bond.
- When atoms form a polar covalent bond, the atom with the greater attraction for electrons has a partial negative charge. The other atom has a partial positive charge.
- The type of atoms in a molecule and its shape are factors that determine whether a molecule is polar or nonpolar.
- Attractions between polar molecules are stronger than attractions between nonpolar molecules.

Vocabulary

covalent bond, *p. 166*
molecule, *p. 166*
polar covalent bond, *p. 168*

6.3 Naming Compounds and Writing Formulas

Key Concepts

- The name of an ionic compound must distinguish the compound from other ionic compounds containing the same elements. The formula of an ionic compound describes the ratio of the ions in the compound.
- The name and formula of a molecular compound describe the type and number of atoms in a molecule of the compound.

Vocabulary

polyatomic ion, *p. 172*

6.4 The Structure of Metals

Key Concepts

- The cations in a metal form a lattice that is held in place by strong metallic bonds between the cations and the surrounding valence electrons.
- The mobility of electrons within a metal lattice explains some of the properties of metals.
- Scientists can design alloys with specific properties by varying the types and amounts of elements in an alloy.

Vocabulary

metallic bond, *p. 176*
alloy, *p. 178*

Thinking Visually

Concept Map Use information from the chapter to complete the concept map below.

 ## Chapter Resources

Print
- ***Chapter and Unit Tests***, Chapter 6 Test A and Test B
- ***Test Prep Resources***, Chapter 6

Technology
- ***Computer Test Bank***, Chapter Test 6
- ***Interactive Textbook***, Chapter 6
- ***Go Online***, PHSchool.com, Chapter 6

Reviewing Content

Choose the letter that best answers the question or completes the statement.

1. When an atom loses an electron, it forms a(n)
   a. anion.
   b. cation.
   c. polyatomic ion.
   d. neutral ion.

2. The charge on a chloride ion in $AlCl_3$ is
   a. 1+.
   b. 3+.
   c. 1−.
   d. 3−.

3. Which pair has the same electron configuration?
   a. Cl^- and Ar
   b. Cl^- and Ar^-
   c. Cl and Ar
   d. Cl^+ and Ar

4. A chemical bond that forms when atoms share electrons is always a(n)
   a. polar bond.
   b. ionic bond.
   c. metallic bond.
   d. covalent bond.

5. When two fluorine atoms share a pair of electrons, the bond that forms is a(n)
   a. polar covalent bond.
   b. ionic bond.
   c. nonpolar covalent bond.
   d. double bond.

6. The chemical formula for magnesium bromide is
   a. MgBr.
   b. $MgBr_2$.
   c. $Mg(II)Br_2$.
   d. Mg_2Br.

7. The compound with the formula $SiCl_4$ is
   a. silicon chloride.
   b. silicon chlorine.
   c. silicon(I) chloride.
   d. silicon tetrachloride.

8. The attraction among water molecules is stronger than the attraction among
   a. sodium and chloride ions.
   b. carbon dioxide molecules.
   c. the atoms in a polyatomic ion.
   d. atoms in a diatomic molecule.

9. Which type of solid is likely to be the best conductor of electric current?
   a. ionic compound
   b. covalent compound
   c. metal element
   d. nonmetal element

10. An alloy contains
   a. at least one metallic element.
   b. at least one nonmetallic element.
   c. only metallic elements.
   d. only nonmetallic elements.

Understanding Concepts

11. What is a stable electron configuration?

12. What does each dot in an electron dot diagram represent?

13. What process changes atoms into ions?

14. What keeps the ions in their fixed positions within a crystal lattice?

15. What are subscripts used for in chemical formulas?

16. Explain why a melted ionic compound is a good conductor of electric current, but a solid ionic compound is a poor conductor of electric current.

17. What distinguishes single, double, and triple covalent bonds?

18. Explain why the covalent bonds in molecules of elements are always nonpolar.

19. Explain why, in a covalent bond between oxygen and hydrogen, the hydrogen atom has a partial positive charge and the oxygen atom has a partial negative charge.

20. What is the name of the binary compound formed from potassium and iodine?

21. Write the formulas for the compounds called copper(I) chloride and copper(II) chloride.

22. Name the compounds represented by the space-filling models labeled A, B, and C.

A **B**   **C**

■ *Sulfur* ■ *Oxygen* ■ *Carbon* ■ *Nitrogen*

23. In general, what determines the strength of metallic bonds?

24. What properties of copper and tin change when these metals are mixed together to form bronze?

25. What advantage of magnesium is retained in magnesium alloys? What disadvantage is reduced?

Chemical Bonds **187**

Assessment

Interactive Textbook If your class subscribes to the Interactive Textbook, your students can go online to access an interactive version of the Student Edition and a self-test.

Reviewing Content

1. b   **2.** c   **3.** a
4. d   **5.** c   **6.** b
7. d   **8.** b   **9.** c
10. a

Understanding Concepts

11. In a stable electron configuration, the highest occupied energy level is filled with electrons.
12. Each dot represents a valence electron.
13. The transfer of electrons
14. Attractions between neighboring cations and anions keep the ions in fixed positions within the lattice.
15. A subscript is used to show the number of atoms of an element in a molecule or the ratio of ions in a crystal lattice.
16. When an ionic compound melts, ions can move away from their fixed locations in the crystal lattice.
17. Two atoms share two electrons in a single bond, four in a double bond, and six in a triple bond.
18. The covalent bonds in molecules of elements are always nonpolar because the atoms have the same attraction for electrons.
19. The oxygen atom has a greater attraction for electrons than the hydrogen atom does.
20. Potassium iodide
21. CuCl and $CuCl_2$
22. A is sulfur trioxide, B is carbon monoxide, and C is nitrogen dioxide
23. In general, the more valence electrons a metal has, the stronger the metal bonds are.
24. A mixture of copper and tin is harder and stronger than either metal in its pure form.
25. The advantage that is retained is that magnesium is a lightweight metal. The disadvantage that is reduced is that magnesium is a soft metal.

⏱ Homework Guide

Section	Questions
6.1	1–3, 11–16, 26, 30, 33
6.2	4–5, 8, 17–19, 27, 34–35, 39–40, 42
6.3	6–7, 20–22, 28–29, 31–32, 36–38
6.4	9–10, 23–25, 41

Critical Thinking

26. All three have the same electron configuration.

27. Molecules and polyatomic ions both contain covalent bonds.

28. Sulfur trioxide: polar covalent bonds; calcium oxide: ionic bonds; iodine: nonpolar covalent bonds

29. Sulfur dichloride, silver(I) sulfate, lithium fluoride, carbon disulfide, calcium hydroxide

30. Q is a metal. X and Z are nonmetals.

31. QX and Q_2Z

32. Cr_2Z_3

33. $:\ddot{F}:\ddot{Z}:\ddot{F}:$

34. Nonpolar covalent bond

Math Skills

35. 8

36. The ratio is two to one anions to cations.

37. BaF_2, Na_2O, $FeSO_4$, and $(NH_4)_2SO_4$

Concepts in Action

38. The correct formula is B.

39. Molecules of carbon dioxide are nonpolar. Molecules of water are polar. The attractive forces are much greater between polar molecules than between nonpolar molecules.

40. The carbonate ion is a polyatomic ion, which contains covalent bonds.

41. Phosphorus has five valence electrons compared to four valence electrons in silicon. The extra electrons are not needed to bond the atoms together and are free to move and carry the current.

42. Ideally, students should note that in both cases the electron will be sharing space with a second electron in orbitals that overlap. In the bond between hydrogen atoms, the electron will be equally attracted to both nuclei. In the bond between hydrogen and oxygen, the electron will have a greater attraction to the oxygen nucleus.

Your students can independently test their knowledge of the chapter and print out their test results for your files.

Critical Thinking

26. Classifying What does a fluoride ion have in common with a neon atom and a sodium ion?

27. Comparing and Contrasting How are molecules and polyatomic ions similar?

28. Classifying Classify the bonds in each of these compounds as ionic, polar covalent, or nonpolar covalent: SO_3, CaO, and I_2.

29. Applying Concepts Write the names for the compounds with these chemical formulas: SCl_2, Ag_2SO_4, LiF, CS_2, and $Ca(OH)_2$.

Use these diagrams to answer Questions 30–34.

30. Using Models Which of the three elements are metals and which are nonmetals?

31. Applying Concepts Element Q forms compounds with element X and with element Z. Write the formulas for these two compounds.

32. Calculating What would the formula be for a compound containing chromium(III) ions and ions of element Z?

33. Applying Concepts Draw an electron dot structure for a compound of fluorine and Z.

34. Predicting If an atom of X reacts with an atom of X, what kind of bond forms?

Math Skills

35. Calculating What is the total number of shared electrons in a carbon dioxide molecule?

36. Making Generalizations What is the ratio of anions to cations in a compound formed by a Group 2A metal and a Group 7A nonmetal?

37. Applying Concepts Write the formulas for barium fluoride, sodium oxide, iron(II) sulfate, and ammonium sulfate.

Concepts In Action

38. Using Models A solution of hydrogen peroxide (H_2O_2) and water is sometimes used to disinfect a cut. Which of the following formulas is the correct structural formula for hydrogen peroxide?

A	B	C
O⎯H⎯H O	H⎯O⎯O⎯H	H⎯H⎯O O

39. Relating Cause and Effect In a carbonated beverage, the main ingredients are water and carbon dioxide. Carbon dioxide gas is released when the bottle is opened. Why is water a liquid but carbon dioxide a gas at room temperature?

40. Classifying The shells shown on page 156 contain the compound calcium carbonate ($CaCO_3$). Explain how this compound can contain both ionic and covalent bonds.

41. Relating Cause and Effect How does adding some phosphorus to silicon make silicon a better conductor of electric current?

42. Writing in Science Compare what happens to the valence electron in a hydrogen atom when the atom bonds with another hydrogen atom and when the atom bonds with an oxygen atom.

Performance-Based Assessment

Designing an Advertisement You own a store that sells bronze bells. Design a quarter-page ad for your store to be published in your local directory of businesses. Write copy for your ad. Describe a photograph to use in the ad. Also supply a sketch showing how you want the copy and the photograph to be laid out on the page.

For: Self-grading assessment
Visit: PHSchool.com
Web Code: cca-1060

Performance-Based Assessment

The ad could include properties of bronze, such as hardness and durability. The ad should stress the sound produced by a bronze bell. (Have examples of ads in a local directory of businesses for students to look at. Students may want to research the cost of a quarter-page ad in the directory.)

Standardized Test Prep for Indiana

Paying Attention to the Details
Sometimes two or more answers to a question are almost identical. If you do not read the answers carefully, you may select an incorrect answer by mistake. In the question below, all the answers include the correct elements in the correct order—metal before nonmetal. However, only one of the answers uses the correct rules for naming $CaCl_2$.

The name for the compound with the formula $CaCl_2$ is

(A) calcium(II) chloride.
(B) calcium chlorine.
(C) calcium dichloride.
(D) calcium chloride.
(E) monocalcium dichloride.

(Answer: D)

Choose the letter that best answers the question or completes the statement.

1. How many electrons does a Group 7A atom need to gain in order to achieve a stable electron configuration?
(A) 0
(B) 1
(C) 2
(D) 7
(E) 8

2. What type of bond forms when electrons are transferred from one atom to another?
(A) nonpolar covalent bond
(B) ionic bond
(C) polar covalent bond
(D) polyatomic bond
(E) metallic bond

3. Metallic bonds form between
(A) cations and protons.
(B) anions and protons.
(C) cations and anions.
(D) cations and electrons.
(E) anions and electrons.

Use the table to answer Questions 4 and 5.

Some Ions and Their Symbols			
Ion Name	Ion Symbol	Ion Name	Ion Symbol
Copper(I)	Cu^+	Nitrate	NO_3^-
Copper(II)	Cu^{2+}	Sulfate	SO_4^{2-}
Iron(II)	Fe^{2+}	Carbonate	CO_3^{2-}
Iron(III)	Fe^{3+}	Phosphate	PO_4^{3-}

4. What is the formula for copper(II) nitrate?
(A) $CuNO_3$
(B) $Cu_2(NO_3)_2$
(C) $Cu(NO_3)_2$
(D) Cu_2NO_3
(E) $CuNO_2$

5. In the compound iron(II) carbonate, the ratio of iron(II) ions to carbonate ions will be
(A) one to one.
(B) two to one.
(C) three to one.
(D) one to two.
(E) one to three.

6. All steels contain
(A) copper and zinc.
(B) copper and tin.
(C) iron and chromium.
(D) chromium and carbon.
(E) iron and carbon.

7. What is the reason that water has a higher boiling point than expected?
(A) Attractions among nonpolar water molecules are strong.
(B) Water molecules have a linear shape.
(C) Water molecules are not very massive.
(D) There are strong attractions among polar water molecules.
(E) There are no attractions among water molecules.

Standards Guide

Question	Standards
2	ICP.5.6
4	ICP.5.6
5	ICP.5.6
7	ICP.3.3

Planning Guide

SECTION OBJECTIVES	STANDARDS		ACTIVITIES and LABS
	NATIONAL	STATE	
7.1 Describing Reactions, pp. 192–198 🕐 1 block or 2 periods **7.1.1** **Interpret** chemical equations in terms of reactants, products, and conservation of mass. **7.1.2** **Balance** chemical equations by manipulating coefficients. **7.1.3** **Convert** between moles and mass of a substance using molar mass. **7.1.4** **Calculate** amounts of reactants or products by using molar mass, mole ratios, and balanced chemical equations.	A-1, A-2, B-2, B-3	ICP5.4, ICP5.5	**SE** Inquiry Activity: How Is Mass Conserved in a Chemical Change? p. 191 **L2** **SE** Quick Lab: Modeling a Mole, p. 196 **L2** **TE** Teacher Demo: Counting Particles, p. 195 **L2** **TE** Build Science Skills: Measuring and Calculating, p. 197 **L2**
7.2 Types of Reactions, pp. 199–205 🕐 1 block or 2 periods **7.2.1** **Classify** chemical reactions as synthesis, decomposition, single-replacement, double-replacement, or combustion reactions. **7.2.2** **Describe** oxidation-reduction reactions, and **relate** them to other classifications of chemical reactions.	A-1, A-2, B-1, B-2, B-3, F-1	ICP5.4, ICP5.5, ICP5.6	**SE** Quick Lab: Identifying a Type of Reaction, p. 203 **L2** **TE** Teacher Demo: Exothermic Reaction, p. 200 **L2** **LM** Investigation 7A: Using Single-Replacement Reactions to Compare Reactivities **L2** **LM** Investigation 7B: Recognizing a Synthesis Reaction **L1**
7.3 Energy Changes in Reactions, pp. 206–209 🕐 1 block or 2 periods **7.3.1** **Describe** the energy changes that take place during chemical reactions. **7.3.2** **Classify** chemical reactions as exothermic or endothermic. **7.3.3** **Explain** how energy is conserved during chemical reactions.	B-2, B-3, B-5, F-1, F-5	ICP5.4, ICP5.5, ICP5.6, ICP5.7	**TE** Build Science Skills: Observing, p. 208 **L2**
7.4 Reaction Rates, pp. 212–215 🕐 1 block or 2 periods **7.4.1** **Explain** what a reaction rate is. **7.4.2** **Describe** the factors affecting chemical reaction rates.	A-1, A-2, B-3, C-1	ICP5.6	**SE** Quick Lab: Observing the Action of Catalysts, p. 214 **L2** **TE** Build Science Skills: Calculating, p. 213 **L2** **TE** Teacher Demo: Temperature and Rate, p. 213 **L2**
7.5 Equilibrium, pp. 216–219 🕐 1 block or 2 periods **7.5.1** **Identify** and **describe** physical and chemical equilibria. **7.5.2** **Describe** the factors affecting chemical equilibrium.	A-1, A-2, B-2, B-3, C-1, E-1, G-1, G-3	ICP3.1, ICP5.5, ICP5.6	**SE** Design Your Own Lab: Manipulating Chemical Equilibrium, pp. 220–221 **L2** **TE** Build Science Skills: Using Models, p. 216 **L2**

RESOURCES
PRINT and TECHNOLOGY

RSW	Section 7.1	**L1**
RSW Math Skill		**L2**
MSPS	Section 7.1	**L2**
T	Chapter 7 Pretest	**L2**
	Section 7.1	**L2**
P	Chapter 7 Pretest	**L2**
	Section 7.1	**L2**
*sci*LINKS **GO**	Conservation of mass	**L2**
SCIENCE NEWS **GO**	Chemical reactions	**L2**

RSW	Section 7.2	**L1**
T	Section 7.2	**L2**
P	Section 7.2	**L2**
*sci*LINKS **GO**	Chemical reactions, Oxidation and reduction	**L2**

RSW	Section 7.3	**L1**
Discovery SCHOOL **DC**	Taming the Flames	**L2**
T	Section 7.3	**L2**
P	Section 7.3	**L2**

RSW	Section 7.4	**L1**
T	Section 7.4	**L2**
P	Section 7.4	**L2**
*sci*LINKS **GO**	Factors affecting reaction rate	**L2**

RSW	Section 7.5	**L1**
T	Section 7.5	**L2**
P	Section 7.5	**L2**
*sci*LINKS **GO**	Factors affecting equilibrium	**L2**

SECTION ASSESSMENT

SE Section 7.1 Assessment, p. 198

iT Section 7.1

SE Section 7.2 Assessment, p. 205

iT Section 7.2

SE Section 7.3 Assessment, p. 209

iT Section 7.3

SE Section 7.4 Assessment, p. 215

iT Section 7.4

SE Section 7.5 Assessment, p. 219

iT Section 7.5

Go Online

Materials for Activities and Labs

Quantities for each group

STUDENT EDITION

Inquiry Activity, p. 191
100-mL graduated cylinder, resealable quart-sized plastic bag, 10-cm × 10-cm piece of paper, effervescent antacid tablet, triple-beam balance

Quick Lab, p. 196
bolt, 2 nuts, 2 washers, balance

Quick Lab, p. 203
piece of zinc, copper(II) sulfate solution, 250-mL beaker, tongs, paper towel

Quick Lab, p. 214
5 test tubes, test-tube rack, marking pencil, dropper pipet, wood splint, platinum wire, 0.1 g manganese dioxide, 5 drops of copper(II) chloride solution, 0.1 g raw potato, graduated cylinder, 25 mL hydrogen peroxide

Design Your Own Lab, pp. 220–221
iodine-starch solution, 150-mL beaker, 4 dropper pipets, spot plate, ascorbic acid solution, chlorine bleach solution

TEACHER'S EDITION

Teacher Demo, p. 195
14 g graphite powder, small beaker, spatula, balance, a bag of rice, stack of paper plates

Build Science Skills, p. 197
copper wire, aluminum foil, water, sodium chloride, hydrogen peroxide, wire snips, metal spatulas, beakers, balances

Teacher Demo, p. 200
balance, evaporating dish, copper powder, ring stand, wire gauze, Bunsen burner, tongs

Build Science Skills, p. 208
beaker, water, thermometer, 1 tsp baking soda, 1 tsp calcium chloride

Build Science Skills, p. 210
fire extinguishers, fire extinguisher ratings

Build Science Skills, p. 213
clay, rulers, plastic knives

Teacher Demo, p. 213
2 chemical light sticks, 2 large beakers, hot water, ice water

Build Science Skills, p. 216
playing cards, watch

Chapter Assessment

CHAPTER ASSESSMENT
SE Chapter Assessment, pp. 223–224
CUT Chapter 7 Test A, B
CTB Chapter 7
iT Chapter 7
PHSchool.com GO
Web Code: cca-1070

STANDARDIZED TEST PREP
SE Chapter 7, p. 225
TP Diagnose and Prescribe

Interactive Textbook with assessment at PHSchool.com

From the Author

David Frank
Ferris State University

Big Ideas

This chapter covers a great deal of information regarding chemical reactions. Students are introduced to two basic conservation laws of chemical reactions: the law of conservation of mass and the law of conservation of energy. A classification scheme for reactions is discussed. Finally, students learn about reaction kinetics (rates) and chemical equilibrium, along with the factors affecting them.

Space and Time If reacting particles collide more frequently or with increased energy, then the rate of a chemical reaction increases. Factors that can make a reaction occur faster include temperature, surface area, stirring, concentration, and catalysts. To keep things simple, students are told that temperature affects the frequency of collision, but you should be aware that higher temperatures also increase the fraction of molecules with sufficient energy to react.

Matter and Change Because the number of reactions can appear overwhelming, students will find it helpful to see relationships between reactions by classifying them. By looking at the chemical equations, students can classify reactions as synthesis, decomposition, single-replacement, double-replacement, and combustion. By looking at electron transfers, students can classify some reactions as oxidation-reduction.

Students learn that the formation of a precipitate or a gas is evidence for a double-replacement reaction. In the next chapter, you may also wish to point out that the reaction between HCl and NaOH is also a double-replacement reaction. Furthermore, these categories overlap. For example, Mg burning in O_2 to produce MgO is an example of synthesis, combustion, and oxidation-reduction.

Energy Diagrams such as Figure 19 are important in understanding the energetics of a reaction. The relative location of the initial product and final reactant lines tells you if a reaction is exothermic or endothermic. The size of the "hump" in the middle is related to the rate at which the reaction takes place.

Chemistry Refresher

Describing Reactions 7.1

Chemical equations are used to describe reactions. The coefficients show the molar ratios of the reactants and products, and they can be changed in order to balance the equation. Chemical equations are balanced to show that mass is conserved in the chemical reaction.

Chemists use the mole, which is an amount containing 6.02×10^{23} particles, to count large numbers of small particles. The mass of one mole of a substance is called a molar mass. The molar mass of an element is the same as its atomic mass expressed in grams. A compound's molar mass is the sum of the atomic masses of its component elements expressed in grams. Molar mass is used to convert between molar and mass amounts of one substance. A mole ratio is used to convert between molar amounts of two different substances in a chemical reaction.

Address Misconceptions

Because reactants are changed into products, students may think that particles can be created or destroyed in ordinary chemical reactions. This is not the case—mass is conserved in all chemical reactions. For a strategy to overcome this misconception, see **Address Misconceptions** on **page 193**.

Types of Reactions 7.2

In a synthesis reaction, two or more substances react to form a single substance. The reverse of a synthesis reaction is a decomposition reaction. A single-replacement reaction is a reaction in which one element takes the place of another element in a compound. Potassium reacting with water is an example of a single-replacement reaction.

General equation for a single-replacement reaction:
$$A + BC \longrightarrow B + AC$$
Equation for potassium reacting with water:
$$2K + 2H_2O \longrightarrow H_2 + 2KOH$$

In a double-replacement reaction, two different compounds exchange positive ions and form two new compounds. In a combustion reaction, a substance reacts rapidly with oxygen, often generating light and heat. Any reaction involving a transfer of electrons can be classified as an oxidation-reduction (redox) reaction.

Go Online
NSTA PD LINKS

For: Teaching methods for chemical reactions
Visit: www.SciLinks.org/PDLinks
Web Code: ccn-0799

Energy Changes in Reactions 7.3

During a chemical reaction, chemical bonds in the reactants are broken and chemical bonds in the products are formed. Breaking bonds requires energy. Forming bonds releases energy. A chemical reaction can be classified as exothermic (releases energy to the surroundings) or endothermic (absorbs energy from the surroundings). Energy is conserved during chemical reactions; the total amount of energy before and after the reaction is the same.

Reaction Rates and Equilibrium 7.4 and 7.5

A reaction rate is the time-rate at which reactants change into products. Generally, reaction rates are increased by a rise in temperature, increased surface area or concentration of reactants, agitation, and catalysts. The effect of a catalyst on reaction energy is illustrated in the diagram below.

Reaction Energy—Catalyzed and Uncatalyzed

- Reaction without catalyst
- Reaction with catalyst

A system is in dynamic chemical equilibrium when there is no change in the concentrations of reactants and products, and reactants and products are forming simultaneously. This can take place only when the forward and reverse reactions occur at the same rate. Equilibria can also be physical in nature. For example, a physical equilibrium can exist between liquid water and water vapor inside a closed container.

Henri Le Châtelier observed that when a system at equilibrium experiences a change, the equilibrium shifts in the direction that relieves the change. Factors affecting chemical equilibrium include shifts in temperature, pressure, and concentration.

Build Reading Literacy

Relate Text and Visuals

Use Graphic Elements to Clarify and Extend

Strategy Help students relate visuals to text, in order to clarify difficult concepts in the text or to understand information beyond that stated in the text. This strategy enables students to focus on their own thought processes as they actively make use of photos and illustrations as tools to support comprehension. Before students begin, choose a section in Chapter 7, such as Section 7.2, pp. 202–203.

Example

1. Have students keep their book closed as you read a few paragraphs aloud, including text that refers to a figure. You may want to think aloud as you read, saying, for example, "I wonder what that would look like?"

2. Then, have students open their book to the passage that you read. Tell them to reread it and then study the figure and its caption carefully. Ask what parts of the passage make more sense when students look at the figure.

3. Point out that visuals also sometimes communicate information that is not in the text. Have students identify any new information that can be learned from the figure.

4. Have students work in pairs, with one reading aloud through the next reference to a figure, and then both working together to discuss how the figure helps them understand the passage or provides additional information.

See p. 207 for a script on how to use the relate text and visuals strategy with students. For additional Build Reading Literacy strategies, see pp. 197, 204, 212, and 218.

ASSESS PRIOR KNOWLEDGE

Use the Chapter Pretest below to assess students' prior knowledge. As needed, review these Science Concepts and Math Skills with students.

Review Science Concepts

Section 7.1 Students should be familiar with chemical and physical properties. Review the information contained in a chemical formula. Have students review the terms *atom, mass, atomic mass,* and *chemical change.*

Section 7.2 Review the common types of evidence for a chemical change. Students should be familiar with the terms *precipitate, chemical change, element, compound, electron,* and *ion.*

Section 7.3 Encourage students to review chemical bond types, how they are named, and how they form. Students should be familiar with various forms of energy.

Sections 7.4 and 7.5 Be sure that students are familiar with the concepts of temperature, surface area, pressure, and concentration.

Review Math Skills

Formulas and Equations, Ratios and Proportions, and Conversion Factors Students need to interpret chemical formulas, balance chemical equations, and be familiar with the manipulation of conversion factors.

Direct students to the **Math Skills** in the **Skills and Reference Handbook** at the end of the student text.

21st Century Learning
Interpersonal and Collaborative Skills

How do scientists classify reactions?

Scientists classify chemical reactions based on the type of reactant or the number of reactants and products. Work in a group to develop a slide-show presentation that summarizes general types of reactions. First, determine how the slide show will be organized. Then work as a group or split up into smaller groups to cover the different reaction types. Present the final slide show in class or publish it on your class Web site.

Indiana's Academic Standards for Science

CHEMICAL ENERGY, REACTIONS, AND BONDING

ICP.5.4: Use the concept of the mole to relate number of moles and the mass of a sample of a pure substance of known chemical composition; **ICP.5.5:** Using conservation principles write and balance chemical equations; **ICP.5.6:** Identify key indicators of a chemical change and classify simple types of chemical reactions. Differentiate between covalent, ionic, hydrogen and Van der Waals bonding, and write formulas for and name compounds of each type; **ICP.5.7:** Explain that in exothermic chemical reactions chemical energy is converted into other forms such as thermal, electrical, light, and sound energy.

PROPERTIES OF MATTER

ICP.3.1: Describe how we use macroscopic properties of matter to model microscopic processes.

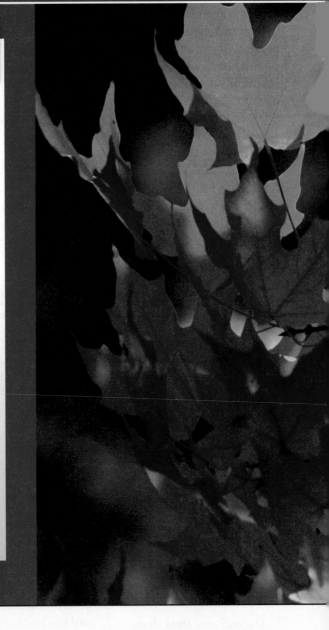

Chapter Pretest

1. Which of the following is an example of a physical change? *(c)*
   a. Wood burns and becomes ash.
   b. A steel nail rusts over time.
   c. Ice melts and becomes water.
   d. Milk curdles when acid is added to it.

2. How do you find the atomic mass of an element? *(The atomic mass of each element is listed on the periodic table.)*

3. Which of the following characteristics can you determine about a substance based on its chemical formula? *(a)*
   a. The number and types of atoms that make up the substance
   b. The mass of an unknown sample of the substance
   c. The melting point of the substance
   d. The density and state of the substance at room temperature

4. Which conversion factor would you multiply 0.020 m by in order to express the quantity in centimeters? *(d)*
   a. $\frac{1000 \text{ m}}{1 \text{ km}}$ **b.** $\frac{1 \text{ km}}{1000 \text{ m}}$
   c. $\frac{1 \text{ m}}{100 \text{ cm}}$ **d.** $\frac{100 \text{ cm}}{1 \text{ m}}$

5. Which is the correct chemical formula for potassium hydroxide? *(b)*
   a. POH   **b.** KOH
   c. P_5OH **d.** K_2OH

Chapter Preview

Discovery CHANNEL SCHOOL

Video Field Trip

Taming the Flames

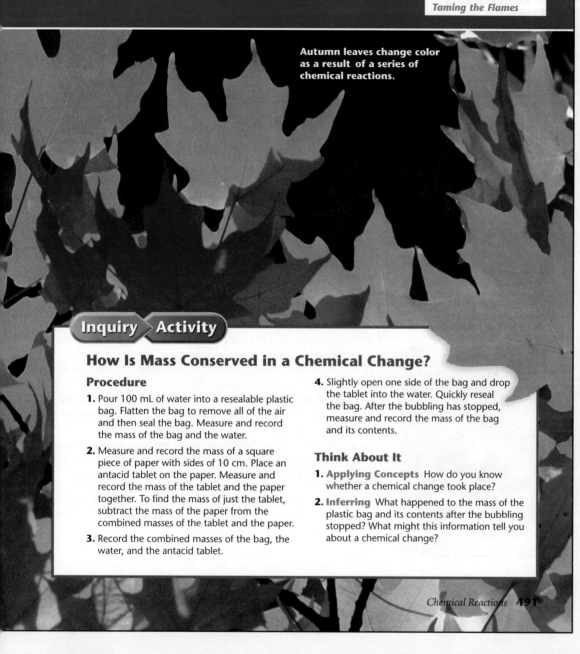

Autumn leaves change color as a result of a series of chemical reactions.

Inquiry Activity

How Is Mass Conserved in a Chemical Change?

Procedure

1. Pour 100 mL of water into a resealable plastic bag. Flatten the bag to remove all of the air and then seal the bag. Measure and record the mass of the bag and the water.

2. Measure and record the mass of a square piece of paper with sides of 10 cm. Place an antacid tablet on the paper. Measure and record the mass of the tablet and the paper together. To find the mass of just the tablet, subtract the mass of the paper from the combined masses of the tablet and the paper.

3. Record the combined masses of the bag, the water, and the antacid tablet.

4. Slightly open one side of the bag and drop the tablet into the water. Quickly reseal the bag. After the bubbling has stopped, measure and record the mass of the bag and its contents.

Think About It

1. **Applying Concepts** How do you know whether a chemical change took place?

2. **Inferring** What happened to the mass of the plastic bag and its contents after the bubbling stopped? What might this information tell you about a chemical change?

Chemical Reactions **191**

Discovery CHANNEL SCHOOL

Video Field Trip

Taming the Flames

Encourage students to view the Video Field Trip "Taming the Flames."

ENGAGE/EXPLORE

Inquiry Activity

How Is Mass Conserved in a Chemical Change? L2

Purpose In this activity, students begin to explain the law of conservation of mass as it applies to chemical reactions.

 Address Misconceptions

This activity can help to remedy the misconception that gases do not have mass or weight.

Skills Focus Observing, Inferring, Measuring

Prep Time 10 minutes

Materials 100-mL graduated cylinder, resealable quart-sized plastic bag, 10-cm × 10-cm piece of paper, effervescent antacid tablet, triple-beam balance

Class Time 10 minutes

Safety Make sure that students tie back hair and loose clothing. Students should put on safety goggles, lab aprons, and plastic gloves before beginning the activity. Make sure that students wipe up any spilled water right away to avoid slips and falls.

Expected Outcome When dissolved in water, the antacid tablet produces bubbles of gas that inflate the bag. This process also produces a fizzing sound and causes the bag to become cooler to the touch.

Think About It

1. The formation of bubbles, the inflation of the bag, the bag getting cooler to the touch, and the fizzing sound provided evidence that a chemical change occurred.

2. The mass of the plastic bag and its contents remained the same. Students may infer that during a chemical change mass is not lost, but conserved.

Visual, Logical, Group

1 FOCUS

Objectives

7.1.1 Interpret chemical equations in terms of reactants, products, and conservation of mass.

7.1.2 Balance chemical equations by manipulating coefficients.

7.1.3 Convert between moles and mass of a substance using molar mass.

7.1.4 Calculate amounts of reactants or products by using molar mass, mole ratios, and balanced chemical equations.

Reading Focus

Build Vocabulary L2

Concept Map Have students construct a concept map of the terms *reactants, products, chemical equations, coefficients,* and *moles.* Instruct students to place the terms in ovals and connect the ovals with lines on which linking words are placed. Students should place the main concept (Describing Reactions) at the top or center and use descriptive linking phrases to connect the terms.

Reading Strategy L2

Answers may vary. Possible answer:
a. How to balance chemical equations
b. An unbalanced equation can be balanced by changing the coefficients.
c. How to convert from mass to moles
d. The mass of a substance can be converted to moles by using the molar mass as a conversion factor.

2 INSTRUCT

Chemical Equations

Use Visuals L1

Figure 1 Have students examine the reaction taking place in the photo. **What clues show that a chemical reaction is taking place?** (*Energy is released in the form of heat and light.*) Mention that one of the reactants, O_2, and the product, CO_2, are colorless gases. **How might a scientist determine that oxygen gas is involved in this reaction?** (*He or she could attempt to burn charcoal in an oxygen-free environment.*)
Visual

7.1 Describing Reactions

Standards: ICP.5.4, ICP.5.5

Reading Focus

Key Concepts

- What is the law of conservation of mass?
- Why must chemical equations be balanced?
- Why do chemists use the mole?
- How can you calculate the mass of a reactant or product in a chemical reaction?

Vocabulary

- reactants
- products
- chemical equation
- coefficients
- mole
- molar mass

Reading Strategy

Monitoring Your Understanding Preview the Key Concepts, topic headings, vocabulary, and figures in this section. List two things you expect to learn. After reading, state what you learned about each item you listed.

What I Expect to Learn	What I Learned
a. _____?_____	b. _____?_____
c. _____?_____	d. _____?_____

Figure 1 Burning is an example of a chemical reaction. When charcoal burns, the carbon in the charcoal reacts with oxygen in the air to produce carbon dioxide and heat.

What type of change is happening in Figure 1? When charcoal burns, it changes into other substances while producing heat and light. Burning is a chemical change. When a substance undergoes a chemical change, a chemical reaction is said to take place. In order to understand chemical reactions, you first must be able to describe them.

Chemical Equations

A useful way of describing a change is to state what is present before and after the change. For example, suppose you wanted to show how your appearance changed as you grew older. You could compare a photo of yourself when you were younger with a photo that was taken recently.

A useful description of a chemical reaction tells you the substances present before and after the reaction. In a chemical reaction, the substances that undergo change are called **reactants.** The new substances formed as a result of that change are called **products.** In Figure 1, the reactants are the carbon in the charcoal and the oxygen in the air. The product of the reaction is carbon dioxide gas.

Using Equations to Represent Reactions During a chemical reaction, the reactants change into products. You can summarize this process with a word equation.

$$\text{Reactants} \longrightarrow \text{Products}$$

Section Resources

Print

- **Reading and Study Workbook With Math Support,** Section 7.1 and **Math Skill:** Balancing Chemical Equations
- **Math Skills and Problem Solving Workbook,** Section 7.1
- **Transparencies,** Chapter Pretest and Section 7.1

Technology

- **Interactive Textbook,** Section 7.1
- **Presentation Pro CD-ROM,** Chapter Pretest and Section 7.1
- **Go Online,** NSTA SciLinks, Conservation of mass; *Science News,* Chemical reactions

To describe the burning of charcoal, you can substitute the reactants and products of the reaction into the word equation as follows.

$$\text{Carbon} + \text{Oxygen} \longrightarrow \text{Carbon dioxide}$$

You can then simplify the word equation by writing the reactants and products as chemical formulas.

$$C + O_2 \longrightarrow CO_2$$

Now you have a chemical equation. A **chemical equation** is a representation of a chemical reaction in which the reactants and products are expressed as formulas. You can read the equation above as, "Carbon and oxygen react and form carbon dioxide," or, "The reaction of carbon and oxygen yields carbon dioxide."

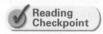 **Reading Checkpoint** *What is a chemical equation?*

Conservation of Mass As a piece of charcoal burns, it gets smaller and smaller until it is finally reduced to a tiny pile of ash. Although the charcoal seems to disappear as it burns, it is actually being converted into carbon dioxide gas. If you measured the mass of the carbon dioxide produced, it would equal the mass of the charcoal and oxygen that reacted.

During chemical reactions, the mass of the products is always equal to the mass of the reactants. This principle, established by French chemist Antoine Lavoisier (1743–1794), is known as the law of conservation of mass. ⬤ **The law of conservation of mass states that mass is neither created nor destroyed in a chemical reaction.** Recall that mass is a measure of the amount of matter. So, this law is also known as the law of conservation of matter. By demonstrating that mass is conserved in various reactions, Lavoisier laid the foundation for modern chemistry.

Figure 2 illustrates how a chemical equation can be restated in terms of atoms and molecules. The equation reads, "One atom of carbon reacts with one molecule of oxygen and forms one molecule of carbon dioxide." Suppose you have six carbon atoms. If each carbon atom reacts with one oxygen molecule to form one carbon dioxide molecule, then six carbon atoms react with six oxygen molecules to form six carbon dioxide molecules. Notice that the number of atoms on the left side of the equation equals the number of atoms on the right. The equation shows that mass is conserved.

For: Links on conservation of mass
Visit: www.SciLinks.org
Web Code: ccn-1071

Figure 2 Whether you burn one carbon atom or six carbon atoms, the equation used to describe the reaction is the same.
Using Models *How do both models of the reaction below show that mass is conserved?*

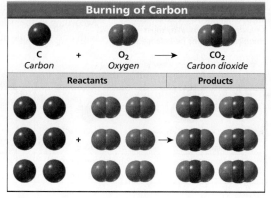

Burning of Carbon

| C Carbon | + | O₂ Oxygen | → | CO₂ Carbon dioxide |

| Reactants | | Products |

Customize for Inclusion Students

Visually Impaired
Provide students with molecular models that use different sizes or textures to identify the different types of atoms. Have them build molecular models that show the reaction for the burning of carbon. Then, have students use the models to demonstrate conservation of mass.

Download a worksheet on conservation of mass for students to complete, and find additional teacher support from NSTA SciLinks.

Answer to . . .

Figure 2 *In both models of the reaction $C + O_2 \longrightarrow CO_2$, the number of atoms of each element on the left equals the number of atoms of each element on the right.*

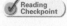 **Reading Checkpoint** *A chemical equation is a representation of a chemical reaction in which the reactants and products are expressed as formulas.*

Balancing Equations
Use Visuals L1

Figure 4 Have students use colored paperclips to model the different atoms of the reactants and products shown in Figure 4. As a class, go over the process of balancing the equation using the paperclips as a visual aid. Have students practice balancing the following equations by making lists of the numbers of each type of atom in the reactants and products as shown in Figure 4.

1. $Na + H_2O \longrightarrow NaOH + H_2$
($2Na + 2H_2O \longrightarrow 2NaOH + H_2$)
2. $HCl + CaCO_3 \longrightarrow CaCl_2 + CO_2 + H_2O$
($2HCl + CaCO_3 \longrightarrow CaCl_2 + CO_2 + H_2O$)
3. $Al + Cl_2 \longrightarrow AlCl_3$
($2Al + 3Cl_2 \longrightarrow 2AlCl_3$)

Students may find it helpful to make two or three models of each reactant and product and then try various combinations, listing and checking the balance of the atoms for each combination.

Visual

For: Activity on balancing equations
Visit: PHSchool.com
Web Code: ccp-1071

Students can view a simulation on how to balance chemical equations.

Figure 3 Water is a compound made up of the elements hydrogen and oxygen.

For: Activity on balancing equations
Visit: PHSchool.com
Web Code: ccp-1071

Figure 4 In the unbalanced equation, the hydrogen atoms are balanced but the oxygen atoms are not. After changing the coefficients, both the hydrogen and oxygen atoms are balanced. *Applying Concepts Why must chemical equations be balanced?*

Balancing Equations

Water is formed by the reaction of hydrogen and oxygen. You can describe the reaction by writing a chemical equation.

$$H_2 + O_2 \longrightarrow H_2O$$

If you examine this equation carefully, you will notice that the number of atoms on the left side does not equal the number of atoms on the right. The equation is not balanced. **In order to show that mass is conserved during a reaction, a chemical equation must be balanced.**

You can balance a chemical equation by changing the **coefficients**, the numbers that appear before the formulas. In the unbalanced equation above, the coefficients are understood to be 1. When you change a coefficient, you change the amount of that reactant or product represented in the chemical equation. As you balance equations, you should never change the subscripts in a formula. Changing the formula changes the identity of that reactant or product.

The first step in balancing an equation is to count the number of atoms of each element on each side of the equation, as shown in Figure 4. The left side of the unbalanced equation has two hydrogen atoms and two oxygen atoms. The right side has two hydrogen atoms and one oxygen atom. The oxygen atoms need to be balanced.

The next step is to change one or more coefficients until the equation is balanced. You can balance the oxygen atoms by changing the coefficient of H_2O to 2.

$$H_2 + O_2 \longrightarrow 2H_2O$$

The oxygen atoms are now balanced. However, the hydrogen atoms have become "unbalanced," with two on the left, and four on the right. To balance the hydrogen atoms, change the coefficient of H_2 to 2.

$$2H_2 + O_2 \longrightarrow 2H_2O$$

The equation is now balanced. Each side of the balanced equation has four hydrogen atoms and two oxygen atoms, as shown in Figure 4. According to the balanced equation, two molecules of hydrogen react with one molecule of oxygen to yield two molecules of water.

Unbalanced Chemical Equation	
H_2 + O_2 ⟶ H_2O	
Reactants	**Product**
2 hydrogen atoms	2 hydrogen atoms
2 oxygen atoms	1 oxygen atom

Balanced Chemical Equation	
$2H_2$ + O_2 ⟶ $2H_2O$	
Reactants	**Product**
4 hydrogen atoms	4 hydrogen atoms
2 oxygen atoms	2 oxygen atoms

Answer to . . .

Figure 4 *To show that mass is conserved during a chemical reaction*

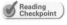 *The first step in balancing a chemical equation is to count the number of atoms of each element on each side of the equation.*

Facts and Figures

Rocket Fuel One of the fuels used to propel the space shuttle is liquid hydrogen, also called LH2. Liquid oxygen, or LOX, serves as the oxidizer. LH2 and LOX for the space shuttle's main engines are stored in separate tanks within a large external fuel tank. The reaction of the hydrogen and oxygen generates thrust and produces water vapor as exhaust gas. It takes about 8.5 minutes for the shuttle to use up its LH2 and LOX supplies, after which the external tank is jettisoned.

Math Skills

Balancing Chemical Equations

Write a balanced equation for the reaction between copper and oxygen to produce copper(II) oxide, CuO.

 Read and Understand
What information are you given?

Reactants: Cu, O_2 Product: CuO

 Plan and Solve
Write a chemical equation with the reactants on the left side and the product on the right.

$$Cu + O_2 \longrightarrow CuO$$

This equation is not balanced. Change the coefficient of CuO in order to balance the number of oxygen atoms.

$$Cu + O_2 \longrightarrow 2CuO$$

Change the coefficient of Cu in order to balance the number of copper atoms.

$$2Cu + O_2 \longrightarrow 2CuO$$

③ Look Back and Check
Is your answer reasonable?

The number of atoms on the left equals the number of atoms on the right.

Math Practice

1. Hydrogen chloride, or HCl, is an important industrial chemical. Write a balanced equation for the production of hydrogen chloride from hydrogen and chlorine.

2. Balance the following chemical equations.
   a. $H_2O_2 \longrightarrow H_2O + O_2$
   b. $Mg + HCl \longrightarrow H_2 + MgCl_2$

3. Ethylene, C_2H_4, burns in the presence of oxygen to produce carbon dioxide and water vapor. Write a balanced equation for this reaction.

Counting With Moles

How many shoes do you own? Because shoes come in twos, you would most likely count them by the pair rather than individually. The counting units you use depend on what you are counting. For example, you might count eggs by the dozen or paper by the ream.

Chemists also need practical units for counting things. Although you can describe a reaction in terms of atoms and molecules, these units are too small to be practical. ● **Because chemical reactions often involve large numbers of small particles, chemists use a counting unit called the mole to measure amounts of a substance.**

A **mole** (mol) is an amount of a substance that contains approximately 6.02×10^{23} particles of that substance. This number is known as Avogadro's number. In chemistry, a mole of a substance generally contains 6.02×10^{23} atoms, molecules, or ions of that substance. For instance, a mole of iron is 6.02×10^{23} atoms of iron.

Figure 5 Shoes are often counted by the pair, eggs by the dozen, and paper by the ream (500 sheets). To count particles of a substance, chemists use the mole (6.02×10^{23} particles).

Chemical Reactions **195**

Math Practice

Solutions L2
1. $H_2 + Cl_2 \longrightarrow 2HCl$
2. a. $2H_2O_2 \longrightarrow 2H_2O + O_2$
   b. $Mg + 2HCl \longrightarrow H_2 + MgCl_2$
3. $C_2H_4 + 3O_2 \longrightarrow 2CO_2 + 2H_2O$
Logical

For Extra Help L1

Only the coefficients, not the subscripts, should change. **Logical**

Direct students to the **Math Skills** in the **Skills and Reference Handbook** at the end of the student text for additional help.

Additional Problems

1. Balance the reaction of silicon with oxygen to form silicon dioxide.
($Si + O_2 \longrightarrow SiO_2$)
2. Balance $Fe + Cl_2 \longrightarrow FeCl_3$.
($2Fe + 3Cl_2 \longrightarrow 2FeCl_3$)
Logical, Portfolio

Counting With Moles

Teacher Demo

Counting Particles L2

Purpose Students see the efficiency of using molar mass to count particles.

Materials 14 g graphite powder, small beaker, spatula, balance, a bag of rice, stack of paper plates

Procedure Count out 1 mole of carbon atoms while a volunteer attempts to count out 1 mole of rice grains (100 grains of rice onto each paper plate). Write the molar mass of carbon on the board and weigh out 12.01 g of graphite. Have students note how few rice grains there are compared to 1 mole. Ask, **How large could 1 mole of rice grains be?** (*1 mole of rice grains could fill more than 10^{13} classrooms that are 10m × 10m × 4m!*)

Expected Outcome Using molar mass to count is more efficient than counting particles one by one. **Visual, Logical**

Quick Lab

Modeling a Mole   L2

Objective
After completing this activity, students will be able to
• use the concept of moles to solve stoichiometric problems.

Skills Focus Observing, Measuring, Predicting, Calculating

Prep Time 5 minutes

Advance Prep Be sure the bolts, nuts, and washers are compatible.

Class Time 20 minutes

Expected Outcome Students will correctly assemble and predict the mass of the molecular model.

Analyze and Conclude
1. The mass of the molecule will equal the sum of the masses of all of its parts.
2. Students can make 10 models.
3. This answer will depend upon the mass of the nuts that are used. For example, if a nut has a mass of 10 g, then students would be able to make 10 models of the molecule.
Kinesthetic, Logical

For Enrichment   L3

Add bolts, washers, and nuts of different masses to the atom collection. Have students assemble a variety of new molecules with the same number of atoms but with different-sized pieces. They can determine whether the mass of the molecule changes and whether it is possible to assemble molecules that are different in structure but have the same mass.
Kinesthetic, Logical

Figure 6 The molar mass of carbon is 12.0 grams. The molar mass of sulfur is 32.1 grams. *Inferring If each of the carbon and sulfur samples contains one mole of atoms, why do the samples have different masses?*

Molar Mass A dozen eggs has a different mass than a dozen oranges. Similarly, a mole of carbon has a different mass than a mole of sulfur, as shown in Figure 6. The mass of one mole of a substance is called a **molar mass.** For an element, the molar mass is the same as its atomic mass expressed in grams. For example, the atomic mass of carbon is 12.0 amu, so the molar mass of carbon is 12.0 grams.

For a compound, you can calculate the molar mass by adding up the atomic masses of its component atoms, and then expressing this sum in grams. A carbon dioxide molecule is composed of one carbon atom (12.0 amu) and two oxygen atoms (2×16.0 amu = 32.0 amu). So carbon dioxide has a molar mass of 44.0 grams.

Mole-Mass Conversions Once you know the molar mass of a substance, you can convert moles of that substance into mass, or a mass of that substance into moles. For either calculation, you need to express the molar mass as a conversion factor. For example, the molar mass of CO_2 is 44.0 grams, which means that one mole of CO_2 has a mass of 44.0 grams. This relationship yields the following conversion factors.

$$\frac{44.0 \text{ g } CO_2}{1 \text{ mol } CO_2} \qquad \frac{1 \text{ mol } CO_2}{44.0 \text{ g } CO_2}$$

Suppose you have 55.0 grams of CO_2. To calculate how many moles of CO_2 you have, multiply the mass by the conversion factor on the right.

$$55.0 \text{ g } CO_2 \times \frac{1 \text{ mol } CO_2}{44.0 \text{ g } CO_2} = 1.25 \text{ mol } CO_2$$

You can check your answer by using the conversion factor on the left.

$$1.25 \text{ mol } CO_2 \times \frac{44.0 \text{ g } CO_2}{1 \text{ mol } CO_2} = 55.0 \text{ g } CO_2$$

Quick Lab

Modeling a Mole

Materials
bolt, 2 nuts, 2 washers, balance

Procedure
1. Measure and record the mass of one bolt, one nut, and one washer. Each piece of hardware will represent an atom of a different element.
2. Assemble the bolt, nuts, and washers together so that they form a model of a molecule known as BN_2W_2.
3. Predict the mass of BN_2W_2.

4. Test your prediction by finding the mass of your model.

Analyze and Conclude
1. **Analyzing Data** Did your prediction match the actual mass of your model? Explain.

2. **Calculating** How many models of your molecule can you make with 20 washers and as many nuts and bolts as you need?

3. **Calculating** How many models of your molecule can you make with 100 grams of nuts and as many bolts and washers as you need?

Chemical Calculations

Think about baking a cake like the one in Figure 7. The directions on a box of cake mix might tell you to add two eggs and one cup of water to the cake mix. Suppose you wanted to make three cakes. Although the directions don't tell you specifically how many eggs and how much water are required for three cakes, you could figure out the amounts. To make three cakes, you would need three times as much of each ingredient—six eggs, three cups of water, and three packages of cake mix.

Chemical equations can be read as recipes for making new substances. Figure 8 shows the balanced equation for the formation of water. You can read this equation as, "Two molecules of hydrogen react with one molecule of oxygen and form two molecules of water." In terms of moles, the equation reads, "Two moles of hydrogen react with one mole of oxygen and form two moles of water." To convert from moles to mass, you need to use the molar masses as conversion factors. Figure 8 shows how the same equation can also be read as, "4.0 grams of H_2 reacts with 32.0 grams of O_2 and forms 36.0 grams of H_2O."

How many grams of oxygen would you need to make 144 grams of water? In chemical reactions, the mass of a reactant or product can be calculated by using a balanced chemical equation and molar masses of the reactants and products. The chemical equation tells you how to relate amounts of reactants to amounts of products. Molar masses let you convert those amounts into masses.

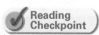 **Reading Checkpoint** *How do you convert from moles to mass?*

Converting Mass to Moles
To calculate how much oxygen is required to make 144 grams of water, you need to begin with a balanced chemical equation for the reaction.

$$2H_2 + O_2 \longrightarrow 2H_2O$$

The first step in your calculations is to determine how many moles of water you are trying to make. By using the molar mass of water, you can convert the given mass of water into moles.

$$144 \text{ g } H_2O \times \frac{1 \text{ mol } H_2O}{18.0 \text{ g } H_2O} = 8.00 \text{ mol } H_2O$$

Formation of Water			
Equation	$2H_2$ +	O_2 →	$2H_2O$
Amount	2 mol	1 mol	2 mol
Molar Mass	2.0 g/mol	32.0 g/mol	18.0 g/mol
Mass (Moles × Molar Mass)	4.0 g +	32.0 g →	36.0 g

Figure 7 A cake recipe tells you how much of each ingredient to use for each cake you bake. **Using Analogies** *How is a cake recipe like a chemical equation?*

Figure 8 In a balanced chemical equation, the number of atoms of each element on the left equals the number of atoms of each element on the right. By using molar masses, you can show that the mass of the reactants equals the mass of the products.

Chemical Reactions **197**

Facts and Figures

Baking Reactions The reaction of sodium bicarbonate ($NaHCO_3$) under heat is one of the chemical reactions that make cakes and muffins rise. Cake recipes may call for baking soda (the common name for sodium bicarbonate) or baking powder (a mixture that contains sodium bicarbonate). When sodium bicarbonate is heated, it breaks down into simpler products according to the following equation.

$$2NaHCO_3 \longrightarrow Na_2CO_3 + H_2O + CO_2$$

The carbon dioxide produced by this reaction causes the cake to rise as it bakes. The CO_2 bubbles that become trapped give baked goods their spongy texture.

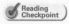

❸ ASSESS

Evaluate Understanding L2

Give students a chemical equation to analyze. Ask them to determine whether the equation is balanced, and to explain how conservation of mass applies. Then, have students write a problem that requires converting from mass of a reactant to mass of a product. Have students exchange their problem with a partner for him or her to solve.

Reteach L1

Use Figure 2 to summarize the key concepts in this section, such as identifying reactants and products, balancing equations, understanding conservation of mass, and determining mole ratios. Have students determine the mole ratio of carbon to carbon dioxide in the balanced equation. *(1:1)*

Solutions

9. $2K + Br_2 \longrightarrow 2KBr$
10. $2Mg + O_2 \longrightarrow 2MgO$

If your class subscribes to the Interactive Textbook, use it to review key concepts in Section 7.1.

Science News provides students with current information on chemical reactions.

For: Articles on chemical reactions
Visit: PHSchool.com
Web Code: cce-1071

Using Mole Ratios Remember the balanced chemical equation for the formation of water. You can read it as, "Two moles of hydrogen react with one mole of oxygen and form two moles of water." Because each mole of oxygen that reacts will yield two moles of water, you can write the following conversion factors, or mole ratios.

$$\frac{1 \text{ mol } O_2}{2 \text{ mol } H_2O} \qquad \frac{2 \text{ mol } H_2O}{1 \text{ mol } O_2}$$

The mole ratio on the left allows you to convert moles of water to moles of oxygen. Now you can calculate how many moles of oxygen are required to produce eight moles of water:

$$8.00 \text{ mol } H_2O \times \frac{1 \text{ mol } O_2}{2 \text{ mol } H_2O} = 4.00 \text{ mol } O_2$$

Converting Moles to Mass The last step is to convert moles of O_2 to grams of O_2 by using the molar mass of O_2 as a conversion factor.

$$4.00 \text{ mol } O_2 \times \frac{32.0 \text{ g } O_2}{1 \text{ mol } O_2} = 128 \text{ g } O_2$$

So, in order to produce 144 grams of H_2O, you must supply 128 grams of O_2. Notice that you used the concept of a mole in two ways to solve this problem. In the first and last step, you used a molar mass to convert between mass and moles. In the middle step, you used the mole ratio to convert moles of a product into moles of a reactant.

Section 7.1 Assessment

Reviewing Concepts

1. 🌐 What is the law of conservation of mass?
2. 🌐 Why does a chemical equation need to be balanced?
3. 🌐 Why do chemists use the mole as a counting unit?
4. 🌐 What information do you need to predict the mass of a reactant or product in a chemical reaction?
5. What is a mole ratio?

Critical Thinking

6. **Applying Concepts** The following equation describes how sodium and chlorine react to produce sodium chloride.

$$2Na + Cl_2 \longrightarrow 2NaCl$$

Is the equation balanced? Explain your answer.

7. **Calculating** Ammonia, NH_3, can be made by reacting nitrogen with hydrogen.

$$N_2 + 3H_2 \longrightarrow 2NH_3$$

How many moles of NH_3 can be made if 7.5 moles of H_2 react with enough N_2?

8. **Calculating** What mass of NH_3 can be made from 35.0 g of N_2?

Math Practice

9. Balance the following equation.

$$K + Br_2 \longrightarrow KBr$$

10. Write a balanced chemical equation for the formation of magnesium oxide, MgO, from magnesium and oxygen.

Section 7.1 Assessment

1. The law of conservation of mass states that mass is neither created nor destroyed.
2. A chemical equation must be balanced in order to demonstrate that mass is conserved.
3. Because chemical reactions often involve large numbers of small particles, the mole $(6.02 \times 10^{23}$ particles) is a practical counting unit for scientists to use.
4. In order to calculate the mass of a reactant or product in a chemical reaction, you need the molar mass of the reactant, the molar mass of the product, and a balanced chemical equation (which tells you the mole ratio between the reactant and product).
5. A mole ratio is a conversion factor that relates two substances that take part in a chemical reaction. A mole ratio can be determined from a balanced chemical equation.
6. Yes, there are two sodium atoms and two chlorine atoms on each side of the equation.
7. $7.5 \text{ mol } H_2 \times \frac{2 \text{ mol } NH_3}{3 \text{ mol } H_2} = 5.0 \text{ mol } NH_3$

8. Molar mass of N_2 is 28.0 g.
$35.0 \text{ g } N_2 \times \frac{1 \text{ mol } N_2}{28.0 \text{ g } N_2} = 1.25 \text{ mol } N_2$
Mole ratio of NH_3:N_2 is 2:1.
$1.25 \text{ mol } N_2 \times \frac{2 \text{ mol } NH_3}{1 \text{ mol } N_2} = 2.50 \text{ mol } NH_3$
Molar mass of NH_3 is 17.0 grams.
$2.50 \text{ mol } NH_3 \times \frac{17.0 \text{ g } NH_3}{1 \text{ mol } NH_3} = 42.5 \text{ g } NH_3$

7.2 Types of Reactions

Reading Focus

Standards: ICP.5.4, ICP.5.5, ICP.5.6

Key Concepts

- What are the general types of chemical reactions?
- How did the discovery of subatomic particles affect the classification of reactions?

Vocabulary

- synthesis reaction
- decomposition reaction
- single-replacement reaction
- double-replacement reaction
- combustion reaction
- oxidation-reduction reaction

Reading Strategy

Previewing Skim the section and begin a concept map like the one below that identifies types of reactions with a general form. As you read, add the general form of each type of reaction.

Types of Reactions

Synthesis | a. _?_ | Single Replacement | b. _?_

A + B → AB | c. _?_ | d. _?_ | e. _?_

T he walls of the cave shown in Figure 9 are solid limestone. When hydrochloric acid is dropped on limestone, a chemical reaction occurs in which a gas is produced. Geologists can use this reaction to determine whether a rock sample contains the mineral calcium carbonate, $CaCO_3$. When a rock containing calcium carbonate reacts with hydrochloric acid, it fizzes. The bubbles contain carbon dioxide gas.

Many other reactions produce carbon dioxide. For example, heating limestone produces carbon dioxide. So does burning gasoline. However, just because two reactions have the same product, you cannot assume that they are the same type of reaction.

Classifying Reactions

Just as you can classify matter into different types, you can classify chemical reactions into different types. Reactions are often classified by the type of reactant or the number of reactants and products. **Some general types of chemical reactions are synthesis reactions, decomposition reactions, single-replacement reactions, double-replacement reactions, and combustion reactions.** Each type describes a different way in which reactants interact to form products.

Figure 9 The walls and other formations of Blanchard Springs Caverns in Arkansas contain the mineral calcium carbonate, $CaCO_3$.

Chemical Reactions **199**

Section Resources

Print
- ***Laboratory Manual,*** Investigations 7A and 7B
- ***Reading and Study Workbook With Math Support,*** Section 7.2
- ***Transparencies,*** Section 7.2

Technology
- ***Interactive Textbook,*** Section 7.2
- ***Presentation Pro CD-ROM,*** Section 7.2
- ***Go Online,*** NSTA SciLinks, Chemical reactions, Oxidation and reduction

---

Section 7.2

1 FOCUS

Objectives

7.2.1 **Classify** chemical reactions as synthesis, decomposition, single-replacement, double-replacement, or combustion reactions.

7.2.2 **Describe** oxidation-reduction reactions, and **relate** them to other classifications of chemical reactions.

Reading Focus

Build Vocabulary [L2]

Word Forms Ask students to write simple definitions of the words *synthesize, decompose,* and *replace.* Then, have students explain how these simple definitions relate to the terms *synthesis reaction, decomposition reaction, single-replacement reaction,* and *double-replacement reaction.* (*To synthesize is to combine and form a complex product, to decompose is to separate into basic parts, and to replace is to take or fill the place of.*)

Reading Strategy [L2]

a. Decomposition **b.** Double replacement **c.** AB ⟶ A + B
d. A + BC ⟶ B + AC
e. AB + CD ⟶ AD + CB

2 INSTRUCT

Classifying Reactions
Integrate Earth Science [L2]

Calcium carbonate in limestone rock is dissolved by water made acidic by carbon dioxide according to the following equation.

$$CaCO_3 + CO_2 + H_2O \rightleftharpoons$$
$$Ca^{2+} + 2HCO_3^-$$

The reverse reaction deposits the calcium carbonate onto a limestone surface. (Note that reaction equilibrium is discussed in depth in Section 7.5.) In this way, water dripping in a limestone cave forms beautiful formations. Have students research cave formations. Ask, **What is the difference between stalactites and stalagmites?** (*Stalactites form on cave ceilings, while stalagmites form on cave floors.*)
Visual

Integrate Biology L2

Biologists often call the decay of organic matter *decomposition* even when the reactions that take place do not follow the general form AB $\longrightarrow$ A + B. While both meanings of *decomposition* are derived from the idea of separating objects into simpler parts, chemists use this term to describe a reaction that leads to the breakdown of a single compound. **Logical**

Teacher **Demo**

Exothermic Reaction L2

Purpose Students observe a synthesis reaction.

Materials balance, evaporating dish, copper powder, ring stand, wire gauze, Bunsen burner, tongs

Procedure Measure and record on the board the mass of the evaporating dish. Measure out 10 g of copper powder and spread it evenly in the evaporating dish. Arrange the wire mesh on the ring stand so that it sits above the Bunsen burner. Place the evaporating dish on the wire mesh and light the Bunsen burner. Heat the copper powder in the evaporating dish for 10–15 minutes. Allow the evaporating dish and its contents to cool and then determine their total mass. Ask, **Was mass conserved in this reaction?** *(Students may answer no, based on the increase in mass.)* Have students calculate the mass of the synthesized product.

Expected Outcome The copper powder turns into black copper(II) oxide, and the product's mass is greater than the original mass of the copper powder. The additional mass comes from the oxygen, which is the other reactant in the synthesis reaction. **Visual, Logical**

Figure 10 Sodium metal reacts vigorously with chlorine to form sodium chloride, NaCl. **Interpreting Photos** *What evidence in this photograph tells you that a chemical reaction is taking place?*

For: Links on chemical reactions
Visit: www.SciLinks.org
Web Code: ccn-1076

Synthesis A **synthesis reaction** is a reaction in which two or more substances react to form a single substance. The reactants may be either elements or compounds. The product synthesized is always a compound. The general equation for a synthesis reaction is

$$A + B \longrightarrow AB$$

Figure 10 shows what happens when sodium reacts with chlorine. The product of this reaction is the compound sodium chloride, which appears as a whitish cloud of solid particles. You are probably more familiar with sodium chloride as table salt. You can describe the synthesis of sodium chloride with the following equation.

$$2Na + Cl_2 \longrightarrow 2NaCl$$

Another example of a synthesis reaction is hydrogen and oxygen reacting to form water.

$$2H_2 + O_2 \longrightarrow 2H_2O$$

This reaction is used to generate electricity for satellites and spacecraft.

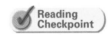
Reading Checkpoint *What is a synthesis reaction?*

Decomposition The opposite of synthesis is decomposition. A **decomposition reaction** is a reaction in which a compound breaks down into two or more simpler substances. The reactant in a decomposition reaction must be a compound. The products may be elements or compounds. The general equation for a decomposition reaction is

$$AB \longrightarrow A + B$$

When electricity passes through water, the water decomposes into hydrogen gas and oxygen gas. You can describe the decomposition of water by writing the following equation.

$$2H_2O \longrightarrow 2H_2 + O_2$$

Notice that this reaction is the opposite of the synthesis of water.

Another example of decomposition occurs in the making of cement. Cement factories use a giant kiln, or oven, to heat a mixture of clay and limestone. The heat causes the calcium carbonate in the limestone to decompose into lime, CaO, and carbon dioxide.

$$CaCO_3 \longrightarrow CaO + CO_2$$

The carbon dioxide escapes the kiln through a smokestack. The clay-and-lime mixture is cooled and ground into cement powder.

The How It Works box on page 201 describes a decomposition reaction that is used to make automobiles safer.

Download a worksheet on chemical reactions for students to complete, and find additional teacher support from NSTA SciLinks.

Customize for English Language Learners

Discussion
Write the general equations for synthesis, decomposition, single-replacement, and double-replacement reactions on the board. Use word equations to explain what is happening in each reaction. For example, you might say, **In a synthesis reaction, chemical A reacts (combines) with chemical B to form a new chemical compound made up of the same elements as those in** **chemicals A and B.** Have students comment on how the equations are alike and how they are different. They may point out that the equation for synthesis appears to be the reverse of the equation for decomposition. Also, they may notice that the replacement reactions involve different particles changing places. Encourage students to use familiar words when describing their observations.

Automobile Safety: Air Bags

Air bags are inflatable cushions built into a car's steering wheel or dashboard. In a crash, the bags inflate, protecting both the driver and the passenger. The whole process takes 0.04 second. **Interpreting Diagrams** *What is the source of the gas that fills an air bag?*

Testing air bags
Air bags have been shown to reduce the risk of serious injury in a head-on collision by 30 percent. New cars have air bags on both the driver and passenger sides.

1 Collision A collision triggers the car's crash sensors, which send an electrical signal to the igniter in the steering wheel.

Crash sensor

Nitrogen gas leaks through holes

Nitrogen gas

Igniter

Electrical signal from crash sensor

Sodium azide pellets decomposing

Ignition unit

Igniter

Sodium azide pellets

Air bag folded into steering wheel

Steering wheel

2 Air bag inflates The igniter sets off a combustion reaction that heats up the sodium azide (NaN_3) contained in the ignition unit. When it is heated, the sodium azide decomposes into metallic sodium (Na) and nitrogen gas (N_2). The nitrogen gas inflates the air bag. The decomposition reaction is $2NaN_3 \rightarrow 2Na + 3N_2$.

Nontoxic residue of secondary reactions

Deflated air bag

3 Air bag deflates The nitrogen escapes through tiny holes in the bag, causing immediate deflation of the air bag. Because sodium is dangerous (due to its high reactivity), the ignition unit also contains other chemicals that react with sodium to form a nontoxic material.

Chemical Reactions **201**

Automobile Safety: Air Bags [L2]

The force of the reaction that inflates an air bag causes the air bag to break out of the steering wheel at up to 200 miles per hour. One way that manufacturers help the bag withstand the friction of this fast movement is by lubricating the bag with powders, such as talcum powder or cornstarch.

Interpreting Diagrams The source of the nitrogen gas that fills an air bag is the reacting sodium azide contained in the ignition unit. When the sodium azide pellets are heated, they decompose into sodium metal and nitrogen gas.
Visual

For Enrichment [L3]

Have students research the benefits and drawbacks of including air bags in automobiles. They may want to find out about the types of injuries caused and prevented by air bags as well as the types of injuries that air bags cannot prevent. **Verbal**

> **Address Misconceptions** [L2]

Many students incorrectly think that the reactants are still present after a reaction has gone to completion. Challenge this misconception by discussing the reaction that takes place when an air bag inflates. After the class has read the feature on air bags, ask students where the nitrogen gas comes from when an air bag inflates. Explain that the nitrogen gas produced from the decomposition of solid sodium azide is exactly like the nitrogen gas in air. Apply this concept later when the class reads about single-replacement reactions that have solid reactants and products.
Verbal

Answer to . . .

Figure 10 *The formation of a cloudy substance and the release of energy (seen in the photo as light) are evidence that a chemical reaction is taking place.*

✔ **Reading Checkpoint**   *A synthesis reaction is a reaction in which two or more substances react to form a single substance.*

Figure 11 A single-replacement reaction occurs when copper wire is submerged in a solution of silver nitrate. As the copper replaces the silver in the silver nitrate solution, the solution turns blue, and silver crystals form on the wire.

Use Visuals L1

Figure 11 Students may note that in the reaction between copper and silver nitrate, the water (part of the silver nitrate solution) doesn't appear as a reactant in the accompanying chemical equation in the text. Ask, **What evidence is there of a chemical change in Figure 11?** *(The solution changes color, and silver crystals form on the wire.)* Explain that when a compound dissociates in water, a physical change has taken place. The water and the dissolved substance remain chemically unchanged. The flask contains the same number of water molecules before and after the reaction takes place. Ask, **If you were to include water in the chemical equation, where would you place it?** *(Water would be on both sides of the equation with equivalent coefficients.)* Explain that just as in a math equation, you can cancel equivalent expressions that appear on both sides of the equation. **Visual**

Figure 12 Potassium reacts with water in a single-replacement reaction that produces hydrogen gas and potassium hydroxide.

Single Replacement

A **single-replacement reaction** is a reaction in which one element takes the place of another element in a compound. Single-replacement reactions have the general form

$$A + BC \longrightarrow B + AC$$

Suppose you dip a coil of copper wire into a solution of silver nitrate and water, as shown in Figure 11. A vivid chemical reaction takes place as the solution turns blue and the submerged part of the wire becomes coated with a silvery metal. In this reaction, the copper replaces the silver in silver nitrate to form copper(II) nitrate. The equation for this reaction is

$$Cu + 2AgNO_3 \longrightarrow 2Ag + Cu(NO_3)_2$$

Notice that one of the products is silver, which you can see adhering to the wire in Figure 12. The other product, copper(II) nitrate, gives the solution its blue color.

Recall that alkali metals are very reactive elements. Figure 12 shows potassium reacting with water. This is another example of a single-replacement reaction, as the element potassium replaces hydrogen in water to form potassium hydroxide, KOH.

$$2K + 2H_2O \longrightarrow H_2 + 2KOH$$

The heat produced by this chemical reaction causes the hydrogen gas to ignite explosively.

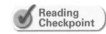 **Reading Checkpoint** *What is a single-replacement reaction?*

Facts and Figures

Activity Series Through experimentation, chemists can compile an activity series, a list of elements arranged in decreasing activity. The elements at the top of the list are the most reactive and will replace those elements at the bottom of the list when they are in compounds. For example, according to the activity series to the right, copper will replace silver in a single-replacement reaction, as in the reaction described in the text. Using the activity series, you could correctly predict that the following single-replacement reaction would take place.

$$Fe + CuSO_4 \longrightarrow FeSO_4 + Cu$$

Activity Series of Metals
Potassium (K)
Calcium (Ca)
Magnesium (Mg)
Zinc (Zn)
Iron (Fe)
Lead (Pb)
Hydrogen (H)
Copper (Cu)
Silver (Ag)

Decreasing Reactivity ↓

Double Replacement

Double Replacement A **double-replacement reaction** is one in which two different compounds exchange positive ions and form two new compounds. The general form of a double replacement reaction is

$$AB + CD \longrightarrow AD + CB$$

Notice that two replacements take place in this reaction. Not only is A replacing C, but C is also replacing A.

Solutions of lead(II) nitrate, $Pb(NO_3)_2$, and potassium iodide, KI, are both colorless. However, when these solutions are mixed, as shown in Figure 13, a yellow precipitate forms as a result of a double-replacement reaction. The equation for this reaction is

$$Pb(NO_3)_2 + 2KI \longrightarrow PbI_2 + 2KNO_3$$

The lead ions in $Pb(NO_3)_2$, trade places with the potassium ions in KI. The products are lead(II) iodide, PbI_2, which precipitates out of solution, and potassium nitrate, KNO_3, which remains in solution.

When geologists test the calcium carbonate content in a rock, they make use of the following double-replacement reaction.

$$CaCO_3 + 2HCl \longrightarrow CaCl_2 + H_2CO_3$$

One of the products of this reaction is calcium chloride, $CaCl_2$. The other product is carbonic acid, H_2CO_3, which decomposes into carbon dioxide gas and water.

$$H_2CO_3 \longrightarrow CO_2 + H_2O$$

Figure 13 When potassium iodide solution is poured into a solution of lead(II) nitrate, a double-replacement reaction takes place. Lead(II) iodide forms as a yellow precipitate.
Comparing and Contrasting *How does a double-replacement reaction differ from a single-replacement reaction?*

Quick Lab

Identifying a Type of Reaction

Materials
piece of zinc, copper(II) sulfate ($CuSO_4$) solution, 250-mL beaker, tongs, paper towel

Procedure

1. Place the zinc in the beaker and add enough $CuSO_4$ solution to cover the zinc as shown. **CAUTION** *Be careful when using chemicals. Copper sulfate is toxic.*

2. After 5 minutes, carefully remove the zinc from the solution using the tongs and place the zinc on the paper towel to dry. Observe any changes that have occurred to the zinc and the solution of $CuSO_4$. **CAUTION** *Follow your teacher's instructions for disposal of used chemicals. Wash your hands with soap or detergent before leaving the laboratory.*

Analyze and Conclude

1. **Observing** What clues indicate that a chemical reaction has taken place?

2. **Applying Concepts** What were the reactants in this reaction? What were the products? Write a balanced chemical equation for the reaction.

3. **Classifying** Is this a single-replacement or double-replacement reaction? Explain.

Chemical Reactions **203**

Quick Lab

Identifying a Type of Reaction   L2

Objective
After completing this activity, students will be able to
- determine whether a chemical reaction has occurred.
- identify a single-replacement reaction.

Skills Focus Observing, Predicting

Prep Time 10 minutes

Advance Prep Purchase zinc strips or cut a zinc sheet into 1" × 2" pieces. While wearing safety goggles and heavy gloves, file down all rough edges. To prepare 0.1 M $CuSO_4$: Dissolve 2.5 g $CuSO_4 \cdot 5H_2O$ in enough water to make 100 mL of solution. Be sure to take proper safety precautions.

Class Time 15 minutes

Safety Students should wear safety goggles, lab aprons, and disposable plastic gloves. They should tie back long hair and secure any loose clothing.

Expected Outcome The section of the zinc strip exposed to the $CuSO_4$ solution will have a distinct copper metal coating and the copper(II) sulfate solution will become darker and less blue in color.

Analyze and Conclude
1. The $CuSO_4$ solution turned less blue and the zinc became coated with reddish copper.

2. Zn and $CuSO_4$; Cu and $ZnSO_4$; $Zn + CuSO_4 \longrightarrow Cu + ZnSO_4$

3. This is a single-replacement reaction because one element replaces another element in a compound. **Visual**

For Enrichment   L2

Have students examine other single metal replacement reactions by placing copper and magnesium in $AgNO_3$, $CuSO_4$, $MgSO_4$, and $ZnSO_4$ solutions. The copper strip will react with $AgNO_3$, and the magnesium strip will react with $AgNO_3$, $CuSO_4$, and $ZnSO_4$. **Kinesthetic**

Answer to . . .

Figure 13 *In a double-replacement reaction, two different compounds exchange positive ions and form two new compounds.*

Reading Checkpoint *A reaction in which one element takes the place of another element in a compound*

Build Reading Literacy L1

Preview Refer to page **36D** in **Chapter 2**, which provides the guidelines for previewing.

Have students preview the text on pp. 204 and 205 related to oxidation and reduction reactions. They should note the headings, the bold-faced key ideas, and the chemical equations. Help students activate their prior knowledge by reviewing the role electrons play in ionic and covalent bonding.
Verbal

Reactions as Electron Transfers

Build Science Skills L2

Classifying Many kinds of reactions are also classified as redox reactions. For example, all combustion reactions are also redox reactions. The easiest reactions to identify as redox reactions contain pure elements. Have students search the section and identify these redox reactions, which have a product or a reactant that is an element.
(2Na + Cl$_2$ ⟶ 2NaCl;
2H$_2$ + O$_2$ ⟶ 2H$_2$O;
2H$_2$O ⟶ 2H$_2$ + O$_2$;
Cu + 2AgNO$_3$ ⟶ Cu(NO$_3$)$_2$ + 2Ag;
2K + 2H$_2$O ⟶ H$_2$ + 2KOH;
CH$_4$ + 2O$_2$ ⟶ CO$_2$ + 2H$_2$O)
Logical

Figure 14 A Bunsen burner generates heat and light by the combustion of natural gas. **Interpreting Photos** *What reactants or products are visible in the reaction shown above?*

Combustion A **combustion reaction** is one in which a substance reacts rapidly with oxygen, often producing heat and light. The burning of natural gas, shown in Figure 14, is an example of combustion. The main component of natural gas is methane, CH_4. When methane burns in an unlimited supply of oxygen, the following reaction occurs.

$$CH_4 + 2O_2 \longrightarrow CO_2 + 2H_2O$$

The products of the reaction are carbon dioxide and water. The combustion of methane also generates both heat and light.

By now you know the chemical equation for the combustion of hydrogen.

$$2H_2 + O_2 \longrightarrow 2H_2O$$

Notice that you could also classify this reaction as the synthesis of water. The classifications for chemical reactions sometimes overlap.

Reactions as Electron Transfers

So far, you have learned that chemical reactions can be identified by the type of reactant or by the number of reactants and products. For example, in a combustion reaction one of the reactants must be oxygen. In a synthesis reaction, two or more reactants combine to form a single product.

As scientists learned more about the structure of the atom, they found different ways to describe how reactions take place. ⬤ **The discovery of subatomic particles enabled scientists to classify certain chemical reactions as transfers of electrons between atoms.** A reaction in which electrons are transferred from one reactant to another is called an **oxidation-reduction reaction,** or redox reaction.

Oxidation For a long time, people have known that metals react with oxygen. Calcium, for instance, reacts with oxygen and forms calcium oxide (CaO), shown in Figure 15. Iron reacts with oxygen and forms rust, or iron(III) oxide (Fe_2O_3). These types of synthesis reactions, in which a metal combines with oxygen, traditionally have been classified as oxidations.

When calcium reacts with oxygen, the following reaction takes place.

$$2Ca + O_2 \longrightarrow 2CaO$$

Notice that while the atoms of both reactants (Ca and O_2) are neutral, the product of the reaction is a compound composed of ions (Ca^{2+} and O^{2-}). When calcium reacts with oxygen, each neutral calcium atom loses two electrons and becomes a calcium ion with a charge of 2+.

$$Ca \longrightarrow Ca^{2+} + 2e^-$$

Figure 15 Calcium oxide, or lime, is produced when calcium burns in the presence of oxygen. In this reaction, the calcium is oxidized and the oxygen is reduced.

204 *Chapter 7*

Facts and Figures

Corrosion of Metals Rust (Fe_2O_3) can result from oxygen and water coming into contact with iron. The corrosion of iron can result in the formation of many substances, including iron(II) oxide, FeO, and hydrated iron(III) oxide, $Fe_2O_3 \cdot nH_2O$. Iron is not the only metal that corrodes. Uncoated aluminum objects oxidize to form white Al_2O_3. Jewelry made of silver tarnishes over time, forming black Ag_2S. Copper pots often develop a distinctive green patina when exposed to the elements.

Any process in which an element loses electrons during a chemical reaction is called oxidation. A reactant is oxidized if it loses electrons. Note that the modern definition of oxidation is much broader than the original meaning. Oxygen doesn't always have to be present in order for an element to lose electrons. For example, when sodium reacts with chlorine, each neutral sodium atom loses one electron and becomes a sodium ion, Na^+.

Reduction As calcium atoms lose electrons during the synthesis of calcium oxide, the oxygen atoms gain electrons. As each neutral oxygen atom gains two electrons, it becomes an ion with a charge of $2-$.

$$O + 2e^- \longrightarrow O^{2-}$$

The process in which an element gains electrons during a chemical reaction is called reduction. A reactant is said to be reduced if it gains electrons.

Oxidation and reduction always occur together. When one element loses electrons, another element must gain electrons. Note that oxidation-reduction reactions do not always involve complete transfers of electrons. For example, in the synthesis of water, hydrogen is oxidized as it partially loses electrons. Oxygen is reduced as it partially gains electrons.

For: Links on oxidation and reduction
Visit: www.SciLinks.org
Web Code: ccn-1072

Section 7.2 Assessment

Reviewing Concepts

1. ⬤ What are five general types of reactions?
2. ⬤ How did the discovery of subatomic particles affect the classification of reactions?
3. The synthesis of water is described by the equation $2H_2 + O_2 \longrightarrow 2H_2O$. How is the decomposition of water related to this reaction? Explain, using a chemical equation.
4. Explain the difference between a single-replacement reaction and a double-replacement reaction.
5. Propane, C_3H_8, is frequently used in camping stoves. When propane undergoes combustion, what are the products formed?
6. Is the reaction represented by the following equation a redox reaction? Explain your answer.

$$2Hg + O_2 \longrightarrow 2HgO$$

Critical Thinking

7. **Predicting** What is the product of the synthesis reaction between magnesium and iodine? Explain your answer.
8. **Classifying** Identify these reactions as synthesis, decomposition, single replacement, double replacement, or combustion.
   a. $Pb(NO_3)_2 + 2HCl \longrightarrow PbCl_2 + 2HNO_3$
   b. $2C_2H_6 + 7O_2 \longrightarrow 4CO_2 + 6H_2O$
   c. $Ca + 2HCl \longrightarrow CaCl_2 + H_2$
   d. $2SO_2 + O_2 \longrightarrow 2SO_3$

Writing in Science

Explanatory Paragraph Write a paragraph explaining why the formation of water can be classified as a synthesis, combustion, or oxidation-reduction reaction.

Chemical Reactions **205**

Section 7.2   Assessment

1. Synthesis reaction, decomposition reaction, single-replacement reaction, double-replacement reaction, and combustion reaction
2. The discovery of subatomic particles allowed scientists to classify certain reactions as transfers of electrons between atoms.
3. In the reaction $2H_2 + O_2 \longrightarrow 2H_2O$, water is formed from its elements. During the decomposition of water, water is broken down into its elements, according to the equation $2H_2O \longrightarrow 2H_2 + O_2$.
4. In a single-replacement reaction, an element replaces another element in one compound. In a double-replacement reaction, two elements replace each other in two different compounds.
5. Carbon dioxide and water
6. Yes, this is a redox reaction because electron transfer takes place. The charge of mercury changes from 0 to 2+ (oxidation). The charge of oxygen changes from 0 to 2− (reduction).
7. MgI_2. In ionic compounds, magnesium has a charge of 2+ and iodine has a charge of 1−.
8. a. Double replacement
   b. Combustion
   c. Single replacement
   d. Synthesis

7.3 Energy Changes in Reactions

① FOCUS

Objectives

7.3.1 Describe the energy changes that take place during chemical reactions.

7.3.2 Classify chemical reactions as exothermic or endothermic.

7.3.3 Explain how energy is conserved during chemical reactions.

Reading Focus

Build Vocabulary   L2

Word-Part Analysis Tell students that the prefix *exo-* means *out* and the prefix *endo-* means *in*. Have students predict the meaning of the terms *exothermic reaction* and *endothermic reaction* given that the word root *thermo* means *heat*. *(An exothermic reaction gives off heat (energy), while an endothermic reaction takes in heat (energy).)*

Reading Strategy   L2

a. Releases energy to the surroundings
b. Absorbs energy from surroundings

② INSTRUCT

Chemical Bonds and Energy
Build Science Skills   L2

Using Models Have students use molecular model kits to make ball-and-stick models for propane, C_3H_8. Explain that the sticks represent bonds and the balls represent atoms in the molecule. Have students count the number of bonds that will break in the combustion of a propane molecule.
Logical, Visual

Reading Focus

 Standards: ICP.5.4, ICP.5.5, ICP.5.6, ICP.5.7

Key Concepts

- What happens to chemical bonds during a chemical reaction?
- What happens to energy during a chemical reaction?

Vocabulary

- ◆ chemical energy
- ◆ exothermic reaction
- ◆ endothermic reaction

Reading Strategy

Comparing and Contrasting Copy the Venn diagram. As you read, complete it to show the differences between exothermic and endothermic reactions.

If you've ever had a barbecue, you may have used a gas grill like the one shown in Figure 16. Many types of gas grills use propane, C_3H_8. You can think of a propane grill as the scene of a chemical reaction—specifically, a combustion reaction. The reactants are propane and oxygen, and the products are carbon dioxide and water. However, the description of this reaction is incomplete unless you consider the heat and light produced. Heat, after all, is the reason for using a propane grill.

Chemical Bonds and Energy

The heat produced by a propane grill is a form of energy. When you write the chemical equation for the combustion of propane, you can include "heat" on the right side of the equation.

$$C_3H_8 + 5O_2 \longrightarrow 3CO_2 + 4H_2O + \text{Heat}$$

This equation states that the heat released in the reaction came from the reactants. **Chemical energy** is the energy stored in the chemical bonds of a substance. A propane molecule has ten single covalent bonds (eight C—H bonds and two C—C bonds). The chemical energy of a propane molecule is the energy stored in these bonds. Likewise, oxygen, carbon dioxide, and water molecules all have energy stored in their chemical bonds.

Figure 16 Many portable barbecue grills burn propane gas.

Section Resources

Print
- *Reading and Study Workbook With Math Support,* Section 7.3
- *Transparencies,* Section 7.3

Technology
- *Interactive Textbook,* Section 7.3
- *Presentation Pro CD-ROM,* Section 7.3

Energy changes in chemical reactions are determined by changes that occur in chemical bonding. ◐ **Chemical reactions involve the breaking of chemical bonds in the reactants and the formation of chemical bonds in the products.** In the combustion of propane, the bonds in propane and oxygen molecules are broken, while the bonds in carbon dioxide and water molecules are formed.

Breaking Bonds As Figure 17 illustrates, each propane molecule reacts with five oxygen molecules. In order for the reaction to occur, eight C—H single bonds, two C—C single bonds, and five O=O double bonds must be broken. Breaking chemical bonds requires energy. This is why propane grills have an igniter, a device that produces a spark. The spark provides enough energy to break the bonds of reacting molecules and get the reaction started.

Forming Bonds Figure 17 also shows you that for each molecule of propane burned, three molecules of carbon dioxide and four molecules of water are formed. This means that six C=O double bonds and eight O—H single bonds are formed in the reaction. The formation of chemical bonds releases energy. The heat and light given off by a propane stove result from the formation of new chemical bonds. The bonds form as the carbon, hydrogen, and oxygen atoms in the propane and oxygen molecules are rearranged into molecules of carbon dioxide and water.

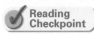 **Reading Checkpoint** *Does breaking chemical bonds require energy or release energy?*

Propane Combustion

C_3H_8	+	$5O_2$	⟶	$3CO_2$	+	$4H_2O$	+	Heat
propane		oxygen		carbon dioxide		water		

8 C–H, 2 C–C		5 O=O	⟶	6 C=O		8 O–H
bonds broken		bonds broken		bonds formed		bonds formed

Figure 17 In order for the combustion of propane to occur, all the chemical bonds in the reactants (propane and oxygen) must be broken. The formation of the chemical bonds in the products completes the reaction.
Inferring How does the chemical energy of the reactants compare to the chemical energy of the products in this reaction?

Chemical Reactions **207**

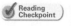
Chemical Reactions **207**

Exothermic and Endothermic Reactions

Build Science Skills

Observing

Purpose Students observe an exothermic process.

Materials beaker, water, thermometer, 1 tsp calcium chloride

Class Time 10 minutes

Procedure Have students fill a beaker with room temperature water and measure its temperature. Then, dissolve 1 tsp of calcium chloride in the water. Have students take the temperature of the solution and identify the process as endothermic or exothermic. Pour the waste solutions down the drain with excess water.

Safety Students should wear gloves and goggles for this activity.

Expected Outcome The temperature increases. The process is exothermic. Logical, Visual, Group

Use Visuals L1

Figure 18 Have students examine the graphs. Ask, **As you go from left to right in each graph, what happens to the reactants?** *(They react to form the products.)* **What point on each graph represents the highest energy?** *(The energy is highest at each curve's peak.)* **What do the double-headed arrows represent?** *(The double-headed arrows represent the difference in chemical energy between the reactants and the products.)* **Which type of reaction has products with a greater amount of energy than the reactants?** *(The products in an endothermic reaction have a greater amount of chemical energy than the reactants.)* Visual

Figure 18 In chemical reactions, energy is either released or absorbed. **A** In an exothermic reaction, energy is released to the surroundings. **B** In an endothermic reaction, energy is absorbed from the surroundings. **Using Graphs** *How do the energy diagrams show that energy is conserved in chemical reactions?*

Exothermic and Endothermic Reactions

Recall that physical changes can release or absorb energy. During an exothermic change, such as freezing, energy is released to the surroundings. During an endothermic change, such as melting, energy is absorbed from the surroundings. Energy also flows into and out of chemical changes. **During a chemical reaction, energy is either released or absorbed.**

Exothermic Reactions A chemical reaction that releases energy to its surroundings is called an **exothermic reaction.** In exothermic reactions, the energy released as the products form is greater than the energy required to break the bonds in the reactants.

Combustion is an example of an extremely exothermic reaction. When 1 mole of propane reacts with 5 moles of oxygen, 2220 kJ (kilojoules) of heat is released. You can use this value to replace "heat" in the combustion equation written earlier.

$$C_3H_8 + 5O_2 \longrightarrow 3CO_2 + 4H_2O + 2220 \text{ kJ}$$

Figure 18A shows how chemical energy changes during an exothermic reaction. Notice that the chemical energy of the reactants is greater than the chemical energy of the products. The difference between these amounts of energy equals the amount of heat given off by the reaction.

In any reaction, the chemical energy reaches a peak before the reactants change into products. This peak represents the amount of energy required to break the chemical bonds of the reactants. Unless reacting particles collide with enough energy to break these bonds, the reaction will not occur. For example, at room temperature, the collisions between propane and oxygen molecules are not energetic enough to result in combustion. However, if you increase the temperature by adding a spark, some of the molecules around the spark move faster and are able to collide with enough energy to react.

208 Chapter 7

Facts and Figures

Activation Energy Reactant particles must collide with enough speed in order to react. Activation energy is the energy required to start a chemical reaction. In an energy diagram, the activation energy is the difference in the energy of the reactants and the energy at the highest point of the curve. Methane gas in a gas stove reacts with oxygen in air to produce carbon dioxide and water.

This combustion reaction provides the flame that heats food. However, simply exposing methane to air is not enough for the reaction to take place. Gas stoves have a pilot light or a sparking device that provides the activation energy needed for the reaction to occur. Once the gas is lit, the energy emitted from the exothermic reaction provides the activation energy for the continued burning of methane.

Endothermic Reactions A chemical reaction that absorbs energy from its surroundings is called an **endothermic reaction.** In an endothermic reaction, more energy is required to break the bonds in the reactants than is released by the formation of the products.

Figure 18B shows the energy diagram for an endothermic reaction. Notice that the energy of the products is greater than the energy of the reactants. The difference between these amounts of energy equals the amount of heat that must be absorbed from the surroundings.

When mercury(II) oxide is heated to a temperature of about 450°C, it breaks down into mercury and oxygen, as shown in Figure 19. The decomposition of mercury(II) oxide is an endothermic reaction that can be described by the following equation.

$$2HgO + 181.7 \text{ kJ} \longrightarrow 2Hg + O_2$$

Because heat is absorbed, the energy term appears on the left side of the equation. For every 2 moles of HgO that decomposes, 181.7 kJ of heat must be absorbed.

Conservation of Energy

In an exothermic reaction, the chemical energy of the reactants is converted into heat plus the chemical energy of the products. In an endothermic reaction, heat plus the chemical energy of the reactants is converted into the chemical energy of the products. In both cases, the total amount of energy before and after the reaction is the same. This principle is known as the law of conservation of energy. You will read more about how energy is conserved later.

Figure 19 The orange-red powder in the bottom of the test tube is mercury(II) oxide. At about 450°C, mercury(II) oxide decomposes into oxygen gas (which escapes from the test tube) and mercury (droplets of which can be seen collecting on the sides of the test tube).

Section 7.3 Assessment

Reviewing Concepts

1. ⊙ What happens to chemical bonds as a chemical reaction occurs?

2. ⊙ How do chemical reactions involve energy?

3. Is the combustion of propane endothermic or exothermic?

4. When propane reacts with oxygen, does the surrounding area become warmer or cooler?

5. Is energy created during an exothermic reaction? Explain.

Critical Thinking

6. **Inferring** Explain why methane does not react with oxygen at room temperature.

7. **Calculating** Methane reacts with oxygen in the following combustion reaction.

$$CH_4 + 2O_2 \longrightarrow CO_2 + 2H_2O$$

What bonds are broken when one molecule of methane reacts with two molecules of oxygen?

Connecting ⊂ Concepts

Chemical Bonds Reread the descriptions of chemical bonds in Sections 6.1 and 6.2. Then, describe the decomposition of mercury(II) oxide. Specify which bonds are ionic and which bonds are covalent.

Chemical Reactions **209**

Conservation of Energy

Address Misconceptions L2

When examining a chemical equation, many students think that energy is being created or destroyed in the reaction. Unlike the situation with conservation of particles, the chemical equation does not clearly show conservation of energy. Challenge this misconception by having students refer to the energy diagrams in Figure 18 for a visual representation of the energy of the reactants and the products.
Visual

3 ASSESS

Evaluate Understanding L2

Have students sketch and label energy diagrams for exothermic and endothermic reactions. Have them discuss the energy diagrams in terms of breaking and forming bonds and conservation of energy.

Reteach L1

Compare and contrast the ways energy is notated in the equation on p. 206, in Figure 17, in Figure 18, and in the equation on p. 208.

Connecting ⊂ Concepts

Mercury(II) oxide, or HgO, is an ionic compound. The decomposition of HgO can be described by the reaction $2HgO \longrightarrow 2Hg + O_2$. For each O_2 molecule formed by the decomposition of HgO, two ionic Hg—O bonds are broken and one covalent O═O double bond is formed.

 Interactive Textbook If your class subscribes to the Interactive Textbook, use it to review key concepts in Section 7.3.

Answer to . . .

Figure 18 *In Figure 18A, the chemical energy of the reactants equals the chemical energy of the products plus the energy released by the reaction. In Figure 18B, the chemical energy of the reactants plus the energy absorbed by the reaction equals the chemical energy of the products.*

Section 7.3 Assessment

1. Chemical reactions involve the breaking of chemical bonds in the reactants and the formation of chemical bonds in the products.

2. During chemical reactions, energy is either released or absorbed.

3. The combustion of propane is exothermic because it releases energy.

4. Warmer. An exothermic reaction releases heat to the surrounding area.

5. No, energy is not created during an exothermic reaction. The energy released by an exothermic reaction was previously stored as chemical energy in the bonds of the reactants.

6. At room temperature, the collisions between methane molecules and oxygen molecules are not energetic enough to cause a reaction.

7. Four C—H single bonds and two O═O double bonds are broken when one molecule of methane burns.

CONCEPTS
— in Action —

Firefighting
Background

Because fires require oxygen, fuel, and intense heat to burn, removing one or more of these components is the best way to put out a fire. Dousing a fire with water cools the fuel and makes it more difficult to heat to the ignition temperature. Backburning and firebreaks remove the fuel that a wildfire needs in order to spread. Smothering a fire reduces the amount of oxygen in the vicinity of the fire.

Build Science Skills

Applying Concepts

Purpose Students identify the types of fires that can occur in the home or laboratory and classify fire extinguishers used to control small fires.

Materials fire extinguishers, fire extinguisher ratings

Class Time 20 minutes

Procedure Tell students that different types of fire extinguishers made for home use can contain water, carbon dioxide, or a dry chemical material—such as sodium bicarbonate or potassium bicarbonate—that decomposes to produce carbon dioxide. Have students examine the different types of fire extinguishers and make note of their contents. Have them list the types of fires each type of extinguisher can put out. Have students apply what they have learned about combustion reactions to determine how each type of fire extinguisher works.

Expected Outcome Extinguishers that contain water can put out ordinary combustibles, such as paper or wood. Water extinguishers reduce the temperature of the fuel. Most dry chemical fire extinguishers can also put out flammable liquids and electrical fires. Dry chemical fire extinguishers smother the fire. Extinguisher ratings are as follows: A extinguishers put out paper and wood fires. B extinguishers put out flammable liquids. C extinguishers put out electrical fires.

Verbal, Logical, Group

Firefighting

Uncontrolled fires threaten lives and property and can have a devastating effect on the environment. To fight fires, it is necessary to understand how they start, and what sustains them.

Fire is the result of combustion, a rapid reaction between oxygen and fuel. During combustion, fuel and oxygen react to form carbon dioxide, water, and heat. Most fires in rural areas, called wildfires, are caused by people being careless with campfires or cigarettes. Arson and lightning are also common causes. Usually the fire starts in an area of dry grass, which will ignite at a temperature of 150–200°C. Burning grass can create enough heat to ignite bushes, and these, in turn, may be tall enough to carry the flames into trees. (Wood has a higher ignition temperature, around 260°C.) Environmental conditions, such as drought that has left vegetation dry, and strong winds, can cause a small fire to spread. Wind also carries fire forward into new areas. Burning twigs and branches that become detached from trees can be blown into new areas of vegetation.

Dousing
Planes or helicopters are used to drop water or a fire-retardant slurry on a large fire. The slurry contains ammonium sulfate, $(NH_4)_2SO_4$, which helps smother the fire.

Firefighter
Firefighters wear protective clothing, helmets, and goggles. This firefighter also carries a shovel for digging trenches to stop a fire spreading.

210 *Chapter 7*

Facts and Figures

Smothering a Fire Various reactions can take place in a fire depending on the type of fuel used. Pure carbon burns according to the following reaction.

$$C + O_2 \longrightarrow CO_2$$

Methane burns according to the following reaction.

$$CH_4 + 2O_2 \longrightarrow 2H_2O + CO_2$$

Draw students to the conclusion that reactions that involve burning have oxygen gas as a reactant. Ask them to speculate as to why covering a small burning object with a blanket can help put out the flames. Explain that smothering the flaming object with the blanket reduces the amount of oxygen available for the reactions.

Backburning
One way to stop a big fire is to start a smaller fire. This technique, called backburning, burns off vegetation between the fireline and the main fire. When the two fires meet, the blaze stops spreading because the land on either side has already been burned.

Boundary of Hanford site

Extent of fire

Smoke plume

Wildfire in Washington State
This satellite picture shows a forest fire that raged for two months in 2000 at the Department of Energy's site at Hanford. The fire was started by a vehicle fire and reached more than 500 square kilometers.

Firebreaks
In parts of the world where wildfires are common, strips of land are cleared of combustible vegetation to create firebreaks. Firefighters also dig firebreaks during fires to prevent fires from spreading.

Going Further

- Write a paragraph explaining how dousing, backburning, and firebreaks affect the chemical reactions involved in wildfires.

- Take a Discovery Channel Video Field Trip by watching "Taming the Flames."

DISCOVERY CHANNEL SCHOOL
Video Field Trip

Going Further

Dousing a wildfire with water deprives the combustion reaction of both oxygen and heat. (Although combustion is an exothermic reaction, heat is still required in order for the reacting particles to collide with enough energy to react, as seen in Figure 18A on p. 208.) Dousing with a chemical gel deprives the fire of oxygen. Both backburning and firebreaks keep wildfires from spreading by depriving the reaction of fuel such as wood and other vegetation.
Verbal

Use Community Resources

Have the class visit a fire station to learn more about fire prevention. Ask a firefighter to talk about the types of methods and chemicals used to prevent and extinguish fires.
Interpersonal

 Video Field Trip

Taming the Flames

After students have viewed the Video Field Trip, ask them the following questions: **Describe how a fire burns, in terms of energy and chemical bonds.** *(The energy from the heat of the flames causes bonds in the fuel and oxygen to break and new bonds to form with the oxygen, releasing more energy to heat the reactants and keep the reaction going.)* **A fire requires heat, fuel, and oxygen to sustain it. List two things a firefighter can do to** remove one of these three ingredients of a fire. **Explain your answer.** *(Student answers may include firefighters can drop chemical gel on a fire to deprive it of oxygen, they can pour water on a fire to cool it and deprive it of oxygen, or they can dig trenches around the burning areas to deny the fire access to new fuel.)* **How do forest managers prevent large, uncontrollable forest fires by intentionally starting small, controlled fires?** *(Material such as leaves and needles, which could help produce large, uncontrollable fires, is cleared away by small, controlled fires. The flammable material that accumulates is called "duff.")*

1 FOCUS

Objectives

7.4.1 **Explain** what a reaction rate is.
7.4.2 **Describe** the factors affecting chemical reaction rates.

Reading Focus

Build Vocabulary L2

LINCS Have students use the LINCS strategy to learn and review the terms *reaction rate, surface area, concentration,* and *catalyst*. In LINCS exercises, students **L**ist what they know about each term, **I**magine a picture that describes the word, **N**ote a "sound-alike" word, **C**onnect the terms to the sound-alike word by making up a short story, and then perform a brief **S**elf-test.

Reading Strategy L2

a. Temperature b. Surface area
c. Stirring d. Concentration
e. Catalysts

2 INSTRUCT

Reactions Over Time
Build Math Skills L1

Ratios and Proportions
To help students understand reaction rate, review other rates that they might be familiar with. As an example of a rate, discuss speed as the ratio of distance traveled over time. In your discussion, be sure that students pay particular attention to the units (miles/hour, etc.). **Logical**

Direct students to the **Math Skills** in the **Skills and Reference Handbook** at the end of the student text for additional help.

Build Reading Literacy L1

Outline Refer to page 156D in **Chapter 6**, which provides the guidelines for outlining.

Have students read the section. Then, have students use the headings as major divisions in an outline. Allow students to refer to their outlines when answering the questions in the Section 7.4 Assessment. **Visual**

7.4 Reaction Rates

Standard: ICP.5.6

Reading Focus

Key Concept
- What does a reaction rate tell you?
- What factors cause reaction rates to change?

Vocabulary
- reaction rate
- catalyst

Reading Strategy
Building Vocabulary
Copy the partially completed web diagram at the right. Then, as you read, complete it with key terms from this section.

You may have heard of athletes "burning Calories" when they exercise. A Calorie is a unit of energy used in the field of nutrition. The average banana, for instance, contains about 100 Calories. The cyclist in Figure 20 can use up, or burn, as many as 10,000 Calories during the course of a race. That adds up to a lot of bananas!

If you eat a banana, you provide your body with about 100 Calories to burn. This energy is released in a series of reactions that take place inside your body. A much faster way of releasing the energy contained in a banana is to burn it—outside the body—in a combustion reaction. In both cases, the total amount of energy released is the same. However, the time it takes for the energy to be released is different in each case.

Figure 20 A cyclist burns the Calories in a banana faster than a person walking would. But burning the banana outside the body would release the energy of the banana even faster.

Reactions Over Time

The progress of any chemical reaction can be measured over time. Different reactions have different durations. Some reactions, such as the explosion of TNT, happen almost instantaneously. Other reactions, such as tree leaves changing color during autumn, happen gradually.

Any change that happens over a period of time can be expressed as a rate. For example, speed is the rate that distance changes over time. A **reaction rate** is the rate at which reactants change into products over time. **Reaction rates tell you how fast a reaction is going.** That is, how fast the reactants are being consumed, how fast the products are being formed, or how fast energy is being absorbed or released.

Section Resources

Print
- **Reading and Study Workbook With Math Support,** Section 7.4
- **Transparencies,** Section 7.4

Technology
- **Interactive Textbook,** Section 7.4
- **Presentation Pro CD-ROM,** Section 7.4
- **Go Online,** NSTA SciLinks, Factors affecting reaction rate

Factors Affecting Reaction Rates

Recall that chemical reactions involve collisions between particles of reactants. The reaction rate depends on how often these particles collide. If the collisions occur more frequently, then the reaction rate increases. If the collisions occur less frequently, then the reaction rate decreases. Almost any reaction rate can be changed by varying the conditions under which the reaction takes place. ⬤ **Factors that affect reaction rates include temperature, surface area, concentration, stirring, and catalysts.**

Temperature Suppose you are frying an egg in a frying pan. What happens if you increase the heat under the pan? The hotter the pan, the faster the egg will cook. Generally, an increase in temperature will increase the reaction rate, while a decrease in temperature will decrease the reaction rate. For instance, you store milk in a refrigerator to slow down the reactions that cause the milk to spoil. These reactions don't stop completely. Even milk stored in a refrigerator will eventually spoil. But the rate of spoiling decreases if the milk is kept cold.

Increasing the temperature of a substance causes its particles to move faster, on average. Particles that move faster are both more likely to collide and more likely to react. If the number of collisions that produce reactions increases, then the reaction rate increases.

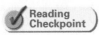 *How does temperature affect reaction rates?*

Surface Area Grain may not strike you as a dangerous material, but it can be explosive under the right conditions. The cause of the fire in Figure 21 was a combustion reaction between grain dust (suspended in the air) and oxygen. The rate of combustion was very rapid due to the small particle size of the grain dust.

The smaller the particle size of a given mass, the larger is its surface area. Imagine using a newspaper to cover the floor of a room. If you keep all the sections folded together, you can only cover a small area. However, if you separate the newspaper into pages and lay them out like tiles, you can cover a much larger area with the same mass of paper.

An increase in surface area increases the exposure of reactants to one another. The greater this exposure, the more collisions there are that involve reacting particles. With more collisions, more particles will react. This is why increasing the surface area of a reactant tends to increase the reaction rate.

For: Links on factors affecting reaction rate
Visit: www.SciLinks.org
Web Code: ccn-1074

Figure 21 This grain elevator in Potlatch, Idaho, exploded when grain dust reacted with oxygen in the air. *Applying Concepts How does surface area affect reaction rates?*

Factors Affecting Reaction Rates
Build Science Skills

 L2

Calculating

Purpose Students learn how to increase surface area.

Materials clay, rulers, plastic knives

Class Time 10 minutes

Procedure Have students make a clay cube, measure its dimensions, and calculate its surface area. Then, have students cut the clay cube in half and calculate the total surface area of the two pieces. Ask, **How does cutting the clay cube in half affect its surface area?** *(Surface area increases.)*

Expected Outcome The more pieces the clay cube is cut into, the greater the surface area becomes. **Logical, Visual**

Temperature and Rate

 L2

Purpose Students observe the effect of temperature on reaction rate.

Materials 2 chemical light sticks, 2 large beakers, hot water, ice water

Procedure Students will observe the same reaction taking place at two different temperatures. Fill one beaker with hot water and the other with ice water. Turn off the room lights. Place an activated light stick in each beaker. Explain that the light sticks glow due to a chemical reaction that gives off light.

Expected Outcome The light stick in hot water will glow more than the one in cold water. **Visual**

Download a worksheet on factors affecting reaction rate for students to complete, and find additional teacher support from NSTA SciLinks.

Answer to . . .

Figure 21 *A surface area increase generally increases the reaction rate.*

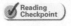 *Increasing the temperature generally increases the reaction rate.*

Customize for Inclusion Students

Visually Impaired
For visually impaired students, consider performing the above demonstration using a reaction that can be observed audibly. For example, place one effervescent tablet in a beaker of cold water and a second effervescent tablet in a beaker of hot water. Have students gather closely around the reaction, or find a way to amplify the reaction sounds. Students should be able to hear a difference in the rates of gas evolution.

Chemical Reactions **213**

Observing the Action of Catalysts [L2]

Objective
After completing this activity, students will be able to
- describe how a catalyst is able to promote a chemical reaction.

Address Misconceptions

Many students see the formation of a new substance with new properties as simply happening, rather than as a result of atoms rearranging. Catalysts can further confuse the issue because they aid the progress of a reaction without being changed by the reaction. Explain that in this Quick Lab, the same reaction takes place in all four test tubes. Use molecular models of hydrogen peroxide to show how the atoms in two H_2O_2 molecules are rearranged to form two water molecules, H_2O, and one molecule of oxygen, O_2.

Skills Focus Observing, Formulating Hypotheses

 Prep Time 15 minutes

Advance Prep Provide a 3% solution of hydrogen peroxide (typical strength sold in stores) solution and 0.1 M $CuCl_2$ (clearly labeled). To make a 0.1 M solution of $CuCl_2$, dissolve 13.5 g $CuCl_2$ in enough water to make 1 L of solution.

Class Time 20 minutes

Safety Review the information in the MSDS for each compound with students before performing the lab. Make sure that students wear safety goggles, lab aprons, and plastic disposable gloves. Avoid skin contact with the compounds, as some are irritants. Students should wash their hands with soap or detergent before leaving the laboratory.

Expected Outcome The platinum wire, manganese dioxide, and raw potato catalyze the release of oxygen bubbles. Copper chloride does not.

Analyze and Conclude
1. The platinum wire produced moderate bubbling, MnO_2 produced vigorous bubbling, $CuCl_2$ produced no reaction, and potato produced foam.
2. MnO_2; potato
3. This test tube served as the control.
Visual, Group

≡Quick Lab

Observing the Action of Catalysts

Materials

5 test tubes, test-tube rack, marking pencil, dropper pipet, wood splint, platinum wire, 0.1 g manganese dioxide (MnO_2), 5 drops of copper(II) chloride ($CuCl_2$) solution, 0.1 g raw potato, graduated cylinder, 25 mL hydrogen peroxide (H_2O_2)

Procedure

1. Label the 5 test tubes from A to E with the marking pencil.
2. Put a small piece of platinum wire in test tube A. Add a tiny amount (about the tip of the wood splint) of MnO_2 to test tube B. Use the dropper pipet to put 5 drops of $CuCl_2$ in test tube C. Put a piece of potato in test tube D. Test tube E should remain empty for now. **CAUTION** MnO_2 and $CuCl_2$ are toxic.
3. Carefully add 5 mL of hydrogen peroxide to test tube A. **CAUTION** Be careful when using chemicals. Observe how fast the bubbles are produced.
4. Repeat Step 3 with test tubes B through E.

Analyze and Conclude

1. **Observing** What effect did the platinum wire, MnO_2, $CuCl_2$, and the potato have on the rate at which the bubbles were produced in the hydrogen peroxide?
2. **Comparing and Contrasting** Which catalyst(s) caused the reaction to go the fastest? The slowest?
3. **Inferring** Why did you put only hydrogen peroxide in test tube E?

Figure 22 The dye solution in the left beaker is more concentrated than the solution in the right. Increasing the concentration of the dye increases the rate of color change in the material.

Stirring You can also increase the exposure of reactants to each other by stirring them. For example, when you wash your clothes in a washing machine, particles of detergent react with particles of the stains on your clothes. This reaction would go slowly if you just left your clothes soaking in a tub of water and detergent. A washing machine speeds up the reaction by stirring the contents back and forth. Collisions between the particles of the reactants are more likely to happen. Stirring the reactants will generally increase the reaction rate.

Concentration Another way you can change the reaction rate is to change the concentration of the reactants. Concentration refers to the number of particles in a given volume. The more reacting particles that are present in a given volume, the more opportunities there are for collisions involving those particles. The reaction rate is faster.

Both of the beakers in Figure 22 contain a piece of material dipped in dye solution. Dyeing is a chemical reaction in which dye particles react with the particles of the material being dyed. The material dipped in the more concentrated dye becomes colored more quickly.

For gases, concentration changes with pressure. The greater the pressure of a gaseous reactant, the greater is its concentration, and the faster is the reaction rate.

⌐ Facts and Figures

Biological Catalysts
Catalysts that speed up reactions in biological systems are called enzymes. See Section 9.4 for a definition of *enzyme*. Enzymes help carry out many of the reactions that take place in the human body. For example, the enzyme lactase helps your body break down lactose, a carbohydrate found in milk. People with lactose intolerance do not produce enough lactase to properly digest milk products.

Catalysts Sometimes you can change a reaction rate by using catalysts. A **catalyst** is a substance that affects the reaction rate without being used up in the reaction. Chemists often use catalysts to speed up a reaction or enable a reaction to occur at a lower temperature. In the making of sulfuric acid, one of the steps involved is the reaction of sulfur dioxide with oxygen to form sulfur trioxide. This reaction happens very slowly without a catalyst such as vanadium(V) oxide.

$$2SO_2 + O_2 \xrightarrow{V_2O_5} 2SO_3$$

Since the catalyst is neither a reactant nor a product, it is written over the arrow. Because the catalyst is not consumed, it can be used to speed up the same reaction over and over again.

Recall that in order for a reaction to take place, the reacting particles must collide with enough energy to break the chemical bonds of those particles. As shown in Figure 23, a catalyst lowers this energy barrier. One way that a catalyst can do this is by providing a surface on which the reacting particles can come together. Imagine that you go to a party and make several new friends. By bringing people together, the party has made it easier for you to form those friendships. Similarly, a catalyst can "invite" reacting particles together so that they are more likely to react.

Reaction Energy—Catalyzed and Uncatalyzed

- Reaction without catalyst
- Reaction with catalyst

Figure 23 The graph above shows how a catalyst lowers the amount of energy required for effective collisions between reacting particles.
Using Graphs *In an exothermic reaction, how does a catalyst affect the amount of energy released?*

Section 7.4 Assessment

Reviewing Concepts
1. ⬤ What does a reaction rate tell you?
2. ⬤ What five factors affect reaction rates?
3. Explain why reactions take place faster at higher temperatures.
4. When you add baking soda to vinegar, the mixture fizzes as carbon dioxide gas is produced. Suppose you added water to the vinegar before you mixed it with the baking soda. What do you think would happen to the rate of carbon dioxide production?
5. How does a catalyst make a reaction go faster?
6. Platinum is a catalyst for the decomposition of hydrogen peroxide into water and oxygen.

$$2H_2O_2 \xrightarrow{Pt} 2H_2O + O_2$$

What would you expect to see if platinum were added to hydrogen peroxide solution?

Critical Thinking
7. **Applying Concepts** Explain why, if you want to store uncooked hamburger meat for a month, you put it in a freezer rather than a refrigerator.
8. **Evaluating** The reaction between magnesium and hydrochloric acid produces hydrogen. If you increase the concentration of HCl, the reaction takes place faster. Could HCl be considered a catalyst for this reaction? Explain your answer.

Writing in Science

Compare and Contrast Paragraph Write a paragraph explaining how temperature, concentration, surface area, and catalysts affect reaction rates.

Chemical Reactions **215**

1 FOCUS

Objectives

7.5.1 Identify and describe physical and chemical equilibria.

7.5.2 Describe the factors affecting chemical equilibrium.

Reading Focus

Build Vocabulary `L2`

Paraphrase To help students understand the vocabulary terms, paraphrase their definitions using words and phrases students are more familiar with. For example, explain that a system is in *equilibrium* when there is no overall change in amounts even though there is a great deal of movement back and forth. A *reversible reaction* is a chemical reaction that can go forward and backward at the same time.

Reading Strategy `L2`

1. Physical equilibrium 2. Chemical equilibrium **B.** Factors affecting chemical equilibrium 3. Concentration

2 INSTRUCT

Types of Equilibria
Build Science Skills `L2`

Using Models

Purpose Students model dynamic equilibrium using playing cards.

Materials playing cards, watch

Class Time 10 minutes

Procedure Have one student use a watch to count seconds out loud one through six every six seconds. Have a second student pull cards from a deck and place them down in rows of six, one card down each second. After three rows of cards have been placed, have a third student begin to remove pairs of cards and place them on the deck every two seconds. Students will observe that the number of rows of cards does not change, because the cards are added and removed at the same rate.

Kinesthetic, Group

7.5 Equilibrium

Standards: ICP.3.1, ICP.5.6

Reading Focus

Key Concepts
- Under what conditions do physical and chemical equilibria occur?
- How do equilibrium systems respond to change?

Vocabulary
- equilibrium
- reversible reaction

Reading Strategy

Outlining As you read, make an outline of the most important ideas in this section.

```
I. Equilibrium
   A. Types of Equilibria
      1. _____
      2. _____
   B. _____
      1. Temperature
      2. Pressure
      3. _____
```

Suppose you're waiting in line for a toll booth at a bridge, like some of the cars shown in Figure 24. You notice that every time a car passes by a toll booth in the direction you are traveling, another car passes through the toll plaza in the opposite direction. The rate of cars entering equals the rate of cars exiting. As a result, the number of cars on either side of the toll plaza remains constant, although cars are continually entering and exiting the bridge.

Types of Equilibria

The traffic at a toll bridge is similar to a system in equilibrium. **Equilibrium** (plural *equilibria*) is a state in which the forward and reverse paths of a change take place at the same rate.

Recall that changes to matter are either physical or chemical. When opposing physical changes take place at the same rate, a physical equilibrium is reached. When opposing chemical changes take place at the same rate, a chemical equilibrium is reached.

Figure 24 About 190,000 vehicles pass through the toll plaza of New York City's Verrazano-Narrows Bridge every day.

216 *Chapter 7*

 Section Resources

Print
- *Reading and Study Workbook With Math Support*, Section 7.5
- *Transparencies*, Section 7.5

Technology
- *Interactive Textbook*, Section 7.5
- *Presentation Pro CD-ROM*, Section 7.5
- *Go Online*, NSTA SciLinks, Factors affecting equilibrium

Physical Equilibrium What happens when you pour some water into a jar and then close the lid? You might think that nothing happens at all. But in fact, some of the water undergoes a physical change by evaporating. As more water evaporates, some of the water vapor condenses. Eventually, the rate of evaporation equals the rate of condensation, and the system reaches equilibrium as shown in Figure 25.

When liquid water is in equilibrium with water vapor, you can describe the system by writing this equation.

$$H_2O(l) \rightleftharpoons H_2O(g)$$

Here, l stands for liquid and g stands for gas. The pair of arrows in this equation indicates that the forward change (evaporation) and the reverse change (condensation) are happening simultaneously and at the same rate. Both the forward and reverse changes are physical changes, so this equation represents a physical equilibrium. **When a physical change does not go to completion, a physical equilibrium is established between the forward and reverse changes.**

Chemical Equilibrium All the chemical equations you have seen so far have been written with single arrows, which suggest that all reactions go to completion in one direction. In reality, however, most reactions are reversible to some extent. A **reversible reaction** is a reaction in which the conversion of reactants into products and the conversion of products into reactants can happen simultaneously.

In the previous section, you read about the synthesis of sulfur trioxide from sulfur dioxide and oxygen. This is actually a reversible reaction that can be expressed as

$$2SO_2(g) + O_2(g) \rightleftharpoons 2SO_3(g)$$

If sulfur dioxide and oxygen are mixed in a closed container, the forward reaction will start to produce sulfur trioxide. However, once molecules of sulfur trioxide form, some of them will change back into the reactants by the reverse reaction. Eventually, the rate of the forward reaction (synthesis) will equal the rate of the reverse reaction (decomposition), and the system will reach equilibrium. **When a chemical reaction does not go to completion, a chemical equilibrium is established between the forward and reverse reactions.** During chemical equilibrium, the reactants change into products just as fast as the products change back into reactants.

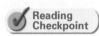 **What happens during chemical equilibrium?**

Figure 25 Liquid water left in a closed container eventually reaches equilibrium with its vapor. *Interpreting Diagrams What do the arrows represent in the diagram above?*

H₂O molecules

For: Links on factors affecting equilibrium
Visit: www.SciLinks.org
Web Code: ccn-1075

Chemical Reactions **217**

Customize for English Language Learners

Think-Pair-Share
Have students work in pairs to think of situations in which there is dynamic equilibrium. Examples include a doorman controlling the number of people who go in and out of an event, a clerk restocking the shelves at a grocery store, and a fountain consisting of a stream of water that pours into an overflowing vessel. Strengthen discussion skills by having students share their examples with the class. Encourage students to examine Figure 24 for an example of equilibrium in a real-world setting. Be sure that students understand that these examples are "open" systems, while dynamic equilibrium is a "closed" system.

Use Visuals **L1**

Figure 25 Have students examine the molecular models of water in the bottle of spring water. Ask, **In which states does water exist inside the bottle?** *(Liquid and vapor)* **Are the molecules of water in the liquid state chemically different than the molecules of water in the vapor state?** *(No, both states of water have the same chemical properties.)* Tell the students that the two states of water are at equilibrium. Ask, **What do you know about the rates of the forward and reverse processes?** *(At equilibrium, the forward and reverse processes occur at the same rate.)* **How is this modeled in Figure 25?** *(The arrows show the same number of molecules leaving the liquid as there are molecules entering the liquid.)* **Visual**

Address Misconceptions **L2**

Many students incorrectly associate equilibrium only with having equal amounts of reactants and products. Challenge this misconception by discussing the following example. A beaker at 0°C contains 2 g of ice and 8 g of water. The rate of melting equals the rate of freezing. Is the system at equilibrium? *(Yes)*
Verbal, Logical

Download a worksheet on factors affecting equilibrium for students to complete, and find additional teacher support from NSTA SciLinks.

Answer to . . .

Figure 25 *The arrows in the diagram shown represent opposing physical changes. The arrows pointing up represent evaporation, as liquid water changes into vapor. The arrows pointing down represent condensation, as the vapor changes into water.*

Reading Checkpoint *During chemical equilibrium, the reactants change into products at the same rate as the products change into reactants.*

Recreating High Altitudes **L2**

Defining the Problem The problem is how to design a training facility that can recreate a high-altitude environment. The design will depend on what property of the air you wish to manipulate.

Organizing Information The equation Hb + O_2 ⇌ HbO_2 describes the hemoglobin-oxygen-oxyhemoglobin system. At high altitudes, the concentration of oxygen decreases, which shifts the equilibrium to the left. In response to the reduced oxyhemoglobin levels, the body produces more hemoglobin.

Creating a Solution The desired shift in the equilibrium happens when you lower the concentration of oxygen. One way you can do this is by reducing the pressure of the air inside the training facility. Another way to lower oxygen concentration is to change the composition of the air within the facility. This can be done by piping in air with a reduced fraction of oxygen. In the second solution, the facility can be operated at normal air pressure.

Presenting Your Plan Students might point out certain structural characteristics of their designs in their proposals. For example, a normal-pressure/low-oxygen facility would require a customized ventilation system that pipes in air with reduced oxygen levels. **Logical**

For Extra Help **L1**

Before they start, make sure students understand what the physical properties of air at a high altitude are. **Logical**

Factors Affecting Chemical Equilibrium
Build Reading Literacy **L1**

Reciprocal Teaching Refer to page **628D** in **Chapter 21**, which provides the guidelines for reciprocal teaching.

Have students read the section with a partner. One partner reads a paragraph out loud. Then, the other partner summarizes the paragraph's contents and explains the main concepts. The partners continue to switch roles with each new paragraph until they have finished the section. **Intrapersonal**

Recreating High Altitudes

An important chemical equilibrium in your blood involves the reaction of hemoglobin (Hb) with oxygen (O_2) to form oxyhemoglobin (HbO_2).

$$Hb + O_2 \rightleftharpoons HbO_2$$

This equilibrium changes with altitude. As you move from lower to higher elevations, the concentration of oxygen in the air decreases, and the equilibrium shifts in the direction that produces less oxyhemoglobin. Your body responds to the shift by producing more hemoglobin. Studies have shown that athletes can improve their performance at sea level by living or training at high altitudes. Some training facilities are designed to recreate high altitudes. Imagine that you are asked to build such a facility.

Defining the Problem In your own words, state the problem you face.

Organizing Information Use Le Châtelier's principle to determine how high altitudes affect this equilibrium system.

Creating a Solution The physical properties of the air inside the training facility include temperature, pressure, and composition. Figure out how to shift the equilibrium in the direction you want by changing one of these properties.

Presenting Your Plan Write a proposal to an athletic team that could benefit from using your training facility. Explain how your facility recreates a high-altitude environment.

Figure 26 French Chemist Henri-Louis Le Châtelier (1850–1936) published the first version of his principle of chemical equilibrium in 1884.

Factors Affecting Chemical Equilibrium

Like reaction rates, chemical equilibria can change depending on the conditions of the reaction. While a reaction rate either increases or decreases in response to a change, an equilibrium shifts. That is, the equilibrium favors either the forward or the reverse reaction. **When a change is introduced to a system in equilibrium, the equilibrium shifts in the direction that relieves the change.** This rule was first observed by Henri Le Châtelier, shown in Figure 26. Today, the rule is known as Le Châtelier's principle.

The making of ammonia is an example of a process in which chemists apply Le Châtelier's principle. Ammonia is an important industrial chemical used to make fertilizers, cleaning agents, dyes, and plastics. The following equation describes the synthesis of ammonia.

$$N_2(g) + 3H_2(g) \rightleftharpoons 2NH_3(g) + Heat$$

Suppose you have a system that contains nitrogen, hydrogen, and ammonia in equilibrium. By applying Le Châtelier's principle, you can predict how this system will be affected by changes in temperature, pressure, and concentration. In the ammonia plant shown in Figure 27, chemists must consider these same factors.

Temperature In the equation for the synthesis of ammonia, heat is written as a product. This tells you that the forward reaction is exothermic. In the reverse reaction, heat is a reactant. So the decomposition of ammonia is endothermic.

What would happen if you increased the temperature of a system that contained nitrogen, hydrogen, and ammonia? According to Le Châtelier's principle, if you added heat to the system, the equilibrium would shift in the direction that removes heat from the system. The system would favor the reverse reaction, which is endothermic. So by increasing the temperature, you would decrease the amount of ammonia.

Pressure Suppose you increased the pressure of the system. According to Le Châtelier's principle, if you increased the pressure, the equilibrium would shift in the direction that decreases the pressure of the system. In order to decrease pressure, the system would favor the reaction that produces fewer gas molecules. You can see that the left side of the equation has four gas molecules, while the right side has two. So by increasing the pressure, you would shift the equilibrium to the right, producing more ammonia.

Concentration A change in concentration of the reactants or products can also affect equilibrium. Suppose you removed ammonia from the nitrogen-hydrogen-ammonia system. Le Châtelier's principle tells you that the equilibrium would shift in the direction that produces ammonia. In order to produce ammonia, the system would favor the forward reaction.

Figure 27 Operating an ammonia plant at relatively low temperature, high pressure, and low ammonia concentration maximizes the amount of ammonia produced.

Section 7.5 Assessment

Reviewing Concepts

1. 💿 What happens when a physical change does not go to completion? What happens when a reaction does not go to completion?

2. 💿 Once a chemical reaction has reached equilibrium, how does the system respond to change?

3. What does the double-ended arrow indicate in the following chemical equation?

$$CaCO_3 \rightleftharpoons Ca^{2+} + CO_3^{2-}$$

4. For which of the following reactions are both reactants and products likely to be found when the reaction appears to be complete? Explain.

$$Mg + O_2 \longrightarrow 2MgO$$

$$HF + H_2O \rightleftharpoons H_3O^+ + F^-$$

Critical Thinking

5. **Inferring** Suppose the following reaction is allowed to come to equilibrium.

$$2NO_2(g) \rightleftharpoons N_2O_4(g)$$

How will increasing the pressure on this system affect the amount of N_2O_4 formed?

6. **Using Models** At 0°C, liquid water is in equilibrium with ice. Make a drawing of water molecules at this temperature, and describe what is happening.

Connecting C Concepts

Phase Changes Write an equation for a system in which the sublimation and deposition of water have reached equilibrium. Use what you studied in Section 3.3 to explain what changes are happening.

Manipulating Chemical Equilibrium **L2**

Objective

After completing this activity, students will be able to

- correctly predict the effect of changes in the concentrations of reactants or products on chemical equilibrium.

Skills Focus Formulating Hypotheses, Designing Experiments, Observing

Prep Time 30 minutes

Advance Prep To prepare 1 L of iodine-starch solution, combine 100 mL of commercial tincture of iodine (2% USP; do not use products labeled decolorized iodine, tincture of iodides, or 7% iodine solution) with 900 mL white vinegar or 1 M acetic acid and 2.5 mL of liquid laundry starch. Do not use spray starch or products labeled concentrated starch. If liquid starch is not available, prepare a stock starch solution by stirring 5 g of cornstarch into 30 mL of cold water to form a smooth suspension. Slowly pour this suspension into 500 mL of boiling water while stirring. Allow the starch solution to cool.

To prepare the ascorbic acid solution, dissolve 7.5 g of ascorbic acid in 1 L of water. To prepare 1 L of bleach solution, combine 250 mL of household chlorine bleach with 750 mL of water.

Class Time 45 minutes

Safety Before performing the lab, review with students the information in the MSDS for each chemical used. Make sure that students wear safety goggles, plastic gloves, and lab aprons.

Expected Outcome Addition of bleach or ascorbic acid shifts the position of equilibrium.

Manipulating Chemical Equilibrium

Chemical reactions tend to go to equilibrium. It is possible to shift the equilibrium by changing the conditions under which the reaction occurs. Factors that can affect chemical equilibrium include the concentration of reactants and products, temperature, and pressure. In this lab, you will observe a chemical reaction and use your observations to predict how one factor will shift the equilibrium of the reaction. Then, you will perform an experiment to test your prediction.

Problem How can you change the equilibrium of a chemical reaction?

Materials

- iodine-starch solution
- 150-mL beaker
- 4 dropper pipets
- spot plate
- ascorbic acid (vitamin C) solution
- chlorine bleach (sodium hypochlorite, NaOCl) solution

Skills Formulating Hypotheses, Designing Experiments, Observing

Procedure

Part A: Observing a Reversible Reaction

1. Pour 50 mL of iodine-starch solution into the 150-mL beaker. The dark color of this solution is due to the presence of iodine molecules (I_2) within the grains of starch. **CAUTION** *Handle iodine solutions with care. Iodine is toxic.*

2. Use a dropper pipet to transfer 3 drops of iodine-starch solution from the beaker to one well on the spot plate.

3. Use another clean dropper pipet to add one drop of ascorbic acid solution to the iodine-starch solution on the spot plate. Continue to add ascorbic acid solution to the mixture on the spot plate, one drop at a time, until the mixture becomes clear. When an iodine molecule reacts with ascorbic acid, the iodine molecule is reduced and breaks down into two colorless iodide ions ($2I^-$).

Sample Data Table

Initial Solution	Solution Added	Quantity Added (mL)	Color of Resulting Mixture

4. Use the third clean dropper pipet to transfer one drop of colorless iodide solution to a second well on the spot plate.

5. Use the last clean dropper pipet to add bleach solution to the drop of colorless iodide solution, one drop at a time. Continue until the dark color of the iodine-starch solution reappears. **CAUTION** *Bleach can damage skin and clothing.* The chlorine bleach (NaOCl) oxidizes iodide ions (I^-), converting them to iodine molecules (I_2).

6. Write a chemical equation showing the equilibrium between iodine molecules and iodide ions. This equation does not need to be balanced. Label the two sides of your equation to indicate which substance appears dark and which appears colorless.

Part B: Design Your Experiment

7. **Predicting** Select one of the solutions used earlier that affects the equilibrium between iodine molecules and iodide ions. Record your prediction of the change you will observe in an iodine-starch solution as you add the solution that you selected.

8. **Designing Experiments** Design an experiment to test your prediction. Your experimental plan should describe in detail how you will perform your experiment.

9. Construct a data table like the sample data table shown, in which to record your observations. (*Note:* Your data table may not be exactly like the sample data table.)

10. Perform your experiment only after your teacher has approved your plan. Record your observations in your data table.
CAUTION *Wash your hands with soap or detergent before leaving the laboratory.*

Analyze and Conclude

1. **Analyzing Data** What factor did you investigate? How did it affect the equilibrium between iodine molecules and iodide ions?

2. **Predicting** How would you expect the equilibrium to change if you added more iodide ions to the mixture? Explain your answer.

3. **Calculating** When chlorine bleach (sodium hypochlorite, NaOCl) oxidizes iodide ions to iodine molecules, sodium hypochlorite is reduced to sodium chloride (NaCl) and water (H_2O). Write a balanced chemical equation for this reaction, beginning with the reactants sodium hypochlorite, iodide ions, and hydrogen ions (H^+).

4. **Drawing Conclusions** How does the addition of more product affect the chemical equilibrium of a reaction?

Go Further Design an experiment to determine whether other substances that are easily oxidized or reduced, such as iron ions, can reduce iodine to iodide, or oxidize iodide to iodine. Then, with your teacher's approval and supervision, perform your experiment.

Procedure

6. $I_2 \rightleftharpoons 2I^-$. The I_2 should be labeled "dark," and the $2I^-$ should be labeled "colorless."

Analyze and Conclude

1. Students should observe that increasing the quantity of chlorine bleach shifts the equilibrium toward iodine molecules, and increasing the quantity of ascorbic acid shifts the equilibrium toward iodide ions.

2. Adding iodide ions would shift the equilibrium toward the formation of more iodine.

3. $NaOCl + 2I^- + 2H^+ \longrightarrow$
$$I_2 + NaCl + H_2O$$

4. Adding more product shifts the equilibrium toward the reactants in a reaction.
Logical, Kinesthetic

Go Further

Evaluate students' plans for clarity and safety before permitting students to proceed with their experiments. Results will depend on the substance chosen. The Fe^{3+} ion can oxidize iodine to iodide.
Logical, Kinesthetic

Study Guide

Study Tip

Make a List
Suggest that students write out a detailed list of everything they need to know for the test a day or two before they take the test. Creating the list is a thorough review in itself. Also, they can use the list to review for the test wherever they are—on their way to and from school, between classes, or during lunch—rather than having to carry around all of their notes and their textbooks.

Thinking Visually

a. Chemical equations
b. Released
c. Endothermic reactions

7.1 Describing Reactions

Key Concepts
- The law of conservation of mass states that mass is neither created nor destroyed.
- In order to show that mass is conserved during a reaction, a chemical equation must be balanced.
- Because chemical reactions often involve large numbers of small particles, chemists use a unit called the mole to measure amounts of a substance.
- In chemical reactions, the mass of a reactant or product can be calculated by using a balanced chemical equation and molar masses.

Vocabulary
reactants, *p. 192;* products, *p. 192;* chemical equation, *p. 193;* coefficients, *p. 194;* mole, *p. 195;* molar mass, *p. 196*

7.2 Types of Reactions

Key Concepts
- The general types of chemical reactions are synthesis reactions, decomposition reactions, single-replacement reactions, double-replacement reactions, and combustion reactions.
- Scientists classify certain chemical reactions as transfers of electrons between atoms.

Vocabulary
synthesis reaction, *p. 200;* decomposition reaction, *p. 200;* single-replacement reaction, *p. 202;* double-replacement reaction, *p. 203;* combustion reaction, *p. 204;* oxidation-reduction reaction, *p. 204*

7.3 Energy Changes in Reactions

Key Concepts
- Chemical reactions involve the breaking of chemical bonds in the reactants and the formation of chemical bonds in the products.
- During a chemical reaction, energy is either released or absorbed.

Vocabulary
chemical energy, *p. 206;* exothermic reaction, *p. 208;* endothermic reaction, *p. 209*

7.4 Reaction Rates

Key Concepts
- Reaction rates tell you how fast a reaction is going.
- Factors that affect reaction rates include temperature, surface area, concentration, stirring, and catalysts.

Vocabulary
reaction rate, *p. 212;* catalyst, *p. 215*

7.5 Equilibrium

Key Concepts
- When a physical change does not go to completion, a physical equilibrium is established between the forward and reverse changes. When a chemical reaction does not go to completion, a chemical equilibrium is established between the forward and reverse reactions.
- When a change is introduced to a system in equilibrium, the equilibrium shifts in the direction that relieves the change.

Vocabulary
equilibrium, *p. 216;* reversible reaction, *p. 217*

Thinking Visually

Concept Map Use information from the chapter to complete the concept map below.

 ## Chapter Resources

Print
- *Chapter and Unit Tests,* Chapter 7 Test A and Test B
- *Test Prep Resources,* Chapter 7

Technology
- *Computer Test Bank,* Chapter Test 7
- *Interactive Textbook,* Chapter 7
- *Go Online,* PHSchool.com, Chapter 7

Assessment

Interactive Textbook with
assessment at PHSchool.com

Reviewing Content

Choose the letter that best answers the question or completes the statement.

1. In the following equation, what are the reactants?
$$NaHCO_3 + HCl \longrightarrow NaCl + H_2O + CO_2$$
   a. $NaHCO_3$ and HCl   b. $NaHCO_3$ and NaCl
   c. HCl and NaCl   d. NaCl, H_2O, and CO_2

2. Which of the following is a statement of the law of conservation of mass?
   a. Mass is created but not destroyed.
   b. Mass is destroyed but not created.
   c. Mass is neither created nor destroyed.
   d. Mass is both created and destroyed, depending on the chemical reaction.

3. The mass of a hydrogen atom is 1.0 amu, and the mass of a carbon atom is 12.0 amu. What is the molar mass of methane, CH_4?
   a. 13.0 amu   b. 13.0 g
   c. 16.0 amu   d. 16.0 g

4. In what type of reaction does one reactant form two or more products?
   a. synthesis   b. decomposition
   c. single replacement   d. double replacement

5. What particle is transferred from one atom to another in a redox reaction?
   a. electron   b. neutron
   c. proton   d. nucleus

6. Which of the following is a single replacement?
   a. $KOH + HCl \longrightarrow KCl + H_2O$
   b. $2Na + 2H_2O \longrightarrow H_2 + 2NaOH$
   c. $2C_2H_6 + 7O_2 \longrightarrow 4CO_2 + 6H_2O$
   d. $H_2O + CO_2 \longrightarrow H_2CO_3$

7. How are reactions related to chemical bonds?
   a. Bonds in the reactants are broken, and bonds in the products are formed.
   b. Bonds in the products are broken, and bonds in the reactants are formed.
   c. Bonds in both the reactants and products are broken.
   d. Bonds are formed in both the reactants and the products.

8. What type of reaction always releases energy?
   a. endothemic   b. exothermic
   c. decomposition   d. oxidation-reduction

9. In general, an increase in temperature
   a. increases reaction rate.
   b. decreases reaction rate.
   c. does not affect reaction rate.
   d. acts as a catalyst.

10. What takes place at chemical equilibrium?
   a. Reactants form more quickly than products.
   b. Products form more quickly than reactants.
   c. Reactants and products stop forming.
   d. Reactants and products form at the same rate.

Understanding Concepts

11. Write the following chemical equation in words.
$$CaCO_3 + Heat \longrightarrow CaO + CO_2$$

12. Explain how a balanced chemical equation shows that mass is conserved.

13. Explain the following diagram in your own words.

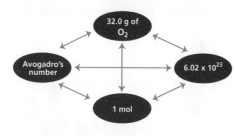

14. Compare oxidation and reduction.

15. Paper burns by combining with oxygen. Why doesn't paper burn every time it contacts oxygen?

16. Give an example of a chemical reaction that occurs slowly. Give another example of a chemical reaction that occurs quickly.

Answer Questions 17–18 based on the equation below.

$$C(s) + H_2O(g) + Heat \rightleftharpoons CO(g) + H_2(g)$$

17. How would you adjust the temperature to increase the amount of product?

18. Does the removal of hydrogen gas as it is produced shift the reaction to the left or the right?

Chemical Reactions **223**

Assessment

 If your class subscribes to the Interactive Textbook, your students can go online to access an interactive version of the Student Edition and a self-test.

Reviewing Content

1. a	2. c	3. d
4. b	5. a	6. b
7. a	8. b	9. a
10. d		

Understanding Concepts

11. Answers may vary. Sample answer: Calcium carbonate reacts under heat to produce calcium oxide and carbon dioxide.

12. A balanced chemical equation has the same number of atoms of each element on both sides, thus showing that mass is neither created nor destroyed.

13. Answers may vary. Sample answer: Avogadro's number equals 6.02×10^{23}, which is the number of particles contained in one mole, which is how many O_2 molecules are in 32.0 g of O_2. Any of the items in the concept web can be expressed in terms of one of the others.

14. In an oxidation reaction, an atom loses (or partially loses) electrons. In a reduction reaction, an atom gains (or partially gains) electrons.

15. In order for a reaction to occur, energy is required to break the chemical bonds of the reactants. At room temperature, there is not enough energy from the surroundings for paper to burst into flames, even though there is enough oxygen present in the air for it to react.

16. Answers will vary. Examples of slow reactions: formation of rust; tarnishing of silver; decomposition of wood or compost. Examples of fast reactions: burning of gasoline; browning of a cut apple; bleaching of clothing.

17. Increasing the temperature would shift the equilibrium to the right and increase the amount of product.

18. Removal of hydrogen would shift the equilibrium to the right.

Homework Guide

Section	Questions
7.1	1–3, 11–13, 19–20, 28–30
7.2	4–6, 14–16, 21–22
7.3	7–8, 23–24, 32
7.4	9, 17, 25–26, 31
7.5	10, 18, 27, 33

Critical Thinking

19. When iron rusts, a color change is one indication that a chemical reaction has taken place. The product that forms (rust) has different properties than the reactants (iron, water, and oxygen).

20. The substances in the candle combine with oxygen to form gaseous products. The total mass of the reactants equals the total mass of the products.

21. A reaction that has two reactants and two products could be a single-replacement reaction, a double-replacement reaction, or a combustion reaction.

22. The burning of magnesium in oxygen could be classified as combustion, synthesis, or oxidation-reduction.

23. In order for chemical bonds to break, energy must be absorbed, so the process is endothermic.

24. In an endothermic reaction, the chemical energy of the reactants plus energy absorbed from the surroundings is converted into the chemical energy of the products. The total energy before and after the reaction is the same.

25. The surface area of B is greater than the surface area of A.

26. An increase in a reactant's surface area increases its exposure to other reactants. If A and B represent the same volume of a reactant, then the reacting particles in B have more opportunities for collisions that may result in reactions. The more collisions between reactants, the faster the reaction rate will be.

27. Both stirring and increasing reactant concentration increase the reaction rate. If you stopped stirring, it would slow down the reaction rate. Because two factors oppose each other (increasing concentration of a reactant and decreasing the stirring of reactants), the overall effect would depend on which factor produced a greater change in the reaction rate.

Math Skills

28. a. $2KI \longrightarrow 2K + I_2$
b. $2Na + 2H_2O \longrightarrow H_2 + 2NaOH$
c. $CH_4 + 2O_2 \longrightarrow CO_2 + 2H_2O$
29. 298 g
30. 0.459 mol

Critical Thinking

19. Observing Explain how you know that a chemical reaction takes place when iron rusts.

20. Inferring As a candle burns, its mass decreases. However, mass is conserved in this reaction. Explain this observation.

21. Making Generalizations In a certain chemical reaction, two reactants undergo change to form two products. Why can't you determine what type of reaction occurred from this information?

22. Applying Concepts Use the reaction that occurs when magnesium burns in oxygen to show how a reaction might be included in more than one category of reaction.

23. Classifying Is breaking bonds an endothermic process or an exothermic process? Explain.

24. Inferring Explain how energy is conserved in an endothermic reaction.

Use the diagram below to answer Questions 25–26.

25. Comparing and Contrasting The volume of the cube in A equals the total volume of the cubes in B. Compare the surface areas of the cubes in A and B.

26. Using Models Use the diagram to explain how surface area affects reaction rates.

27. Predicting You are performing an experiment and want to increase the rate of reaction. You stop stirring the reactants and, instead, increase the concentration of one reactant. Can you expect the reaction to proceed at a faster rate? Explain.

Math Skills

28. Applying Concepts Balance each of the following chemical equations.
  a. $KI \longrightarrow K + I_2$
  b. $Na + H_2O \longrightarrow H_2 + NaOH$
  c. $CH_4 + O_2 \longrightarrow CO_2 + H_2O$

29. Calculating What mass of KBr is contained in 2.50 moles of the compound?

30. Calculating How many moles of Na_2CrO_4 are contained in 74.3 grams of the compound?

Concepts in Action

31. Inferring Kept at room temperature, batteries will eventually lose their charge. Why will keeping batteries in the freezer make them last longer?

32. Drawing Conclusions Octane, C_8H_{18}, is one of the compounds present in gasoline. The products of the burning of octane are water and carbon dioxide. In this reaction, which contain more energy, the bonds in the reactants or the bonds in the products? Explain.

33. Writing in Science Write a paragraph describing a chemical reaction that you have observed recently.

Performance-Based Assessment

Designing an Experiment Choose a chemical reaction that reaches equilibrium and includes at least one gas. Design an experiment that will show the effects of concentration, temperature, and pressure on the system. You will not actually perform the experiment, so you are not limited by the equipment available in your laboratory. Prepare a lab report that includes a hypothesis, all steps of the procedure, and any expected results.

For: Self-grading assessment
Visit: PHSchool.com
Web Code: cca-1070

Concepts in Action

31. Lowering the temperature decreases the rate of reaction of the materials in the battery.
32. The burning of octane is exothermic—it releases energy. In an exothermic reaction, the chemical energy of the reactants equals the amount of energy released plus the chemical energy of the products. Therefore, the bonds in the reactants (octane and oxygen) contain more energy than the bonds in the products (water and carbon dioxide).

33. Students' answers may include word equations of common reactions, observations that can be interpreted as evidence of chemical change, or an inferred classification of the reaction.

Test-Taking Tip

Calculating
When balancing chemical equations, follow these tips:

- Never change the subscript in any formula. Change only the coefficients.
- First, balance the atom that is most obviously unbalanced by placing a coefficient in front of the appropriate formula.
- Next, balance other atoms by placing coefficients in front of appropriate formulas.
- Finally, balance any atom that appears by itself in a formula (such as O_2, H_2, or Ca).
- Count the number of atoms of each element on both sides of the equation. If they are not equal, continue balancing.

Practice using these tips in Questions 1 and 3.

Choose the letter that best answers the question or completes the statement.

1. Balance this chemical equation.

$$MgO + H_3PO_4 \longrightarrow Mg_3(PO_4)_2 + H_2O$$
- (A) $3MgO + 2H_3PO_4 \longrightarrow Mg_3(PO_4)_2 + 3H_2O$
- (B) $3MgO + 2H_3PO_4 \longrightarrow Mg_3(PO_4)_2 + 2H_2O$
- (C) $6MgO + 2H_3PO_4 \longrightarrow Mg_3(PO_4)_2 + 3H_2O$
- (D) $6MgO + 2H_3PO_4 \longrightarrow 2Mg_3(PO_4)_2 + 6H_2O$
- (E) $6MgO + 4H_3PO_4 \longrightarrow 2Mg_3(PO_4)_2 + 3H_2O$

Questions 2 and 3 refer to the following reaction.

$$C_4H_{10} + O_2 \longrightarrow CO_2 + H_2O$$

2. What type of reaction is described by this equation?
- (A) synthesis
- (B) decomposition
- (C) combustion
- (D) double replacement
- (E) single replacement

3. Balance the equation for the reaction between butane (C_4H_{10}) and oxygen, and then determine how many grams of CO_2 are formed when 5.00 grams of C_4H_{10} react.
- (A) 1.65 grams
- (B) 3.79 grams
- (C) 15.1 grams
- (D) 20.0 grams
- (E) 26.4 grams

4. Which equation describes a synthesis?
- (A) $Ba(OH)_2 + 2HCl \longrightarrow BaCl_2 + 2H_2O$
- (B) $CH_4 + 2O_2 \longrightarrow CO_2 + 2H_2O$
- (C) $Zn + CuSO_4 \longrightarrow Cu + ZnSO_4$
- (D) $2H_2 + O_2 \longrightarrow 2H_2O$
- (E) $CaCO_3 \longrightarrow CaO + CO_2$

Use the energy diagram to answer Question 5.

Reaction Energy for $A_2 + 2B \rightleftharpoons 2AB$

Chemical Energy

$A_2 + 2B$

Energy barrier

2AB

Reaction Progress →

5. What effect would a catalyst have on the reaction $A_2 + 2B \rightleftharpoons 2AB$?
- (A) It gives the products more energy.
- (B) It makes the reaction endothermic.
- (C) It gives the reacting particles more energy.
- (D) It provides a new reaction pathway for the reactants.
- (E) none of the above

6. The following equation shows the formation of ammonia (NH_3) from nitrogen (N_2) and hydrogen (H_2). This reaction is in equilibrium.

$$N_2(g) + 3H_2(g) \rightleftharpoons 2NH_3(g) + Heat$$

If the pressure of the system is decreased, the equilibrium will shift
- (A) to the right because there are fewer moles of gas on the product side of the equation.
- (B) to the left because there are more moles of gas on the reactant side of the equation.
- (C) to the right because a drop in pressure brings the reactants together so they can react.
- (D) to the left because a drop in pressure pulls the product molecules apart.
- (E) in neither direction because pressure does not affect chemical equilibriums.

Standards Guide

Question	Standards
1	ICP.5.5
2	ICP.5.5
3	ICP.5.5
4	ICP.5.5
5	ICP.5.5
6	ICP.5.4

Performance-Based Assessment

Answers will vary. One of the reactions chosen might be the decomposition of hydrogen peroxide to form water and oxygen. For this reaction, increasing the pressure would shift the equilibrium to the left (in the direction of synthesis); increasing the temperature would shift the equilibrium to the right (in the direction of decomposition) as the reaction is endothermic; and removing oxygen from the system would decrease the concentration of products and shift the equilibrium to the right (in the direction of decomposition).

Your students can independently test their knowledge of the chapter and print out their test results for your files.

Planning Guide

Use these planning tools

Easy Planner
Teacher Express

SECTION OBJECTIVES	STANDARDS		ACTIVITIES and LABS
	NATIONAL	STATE	
8.1 Formation of Solutions, pp. 228–234 ⏱ 1 block or 2 periods **8.1.1 Describe** how a substance can dissolve in water by dissociation, dispersion, or ionization. **8.1.2 Describe** how the physical properties of a solution can differ from those of its solute and solvent. **8.1.3 Identify** energy changes that occur during the formation of a solution. **8.1.4 Describe** factors affecting the rate at which a solute dissolves in a solvent.	A-1, A-2, B-2, B-3, B-6, F-1	ICP.3.2, ICP.3.3	**SE** Inquiry Activity: How Do Shaking and Heating Affect a Carbonated Beverage? p. 227 **L2** **SE** Quick Lab: Comparing Heats of Solution, p. 232 **L2** **TE** Teacher Demo: Freezing Points of Solutions, p. 231 **L2**
8.2 Solubility and Concentration, pp. 235–239 ⏱ 1 block or 2 periods **8.2.1 Define** solubility and **describe** factors affecting solubility. **8.2.2 Classify** solutions as unsaturated, saturated, or supersaturated. **8.2.3 Calculate** and **compare** and **contrast** solution concentrations expressed as percent by volume, percent by mass, and molarity.	B-2, E-1	ICP.3.2, ICP.3.3	**TE** Teacher Demo: Crystallization, p. 236 **L2** **TE** Build Science Skills: Measuring, p. 237 **L2** **LM** Investigation 8B: Comparing Solubilities and Rates of Dissolving **L1**
8.3 Properties of Acids and Bases, pp. 240–245 ⏱ 1 block or 2 periods **8.3.1 Define** acid and **describe** some of the general properties of an acid. **8.3.2 Define** base and **describe** some of the general properties of a base. **8.3.3 Identify** a neutralization reaction, and **describe** the reactants and products of neutralization. **8.3.4 Explain** how acids and bases can be defined as proton donors and proton acceptors.	A-1, A-2, B-2, B-3, F-1	ICP.3.1, ICP.5.5	**SE** Quick Lab: Using an Indicator, p. 243 **L2** **SE** Exploration Lab: Preparing a Salt by Neutralization, pp. 254–255 **L2** **TE** Teacher Demo: Neutralization Reaction, p. 244 **L2** **LM** Investigation 8A: Comparing Antacids **L2**
8.4 Strength of Acids and Bases, pp. 246–249 ⏱ 1 block or 2 periods **8.4.1 Define** pH, and **relate** pH to hydronium ion concentration in a solution. **8.4.2 Distinguish** between strong acids and weak acids, and between strong bases and weak bases. **8.4.3 Define** buffer, and **describe** how a buffer can be prepared. **8.4.4 Explain** how electrolytes can be classified.	A-1, A-2, B-2, B-3, C-1, F-1, G-1, G-2, G-3	ICP.3.1, ICP.5.1, ICP.5.5, ICP.5.6, ICP.6.3	**SE** Quick Lab: Making a Battery, p. 248 **L2**

RESOURCES
PRINT and TECHNOLOGY

RSW Section 8.1	**L1**
T Chapter 8 Pretest	**L2**
Section 8.1	**L2**
P Chapter 8 Pretest	**L2**
Section 8.1	**L2**
GO Solutions	**L2**

RSW Section 8.2	**L1**
MSPS Section 8.2	**L2**
RSW Math Skill	**L2**
T Section 8.2	**L2**
P Section 8.2	**L2**

PLM Lab 3: Preparing a Salt by Neutralization	**L2**
RSW Section 8.3	**L1**
T Section 8.3	**L2**
P Section 8.3	**L2**
GO Bases	**L2**

RSW Section 8.4	**L1**
DC Suspended in Blood	**L2**
T Section 8.4	**L2**
P Section 8.4	**L2**
GO pH	**L2**

SECTION ASSESSMENT

SE Section 8.1 Assessment, p. 234

iT Section 8.1

SE Section 8.2 Assessment, p. 239

iT Section 8.2

SE Section 8.3 Assessment, p. 245

iT Section 8.3

SE Section 8.4 Assessment, p. 249

iT Section 8.4

Go Online

Go online for these Internet resources.
PHSchool.com
Web Code: cca-1080

NSTA SCiLINKS
Web Code: ccn-1081
Web Code: ccn-1083
Web Code: ccn-1084

Materials for Activities and Labs

Quantities for each group

STUDENT EDITION

Inquiry Activity, p. 227
plastic bottle of carbonated beverage, small balloon, bucket, hot water

Quick Lab, p. 232
2 large test tubes, 10-mL graduated cylinder, distilled water, thermometer, 1 g KCl, 5 mL 95% isopropyl alcohol solution, stirring rod

Quick Lab, p. 243
1/4 cup frozen blueberries, foam cup, spoon, 4 small plastic cups, 2 dropper pipets, lemon juice, white vinegar, window cleaner, baking soda

Quick Lab, p. 248
1 large fresh lemon, plastic knife, zinc strip, 2 copper strips, multimeter

Exploration Lab, pp. 254–255
3 dropper pipets, labels, 10-mL graduated cylinder, test tube rack, 2 10-mL test tubes, distilled water, hydrochloric acid, sodium hydroxide solution, 3 stirring rods, phenolphthalein solution, 2 25-mL beakers, pH paper, large watch glass, 100-mL beaker, hot plate

TEACHER'S EDITION

Teacher Demo, p. 231
2 trays, ice, rock salt, water, 2 small plastic containers (clear), thermometer

Teacher Demo, p. 236
beakers, 200 g sodium acetate trihydrate, distilled water, spatula, hot plate

Build Science Skills, p. 237
2 400-mL beakers, water, ice, hot plate, 2 70-mL test tubes, salt, scoop, 2 stirring rods, thermometer, weigh paper, balance, test tube tongs

Teacher Demo, p. 244
2 lemons, beaker, 0.1-M solution of NaOH, phenolphthalein solution (indicator), syringe, knife

Build Science Skills, p. 251
calcium hydroxide (pickling lime); 2 large, sealable jars; clear plastic cups; straws; stopwatches; jump ropes

Chapter Assessment

CHAPTER ASSESSMENT

SE	Chapter Assessment, pp. 257–258
CUT	Chapter 8 Test A, B
CTB	Chapter 8
iT	Chapter 8

PHSchool.com GO
Web Code: cca-1080

STANDARDIZED TEST PREP

SE	Chapter 8, p. 259
TP	Diagnose and Prescribe

Interactive Textbook with assessment at PHSchool.com

Before you teach

From the Author

David Frank
Ferris State University

Big Ideas
In this chapter, students are reintroduced to the homogeneous mixtures called solutions. Some characteristic properties result when solutions form, such as an increase in the boiling point and a decrease in the melting point of the solvent. Students then learn some of the properties of acids and bases, which have characteristic properties when dissolved in water.

Space and Time Point out to students that the factors that affect the rate of dissolving are similar to the factors that affect the rate of a chemical reaction. In both cases, the rates increase when collisions between particles take place more frequently. Thus, stirring, increased temperature, and increased surface area reduce the amount of time required to form a solution.

Matter and Change Take care to help students distinguish between the concentration of an acid and its strength. The concentration of an acid simply refers to how much is dissolved in water. The strength of an acid is related to the concept of equilibrium developed in the last chapter. A strong acid ionizes almost completely in water. A weak acid, however, reaches an equilibrium in which ionization occurs to only a small extent. A 1-M solution of the strong acid HCl, therefore, has a lower pH than a 1-M solution of CH_3COOH. However, the relatively dilute solution of 1.0×10^{-6} M HCl is still a strong acid, in spite of its relatively high pH, because the HCl still ionizes almost completely in water.

Forces and Motion The concept of polarity is applied in this chapter to the solution process. Due to the charges in both substances, ionic compounds are more likely to dissolve in polar substances than in nonpolar substances.

Energy The formation of a solution may be either endothermic or exothermic. This depends on the relative amount of energy used to break attractions between solute particles and solvent particles and the amount of energy released when new interactions between solute and solvent are formed.

Chemistry Refresher

Colligative Properties of Solutions 8.1

Dissolving a solute in a solvent results in a solution whose boiling point and freezing point are different than those of either the solute or the solvent. Colligative properties, such as freezing point depression and boiling point elevation, are properties of solutions that depend on the number of solute particles dissolved and not on the identity of the solute. Solutions of equal molarity do not necessarily have equal concentrations of solute particles. For example, 1 mole of a dissociating solute, such as NaCl, produces more particles in solution than 1 mole of a nondissociating solute, such as glucose. A third colligative property is osmotic pressure, or the pressure required to prevent the diffusion of pure solvent across a semipermeable membrane that separates a solution from the pure solvent.

Address Misconceptions

Many students do not differentiate between solvent and solute particles when learning about solutions. However, a solution's properties are determined by the different types of particles that constitute it. For a strategy to overcome this misconception, see **Address Misconceptions** on **page 229**.

Solubility 8.2

Solubility can be described as the amount of solute dissolved in a saturated solution. The solubility of one substance in another depends on several factors, including the polarity of the solvent, temperature, and pressure. Solutions can be described as unsaturated, saturated, or supersaturated. When a solute crystallizes out of a supersaturated solution, as shown above, the solution that remains is saturated.

For: Teaching methods for solutions, acids, and bases
Visit: www.SciLinks.org/PDLinks
Web Code: ccn-0899

Describing Acids and Bases 8.3 and 8.4

Address Misconceptions

Some students may think that pure water is a good conductor of electricity. However, the number of ions in pure water is not great enough to carry an electric current. For a strategy to overcome this misconception, see **Address Misconceptions** *on* **page 249.**

Acids are compounds that produce hydronium ions (H_3O^+) in water. Bases are compounds that produce hydroxide ions (OH^-) when dissolved in water. Acids can also be classified as proton donors, while bases can be classified as proton acceptors. Both acids and bases are examples of electrolytes, or compounds that form ions when in solution. Students may have trouble grasping the difference between the concentration and strength of an acid or base.

The concentration of hydronium ions in solution is described by pH. The degree to which ions form in solution is described by strength. For example, a very dilute strong acid will have few hydronium ions in solution, yet the acid is still classified as strong. Conversely, a very concentrated weak acid may have relatively many hydronium ions in solution, yet the acid is still classified as weak.

The pH Scale 8.4

The pH scale runs from 0 to 14, with 0 being very acidic, 7 being neutral, and 14 being very basic. Note that the pH scale is logarithmic, which means that solutions that differ by 1 pH unit have hydronium ion concentrations that differ by a factor of 10.

pH Values for Common Substances

Drain cleaner
Ammonia
Soap
Baking Soda
Distilled water
Milk
White bread
Tomato
Oranges
Vinegar
Lemons
Car battery acid

pH / Hydronium Concentration

The relationship between pH and hydronium ion concentration (given in molarity) is described by the following equation:

$$pH = -\log_{10} [H_3O^+]$$

Solutions can also be described by the pOH scale. A solution's pOH can be determined using the following equation:

$$pOH = -\log_{10} [OH^-]$$

The pOH scale is the opposite of pH scale. A very basic solution will have a low pOH, and a very acidic solution will have a high pOH.

Build Reading Literacy

Compare and Contrast

Identify Similarities and Differences

Strategy Help students read and understand material that discusses two or more related topics or concepts. This strategy helps students identify similarities and differences, thus enabling them to link prior knowledge with new information. Before students begin, assign a section in Chapter 8 for them to read, such as Section 8.2, pp. 235–239.

Example

1. Have students compare two or more topics or concepts under a section heading. Tell them that when they compare, they should focus on both similarities and differences. Remind them to look for these signal words:

- **Similarities:** *similar, similarly, also, just as, like, likewise, in the same way*
- **Differences:** *but, however, although, whereas, on the other hand, different, unlike*

2. Have students contrast two or more topics or concepts. Remind students that when they contrast, they should focus only on differences.

3. Have students create a chart or diagram comparing or contrasting two or more topics or concepts they read about in the section. Suggest that they create either a compare/contrast table or a Venn diagram to present their information.

See p. 241 for a script on how to use the compare and contrast strategy with students. For additional Build Reading Literacy strategies, see pp. 229, 236, and 246.

ASSESS PRIOR KNOWLEDGE

Use the Chapter Pretest below to assess students' prior knowledge. As needed, review these Science Concepts and Math Skills with students.

Review Science Concepts

Section 8.1 Go over atomic structure and the difference between ionic and molecular compounds. Review physical properties, including conductivity, freezing point, and boiling point. Be sure that students understand the difference between endothermic and exothermic processes.

Section 8.2 Encourage students to recall what they have learned about polar versus nonpolar substances. Review the concept of concentration and the use of units, such as liters, moles, and grams.

Section 8.3 Review chemical properties including reactivity. Encourage students to review different types of reactions, including double and single replacement reactions. Go over terms such as *proton, valence electron, ion,* and *positive* and *negative charge.*

Section 8.4 Review the definitions of chemical and physical equilibrium. Encourage students to recall how to describe a solution's concentration.

Review Math Skills

Line Graphs Students will need to know how to interpret line graphs in order to complete the Chapter 8 Assessment.

Direct students to the **Math Skills** in the **Skills and Reference Handbook** at the end of the student text.

8 Solutions, Acids, and Bases

21st Century Learning
Communication Skills

Why is soil acidity important in gardening?

In order for their plants to thrive, gardeners and farmers need to be mindful of the acidity of the soil. Suppose you are planning a small garden for your neighborhood. Use the library or Internet to find out the typical soil acidity for your area and how this affects the variety of plant life. Talk to a local gardener, farmer, or plant nursery worker to find out how soil acidity is measured and maintained. Then write a paragraph that outlines your plan for the garden, making sure to discuss soil pH considerations.

Indiana's Academic Standards for Science

PROPERTIES OF MATTER
ICP.3.1: Describe how we use macroscopic properties of matter to model microscopic processes; **ICP.3.2:** Study the characteristics of solids, liquids, and gases and their changes of state and interpret them in terms of a molecular model which describes their energies and motions; **ICP.3.3:** Understand how thermal energy (the microscopic motions of the atoms and/or molecules) is related to the macroscopic concept of temperature. Examine the differences in these concepts by measuring the temperature changes of water as it is heated or cooled.

CHEMICAL ENERGY, REACTIONS, AND BONDING
ICP.5.1: Recognize and describe physical properties of matter and use these to differentiate between pure substances and mixtures; **ICP.5.5:** Using conservation principles write and balance chemical equations; **ICP.5.6:** Identify key indicators of a chemical change and classify simple types of chemical reactions. Differentiate between covalent, ionic, hydrogen and Van der Waals bonding, and write formulas for and name compounds of each type.

ELECTRICAL ENERGY PROPAGATION AND MAGNETISM
ICP.6.3: Using the example of electrolysis and its application in batteries, explain the relationship between chemical reactions and electrical energy.

This cave formed gradually as rainwater seeped through limestone rock and dissolved the calcium carbonate in the limestone.

Chapter Pretest

1. Describe the charge and location within an atom of the following subatomic particles: protons, electrons, and neutrons. *(Protons: positive; in the nucleus. Electrons: negative; in the electron cloud surrounding the nucleus. Neutrons: neutral; in the nucleus)*

2. True or False: Both molecular and ionic compounds contain covalent bonds. *(False)*

3. Conductivity, freezing point, and boiling point are all *(c)*

   a. related to volume.
   b. chemical properties.
   c. physical properties.
   d. related to mass.

4. Which of the following is always true of a polar covalent bond? *(a)*

   a. One atom in the bond has a partial negative charge.
   b. One atom in the bond is an ion.
   c. Both atoms in the bond are of the same element.
   d. Both atoms in the bond have partial positive charges.

5. How many moles are in 32.0 g of O_2 gas, which has a molar mass of 16.0 g? *(2.00 moles)*

6. Describe chemical equilibrium. *(Forward and reverse reactions take place at the same rate.)*

Video Field Trip

Suspended in Blood

Inquiry Activity

How Do Shaking and Heating Affect a Carbonated Beverage?

Procedure

1. Remove the cap from a plastic bottle of carbonated beverage (a solution of carbon dioxide in water). Observe what happens.

2. Fit a balloon tightly over the top of the bottle. Holding the bottle over a sink, shake it several times from side to side. Observe any changes in the balloon and the liquid.

3. Place the bottle in a bucket of hot water. Observe any further changes in the balloon.

Think About It

1. **Observing** What happened when you removed the cap from the bottle?

2. **Inferring** What caused the balloon to expand?

3. **Drawing Conclusions** How did shaking affect the rate of the change in the beverage?

4. **Applying Concepts** How would storing a carbonated beverage in a refrigerator affect what happens when the cap is removed?

Solutions, Acids, and Bases **227**

Video Field Trip

Suspended in Blood

Encourage students to view the Video Field Trip "Suspended in Blood."

ENGAGE/EXPLORE

Inquiry Activity

How Do Shaking and Heating Affect a Carbonated Beverage? L2

Purpose In this activity, students begin to describe the effects of temperature and agitation on the solubility of a gas in a liquid.

⚑ **Address Misconceptions**

Students may think that solutes can be only liquids or solids. Challenge this misconception by asking students to explain their observations in this activity.

Skills Focus Observing, Inferring

🕐 **Prep Time** 5 minutes

Materials plastic bottle of carbonated beverage, small balloon, bucket, hot water

Class Time 15 minutes

Safety Have students wipe up any liquid spilled on the floor.

Expected Outcome Prior to opening the bottle, students will not see any bubbles. Once the bottle is opened, bubbles will begin to appear in the liquid. A little foam may appear depending on whether the bottle was shaken prior to opening. After the balloon is placed on the bottle and the bottle is shaken, the balloon will inflate somewhat due to carbon dioxide being released. If the beverage is at room temperature, there will be more bubbles than if the beverage was chilled.

Think About It

1. After the cap is removed, many bubbles appear in the liquid.

2. Acceptable answers include suggesting that a gas was dissolved in the liquid and that shaking the bottle allowed the gas to escape.

3. Shaking the beverage caused bubbles to form more rapidly (thus inflating the balloon).

4. Storing the beverage in a refrigerator would reduce the formation of bubbles.

Visual

1 FOCUS

Objectives

8.1.1 Describe how a substance can dissolve in water by dissociation, dispersion, or ionization.

8.1.2 Describe how the physical properties of a solution can differ from those of its solute and solvent.

8.1.3 Identify energy changes that occur during the formation of a solution.

8.1.4 Describe factors affecting the rate at which a solute dissolves in a solvent.

Reading Focus

Build Vocabulary L2

Word Forms Ask students to name the verb forms for the three types of dissolving: *dissociation, dispersion,* and *ionization. (Dissociate, disperse, and ionize)* Give a definition of each term and have students discuss how these words give clues as to what type of particle is involved in each type of dissolving.

Reading Strategy L2

a. Physical change
b. Ions are present before and after.
c. Chemical change
d. Ions are present after, but not before.

2 INSTRUCT

Integrate Biology L2

To avoid decompression sickness, or "the bends," scuba divers make "decompression stops" as they return to the surface. They rise from deeper waters very slowly and pause periodically to allow the dissolved gases to come out of solution. Scuba divers are at risk for the bends even in water as shallow as 10 m. However, the bends is not a problem for diving animals or people who dive without scuba tanks. Ask, **Why do you think decompression sickness is not a risk when diving without scuba tanks?** *(People who dive without scuba tanks take one breath at the surface and hold it while diving underwater. They have the same amount of gas in their body at the surface as they have throughout the dive, so they do not get a dangerous level of dissolved gases in their blood and tissues.)* **Logical**

8.1 Formation of Solutions

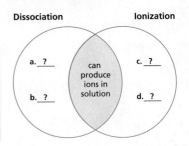

Standards: ICP.3.2, ICP.3.3

Reading Focus

Key Concepts

- What are three processes that can occur when substances dissolve?
- What are some properties of a solution that differ from those of its solvent and solutes?
- What happens to energy when a solution forms?
- What factors affect the rate of dissolving?

Vocabulary

- solute
- solvent
- dissociation
- dispersion
- ionization

Reading Strategy

Comparing and Contrasting Copy the Venn diagram below. Contrast dissociation and ionization by listing the ways they differ.

Dissociation   Ionization

a. ?   can produce ions in solution   c. ?

b. ?   d. ?

Figure 1 If divers surface too quickly from great depths, the nitrogen that has dissolved in their blood and other tissues bubbles out of solution. These bubbles can become trapped in joints and cause great pain, a condition called "the bends."

Scuba divers, like the one in Figure 1, are able to breathe underwater with the aid of a tank containing compressed air. Like the air you breathe at sea level, the air inside the tank contains about 78 percent nitrogen. As a scuba diver descends to greater depths, the pressure of the air in the diver's lungs increases. At a depth of 10 meters, the air in the diver's lungs is already twice the pressure of the air at sea level.

The human body consists mainly of water. When gases come in contact with water, they dissolve in the water to form a solution. The deeper a scuba diver goes, the greater is the air pressure in her lungs, and the more nitrogen dissolves in the blood and tissues of her body.

The idea of a gas dissolving may seem strange to you. When you hear the word *dissolve*, you probably think of a solid dissolving in a liquid, such as sugar added to tea. However, any states of matter—solid, liquid, and gas—can become part of a solution. For a solution to form, one substance must dissolve in another.

 Section Resources

Print

- **Reading and Study Workbook With Math Support,** Section 8.1
- **Transparencies,** Chapter Pretest and Section 8.1

Technology

- **Interactive Textbook,** Section 8.1
- **Presentation Pro CD-ROM,** Chapter Pretest and Section 8.1
- **Go Online,** NSTA SciLinks, Solutions

Types of Solutions		
Solute	Solvent	Example
Gas	Gas	Air (oxygen, carbon dioxide in nitrogen)
Liquid	Gas	Water in air
Gas	Liquid	Carbonated beverage (carbon dioxide in water)
Liquid	Liquid	Vinegar (acetic acid in water)
Solid	Liquid	Sugar water (sugar in water)
Solid	Solid	Stainless steel (Chromium and nickel in iron)

Dissolving

Recall that a solution is a homogeneous mixture of two or more substances. Every solution has two types of components. A **solute** is a substance whose particles are dissolved in a solution. The substance in which the solute dissolves is called the **solvent.** For example, seawater is a solution in which salt is the solute and water is the solvent.

Solutes and solvents can take the form of a solid, liquid, or gas. The solution takes the state of the solvent. Figure 2 lists some common solutions and the states of their respective solutes and solvents. Air, for instance, is a solution of several gases dissolved in another gas. Nitrogen, making up about 78 percent of air, is the solvent. Oxygen, carbon dioxide, argon, and other gases are solutes.

You are probably most familiar with solutions in which water is the solvent. Carbonated drinks, hot tea, and seawater are just a few examples of the many water-based solutions you might have encountered. ⊂●⊃ **Substances can dissolve in water in three ways—by dissociation, dispersion, and ionization.**

Dissociation of Ionic Compounds
For a solute to dissolve in water, the solute and solvent particles must attract one another. However, the particles within the solute are attracted to one another, and the particles within the solvent are attracted to one another. So before a solution can form, the attractions that hold the solute together and the solvent together must be overcome.

Figure 3 illustrates how a sodium chloride crystal dissolves in water. Sodium chloride is an ionic compound. Water is a polar molecule, and is attracted to the ions in the solute. The crystal dissolves as the sodium and chlorine ions are pulled into solution, one by one, by the surrounding water molecules. The process in which an ionic compound separates into ions as it dissolves is called **dissociation.**

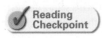

How does sodium chloride dissolve in water?

Figure 2 A stainless steel pot or pan is a solution of chromium and nickel in iron. In a solution, the solvent is the substance in the greatest quantity.

Figure 3 When an ionic compound dissolves in water, the charged ends of water molecules surround the oppositely charged ions.

1

2

3

◯ Cl⁻ ● Na⁺ ● H₂O

Solutions, Acids, and Bases **229**

Dissolving
Build Reading Literacy L1

Relate Text and Visuals Refer to page **190D** in **Chapter 7,** which provides the guidelines for relating text and visuals.

Have students read the text on pp. 229–230 describing different ways in which a substance can dissolve in water. Then, have students form groups of three. Each student will choose a type of dissolving. Encourage students to use Figure 3, Figure 4, or the diagram in the passage to explain to their group what happens on the particle level when substances dissolve by dissociation, dispersion, or ionization.
Visual, Logical

Address Misconceptions L2

Many students do not differentiate between solvent and solute particles when learning about solutions. Challenge this misconception by having students examine the keys at the bottom of Figure 3 and Figure 4. Have them note the different colors and sizes used to differentiate between solvent and solute particles. Point out that these figures show models of particles in order to represent the movement and relationship of solvent and solute particles. The figures do not show what the atoms, molecules, and ions actually look like. For example, the colors, shapes, and relative sizes of the particles are symbolic and do not represent the actual characteristics of the particles.
Visual

Customize for Inclusion Students

Hearing Impaired
If you have students with hearing impairments, have students draw what happens to solvent and solute particles during dissociation, dispersion, and ionization. Encourage them to label their illustrations and provide brief written descriptions.

Answer to . . .

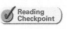 *Sodium chloride dissolves by dissociating into ions.*

Figure 4 Have students examine Figure 4. Ask, **What symbol is used to represent water molecules?** *(A larger red sphere with two smaller blue spheres attached)* **How are the sugar molecules arranged in the beginning?** *(The sugar molecules are arranged in a packed crystal.)* **What symbol is used to represent sugar molecules?** *(A purple, two-ringed structure, with the rings joined at one point)* **How are the sugar molecules arranged in the end?** *(The sugar molecules are spread out and mixed in uniformly with the water molecules.)* **Visual**

Build Science Skills   L2

Predicting Have students look at the figure in the text on ionization of molecular compounds. Ask, **What ions would be produced as molecules of hydrogen bromide, HBr, dissolved in water?** *(Hydronium ions [H_3O^+] and bromide ions [Br^-])* **Logical, Visual**

Sugar
Water

Figure 4 Saliva dissolves the sugar in hard candy by dispersion. As water molecules collide with sugar crystals, attractions develop between the water molecules and sugar molecules at the surface of the solid.

Dispersion of Molecular Compounds When you place a piece of hard candy on your tongue, the sweet taste spreads, or disperses, throughout your mouth. The water in your saliva dissolves the sugar and flavoring in the candy. Sugar dissolves in water by **dispersion,** or breaking into small pieces that spread throughout the water.

Both sugar and water are polar molecules, so they attract one another. Because the water molecules are constantly moving, they collide frequently with the surface of the sugar crystals, as shown in Figure 4. Attractions form between the water molecules and the exposed sugar molecules. When enough water molecules have surrounded a sugar molecule, the attractions between them are great enough to overcome the attractions holding the sugar molecule to the surface of the crystal. The sugar molecule breaks free, and is pulled into solution by the water molecules.

As more sugar molecules break free of the crystal, another layer of sugar molecules is exposed to the water, and the process repeats. The solute particles become evenly spread throughout the solvent.

Reading Checkpoint   *How does sugar dissolve in water?*

Ionization of Molecular Compounds Hydrogen chloride, HCl, is a molecular compound in which a hydrogen atom and a chlorine atom share a pair of electrons. Recall that a hydrogen atom has only one proton and one electron. When HCl gas dissolves in water, the hydrogen proton from each HCl molecule is transferred to a water molecule. For each HCl molecule that reacts, a hydronium ion, H_3O^+, and a chloride ion, Cl^-, are produced.

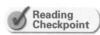

Notice that when hydrogen chloride and water form a solution, two molecular compounds react to form two ions. The process in which neutral molecules gain or lose electrons is known as **ionization.** Unlike dissociation and dispersion, which are physical changes, dissolving by ionization is a chemical change. The solution that results contains new substances. When a solute dissolves by dissociation, the ions pulled into solution are the same ions present in the solute. When a solute dissolves by ionization, the ions in solution are formed by the reaction of solute and solvent particles.

Properties of Liquid Solutions

The physical properties of salt are clearly different from the physical properties of water. But how do the properties of a saltwater solution compare to those of its solute and solvent? ⊖ **Three physical properties of a solution that can differ from those of its solute and solvent are conductivity, freezing point, and boiling point.**

Conductivity Solid sodium chloride is a poor conductor of electric current. But when sodium chloride dissociates in water, the sodium and chloride ions are able to move freely. The ions in solution will then conduct an electric current. Hydrogen chloride gas is also a poor conductor of electric current. However, when hydrogen chloride ionizes in water, the resulting solution conducts an electric current.

Freezing Point and Boiling Point If you live in a cold climate, you are probably familiar with icy roads like the one in Figure 5. You may have seen snowplows or salt trucks spreading magnesium chloride, $MgCl_2$, or a similar ionic compound on these icy roads. When magnesium chloride dissolves in melting ice and snow, it dissociates into magnesium (Mg^{2+}) ions and chloride (Cl^-) ions. As Figure 6A shows, ice forms when water molecules are able to arrange themselves in a rigid, honeycomb-like structure. In Figure 6B, the presence of magnesium and chloride ions, which are attracted to the water molecules, interferes with the freezing process. The freezing point of water at sea level is 0°C. When icy roads are salted with magnesium chloride, the resulting solution can have a freezing point as low as −15°C.

A solute can also raise the boiling point of the solvent. For example, the coolant used in most car radiators is a solution containing water and ethylene glycol, $C_2H_6O_2$. Water at sea level boils at 100°C. Adding ethylene glycol to water raises the boiling point. The resulting solution helps prevent the engine from overheating. Because ethylene glycol also lowers the freezing point of water, the coolant does not freeze during spells of cold weather.

Figure 5 Salt spread on icy roads lowers the freezing point of water.

Figure 6 The presence of solute particles affects how a solvent freezes. **A** Pure water freezes in a hexagonal pattern. **B** In water "salted" with $MgCl_2$, the dissociated Mg^{2+} and Cl^- ions disrupt the formation of ice crystals. **Using Models** *How do the interactions between Mg^{2+} and H_2O differ from the interactions between Cl^- and H_2O?*

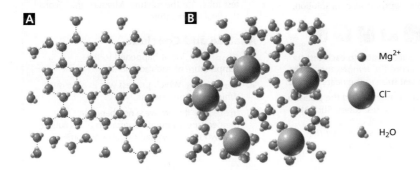

A   **B**

- Mg²⁺
- Cl⁻
- H₂O

Solutions, Acids, and Bases **231**

Facts and Figures

Structure of Ice The unusual structure of ice is due to the formation of hydrogen bonds between molecules and the angle between water's two O–H bonds. Because the formation of hydrogen bonds in place of weaker intermolecular forces releases energy, hydrogen bonding is energetically favorable. Thus, the open structure of ice maximizes the number of hydrogen bonds that can form among water molecules. Adding a solute prevents the water molecules from achieving this low energy structure.

Solutions, Acids, and Bases 231

Heat of Solution

Comparing Heats of Solution **L2**

Objective
After completing this activity, students will be able to
• determine whether a solution process is exothermic or endothermic.

Skills Focus Observing, Measuring, Classifying, Inferring

 Prep Time 15 minutes

Class Time 15 minutes

Safety Caution students to use the stirring rod, not the thermometer, to stir the solutions. Do not use mercury thermometers. Have students observe safety symbols and wear safety goggles, plastic gloves, and lab aprons.

Teaching Tips
• Dispose of all waste solutions in the sink with excess water.

Expected Outcome The potassium chloride solution process is endothermic, and the temperature should fall. The alcohol solution process is exothermic, and the temperature should rise.

Analyze and Conclude
1. The temperature of the potassium chloride solution fell. The temperature of the alcohol solution rose.
2. The alcohol solution process is exothermic. The potassium chloride solution process is endothermic.
3. Assuming that the solute dissolved, students should infer that the amount of energy absorbed as the particles separated would be equal (or very similar) to the amount of energy released when the solution formed.
Visual, Logical

For: Links on solutions
Visit: www.SciLinks.org
Web Code: ccn-1081

Heat of Solution

When sodium hydroxide, NaOH, dissolves in water, the solution becomes warmer. The solution releases energy to the surroundings. In contrast, when ammonium nitrate, NH_4NO_3, dissolves in water, the solution becomes colder. The solution absorbs energy from the surroundings. 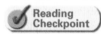 **During the formation of a solution, energy is either released or absorbed.**

Like chemical reactions, the solution process can be described as exothermic or endothermic. Dissolving sodium hydroxide in water is exothermic, as it releases heat. Dissolving ammonium nitrate in water is endothermic, as it absorbs heat. The How It Works box on page 233 describes how dissolving ammonium nitrate is used in cold packs.

In order for a solution to form, both the attractions among solute particles and the attractions among solvent particles must be broken. Breaking attractions requires energy. As the solute dissolves, new attractions form between solute and solvent particles. The formation of attractions releases energy. The difference between these energies is known as the heat of solution. For example, dissolving one mole of sodium hydroxide in water releases 44.5 kilojoules of heat. In this exothermic change, energy is released as NaOH and H_2O form new attractions. It is 44.5 kilojoules greater than the energy required to break the attractions among NaOH crystals and among H_2O molecules.

Reading Checkpoint *Does the breaking of attractions among solvent particles release energy or absorb energy?*

Comparing Heats of Solution

Materials
2 large test tubes, 10-mL graduated cylinder, distilled water, thermometer, 1 g potassium chloride, 5 mL 95% isopropyl alcohol solution, stirring rod

Procedure

1. Add 5 mL of distilled water to each test tube. Measure and record the temperature of the water in each test tube to the nearest 0.2°C.

2. Remove the thermometer. Add the potassium chloride to one of the test tubes. Stir until the potassium chloride dissolves.
   CAUTION: *Use the stirring rod, not the thermometer, to stir the solution.*

3. Measure and record the final temperature of the solution. Rinse the thermometer.

4. Add 5 mL of the alcohol solution to the second test tube. Stir the mixture. Measure and record the final temperature.

Analyze and Conclude

1. **Observing** What happened to the temperature of each solution?

2. **Classifying** Which process was exothermic? Which was endothermic?

3. **Inferring** If there were no change in temperature during the formation of a solution, how would you explain this observation?

Download a worksheet on solutions for students to complete, and find additional teacher support from NSTA SciLinks.

HOW It Works

Cold Packs

Instant hot and cold packs are often used by athletes to treat injuries. Hot packs are also used in cold weather to warm hands and feet. Both types of pack work through the action of chemicals that either release or absorb heat when they dissolve in water. One type of cold pack is shown below. **Inferring** *How does shaking the pack after squeezing it affect the rate of dissolving?*

Using a cold pack
A cold pack removes heat from the inflammation around an injury. It also decreases the size of capillaries (small blood vessels) in the injured area, which reduces swelling and bruising.

A **Inside the pack** A cold pack consists of two sealed bags, one inside the other. The strong outer bag contains solid ammonium nitrate powder. The thin-walled inner bag contains water.

Outer bag

Ammonium nitrate powder

Water in inner bag

B **Squeezing the pack** When the pack is squeezed, the inner bag containing the water bursts. The water rushes into the outer bag where it dissolves the ammonium nitrate.

Inner bag bursts.

Ammonium nitrate dissolves in water.

C **Heat absorbed** As the ammonium nitrate dissolves, it absorbs energy from the water. This causes the temperature of the solution in the bag to drop rapidly. The pack is then ready for use.

Heat absorbed

Solutions, Acids, and Bases **233**

Build Science Skills

Inferring Have students examine the description of what happens when NaOH dissolves in water. Tell them that the solute-solute attractions that are broken when NaOH dissociates are the ionic bonds between Na^+ and OH^- ions. Ask, **What solute-solute attractions are broken when molecular compounds dissolve through dispersion?** *(The intermolecular attractions between the solute molecules)*
Logical

HOW It Works

Cold Packs

The heat of solution for ammonium nitrate, NH_4NO_3, is 25.7 kJ/mol. This means that 25.7 kJ are absorbed when one mole, or about 80 g, of ammonium nitrate is dissolved in water. The amount of cooling that occurs depends on the amount of solid ammonium nitrate present in the cold pack.

Interpreting Diagrams Like stirring a mixture, shaking the bag moves more dissolved ions away from the surface of the solid ammonium nitrate and allows for more collisions between solute and solvent particles.
Visual

For Enrichment

Interested students can design a method for testing the effectiveness of different brands of hot or cold packs. They might compare how hot or cold each brand makes a sample of water. Alternatively, they might determine how long a desired temperature range is maintained by each brand.
Kinesthetic

Facts and Figures

Instant Hot Packs Many hot packs use a mechanism similar to that of cold packs in order to produce the opposite effect. Hot packs can use calcium chloride, $CaCl_2$, or magnesium sulfate, $MgSO_4$, which have negative heats of solution. Both substances have other home uses. Calcium chloride is used to keep pickles crisp and magnesium sulfate is used as bath salts.

Another type of hot pack uses a super-saturated solution of sodium acetate, $NaC_2H_3O_2$. Clicking a disk in the pack causes the solute to crystallize, which is an exothermic process. These hot packs are reusable because placing the pack in boiling water causes the solute crystals to go back into solution.

Answer to . . .

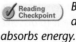 Reading Checkpoint *Breaking attractions among solvent particles absorbs energy.*

Factors Affecting Rates of Dissolving

Address Misconceptions **L2**

The text states that increasing temperature speeds up the rate of dissolving. There are some exceptions to this rule. In the next section, students will read about the relationship between temperature and the solubility of gases. Gases (and some solids) are more soluble as the temperature of the solution decreases. Have students speculate as to how increasing the temperature of a solution affects the solubility of a gas. **Logical**

3 ASSESS

Evaluate Understanding **L2**

Have students draw illustrations that represent the terms *solvent, solute, dissociation, dispersion,* and *ionization* on index cards. Then, have students shuffle the cards and exchange them with a partner. The partner then tries to identify what each illustration represents.

Reteach **L1**

Use Figures 3, 4, and 6 to summarize key concepts about solutions, including dissociation, dispersion, and freezing point depression.

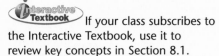

Factors that affect chemical reaction rates include temperature, surface area, concentration, stirring, and catalysts. Rates of dissolving are affected by temperature, surface area, and stirring.

Interactive Textbook If your class subscribes to the Interactive Textbook, use it to review key concepts in Section 8.1.

Figure 7 The rate of dissolving can be increased by reducing the particle size of the solute, by stirring, and by heating the solvent. **Predicting** *How does changing the temperature setting on a washing machine affect how fast the detergent will dissolve?*

Crushed solid

Stirring

Heat

Factors Affecting Rates of Dissolving

You already know that sugar dissolves in water. But what do you know about the rate at which it dissolves? Like rates of chemical reactions, rates of dissolving depend on the frequency and energy of collisions that occur between very small particles. During a chemical reaction, collisions occur between particles of the reactants. During the formation of a solution, collisions occur between particles of the solute and solvent. **Factors that affect the rate of dissolving include surface area, stirring, and temperature.**

When a sugar cube dissolves in water, the dissolving takes place at the surfaces of the cube. The greater the surface area of a solid solute, the more frequent the collisions are between solute and solvent particles. More collisions result in a faster rate of dissolving. You can increase the surface area of a solid by dividing it into smaller particles. The more finely divided a solid solute, the faster it dissolves. For example, one gram of granulated sugar dissolves faster in water than a 1-gram sugar cube.

You can also make sugar dissolve faster by stirring the mixture. Stirring moves dissolved particles away from the surface of the solid, and allows for more collisions between solute and solvent particles.

Another way to speed up the rate of dissolving is to increase the temperature of the solvent. For example, sugar dissolves faster in warm water than it does in cold water. Increasing the temperature of a solvent causes its particles to move faster, on average. As a result, both the number of collisions and the energy of these collisions with solute particles increase. The solute goes into solution more quickly.

Section 8.1 Assessment

Reviewing Concepts

1. What are three ways that substances can dissolve in water?
2. What physical properties of a solution differ from those of its solutes and solvent?
3. How does the formation of a solution involve energy?
4. What factors affect dissolving rates?

Critical Thinking

5. **Comparing and Contrasting** Compare the processes by which sugar crystals and hydrogen chloride gas dissolve in water.

6. **Predicting** Suppose you put equal amounts of pure water and salt water into separate ice cube trays of the same size and shape. When you put both trays in the freezer, what would you expect to happen?

Connecting Concepts

Reaction Rates In Section 7.3, factors affecting chemical reaction rates are discussed. Find out which of these factors also affect rates of dissolving.

Section 8.1 Assessment

1. Dispersion, dissociation, and ionization
2. Conductivity, boiling point, and melting point
3. Breaking the attractions among solute particles and the attractions among solvent particles absorbs energy. Energy is released as new attractions form between solute and solvent particles.
4. Rates of dissolving are affected by temperature, surface area, and stirring.

5. Sugar crystals dissolve by dispersion, which means that the sugar molecules break away from the surface of the crystals as water molecules surround them. Hydrogen chloride gas dissolves in water by ionization, which means that a hydrogen proton is transferred from the hydrogen chloride molecule to a water molecule, forming a hydronium ion and a chloride ion.
6. The pure water would freeze before the saltwater because the salt would lower the freezing point of the water.

Answer to . . .

Figure 7 *Increasing the temperature setting causes the detergent to dissolve at a faster rate.*

8.2 Solubility and Concentration

Standards: ICP.3.2, ICP.3.3

Reading Focus

Key Concepts

- How are solutions with different amounts of solute described?
- What factors determine the solubility of a solute?
- What are three ways to measure the concentration of a solution?

Vocabulary

- solubility
- saturated solution
- unsaturated solution
- supersaturated solution
- concentration
- molarity

Reading Strategy

Previewing Copy the table below. Before you read the section, rewrite the green topic headings as *how, why,* and *what* questions. As you read, write an answer to each question.

Question	Answer
What is solubility?	a. _____?_____
b. _____?_____	Solvent, temperature, and pressure
c. _____?_____	d. _____?_____

Have you ever prepared a pitcher of lemonade or iced tea? Fresh lemonade is a solution of water, lemon juice, and sugar. Water is the solvent. Lemon juice and sugar are the solutes.

You might be surprised at how much sugar can dissolve in water. However, there is a limit to the amount of sugar that can dissolve in a given amount of water. Once that limit is reached, no more sugar will dissolve, and you cannot make the solution taste any sweeter.

Solubility

The maximum amount of a solute that dissolves in a given amount of solvent at a constant temperature is called **solubility.** Solubilities are usually expressed in grams of solute per 100 grams of solvent at a specified temperature. Figure 8 lists the solubilities of some common substances in water at 20°C. Notice that table sugar is more soluble in water than table salt, which is more soluble than baking soda.

Knowing the solubility of a substance can help you classify solutions based on how much solute they contain. **Solutions are described as saturated, unsaturated, or supersaturated, depending on the amount of solute in solution.**

Solubility in 100 g of Water at 20°C

Compound	Solubility (g)
Table salt (NaCl)	36.0
Baking soda (NaHCO₃)	9.6
Table sugar ($C_{12}H_{22}O_{11}$)	203.9

Figure 8 At a given temperature, different solutes have different solubilities in water. **Calculating** *At 20°C, how much baking soda can dissolve in 200 grams of water?*

Section 8.2

1 FOCUS

Objectives

8.2.1 **Define** solubility and **describe** factors affecting solubility.

8.2.2 **Classify** solutions as unsaturated, saturated, or supersaturated.

8.2.3 **Calculate** and **compare** and **contrast** solution concentrations expressed as percent by volume, percent by mass, and molarity.

Reading Focus

Build Vocabulary

Word-Part Analysis Ask students what words they know that have the prefix *super-. (Superhero, supersonic, supervise)* Give a definition of the word part. (*Super-* means "above.") Have students predict the meaning of *supersaturated,* given that *saturated* means "unable to hold more." (*Supersaturated* means "holding an amount over the normal level.")

Reading Strategy

a. The maximum amount of solute that dissolves in a given amount of solvent at a given temperature
b. What factors affect solubility?
c. How is the concentration of a solution expressed?
d. Percent by volume, percent by mass, molarity

2 INSTRUCT

Solubility

Build Science Skills

Calculating Have students answer the following questions: Suppose you add 60 g of lead nitrate, Pb(NO₃)₂, to 100 g of water at 20°C. After you stir it, 8 g of lead nitrate remains undissolved. **What is the solubility of lead nitrate at 20°C?** *(52 g per 100 g of water)* **If you add 44 g of table salt to 100 g of water at 20°C, how many grams will remain undissolved?** *(8 g)*
Logical

Answer to . . .

Figure 8 *19.2 g*

Build Reading Literacy L1

Outline Refer to page **156D** in **Chapter 6**, which provides the guidelines for outlining.

Have students read the section. Then, have them use the headings as major divisions in an outline. Have students refer to their outlines when answering the questions in the Section 8.2 Assessment. **Verbal**

Address Misconceptions L2

Some students think that when things dissolve they "disappear" and are no longer there. Challenge this misconception by reviewing the law of conservation of mass. Explain that mass is conserved in all ordinary chemical and physical processes, including solutes dissolving and coming out of solution. Have students examine the beakers on this page. Explain that even though you cannot see the solute in the first beaker, it is still there. Adding a crystal causes the solute to come out of solution and become visible again. **Visual**

Teacher Demo

Crystallization L2

Purpose Students observe crystallization of a solute from a supersaturated solution.

Materials beakers, 200 g sodium acetate trihydrate, distilled water, spatula, hot plate (An alternative to sodium acetate trihydrate is sodium thiosulfate hydrate.)

Procedure The day before, prepare a supersaturated solution consisting of 200 g sodium acetate trihydrate dissolved in 20 mL distilled water. Heat the solution until all of the solute has dissolved. Allow to cool overnight. (Consider preparing multiple solutions in case one crystallizes while it is cooling.) Tell the class that you have prepared a supersaturated solution. Add a crystal of sodium acetate to the cooled solution.

Expected Outcome Upon adding the crystal, the solute will crystallize out of solution and form a solid mass. Be prepared in case the beaker breaks due to expansion of the contents. Have students stand a safe distance away, and do not let students pick up broken glass if the beaker does break. **Visual**

Figure 9 A supersaturated solution is analogous to the overloaded man shown above. One wrong step, and he might drop all the boxes. In the photo sequence below, a single crystal of sodium acetate, $NaC_2H_3O_2$, is added to a supersaturated solution of sodium acetate in water. The excess solute rapidly crystallizes out of the solution.

Saturated Solutions Table sugar is very soluble in water. At 20°C, 203.9 grams of table sugar will dissolve in 100 grams of water. What will happen if you try to dissolve more than 203.9 grams of table sugar in the same amount of water? The extra sugar will not go into solution. The solution is already saturated. A **saturated solution** is one that contains as much solute as the solvent can hold at a given temperature. When a solution is saturated, the solvent is "filled" with solute. If you add more solute, it will not dissolve.

Unsaturated Solutions A solution that has less than the maximum amount of solute that can be dissolved is called an **unsaturated solution.** For example, many of the beverages you drink are unsaturated solutions of sugar in water. If you sweeten your lemonade with a spoonful of sugar, and the sugar dissolves, you know that the solution is unsaturated. As long as the amount of solute is less than the solubility at that temperature, the solution is unsaturated.

Supersaturated Solutions Have you ever tried to carry more books than you can easily manage? If you're not careful, you'll drop them all because the load is so unstable. Similarly, a solvent can sometimes dissolve more solute than you might expect, based on its solubility. Solubility is given at a specific temperature, such as 20°C. If you heat a solvent above that temperature, more solute may dissolve. If you then carefully cool the solvent back to 20°C without jarring it, you may be able to keep the extra solute in solution.

A **supersaturated solution** is one that contains *more* solute than it can normally hold at a given temperature. Supersaturated solutions are very unstable. If even a tiny crystal of the solute falls into a supersaturated solution, the extra solute can rapidly deposit out of solution, as shown in Figure 9.

Reading Checkpoint *How does a supersaturated solution differ from a saturated solution?*

Customize for English Language Learners

Discussion
Students who are learning English can benefit from real-life examples that relate to science content. Encourage students to think of observations they may have made about factors that affect solubility. For example, perhaps they have seen that vinegar and oil salad dressing separates into layers. Also, they may have noticed that carbonated beverages taste "flat" when they are warm. Encourage students to share their observations with the class.

Factors Affecting Solubility

Have you ever had to clean oil or grease from your hands? If you rinse your hands in water alone, the oil remains on your hands. But if you use soapy water, you can easily rinse the oil off your hands. Oil is soluble in soapy water, but not in pure water. Solubility varies not only with the solvent used, but also with the conditions of the solution process. ⟶ **Three factors that affect the solubility of a solute are the polarity of the solvent, temperature, and pressure.**

Polar and Nonpolar Solvents Oil does not dissolve in water because oil molecules are nonpolar and water molecules are polar. A common guideline for predicting solubility is "like dissolves like." Solution formation is more likely to happen when the solute and solvent are either both polar or both nonpolar. Figure 11 illustrates how soapy water dissolves oil. A soap molecule has a polar end, which attracts water molecules, and a nonpolar end, which attracts oil. The soap molecules break up the oil into small droplets that are soluble in water.

Temperature When you add a large amount of sugar to cold tea, only a small amount dissolves. If you add the same amount of sugar to the same amount of hot tea, more sugar will dissolve. In general, the solubility of solids increases as the solvent temperature increases.

When a glass of cold water warms up to room temperature, bubbles form on the inside of the glass. These bubbles are gases that were dissolved in the water. They come out of the solution as the water temperature rises. Unlike most solids, gases usually become less soluble as the temperature of the solvent increases.

Pressure How do manufacturers produce a carbonated beverage? They use pressure to force carbon dioxide (CO_2) to dissolve in the liquid. Increasing the pressure on a gas increases its solubility in a liquid. The pressure of CO_2 in a sealed 12-ounce can of soda at room temperature can be two to three times atmospheric pressure.

Figure 10 Generally, a solute is more likely to dissolve in a "like" solvent than an "unlike" solvent. **Classifying** *How is saltwater an example of "like dissolving in like"?*

Solvent-Solute Combinations

Solvent Type	Solute Type	Will Solution Form?
Polar	Polar (or ionic)	More likely
Polar	Nonpolar	Not likely
Nonpolar	Polar (or ionic)	Not likely
Nonpolar	Nonpolar	More likely

Figure 11 Soaps and detergents are used to remove grease and oil stains. Soap molecules form attractions to both polar water molecules and nonpolar oil molecules. As the water flows away, it carries the oil with it.

Water molecule — Polar end of soap molecule — Nonpolar end of soap molecule — Grease

Solutions, Acids, and Bases **237**

Facts and Figures

Micelles and Soap When the nonpolar ends of soap molecules clump together in water in such a way that their polar ends radiate outward, they make a ball-shaped formation called a *micelle*. When a mixture of water and soap is mixed, the small micelles become suspended in the water. Because the micelles scatter light, soapy water is cloudy. The process for making soap is discussed in Section 8.3.

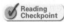

Concentration of Solutions

Build Science Skills

Interpreting Diagrams Have students examine the label in Figure 12. Then, have students calculate the volume of real cranberry juice in 300 mL of Smith's Cranberry Juice. *(81 mL)*
Logical

 Problem-Solving Activity

Putting the Fizz Into Carbonated Beverages **L2**

Defining the Problem The problem is how to find a supplier of carbon dioxide for adding carbonation to beverages and how to keep the levels of carbon dioxide in the beverages constant.

Organizing Information Examples of reactions that create carbon dioxide include reacting vinegar and baking soda, fermentation in yeast, cellular respiration in plants and animals, and combustion of carbon compounds. Students will need to find out what kinds of manufacturers produce large amounts of carbon dioxide gas. They will also need to find out how temperature, pressure, and type of solvent affect the solubility of gases.

Creating a Solution Students may choose a gas or petroleum company as a supplier. (CO_2 is also a by-product in fertilizer and fermentation processes.) Two factors that affect solubility of a gas in a liquid are temperature and pressure.

Presenting Your Plan Acceptable proposals should include reasons for choosing the supplier, such as low cost, facility of distribution, or quality of product. To regulate carbonation levels, the factory can manipulate the temperature and pressure at which CO_2 dissolves. The solubility of a gas increases as pressure increases and temperature decreases.
Logical

For Extra Help **L1**

Encourage students to be creative in their research. They do not have to limit their research to the library or Internet. Students may want to call a local restaurant that serves carbonated fountain drinks to find out where they get their carbon dioxide. They could also call or visit a local bottling company.
Interpersonal

SMITH'S
Cranberry Juice
Black River Falls, Wisconsin

Contains 27% Cranberry Juice

INGREDIENTS: Filtered Water, Cranberry Juice (Cranberry Juice from Concentrate and Cranberry Juice), High Fructose Corn Syrup, Ascorbic Acid (Vitamin C)

Figure 12 The juice squeezed from fruit is already a solution. Most bottled or canned juices are less-concentrated solutions of fruit juices, made by adding water. Percent by volume is a way to measure the concentration of one liquid dissolved in another.

Concentration of Solutions

How do you take your tea? Some people prefer their tea very concentrated, so they leave the tea bag in hot water for several minutes. Other people immerse the tea bag for only a minute or two, because they prefer their tea much less concentrated, or dilute. The resulting solutions differ in how much solute is present. The **concentration** of a solution is the amount of solute dissolved in a specified amount of solution. 🔵 **Concentration can be expressed as percent by volume, percent by mass, and molarity.**

Percent by Volume Fruit juice bottles often have labels, such as the one in Figure 12, that state the percentage of "real juice" in the bottle. For example, if 27 percent of the total volume of liquid is fruit juice, the concentration of fruit juice is 27 percent by volume. Use the following equation to calculate concentration as a percent by volume.

$$\text{Percent by volume} = \frac{\text{Volume of solute}}{\text{Volume of solution}} \times 100\%$$

Percent by Mass Concentration expressed as a percent by mass is more useful when the solute is a solid. Percent by mass is the percent of a solution's total mass that is accounted for by a solute.

$$\text{Percent by mass} = \frac{\text{Mass of solute}}{\text{Mass of solution}} \times 100\%$$

Suppose you have 100 grams of a solution of sugar in water. After allowing the water to evaporate, 15 grams of sugar remain. So, the concentration of sugar in the solution was 15 percent by mass.

 Problem-Solving Activity

Putting the Fizz Into Carbonated Beverages

You have been asked to find a supplier of carbon dioxide for a factory that produces carbonated beverages. You also must find out how to regulate the carbonation levels of the beverages produced.

Defining the Problem Describe your task in your own words.

Organizing Information Find examples of chemical reactions that produce carbon dioxide. What industries use such reactions? In addition, list and review the general factors affecting solubility.

Creating a Solution Choose a business or industry to supply your factory with carbon dioxide. Figure out how the solubility of a gas in a liquid varies under different conditions.

Presenting Your Plan Write a proposal to the manager of your factory. Explain your choice of a carbon dioxide supplier, and describe how to regulate carbonation levels of the beverages produced.

238   *Chapter 8*

Facts and Figures

Molality Another way of describing solution concentration is called *molality*. Molality is defined as the number of moles of solute per kilogram of solvent, and is represented by a lower case *m*. The advantage of using molality over molarity to describe concentrations is that molality does not involve volume and thus does not change with changes in temperature. For this reason, molality is often used in calculations involving colligative properties (such as freezing point depression and boiling point elevation) that are observed over a range of temperatures.

Molarity Suppose you add 10 grams of sodium chloride to 100 milliliters of water. Then, in a different container, you add 10 grams of table sugar to 100 milliliters of water. Do the two solutions contain the same number of solute particles? No, they do not, because the two different solutes have different molar masses.

To compare the number of solute particles in solutions, chemists often use moles to measure concentration. Recall that a mole is the amount of a substance that contains approximately 6.02×10^{23} particles of that substance. **Molarity** is the number of moles of a solute dissolved per liter of solution. Use the following equation to calculate molarity.

$$\text{Molarity} = \frac{\text{Moles of solute}}{\text{Liters of solution}}$$

To make a 1-molar (1M) solution of sodium chloride in water, first calculate the molar mass of the solute. Sodium chloride, NaCl, has a molar mass of 58.5 grams. If 58.5 grams of sodium chloride is mixed with enough water to make one liter of solution, the resulting solution is 1-molar.

Table sugar, $C_{12}H_{22}O_{11}$, has a molar mass of 342 grams. To make a 1-molar solution of table sugar in water, 342 grams of table sugar must be added to enough water to make one liter of solution.

Figure 13 A 1M NaCl solution contains 58.5 grams of NaCl per liter of solution. **Calculating** *How much solute would you need to make to make one liter of a 0.2-molar solution of sodium chloride in water?*

Section 8.2 Assessment

Reviewing Concepts

1. ⊙ What terms are used to describe solutions with different amounts of solute?
2. ⊙ List three factors that affect solubility.
3. ⊙ What are three ways to measure the concentration of a solution?
4. What is the effect of pressure on the solubility of a gas?
5. Compare a 2-molar solution of salt water with a 2-molar solution of sugar water. How are they similar? How are they different?

Critical Thinking

6. **Problem Solving** How would you figure out the solubility of an unknown solid in water?

7. **Inferring** Despite the name, dry cleaning does involve the use of liquid solvents. Why would a dry cleaner use both polar and nonpolar cleaning solvents?
8. **Calculating** Use the periodic table to find the mass of potassium nitrate (KNO_3) needed to make 1 liter of 1-molar solution.

Writing in Science

Compare and Contrast Paragraph Write a paragraph comparing the different ways that concentration can be expressed. (*Hint*: Describe what quantities must be measured for each type of concentration calculation.)

Solutions, Acids, and Bases **239**

Section 8.2 Assessment

1. Unsaturated, saturated, and supersaturated
2. Polarity of the solute and solvent, temperature, and pressure
3. Percent by volume, percent by mass, and molarity
4. It increases the solubility of a gas.
5. The molar concentrations of the solutions are identical; each contains the same number of moles of solute per liter of solution. The solutions differ in percent by mass concentration; the sugar water solution contains more

grams of solute per gram of solution than the saltwater solution.
6. Measure the mass of a beaker containing 100 g of water. Add the unknown solid, while stirring, until no more dissolves. Measure the mass of the beaker and its contents again. Measure the temperature of the solution. The difference in mass is the solubility of the unknown solid in grams per 100 g of water.
7. To remove both polar and nonpolar stains
8. 101.1 g

Build Math Skills **L1**

Calculating With Significant Figures
Have students solve the following problems and express their answers using the correct significant figures. **What is the molarity of a solution consisting of 111 g of $CaCl_2$ dissolved in enough water to make 2.0 L of solution?** *(0.50 M)* **What volume of a 2.00-M solution KI in water contains 5.96 moles of solute?** *(2.98 L)* **Logical**

Direct students to the **Math Skills** in the **Skills and Reference Handbook** at the end of the student text for additional help.

3 ASSESS

Evaluate Understanding **L2**

Have students write three math problems (with solutions) based on the equations given for percent by volume, percent by mass, and molarity. Have students take turns analyzing and solving the problems in class. Note that even incorrectly worded problems are useful because students can be asked to identify and correct the errors.

Reteach **L1**

Use the table on p. 235 to review solubility. Have students describe how much solute would be in an unsaturated, saturated, and supersaturated solution of each type of solute given in the table. For example, any amount less than 36.0 g of sodium chloride in 100 g of water would be an unsaturated solution.

Writing in Science

Concentration can be expressed in at least three different ways—percent by volume, percent by mass, and molarity. To determine percent by volume, you need to find the volume of solute and the volume of solution. To determine percent by mass, you need to find the mass of solute and the mass of solution. To determine molarity, you need to find the moles of solute and the volume of solution (in liters).

Interactive Textbook If your class subscribes to the Interactive Textbook, use it to review key concepts in Section 8.2.

Answer to . . .

Figure 13 *11.7 g*

8.3 Properties of Acids and Bases

1 FOCUS

Objectives

8.3.1 **Define** acid and **describe** some of the general properties of an acid.

8.3.2 **Define** base and **describe** some of the general properties of a base.

8.3.3 **Identify** a neutralization reaction, and **describe** the reactants and products of neutralization.

8.3.4 **Explain** how acids and bases can be defined as proton donors and proton acceptors.

Reading Focus

Build Vocabulary L2

Concept Map Have students construct a concept map of the vocabulary terms used in this section. Instruct students to place the vocabulary terms in ovals and connect the ovals with lines on which linking words are placed. Students should place the main concept (Properties of Acids and Bases) at the top or the center. As they move away from the main concept, the content should become more specific.

Reading Strategy L2

b. A compound that produces hydronium ions when dissolved in water **d.** A compound that produces hydroxide ions when dissolved in water **f.** Any ionic compound that forms when an acid reacts with a base

2 INSTRUCT

Identifying Acids

Address Misconceptions L2

Many students think that all acids are harmful or that all harmful chemicals are acids. Challenge these misconceptions by asking, **What juices might contain acids?** *(Orange juice, lemon juice, and tomato juice are all acidic.)* **Do you know of any acid that exists normally in your body?** *(Stomach acid contains hydrochloric acid, which aids in digestion.)*
Verbal

Standards: ICP.3.1, ICP.5.5

Reading Focus

Key Concepts

- What are some general properties of acids and bases?
- What are the products of neutralization?
- What are proton donors and proton acceptors?

Vocabulary

- ◆ acid
- ◆ indicator
- ◆ base
- ◆ neutralization
- ◆ salt

Reading Strategy

Using Prior Knowledge Before you read, copy the table below and write your definition for each vocabulary term. After you read, write the scientific definition of each term and compare it with your original definition.

Term	Your Definition	Scientific Definition
Acid	a. ?	b. ?
Base	c. ?	d. ?
Salt	e. ?	f. ?

Figure 14 Soap making involves the use of a base such as sodium hydroxide or potassium hydroxide.

One of the chemicals used to make the soaps shown in Figure 14 is sodium hydroxide. In traditional soap making, sodium hydroxide is added to a mixture of melted animal or vegetable fats. As the mixture is brought to a boil, the sodium hydroxide reacts with the fats. The products of the reaction are glycerol (a colorless, syrupy liquid) and soap. After the glycerol is separated from the soap, the soap is purified. Other chemicals are then mixed with the soap to give it a particular scent and color.

Sodium hydroxide belongs to a class of compounds, known as bases, that share some physical and chemical properties. Bases are related to another class of compounds called acids. As you will discover, there are several differences among acidic solutions, basic solutions, and solutions that have properties of neither an acid nor a base.

Identifying Acids

An **acid** is a compound that produces hydronium ions (H_3O^+) when dissolved in water. Recall that when hydrogen chloride gas dissolves in water, it ionizes and forms hydronium ions and chloride ions.

$$HCl + H_2O \longrightarrow H_3O^+ + Cl^-$$

The solution that results is called hydrochloric acid. Figure 15 lists some common acids and their uses.

240 Chapter 8

Section Resources

Print
- *Laboratory Manual*, Investigation 8A
- *Reading and Study Workbook With Math Support*, Section 8.3
- *Transparencies*, Section 8.3

Technology
- *Probeware Lab Manual*, Lab 3
- *Interactive Textbook*, Section 8.3
- *Presentation Pro CD-ROM*, Section 8.3
- *Go Online*, NSTA SciLinks, Bases

Common Acids		
Name	Formula	Use
Acetic acid	CH_3COOH	Vinegar
Carbonic acid	H_2CO_3	Carbonated beverages
Hydrochloric acid	HCl	Digestive juices in stomach
Nitric acid	HNO_3	Fertilizer production
Phosphoric acid	H_3PO_4	Fertilizer production
Sulfuric acid	H_2SO_4	Car batteries

Figure 15 The table lists names, formulas, and uses for several common acids.
Inferring **What products are formed when nitric acid ionizes in water?**

Build Reading Literacy L1
Compare and Contrast Refer to page **226D** in this chapter, which provides the guidelines for comparing and contrasting.

Have students read the section. As they read, they should create lists of how acids and bases are similar and different. **Verbal**

Acids have certain chemical and physical properties that are similar. ⬛ **Some general properties of acids include sour taste, reactivity with metals, and ability to produce color changes in indicators.**

Sour Taste Foods that taste sour often contain acids. For example, lemons, grapefruits, limes, and oranges all contain citric acid. The vinegar used in salad dressings contains acetic acid, CH_3COOH. Dairy products that have spoiled contain butyric (byoo THIR ik) acid. While many of the foods you eat contain acids, you should never test an acid by tasting it.

Reactivity With Metals When you use aluminum foil to cover a bowl of leftover spaghetti sauce or other foods containing tomatoes, the foil often turns dark. The foil may also develop small holes, and the food may acquire a metallic taste. Tomatoes contain citric acid, which reacts with metals such as aluminum.

The reaction between an acid and a metal is an example of a single-replacement reaction. For example, when zinc is added to a test tube containing hydrochloric acid, bubbles form in the tube. The following equation describes the reaction.

$$Zn + 2HCl \longrightarrow H_2 + ZnCl_2$$

As the zinc replaces hydrogen in hydrochloric acid, hydrogen gas and zinc(II) chloride are produced.

Color Changes in Indicators An **indicator** is any substance that changes color in the presence of an acid or base. One of the most common indicators used is litmus, a kind of dye derived from plants called lichens (LY kens). Litmus paper, shown in Figure 16, is made by coating strips of paper with litmus. Blue litmus paper turns red in the presence of an acid. If you drop an unknown solution onto blue litmus paper and the litmus paper turns red, you can classify the solution as an acid.

Figure 16 Litmus paper is an indicator that changes color in the presence of acids and bases. When blue litmus paper touches an acid, it turns red. Apples contain several acids, including malic acid, ascorbic acid (vitamin C), and citric acid.

Solutions, Acids, and Bases **241**

Customize for Inclusion Students

Behaviorally Disordered
Have students collect soil samples from various locations near the school and their homes. Have them note the types of plants that are found in the locations where they collected their samples. Provide students with water test kits so they can determine the pH of each sample. Have students determine if there is a correlation between the types of plants that grow in an area and the pH of the soil.

Answer to . . .
Figure 15 NO_3^- *and* H_3O^+

Identifying Bases
Build Science Skills L2

Observing Encourage students to bring in various products from home and test each product with litmus paper. Many of the following products contain acids: fruit juices, vinegar, carbonated beverages, milk, and fertilizers. Many of the following products contain bases: cleaning products, detergents, soaps, deodorants, and antacids. Avoid having students bring in corrosive products such as car batteries or drain cleaners. As a class, make a chart that classifies each product as acidic, neutral, or basic.
Visual

Build Science Skills L2

Comparing and Contrasting Have students examine the table in Figure 17. Ask, **What do the bases listed in the table have in common?** *(They all contain OH⁻, hydroxide ions.)* **How do the bases differ?** *(They have different cations and different numbers of hydroxide ions.)*
Logical

Download a worksheet on bases for students to complete, and find additional teacher support from NSTA SciLinks.

For: Links on bases
Visit: www.SciLinks.org
Web Code: ccn-1083

Identifying Bases

Sodium hydroxide, NaOH, is an example of a base. A **base** is a compound that produces hydroxide ions (OH^-) when dissolved in water. When sodium hydroxide dissolves in water, it dissociates into sodium ions and hydroxide ions.

$$NaOH \longrightarrow Na^+ + OH^-$$

Figure 17 lists some common bases and their uses. Like acids, bases have certain physical and chemical properties that you can use to identify them. **Some general properties of bases include bitter taste, slippery feel, and ability to produce color changes in indicators.** Unlike acids, bases usually do not react with metals. However, low reactivity with metals is not considered a general property of bases. For example, sodium hydroxide reacts very vigorously with metals such as aluminum and zinc.

Bitter Taste Have you ever tasted unsweetened chocolate (sometimes called baking chocolate)? Without sugar, chocolate tastes bitter. Cacao beans contain a base called theobromine that gives unsweetened chocolate its bitter taste.

Many cough syrups and other liquid medicines contain similar bases. Fruit flavorings are often added to mask the taste of these basic solutions.

Slippery Feel Bases feel slippery. Wet soap and many cleaning products that contain bases are slippery to the touch. When wet, some rocks feel slippery because the water dissolves compounds trapped in the rocks, producing a basic solution.

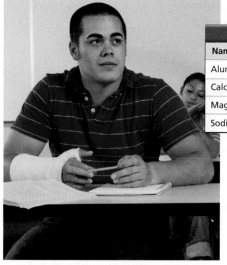

Common Bases		
Name	**Formula**	**Uses**
Aluminum hydroxide	$Al(OH)_3$	Deodorant, antacid
Calcium hydroxide	$Ca(OH)_2$	Concrete, plaster
Magnesium hydroxide	$Mg(OH)_2$	Antacid, laxative
Sodium hydroxide	NaOH	Drain cleaner, soap production

Figure 17 A base is a compound that produces hydroxide ions when dissolved in water. The plaster in this boy's cast contains a base. Bases are also commonly found in products used for cleaning.

Quick Lab

Using an Indicator

Materials
one quarter cup of frozen blueberries, foam cup, spoon, 4 small plastic cups, 2 dropper pipets, lemon juice, white vinegar, window cleaner, baking soda

Procedure

1. Place the blueberries in the foam cup and mash them with the spoon. Try to get as much juice out of the berries as possible. You will use the juice as an indicator.

2. Use the spoon to remove most of the crushed berries and discard them as directed by your teacher. Leave as much juice behind as possible.

3. Use a dropper pipet to place a few drops of lemon juice (which is acidic) in one of the plastic cups. Use a second pipet to add one drop of your indicator to the lemon juice. Swirl the cup. Record your observations.

4. Rinse out the pipets with water. Repeat Step 3, using vinegar and then window cleaner in place of lemon juice. Record your observations.

5. Place several drops of the indicator in the last plastic cup. Add a small pinch of baking soda to the cup. Swirl the cup. Record your observations.

Analyze and Conclude

1. **Classifying** Use your observations to determine how the color of blueberry juice changes in acids and bases.

2. **Drawing Conclusions** How does the blueberry indicator help you determine whether a material is an acid or a base?

3. **Inferring** Why does the color of the blueberry indicator change less when added to acids than when added to bases?

Color Changes in Indicators Bases turn red litmus paper blue. The litmus paper will change back to red if you drop an acidic solution on it.

Phenolphthalein (fee nol THAY leen) is another example of an acid-base indicator. In a solution containing a base, phenolphthalein is red. In a solution containing an acid, phenolphthalein is colorless.

Some flowers, like the hydrangeas shown in Figure 18, contain natural indicators. The color of the flowers depends on whether the plant is growing in acidic or basic soil. When hydrangeas grow in acidic soil, the flowers are bluish-purple. When hydrangeas grow in basic soil, the flowers are pink. By manipulating the acidity of the soil, gardeners can determine the color of the flowers.

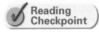 **Reading Checkpoint** *What color does litmus paper turn in a base?*

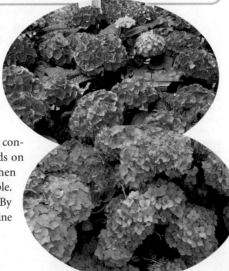

Figure 18 Soil acidity can affect the color of flowers such as hydrangeas.

Solutions, Acids, and Bases **243**

Facts and Figures

Litmus Paper Litmus paper contains a combination of several organic compounds that come from a species of lichen. Originally litmus was used as a dye. Today, some of these compounds are also used in perfume making and antibiotics.

 Quick Lab

Using an Indicator **L2**

Objective
After completing this activity, students will be able to
• extract an indicator from blueberries and use it to classify substances as acids or bases.

Skills Focus Observing, Classifying, Drawing Conclusions, Inferring

🕐 **Prep Time** 15 minutes

Advanced Prep Provide ammonia-based window cleaner because alcohol-based window cleaner may not be basic.

Class Time 15 minutes

Safety Have students observe safety symbols and wear safety goggles and lab aprons.

Teaching Tips
• Have students dispose of crushed berries in the trash.
• Dispose of all waste solutions in the sink with excess water.

Expected Outcome The indicator will stay purple with lemon juice and vinegar. It will turn green with window cleaner and baking soda.

Analyze and Conclude
1. Lemon juice and vinegar contain acids and do not change the color of the indicator. Window cleaner and baking soda contain bases and change the color of the indicator to green.
2. It is purple in an acid and green in a base.
3. Blueberries contain acid. The indicator does not change color in an acid because it is already indicating an acid.
Visual, Logical

For Enrichment **L3**
Have students use their blueberry indicator on other substances, such as a carbonated beverage, deionized water, and a laundry detergent solution. Ask them if they can conclude that a substance, such as water, is acidic if it does not turn the indicator green. Have them test their inferences using litmus paper.
Visual, Logical

Answer to . . .

 Reading Checkpoint *Blue*

Solutions, Acids, and Bases **243**

Neutralization and Salts

Neutralization Reaction L2

Purpose Students observe a neutralization reaction.

Materials 2 lemons, beaker, 0.1-M solution of NaOH, phenolphthalein solution (indicator), syringe, knife

Procedure Tell students that the phenolphthalein solution is an indicator that is pink in the presence of bases. Pour a small amount of the 0.1-M NaOH solution in the beaker. Add a couple of drops of indicator. Have students note the pink color. Explain that you are going to try to turn one of the lemons pink by injecting it with the base and indicator. Use the syringe to inject the NaOH solution into one of the lemons. Wait a few moments and then cut open both lemons.

Safety Use caution when handling the base solution. Sodium hydroxide is corrosive. In case of spills, clean thoroughly with water. Have students wear safety goggles, plastic gloves, and lab aprons should they handle the demo materials. Do not allow students to handle the syringe.

Expected Outcome Both lemons will have their normal color. Explain that a neutralization reaction occurred. The base reacted with the acid in the lemons to produce a salt. You cannot use phenolphthalein to turn a lemon pink unless you add enough base to react with all of the acid in the lemon with some base left over. The amount of base required to neutralize a lemon depends on the amount of juice in the lemon and the amount of acid the juice contains. Pour a small amount of the base (with indicator) solution onto the cut face of one of the lemons to allow students to observe the pink color of the basic solution disappear as the base is neutralized.
Visual

Neutralization and Salts

When people eat fish, they sometimes squeeze lemon juice over the fish. Fish contains bases that can leave a bitter taste. Lemon juice contains acids, such as citric acid. By squeezing lemon juice over the fish, the citric acid reacts with the bases in the fish, and the fish tastes less bitter.

The reaction between an acid and a base is called **neutralization.** During neutralization, the negative ions in an acid combine with the positive ions in a base to produce an ionic compound called a **salt.** At the same time, the hydronium ions from the acid combine with the hydroxide ions from the base to produce water. ⬤ **The neutralization reaction between an acid and a base produces a salt and water.**

For example, when hydrochloric acid reacts with sodium hydroxide, the following neutralization reaction occurs.

$$(H_3O^+ + Cl^-) + (Na^+ + OH^-) \longrightarrow 2HOH + (Na^+ + Cl^-)$$

| acid | base | water | salt |

The products of the reaction are a salt made up of sodium and chloride ions, and water. If you let the water in the resulting solution evaporate, the sodium and chloride ions would begin to crystallize out of solution, forming table salt.

Table salt is the most common example of a salt compound. Other common salts are listed in Figure 19. For instance, baking soda, $NaHCO_3$, is produced during the neutralization reaction between sodium hydroxide and carbonic acid, H_2CO_3. The other product is water. The ocean contains many dissolved salts, including chlorides and sulfates of potassium, calcium, magnesium, and sodium. Many of these salts go into solution as seawater washes against rocks.

Figure 19 The common salts listed in the table can all be made by reacting an acid with a base. One of these salts, sodium carbonate, was used to make the glass for the vases shown below. *Inferring* **Name an acid and a base that could react to form potassium chloride, KCl.**

Common Salts		
Name	**Formula**	**Uses**
Sodium chloride	NaCl	Food flavoring, preservative
Sodium carbonate	Na_2CO_3	Used to make glass
Potassium chloride	KCl	Used as a salt substitute to reduce dietary intake of sodium
Potassium iodide	KI	Added to table salt to prevent iodine deficiency
Magnesium chloride	$MgCl_2$	De-icer for roads
Calcium carbonate	$CaCO_3$	Chalk, marble floors, and tables
Ammonium nitrate	NH_4NO_3	Fertilizer, cold packs

244 *Chapter 8*

Facts and Figures

Differing Definitions The definitions for acids and bases given on the previous pages are similar to those described by Swedish physicist Svante Arrhenius in 1884. Note that acids do not necessarily contain hydronium ions and bases do not necessarily contain hydroxide ions. An alternative way of defining acids and bases was developed independently in 1923 by J. N. Brønsted and T. M. Lowry and is described on p. 245. A Brønsted-Lowry base is a proton acceptor, while a Brønsted-Lowry acid is a proton donor. The distinction is important when describing nonaqueous solutions.

Proton Donors and Acceptors

Recall that hydronium ions (H_3O^+) are produced when acids dissolve in water. When an acid and a base react in water, a proton from the hydronium ion from the acid combines with the hydroxide ion (OH^-) from the base to form water (H_2O). Acids lose, or "donate," protons. Bases "accept" protons, forming water, a neutral molecule. ● **Acids can be defined as proton donors, and bases can be defined as proton acceptors.** This definition allows you to classify a wider range of substances as acids or bases.

Based on the definitions of acids and bases that you read earlier in this section, water is neither an acid nor a base. However, using the proton-donor or proton-acceptor definition, water can act as either an acid or a base depending on the compound with which it reacts.

Figure 20 shows the ionization of hydrogen chloride and ammonia as they form solutions. In the first reaction, water acts as a base. It accepts a proton from hydrogen chloride and becomes a hydronium ion. In the second reaction, water acts as an acid. It donates a proton to the ammonia, which acts as a base. The resulting solution contains hydroxide ions and ammonium ions, NH_4^+.

Figure 20 In the first reaction, water acts as a base, accepting a proton from hydrogen chloride. In the second reaction, water acts as an acid, donating a proton to the ammonia.
Applying Concepts **What acts as the proton donor in the first reaction?**

Section 8.3 Assessment

Reviewing Concepts

1. ● List three general properties of acids.
2. ● List three general properties of bases.
3. ● What are the two products of a neutralization reaction?
4. ● What are the proton-donor and proton-acceptor definitions of acids and bases?
5. What ion is present in all common acid solutions?

Critical Thinking

6. **Using Analogies** Commercials for antacids often claim these products neutralize stomach acid. Antacids are bases. Think of an analogy for the way in which antacids neutralize acids.

7. **Applying Concepts** In the following equation, which reactant is a proton donor? Which is a proton acceptor?
$$HNO_3 + H_2O \longrightarrow H_3O^+ + NO_3^-$$

Connecting ⊂ Concepts

Classifying Reactions Compare neutralization with the types of chemical reactions described in Section 7.2. To which type of reaction is neutralization most similar? Explain your choice.

Figure 20 Have students examine and read the caption for Figure 20. **How many reactions are represented in the figure?** *(2)* **How are atoms represented in this figure?** *(Atoms are represented by their chemical symbol and small, orange dots.)* **What do the small, orange dots represent?** *(Valence electrons)* **What do the positive and negative signs represent?** *(The charge of each ion)* **How can you tell which substance is the proton donor?** *(When that substance loses an H, a proton)* **What happens to a proton donor in this figure after it donates a proton?** *(It becomes a negative ion.)*
Visual

3 ASSESS

Evaluate Understanding L2

Have students write the equation for a neutralization reaction and label each reactant or product as an acid, base, salt, proton donor, or proton acceptor. Then, have them indicate the color each reactant and product would turn red and blue litmus paper.

Reteach L1

Use Figure 20 to summarize the key features of acids, bases, and neutralization reactions.

Connecting ⊂ Concepts

Neutralization is an example of a double-replacement reaction. During neutralization, an acid and a base exchange positive ions, forming water and a salt.

Interactive Textbook If your class subscribes to the Interactive Textbook, use it to review key concepts in Section 8.3.

Section 8.3 Assessment

1. They taste sour, react with certain metals, and turn blue litmus paper red.
2. They taste bitter, feel slippery, and turn red litmus paper blue.
3. Water and a salt
4. Acids are proton donors, and bases are proton acceptors.
5. Hydronium (H_3O^+)
6. Acceptable answers include saying that it's like a positive number canceling out a negative number of the same value when added: $6+ (-6) = 0$
7. HNO_3 is the proton donor, and H_2O is the proton acceptor.

Answer to . . .

Figure 19 *Potassium hydroxide (KOH) and hydrogen chloride (HCl)*

Figure 20 *Hydrogen chloride*

---

1 FOCUS

Objectives

8.4.1 **Define** pH, and **relate** pH to hydronium ion concentration in a solution.

8.4.2 **Distinguish** between strong acids and weak acids, and between strong bases and weak bases.

8.4.3 **Define** buffer, and **describe** how a buffer can be prepared.

8.4.4 **Explain** how electrolytes can be classified.

Reading Focus

Build Vocabulary   L2

Word Meanings Ask students to brainstorm examples of product advertising that contain the terms *pH, electrolyte,* or *buffer.* (*Students may have heard of beauty products described as "pH-balanced," some sports beverages contain electrolytes, and many antacids contain buffers.*) Have students look up the definition of each term and speculate what is meant by the advertisers' claims. (*Answers may include that some deodorants differ in acidity, sports drinks contain ions in solution, and some antacids can be used to resist large changes in pH.*)

Reading Strategy   L2

a. Ionizes almost completely when dissolved in water
b. Is a strong electrolyte
c. Dissociates almost completely when dissolved in water

2 INSTRUCT

Build Reading Literacy   L1

Identify Main Idea/Details Refer to page **98D** in **Chapter 4**, which provides the guidelines for identifying main idea and details.

Have students read the section and make a list of the main headings on each page. Under each heading, have them identify the main idea of the passage. Have students refer to their lists when answering the questions in the Section 8.4 Assessment.
Verbal

8.4 Strength of Acids and Bases

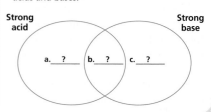

Standards: ICP.3.1, ICP.5.5, ICP.6.3

Reading Focus

Key Concepts

- How is pH used to describe the concentration of acids and bases?
- How do strong acids and bases differ from weak acids and bases?
- Why are strong acids and bases good electrolytes?

Vocabulary

- pH
- buffer
- electrolyte

Reading Strategy

Comparing and Contrasting Copy the Venn diagram below. As you read, complete the diagram by comparing and contrasting acids and bases.

Strong acid   Strong base

a. ? b. ? c. ?

Figure 21 Sodium bicarbonate, or baking soda, is often added to swimming pools to regulate the acidity of the water.

On a hot summer day, you might go swimming in a pool with some of your friends. As the water evaporates from your skin, you feel cooler and refreshed.

Have you ever thought about how the water in a swimming pool is made safe for swimming? You may have noticed the odor of chlorine at a backyard swimming pool or at larger municipal pools. Certain compounds of chlorine are dissolved in the water. These compounds prevent the growth of bacteria that could make you sick.

The concentration of hydronium ions in solution must be carefully controlled in a swimming pool. If there are too many or too few hydronium ions, then the right compounds of chlorine will not be present. Figure 21 shows a pool maintenance worker adding sodium bicarbonate, $NaHCO_3$, to the water. Sodium bicarbonate can be used to lower the concentration of hydronium ions in solution.

How can you describe the acidity or basicity of a solution? One way is to determine the concentration of hydronium or hydroxide ions present in solution. Another way is to describe how readily those hydronium ions or hydroxide ions formed.

Section Resources

Print
- *Reading and Study Workbook With Math Support,* Section 8.4
- *Transparencies,* Section 8.4

Technology
- *Interactive Textbook,* Section 8.4
- *Presentation Pro CD-ROM,* Section 8.4
- *Go Online,* NSTA SciLinks, pH

Car battery acid　Lemons　Oranges　White bread　Distilled water　Soap　Drain cleaner

0　1　2　3　4　5　6　7　8　9　10　11　12　13　14

Most acidic　　　　　　　　　Neutral　　　　　　　　　　*Most basic*

Vinegar　Tomato　Milk　　　　　Baking soda　Ammonia

The pH Scale

Chemists use a number scale from 0 to 14 to describe the concentration of hydronium ions in a solution. It is known as the pH scale. The **pH** of a solution is a measure of its hydronium ion concentration. A pH of 7 indicates a neutral solution. Acids have a pH less than 7. Bases have a pH greater than 7.

Notice in Figure 22 that water falls in the middle of the pH scale. Water ionizes slightly according to the following reaction.

$$2H_2O \rightleftharpoons H_3O^+ + OH^-$$

The arrow pointing to the left is longer than the arrow pointing to the right to show that water contains more molecules than ions. Water is neutral because it contains small but equal concentrations of hydronium ions and hydroxide ions. At 25°C, the concentration of both H_3O^+ and OH^- in water is 1.0×10^{-7} M. Pure water has a pH of 7.

If you add an acid to water, the concentration of H_3O^+ increases and the concentration of OH^- decreases. Suppose you have a hydrochloric acid solution in which the concentration of H_3O^+ is 0.10 M (or 1.0×10^{-1} M). The solution has a pH of 1. 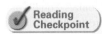 **The lower the pH value, the greater the H_3O^+ ion concentrtion in solution is.**

If you add a base to water, the concentration of OH^- increases and the concentration of H_3O^+ decreases. Consider a sodium hydroxide solution in which the concentration of OH^- is 0.10 M. The concentration of H_3O^+ in this solution is 1.0×10^{-13} M, which corresponds to a pH of 13. **The higher the pH value, the lower the H_3O^+ ion concentration is.**

> **Reading Checkpoint**　*What is the pH of pure water?*

Strong Acids and Bases

Recall that some reactions go to completion while others reach equilibrium. When certain acids and bases dissolve in water, the formation of ions from the solute almost goes to completion. Such acids and bases are classified as *strong*.

Figure 22 The pH scale can help you classify solutions as acids or bases.
Comparing and Contrasting
The desired pH range of chlorinated water in swimming pools is 7.2 to 7.8. How does the concentration of hydronium ions in this solution compare to that of lemon juice?

For: Links on pH
Visit: www.SciLinks.org
Web Code: ccn-1084

Solutions, Acids, and Bases **247**

The pH Scale
Use Visuals　L1

Figure 22 Have students examine Figure 22 of the pH scale. Ask, **In which direction would you find substances that are more acidic?** *(To the left)* **Would a solution with a pH of 11 be an acid or a base?** *(A base)* **What is the pH of ammonia?** *(11.5)* **Compare the pH and acidity of oranges and tomatoes.** *(Oranges have a lower pH than tomatoes and are therefore more acidic.)* **Visual**

Build Math Skills　L1

Exponents Many students have a hard time interpreting positive and negative exponents. Be sure that they understand that a value with a large negative exponent is significantly smaller than a value with a small negative exponent. **Logical**

Direct students to the **Math Skills** in the **Skills and Reference Handbook** at the end of the student text for additional help.

Strong Acids and Bases
Integrate Biology　L2

Explain that the stomach contains a dilute solution of hydrochloric acid, HCl. Even though the solution is dilute, HCl is a strong acid, which means it ionizes completely in solution. Have students find out how this strong acid aids in digestion. Have them make a poster illustrating the stomach's role in digestion and explain how food is digested by stomach acid. *(Stomach acid works with enzymes to help break down proteins. Contraction of stomach muscles helps to mix the food, acid, and enzymes, turning food into a semiliquid.)* **Visual, Verbal**

Download a worksheet on pH for students to complete, and find additional teacher support from NSTA SciLinks.

Answer to . . .

Figure 22 *Concentration of hydronium ions in lemon juice is greater.*

> **Reading Checkpoint**　7

Solutions, Acids, and Bases **247**

Weak Acids and Bases

Making a Battery L2

Objective
After completing this activity, students will be able to
- make a battery using a lemon as a source for electrolytes.

Skills Focus Observing, Predicting

 Prep Time 5 minutes

Advance Prep Use tin strips to cut copper and zinc into 2–5 cm strips. Strip the ends if using insulated wires. File down the rough edges of the metal strips. Wear heavy leather gloves when preparing the strips.

Class Time 10 minutes

Safety Have students observe safety symbols and wear lab aprons.

Teaching Tips
- Have students throw used lemons away.
- Clean used copper and zinc strips and save them for reuse.
- Current is the rate at which charge flows through a wire and is expressed in amps, while voltage is expressed in volts. Potential difference is a measure of the work required to carry positive charge from one point to another and is expressed in volts.

Expected Outcome The battery will probably produce less than 1 volt and a very small current, about 0.0001 amp. The actual voltage and current depend on how juicy the lemon is, how far apart the electrodes are placed, and how deep they go into the fruit.

Analyze and Conclude
1. There is no voltage when using two copper strips. Values between 0.5 V and 1 V are typical when using the copper and zinc strips.
2. A basic solution is also electrolytic and may provide a similar result.
Visual, Kinesthetic

For Enrichment L3

Have students perform this lab with metals to determine which pairs of metals produce the greatest voltages. Then, refer them to a chemistry text to read about electronegativity. (Pairs of metals that are far apart in the electromotive series produce the greatest voltages.)
Kinesthetic

Quick Lab

Making a Battery

Materials

1 large fresh lemon, plastic knife, zinc strip, 2 copper strips, multimeter

Procedure
1. Roll the lemon between your hands until it softens.
2. Use the knife to carefully cut two parallel slits in the lemon about 1 cm apart. Push the copper strips into the slits to a depth of 2 to 3 cm. Don't allow the strips to touch.
3. Attach the copper strips to the terminals of the multimeter. Observe the reading and record it.
4. Replace one of the copper strips with the zinc strip and repeat step 3.

Analyze and Conclude
1. **Observing** What was the reading on the multimeter when you used two copper strips? A copper and a zinc strip?
2. **Predicting** Lemon juice is acidic. Would a basic solution provide a similar result?

Strong Acids When hydrogen chloride dissolves in water, almost all of its molecules ionize. After the reaction, there are about the same number of hydronium ions in solution as there were molecules of HCl to begin with. The products do not reform reactant molecules. HCl is an example of a strong acid. **When strong acids dissolve in water, they ionize almost completely.** Other strong acids include sulfuric acid, H_2SO_4, and nitric acid, HNO_3.

Strong Bases When dissolved in water, sodium hydroxide almost completely dissociates into sodium and hydroxide ions. Sodium hydroxide is an example of a strong base. **Strong bases dissociate almost completely in water.** Other strong bases include calcium hydroxide, $Ca(OH)_2$, and potassium hydroxide, KOH.

Weak Acids and Bases

The citric acid in orange juice and the acetic acid in vinegar are *weak* acids. Toothpaste and shampoo contain *weak* bases. **Weak acids and bases ionize or dissociate only slightly in water.**

Weak Acids A solution of acetic acid, CH_3COOH, and water can be described by the following equation.

$$CH_3COOH + H_2O \rightleftharpoons CH_3COO^- + H_3O^+$$

The equilibrium favors the reactants over the products, so few ions form in solution. A weak acid forms fewer hydronium ions than a strong acid of the same concentration. This also means that a weak acid has a higher pH than a strong acid of the same concentration.

It is important to understand the difference between concentration and strength. Concentration is the amount of solute dissolved in a given amount of solution. Strength refers to the solute's tendency to form ions in water. You cannot assume that a strong acid has a low pH, because its concentration also affects pH. For instance, a dilute solution of HCl (a strong acid) can have a pH of 6. But a concentrated solution of acetic acid (a weak acid) can have a pH of 3.

Weak Bases Ammonia, NH_3, is a colorless gas with a distinctive smell. When it dissolves in water, very little of it ionizes. Equilibrium favors the reactants, so few NH_4^+ and OH^- ions are produced.

$$NH_3 + H_2O \rightleftharpoons NH_4^+ + OH^-$$

Buffers Weak acids and bases can be used to make buffers. A **buffer** is a solution that is resistant to large changes in pH. Buffers can be prepared by mixing a weak acid and its salt or a weak base and its salt. Because a buffer can react with both an acid and a base, its pH remains relatively constant.

Facts and Figures

Buffered Aspirin Many drugs contain buffers to offset the effects they might have upon ingestion. For example, acetylsalicylic acid is the ingredient in aspirin medication that relieves pain. Many of the kinds of aspirin available for consumer use are buffered to minimize the acidity of aspirin.

Electrolytes

Sports drinks, like the one shown in Figure 23, taste salty because they contain salts of elements such as sodium, potassium, and calcium. Salts are examples of electrolytes. An **electrolyte** is a substance that ionizes or dissociates into ions when it dissolves in water. The resulting solution can conduct electric current. The electrolytes in sports drinks help restore the balance of ions in your body.

Electrolytes can be classified as strong or weak. **Strong acids and bases are strong electrolytes because they dissociate or ionize almost completely in water.** For example, sodium hydroxide is a strong electrolyte that produces many ions in water. Salts are also strong electrolytes. When potassium chloride dissolves in water, it dissociates into potassium and chloride ions. In contrast, acetic acid is a weak electrolyte because it only partially ionizes.

Batteries and other portable devices that produce electricity also contain electrolytes. Car batteries use lead plates in combination with the electrolyte sulfuric acid to produce electricity. Space shuttles use devices called fuel cells that provide electricity to power all the crafts' devices. Fuel cells use the strong base potassium hydroxide as an electrolyte. Instead of metal electrodes, the fuel cells use oxygen and hydrogen brought from Earth. At the same time that the fuel cells provide electrical energy to power a space shuttle, they also produce water that the crew can use.

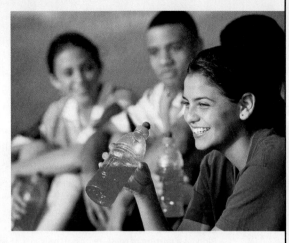

Figure 23 Drinking sports drinks after exercising can restore the balance of ions in your body.

Section 8.4 Assessment

Reviewing Concepts

1. How is pH related to the concentration of hydronium ions in solution?
2. What determines the degree to which an acid or base is weak or strong?
3. Are strong acids and bases good electrolytes? Explain why or why not.
4. Why is pure water neutral?
5. What is a buffer?

Critical Thinking

6. **Comparing and Contrasting** Explain how the concentration of an acid differs from the strength of an acid.

7. **Relating Cause and Effect** Suppose you add another liter of water to 1 liter of a 1-molar solution of hydrochloric acid. What happens to the number of hydronium ions in solution? What happens to the concentration?

Writing in Science

Explanatory Paragraph Explain the concept of a pH scale, and compare the pH values of acids, bases, and pure water. (*Hint:* Use examples from Figure 22 to help you describe the range of the pH scale.)

Address Misconceptions L2

Many students think that pure water is a good conductor of electricity. Though pure water has some ions due to self-ionization, the number of ions in pure water is not great enough to carry an electric current. Explain that practically all water obtained from traditional sources contains electrolytes. Thus, it is very difficult to find water that will not conduct electricity. Even deionized water samples may have some dissolved ions depending on the effectiveness of the deionizer or the method of storage. **Verbal**

3 ASSESS

Evaluate Understanding L2

Encourage students to make a note card for each of the Key Concepts questions listed on p. 246. Then, ask them to make a note card that answers each question using one of the boldfaced key points in this section. Have them make three more sets of note cards using the vocabulary terms and their definitions. Encourage students to review the information on their cards.

Reteach L1

As a class, make a chart that lists what strong acids, strong bases, and strong electrolytes have in common. Do the same for weak acids, weak bases, and weak electrolytes.

Writing in Science

Acceptable answers include explaining that a pH scale allows you to describe how acidic or basic a solution is. Solutions with a pH lower than 7, such as vinegar, are acidic. Solutions with a pH higher than 7, such as household ammonia, are basic. Solutions with a pH of 7 (the same as pure water) are neutral.

 Interactive Textbook If your class subscribes to the Interactive Textbook, use it to review key concepts in Section 8.4.

Section 8.4 Assessment

1. Solutions with a low pH have a high concentration of hydronium ions in solution and are acidic. Solutions with a high pH have a low concentration of hydronium ions in solution and are basic.
2. The degree to which an acid or base dissociates or ionizes when dissolved in water determines whether it is weak or strong.
3. Strong acids and bases are strong electrolytes because they dissociate or ionize almost completely when dissolved in water.

4. Pure water is neutral because it contains equal concentrations of hydronium and hydroxide ions.
5. A buffer is a solution that is resistant to large changes in pH.
6. The concentration of an acid is the amount of solute dissolved in a given amount of solution. The strength of an acid refers to the solute's tendency to form ions in water.
7. The number of hydronium ions stays the same. The concentration decreases because there are fewer ions per liter.

River of Life L2

Background

When blood pH falls outside of the normal range, 7.35–7.45, a person may experience acidosis or alkalosis.

Acidosis occurs when blood has a pH as low as 7.2. It can arise from the blood having too much carbon dioxide due to poor breathing, production of acids due to high glucose levels in the urine (a symptom of diabetes), and loss of bicarbonate due to severe diarrhea. Alkalosis occurs when blood has a pH above 7.45. It can arise from the blood having too little carbon dioxide due to hyperventilation, the loss of stomach acid due to vomiting, and the presence of high levels of bicarbonate in fluids delivered intravenously (through an IV).

River of Life

Just as rivers are used to transport products and raw materials, blood connects the body's living cells, delivering nutrients and carrying away wastes. The exact composition of this red liquid changes continuously as it flows through the body.

Liquid tissue
Blood is a mixture of cells—red blood cells, white blood cells, and platelets—suspended in a water-based solution called plasma. Nutrients, vitamins, and minerals also travel in blood, dissolved in the plasma. The cells and other substances remain suspended in the blood because the heart's pumping action keeps the blood moving.

Red blood cell

White blood cell

Blood components
When left to sit, blood separates into its parts. About 55 percent makes up the liquid top layer and 45 percent makes up the cellular layer below.

Plasma *This liquid part of the blood is about 90 percent water. The other 10 percent includes many dissolved substances, such as proteins and glucose.*

White blood cells and platelets *White blood cells help the body fight disease. Platelets help the blood to clot when bleeding occurs.*

Red blood cells *These cells contain the compound hemoglobin, which carries oxygen from the lungs to cells throughout the body.*

250 *Chapter 8*

Blood flow
The body's circulation system contains two circuits. In the first, blood is pumped by the heart to the lungs. As oxygenated blood returns to the heart, it is pumped to the remaining tissues in the body through the second circuit.

Lungs In the lungs, carbon dioxide is removed from the blood, and oxygen is taken up by red blood cells.

Heart The heart pumps oxygenated blood, shown in red, from the lungs around the body. At the same time, the heart pumps deoxygenated blood, shown in blue, back to the lungs.

Cells Oxygen is delivered to each cell in the body, and carbon dioxide is removed.

Platelet

Maintaining blood pH levels

For the body to function normally, blood pH must be kept within a narrow range. Buffer systems ensure pH levels are maintained within that range. A buffer is a chemical or a combination of chemicals that can absorb either hydrogen ions (H^+) or hydroxide ions (OH^-). Buffers maintain a relatively constant hydrogen ion concentration. Hydrogen ions produced by chemical reactions in the body are the main threat to your blood's pH. A very important blood buffer system consists of hydrogen carbonate ions (HCO_3^-) and carbonic acid (H_2CO_3) as shown in this equation.

$$HCO_3^- + H^+ \rightleftharpoons H_2CO_3$$

Carbon dioxide (CO_2) dissolved in the blood acts as an acid. It forms carbonic acid when dissolved in water, and donates hydrogen ions when they are needed. Hydrogen carbonate, produced by the kidneys, is a base that soaks up hydrogen ions when there are too many of them, and transports them to the lungs where the acid is excreted as carbon dioxide.

Solutions, Acids, and Bases **251**

(continued)

Using Blood
Build Science Skills   **L3**

Inferring Explain that when a recipient's blood serum contains antibodies that react to the antigens on the surface of a donor's blood cells, it will produce a potentially fatal clumping of blood cells. Each blood type has a particular combination of antigens and antibodies. You can always receive blood of your own type. However, depending on your blood type, you may or may not be able to receive blood of another type. Give the following information to students.

- Type A blood has Type A antigens on its blood cells and anti-B antibodies in its serum.
- Type B blood has Type B antigens on its cells and anti-A antibodies in its serum.
- Type AB blood has both Type A and Type B antigens on its blood cells, but neither anti-A nor anti-B antibodies in its serum.
- Type O blood contains neither A nor B antigens on its cells but has both anti-A and anti-B antibodies in its serum. Ask, **Can you deduce which type of blood a person would need to donate to anyone?** (People with Type O blood are universal donors.) **Can you deduce which type of blood a person would need to have to be able to receive all other types?** (People with Type AB blood are universal receivers.)
Logical

CONCEPTS in Action

Using Blood

Because blood is continuously replenished by the body, it can be taken from healthy people and made available for those who need it—whether because of blood loss in accidents or surgery, or to treat illnesses such as anemia or cancer.

Blood banks store blood from donors, or sometimes from a patient, for use during a planned surgery. Once collected, compounds are added to prevent clotting. Most blood is separated into components. For example, plasma can be stored at −18°C for up to 12 months, while platelets are stored at room temperature and must be used within 5 days.

Charles Drew
During the 1940s, physician and inventor Charles Drew developed methods for separating and storing blood on a large scale, providing the basis for today's Red Cross centers.

1900: Karl Landsteiner discovers three of the main blood groups (A, B, and O). The fourth group, AB, is discovered in 1902.

1932: First blood bank is established in Russia, followed in 1937 by the first United States hospital blood bank in Chicago.

1940: Charles Drew pioneers large-scale separation and storage of blood plasma.

1948: American Red Cross establishes a national blood collection and distribution program.

Tube containing blood spun at high speed

Centrifuge
A centrifuge works like the spin cycle on a washing machine to separate blood quickly into its different components.

252   *Chapter 8*

Facts and Figures

Blood Types Some blood types are rarer than others. The following chart lists the approximate percentage of each blood type in the U.S. population.

Blood Type	Percentage of U.S. Population
O positive	38%
A positive	34%
B positive	9%
O negative	7%
A negative	6%
AB positive	3%
B negative	2%
AB negative	1%

Blood bag *The use of whole blood in transfusions has been reduced in recent years but it is retained as a treatment option in cases of massive blood loss.*

Blood Transfusion

Each year, more than 4 million people in the United States receive a blood transfusion, either of whole blood or of a blood component, such as plasma or platelets. Before being stored, blood from a donor is tested to make sure it is safe.

Donated blood

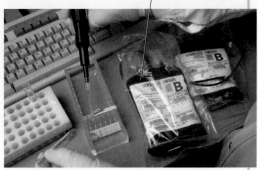

Crossmatching blood
Blood groups are used to determine which blood can be given to whom. Antigens, or molecular markers on the surface of red blood cells, determine the type of blood a person can safely receive in a transfusion. If blood of incompatible types is mixed, the red blood cells form clumps instead of mixing properly. These clumps can block blood vessels and even cause death.

1950: Plastic blood bags are introduced for blood storage, allowing blood to be frozen at lower temperatures and for longer periods.

1985: First HIV testing of donor blood is carried out, followed by other tests to protect transfusion patients from disease.

Going Further

- Research and write a paragraph about the work of Charles Drew. What methods did he use to prolong the storage time for whole blood? Why did he decide to separate whole blood into plasma and cells for storage?
- Take a Discovery Channel Video Field Trip by watching "Suspended in Blood."

DISCOVERY CHANNEL **SCHOOL**
Video Field Trip

Solutions, Acids, and Bases **253**

Preparing a Salt by Neutralization

L2

Objective

After completing this activity, students will be able to

- perform a neutralization reaction.
- determine the indicating colors of an indicator.
- detect the occurrence of a neutralization reaction using an indicator.

Skills Focus Observing, Measuring, Analyzing Data

 Prep Time 20 minutes

Advance Prep Prepare solutions of 1 M hydrochloric acid and 1 M sodium hydroxide. To help students keep track of their solutions, prepare sets of labeled test tubes for each group of students. Provide each group with about 8 mL of each solution. Provide phenolphthalein solution in a dropper bottle.

Class Time 60 minutes (2 class periods)

Safety Students should use caution with the acid and base solutions. Remind students never to taste anything (e.g., salt) in a lab. Hydrochloric acid and sodium hydroxide are corrosive. In case of spills, clean thoroughly with water. Caution students not to touch the hot plate or the heated beaker. Have students observe safety symbols and wear safety goggles, plastic gloves, and lab aprons.

Sample Data

Materials	Observations
1 mL	22 drops
HCl + phenolphthalein	clear
NaOH + phenolphthalein	pink
Drops of HCl used	88 drops
mL of HCl used	4 mL
Drops of NaOH used	88 drops
mL of NaOH used	4 mL
pH of final solution	7

Exploration Lab

Preparing a Salt by Neutralization

In this lab, you will prepare table salt by reacting hydrochloric acid (HCl) with sodium hydroxide (NaOH). To be sure that all of the acid and base have reacted, you will use phenolphthalein. You will first have to test the colors of this indicator with a known acid and base. After the acid and base have reacted, you will measure the pH of the solution with pH paper. Finally, you will evaporate the water and collect the sodium chloride.

Problem
How can you produce a salt by neutralization?

Materials
- 3 dropper pipets
- labels
- 10-mL graduated cylinder
- test tube rack
- 2 10-mL test tubes
- distilled water
- hydrochloric acid
- sodium hydroxide solution
- 3 stirring rods
- phenolphthalein solution
- 2 25-mL beakers
- pH paper
- large watch glass
- 100-mL beaker
- hot plate

For the probeware version of this lab, see Probeware Lab Manual, Lab 3.

Skills
Observing, Measuring, Analyzing Data

Procedure

Part A: Preparing for the Experiment

1. On a separate sheet of paper, copy the data table shown.

Data Table	
Material(s)	Observation
1 mL	_____ drops
HCl + phenolphthalein	_____ (color)
NaOH + phenolphthalein	_____ (color)
Drops of HCl used	_____ drops
mL of HCl used	_____ mL
Drops of NaOH used	_____ drops
mL of NaOH used	_____ mL
pH of final solution	_____

2. Place about 10 mL of distilled water in a 25-mL beaker. Set the graduated cylinder on the table and add distilled water to the 5-mL mark. Be sure that the *bottom* of the meniscus is on the 5-mL line.

3. To determine the number of drops in 1 mL, use a clean dropper pipet to add 1 mL of water to the graduated cylinder. Hold the dropper pipet straight up and down with the tip of the dropper pipet just inside the mouth of the cylinder. As your partner watches the liquid level in the cylinder, add drops of water one at a time while counting the drops. Continue adding drops until the liquid level reaches 6 mL. Record the number of drops in 1 mL.

4. Label one clean dropper pipet *Hydrochloric acid (HCl)* and the other *Sodium hydroxide (NaOH)*.

5. Using the HCl dropper pipet, add 3 mL of hydrochloric acid to a clean test tube. **CAUTION** *Hydrochloric acid is corrosive. In case of spills, clean thoroughly with water.* Add 2 to 3 drops of phenolphthalein to the test tube. Use a clean stirring rod to mix the hydrochloric acid and indicator. Record your observations.

6. Using the dropper pipet labeled NaOH, add 3 mL of sodium hydroxide solution to a clean test tube. **CAUTION** *Sodium hydroxide is corrosive. In case of spills, clean thoroughly with water.* Add 2 to 3 drops of phenolphthalein to the test tube. Use a clean stirring rod to mix the sodium hydroxide solution and indicator. Record your observations.

Part B: Making the Salt

7. Using the HCl dropper pipet, add 4 mL of hydrochloric acid to a clean 25-mL beaker. Record the number of drops you used. Add 2 to 3 drops of phenolphthalein to the beaker.

8. Use the NaOH dropper pipet to add sodium hydroxide drop by drop to the beaker of hydrochloric acid and phenolphthalein, stirring constantly. Count the drops as you add them. As a pink color remains longer, add the drops more slowly.

• When determining the number of drops in a milliliter, one student should place the tip of the dropper inside the opening of the graduated cylinder and count the drops while a second student kneels to examine the graduated cylinder at eye level.
• Students should read the level of the graduated cylinder while it is sitting on a flat surface. Remind students to read the bottom of the meniscus when making volume measurements.
• Show students how to label the pipets.
• The size of the beaker used in Step 12 depends on the size of the evaporating dish. A small evaporating dish may require a smaller beaker.
• Combine all waste solutions, and add acid or base until litmus indicates neutrality. Dispose of the neutral solution in the sink with excess water.

Expected Outcome It will take approximately the same number of milliliters of each solution to reach the pink endpoint.

Analyze and Conclude

1. See Expected Outcome. Students should recognize that they used equal volumes of base and acid.

2. The concentrations are the same.

3. It would have taken twice as much base to reach the color change.

Visual, Kinesthetic, Logical

Go Further

Have students perform a quantitative analysis to determine the identity of unknown solutions of NaOH. Prepare three solutions of NaOH (1 M, 0.5 M, and 0.1 M). Label them Solutions A, B, and C. Have students perform Steps 7–10 for each of the three unknown solutions. Using their results, they should identify each solution. It may be necessary to tell them which concentrations are expected.

Logical

9. Continue to add and count the drops of sodium hydroxide until a light pink color remains for at least 30 seconds. (Note: If you add too much sodium hydroxide, add a few more drops of hydrochloric acid until the color disappears.) Record any additional drops of hydrochloric acid that you added. Then, carefully add sodium hydroxide until one drop produces a lasting pink color. Record the total number of drops of sodium hydroxide used.

10. Use a piece of pH paper to determine the pH of the final solution. Record the pH. If the pH is higher than 7.0, add hydrochloric acid drop by drop, testing the pH with pH paper after each drop, until the pH is equal to 7.0. Record the pH and the total number of drops of HCl you added.

11. Use the solution in the beaker to fill the watch glass halfway.

12. Fill the 100-mL beaker about half full of water. Place the beaker on top of the hot plate.

13. Set the watch glass on top of the beaker.

14. Turn on the hot plate to a low setting. Adjust the heat as the water in the beaker warms. The water should simmer, but not boil.

CAUTION *Do not touch the hot plate or the beaker.* Heat until a solid is visible at the edges of the water in the watch glass and the water is nearly evaporated. Turn off the heat.

15. Allow the remaining water to evaporate. Observe the contents of the watch glass. Record your observations.

16. When the watch glass has cooled, dispose of the contents as directed by your teacher. Clean up your equipment. Wash your hands with soap and water.

Analyze and Conclude

1. **Comparing and Contrasting** What was the total amount of hydrochloric acid used to make the neutral solution? What was the total amount of sodium hydroxide? How do the amounts compare?

2. **Drawing Conclusions** What do you conclude about the concentrations of hydrochloric acid and sodium hydroxide in the solutions?

3. **Predicting** If the acid had been twice as concentrated as the base, how would your data have changed?

Solutions, Acids, and Bases **255**

Probeware Lab Manual Versions of this lab for use with probeware available from Pasco, Texas Instruments, and Vernier are in Probeware Lab Manual.

Study Guide

Study Tip

Customize Your Notes
Customizing your notes can help you remember important concepts. For example, if you like to draw, you may include illustrations that help you remember facts or terms. If you are better at organizing, use color coding or highlighting to link ideas or make facts more memorable.

Thinking Visually

a. Neutralization
b. Water
c. Salt

Assessment

 If your class subscribes to the Interactive Textbook, your students can go online to access an interactive version of the Student Edition and a self-test.

Reviewing Content

1. d	**2.** a	**3.** d
4. b	**5.** a	**6.** c
7. c	**8.** b	**9.** a
10. d		

Understanding Concepts

11. Increasing the temperature of a solvent decreases the solubility of a gas.
12. More energy is released when the solution forms than is absorbed when the solute and solvent molecules separate and break apart.
13. It provides more surface area that the solvent can contact.
14. An unsaturated solution contains less solute than it can hold at a given temperature; a saturated solution contains as much solute as it can hold at a given temperature; and a supersaturated solution contains more solute than it can hold at a given temperature.

8.1 Formation of Solutions

Key Concepts

- Substances can dissolve in water in three ways—through dissociation, dispersion, and ionization.
- Three physical properties of a solution that can differ from those of its solute and solvent are conductivity, freezing point, and boiling point.
- During the formation of a solution, energy is either released or absorbed.
- Factors that affect the rate of dissolving include surface area, temperature, and stirring.

Vocabulary

solute, p. 229; solvent, p. 229; dissociation, p. 229; dispersion, p. 230; ionization, p. 230

8.2 Solubility and Concentration

Key Concepts

- Solutions are described as unsaturated, saturated, or supersaturated, depending on the amount of solute in solution.
- Three factors that affect the solubility of a solute are the type of bonding in the solute and solvent, temperature, and pressure.
- Concentration can be expressed as percent by volume, percent by mass, and molarity.

Vocabulary

solubility, p. 235; saturated solution, p. 236; unsaturated solution, p. 236; supersaturated solution, p. 236; concentration, p. 238; molarity, p. 239

8.3 Properties of Acids and Bases

Key Concepts

- Acids taste sour, react with certain metals, and turn blue litmus paper red. Bases taste bitter, feel slippery, and turn red litmus paper blue.
- The neutralization reaction between an acid and a base produces a salt and water.
- Acids can be defined as proton donors, and bases can be defined as proton acceptors.

Vocabulary

acid, p. 240; indicator, p. 241; base, p. 242; neutralization, p. 244; salt, p. 244

8.4 Strength of Acids and Bases

Key Concepts

- The lower the pH value, the greater the H_3O^+ ion concentration is. The higher the pH value, the lower the H_3O^+ ion concentration is.
- The strength of an acid or a base depends on the degree to which it dissociates or ionizes in water.
- Strong acids and bases are good electrolytes because they produce many ions in solution.

Vocabulary

pH, p. 247; buffer, p. 248; electrolyte, p. 249

Thinking Visually

Concept Map Use the information on acids and bases to complete the concept map below.

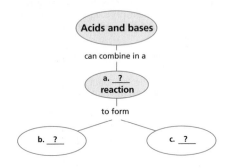

Chapter Resources

Print
- **Chapter and Unit Tests,** Chapter 8 Test A and Test B
- **Test Prep Resources,** Chapter 8

Technology
- **Computer Test Bank,** Chapter Test 8
- **Interactive Textbook,** Chapter 8
- **Go Online,** PHSchool.com, Chapter 8

Reviewing Content

Choose the letter that best answers the question or completes the statement.

1. The parts of a solution are the
 a. salt and vapor.   **b.** solvent and solid.
 c. solute and water.   **d.** solute and solvent.

2. In a solution, the solute is the substance that
 a. dissolves in the solvent.
 b. is in the greatest quantity.
 c. is the liquid.
 d. is a solid.

3. Sugar dissolves in water through
 a. ionization.   **b.** dissociation.
 c. neutralization.   **d.** dispersion.

4. Ionic compounds produce ions in solution by
 a. ionization.   **b.** dissociation.
 c. evaporation.   **d.** dispersion.

5. The process by which some molecular compounds dissolve in water to form ions is
 a. ionization.   **b.** dissociation.
 c. neutralization.   **d.** dispersion.

6. The boiling point of a liquid solution is
 a. the same as the boiling point of the solvent.
 b. the same as the boiling point of the solute.
 c. higher than the boiling point of the solvent.
 d. lower than the boiling point of the solvent.

7. Which of the following is NOT characteristic of an acid?
 a. tastes sour
 b. reacts with metals
 c. turns litmus paper blue
 d. produces H_3O^+ ions in solution

8. The reaction between an acid and a base is called
 a. ionization.   **b.** neutralization.
 c. dissociation.   **d.** dispersion.

9. A solution of sodium hydroxide in water is most likely to have a pH close to
 a. 14.   **b.** 7.
 c. 5.   **d.** 3.

10. Substances that form ions when dissolved in water are
 a. solutions.   **b.** molecules.
 c. polar.   **d.** electrolytes.

Understanding Concepts

11. How does increasing the temperature of a solvent affect the solubility of a gas?

12. Explain why the temperature of water might increase when a solution forms.

13. Explain why crushing a solute increases the rate of solution.

14. Name and describe the three types of solutions.

15. Explain why oil does not dissolve in water.

16. Describe how you might increase the solubility of a solid in a liquid.

17. Explain how a solution can be both dilute and saturated.

18. Describe three different ways in which the concentration of a solution can be reported.

19. Define and give an example of an acid and of a base.

20. List the properties of acids and bases. Which of the properties would you use to safely test whether an unknown substance was an acid or a base?

21. If you add hydrochloric acid (HCl) to magnesium (Mg) metal, what will you observe? What products form in this reaction?

22. Identify each of the following compounds as an acid, base, or salt: LiOH, H_2CO_3, $Ba(OH)_2$, and KCl.

23. What determines the strength of an acid?

24. What happens when a solution of nitric acid (HNO_3) is added to a solution of potassium hydroxide (KOH)? What are the products?

25. Which of the following compounds can react with H_2SO_4 to form a salt: NaCl, $Ca(OH)_2$, HF, $AlCl_3$, H_2O, $Mg(OH)_2$? Name the salt(s) that would form.

Assessment (continued)

15. Oil is a nonpolar substance. Water is a polar substance. Water molecules attract one another much more than they attract the oil. Therefore, the water stays together and doesn't mix with the oil.

16. You could heat the liquid.

17. If the solute isn't very soluble, the solution can be saturated and still have very little solute in it, so it would be dilute.

18. Percent by volume (volume of solute divided by volume of solution multiplied by 100%), percent by mass (mass of solute divided by mass of solution multiplied by 100%), and molarity (moles of solute divided by liters of solution).

19. An acid produces hydronium ions in solution. Acceptable answers include hydrochloric acid, citric acid, and acetic acid. A base produces hydroxide ions in solution. Acceptable answers include sodium hydroxide, calcium hydroxide, and ammonia.

20. Acids taste sour, react with metals, and turn blue litmus paper red. Bases taste bitter, feel slippery, and turn red litmus paper blue. Acceptable answers include use of litmus paper.

21. You would observe bubbles of hydrogen gas forming on the metal. The products are magnesium chloride ($MgCl_2$) and hydrogen gas (H_2).

22. LiOH is a base, H_2CO_3 is an acid, $Ba(OH)_2$ is a base, and KCl is a salt.

23. The strength of an acid is determined by how completely it ionizes when dissolved in water.

24. A neutralization reaction occurs. The products are potassium nitrate and water.

25. $Ca(OH)_2$ and $Mg(OH)_2$. The salts would be calcium sulfate and magnesium sulfate.

Solutions, Acids, and Bases **257**

Homework Guide

Section	Questions
8.1	1–6, 12
8.2	11, 13–17
8.3	7–8, 18–21, 23–24
8.4	9–10, 22

Critical Thinking

26. NaCl is an ionic compound. When it is added to water, its ions dissociate. The ions are then pulled into solution by the polar water molecules. HCl is a polar molecular compound. When HCl is added to water, a proton is transferred from HCl to the water molecule, forming H_3O^+ and Cl^- ions. This process is an example of ionization.

27. $(0.50 \text{ mol/L})(3.0 \text{ L})(342 \text{ g/mol}) = 513 \text{ g}$

28. 9, because it is a base. If the pH were 4, it would be an acid and would be more likely to react with the metal.

29. X is a base. Z is an acid. Y could be water.

Math Skills

30. Potassium nitrate
31. It would be supersaturated.
32. 85 g

Concepts in Action

33. Acceptable answers may include the following steps: Obtain several different brands of antacids. Read the directions and measure out one dose of each antacid. Dissolve the doses in distilled water in separate beakers. Add to each beaker an indicator that changes color at a pH of about 7. Prepare a solution of HCl with a pH of 1, 2, or 3. Add hydrochloric acid to each beaker one drop at a time, counting the drops and stirring, until the indicator changes color and the color remains for at least 30 seconds. The antacid that requires the most drops is the most effective at neutralizing stomach acid. (Note: As some antacids are not very soluble in water, this experiment might require a "back titration," in which excess acid is added to dissolve all of the antacid, and the unreacted acid is then titrated with a base.)

34. Antacid A keeps stomach contents within the normal acid range. Antacid B changes stomach contents to a basic solution, which is not normal. The stomach contents must be acid to digest food. Antacid A is the more healthful choice.

35. Students should recognize that adding water to the acid will only dilute it and cause it to spread further. If workers sprinkled a powdered solid base over the acid, the base would dissolve and then neutralize the acid. An indicator could be used to determine if all the acid has been neutralized. The

Critical Thinking

26. Comparing and Contrasting Compare what happens when NaCl and HCl are added to water.

27. Calculating The molar mass of sucrose, or table sugar, is 342 grams. Calculate how many grams of sucrose are required to make 3.0 liters of 0.50 M sucrose solution.

28. Applying Concepts A solution is an acid or a base, and it doesn't react with metal. Is its pH more likely to be 4 or 9? Explain your answer.

29. Inferring You have equal amounts of three colorless liquids, X, Y, and Z. An indicator is yellow in a pH of 8 or less and blue in a pH of 8 or more. The indicator turns blue in X and yellow in Y and Z. When you add liquid Z to X, the indicator turns yellow. When you add Z to Y, the solution remains yellow. Which liquid could be water?

Math Skills

Use the graph to answer Questions 30–32.

Solubilities of Salts

(y-axis: Solubility (g/100 mL of water); x-axis: Temperature (°C))

Curves labeled: Potassium nitrate, Sodium nitrate, Sodium chloride

30. Using Graphs Which compound is the most soluble at 75°C?

31. Interpreting Diagrams What kind of solution would you have if it contained 50 grams of sodium chloride in 100 mL of water at 30°C?

32. Calculating How many grams of sodium nitrate would you need to make 100 mL of a saturated solution at 25°C?

Concepts in Action

33. Designing an Experiment Commercials often say that antacids "neutralize excess stomach acid." Stomach acid is hydrochloric acid with a pH of around 1–4 depending on what and how recently you have eaten. Design an experiment to test how effective various brands of antacids are at neutralizing stomach acid.

34. Making Judgments A single dose of antacid A changes the pH of stomach contents from 1 to 3. A single dose of antacid B changes the pH of stomach contents from 1 to 8. Which antacid would you choose to use? Explain your answer.

35. Writing in Science You are in charge of writing the directions for a safety workers' training manual. The manual tells workers what to do if a train carrying nitric acid derails and the acid spills. What are some things they could do to clean up the spill? Write the procedures in steps, explaining why each step is done.

Performance-Based Assessment

Making a Display Prepare a classroom display on the importance of acids and bases in daily life. Include information on the properties of acids and bases, as well as examples of where they are found in daily life. Research ways in which manufacturers use acids and bases to produce common items and include that information in your display.

Go Online
PHSchool.com

For: Self-grading assessment
Visit: PHSchool.com
Web Code: cca-1080

resulting mixture (containing water and a salt) could then be cleaned up safely like any other liquid spill.

Performance-Based Assessment

Acceptable displays include listing and illustrating the properties and examples of acids and bases discussed in this chapter. Acids and bases are used in a variety of ways to manufacture common items. Examples include sulfuric acid in the production of rayon, glue, and paper; nitric acid in the production of fertilizers, explosives, and nylon; and sodium hydroxide in the production of rayon, paper, and soap.

Standardized Test Prep for Indiana

 Standards Guide

Question	Standards
5	ICP.5.6

Test-Taking Tip

Some test questions may include a drawing of lab equipment. It is important that you carefully study the information presented in the question as well as the picture provided. Keep these tips in mind when answering a question with lab equipment drawings:

- Identify the equipment shown so you can determine what information the drawing can or cannot give you.
- Think of similar labs or questions you may have seen. These may help you determine the information available from the drawing.
- The drawings may not be drawn to scale. You must read and interpret the scales and increments carefully.
- Carefully read the question. You may not need all the information presented in the drawing or you may need more information than is presented in the drawing.

Practice using these tips in Question 6.

1. Which of the following will NOT increase the rate at which a solute dissolves in a solvent?
 (A) increasing the surface area of the solute
 (B) stirring the solvent
 (C) increasing the temperature
 (D) increasing the particle size of the solute
 (E) agitating the mixture

2. At 20°C, a saturated solution contains 36 g of NaCl and 100 mL of water. All the solid is dissolved. What happens if the solution is slowly cooled to 0°C?
 (A) It freezes.
 (B) It becomes supersaturated.
 (C) The pressure on it increases greatly.
 (D) More NaCl could be dissolved in it.
 (E) The NaCl reacts with the water.

3. Which pH indicates a solution of an acid?
 (A) pH = 3
 (B) pH = 7
 (C) pH = 9
 (D) pH = 14
 (E) pH = 19

4. Which substance is a weak base?
 (A) NaCl
 (B) NH_3
 (C) HCl
 (D) HF
 (E) KOH

5. What reaction occurs when a solution of hydrochloric acid, HCl, is mixed with a solution of calcium hydroxide, $Ca(OH)_2$?
 (A) $Cl + Ca(OH) \longrightarrow HCa + Cl(OH)_2$
 (B) $HCl + Ca(OH)_2 \longrightarrow H(OH)_2 + CaCl$
 (C) $2HCl + Ca(OH)_2 \longrightarrow 2H_2O + CaCl_2$
 (D) $2HCl + Ca(OH)_2 \longrightarrow H_2Ca + 2ClOH$
 (E) $HCl + Ca(OH)_2 \longrightarrow$ no reaction occurs

0.1 M HCl   0.1 M NaOH

6. If the contents of the two beakers shown above are mixed, the resulting solution
 (A) will turn red litmus paper blue.
 (B) will turn blue litmus paper red.
 (C) will resist large changes in pH.
 (D) will react with metals.
 (E) will not change the color of red or blue litmus paper.

Solutions, Acids, and Bases **259**

Your students can independently test their knowledge of the chapter and print out their test results for your files.

Planning Guide

SECTION OBJECTIVES	STANDARDS		ACTIVITIES and LABS
	NATIONAL	STATE	
9.1 Carbon Compounds, pp. 262–269 🕐 1 block or 2 periods **9.1.1 Relate** the structures of three forms of carbon to their properties. **9.1.2 Explain** why there are millions of different organic compounds. **9.1.3 Relate** the number and arrangement of carbon atoms in hydrocarbons to their properties. **9.1.4 Distinguish** unsaturated from saturated hydrocarbons. **9.1.5 Classify** hydrocarbons using structural formulas and names. **9.1.6 Describe** the formation, composition, and uses of three types of fossil fuels. **9.1.7 Distinguish** complete combustion from incomplete combustion of fossil fuels. **9.1.8 Describe** the effects of some products of the combustion of fossil fuels.	A-1, A-2, B-3, C-5, D-2, F-1, F-2, F-3, F-4, F-5, G-1, G-2, G-3	ICP.3.2, ICP.5.5, ICP.8.2, ICP.8.4	**SE** Inquiry Activity: Do All Carbon Compounds Have Similar Properties? p. 261 **L2** **SE** Quick Lab: Comparing Isomers, p. 265 **L2** **TE** Teacher Demo: Comparing Models of Molecules, p. 264 **L2** **TE** Teacher Demo: Fractional Distillation, p. 267 **L2**
9.2 Substituted Hydrocarbons, pp. 272–274 🕐 1 block or 2 periods **9.2.1 Classify** substituted hydrocarbons based on their functional groups. **9.2.2 Describe** some properties and reactions of five types of substituted hydrocarbons.	A-1, B-2, F-1, F-3, F-4, F-5	ICP.3.2, ICP.3.3	**TE** Teacher Demo: Modeling Functional Groups, p. 272 **L2**
9.3 Polymers, pp. 275–280 🕐 1 block or 2 periods **9.3.1 Distinguish** a monomer from a polymer. **9.3.2 Compare** three examples of synthetic polymers. **9.3.3 Describe** the structures and functions of four types of natural polymers.	B-2, C-1, C-2, C-5, G-1, G-3	ICP.8.2, ICP.8.4	**SE** Quick Lab: Distinguishing Sugars from Starches, p. 278 **L2** **LM** Investigation 9A: Testing for Nutrients in Foods **L2** **LM** Investigation 9B: Comparing Cross-Linked Polymers **L1**
9.4 Reactions in Cells, pp. 282–284 🕐 1 block or 2 periods **9.4.1 Compare** photosynthesis and cellular respiration. **9.4.2 Explain** how enzymes and vitamins help reactions take place in cells.	A-1, A-2, B-3, C-1, C-5, F-1	ICP.5.6, ICP.5.7	**SE** Consumer Lab: Comparing Vitamin C in Fruit Juices, p. 285 **L2** **TE** Teacher Demo: Photosynthesis and Cellular Respiration, p. 283 **L2** **TE** Teacher Demo: Denaturing an Enzyme, p. 284 **L2**

RESOURCES
PRINT and TECHNOLOGY

RSW Section 9.1   L1
RSW Math Skill   L2
DC Clean Energy   L2
T Chapter 9 Pretest   L2
    Section 9.1   L2
P Chapter 9 Pretest   L2
    Section 9.1   L2
SCILINKS **GO** Fossil fuels   L2

RSW Section 9.2   L1
MSPS Section 9.2   L2
T Section 9.2   L2
P Section 9.2   L2

RSW Section 9.3   L1
T Section 9.3   L2
P Section 9.3   L2
SCILINKS **GO** Polymers   L2

RSW Section 9.4   L1
T Section 9.4   L2
P Section 9.4   L2
SCIENCE NEWS **GO** Organic chemistry and biochemistry   L2

SECTION ASSESSMENT

SE Section 9.1 Assessment, p. 269
iT Section 9.1

SE Section 9.2 Assessment, p. 274
iT Section 9.2

SE Section 9.3 Assessment, p. 280
iT Section 9.3

SE Section 9.4 Assessment, p. 284
iT Section 9.4

Go Online

Go online for these Internet resources.

PHSchool.com
Web Code: cca-1090
Web Code: cch-1090

NSTA SCILINKS
Web Code: ccn-1091
Web Code: ccn-1093

SCIENCE NEWS
Web Code: cce-1094

Materials for Activities and Labs

Quantities for each group

STUDENT EDITION

Inquiry Activity, p. 261
sucrose (table sugar), cellulose (paper), isopropyl alcohol, polystyrene (foam cup), polypropylene (food storage container)

Quick Lab, p. 265
30 marshmallows, 70 raisins, 50 toothpicks

Quick Lab, p. 278
1 slice each of potato, ripe apple, and bread; 15 mL cornstarch; 15 mL table sugar; iodine in dropper bottle; 6 small paper plates

Consumer Lab, p. 285
apple juice, variety of other fruit juices, test tubes and rack, 10-mL graduated cylinder, methylene blue indicator, dropper pipet, stirring rods

TEACHER'S EDITION

Teacher Demo, p. 264
molecular model kit

Teacher Demo, p. 267
distillation apparatus with stand, 50 mL water, 50 mL ethanol, 60 mL mineral oil, hot plate, 60-mL beakers (6), concave glass beaker covers (3), shield, dropper pipets (5)

Build Science Skills, p. 270
100-mL beaker containing 1:1 mixture of sulfur powder and coal dust, plastic pipet, 100-mL graduated cylinder, stirring rod, distilled water, 100-mL beaker

Teacher Demo, p. 272
any appliance that has attachments with different functions

Teacher Demo, p. 283
methylene blue, water, 500-mL beaker, *elodea* sprig, straw

Teacher Demo, p. 284
potato, sharp knife, cutting surface, 3% hydrogen peroxide solution, water, 500-mL beakers (2), hot plate

Chapter Assessment

CHAPTER ASSESSMENT

SE Chapter Assessment, pp. 287–288
CUT Chapter 9 Test A, B
CTB Chapter 9
iT Chapter 9
PHSchool.com GO
Web Code: cca-1090

STANDARDIZED TEST PREP

SE Chapter 9, p. 289
TP Diagnose and Prescribe

InteractiveTextbook with assessment at PHSchool.com

Before you teach

From the Author

David Frank
Ferris State University

Big Ideas
So far, students have focused on three major areas of chemistry. In analytical chemistry, the composition of matter is the primary focus. In physical chemistry, laws and theories that describe the behavior of matter take center stage. Inorganic chemistry excludes most carbon compounds, but includes the elemental forms of carbon. In Chapter 9, students study a few organic compounds and get a glimpse of biochemistry, an area in which inorganic and organic compounds play key roles.

Space and Time At room temperature, there is no visible reaction between sucrose and oxygen to release energy stored in this sugar. So how is the energy released in cells at a temperature only slightly higher than room temperature? Protein catalysts allow reactions in cells to take place quickly at body temperature.

Matter and Change When students first encounter organic molecules, they may be intimidated by the complex structures. If possible, use three-dimensional models to support the structural formulas shown in the text. Once students understand how hydrocarbons are classified, they study a few examples of substituted hydrocarbons to see how functional groups affect the properties of organic compounds. Section 9.3 shows how functional groups link monomers in polymers.

Forces and Motion In Section 9.3, students see how the intermolecular forces of attraction they studied in Chapter 6 and applied to solutions in Chapter 8 can also be applied to polymers. Help students understand that concepts in chemistry hold true for all types of matter.

Energy In this chapter, students have numerous opportunities to apply what they learned about chemical reactions in Chapter 7. Students get to compare the exothermic combustion reactions of fossil fuels to the process in cells that releases energy from food—cellular respiration. They also get to see how cellular respiration and the endothermic process of photosynthesis are related through their reactants and products.

Chemistry Refresher

Organic Compounds 9.1

Chemists in the early 1800s thought that living things possessed a vital force that distinguished them from non-living things, an idea known as *vitalism*. The term *organic* referred to substances found only in living organisms and *inorganic* referred to all other substances. Organic substances, chemists reasoned, could be used to produce inorganic substances. But inorganic substances lacked the vital force required to produce organic substances. In 1828, Friedrich Wöhler took the first step in

Address Misconceptions

Students often explain the formula and structure of methane by saying that carbon needs four bonds. The type and number of bonds in a compound can be explained by the structures of the atoms that form the bonds. For a strategy to overcome this misconception, see **Address Misconceptions** *on* **page 263.**

disproving vitalism. During a systematic study of cyanates, he mixed two inorganic substances and produced the organic substance urea. Today the term *organic* refers to compounds containing carbon and hydrogen, often combined with a few other elements. In general, organic compounds contain carbon-to-hydrogen bonds, and inorganic compounds, such as carbides and carbonates, do not. There is rarely a one-to-one correlation between a chemical formula and an organic compound. (There are nine different compounds with the formula C_7H_{16}.)

The shape of a molecule depends on the bond lengths and bond angles between atoms. Bond length is the distance between the nuclei of bonded atoms. Bond lengths are usually reported in picometers (pm) or angstroms (Å). Generally, bond length decreases as the number of bonds between two atoms increases. The type of bond also affects the angle between atoms in the molecule. In all three examples shown, the arrangement of the hydrogen atoms minimizes repulsion between electron clouds.

$$H \overset{109.5°}{\underset{1.54\ pm}{C-C}} H$$
Ethane

$$H \overset{121.7°}{\underset{1.34\ pm}{C=C}} H$$
Ethene

$$\overset{180°}{H-C\equiv C-H} \\ 1.21\ pm$$
Ethyne

Go Online

NSTA

PDLiNKS

For: Teaching methods for carbon chemistry
Visit: www.SciLinks.org/PDLinks
Web Code: ccn-0999

Naming Organic Compounds 9.2

The International Union of Pure and Applied Chemistry (IUPAC) established rules for naming organic compounds. In their system, names have a root that is based on the longest continuous chain of carbon atoms (or rings in aromatic hydrocarbons). A suffix is used for different classes of compounds (such as -*ol* for alcohols). Prefixes are used to indicate the location of branches or functional groups along the carbon chain. In the IUPAC system, isopropyl alcohol is 2-propanol. This name indicates that an −OH group is attached to the central carbon in a three-carbon chain.

Formation of Polymers 9.3

Polymers form by addition or condensation. The formation of polyethylene is an example of addition polymerization. Electrons in the double bond of an ethene molecule can form single bonds with carbon atoms in two other ethene molecules. In condensation polymerization, monomers are joined through a reaction that eliminates a small molecule. The illustration shows how water is eliminated when the carboxyl group of one amino acid joins to the amino group of a second amino acid. Each R represents a hydrocarbon chain.

Reactions in Cells 9.4

Address Misconceptions

Students may confuse cellular respiration, respiration, and breathing. For a strategy to overcome this misconception, see **Address Misconceptions** on **page 283**.

Chemical reactions in cells are classified as catabolic or anabolic. Catabolic reactions break down compounds into simpler substances and release energy. Cellular respiration is a catabolic process. Anabolic reactions use energy to build complex molecules from simpler substances. Photosynthesis is an anabolic process. When chlorophyll molecules in plant cells absorb light, electrons in the molecules are promoted to higher energy levels. A series of carrier molecules transport these high-energy electrons to locations where the energy is used to build complex molecules, including carbohydrates.

Build Reading Literacy

Relate Cause and Effect

Understanding How and Why Things Occur

Strategy Help students read and understand relationships between events. Cause-effect relationships are integral to science, so it is very important that students understand the cause-effect relationships developed in the text. Before students begin, assign a passage in Chapter 9 for them to read, such as pp. 267–269 in Section 9.1.

Example

1. Remind students that a cause is what makes something happen and the effect is what happens as a result. Point out that in science, many actions cause other actions to occur.
2. Have students identify cause-effect relationships in the passage. Remind them that the text does not always directly state the cause-effect relationship, but in many cases clue words or phrases do point out such a connection: *because, so, since, results, therefore, cause, lead to.* For example, Rain is always slightly acidic *because* carbon dioxide dissolves in water droplets and forms carbonic acid.
3. Then, explain that causes and effects often occur in chains, with effects becoming causes of later effects. Have students find a cause-effect chain and show it in the form of a flowchart. (insufficient oxygen for complete combustion $\longrightarrow$ carbon monoxide produced $\longrightarrow$ inhaled and absorbed by blood $\longrightarrow$ hemoglobin cannot carry oxygen to cells)

See p. 262 for a script on how to use the relate cause and effect strategy with students. For additional Build Reading Literacy strategies, see pp. 273, 275, and 282.

ASSESS PRIOR KNOWLEDGE

Use the Chapter Pretest below to assess students' prior knowledge. As needed, review these Science Concepts and Math Skills with students.

Review Science Concepts

Section 9.1 Review covalent bonding in general and the difference between single and double covalent bonds. Encourage students to recall the number of bonds carbon can form. Review how to interpret chemical formulas and chemical equations.

Sections 9.2 and 9.3 Have students review how physical properties, such as boiling points, are used to identify a substance. Discuss attractions between molecules.

Section 9.4 Review exothermic and endothermic reactions. Have students recall the role of a catalyst in a chemical reaction.

Review Math Skills

Data Tables Students will need to be familiar with analyzing data presented in tables about compounds and their properties.

Direct students to the **Math Skills** in the **Skills and Reference Handbook** at the end of the student text.

CHAPTER

9 Carbon Chemistry

21st Century Learning
Global Awareness

What fossil fuels are used to create electricity?

Fossil fuels account for the great majority of the world's energy use. Research online to identify the types of fossil fuels used by power plants to generate electricity. Determine the pros and cons of these fuels, and find out how much electricity is produced in the United States using each type of fossil fuel. Create a multimedia presentation summarizing your research.

 Indiana's Academic Standards for Science

PHYSICAL SCIENCE
SC.912.P.8.7: Interpret formula representations of molecules and compounds in terms of composition and structure.

LIFE SCIENCE
SC.912.L.16.10: Evaluate the impact of biotechnology on the individual, society and the environment, including medical and ethical issues; **SC.912.L.17.11:** Evaluate the costs and benefits of renewable and nonrenewable resources; **SC.912.L.17.15:** Discuss the effects of technology on environmental quality; **SC.912.L.17.16:** Discuss the large-scale environmental impacts resulting

ENVIRONMENT, ECONOMICS
ICP.8.2: Describe the benefits and risks of the development of non-renewable forms of energy such as coal, oil, natural gas and uranium fission sources; **ICP.8.4:** Describe how efficient use of renewable and non-renewable energy sources is essential to maintaining an acceptable environment.

CHEMICAL ENERGY, REACTIONS, AND BONDING
ICP.5.5: Using conservation principles write and balance chemical equations; **ICP.5.6:** Identify key indicators of a chemical change and classify simple types of chemical reactions. Differentiate between covalent, ionic, hydrogen and Van der Waals bonding, and write formulas for and name compounds of each type; **ICP.5.7:** Explain that in exothermic chemical reactions chemical energy is through science and which questions are outside the boundaries of scientific investigation. (Also: SC.912.N.1.1)

260 *Chapter 9*

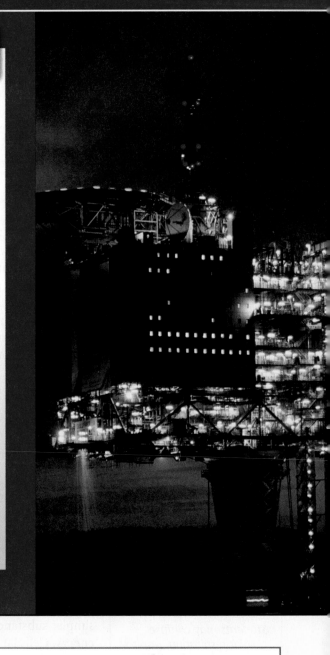

Chapter Pretest

1. What kind of bonds are found in molecules? *(Covalent bonds)*
2. How many electrons are shared in a double bond? *(4)*
3. How many bonds can a carbon atom form? *(4)*
4. Tell which of the following are formulas for a molecular compound. *(b and c)*
  a. H_2 b. CO_2
  c. CH_4 d. NaCl

5. In the following chemical equation, how many hydrogen atoms are in a molecule of the product? *(2)*
  $2H_2 + O_2 \longrightarrow 2H_2O$
6. Which of these properties can be used to separate substances in a mixture? *(a)*
  a. boiling point
  b. hardness
  c. malleability
  d. flammability

7. True or False: Attractions between molecules are stronger than covalent bonds. *(False)*
8. True or False: An exothermic reaction releases energy. *(True)*
9. How does a catalyst affect the progress of a chemical reaction? *(It lowers the energy barrier, which increases the reaction rate.)*

Chapter Preview

9.1   Carbon Compounds   9.3   Polymers

9.2   Substituted Hydrocarbons   9.4   Reactions in Cells

Video Field Trip

Clean Energy

This drilling platform will be used to pump petroleum from layers of rock beneath the ocean floor.

 Inquiry ⟩ **Activity**

Do All Carbon Compounds Have Similar Properties?

Procedure

1. Examine samples of sucrose, cellulose, isopropyl alcohol, polystyrene, and polypropylene. All five compounds contain carbon and hydrogen. Sucrose, cellulose, and isopropyl alcohol contain oxygen, too.

2. Record a set of physical properties for each compound. Include some of the properties you studied in Chapter 2.

Think About It

1. **Making Generalizations** Is there any property you observed that you could use to classify a compound as a carbon compound?

2. **Formulating Hypotheses** Why does carbon form many more compounds than other elements do? (*Hint:* How many valence electrons does carbon have and what type of bonds does it form?)

Carbon Chemistry **261**

Video Field Trip

Clean Energy

Encourage students to view the Video Field Trip "Clean Energy."

1 FOCUS

Objectives

9.1.1 Relate the structures of three forms of carbon to their properties.

9.1.2 Explain why there are millions of different organic compounds.

9.1.3 Relate the number and arrangement of carbon atoms in hydrocarbons to their properties.

9.1.4 Distinguish unsaturated from saturated hydrocarbons.

9.1.5 Classify hydrocarbons using structural formulas and names.

9.1.6 Describe the formation, composition, and uses of three types of fossil fuels.

9.1.7 Distinguish complete combustion from incomplete combustion of fossil fuels.

9.1.8 Describe the effects of some products of the combustion of fossil fuels.

Reading Focus

Build Vocabulary   L2

Concept Map Have students make a concept map with the word *hydrocarbons* as the starting point. The diagram should include the following terms: *saturated hydrocarbons, unsaturated hydrocarbons, alkanes, alkenes, alkynes, aromatic hydrocarbons, branched chain, straight chain,* and *rings.*

Reading Strategy   L2

a. Rigid three-dimensional network **b.** Widely spaced layers **c.** Hollow spheres with a surface of carbon atoms arranged in alternating hexagons and pentagons

2 INSTRUCT

Build Reading Literacy   L1

Relate Cause and Effect Refer to page **260D** in this chapter, which provides the guidelines for relating cause and effect.

Have students read p. 262. Ask, **What caused scientists to change the definition of an organic compound?** *(Wöhler synthesized urea, an organic compound produced by many organisms.)* **Logical**

9.1 Carbon Compounds

Standards: ICP.3.2, ICP.5.5, ICP.8.2, ICP.8.4

Reading Focus

Key Concepts

- What are three forms of carbon?
- What factors determine the properties of a hydrocarbon?
- What are the three types of unsaturated hydrocarbons?
- What are the three main fossil fuels and the two primary products of their combustion?

Vocabulary

- organic compound
- network solid
- hydrocarbon
- saturated hydrocarbon
- isomers
- unsaturated hydrocarbon
- aromatic hydrocarbons
- fossil fuels

Reading Strategy

Previewing Copy the table below. Before you read, use the models in Figure 2 to describe the arrangement of carbon atoms in each form of carbon.

Forms of Carbon Compounds	
Diamond	a. ?
Graphite	b. ?
Buckminsterfullerene	c. ?

Figure 1 A whale's survival depends on carbon compounds. Carbon compounds form the structures of a whale's cells and control reactions that take place in those cells. The instructions for these processes are stored in organic compounds.

Until 1828, chemists divided compounds into compounds that chemists could produce and compounds that only organisms could produce. The compounds produced by *organisms* were called *organic* compounds. In 1828, a German chemist, Friedrich Wöhler, mixed silver cyanate, AgOCN, with ammonium chloride, NH_4Cl. He expected to make ammonium cyanate. Instead, he produced urea, $(NH_2)_2CO$, which is a product of reactions that occur in the livers of many organisms. Wöhler had synthesized an organic compound.

An **organic compound** contains carbon and hydrogen, often combined with a few other elements, such as oxygen and nitrogen. There are millions of organic compounds—more than 90 percent of all known compounds. Remember that carbon has four valence electrons. So, a carbon atom can form four single covalent bonds, or a double bond and two single bonds, or a triple bond and a single bond. Most of the bonds in organic compounds are carbon-to-carbon bonds or carbon-to-hydrogen bonds.

Section Resources

Print
- *Reading and Study Workbook With Math Support,* Section 9.1 and **Math Skill:** Balancing Equations for Organic Reactions
- *Transparencies,* Chapter Pretest and Section 9.1

Technology
- *Interactive Textbook,* Section 9.1
- *Presentation Pro CD-ROM,* Chapter Pretest and Section 9.1
- *Go Online,* NSTA SciLinks, Fossil fuels

A

B

C

Diamond

Graphite

Buckminsterfullerene

Forms of Carbon

The element carbon exists in several forms with different properties. **Diamond, graphite, and fullerenes are forms of carbon.** In each form, there is a different arrangement of bonded carbon atoms.

Diamond Cutting, grinding, and drilling tools are often coated with diamond because no substance is harder than diamond. Diamond is an example of a network solid. In a **network solid,** all the atoms are linked by covalent bonds. A network solid is sometimes described as a single molecule. Figure 2A shows how the carbon atoms are linked in diamond. Covalent bonds connect each carbon atom in diamond to four other carbon atoms. The three-dimensional structure that results is rigid, compact, and strong. Diamond is harder than other substances because cutting a diamond requires breaking many covalent bonds.

Graphite A second form of carbon, graphite, has very different properties from diamond. It is extremely soft and slippery. Figure 2B shows how the carbon atoms in graphite are arranged in widely spaced layers. Within each layer, each carbon atom forms strong covalent bonds with three other carbon atoms. Between graphite layers the bonds are weak, which allows the layers to slide easily past one another. Because graphite is soft and slippery, it is a good lubricant for moving metal parts in machinery. Pencil "lead" is a mixture of graphite and clay. The layered structure of graphite explains why you can make pencil marks on paper and why the marks can be erased easily.

Fullerenes In 1985, researchers discovered a third form of carbon in the soot produced when some carbon compounds burn. Fullerenes are large hollow spheres, or cages, of carbon. These cages have since been found in meteorites. Figure 2C shows a model of a cage made from 60 carbon atoms. On the surface of the cage, the atoms form alternating hexagons and pentagons, like a soccer ball cover. The C_{60} molecule is called buckminsterfullerene after Buckminster Fuller, an architect who designed domes with similar geometric patterns.

Figure 2 There are several forms of carbon. **A** In diamond, carbon atoms are arranged in a rigid, three-dimensional network. **B** In graphite, the atoms are arranged in layers. **C** In fullerenes, carbon atoms are arranged in hollow spheres. *Predicting Are the properties of fullerenes more like those of diamond or of graphite? Give a reason for your choice.*

For: Activity on carbon bonding
Visit: PHSchool.com
Web Code: ccp-1091

Carbon Chemistry **263**

Saturated Hydrocarbons

Integrate Language Arts

Tell students that one definition of *saturated* is "filled to capacity." So saturated can mean "the inability to contain, absorb, receive, or hold." For example, the ground may be saturated with water after a heavy rainstorm, meaning it can absorb no more water. Have students use these meanings to paraphrase the definition of the vocabulary term *saturated hydrocarbon*. (*Possible answer: In a saturated hydrocarbon, carbon atoms do not have the capacity to bond to additional hydrogen atoms.*)
Verbal

Teacher ▷ **Demo**

Comparing Models of Molecules   L2

Purpose Students compare ball-and-stick models and structural formulas for methane and propane.

Materials molecular model kit

Procedure Write the structural formulas and chemical formulas for methane and propane on the board. Remind students that a structural formula provides more information than a molecular formula because it shows how the atoms are arranged in a molecule. Then, show students ball-and-stick models for methane and propane. Explain that a ball-and-stick model shows the angles between atoms in a molecule and the overall shape of the molecule. (Students may recall methane's tetrahedral shape from the Quick Lab in Section 6.3.) The bond angle between carbon and hydrogen is 109.5° in methane and propane.

Expected Outcome Students observe the similarities and differences between the structures of methane and propane molecules.
Visual, Logical

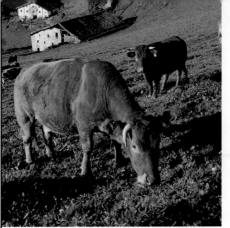

Figure 3 Microorganisms in the stomachs of a cow produce more than 500 liters of methane (CH₄) per day.

Figure 4 Molecules of ethane, propane, pentane, and octane have two, three, five, and eight carbon atoms, respectively. **Making Generalizations** *How does increasing the number of carbon atoms affect the boiling point of a straight-chain alkane?*

Saturated Hydrocarbons

Grass contains a compound called cellulose. Most organisms, including the grazing cows in Figure 3, cannot digest cellulose. However, microorganisms in cows' stomachs break down cellulose into smaller molecules that cows can digest. One of the products of this process is methane, CH_4, which is a hydrocarbon. A **hydrocarbon** is an organic compound that contains only the elements hydrogen and carbon. Methane is a saturated hydrocarbon. In a **saturated hydrocarbon,** all of the bonds are single bonds. A saturated hydrocarbon contains the maximum possible number of hydrogen atoms for each carbon atom. Another name for a saturated hydrocarbon is an alkane. Names of alkane compounds end in –*ane*, as in methane and propane.

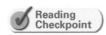 **Factors that determine the properties of a hydrocarbon are the number of carbon atoms and how the atoms are arranged.** A hydrocarbon molecule can contain one carbon atom, as in methane, or more than 30 carbon atoms, as in asphalt. The carbon atoms can be arranged in a straight chain, a branched chain, or a ring.

Straight Chains Figure 4 lists the names, molecular formulas, structural formulas, and boiling points for four straight-chain alkanes. Recall that a molecular formula shows the type and number of atoms in a molecule of the compound. A structural formula shows how those atoms are arranged. The number of carbon atoms in a straight-chain alkane affects the state of the alkane at room temperature. Methane and propane are gases. Pentane and octane are liquids. The more carbon atoms, the higher the boiling point is.

✓ **Reading Checkpoint** *What is another name for a saturated hydrocarbon?*

Some Straight-Chain Alkanes				
Name	Methane	Propane	Pentane	Octane
Molecular Formula	CH_4	C_3H_8	C_5H_{12}	C_8H_{18}
Structural Formula	H | H—C—H | H	H H H | | | H—C—C—C—H | | | H H H	H H H H H | | | | | H—C—C—C—C—C—H | | | | | H H H H H	H H H H H H H H | | | | | | | | H—C—C—C—C—C—C—C—C—H | | | | | | | | H H H H H H H H
Boiling Point	−161.5°C	−42.1°C	36.0°C	125.6°C

Facts and Figures

Naming Hydrocarbons Names of straight- and branched-chain hydrocarbons use prefixes to indicate the number of carbon atoms in the longest continuous chain. Except for *meth-* (1), *eth-* (2), and *prop-* (3), the prefixes used match those shown in Figure 20 on p. 175. For branched-chain hydrocarbons, the carbon atoms in the longest continuous chain are numbered beginning at one end of the chain. Prefixes that combine a numeral and a group designation are used to show the type and location of branches. Using this system, the official name for isobutane (shown in Figure 5) is 2-methylpropane.

Quick Lab

Comparing Isomers

Materials

30 marshmallows, 70 raisins, 50 toothpicks

Procedure

1. Use marshmallows to represent carbon atoms, and raisins to represent hydrogen atoms, as in the model of propane shown. **CAUTION** *Do not eat anything in the laboratory.* Break the toothpicks in half to represent single bonds. Build models of five different isomers of hexane (C_6H_{14}).

2. For each model, attach all six carbon atoms first. Then attach hydrogen atoms until each carbon atom has four bonds.

Analyze and Conclude

1. **Using Models** Draw a structural formula for each isomer.

2. **Predicting** Would pentane (C_5H_{12}) or heptane (C_7H_{16}) have more isomers than hexane? Explain your answer.

Branched Chains Look at the butane and isobutane formulas in Figure 5. Both compounds have a molecular formula of C_4H_{10}, but their structural formulas are different. In isobutane, there is a branch at the point where a carbon atom bonds to three other carbon atoms.

Compounds with the same molecular formula but different structural formulas are **isomers.** Differences in structure affect some properties of isomers. Butane boils at –0.5°C, but isobutane boils at –11.7°C. The number of possible isomers increases rapidly each time an additional carbon atom is added to the chain. For example, octane (C_8H_{18}) has 18 isomers, while decane ($C_{10}H_{22}$) has 75.

Rings Figure 5 also shows the structural formula for cyclobutane. The carbon atoms in cyclobutane are linked in a four-carbon ring. Because each carbon atom forms bonds with two other carbon atoms, it can bond with only two hydrogen atoms. So cyclobutane (C_4H_8) molecules have two fewer hydrogen atoms than butane (C_4H_{10}) molecules. Most ring alkanes, or cyclic hydrocarbons, have rings with five or six carbons.

Butane C_4H_{10}	Isobutane C_4H_{10}	Cyclobutane C_4H_8

Figure 5 Butane, isobutane, and cyclobutane represent three ways that carbon atoms are arranged in an alkane—in a straight chain, in a branched chain, and in a ring. *Classifying* **Explain why butane and cyclobutane are not isomers.**

Carbon Chemistry **265**

Facts and Figures

Hydrocarbons An isomer with branches often has a lower boiling point than its corresponding straight-chain isomer because less efficient packing results in weaker intermolecular forces. There is a strain on rings with only three or four carbon atoms because of the bond angles between the carbon atoms.

In general, unsaturated hydrocarbons are more reactive than saturated hydrocarbons because atoms or groups of atoms can be added to the molecule at the locations of double and triple bonds. Combustion reactions are the exception to this trend.

Quick Lab

Comparing Isomers   L2

Objective

After completing this activity, students will be able to

• use structural formulas and models to describe the isomers of hexane.

Skills Focus Observing, Predicting, Using Models

Prep Time 10 minutes.

Materials 30 marshmallows, 70 raisins, 50 toothpicks

Advance Prep Set out raisins, marshmallows, and toothpicks in a central location.

Class Time 15–20 minutes

Safety Remind students never to eat anything in the laboratory.

Teaching Tips

• Display ball-and-stick models that are initially oriented with the branches at opposite ends. Rotate one model 180° to show that the structural formulas represent the same isomer.

Expected Outcome Students should be able to draw the structural formulas for the isomers of hexane.

Analyze and Conclude

1. There are five straight- and branched-chain isomers of hexane:
(1) C–C–C–C–C–C (hexane)

(2) C–C–C–C–C (3) C–C–C–C–C
     | |
     C   C
(2-methylpentane) (3-methylpentane)

(4) C–C–C–C (5) C
     | | |
     C C   C–C–C–C
(2, 3-dimethylbutane) |
                         C
                (2, 2-dimethylbutane)

2. Heptane. The greater the number of carbon atoms, the greater the possibility for different lengths and locations of branches along a central chain.
Logical

Answer to . . .

Figure 4 *The boiling point increases.*

Figure 5 *Cyclobutane and butane do not have the same formula.*

Unsaturated Hydrocarbons

Integrate Social Studies `L2`

Friedrich August Kekulé claimed to have developed the model for the ring structure of benzene after he had a dream about a snake chasing its own tail. Have students find out more about this German chemist's work. Ask, **What other major contribution did Kekulé make to organic chemistry?** *(In 1854, he was one of the first to theorize that carbon forms four bonds.)*
Verbal

Integrate Health `L2`

The terms *saturated* and *unsaturated* are also used to describe fats. The term *fat* is commonly used to refer to the fats and oils that are obtained from animals and plants. (These fats are esters that form when fatty acids react with glycerol, an alcohol with three −OH groups.) There are three long hydrocarbon chains in each fat molecule. The chains contain an even number of carbon atoms (typically between 12 and 24). If the hydrocarbon chains contain only single bonds, then the fat is classified as a saturated fat. If there are one or more double or triple bonds in the hydrocarbon chains, then the fat is classified as an unsaturated fat. Unsaturated fats, such as corn oil and olive oil, are generally liquids at room temperature. Saturated fats, such as butter and bacon grease, tend to be solids at room temperature. A diet high in saturated fats has been linked to heart disease. Have students examine food labels to determine which types of foods contain saturated and unsaturated fats. You may also ask students to research whether cooking with unsaturated fats, such as olive oil, provides any health benefits other than preventing heart disease.
Visual

Figure 6 There are three types of unsaturated hydrocarbons.
A Ethene is an alkene that controls the ripening of a tomato.
B Ethyne is an alkyne used in torches that cut metals or weld them together. **C** Kekulé figured out the ring structure of the aromatic hydrocarbon benzene.

A

B

C

Unsaturated Hydrocarbons

A hydrocarbon that contains one or more double or triple bonds is an **unsaturated hydrocarbon.** These hydrocarbons are classified by bond type and the arrangement of their carbon atoms. ⬤ **There are three types of unsaturated hydrocarbons—alkenes, alkynes, and aromatic hydrocarbons.**

Ethene   Ethyne   Benzene

Alkenes Many fruit-bearing plants produce ethene (C_2H_4), which controls the rate at which fruits, such as the tomato in Figure 6A, ripen. There is a double bond between the two carbon atoms in ethene. Hydrocarbons that have one or more carbon-carbon double bonds are alkenes. The names of alkenes end in *–ene*. Plastics used in trash bags and milk jugs are produced by reactions involving ethene.

Alkynes In 1895, Henry-Louis Le Châtelier reported that a flame produced when ethyne burned had a temperature about 1000°C higher than a flame produced when hydrogen burns. Ethyne (C_2H_2), also known as acetylene, is an alkyne. Alkynes are straight- or branched-chain hydrocarbons that have one or more triple bonds. Alkyne names end in *–yne*.

Alkynes are the most reactive hydrocarbon compounds. The welder in Figure 6B is burning a mixture of oxygen and acetylene in an oxyacetylene torch. The temperature of the flame produced approaches 3500°C. At that temperature, most metals can be melted and welded together. The acetylene and oxygen are stored under pressure in tanks.

Aromatic Hydrocarbons The Belgian stamp in Figure 6C honors Friedrich Kekulé (1829–1896), who figured out that benzene (C_6H_6) is an unsaturated hydrocarbon with a ring structure. Although the formula shows alternating single and double bonds, the six bonds in the ring are identical. Six of the valence electrons are shared by all six carbon atoms. Hydrocarbons that contain similar ring structures are known as **aromatic hydrocarbons.** The name was chosen because many of these compounds have strong aromas or odors.

Reading Checkpoint   *What is an unsaturated hydrocarbon?*

Fossil Fuels

Some hydrocarbons were formed from plants and animals that lived in Earth's oceans and swamps millions of years ago. After those plants and animals died, they were buried under layers of rock and soil. High temperature and pressure deep in Earth's crust changed those remains into deposits of hydrocarbons called fossil fuels. **Fossil fuels** are mixtures of hydrocarbons that formed from the remains of plants or animals. ⬤ **Three types of fossil fuels are coal, natural gas, and petroleum.** The type of fossil fuel produced depends on the origin of the organic material and the conditions under which it decays.

Coal The ferns in Figure 7A are similar to those that produced the coal in Figure 7B. Coal is a solid fossil fuel that began to form about 300 million years ago in ancient swamps. Giant tree ferns and other plants were buried in those swamps. After millions of years of pressure, the plant remains produced a mixture of hydrocarbons. Most of the hydrocarbons in coal are aromatic hydrocarbons with high molar masses. These compounds have a high ratio of carbon to hydrogen. So burning coal produces more soot than burning other fossil fuels does.

Natural Gas The second main fossil fuel, natural gas, formed from the remains of marine organisms. Natural gas is mostly methane. It also contains ethane, propane, and isomers of butane. Natural gas is distributed through a network of underground pipes. It is used for heating and cooking, and to generate some electricity. Deposits of natural gas are found with deposits of coal and petroleum. Enormous amounts of unused natural gas resources also exist as methane frozen together with water, called methane hydrate. Methane hydrate is found in Arctic soils and in offshore sediments.

Petroleum The third main fossil fuel, petroleum, also formed from the remains of marine organisms. Petroleum, often known as crude oil, is pumped from deep beneath the Earth's surface. It is a complex liquid mixture of hydrocarbons, comprised mainly of long-branched alkanes and alkenes. For petroleum to be useful, it must be separated into simpler mixtures, or fractions, such as gasoline and heating oil.

Figure 7 Fossil fuels form from the remains of plants and animals. **A** The ferns shown are similar to ferns that lived millions of years ago. **B** The imprints of ferns left on the lump of coal are evidence that the coal formed when plant remains were compressed under layers of rock and soil.

For: Links on fossil fuels
Visit: www.SciLinks.org
Web Code: ccn-1091

Carbon Chemistry **267**

Teacher ⟩ **Demo**

Fractional Distillation L2

Purpose Students will observe fractional distillation of a mixture of organic compounds.

Materials Distillation apparatus with stand, 50 mL water, 50 mL ethanol, 60 mL mineral oil, hot plate, 60-mL beakers (6), concave glass beaker covers (3), shield, dropper pipets (5).

Procedure Explain that fractional distillation is a method of separating mixtures using differences in boiling points. Measure 50 mL of water and 50 mL of ethanol in two different beakers and mix them together in the distillation chamber. Heat the mixture, keeping the temperature at about 85°C, just above the boiling point of ethanol and below the boiling point of water. Three times during the process, collect the distilled liquid (distillate) in a separate beaker, and cover the beaker. After you complete the distillation, place a drop of pure ethanol and a drop of pure water in a beaker of mineral oil. Next, place a drop from each beaker of distilled liquid into the mineral oil. Have students notice whether the drops float or how quickly they sink.

Safety Place a blast shield between the equipment and students. Use mitts or tongs to handle hot glass.

Expected Outcome The ethanol will collect more rapidly in the catch beaker. Pure ethanol floats in mineral oil, and pure water sinks. Students can infer the relative concentrations of ethanol and water in each distillate sample by the behavior of the drops in the mineral oil. **Visual**

Download a worksheet on fossil fuels for students to complete, and find additional teacher support from NSTA SciLinks.

Answer to . . .

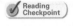 *A hydrocarbon that contains one or more double or triple bonds*

Build Science Skills **L2**

Problem Solving Tell students that they are given an unknown alkane. Have them use Figure 8 to answer the following question. Ask, **How could you determine if the alkane is one of the components of gasoline?** *(If its boiling point is between 40°C and 100°C, then the alkane may be a component of gasoline.)*
Visual, Logical

FYI

In industry documents that describe fractional distillation, there is variation in the names of the fractions collected, the length of the carbon chains in a fraction, and the temperature range at which a fraction is collected. There *is* agreement on how the process separates the numerous substances in petroleum into fractions.

Combustion of Fossil Fuels
Build Math Skills **L1**

Balancing Equations Remind students that only the coefficients in front of the formulas, and not the subscripts in the formulas, may be changed when they balance an equation. Have students practice balancing the equation for the complete combustion of ethane:

$C_2H_6 + O_2 \longrightarrow CO_2 + H_2O$

$(2C_2H_6 + 7O_2 \longrightarrow 4CO_2 + 6H_2O)$

Then, have students determine the balanced equation for incomplete combustion of ethane.

$(2C_2H_6 + 5O_2 \longrightarrow 4CO + 6H_2O)$
Logical

Direct students to the **Math Skills** in the **Skills and Reference Handbook** at the end of the student text for additional help.

Figure 8 The petroleum pumped from underground deposits is a complex mixture of hydrocarbons. **A** At a refinery, petroleum is separated into mixtures called fractions. **B** The diagram shows some of the fractions that can be collected from a distillation tower. The labels provide data on the compounds within a fraction. For example, compounds in kerosene have from 12 to 16 carbon atoms and condense at temperatures between 200°C and 250°C. **Interpreting Diagrams** *How many carbon atoms are there in the compounds in the petroleum gas fraction?*

Petroleum gas
< 40°C
C_1 to C_4

Gasoline
40°–200°C
C_5 to C_{12}

Kerosene, jet fuel
200°–250°C
C_{12} to C_{16}

Heating oil
250°–300°C
C_{15} to C_{18}

Lubricating oil
300°–370°C
$\geq C_{19}$

Residue, asphalt
$\geq C_{25}$

Distillation Tower

Crude oil vapors

Crude oil

Heating burner

For: Activity on photochemical smog
Visit: PHSchool.com
Web Code: ccc-1090

The diagram in Figure 8B shows how petroleum is separated into fractions through a type of distillation called fractional distillation. When petroleum is heated in a distillation tower, most of the hydrocarbons vaporize. The vapors rise through the tower and condense as the temperature decreases. Compounds with higher boiling points condense first. They are collected near the bottom of the tower.

Combustion of Fossil Fuels

The energy released from fossil fuels through combustion is used to heat buildings, cook food, or for transportation. Recall that energy from the combustion of propane heats the air in a hot-air balloon.

$$C_3H_8 + 5O_2 \longrightarrow 3CO_2 + 4H_2O \text{ (complete combustion)}$$

The primary products of the complete combustion of fossil fuels are carbon dioxide and water. Burning fossil fuels increases the amount of carbon dioxide in the atmosphere. This increase may affect temperatures, amounts of rain, and sea levels worldwide. Some sulfur and nitrogen are in fossil fuels, and air contains nitrogen. So nitrogen oxides and sulfur dioxide are produced during the combustion of fossil fuels.

Incomplete Combustion In stoves and furnaces, there may not be enough oxygen available for complete combustion of all the fuel. So a deadly gas, carbon monoxide, is produced. This colorless, odorless gas can be inhaled and absorbed by blood. It keeps hemoglobin from carrying oxygen to cells. Safety experts recommend that homes heated with natural gas or heating oil have carbon monoxide detectors.

$$2C_3H_8 + 7O_2 \longrightarrow 6CO + 8H_2O \text{ (incomplete combustion)}$$

When fossil fuels undergo incomplete combustion in factories or power plants, they also produce tiny particles of carbon. Inhaling these particles can cause heart and lung problems.

Find links to additional activities and have students monitor phenomena that affect Earth and its residents.

Facts and Figures

Octane Number Octane ratings are used to compare blends of gasoline. Two substances found in gasoline are used as reference fuels: *n*-heptane and isooctane (2,2,4-trimethylpentane). Because *n*-heptane self-ignites when compressed, it burns too rapidly, causing a knocking sound in a poorly performing engine. Isooctane will not self-ignite if it is compressed before sparking. The octane rating describes a blend as though it contained only *n*-heptane and isooctane. With an octane rating of 89, gasoline performs as if it contained 89% isooctane and 11% *n*-heptane. With a higher octane rating, the possibility of knocking is lower.

Figure 9 This statue of George Washington was sculpted from marble in 1918. The photograph was taken in the 1990s. The damage was done by calcium carbonate in the marble reacting with sulfuric acid in acid rain.

Acid Rain The combustion of fossil fuels causes the acidity of rain to increase. Rain is always slightly acidic, with a pH of about 5.6, because carbon dioxide dissolves in water droplets and forms carbonic acid, H_2CO_3. Sulfur dioxide and nitrogen oxides released into the atmosphere also dissolve in water, forming sulfuric acid, H_2SO_4, and nitric acid, HNO_3. The pH of rain containing sulfuric acid and nitric acid can be as low as 2.7. These acids damage stone structures like the statue in Figure 9. They also damage metal and concrete.

For: Activity on acid rain
Visit: PHSchool.com
Web Code: ccc-1091

Section 9.1 Assessment

Reviewing Concepts

1. Name three forms of carbon.
2. What two factors can affect the properties of a hydrocarbon?
3. Name the three categories of unsaturated hydrocarbons.
4. Name the three main fossil fuels.
5. What are the two primary products of the complete combustion of fossil fuels?
6. What are three ways that carbon atoms can be arranged in hydrocarbon molecules?

Critical Thinking

7. **Classifying** Why isn't carbon dioxide considered an organic compound?
8. **Applying Concepts** Draw structural formulas for the two branched-chain isomers of pentane, C_5H_{12}.

Connecting C Concepts

Saturation Compare the way *saturated* and *unsaturated* are used in describing hydrocarbons to how they were used in describing solutions in Section 8.2.

Carbon Chemistry **269**

Build Math Skills L1

Interpreting Equations Write the equations for the complete and incomplete combustion of propane on the board. Ask, **Why are there 5 moles of oxygen in the equation for the complete combustion, but 7 moles of oxygen in the equation for the incomplete combustion?** Let students figure out that the number of moles of methane is not the same in the two equations. Then, multiply the coefficients in the first equation by 2 to show that the amount of oxygen used is greater.
Logical

Direct students to the **Math Skills** in the **Skills and Reference Handbook** at the end of the student text for additional help.

3 ASSESS

Evaluate Understanding

Have students make flashcards for the key concepts and vocabulary in this section. For example, for each type of unsaturated hydrocarbon, they can make a card that has an example and a definition. Students can use the flashcards to quiz one another.

Reteach L1

Use the structural formulas in the text on pp. 265 and 266 to review each type of hydrocarbon.

Connecting C Concepts

In a saturated solution, the solvent contains the maximum amount of solute at a given temperature. A saturated hydrocarbon contains the maximum number of hydrogen atoms for each carbon atom. More solute can be added to an unsaturated solution. More hydrogen atoms can be added to an unsaturated hydrocarbon.

 If your class subscribes to the Interactive Textbook, use it to review key concepts in Section 9.1.

Section 9.1 Assessment

1. Diamond, graphite, and fullerenes are forms of carbon.
2. Factors that determine the properties of a hydrocarbon are the number of carbon atoms and how the atoms are arranged.
3. The three types of unsaturated hydrocarbons are alkenes, alkynes, and aromatic hydrocarbons.
4. Three types of fossil fuels are coal, natural gas, and petroleum.
5. Carbon dioxide and water
6. As a straight chain, a branched chain, or a ring
7. Carbon dioxide does not contain any hydrogen atoms.
8.
```
C–C–C–C              C
    |                |
    C              C–C–C
(2-methylbutane)     |
                     C
              (2, 2-dimethylpropane)
```

Answer to . . .

Figure 8 *Molecules of compounds in petroleum gas contain one to four carbon atoms.*

Carbon Chemistry 269

Breathing Easy `L2`
Background

The Department of Energy began The Clean Coal Technology Program in response to concerns about acid rain. The diagram illustrates some of the methods used to reduce emissions of nitrogen oxides and sulfur dioxide. (1) Sulfur that is not bonded to carbon is removed when coal is crushed and washed. (2) Jets of air keep limestone and crushed coal suspended so that the limestone can react with the sulfur dioxide. Because the temperature in the furnace is low and the amount of air is limited, most of the oxygen reacts with fuel, not nitrogen. (7) Smokestacks may contain electrostatic precipitators and scrubbers. As particles of ash pass through the precipitator, they gain a charge. They can be collected on a plate with an opposite charge. In one type of scrubber, limewater is sprayed into the stream of waste gases. The calcium hydroxide reacts with sulfur dioxide and forms solid calcium sulfate.

Build Science Skills `L2`
Observing

ACTIVITY

Purpose In this activity, students will use physical properties to separate a mixture of coal and sulfur.

Materials 100-mL beaker containing a 1:1 mixture of sulfur powder and coal dust, 100-mL graduated cylinder, stirring rod, distilled water, plastic pipet, 100-mL beaker

Class Time 10–15 minutes

Procedure Provide each group with a beaker containing 10 g of the sulfur-coal mixture. Have them add 30 mL of water to the beaker and mix using a stirring rod. Allow layers to form in the mixture. Next, have students use a pipet to transfer the layer of water containing coal dust to a second beaker. Stir the mixture and allow layers to form again. Have students compare their activity to the process described in Step 1 of the diagram.

Safety Students should wear safety goggles and aprons.

CONCEPTS in Action

Breathing Easy

Coal-burning power stations produce more than half the electricity in the United States. An average coal-burning power station emits about 10,000 tons each of sulfur dioxide and nitrogen oxides each year.

Oxides of sulfur and nitrogen cause smog and acid rain, and can irritate your lungs. The Clean Coal Technology Program in the United States encourages the development of technologies that reduce emissions of these harmful gases. The diagram shows how these emissions are reduced. The process begins when sulfur is washed from the surface of coal and ends when cleaner air is released into the atmosphere. Researchers are also exploring ways to capture the carbon dioxide that is produced to keep it from entering the atmosphere.

1 Washing coal The coal is crushed and washed to remove sulfur from its surface. When the coal is placed in a water-filled tank, the coal floats to the surface while the sulfur impurities sink to the bottom.

2 Furnace 1 A mixture of coal and limestone floats on a stream of hot air in the furnace. Calcium carbonate in the limestone reacts with sulfur dioxide to form calcium sulfate. The amount of air is limited and the temperature is held low to keep nitrogen from reacting with oxygen.

3 Cyclone separator The cyclone separates the unburned fuel from the hot gases.

4 Furnace 2 Unburned coal from the first furnace is transferred into furnace 2 for further burning. More limestone is added to react with any sulfur dioxide produced.

Facts and Figures

Catalytic Converters The combustion of petroleum products in internal combustion engines produces emissions that contribute to air pollution. In a vehicle's exhaust system, there is a catalytic converter. This device contains a mixture of catalysts for the oxidation of carbon monoxide and unburned hydrocarbons to carbon dioxide and water and the reduction of nitrogen oxides to nitrogen. The catalysts may be transition metals, such as platinum palladium, and rhodium; or oxides of transition metals, such as CuO and Cr_2O_3.

Electric generator

Gas turbine

Steam turbine

Chimney

Particle filters

Condenser

6 Particle filter Hot gases from the furnaces are fed through filters made of tightly woven fabric. The filters trap tiny particles of coal and ash and prevent them from entering the gas turbine.

Steam out

Boiler

Steam out

Water in

5 Boiler Water from the condenser flows through pipes in the boiler. Hot gases from furnace 2 are fed into the boiler to heat the water. The steam created is used to spin a steam turbine. The exhaust gases are recycled back to furnace 2.

Heat exchanger

7 Heat exchanger Waste gases are cooled in the heat exchanger by a coil containing cold water. The cooled and cleaned gases, containing dramatically reduced amounts of sulfur dioxide and nitrogen oxides, are emitted from the chimney.

Going Further

- Research the process of coal gasification. Write a paragraph describing one of the methods used to convert coal into flammable gases. What gases are produced? What are the benefits of coal gasification? Are there any problems with the technology?

- Take a Discovery Channel Video Field Trip by watching "Clean Energy."

 DISCOVERY CHANNEL SCHOOL **Video Field Trip**

Carbon Chemistry **271**

Expected Outcome Most of the sulfur will settle to the bottom of the first beaker while the coal dust floats. Any remaining sulfur will settle to the bottom of the second beaker. This activity demonstrates what happens when coal is crushed and washed prior to burning.
Visual, Kinesthetic

Going Further   L3

The United States Department of Energy has funded research into coal gasification. They are encouraging the development of methods for converting solid coal into gases that can be used to generate power. During gasification, coal reacts with steam and oxygen at a high temperature and pressure. The methods produce a mixture of gases. Hydrogen and carbon monoxide are typical products. The hydrogen can be separated from the raw mixture and used directly as fuel or it can be combined with carbon monoxide to produce methane. Any carbon dioxide produced is captured for commercial applications or sequestered to prevent its release into the atmosphere.

If students search the Internet, they will find descriptions of multiple methods for coal gasification, and information on the advantages and drawbacks of the methods. The main advantages of coal gasification are a reduction in air pollution and an increase in efficiency (more energy produced from the same amount of coal). For now, drawbacks include the cost of equipment and a higher cost per kilowatt for power generation. Other drawbacks are the amount of water required and the amount of wastewater produced.
Verbal, Portfolio

 DISCOVERY CHANNEL SCHOOL   **Video Field Trip**

Clean Energy

After students have viewed the Video Field Trip, ask them the following questions: **What substances does a fuel cell use to produce energy? What form of energy is produced?** *(The fuel cell uses oxygen [from air] and hydrogen. The fuel cell produces electrical energy.)* **What technological advance made fuel cells more efficient?** *(The development of a new kind of membrane to separate the oxygen and hydrogen)* **Give one advantage** that a fuel cell has over an internal combustion engine.** *(Student answers may include having no moving parts, producing only water as a product, and being quieter.)* **What advantage does a vehicle that uses a fuel cell have over a vehicle that uses batteries?** *(As long as fuel is provided, the fuel cell will continue to work.)* **If fuel cells are more efficient (that is, if they have a higher ratio of output energy to input energy) than internal combustion engines, why do most cars still have internal combustion engines?** *(Because of the large investment already made in internal engine technology)*

Carbon Chemistry 271

1 FOCUS

Objectives

9.2.1 Classify substituted hydrocarbons based on their functional groups.

9.2.2 Describe some properties and reactions of five types of substituted hydrocarbons.

Reading Focus

Build Vocabulary   L2

Word Forms Before students read this section, have them look up the words *substitute* and *functional*. Then, have students write a prediction for the meanings of the terms *substituted hydrocarbon* and *functional group*. After students study the section, have them look at their predictions and discuss any differences between their predictions and the definitions in the text.

Reading Strategy   L2

a. alcohol b. organic acid
c. organic base

2 INSTRUCT

Teacher Demo

Modeling Functional Groups   L2

Purpose Students make an analogy between an appliance's attachments and functional groups.

Materials Any appliance that has attachments with different functions

Procedure Demonstrate how the appliance works. Show students how each attachment performs a different function. Use these differences to explain how functional groups determine the properties of substituted hydrocarbons.

Safety Handle the appliance and its attachments according to the manufacturer's safety recommendations.

Expected Outcome Students will be able to compare the attachments of an appliance to functional groups in substituted hydrocarbons.
Visual, Logical

9.2 Substituted Hydrocarbons

Standards: ICP.3.2, ICP.3.3

Reading Focus

Key Concepts

- What functional groups are found in alcohols, organic acids, and organic bases?
- How are esters formed?

Vocabulary

- substituted hydrocarbon
- functional group

Reading Strategy

Monitoring Your Understanding Copy the table. As you read, complete the table by connecting each functional group with the type of compound that contains the functional group.

Functional Group	Type of Compound
–OH	a. ?
–COOH	b. ?
–NH₂	c. ?

The electric drill in Figure 10 can be used to drill holes, tighten a screw, or sand a rough surface. To change the function of the drill, you replace, or substitute, an attachment. A carbon atom in an organic compound can have four attachments. In a methane molecule (CH_4), the carbon atom has four identical attachments—its hydrogen atoms. When methane reacts with chlorine, chlorine atoms replace hydrogen atoms.

$$CH_4 + Cl_2 \longrightarrow CH_3Cl + HCl$$

Chloromethane and hydrogen chloride are products of the reaction between methane and chlorine. So are compounds with two, three, or four chlorine atoms. Organic compounds containing chlorine or other halogens are halocarbons. Almost all the halocarbons found on Earth were released from refrigerators, air conditioners, or aerosol sprays. Researchers have established that halocarbons containing chlorine and fluorine deplete Earth's protective ozone layer. The manufacture of chlorofluorocarbons has been restricted since 1990.

A hydrocarbon in which one or more hydrogen atoms have been replaced by an atom or group of atoms is a **substituted hydrocarbon.** The substituted atom or group of atoms is called a **functional group** because it determines the properties of the compound. Alcohols, organic acids, organic bases, and esters are substituted hydrocarbons.

Figure 10 Hydrocarbons in which some hydrogen atoms have been replaced can be compared to an electric drill with attachments.
Inferring *What determines the function of the drill, the drill itself or the attachments?*

hole saw bit

Forstner drill bit

Phillips screwdriver bit

twist drill bit

drum sander

272   *Chapter 9*

Section Resources

Print

- ***Reading and Study Workbook With Math Support,*** Section 9.2
- ***Math Skills and Problem Solving Workbook,*** Section 9.2
- ***Transparencies,*** Section 9.2

Technology

- ***Interactive Textbook,*** Section 9.2
- ***Presentation Pro CD-ROM,*** Section 9.2

Exploring Boiling Points of Chlorocarbons

Use the data given to construct a graph with *Number of Chlorine Atoms,* from 0 to 4, on the horizontal axis and *Boiling Point* on the vertical axis. Draw a smooth curve connecting the points.

1. **Using Graphs** Predict the boiling point of dichloromethane.

2. **Relating Cause and Effect** What effect does increasing the number of chlorine atoms have on the boiling point?

Boiling Points of Methane and Its Substituted Chlorocarbons		
Name	Formula	Boiling Point (°C)
Methane	CH_4	−161
Chloromethane	CH_3Cl	−24
Dichloromethane	CH_2Cl_2	?
Trichloromethane	$CHCl_3$	61
Tetrachloromethane	CCl_4	77

3. **Formulating Hypotheses** Why is the boiling point of CH_3Br higher than the boiling point of CH_3Cl? (*Hint:* Compare the atomic masses for bromine and chlorine.)

Alcohols

Methanol, CH_3OH, is used as a fuel in some motorcycles. Ethanol, CH_3CH_2OH, is often mixed with gasoline to help the gasoline burn more completely. Methanol and ethanol are alcohols. The name of an alcohol ends in –*ol*. ◯ **The functional group in an alcohol is a hydroxyl group, –OH.** When a halocarbon reacts with a base, the products are an alcohol and salt.

$$CH_3Cl + NaOH \longrightarrow CH_3OH + NaCl$$

An alcohol can also be made by reacting an alkene with water.

H   H
 \\ /
  C=C   +   H–OH   —H⁺→   H–C–C–H
 / \\   H OH
H   H   H–C–C–H
                                     H H

Ethene   **Water**   **Ethanol**

Organic Acids and Bases

The sharp, sour taste of a lemon comes from citric acid, an organic acid. ◯ **The functional group in organic acids is a carboxyl group, –COOH.** Names of organic acids end in -*oic*. Organic acids tend to have sharp tastes and strong odors. The simplest organic acid is methanoic acid, which is also known as formic acid. Vinegar is a solution of water and the organic acid ethanoic acid, which is usually referred to as acetic acid. If the ants in Figure 11 sprayed the formic acid they produce on your skin, your skin would itch or burn.

Methanoic acid   **Ethanoic acid**

     O   H   O
     ‖ | ‖
H – C – OH   H – C – C – OH
                               |
                               H

Figure 11 Birds sometimes will sit on an ants' nest and allow the ants to crawl over them. The methanoic acid sprayed by the ants is a natural pesticide that kills mites in the birds' feathers.

Carbon Chemistry **273**

Exploring Boiling Points of Chlorocarbons

1. Acceptable answers include temperatures between −24°C and 61°C. (The boiling point of dichloromethane is 40°C.)
2. As the number of chlorine atoms increases, the boiling point increases.
3. Bromine is more massive than chlorine.

For Extra Help L1

Demonstrate how to use a curve on a graph to estimate the value of an unknown data point. Find the appropriate value on the horizontal axis. Use a ruler to intersect the curve above that value. Turn the ruler 90° and read the vertical value for the intersection point. **Visual**

Alcohols
Build Science Skills L2

Applying Concepts Ask students to predict the products for the complete combustion of methanol and ethanol. Then, have them write balanced equations for these reactions.

$$2CH_3OH + 3O_2 \longrightarrow 2CO_2 + 4H_2O$$
$$C_2H_5OH + 3O_2 \longrightarrow 2CO_2 + 3H_2O$$

Logical

FYI

There are multiple methods for the formation of alcohols, including fermentation and reduction of aldehydes and ketones.

Organic Acids and Bases
Build Reading Literacy

Compare and Contrast Refer to page **226D** in **Chapter 8**, which provides guidelines for comparing and contrasting.

Have students read the text on pp. 273–274 related to organic acids and bases. Ask, **How do organic acids and bases differ?** (*Organic acids have a carboxyl group, while organic bases have an amino group.*) **How are organic acids and bases similar?** (*They are substituted hydrocarbons with strong odors.*)
Verbal

Customize for Inclusion Students

Learning Disabled
Make concept maps for each section and cover them with clear contact paper. Then, cut the maps into puzzle pieces. Provide students with the pieces and have them put the puzzle together. After students complete the puzzle, have them make flashcards with concept connections and added notes. For example,

students may have cards with the names of compounds on one side and structural formulas on the other. They may also have key concept cards with an important word missing: _____ **form when organic acids react with alcohols.** The answer on the back of the card would be *Esters.*

Answer to . . .

Figure 10 *The attachments determine the specific function of the drill.*

Esters

Address Misconceptions `L2`

Students may not know that an object has an odor because molecules from substances in the object interact with chemoreceptors in the nose. Studying esters is a good way to challenge this misconception. Have students smell some fragrant objects, such as apples, bananas, or flowers. Explain that some of the compounds responsible for the odors are esters.
Logical, Kinesthetic

Use Community Resources `L2`

Have a pharmacist speak to the class about how functional groups determine the effect of a medicine. Have students ask how to find information on the chemical composition of active ingredients in prescription and over-the-counter drugs.
Interpersonal

3 ASSESS

Evaluate Understanding `L2`

Have students design and play a matching game that uses cards that identify the formulas and characteristics of each functional group described in the section.

Reteach `L1`

Use short phrases to summarize the characteristics of functional groups. For example, say that amines smell like rotten fish and esters have pleasant smells, like some flowers. Review other characteristics, such as chemical structure, for each functional group.

Connecting C Concepts

Replacing a halogen with a hydroxyl group is a double-replacement reaction because the hydroxyl group and the halogen exchange places. The reaction of alkenes with water to produce an alcohol is a synthesis reaction because two reactants join to form one product.

Interactive Textbook If your class subscribes to the Interactive Textbook, use it to review key concepts in Section 9.2.

Figure 12 Many compounds in rose petals contribute to the fragrance of a rose. Some of these compounds are esters, which tend to have pleasant, sweet odors.

Do you know the smell of rotten fish? Then you've encountered a type of substituted hydrocarbon called an amine. Amines are organic bases. **The functional group in an amine is an amino group, $-NH_2$.** Amines are found in paints, dyes, and disinfectants. In Section 9.3 you will study the role organic bases play in the formation of organic compounds that are essential for life.

Esters

One group of substituted hydrocarbons accounts for the flavors of many foods and the pleasant odor of many flowers. These compounds are known as esters. **Esters form when organic acids react with alcohols.** The second product of the reaction is water. For example, ethanoic acid can react with methanol to produce methyl ethanoate (methyl acetate). The reaction is reversible.

$$
\underset{\textbf{Ethanoic acid}}{
\begin{array}{c} H\ O \\ |\ \ || \\ H-C-C-OH \\ | \\ H \end{array}}
+
\underset{\textbf{Methanol}}{
\begin{array}{c} H \\ | \\ HO-C-H \\ | \\ H \end{array}}
\underset{}{\overset{H^+}{\rightleftharpoons}}
\underset{\textbf{Methyl ethanoate}}{
\begin{array}{c} H\ O\ \ \ H \\ |\ \ ||\ \ \ | \\ H-C-C-O-C-H \\ |\ \ \ \ \ \ \ \ \ | \\ H\ \ \ \ \ \ \ \ H \end{array}}
+ \underset{\textbf{Water}}{HOH}
$$

Esters are used in many processed foods to produce flavors such as strawberry, banana, and grape. Flowers like the roses in Figure 12 produce esters and other compounds with distinctive odors that attract insects for pollination. Sometimes, the compounds produced by the plant mimic compounds produced by the insect.

Section 9.2 Assessment

Reviewing Concepts

1. What functional groups are found in alcohols, organic acids, and organic bases?
2. What types of compounds can react to produce esters?
3. What is a substituted hydrocarbon?
4. When a halocarbon reacts with a base, what products are produced?
5. What are two properties of organic acids?

Critical Thinking

6. **Classifying** An unknown compound has no noticeable odor. Explain why the compound is unlikely to be an organic acid, an organic base, or an ester.

7. **Inferring** What kind of organic compound gives a vitamin-C tablet its sour taste?
8. **Applying Concepts** Name one kind of substituted hydrocarbon you would expect to find in artificially flavored grape jelly.

Connecting C Concepts

Types of Reactions Alcohols can be made by reacting halocarbons with bases, or alkenes with water. Review the general types of reactions presented in Section 7.2. Which types best describe the two methods for producing an alcohol? Explain your choices.

Section 9.2 Assessment

1. Alcohols have hydroxyl groups, organic acids have carboxyl groups, and organic bases have amino groups.
2. Esters form when organic acids react with alcohols.
3. A hydrocarbon in which a functional group has been substituted for a hydrogen atom

4. An alcohol and a salt
5. Organic acids contain carboxyl groups and have a sharp, sour taste and a strong smell.
6. Organic acids, organic bases, and esters tend to have noticeable smells.
7. An organic acid
8. An ester

9.3 Polymers

Standards: ICP.8.2, ICP.8.4

Reading Focus

Key Concepts
- What is one way that polymers can be classified?
- What are three examples of synthetic polymers?
- What are four types of polymers that organisms can produce?

Vocabulary
- polymer
- monomers
- carbohydrates
- nucleic acids
- amino acid
- protein

Reading Strategy
Identifying Main Ideas Before you read, copy the concept map. As you read, complete the map to summarize two main ideas about polymers.

F reight trains, like those in Figure 13, use different types of cars to transport goods. A flatcar with no sides or roof is used to haul steel beams. Grain is carried in covered hoppers, which have a hatch at the top and a chute at the bottom. Liquids travel in tank cars. The cars on a train may be all the same type or a mixture of different types. On average, about 100 cars are linked together behind the locomotive on a freight train.

Like freight trains, some molecules are built up from smaller units linked together. A **polymer** is a large molecule that forms when many smaller molecules are linked together by covalent bonds. The smaller molecules that join together to form a poly- mer are **monomers.** *Poly-* means "many." *Mono-* means "one." In some polymers, there is only one type of monomer. Other polymers have two or more kinds of monomers.

Polymers can be classified as natural polymers or synthetic polymers. Many important types of biological molecules are natural polymers. Organisms produce these polymers in their cells. Synthetic polymers are developed by chemists in research laboratories and manufactured in factories. Both types of polymers have industrial uses. For example, silk and cotton fabrics are woven from natural polymer fibers, while polar fleece is made from a synthetic polymer.

Figure 13 Couplers that interlock like the fingers of your hands connect one railroad car to another. Many cars can be joined together to form a train because there is a coupler on both ends of a car. **Using Analogies** *How is a polymer like a train?*

Carbon Chemistry **275**

Section Resources

Print
- *Laboratory Manual,* Investigations 9A and 9B
- *Reading and Study Workbook With Math Support,* Section 9.3
- *Transparencies,* Section 9.3

Technology
- *Interactive Textbook,* Section 9.3
- *Presentation Pro CD-ROM,* Section 9.3
- *Go Online,* NSTA SciLinks, Polymers

Section 9.3

1 FOCUS

Objectives
9.3.1 **Distinguish** a monomer from a polymer.
9.3.2 **Compare** three examples of synthetic polymers.
9.3.3 **Describe** the structures and functions of four types of natural polymers.

Reading Focus

Build Vocabulary   L2

Word-Part Analysis Have students break the vocabulary terms *polymer, monomer,* and *carbohydrate* into roots, prefixes, or suffixes. Students may need to use a dictionary to find the meanings of some parts. (*Monomer has the prefix* mono- *meaning "one." Monomers are the single units that make up polymers. Polymer has the prefix* poly- *meaning "many." Polymers contain many monomers. Carbohydrate has the prefix* carbo-, *which means it contains carbon, and the suffix* -hydrate, *which means it also contains the components of water— hydrogen and oxygen.*)

Reading Strategy   L2
a. monomers
b. and c. natural/synthetic

2 INSTRUCT
Build Reading Literacy   L1

Use Prior Knowledge Refer to page **2D** in **Chapter 1,** which provides guidelines for using prior knowledge.

Before students read, ask them to list different fibers used to make fabrics, such as wool and polyester. Have them discuss which fibers they think are natural and identify their sources.
Verbal, Intrapersonal

Answer to . . .

Figure 13 *Like a train, a polymer is made up of single units that are joined together.*

Carbon Chemistry   275

Synthetic Polymers

Use Visuals L1

Figure 14 Have students look at the objects in Figure 14. Ask, **What are some physical properties of rubber, nylon, and polyethylene?** *(Possible answer: Rubber resists wear. Nylon is durable and strong. High-density polyethylene is hard.)* **What are some ways that each of the polymers is used?** *(Possible answer: Rubber is used for tires and as an adhesive. Nylon is used for parachutes, windbreakers, fishing line, carpets, and rope. Polyethylene is used for milk bottles and plastic wrap.)* **Visual, Logical**

Integrate Social Studies L2

Natural rubber collected from trees is soft and sticky. In 1839, Charles Goodyear found that when sulfur is added to rubber and the mixture is heated, the rubber is no longer sticky. Have students research other topics related to polymers. Possible topics include the discovery of nylon, the discovery of artificial silk (later called rayon) by Hilaire de Chardonnet, or the use of polymers in the film industry. Students may also want to research current efforts to recycle plastics, including the codes used on plastic products. Have students use posters or computer graphics to prepare a report on their research. **Verbal, Portfolio**

Download a worksheet on polymers for students to complete, and find additional teacher support from NSTA SciLinks.

Figure 14 Synthetic polymers are used to make tires, ropes, and plastic objects. **A** About half the rubber produced in the world is used to manufacture tires. **B** Nylon is a good choice for a rope because its fibers are strong and do not wear out easily. **C** The hard plastic shapes are made from a high-density polyethylene polymer. **Inferring** *At room temperature, polymers are most likely to exist as which state of matter?*

For: Links on polymers
Visit: www.SciLinks.org
Web Code: ccn-1093

Synthetic Polymers

The properties of a polymer depend on the type and number of monomers in the polymer. 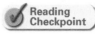 **Rubber, nylon, and polyethylene are three examples of compounds that can be synthesized.**

Rubber The sap collected from rubber trees in tropical regions contains rubber. So why would a chemist make synthetic rubber? The supply of natural rubber is limited. During World War II, the allies could not obtain natural rubber. Chemists worked hard to produce a synthetic rubber, using hydrocarbons from petroleum. Natural rubber and synthetic rubbers contain different monomers and have different properties. The tires in Figure 14A will resist wear and be less likely to leak if they are made of synthetic rubber. Rubber is used as an adhesive. The How It Works box on page 277 explains how adhesives work.

Nylon In the 1930s, Wallace Carothers was trying to produce a synthetic polymer to replace silk. The polymer he produced was nylon, which has properties not found in natural polymers. Nylon fibers are very strong, durable, and shiny. Nylon is used in parachutes, windbreakers, fishing line, carpets, and ropes like the one in Figure 14B.

Polyethylene Plastic milk bottles, plastic wrap, and the plastic shapes in Figure 14C are made of polyethylene. This polymer forms when ethene (or ethylene) molecules link head to tail. The number of carbon atoms in a polyethylene chain affects the properties of the polymer. The more carbon atoms in the chain, the harder the polymer is.

$$n \ \underset{H}{\overset{H}{C}} = \underset{H}{\overset{H}{C}} + \underset{H}{\overset{H}{C}} = \underset{H}{\overset{H}{C}} + \underset{H}{\overset{H}{C}} = \underset{H}{\overset{H}{C}} \longrightarrow \left(\underset{H}{\overset{H}{C}} - \underset{H}{\overset{H}{C}} - \underset{H}{\overset{H}{C}} - \underset{H}{\overset{H}{C}} - \underset{H}{\overset{H}{C}} - \underset{H}{\overset{H}{C}} \right)_n$$

Reading Checkpoint *What determines the hardness of polyethylene?*

Customize for English Language Learners

Think-Pair-Share
Have students work in pairs to think of more analogies for polymers. Examples include beads in a necklace and links in a chain. Strengthen discussion skills by having students share their examples with the class.

Answer to . . .

Figure 14 *Polymers are most likely to be solids at room temperature.*

Reading Checkpoint *The hardness of polyethylene is determined by the number of carbon atoms in the chain. The more carbon atoms there are, the harder the polymer is.*

Synthetic Adhesives

Adhesion is the force of attraction between molecules of different substances whose surfaces are in contact. These forces are rarely strong enough to bind two surfaces together. An adhesive placed between the surfaces binds them together. Most adhesives are synthetic polymers. The diagram illustrates how some adhesives work. The adhesive remains liquid until the surfaces are in position. Then the adhesive sets. **Interpreting Diagrams** *Explain the purpose of a stabilizer in an adhesive.*

It also sticks handles to teapots.

Permanent adhesion
An epoxy resin was used to attach the automobile to the billboard. Epoxy resins are often stored in two parts that are mixed just before the epoxy is used. Strong binding forces in these adhesives make them heat- and water-resistant.

1 Liquid adhesive
In a typical adhesive, monomer molecules and a stabilizer are in a solvent. The stabilizer stops the monomers from forming a solid polymer.

Tube

Monomer molecule

Stabilizer

Solvent

2 Applying the adhesive Some of the liquid is squeezed onto one of the surfaces to be joined.

Monomers join together.

Temporary adhesion
The sticky strip on a reusable note is an adhesive containing tiny spheres. The spheres limit the amount of surface area that makes contact, so the note sticks lightly and repositions easily.

3 The adhesive sets
Contact with water in the air and on the surfaces being joined makes the stabilizer inactive. The monomers then begin to join together to form a polymer. As the chain lengthens, the adhesive changes from a liquid to a solid.

Types of adhesion
Adhesion can work in three ways. Molecules of the polymer may fill crevices in the surfaces being connected. The molecules may also be attracted to one another by intermolecular forces, or they may react by forming covalent bonds.

Carbon Chemistry **277**

Synthetic Adhesives L2

The invention of reusable notes began in 1968 when Dr. Spencer Silver was attempting to make a strong adhesive. One of the adhesives he produced was just strong enough to hold papers together, but it was weak enough that the papers could be separated without damage. Silver tried to develop a use for the weak adhesive, but it was his colleague, Art Fry, who realized the adhesive's potential. While singing in a choir, Fry was bothered by bookmarks slipping out of pages. By applying some of the weak adhesive to paper, Fry developed a reusable bookmark that could stick to pages without harming them. The adhesive is now used to produce the familiar, multi-colored reusable notes.

Interpreting Diagrams Stabilizers are used to prevent the adhesive monomers from forming a solid polymer.
Logical

For Enrichment L3

Have students work in pairs and devise an experiment to compare two types of commercially-available adhesives. Remind them to start by forming a hypothesis and writing a plan for their experiment. Suggest that they develop a number scale for reporting how well each adhesive binds two surfaces together. Materials may include paper, metal foil, or wooden craft sticks.
Kinesthetic, Logical

FYI

Although the terms are used inter-changeably, *glue* refers to natural products and *adhesives* refers to synthetics.

Natural Polymers

Distinguishing Sugars From Starches [L2]

Objective

After completing this activity, students will be able to

• use iodine to test for the presence of starch in foods.

Skills Focus Observing, Formulating Hypotheses, Inferring

 Prep Time 15 minutes

Materials 1 slice each of potato, ripe apple, bread; 15 mL cornstarch; 15 mL table sugar; iodine in a dropper bottle; 6 small paper plates

Advance Prep Cut apples, potatoes, and bread into small cubes (about 1 cm³). Place iodine solution in labeled dropper bottles.

Class Time 10–15 minutes

Safety Students should wear safety goggles and aprons. Remind students not to eat anything in the lab. If students slice their own apples and potatoes, remind them to be careful when handling sharp objects.

Teaching Tips

• Do not slice the apples and potatoes until right before class. Oxidation will cause them to turn brown, making it difficult to observe the results.

• Make sure that the apples are very ripe, but not rotten. In an unripe apple, all of the starch may not be converted to sugar, and students may get a positive result. Test one apple in advance.

Expected Outcome Iodine solution changes color in the presence of starch. Iodine will change from orange-rust to brown or blue-black with the cornstarch, potato, and bread. Iodine will not change color with the sugar or the apple.

Analyze and Conclude

1. Iodine will change color with starch, but not with a sugar.
2. The cornstarch, potato, and bread contain starch.
3. Possible answers include corn, flour, cereals, or any of the foods shown in Figure 15.
Visual, Logical

⊒Quick⟩Lab

Distinguishing Sugars From Starches

Materials

1 slice each of potato, ripe apple, and bread; 15 mL cornstarch; 15 mL table sugar; iodine in dropper bottle; 6 small paper plates

Procedure

1. Place one sample of each food on a paper plate. **CAUTION** *Never eat anything in a lab.*

2. Place 2 to 3 drops of iodine solution on the cornstarch. Record your observations.

3. Repeat Step 2 using sugar instead of cornstarch.

4. Place 2 to 3 drops of iodine on each of the other food samples. Record your observations.

Analyze and Conclude

1. **Classifying** How can an iodine solution be used to distinguish a sugar from a starch?

2. **Drawing Conclusions** Which of the food samples contained starch?

3. **Predicting** What other foods would turn dark when tested with iodine solution?

Figure 15 All the foods shown contain starch, which is a polymer of the simple sugar glucose. **Observing** *Identify foods that you recognize in the photograph.*

Natural Polymers

Almost all of the large molecules produced by organisms are polymers. **Four types of polymers produced in plant and animal cells are starches, cellulose, nucleic acids, and proteins.**

Starches Many animals are attracted to sweet-tasting foods. The compounds responsible for this sweetness are often sugars. Simple sugars have the formula $C_6H_{12}O_6$. They can exist as straight chains or rings. The simple sugars glucose and fructose can react to form sucrose (table sugar). Glucose monomers join to form starches as shown below.

Glucose   A type of starch found in plants

Typically, a starch contains hundreds of glucose monomers. Plants store starches for food and to build stems, seeds, and roots. Flour for the bread, pasta, and tortillas shown in Figure 15 is made by grinding the seeds of grains, such as wheat and corn. Simple sugars, slightly more complex sugars such as sucrose, and polymers built from sugar monomers are all classified as **carbohydrates.**

Cellulose The carbohydrate cellulose is the main component of cotton and wood. It is the most abundant of all organic compounds found in nature. Cellulose molecules contain 3000 or more glucose monomers. Cellulose gives strength to plant stems and tree trunks. Most animals cannot digest cellulose.

278 *Chapter 9*

⌐ Facts and Figures ───────

Starchy Root Cassava is a starchy tuber that is a food staple for many people in South America, West Africa, and the Caribbean. Cassava is similar to the sweet potato, except that some varieties contain prussic acid. If not prepared by grating, pressing, and heating, cassava is toxic. Tapioca is a product of cassava roots.

Nucleic Acids There are molecules in each cell of a plant or animal that store information about its structures and functions. These molecules are nucleic acids. **Nucleic acids** are large, nitrogen-filled polymers found mainly in the nuclei of cells. There are two types of nucleic acid, deoxyribonucleic acid (DNA) and ribonucleic acid (RNA).

The monomers in a nucleic acid are nucleotides. Figure 16A shows the three parts of a DNA nucleotide. The yellow circle represents a phosphate group. The green pentagon represents deoxyribose sugar, which has a five-atom ring. The purple rectangle represents an organic base. The bases in DNA are adenine, thymine, cytosine, and guanine.

When two strands of DNA line up as shown in Figure 16B, an adenine base always pairs up with a thymine base, and a cytosine base always pairs up with a guanine base. These pairs of bases are arranged like the rungs of a ladder. The strands are held together by strong intermolecular attractions between hydrogen atoms on one strand and nitrogen or oxygen atoms on the other strand. Figure 16C shows how the strands twist around each other in a structure called a double helix. The order of the base pairs in a strand is a code that stores information that is used to produce proteins.

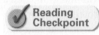 **Reading Checkpoint** *What are the two types of nucleic acids?*

A

B
- ⬤ Phosphate
- ⬠ Deoxyribose sugar
- ▪ Adenine
- ◢ Thymine
- ▪ Cytosine
- ▪ Guanine

C

Figure 16 Nucleic acids are polymers that store the genetic information that gives the girls in the photograph their distinct physical characteristics.
A The monomers in DNA have three components—a phosphate group, a sugar, and one of four organic bases. **B** Two strands of DNA are held together by intermolecular attractions between the organic bases.
C The shape of DNA is like a twisted ladder. Phosphate-sugar chains form the sides of the ladder. The rungs of the ladder are pairs of bases.

Carbon Chemistry **279**

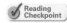

Build Science Skills `L2`

Comparing and Contrasting Have students compare and contrast proteins and nucleic acids. Ask, **What do these two types of polymers have in common?** *(Both have important biological functions, and the monomers of both are acids.)* **How do these two types of polymers differ?** *(The monomers in nucleic acids are nucleotides. The monomers in proteins are amino acids.)* **Logical**

Integrate Health `L2`

Eggs, milk, meat, and fish usually contain all the essential amino acids. Individual plant foods do not. A strict vegetarian must eat a combination of foods to obtain all the essential amino acids. Have students research and prepare posters showing foods (such as beans and rice) that provide the complete set of essential amino acids.
Visual

3 ASSESS

Evaluate Understanding `L2`

Have students write down the following list of polymers: polyethylene, starch, cellulose, nucleic acids, and proteins. Then, have students identify the monomers for each polymer.

Reteach `L1`

Use the equation in the text on pp. 276 and 278 to compare a synthetic and a natural polymer.

Writing in Science

Paragraphs should include the following. Similarities: made up of smaller molecules called monomers that are linked together by covalent bonds. Differences: synthetic polymers are developed by chemists; organisms produce natural polymers.

Interactive Textbook If your class subscribes to the Interactive Textbook, use it to review key concepts in Section 9.3.

Answer to . . .

Figure 17 *Possible answers include: seafood, meat, beans, and nuts.*

Figure 17 The foods shown are all good protein sources.
Classifying *Group the foods into three or four categories.*

Proteins Recall that organic acids contain a –COOH group and organic bases, or amines, contain an –NH_2 group. There is one substituted hydrocarbon that contains both groups. An **amino acid** is a compound that contains both carboxyl and amino functional groups in the same molecule. There are about 20 amino acids that your body needs to function.

Glycine   Phenylalanine

Your cells can manufacture some, but not all, of the amino acids. For example, your body can make glycine, but not phenylalanine. The essential amino acids that your body cannot make must come from foods like those in Figure 17.

Your cells use amino acids as the monomers for constructing protein polymers. A **protein** is a polymer in which at least 100 amino acid monomers are linked through bonds between an amino group and a carboxyl group. The instructions for making proteins are stored in DNA. Proteins make up the fibers of your muscles, your hair and fingernails, and the hemoglobin in your blood. Your body may contain as many as 300,000 different proteins.

Section 9.3 Assessment

Reviewing Concepts

1. Describe a way that polymers can be classified.
2. Name three synthetic polymers.
3. Describe What are four types of polymers that can be found in the cells of organisms?
4. What are the three parts of a nucleotide?
5. What holds the bases together in DNA?
6. What two functional groups are found in amino acids?

Critical Thinking

7. **Using Analogies** Which natural polymers are like a train with identical freight cars and which are like a train with a mixture of different cars?

8. **Inferring** There is another system for classifying carbohydrates that uses the categories monosaccharides, disaccharides, and polysaccharides. Where would you place glucose, sucrose, and cellulose in this classification system? Give a reason for your answer.

Compare-Contrast Paragraph Write a paragraph comparing natural and synthetic polymers in general. How are they similar? How are they different?

Section 9.3   Assessment

1. The two main types of polymers are natural and synthetic.
2. Rubber, nylon, and polyethylene
3. Starches, cellulose, nucleic acids, and proteins
4. Organic base, phosphate group, and a sugar
5. Strong intermolecular attractions
6. Amino acids contain a carboxyl group and an amino group.

7. Starches and cellulose are like trains with identical cars, and proteins and nucleic acids are like trains with a mixture of different cars.
8. Glucose is a monosaccharide because its molecules are single sugar units. Sucrose is a disaccharide because its molecules contain a glucose unit and a fructose unit linked together. Cellulose is a polysaccharide because it contains many glucose units linked together.

Genetically Modified Organisms: Modern Miracles or *Frankenfoods*?

People have been selectively breeding plants and animals for many years. Selective breeding works over generations to enhance or eliminate specific traits in an organism. Today, through genetic engineering, scientists can isolate and combine genes to create a genetically modified organism that would never exist in nature. Crops, such as corn and soy, are sometimes modified to avoid damage from weeds, insects, or viruses.

Here's an example. A bacterium called *Bacillus thurlingensis*, found in soil, creates a type of protein that kills insect larvae. Splicing the genes that encode this protein from that bacterium into corn DNA creates a new strain of corn. This genetically modified corn is protected against the corn borer, a pest that causes billions of dollars of damage to crops each year. This new strain of corn reduces the need to spray corn crops with pesticides.

The Viewpoints

Genetic modification is a beneficial tool.

The population of the world is expected to grow by roughly two billion people in the next 20 years, but the amount of farming land might actually decrease because of development and other factors. Genetic modification allows people to grow food more productively by using helpful gene traits that can make crops and livestock more resistant to pests and diseases.

Genetic modification can also help to reduce certain health issues. For example, golden rice is a type of rice that has added genes that make it rich in beta-carotene, a form of vitamin A. Golden rice can help to reduce vitamin A deficiencies in populations that rely predominantly on rice as their staple food.

Genetic modification is a dangerous practice.

Selective breeding does not create plants or animals that would be impossible in nature. Conversely, genetic modification creates unnatural creatures. Furthermore, it is impossible to predict the effects these new life forms could have on the environment. Inserting a bacterial gene into a plant could have unknown repercussions. Will the inserted gene be harmful to people? Will insects that are not pests also be harmed? In addition, once genetically modified organisms are out in the world, they could be difficult to contain. For example, the pollen from genetically modified plants could pollinate other plants to create new, unknown hybrids, which might have further unexpected effects on the environment.

Research and Decide

1. **Defining the Issue** In your own words, describe why genetically modified organisms are controversial.

2. **Analyzing the Viewpoints** List three arguments that support the use of genetic modification. List three arguments made by people who think that genetic modification is a dangerous idea.

3. **Forming Your Opinion** Traditionally, farmers store and sow the seeds of crops from previous years. However, many genetically modified crops produce sterile seeds. Farmers who grow these genetically modified crops must buy new seeds each year from seed companies. Are there advantages to this type of arrangement? Are there disadvantages? Explain your answer.

Go Online

NSTA *SciLINKS*

For: Links on polymers
Visit: www.SciLinks.org
Web Code: ccn-1093

Genetically Modified Organisms: Modern Miracles or *Frankenfoods*?

Background

Husbandry is the selective breeding of animals. The array of dog breeds is a good example of how traits can be manipulated within a species. Farmers used selective hybridization and grafting to improve crops, for example, developing sweet corn from native hard-kernel strains, or exotic fruit, such as the kiwi.

Scientists now can map the genomes of different organisms and locate genes that were linked to specific traits. Through recombinant DNA technology, or genetic engineering, scientists use enzymes to splice the area with the desired gene and use bacteria to make multiple copies of the gene. Using a variety of techniques, the gene copies are then inserted into the DNA of the target organism cell, creating the new, genetically modified genome.

Answers

1. Gene modification has much potential to help people, but its safety is unknown.

2. Acceptable answers in favor of pursuing genetic modification include the ability to feed more people, improve nutrition, and make food-based medicine. Acceptable answers in favor of restricting or banning genetic modification include unknown health risks to humans, to other organisms, and to the environment; the inability to control the spread of genetically modified material such as seeds and pollen in the environment; and the creation of gene or species combinations that are impossible in nature without fully understanding the effects.

3. As an advantage, students should identify the prevention of crossbreeding with wild-type plants. Disadvantages are the farmers' need to buy seed every year, and their inability to grow the plants from their own seed stocks from year to year.

Go Online
PHSchool.com

Download a worksheet on polymers for students to complete, and find additional teacher support from NSTA SciLinks.

1 FOCUS

Objectives

9.4.1 Compare photosynthesis and cellular respiration.

9.4.2 Explain how enzymes and vitamins help reactions take place in cells.

Reading Focus

Build Vocabulary   L2

Web Diagram Have students create a web diagram relating the terms *photosynthesis, cellular respiration, glucose, energy, carbohydrates, digestion,* and *polymers.*

Reading Strategy   L2

a. During photosynthesis, energy from sunlight is converted into chemical energy.
b. During cellular respiration, the energy stored in products of photosynthesis is released.
c. Enzymes and vitamins are compounds that help cells function efficiently at normal body temperature.

2 INSTRUCT

Photosynthesis
Build Reading Literacy   L1

Sequence Refer to page **290D** in **Chapter 10**, which provides guidelines for using a sequence.

Have students create a flowchart that follows a carbon atom through photosynthesis and cellular respiration. Have students mark where oxygen, water, and energy enter and exit the overall process.
Verbal

Integrate Biology   L2

In green plants, chlorophyll a and b are the dominant light-absorbing pigments. These pigments and others contribute to the color of leaves and allow plants to absorb the energy of sunlight. Have interested students research chlorophyll's structure. *(Chlorophyll has a flat, star-shaped structure with a Mg^{2+} ion in the center.)*
Logical

9.4 Reactions in Cells

Standards: ICP.5.6, ICP.5.7

Reading Focus

Key Concepts

- What energy conversion takes place during photosynthesis?
- How are photosynthesis and cellular respiration related?
- What molecules help cells function efficiently?

Vocabulary

- photosynthesis
- enzymes
- vitamins

Reading Strategy

Summarizing Copy the table. As you read, complete the table by recording a main idea for each heading.

Heading	Main Idea
Photosynthesis	a. ?
Cellular Respiration	b. ?
Enzymes and Vitamins	c. ?

Figure 18 Unlike a plant, this runner must get the energy he needs from the food he eats.

For thousands of years, people used whale oil and other animal fats as fuels for their lamps. As fats burn, they combine with oxygen and produce carbon dioxide and water. They also release energy in the form of heat and light. In a lamp, combustion takes place rapidly. In the cells of organisms, a more controlled version of the process releases energy stored in molecules. Some of the energy released helps maintain your internal body temperature at or close to 37°C.

Reactions that take place in cells follow the same rules as reactions that take place in a research laboratory or classroom. Some reactions go to completion and some reach an equilibrium point. Many reactions occur in solution and catalysts are often needed. Energy is transferred and energy is converted from one form to another. Photosynthesis and cellular respiration are two processes that allow organisms to meet their energy needs.

Photosynthesis

The sun is the primary source of energy for most plants and animals. During **photosynthesis,** plants chemically combine carbon dioxide and water into carbohydrates. The process requires light and chlorophyll, a green pigment in plants. This equation summarizes the process.

$$6H_2O + 6CO_2 + Energy\ (light) \longrightarrow C_6H_{12}O_6 + 6O_2$$

 During photosynthesis, energy from sunlight is converted into chemical energy. Photosynthesis involves a complex series of chemical reactions. When all the reactions are complete, the energy from sunlight has been stored in the covalent bonds of molecules.

Section Resources

Print
- *Reading and Study Workbook With Math Support,* Section 9.4
- *Transparencies,* Section 9.4

Technology
- *Interactive Textbook,* Section 9.4
- *Presentation Pro CD-ROM,* Section 9.4
- *Go Online,* Science News, Organic chemistry and biochemistry

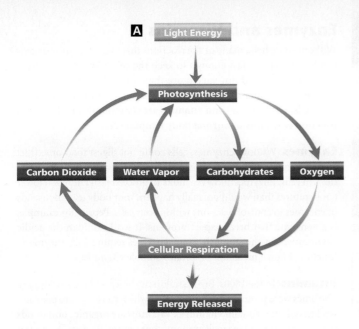

Cellular Respiration

What does your body need energy for, besides maintaining a constant body temperature? Everything! It takes energy to laugh or cry, to heal a bone or a paper cut, to climb a rope or a staircase, or even to sleep. During cellular respiration, the energy stored in the products of photosynthesis is released. Like photosynthesis, cellular respiration is a complex series of reactions. This equation is a summary of the overall process.

$$C_6H_{12}O_6 + 6O_2 \longrightarrow 6H_2O + 6CO_2 + Energy \text{ (heat)}$$

Figure 19 summarizes the relationship between photosynthesis and cellular respiration. Each process produces the reactants for the other process. Carbon dioxide and water are reactants in photosynthesis and products of cellular respiration. Carbohydrates and oxygen are reactants in cellular respiration and products of photosynthesis.

In the equation for cellular respiration, glucose is reacting with oxygen. The glucose can come from simple sugars or from starches, because starch is a polymer of glucose. During digestion, starch breaks down into glucose. This process is an example of depolymerization. Fats are also a good source of energy. One gram of fat produces twice the energy of one gram of a carbohydrate.

 Reading Checkpoint *Which produces more energy per gram, a carbohydrate or a fat?*

For: Activity on phytoplankton
Visit: PHSchool.com
Web Code: ccc-1094

Customize for Inclusion Students

Gifted
Some organisms release the energy stored in compounds through an anaerobic process called fermentation. (Anaerobic means "in the absence of oxygen.") The products of the fermentation of carbohydrates are ethanol and carbon dioxide.

$$C_6H_{12}O_6 \longrightarrow 2CH_3CH_2OH + 2CO_2$$

Have students research and write a short report about fermentation. Suggest that they include information about common examples of fermentation. Many commercial products, including cheese, antibiotics, and vitamins, are produced by fermentation. Students might also want to research what causes lactic acid to build up in muscles and how athletes can reduce this process.

Cellular Respiration

Cellular Respiration

Address Misconceptions L2

Students may confuse cellular respiration, respiration, and breathing. Explain that cellular respiration is a chemical process that releases energy stored in molecules. During respiration, oxygen and carbon dioxide are exchanged between cells, blood, and air in the lungs. Breathing is the movement of air into and out of the lungs by inhalation and exhalation. **Verbal**

Teacher > **Demo**

Photosynthesis and Cellular Respiration L2

Purpose Students learn about the products of photosynthesis and cellular respiration.

Materials methylene blue, water, 500-mL beaker, *elodea* sprig, straw

Procedure Explain that methylene blue turns orange in the presence of carbon dioxide. Place five drops of methylene blue in a beaker of water. Use the straw to blow into the water. After the solution changes color, remove the straw. Place an *elodea* sprig into the solution and place the beaker in sunlight. Have students notice the color change every five minutes for the next thirty minutes.

Safety Do not ingest any of the methylene blue.

Expected Outcome The solution turns orange when it absorbs carbon dioxide from exhaled air. As the elodea removes carbon dioxide from the solution, the color changes back to blue. **Visual**

Go Online PLANETDIARY

Find links to additional activities and have students monitor phenomena that affect Earth and its residents.

Answer to . . .

 Reading Checkpoint *A fat*

Enzymes and Vitamins

Teacher > Demo

Denaturing an Enzyme **L2**

Purpose Students will observe how enzyme activity is affected by temperature.

Materials potato, sharp knife, cutting surface, 3% hydrogen peroxide solution, water, 500-mL beakers (2), hot plate

Procedure Fill a beaker halfway with water and use the hot plate to boil the water. Cut a potato into small cubes (about 1 cm³). Place some of the cubes in the boiling water and allow them to cook for several minutes. Fill a second beaker halfway with hydrogen peroxide solution. Place some of the raw cubes in the hydrogen peroxide solution. Have students observe the gas bubbles that form on the surface of the potato cubes. Explain that an enzyme in the potato is speeding up the reaction that decomposes hydrogen peroxide into water and oxygen. Explain that enzymes lose their ability to speed up reactions when they are damaged by an increase in temperature. Place some of the cooked potato cubes in the hydrogen peroxide and have students note that gas bubbles do not form (or form at a much slower rate). **Visual**

3 ASSESS

Evaluate Understanding **L2**

Have groups of students write four review questions with answers.

Reteach **L1**

Have students use Figure 19 to review the relationships between photosynthesis and cellular respiration.

Writing in Science

The masses of the vitamins in the pills are small (micrograms) compared to the masses of the minerals (milligrams).

 If your class subscribes to the Interactive Textbook, use it to review key concepts in Section 9.4.

Answer to . . .

Figure 20 *Soluble in water*

Figure 20 Lemons, limes, and oranges are sources of vitamin C. **Drawing Conclusions** *Is vitamin C soluble in fat or in water?*

For: Articles on biochemistry
Visit: PHSchool.com
Web Code: cce-1094

Enzymes and Vitamins

Without some help, many of the reactions that take place in your cells would not happen fast enough to keep the cells alive. Your internal temperature should not vary more than a few degrees from 37°C. So you cannot increase the temperature to speed up a reaction in your cells. ⊖ **Enzymes and vitamins are compounds that help cells function efficiently at normal body temperature.**

Enzymes Without enzymes, cells could not digest food or extract energy from food. **Enzymes** are proteins that act as catalysts for reactions in cells. Enzymes allow reactions to proceed faster at much lower temperatures than would normally happen. Your body uses thousands of enzymes to control reactions within your cells. Pepsin, for example, is an enzyme that breaks apart proteins. It works only in the acidic environment of the stomach. Some enzymes require a co-enzyme to function, often a metal ion or a water-soluble vitamin.

Vitamins In the 1800s, British sailors ate limes on long sea voyages. The limes were protection against scurvy, which causes severe pain and weakness. Limes contain vitamin C. **Vitamins** are organic compounds that organisms need in small amounts, but cannot produce. A vitamin that dissolves in water, such as vitamin C, gets eliminated from the body and must be replaced daily. A vitamin that dissolves in fats, such as vitamin A, can build up over time in body tissues. Taking excess amounts of fat-soluble vitamins may be harmful.

Section 9.4 Assessment

Reviewing Concepts

1. ⊖ What happens to sunlight during photosynthesis?

2. ⊖ Describe the relationship between photosynthesis and cellular respiration.

3. ⊖ What molecules improve the efficiency of cell functions?

4. What happens to starch during digestion?

5. Why can't an increase in temperature be used to speed up reactions in cells?

Critical Thinking

6. **Formulating Hypotheses** Why must combustion in cells take place in multiple steps?

7. **Drawing Conclusions** Some bacteria do not require oxygen. How would the disappearance of plants affect these bacteria?

8. **Inferring** What affect could a lack of essential amino acids have on reactions in a person's body?

Writing in Science

Explanatory Paragraph Check the label on a package of multivitamins and minerals. Compare the masses of the minerals to the masses of the vitamins included in a single pill. Discuss any trend that you detect.

Section 9.4   Assessment

1. Sunlight is converted into chemical energy.
2. The products of one process are the reactants in the other.
3. Enzymes and vitamins
4. Starch is broken down into glucose, which can be used in cellular respiration.
5. The internal temperature should not vary more than a few degrees from 37°C.
6. Multiple steps allow the cells to release the energy stored in chemical bonds in smaller amounts, rather than all at once, which could cause the temperature in a cell to rise.
7. It's likely that these bacteria would not be affected because they do not require the oxygen that plants produce during photosynthesis.
8. Without these essential amino acids, the body would not be able to produce enzymes needed for cellular reactions.

Comparing Vitamin C in Fruit Juices

Various brands of juices claim to be good sources of vitamin C, but which juices are the best sources? Vitamin C is an organic acid called ascorbic acid. Like other acids, vitamin C reacts with indicators to produce a color change. This reaction can be used to determine the amount of vitamin C present in foods, such as fruit juices. In this lab, you will add an indicator to a sample of apple juice. The indicator will change color when all the vitamin C has reacted. Then you will test and compare the vitamin C content in other juices with the results for apple juice.

Problem
Which juice provides the most vitamin C?

Materials
- apple juice
- a variety of other fruit juices
- test tubes and rack
- 10-mL graduated cylinder
- methylene blue indicator in dropper bottle
- stirring rods

Skills
Observing, Measuring, Analyzing Data

Procedure

Part A: Measuring Vitamin C in Apple Juice

1. On a sheet of paper, copy the data table.
2. Use a graduated cylinder to measure 10 mL of apple juice. Pour the juice into a test tube.

Data Table	
Type of Juice	**Number of Drops**
Apple	

3. Add a drop of methylene blue indicator to the test tube. Stir until the color of the indicator disappears.
4. Add more indicator, one drop at a time, stirring after each addition. Count the drops you add. Stop adding the indicator when the last drop of indicator does not change color. Record the number of drops you used.

Part B: Measuring Vitamin C in Other Juices

5. Formulate and record a hypothesis about which juice will have the greatest amount of vitamin C. You will need to decide which variables must be kept the same, as well as how to account for bits of solid in some juices.
6. List the steps in your procedure and write the names of each of the juices to be tested in the left column of your data table.
7. Have your teacher check your procedure before you begin your experiment.

Analyze and Conclude

1. **Using Graphs** Make a bar graph of your data. Which juice required the most drops of indicator? Which required the least?
2. **Drawing Conclusions** Based on your data, which juice contained the most vitamin C? How did you reach this conclusion?
3. **Evaluating and Revising** What unexpected problems did you encounter? Explain how you could revise your procedure to avoid these problems.

Carbon Chemistry **285**

Science News provides students with current information on biochemistry.

Comparing Vitamin C in Fruit Juices   L2

Objective
After completing this activity students will be able to
- use an indicator to compare the amount of vitamin C in fruit juices.

Skills Focus Formulating Hypotheses, Analyzing Data, Controlling Variables, Using Graphs and Charts

Prep Time 15–20 minutes

Advance Prep Place labeled containers of apple juice and other fruit juices, plus dropper bottles of methylene blue indicator solution, in a central location.

Class Time 20 minutes

Safety Students should wear safety goggles, aprons, and gloves. Remind students never to drink anything in the laboratory.

Expected Outcome In Part A, students will find that a permanent color change occurs after a certain number of drops of indicator are added to the juice. In Part B, students will produce write-ups that include a hypothesis; a discussion of variables and how they will be controlled; a procedure with directions; and a data table in which to record the data.

Analyze and Conclude
1. The graph and answers will vary depending on the samples tested.
2. The juice that required the most drops of indicator is the one that contains the most vitamin C.
3. Acceptable answers include that juices with large amounts of pulp were difficult to compare with clear juices with the same volume. (Students may suggest filtering those samples.) Students may also say that dark juices, such as prune juice or grape juice, obscured the color change. (Students might suggest diluting all samples with the same amount of distilled water.)
Visual, Logical, Portfolio

Going Further
Methylene blue reacts with all organic acids. Students can use it to find the total amount of organic acids in fruits and vegetables. With a blender and distilled water, they can make liquid samples to test. They must control the amount of food, the amount of water added, and the time of blending.
Visual, Logical

Study Tip

Organize New Information
After studying all of the sections in the chapter, have students examine connections between concepts in different sections. Use concept maps or web diagrams to study the relationships between carbon compounds, substituted hydrocarbons, polymers, and cellular reactions.

Thinking Visually

a. fossil fuels
b. c. d. in any order: petroleum, coal, natural gas

9.1 Carbon Compounds

Key Concepts

- Diamond, graphite, and fullerenes are forms of carbon. Diamond is a network solid. Graphite forms layers that slide past one another. Fullerenes are large hollow spheres or cages of carbon.
- Factors that determine the properties of a hydrocarbon are the number of carbon atoms and how the atoms are arranged. Hydrocarbons can form a straight chain, a branched chain, or a ring.
- There are three types of unsaturated hydrocarbons—alkenes, alkynes, and aromatic hydrocarbons.
- Three types of fossil fuels are coal, petroleum, and natural gas. The primary products of the complete combustion of fossil fuels are carbon dioxide and water.

Vocabulary

organic compound, *p. 262;* network solid, *p. 263;* hydrocarbon, *p. 264;* saturated hydrocarbon, *p. 264;* isomers, *p. 265;* unsaturated hydrocarbon, *p. 266;* aromatic hydrocarbons, *p. 266;* fossil fuels, *p. 267*

9.2 Substituted Hydrocarbons

Key Concepts

- The functional group in an alcohol is a hydroxyl group, –OH. The functional group in an organic acid is a carboxyl group, –COOH. The functional group in an amine is an amino group, –NH$_2$.
- Esters form when organic acids react with alcohols.

Vocabulary

substituted hydrocarbon, *p. 272*
functional group, *p. 272*

9.3 Polymers

Key Concepts

- Polymers can be classified as natural polymers or synthetic polymers.
- Rubber, nylon, and polyethylene are three examples of compounds that can be synthesized.
- Four types of polymers produced in plant and animal cells are starches, cellulose, nucleic acids, and proteins.

Vocabulary

polymer, *p. 275;* monomers, *p. 275;* carbohydrates, *p. 278;* nucleic acids, *p. 279;* amino acid, *p. 280;* protein, *p. 280*

9.4 Reactions in Cells

Key Concepts

- During photosynthesis, energy from sunlight is converted into chemical energy.
- During cellular respiration, the energy stored in the products of photosynthesis is released .
- Enzymes and vitamins help cells function efficiently at normal body temperature.

Vocabulary

photosynthesis, *p. 282;* enzymes, *p. 284;* vitamins, *p. 284*

Thinking Visually

Concept Map Copy the concept map onto a sheet of paper. Use information from the chapter to complete it.

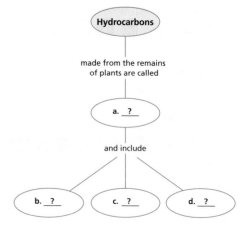

Chapter Resources

Print
- ***Chapter and Unit Tests,*** Chapter 9 Test A and Test B
- ***Test Prep Resources,*** Chapter 9

Technology
- ***Computer Test Bank,*** Chapter Test 9
- ***Interactive Textbook,*** Chapter 9
- ***Go Online,*** PHSchool.com, Chapter 9

Reviewing Content

Choose the letter that best answers the question or completes the statement.

1. How many bonds can a carbon atom form?
  a. two   **b.** four
  c. six   **d.** seven

2. Two compounds that have the same molecular formula but different structural formulas are
  a. isomers.   **b.** isotopes.
  c. alkanes.   **d.** alkenes.

3. Which compound has a triple bond?
  a. alkene   **b.** alkyne
  c. alkane   **d.** alcohol

4. The primary products of complete combustion of fossil fuels are
  a. carbon monoxide and water.
  b. carbon dioxide and water.
  c. carbon dioxide and carbon monoxide.
  d. methane and water.

5. What is an organic compound with at least one hydroxyl group called?
  a. an organic acid
  b. an alkyne
  c. an organic base
  d. an alcohol

6. Amines all contain atoms of
  a. oxygen.   **b.** nitrogen.
  c. sulfur.   **d.** chlorine.

7. The monomers for protein molecules are
  a. ethene.   **b.** nucleic acids.
  c. amino acids.   **d.** ethanoic acids.

8. A nucleotide does not contain a(n)
  a. organic base.
  b. organic acid.
  c. sugar.
  d. phosphate group.

9. Reactions in cells take place at about
  a. 100°C.   **b.** 0°C.
  c. 40°C.   **d.** 60°C.

10. An enzyme is a
  a. protein.   **b.** vitamin.
  c. lipid.   **d.** carbohydrate.

Understanding Concepts

11. How did the synthesis of urea change the definition of an organic compound?

12. Why is diamond extremely hard but graphite is extremely soft?

13. What is a saturated hydrocarbon?

14. Why can an acetylene torch be used to weld metals together?

15. How are fossil fuels formed?

16. How are the hydrocarbons in petroleum separated into fractions?

17. Why is it important to make sure that there is plenty of air around a gas burner such as the one shown below?

18. How is acid rain produced?

19. What is a functional group?

20. Why is ethanol added to gasoline?

21. What types of substituted hydrocarbons can react to form esters?

22. Explain why natural and synthetic rubber have different properties.

23. What do cellulose and starch have in common?

24. What are the products of photosynthesis? What are the products of cellular respiration?

25. What role do enzymes play in cells?

Carbon Chemistry **287**

 Interactive Textbook   If your class subscribes to the Interactive Textbook, your students can go online to access an interactive version of the Student Edition and a self-test.

Reviewing Content

1. b   **2.** a   **3.** b
4. b   **5.** d   **6.** b
7. c   **8.** b   **9.** c
10. a

Understanding Concepts

11. Because urea was synthesized in a laboratory, the definition of organic compounds changed from compounds produced by organisms to compounds containing carbon and hydrogen, often combined with a few other elements.

12. Diamond is hard because of its rigid, three-dimensional network structure. Graphite is soft because the bonds between graphite layers are weak.

13. A saturated hydrocarbon is a hydrocarbon that contains only single bonds.

14. The temperature of the flame in an oxyacetylene torch approaches 3500°C, a temperature high enough to melt most metals.

15. High temperatures and pressures changed the buried remains of plants and animals into mixtures of hydrocarbons.

16. The hydrocarbons are heated until they vaporize. The vapors rise in a distillation tower and condense as the temperature decreases. Those with higher boiling points condense first.

17. A lack of air can cause incomplete combustion, which produces carbon monoxide.

18. When fossil fuels are burned, sulfur dioxide and nitrogen oxides are produced. These oxides dissolve in water droplets, forming sulfuric acid and nitric acid.

19. A functional group is an atom or group of atoms that replace a hydrogen atom in a hydrocarbon.

20. Ethanol helps the gasoline burn more completely.

21. Organic acids and alcohols

22. They contain different monomers.

23. Both are polymers of glucose.

24. The products of photosynthesis are oxygen and carbohydrates. The products of cellular respiration are carbon dioxide and water.

25. Enzymes act as catalysts for reactions that take place in cells.

 Homework Guide

Section	Questions
9.1	1–4, 11–18, 26, 33–36, 39
9.2	5–6, 19–21, 27–28, 31–32
9.3	7–8, 22–23, 29, 37
9.4	9–10, 24–25, 30, 38

Critical Thinking

26. No, because methane contains only one carbon atom, which eliminates the possibility of branching.

27. Double and triple bonds can be classified as functional groups because they affect the characteristic chemical properties of unsaturated compounds.

28. The compounds are classified as: alkane, alkyne, alcohol. The word endings identify the type of compound.

29. Students are likely to say that starches and proteins can be eaten. Silk, cotton, and rubber can be worn.

30. Acceptable answers include: Because vitamins are defined as substances that organisms cannot produce, strictly speaking, vitamin D should not be classified as a vitamin.

Math Skills

31. Alcohol 1

32. Alcohol 1 and Alkane 3

33. Alkane 1 is likely to have the fewest carbon atoms, and Alkane 3 is likely to have the most carbon atoms because the more carbon atoms an alkane has, the higher its boiling point.

Concepts in Action

34. You could test to see if the boiling point remains constant as the mixture boils or if the temperature changes (indicating more than one substance in the mixture).

35. There would be an immediate increase in carbon dioxide from combustion and a long-term increase because there would be fewer plants to absorb carbon dioxide for use in photosynthesis.

36. Possible answer: Because fossil fuels have been relatively inexpensive and plentiful, there has not been sufficient incentive to invest in alternative technologies.

37. Cells use the essential amino acids stored in ingested proteins as raw materials to manufacture proteins.

38. The termite has enzymes that allow the reaction to occur at the body temperature of a termite.

39. Sample answer: death of organisms; burial of remains; action of high temperatures and pressures over time; drilling or mining; fractional distillation; delivery to gas station; pumping into tank.

Critical Thinking

26. Predicting Does methane have isomers? Explain your answer.

27. Forming Operational Definitions Present an argument for classifying double and triple bonds as functional groups. *(Hint:* What is the role of a functional group in a compound?)

28. Classifying Based on their names, classify each of these compounds: octacosane, pentyne, and octanol. What information did the names provide that helped you classify the compounds?

29. Classifying Which natural polymers can be eaten for breakfast? Which natural polymers can be worn to school?

30. Applying Concepts When your skin is exposed to sunlight, cells in your skin produce vitamin D. Should vitamin D be classified as a vitamin? Give a reason for your answer.

Math Skills

Use this table to answer Questions 31–33.

Selected Properties of Fuels

Fuels	Melting Point (°C)	Boiling Point (°C)
Alcohol 1	6	228
Alcohol 2	26	83
Alkane 1	−183	−162
Alkane 2	−138	0
Alkane 3	−57	126

31. Analyzing Data Which fuel is a liquid across the greatest range of temperature?

32. Using Tables At 20°C, which fuels would be liquid?

33. Analyzing Data Look at the data for the three unknown alkanes. Which alkane is likely to have the fewest carbon atoms? Which is likely to have the most carbon atoms? Give a reason for your choices.

Concepts in Action

34. Designing Experiments You work at a refinery and want to know whether a fraction you have collected from a distillation tower is a single substance or a mixture. What kind of test could you do to find out?

35. Relating Cause and Effect What are two ways that a large forest fire might affect the amount of carbon dioxide in the atmosphere?

36. Making Judgments Why do you think progress in solar energy, wind power, and other alternative forms of energy has been slow?

37. Drawing Conclusions If the cells in your body can manufacture proteins, why are proteins an important part of a balanced diet?

38. Comparing and Contrasting When wood burns, the cellulose in wood is converted to carbon dioxide and water. The same products are produced when a termite digests wood, but the process occurs at a much lower temperature. Explain the difference in temperature.

39. Writing in Science Describe the series of events that starts with the death of a group of ancient ocean organisms and ends with filling the tank of an automobile with gasoline. *(Hint:* Consider making a flow chart of events first.)

Performance-Based Assessment

Animating a Process Make a flip book that begins with the sun providing energy for photosynthesis in a plant. It should proceed through photosynthesis, and then show how the products of photosynthesis are used in cellular respiration. Complete the book by showing the products of cellular respiration about to be used for photosynthesis.

For: Self-grading assessment
Visit: PHSchool.com
Web Code: cca-1090

Performance Based Assessment

Acceptable flip books should have pages showing the conversion of light energy to chemical energy, storage of chemical energy, and use of chemical energy in cellular respiration.

Your students can independently test their knowledge of the chapter and print out their test results for your files.

Standardized Test Prep for Indiana

 Standards Guide

Question	Standards
2	ICP.4.3

Test-Taking Tip

Make Logical Connections

A cause-and-effect statement may seem to be true when it is false. The statement may seem true because the descriptions of the cause and the effect are both accurate. However, there is no logical connection between the cause and the effect. In the question below, the opening phrase contains an accurate statement about body temperature. Most of the answers are accurate, too. But only one answer provides a logical effect of the statement in the opening phrase.

Because body temperature cannot vary more than a few degrees from 37°C,
 (A) cellular respiration releases energy stored in covalent bonds.
 (B) carbohydrates are good sources of energy.
 (C) enzymes are required for reactions in cells.
 (D) fats are good sources of energy.
 (E) energy cannot be released in cells.

(Answer: C)

Choose the letter that best answers the question or completes the statement.

1. Benzene is classified as an aromatic hydrocarbon because
 (A) it has a strong odor.
 (B) it contains only carbon and hydrogen.
 (C) it is a compound found in coal.
 (D) it has an unsaturated ring structure.
 (E) it has a saturated ring structure.

2. How are photosynthesis and cellular respiration related?
 (A) They both occur in all living organisms.
 (B) They both consume more energy than they produce.
 (C) They both produce water and carbon dioxide.
 (D) Cellular respiration stores energy, and photosynthesis releases it.
 (E) Photosynthesis stores energy, and cellular respiration releases it.

3. Which type of compound forms when amino acids are linked together?
 (A) nucleic acid
 (B) protein
 (C) carbohydrate
 (D) organic acid
 (E) ester

4. What type of substituted hydrocarbon contains the functional group –OH?
 (A) halocarbon
 (B) alcohol
 (C) ester
 (D) organic base
 (E) organic acid

Use the diagram to answer Questions 5 and 6. The diagram shows a combustion apparatus used to identify hydrocarbons.

A   B

5. A sample of a hydrocarbon is in the glass tube. What gas is in the green tank?
 (A) nitrogen
 (B) carbon dioxide
 (C) oxygen
 (D) methane
 (E) acetylene

6. The containers labeled A and B absorb the primary products of the reaction that occurs in the tube. Those products are
 (A) carbon dioxide and water.
 (B) carbon monoxide and water.
 (C) oxides of sulfur and nitrogen.
 (D) sulfuric and nitric acid.
 (E) carbon dioxide and carbon monoxide.

Carbon Chemistry **289**

Planning Guide

SECTION OBJECTIVES	STANDARDS		ACTIVITIES and LABS
	NATIONAL	STATE	
10.1 Radioactivity, pp. 292–297 🕐 1 block or 2 periods **10.1.1 Describe** the process of nuclear decay. **10.1.2 Classify** nuclear radiation as alpha particles, beta particles, or gamma rays. **10.1.3 Balance** nuclear equations. **10.1.4 Identify** sources of nuclear radiation, and **describe** how nuclear radiation affects matter. **10.1.5 Describe** methods of detecting nuclear radiation.	A-1, B-1, B-6, D-1, F-1, F-5, G-1, G-2, G-3	ICP.7.7	**SE** Inquiry Activity: What Happens When an Atom Decays? p. 291 **L2** **TE** Teacher Demo: Stopping Radiation, p. 294 **L2** **LM** Investigation 10B: Detecting Radiation **L1**
10.2 Rates of Nuclear Decay, pp. 298–301 🕐 1 block or 2 periods **10.2.1 Define** half-life, and **relate** half-life to the age of a radioactive sample. **10.2.2 Compare** and **contrast** nuclear reaction rates with chemical reaction rates. **10.2.3 Describe** how radioisotopes are used to estimate the age of materials.	A-1, A-2, B-1, B-3	ICP.7.7	**SE** Quick Lab: Modeling Half-Life, p. 300 **L2** **TE** Teacher Demo: Predicting Decay, p. 299 **L2** **LM** Investigation 10A: Modeling Radioactive Decay **L2**
10.3 Artificial Transmutation, pp. 303–305 🕐 1 block or 2 periods **10.3.1 Describe** and **identify** examples of transmutation. **10.3.2 Describe** how transuranium elements are synthesized. **10.3.3 Explain** how particle accelerators have been used in scientific research.	A-1, A-2, B-1, B-6, E-2, F-1, F-5, G-1, G-2, G-3	ICP.7.2, ICP.7.7	**SE** Quick Lab: Modeling Transmutation, p. 304 **L2**
10.4 Fission and Fusion, pp. 308–315 🕐 1 block or 2 periods **10.4.1 Compare** and **contrast** nuclear forces. **10.4.2 Describe** the process of nuclear fission. **10.4.3 Explain** how nuclear reactors are used to produce energy. **10.4.4 Describe** the process of nuclear fusion.	A-1, A-2, B-1, E-2, F-1, F-2, F-4, F-5, G-1, G-2, G-3	ICP.3.1, ICP.7.3, ICP.7.4, ICP.7.5, ICP.7.6, ICP.7.7, ICP.7.8	**SE** Exploration Lab: Modeling a Chain Reaction, pp. 316–317 **L2** **TE** Teacher Demo: Nuclear Processes, p. 311 **L2**

RESOURCES
PRINT and TECHNOLOGY

SECTION
ASSESSMENT

RSW Section 10.1 **L1**

RSW Math Skill **L2**

MSPS Section 10.1 **L2**

T Chapter 10 Pretest **L2**
   Section 10.1 **L2**

P Chapter 10 Pretest **L2**
   Section 10.1 **L2**

PLANETDIARY GO Radioactivity
   activity **L2**

SE Section 10.1 Assessment, p. 297

iT Section 10.1

RSW Section 10.2 **L1**

T Section 10.2 **L2**

P Section 10.2 **L2**

SCLINKS GO Half-Life **L2**

SE Section 10.2 Assessment, p. 301

iT Section 10.2

RSW Section 10.3 **L1**

DC Nuclear Medicine **L2**

T Section 10.3 **L2**

P Section 10.3 **L2**

SE Section 10.3 Assessment, p. 305

iT Section 10.3

RSW Section 10.4 **L1**

T Section 10.4 **L2**

P Section 10.4 **L2**

SCLINKS GO Fission **L2**

SE Section 10.4 Assessment, p. 315

iT Section 10.4

Go Online

Go online for these Internet resources.

PHSchool.com
   Web Code: cca-1100
   Web Code: cch-1102

NSTA SCLINKS
   Web Code: ccn-1102
   Web Code: ccn-1104

PLANETDIARY
   Web Code: ccc-1101

Materials for Activities and Labs

Quantities for each group

STUDENT EDITION

Inquiry Activity, p. 291
green and purple beads

Quick Lab, p. 300
100 1-cm squares of wallpaper, large plastic bag, graph paper

Quick Lab, p. 304
periodic table, 2 sheets of unlined white paper, 32 green beads, 32 purple beads

Exploration Lab, pp. 316–317
20 dominoes, watch with a second hand (or stopwatch), metric ruler

TEACHER'S EDITION

Teacher Demo, p. 294
medical X-ray image or photograph of a medical X-ray image

Teacher Demo, p. 299
hot plate, 250-mL or 500-mL beaker, glass plate, popcorn, cooking oil

Build Science Skills, p. 307
500-mL beaker; sponges; shallow pans; food coloring; 1-cm strips of thin and thick cardboard, newspaper, and waxed paper; paper towels

Teacher Demo, p. 311
bubble solution, 2 bubble wands

Chapter Assessment

CHAPTER ASSESSMENT

SE Chapter Assessment, pp. 319–320
CUT Chapter 10 Test A, B
CTB Chapter 10
iT Chapter 10
PHSchool.com GO
Web Code: cca-1100

STANDARDIZED TEST PREP

SE Chapter 10, p. 321
TP Diagnose and Prescribe

Interactive Textbook with assessment at PHSchool.com

Before you teach

From the Author

David Frank
Ferris State University

Big Ideas

In the chapters leading to this one, students have focused on chemical changes. They have learned how electrons move around in these changes, as ionic or covalent bonds are broken or formed. In nuclear chemistry, students will study processes that take place when the nuclei of atoms are affected. Unlike the processes of earlier chapters, the numbers of neutrons and protons will change, and atoms of one element become atoms of another.

Space and Time Spontaneous nuclear decay processes follow first order kinetics. As a consequence, nuclear decays have a well-defined and constant half-life. One application of nuclear decay is to determine the ages of objects. Carbon-14 is incorporated into all living things, so carbon-14 dating is one method used for dating. Carbon-14 has a half-life of 5730 years. Radioisotopes with longer half-lives can be used to determine the age of rocks.

Matter and Change Students will first study the decay processes of a radioactive substance. Three types of nuclear radiation may be emitted: alpha particles, beta particles, or gamma rays. The first two types are associated with the change of an atom into an atom of another element or into a different isotope of the same element. Students will then study fission and fusion processes.

Forces and Motion Electrostatic forces, the attractions between particles of opposite charge and repulsions between particles of similar charge, have already been introduced. A student might wonder why a nucleus remains intact, given that it consists of positively charged protons and uncharged neutrons. Strong nuclear forces, which act over very short differences, keep these particles together.

Energy Compared to the physical and chemical changes that students have already studied, nuclear changes involve tremendous amounts of energy. During processes such as fusion, the products have less mass than the reactants, and large amounts of energy are released.

Chemistry Refresher

Nuclear Radiation 10.1

Radioactivity is the process in which an unstable atomic nucleus emits radiation in the form of particles and energy. The release of charged particles from a nucleus results in the formation of a different isotope with a different atomic number and/or atomic mass. Unlike stable isotopes, radioisotopes spontaneously decay into other isotopes.

Three common types of nuclear radiation are alpha particles, beta particles, and gamma rays. Nuclear radiation can ionize atoms. When cells of living tissue are exposed to nuclear radiation, they may no longer function properly. Nuclear radiation can be monitored using devices such as Geiger counters and film badges.

> **Address Misconceptions**
>
> *Students may mistakenly think that gamma rays, X-rays, and visible light are unrelated.* However, they are all part of a continuous magnetic spectrum, and for that reason, all three affect a photographic plate in the same way. For a strategy to overcome this misconception, see **Address Misconceptions** on **page 292.**

Half-Life and Radiocarbon Dating 10.2

The rate at which radioisotopes undergo nuclear decay is constant for each isotope under all conditions and depends on the number (fraction) of nuclei present. The amount of time required for half the atoms of a sample of a radioisotope to decay is called the half-life of the radioisotope.

Because the nuclear decay rate for a given radioisotope is constant, it can be used to measure the passage of time. Carbon-14 is a radioisotope commonly used for this purpose, through a method called radiocarbon dating. The small fraction of carbon atoms in the atmosphere that are carbon-14 has remained roughly constant for thousands of years. The carbon-14 is produced by the interaction of cosmic rays from outer space with Earth's atmosphere. All living organisms take in carbon, a certain percentage of which is carbon-14. When an organism dies, it no longer takes in carbon-14. The amount of carbon-14 in the dead organism decreases over time as the radioactive carbon undergoes beta decay to form nitrogen-14. Scientists can measure the ratio of carbon-14 to carbon-12 in the remains of the organism, and use this ratio to estimate how long ago the organism died.

Artificial Transmutation 10.3

During nuclear decay, atoms of one element change into atoms of another element. This change is called transmutation. Scientists carry out artificial transmutations by bombarding atomic nuclei with high-energy particles. This process can be used to synthesize transuranium elements (elements with atomic numbers greater than 92), which are not usually found in nature.

Nuclear Forces and Reactions 10.4

Address Misconceptions

Students may incorrectly think that the sun is burning because the sun gives off heat and light. In fact, the light and heat from the sun are a result of nuclear reactions. For a strategy to overcome this misconception, see **Address Misconceptions** on **page 315.**

The subatomic particles in the nucleus are held together by strong nuclear forces. Repulsive electric forces between protons exist. In small nuclei, the strong nuclear forces are generally much greater than the electric forces. In very large nuclei, however, the opposing nuclear forces become similar in strength, resulting in an unstable nucleus.

A large, unstable nucleus may undergo nuclear fission, in which it splits into two smaller nuclei. Fission releases neutrons and a considerable amount of energy. In the presence of many unstable nuclei, fission can lead to a chain reaction, which can be either uncontrolled or controlled. An atomic bomb explosion is an example of an uncontrolled chain reaction. A controlled chain reaction occurs in the reactor of a nuclear power plant.

Another type of nuclear reaction is called fusion, in which two nuclei combine to form one larger nucleus. Fusion reactions release a tremendous amount of energy. The sun is powered by a fusion reaction in which hydrogen nuclei are fused together to form helium nuclei.

Neutron

Krypton-91
$^{91}_{36}$Kr

Energy

$^{235}_{92}$U
Uranium-235

$^{236}_{92}$U
Uranium-236
(very unstable)

$^{142}_{56}$Ba
Barium-142

Go Online
NSTA
PD LINKS

For: Teaching methods for nuclear chemistry
Visit: www.SciLinks.org/PDLinks
Web Code: ccn-1099

Build Reading Literacy

Sequence

Ordering Events

Strategy Help students understand and visualize the steps in a process, or the order in which events occur. Sequences frequently involve cause-effect relationships. Readers can construct graphic organizers to help themselves visualize and comprehend a sequence. For most sequences, flowcharts are the graphic of choice. However, cycle diagrams are more appropriate for cycles. Before students begin, locate a description in the text of a several-step process or a chain of causes and effects, such as those in Section 10.4 related to a fission chain reaction (p. 311) or nuclear power generation (p. 314).

Example

1. Have students read the passage, thinking about what takes place first, second, third, and so on. Point out that the text will not always use order words such as *first, next, then,* and *finally.*
2. Review the passage, listing the steps or events in order.
3. If the passage describes a chain of steps or events, draw a flowchart on the board, having students tell the sequence of events, steps, or causes and effects, and writing each part of the process in a separate box.

4. If the passage describes a cycle, use a cycle diagram to show the sequence.

5. Have students locate additional examples of sequential relationships in the text or visuals of the chapter. Students can depict the steps or events using graphic organizers.

See p. 309 for a script on how to use the sequence strategy with students. For additional Build Reading Literacy strategies, see pp. 293 and 304.

ASSESS PRIOR KNOWLEDGE

Use the Chapter Pretest below to assess students' prior knowledge. As needed, review these Science Concepts and Math Skills with students.

Review Science Concepts

Section 10.1 Encourage students to recall what they have learned about balancing chemical equations. Review how chemical equations show conservation of mass.

Section 10.2 Encourage students to remember what they have learned about the rates of chemical reactions. To prepare students for a discussion of half-life, ask students to recall basic probability calculations.

Section 10.3 Review the different parts of the periodic table. Encourage students to recall the location of uranium and the elements heavier than uranium in the periodic table.

Section 10.4 Ask students to recall what they have learned about modern models of the atom.

Review Math Skills

Equations and Formulas Students will need to manipulate variables and constants to solve for unknowns in equations representing nuclear decay.

Direct students to the **Math Skills** in the **Skills and Reference Handbook** at the end of the student text.

CHAPTER
10 Nuclear Chemistry

21st Century Learning
Communication Skills

How is radiocarbon dating used to date objects?

The use of radioisotopes to date rocks and artifacts has helped scientists piece together a clearer picture of Earth's past. Use the library or Internet to learn more about an archaeological site that you have heard about in the news. Find out how the age of the site was determined. Digitally record a podcast about the site and the methods used by scientists to date the site and/or its artifacts. Post the podcast on your class Web site.

Indiana's Academic Standards for Science

NUCLEAR ENERGY (FISSION/FUSION)
ICP.7.2: Differentiate between protons, neutrons, and electrons and determine the number of these subatomic particles in each atom; **ICP.7.3:** Understand that the stability of nuclei depends on the numbers of neutrons and protons; **ICP.7.4:** Understand that fission results from large, less stable nuclei decomposing to form smaller, more stable nuclei; **ICP.7.5:** Understand that fusion results from two smaller nuclei combining to form one larger nucleus; **ICP.7.6:** Understand that the energy radiated from the sun derives from the fusion process; **ICP.7.7:** Describe the various forms of emission that are typical of radioactive decay; **ICP.7.8:** Relate the fission process to the human development and use of the fission process in war (uncontrolled) and in peace (controlled).

Also covered: ICP.3.1

This false-color image from a bubble chamber shows the tracks of subatomic particles at high speed.

290 *Chapter 10*

Chapter Pretest

1. According to the law of conservation of mass, if element X has a molar mass of 3 g/mol, and element Y has a molar mass of 5 g/mol, what must be the total mass of products formed when one mole of the compound X_2Y decomposes? *(11 g)*

2. True or False: A reaction rate is the rate at which reactants change into products over time. *(True)*

3. If you tossed 128 coins in the air, about how many could you expect to land heads up? *(b)*
   a. About 178   **b.** About 64
   c. About 32   **d.** Almost none

4. Suppose you were to remove any coins that landed heads up, and then toss the remaining coins in the air. How many times could you expect to repeat this process until you had removed all of the coins? *(About 7 times)*

5. The element uranium belongs to *(d)*
   a. Group 7A (halogens).
   b. Group 8A (noble gases).
   c. the lanthanide series.
   d. the actinide series.

6. Which subatomic particles are found in the nucleus? *(Protons and neutrons)*

Chapter Preview

10.1 Radioactivity
10.2 Rates of Nuclear Decay
10.3 Artificial Transmutation
10.4 Fission and Fusion

Discovery
SCHOOL
Video Field Trip
Nuclear Medicine

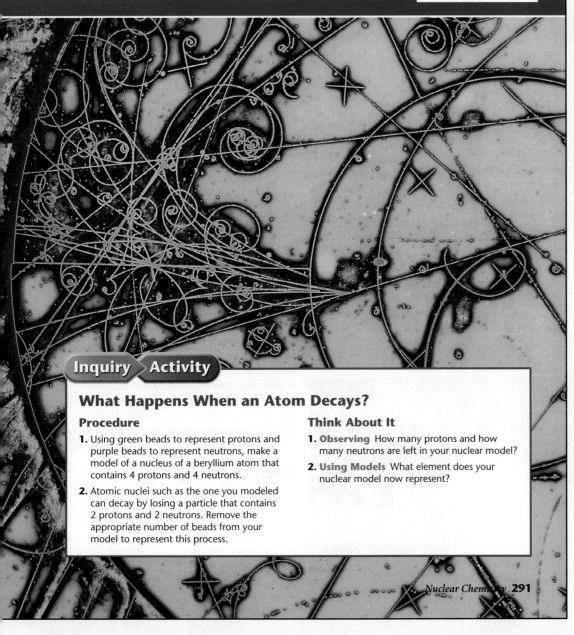

Inquiry Activity

What Happens When an Atom Decays?

Procedure

1. Using green beads to represent protons and purple beads to represent neutrons, make a model of a nucleus of a beryllium atom that contains 4 protons and 4 neutrons.

2. Atomic nuclei such as the one you modeled can decay by losing a particle that contains 2 protons and 2 neutrons. Remove the appropriate number of beads from your model to represent this process.

Think About It

1. **Observing** How many protons and how many neutrons are left in your nuclear model?

2. **Using Models** What element does your nuclear model now represent?

Nuclear Chemistry **291**

ENGAGE/EXPLORE

Inquiry Activity

What Happens When an Atom Decays? **L2**

Purpose In this activity, students begin to describe one mechanism of atomic decay that causes atoms to change from one element to another.

🚩 **Address Misconceptions**

Students may think that elements are unchangeable, and they may doubt that an atom of one element can change to another. Challenge this misconception by asking students to discuss the outcome of this activity. This activity demonstrates how elements can change, though it does not prove that such changes actually occur.

Skills Focus Using Models

🕐 **Prep Time** 5 minutes

Materials green and purple beads

Class Time 10 minutes

Expected Outcome The model will demonstrate the decay of $^{8}_{4}Be$ to $^{4}_{2}He$ by loss of an alpha particle (two protons and two neutrons).

Think About It
1. Two protons and two neutrons are left in the model.
2. The model represents helium.
Kinesthetic, Logical

Discovery
SCHOOL
Video Field Trip
Nuclear Medicine

Encourage students to view the Video Field Trip "Nuclear Medicine."

❶ FOCUS

Objectives

10.1.1 Describe the process of nuclear decay.

10.1.2 Classify nuclear radiation as alpha particles, beta particles, or gamma rays.

10.1.3 Balance nuclear equations.

10.1.4 Identify sources of nuclear radiation, and **describe** how nuclear radiation affects matter.

10.1.5 Describe methods of detecting nuclear radiation.

Reading Focus

Build Vocabulary   L2

Word-Part Analysis Point out the two vocabulary terms that contain the word *radiation (nuclear radiation, background radiation).* Explain that the word comes from a Latin word meaning "to spread out from a point."

Reading Strategy   L2

Student answers may include:
a. Nuclear decay is the spontaneous change of one isotope into another.
b. What are the types of nuclear radiation? **c.** What are the effects of nuclear radiation? **d.** One effect of nuclear radiation is the ionization of matter. **e.** How can nuclear radiation be detected? **f.** Nuclear radiation can be detected by a Geiger counter or film badge.

❷ INSTRUCT

Nuclear Decay

Address Misconceptions   L2

Many students think that gamma rays, X-rays, and visible light are unrelated. Point out that all three are different parts of the continuous electromagnetic spectrum. Explain that the photographic plate in Becquerel's experiment detected all three kinds of electromagnetic waves. Just as photographic film can detect visible light, it can detect X-rays and gamma rays emitted during nuclear decay. Students will read about the electromagnetic spectrum in Chapter 18. **Logical**

10.1 Radioactivity

Standard: ICP.7.7

Reading Focus

Key Concepts

- What happens during nuclear decay?
- What are three types of nuclear radiation?
- How does nuclear radiation affect atoms?
- What devices can detect nuclear radiation?

Vocabulary

- ◆ radioactivity
- ◆ radioisotope
- ◆ nuclear radiation
- ◆ alpha particle
- ◆ beta particle
- ◆ gamma ray
- ◆ background radiation

Reading Strategy

Previewing Copy the table below. Before you read the section, rewrite the topic headings as *how, why,* and *what* questions. As you read, write an answer to each question.

Question	Answer
What is nuclear decay?	a. _____?_____
b. _____?_____	Alpha, beta, gamma
c. _____?_____	d. _____?_____
e. _____?_____	f. _____?_____

Figure 1 Due to rainy weather, Henri Becquerel postponed his intended experiment with uranium salts. **A** Without any exposure to sunlight, the salts still produced a foggy image on a photographic plate. **B** For his discovery of radioactivity, Becquerel shared the 1903 Nobel Prize for Physics with Marie and Pierre Curie.

In 1896, French physicist Antoine Henri Becquerel (1852–1908) was experimenting with uranium salts. He hypothesized that the salts, which glow after being exposed to light, produced X-rays while they glowed. To test his hypothesis, Becquerel performed an experiment. First, he wrapped a photographic plate in paper. Then, he placed some uranium salts on the plate and set it outside in the sunlight, which caused the salts to glow. When Becquerel developed the plate, he got a foggy image. At the time, Becquerel thought that X-rays from the salts had penetrated the paper and fogged the plate.

Like any good scientist, Becquerel wanted to repeat his experiment, but a spell of bad weather forced him to wait. In the meantime, he left a wrapped photographic plate and uranium salts in a desk drawer. After several days, Becquerel decided to develop the plate without exposing the uranium to sunlight. To his surprise, he got the foggy image shown in Figure 1A. Later, Becquerel determined that the uranium salts had emitted rays that had never been observed before.

Nuclear Decay

Becquerel's experiment marked the discovery of radioactivity. **Radioactivity** is the process in which an unstable atomic nucleus emits charged particles and energy. Any atom containing an unstable nucleus is called a radioactive isotope, or **radioisotope** for short.

Section Resources

Print
- *Laboratory Manual,* Investigation 10B
- *Reading and Study Workbook With Math Support,* Section 10.1 and **Math Skill:** Nuclear Equations for Alpha Decay
- *Math Skills and Problem Solving Workbook,* Section 10.1
- *Transparencies,* Chapter Pretest and Section 10.1

Technology
- *Interactive Textbook,* Section 10.1
- *Presentation Pro CD-ROM,* Chapter Pretest and Section 10.1
- *Go Online, Planet Diary,* Radioactivity activity

Radioisotopes of uranium—primarily uranium-238—were the source of radioactivity in Becquerel's experiment. (Recall that the name of an isotope includes its mass number.) Another common radioisotope is carbon-14, which can be found in fossils like the ones shown in Figure 2.

Unlike stable isotopes such as carbon-12 or oxygen-16, radioisotopes spontaneously change into other isotopes over time. When the composition of a radioisotope changes, the radioisotope is said to undergo nuclear decay. ☁ **During nuclear decay, atoms of one element can change into atoms of a different element altogether.** For example, uranium-238 decays into thorium-234, which is also a radioisotope.

Types of Nuclear Radiation

Scientists can detect a radioactive substance by measuring the nuclear radiation it gives off. **Nuclear radiation** is charged particles and energy that are emitted from the nuclei of radioisotopes. ☁ **Common types of nuclear radiation include alpha particles, beta particles, and gamma rays.** Figure 3 shows the properties of these three types of radiation.

Alpha Decay When a uranium-238 sample decays, it emits alpha particles. An **alpha particle** is a positively charged particle made up of two protons and two neutrons—the same as a helium nucleus. It has a 2+ charge. The common symbol for an alpha particle is ${}^4_2\text{He}$. The subscript is the atomic number (the number of protons). The superscript is the mass number (the sum of the numbers of protons and neutrons). Another symbol for an alpha particle is the Greek letter α.

Alpha decay, which refers to nuclear decay that releases alpha particles, is an example of a nuclear reaction. Like chemical reactions, nuclear reactions can be expressed as equations. The following nuclear equation describes the alpha decay of uranium-238.

$$ {}^{238}_{92}\text{U} \rightarrow {}^{234}_{90}\text{Th} + {}^4_2\text{He} $$

In alpha decay, the product isotope has two fewer protons and two fewer neutrons than the reactant isotope. In the equation above, the mass number on the left (238) equals the sum of the mass numbers on the right (234 + 4). Also, the atomic number on the left (92) equals the sum of the atomic numbers on the right (90 + 2). In other words, the equation is balanced.

Alpha particles are the least penetrating type of nuclear radiation. Most alpha particles travel no more than a few centimeters in air, and can be stopped by a sheet of paper or by clothing.

Figure 2 About 26,000 years ago, more than 100 mammoths died at a sinkhole in Hot Springs, South Dakota. Scientists figured out how old the remains were by measuring amounts of the radioisotope carbon-14 contained in the mammoth bones.

Figure 3 Within a few years of Becquerel's discovery of radioactivity, Ernest Rutherford classified three types of nuclear radiation based on his own studies of uranium compounds. *Comparing and Contrasting How do alpha particles, beta particles, and gamma rays differ in terms of charge? In terms of mass?*

Characteristics of Nuclear Radiation				
Radiation Type	**Symbol**	**Charge**	**Mass (amu)**	**Common Source**
Alpha particle	α, ${}^4_2\text{He}$	2+	4	Radium-226
Beta particle	β, ${}^0_{-1}\text{e}$	1−	$\frac{1}{1836}$	Carbon-14
Gamma ray	γ	0	0	Cobalt-60

Types of Nuclear Radiation
Build Science Skills L2

Inferring Have students look at Figure 3, which shows the particles emitted in nuclear decay. Explain that a nucleus that emits an alpha particle gives up two protons and two neutrons (a helium nucleus). A nucleus that emits a beta particle (an electron) gives up a neutron but gains a proton, because a neutron decomposes into a proton and an electron during beta decay. Ask, **Which type of radioactive decay causes the largest change in the atomic number of a nucleus?** *(Alpha decay, which reduces the atomic number of the nucleus by two)*
Logical, Visual

Build Reading Literacy L1

Compare and Contrast Refer to page **226D** in **Chapter 8**, which provides the guidelines for comparing and contrasting.

Ask students to construct a compare/contrast table. Have them skim the sections on alpha decay, beta decay, and gamma decay. Then, ask students to describe similarities and differences of the decay types in their table.
Verbal, Visual

Customize for English Language Learners

Build a Science Glossary
Encourage English language learners to make a science glossary as they read the section. Suggest that they start with the vocabulary terms and then add any other new terms they encounter. Encourage students to copy the table in Figure 3 into their glossary, as these particles are key to understanding the chapter. Model how to divide words into parts such as prefix, root word, and suffix. Posting a list of suffixes and prefixes with their meanings in the classroom will help students when they encounter new words.

Answer to . . .

Figure 3 *Alpha particles have a charge of 2+; beta particles have a charge of 1−; gamma rays have no charge. Alpha particles have a mass of 4 amu; beta particles have a mass of $\frac{1}{1836}$ amu; and gamma rays have no mass.*

Use Visuals

Figure 4 Emphasize that beta and gamma rays will pass through paper and that gamma rays will also pass through a thin sheet of aluminum. Ask, **What materials would effectively shield a radioactive source that emitted only beta particles?** (Aluminum or concrete) **Why might concrete be insufficient protection from gamma rays?** (Some gamma rays will pass through concrete, and a concrete wall would have to be several meters thick to ensure that the gamma rays were effectively blocked.) **Visual, Logical**

Teacher Demo

Stopping Radiation   L2

Purpose Demonstrate to students that radiation can be blocked to varying degrees by different materials.

Materials medical X-ray image or photograph of a medical X-ray image

Procedure Show students the medical X-ray image. Tell students that where the X-rays reached the film, it is black, and where the X-rays were completely blocked, the film is clear. When light shines through the clear part of the X-ray, it looks white. Ask, **Which blocks X-rays better, bone or soft tissue?** (Bone, because the white area on the image means that the X-rays did not reach the film.) **How can X-rays tell you about the thickness of bone?** (Thick bone is really clear on the film or white in the image because it absorbs most of the X-rays. Thinner bone is light gray because some X-rays pass through the bone.) **What do you think a metal object would look like on an X-ray image?** (It would be white because it would block the X-rays.)

Expected Outcome Students should be able to relate the penetrating power of X-rays to the penetrating power of nuclear radiation. **Visual, Verbal**

Go Online
PLANETDIARY

Find links to additional activities and have students monitor phenomena that affect Earth and its residents.

Go Online
PLANETDIARY

For: Activity on radiation
Visit: PHSchool.com
Web Code: ccc-1101

Figure 4 Alpha particles (shown in red) are the least penetrating type of nuclear radiation. Gamma rays (shown in green) are the most penetrating. A concrete slab can block most but not all of the gamma rays released by a radioactive source.
Interpreting Diagrams *Which type of radiation can penetrate paper but is blocked by aluminum foil?*

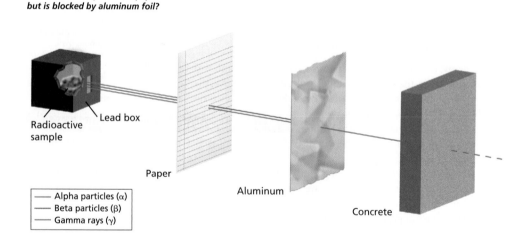

Radioactive sample
Lead box
Paper
Aluminum
Concrete

— Alpha particles (α)
— Beta particles (β)
— Gamma rays (γ)

294   *Chapter 10*

Beta Decay When thorium-234 decays, it releases negatively charged radiation called beta particles. A **beta particle** is an electron emitted by an unstable nucleus. In nuclear equations, a beta particle is written as $_{-1}^{0}e$ or β. Because of its single negative charge, a beta particle is assigned an atomic number of -1. In Chapter 4, you learned that an electron has very little mass when compared with a proton. For this reason, a beta particle is assigned a mass number of 0.

How can an atomic nucleus, which has a positive charge, emit a negatively charged particle? During beta decay, a neutron decomposes into a proton and an electron. The proton stays trapped in the nucleus, while the electron is released. The following equation describes the beta decay of thorium-234.

$$_{90}^{234}\text{Th} \rightarrow \, _{91}^{234}\text{Pa} + \, _{-1}^{0}e$$

In beta decay, the product isotope has one proton more and one neutron fewer than the reactant isotope. The mass numbers of the isotopes are equal because the emitted beta particle has essentially no mass.

Due to their smaller mass and faster speed, beta particles are more penetrating than alpha particles. As Figure 4 illustrates, beta particles pass through paper, but can be stopped by a thin sheet of metal.

 Reading Checkpoint   *What is a beta particle?*

Gamma Decay Not all nuclear radiation consists of charged particles. A **gamma ray** is a penetrating ray of energy emitted by an unstable nucleus. The symbol for a gamma ray is γ. Gamma radiation has no mass and no charge. Like X-rays and visible light, gamma rays are energy waves that travel through space at the speed of light.

Facts and Figures

Explaining Energy The amount of energy emitted in alpha and gamma decay is equal to the energy difference of the nucleus before and after emission. However, this is not true in beta decay. Physicists had difficulty explaining this discrepancy, because the law of conservation of energy states that the total energy should remain unchanged during the process. In 1930, physicist Wolfgang Pauli proposed that an undetected particle, called the neutrino, was emitted along with the beta particles, accounting for some of the energy change in beta decay. In 1956, the neutrino was directly observed for the first time by American physicists Frederick Reines and Clyde Cowan.

Math Skills

Balancing Nuclear Equations

Write a balanced nuclear equation for the alpha decay of polonium-210.

 Read and Understand

What information are you given?

Reactant isotope = polonium-210

Radiation emitted = $^4_2$He (alpha particle)

Use the periodic table to obtain the atomic number of polonium.

Reactant isotope = $^{210}_{84}$Po

2 Plan and Solve

What unknowns are you trying to calculate?

Atomic number of product isotope, Z = ?

Mass number of product isotope, A = ?

Chemical symbol of product isotope, X = ?

What equation contains the given information?

$$^{210}_{84}\text{Po} \rightarrow {}^A_Z\text{X} + {}^4_2\text{He}$$

Write and solve equations for atomic mass and atomic number.

$210 = A + 4$ $84 = Z + 2$

$210 - 4 = A$ $84 - 2 = Z$

$206 = A$ $82 = Z$

According to the periodic table, the element with an atomic number of 82 is lead, Pb. So, X is Pb. The balanced nuclear equation is shown below.

$$^{210}_{84}\text{Po} \rightarrow {}^{206}_{82}\text{Pb} + {}^4_2\text{He}$$

 Look Back and Check

Is your answer reasonable?

The mass number on the left equals the sum of the mass numbers on the right. The atomic number on the left equals the sum of the atomic numbers on the right. The equation is balanced.

Math Practice

1. Write a balanced nuclear equation for the alpha decay of thorium-232.

2. Write a balanced nuclear equation for the beta decay of carbon-14.

3. Determine the product of alpha decay for americium-241.

4. Determine the product of beta decay for strontium-90.

Nuclear Chemistry **295**

Math Practice

Solutions L2

1. $^{232}_{90}$Th $\longrightarrow {}^A_Z$X + $^4_2$He

$A = 232 - 4 = 228$

$Z = 90 - 2 = 88$

X = Ra

$^{232}_{90}$Th $\longrightarrow {}^{228}_{88}$Ra + $^4_2$He

2. $^{14}_6$C $\longrightarrow {}^A_Z$X + $^0_{-1}$e

$A = 14 - 0 = 14$

$Z = 6 - (-1) = 7$

X = N

$^{14}_6$C $\longrightarrow {}^{14}_7$N + $^0_{-1}$e

3. $^{241}_{95}$Am $\longrightarrow {}^A_Z$X + $^4_2$He

$A = 241 - 4 = 237$

$Z = 95 - 2 = 93$

X = Np

^A_ZX = $^{237}_{93}$Np

4. $^{90}_{38}$Sr $\longrightarrow {}^A_Z$X + $^0_{-1}$e

$A = 90 - 0 = 90$

$Z = 38 - (-1) = 39$

X = Y

^A_ZX = $^{90}_{39}$Y

Logical

For Extra Help L1

Remind students that when they write and solve the equation for atomic mass and atomic number, they must remember to change the sign of the constant when it is moved to the left side of the equation.

Logical

Direct students to the **Math Skills** in the **Skills and Reference Handbook** at the end of the student text for additional help.

Additional Problems

1. Write a balanced nuclear equation for the alpha decay of uranium-238.
($^{238}_{92}U \longrightarrow {}^{234}_{90}Th + {}^4_2He$)

2. Write a balanced nuclear equation for the beta decay of sodium-24.
($^{24}_{11}Na \longrightarrow {}^{24}_{12}Mg + {}^0_{-1}e$)

Logical, Portfolio

Answer to . . .

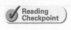 *A beta particle is an electron emitted by an unstable nucleus.*

Figure 4 *Gamma rays are the most penetrating type of nuclear radiation shown in the diagram.*

Effects of Nuclear Radiation

Use Community Resources **L2**

Arrange to have someone from your state or local health department come to your class to talk about the hazards of radon. Have students prepare questions for the speaker in advance. The speaker can inform students about the possible dangers of radon in their homes and what kinds of tests are available. The speaker may also provide information on what the EPA considers to be safe radon levels. Have pairs or groups of students write thank-you notes to the speaker, incorporating a few of the facts that students learned from the presentation. **Interpersonal, Group**

Integrate Earth Science **L2**

Radon is a naturally occurring radioactive element that is formed in the decay chain of uranium-238. Uranium can be found in almost all rocks and soil. Fortunately, in most areas the amount of uranium in rocks and soil is very small. Higher concentrations of uranium and its minerals are commonly found in light colored igneous rocks, granite, dark shale, phosphate-containing sedimentary rocks, and metamorphic rocks derived from these rocks. Soils derived from these rocks also have high uranium concentrations. Encourage students to work in small groups to research the concentrations of uranium in their community. They may use library resources, such as the Internet, to assist them in their research. **Group, Portfolio**

Figure 5 The mineral autunite is an important source of uranium.

Figure 6 Radon gas is produced underground as the uranium in rocks and soil decays. As the radon seeps up through the ground, it can get into buildings by passing through cracks or holes in their foundations. *Inferring How would ventilation of the basement affect radon levels in the house shown below?*

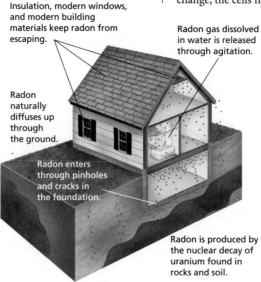

Insulation, modern windows, and modern building materials keep radon from escaping.

Radon gas dissolved in water is released through agitation.

Radon naturally diffuses up through the ground.

Radon enters through pinholes and cracks in the foundation.

Radon is produced by the nuclear decay of uranium found in rocks and soil.

296 Chapter 10

During gamma decay, the atomic number and mass number of the atom remain the same, but the energy of the nucleus decreases. Gamma decay often accompanies alpha or beta decay. For example, thorium-234 emits both beta particles and gamma rays (abbreviated as γ) as it decays.

$$^{234}_{90}\text{Th} \rightarrow {}^{234}_{91}\text{Pa} + {}^{0}_{-1}\text{e} + \gamma$$

Gamma rays are much more penetrating than either alpha particles or beta particles. It can take several centimeters of lead or several meters of concrete to stop gamma radiation.

Effects of Nuclear Radiation

You may not realize it, but you are exposed to nuclear radiation every day. Most of this is **background radiation,** or nuclear radiation that occurs naturally in the environment. Radioisotopes in air, water, rocks, plants, and animals all contribute to background radiation. Most rocks, such as the one in Figure 5, contain at least trace amounts of radioactive elements. Another source of background radiation is cosmic rays. Cosmic rays are streams of charged particles (mainly protons and alpha particles) from outer space. Collisions between cosmic rays and Earth's atmosphere shower the surface below with nuclear radiation. All this radioactivity may sound dangerous. However, background radiation levels are generally low enough to be safe.

When nuclear radiation exceeds background levels, it can damage the cells and tissues of your body. ◯ **Nuclear radiation can ionize atoms.** When cells are exposed to nuclear radiation, the bonds holding together proteins and DNA molecules may break. As these molecules change, the cells may no longer function properly.

Alpha particles, beta particles, and gamma rays are all forms of ionizing radiation. Alpha particles can cause skin damage similar to a burn, but they are not a serious health hazard unless an alpha-emitting substance is inhaled or eaten. For example, radon gas is a potentially dangerous natural source of alpha particles because it can be inhaled. Radon-222 is formed through a series of nuclear decays that begins with uranium-238 in rocks deep underground. As radon-222 is produced, it seeps upward toward the surface. It sometimes collects in the basements of buildings that lack proper ventilation, as shown in Figure 6. Prolonged exposure to radon-222 can lead to lung cancer.

Facts and Figures

Radon Radon is a colorless, odorless, tasteless gas. The most stable isotope, radon-222, is produced by the alpha decay of radium-226. The fact that radon may be a serious health hazard was not recognized until the late 1980s. Today, radon is considered by some to be the second leading cause of lung cancer in the United States, after smoking. Cigarette smokers who become exposed to radon are at particularly high risk of lung cancer.

There are three naturally occurring isotopes of radon. Radon-222 has the longest half-life, 3.82 days. Radon-220, with a half-life of 51.5 seconds, is formed in the decay chain of thorium-232. Radon-219, with a half-life of 3.92 seconds, is formed in the decay chain of actinium-227.

Answer to . . .

Figure 6 *Radon enters buildings from underground. Therefore, ventilating the basement of the house in Figure 6 would help reduce overall radon levels.*

When exposure to nuclear radiation is external, the amount of tissue damage depends on the penetrating power of the radiation. For example, beta particles can damage tissues in the body more than alpha particles, but less than gamma rays. Gamma rays can penetrate deeply into the human body, potentially exposing all organs to ionization damage.

Detecting Nuclear Radiation

Although you can't see, hear, or feel the radioactivity around you, scientific instruments can measure nuclear radiation. ⊂⊃ **Devices that are used to detect nuclear radiation include Geiger counters and film badges.** A Geiger counter, shown in Figure 7, uses a gas-filled tube to measure ionizing radiation. When nuclear radiation enters the tube, it ionizes the atoms of the gas. The ions produce an electric current, which can be measured. The greater the amount of nuclear radiation, the greater the electric current produced in the tube is.

Recall that in Becquerel's experiment, nuclear radiation left an image on a photographic plate. Today, many people who work with or near radioactive materials wear film badges to monitor their exposure to nuclear radiation. A film badge contains a piece of photographic film wrapped in paper. The film is developed and replaced with a new piece periodically. The exposure on the film indicates the amount of radiation exposure for the person wearing the badge.

Figure 7 Wearing protective clothing, a firefighter uses a Geiger counter to test the ground for radioactivity. Firefighters sometimes help clean up accidents involving radioactive materials.

Section 10.1 Assessment

Reviewing Concepts

1. ⊂⊃ How does an element change during nuclear decay?
2. ⊂⊃ What are three types of nuclear radiation?
3. ⊂⊃ How are atoms affected by nuclear radiation?
4. ⊂⊃ What devices can be used to detect nuclear radiation?
5. How do types of nuclear radiation differ in electric charge?
6. Describe the penetrating power of each common type of radiation.
7. What is background radiation? List some of its sources.

Critical Thinking

8. **Predicting** What is the effect of beta decay on the composition of a nucleus?
9. **Inferring** Why do you think airplane pilots wear film badges?

Math Practice

10. Write a balanced nuclear equation for the alpha decay of radium-226.
11. Write a nuclear equation that describes the beta decay of hydrogen-3.

Detecting Nuclear Radiation

Use Visuals   L1

Figure 7 Have students carefully examine the photograph. Ask, **Why is it important to wear protective clothing around radioactive materials?** *(Protective clothing keeps radioactive materials away from skin.)* Tell students that the EPA recommends heavy clothing as protection from beta radiation. Ask, **Does a Geiger counter protect against the effects of nuclear radiation?** *(No. The Geiger counter serves only as a monitoring device, not a shielding device.)* **Visual, Logical**

3 ASSESS

Evaluate Understanding   L2

Randomly ask students to name the symbol or charge for each type of nuclear decay.

Reteach   L1

Use Figure 4 to summarize the three different types of nuclear decay and how each type affects matter.

Math Practice

Solutions

10. $^{226}_{88}\text{Ra} \longrightarrow ^{A}_{Z}\text{X} + ^{4}_{2}\text{He}$
$A = 226 - 4 = 222$; $Z = 88 - 2 = 86$;
$X = \text{Rn}$; $^{226}_{88}\text{Ra} \longrightarrow ^{222}_{86}\text{Rn} + ^{4}_{2}\text{He}$

11. $^{3}_{1}\text{H} \longrightarrow ^{A}_{Z}\text{X} + ^{0}_{-1}\text{e}$
$A = 3 - 0 = 3$; $Z = 1 - (-1) = 2$;
$X = \text{He}$; $^{3}_{1}\text{H} \longrightarrow ^{3}_{2}\text{He} + ^{0}_{-1}\text{e}$

Interactive Textbook If your class subscribes to the Interactive Textbook, use it to review key concepts in Section 10.1.

Section 10.1 Assessment

1. During nuclear decay, atoms of one element can change into atoms of another element.
2. Three types of nuclear radiation are alpha particles, beta particles, and gamma rays.
3. Nuclear radiation can ionize atoms.
4. Geiger counters and film badges are two devices used to detect nuclear radiation.
5. Alpha particles have a charge of 2+; beta particles have a charge of 1−; gamma rays have no charge.

6. Alpha particles are the least penetrating. Most alpha particles can be stopped by a sheet of paper or by clothing. Beta particles pass through paper, but can be stopped by metal foil. Gamma rays, which are much more penetrating than either alpha particles or beta particles, can pass through several meters of concrete.
7. Background radiation is nuclear radiation that occurs naturally in the environment. Sources of background radiation include cosmic rays, and rocks and minerals that contain radioactive elements.

8. In beta decay, a neutron decomposes into a proton and an electron. Therefore, the mass number stays the same while the atomic number (the number of protons) increases by one. The net effect of beta decay is that the number of neutrons in the nucleus decreases by one and the number of protons increases by one.
9. Because they work at high altitudes, pilots are exposed to high levels of background radiation from cosmic rays. To monitor their radiation exposure, pilots wear film badges.

1 FOCUS

Objectives

10.2.1 Define half-life, and **relate** half-life to the age of a radioactive sample.

10.2.2 Compare and **contrast** nuclear reaction rates with chemical reaction rates.

10.2.3 Describe how radioisotopes are used to estimate the age of materials.

Reading Focus

Build Vocabulary L2

Paraphrase Have students write a definition of *half-life* in their own words. After students read the section, ask them to draw a diagram that illustrates the definition.

Reading Strategy L2

a. Carbon-14
b. 50,000

2 INSTRUCT

Build Science Skills L2

Drawing Conclusions Ask students to look at Figure 8. Tell them that if the object is made of an organic (once-living) material, the object's carbon-14 content can be used to determine its age. Ask, **The tools shown in the photo are made of stone. Do you think the stone tools contain carbon-14?** *(No, stone is not an organic material.)* **The caption states that the objects are estimated to be 15,000 years old. If the stone tools were not used to determine this age, then what was?** *(The people who made the stone tools also made and used other, organic-based objects. These objects, perhaps made of cloth or wood, were used to determine the age.)*
Logical

10.2 Rates of Nuclear Decay

 Standard: ICP.7.7

Reading Focus

Key Concepts

- How do nuclear decay rates differ from chemical reaction rates?
- How do scientists determine the age of an object that contains carbon-14?

Vocabulary

- half-life

Reading Strategy

Identifying Details Copy the concept map below. As you read, complete it to identify details about radiocarbon dating.

Radiocarbon dating

uses the radioisotope

a. _?_

can be used to date objects as old as

b. _?_ years

A well-known theory is that early Americans were people from Siberia who crossed the Bering Strait into Alaska about 13,000 years ago. However, this theory has been challenged by recent scientific discoveries. In the 1990s, archaeologists working at a site in Cactus Hill, Virginia, found stone tools, charcoal, and animal bones that were at least 15,000 years old. Some of the artifacts were as much as 17,000 years old. The age of these artifacts suggests that the first Americans reached the continent much earlier than formerly thought. Some archaeologists have since revised their theories on the origin of America's earliest ancestors. One possible explanation is that the first Americans were people from Europe who crossed the Atlantic Ocean by using boats.

Figure 8 shows some of the artifacts from the Cactus Hill site. They certainly look very old, but the archaeologists needed to find out *how* old. One clue that can reveal the age of an object is how many radioactive nuclei it contains. Because most materials contain at least trace amounts of radioisotopes, scientists can estimate how old they are based on rates of nuclear decay.

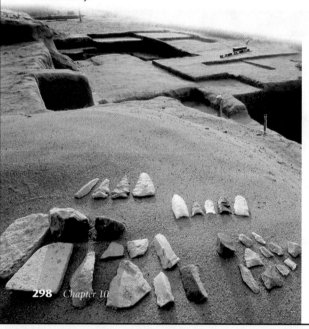
Figure 8 These stone tools from the archaeological site in Cactus Hill, Virginia, are at least 15,000 years old. Scientists estimated the age of the site based on rates of nuclear decay.

298 Chapter 10

 Section Resources

Print
- *Laboratory Manual,* Investigation 10A
- *Reading and Study Workbook With Math Support,* Section 10.2
- *Transparencies,* Section 10.2

Technology
- *Interactive Textbook,* Section 10.2
- *Presentation Pro CD-ROM,* Section 10.2
- *Go Online,* NSTA SciLinks, Half-Life

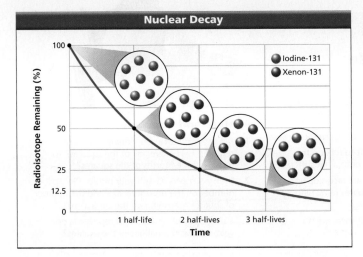

Nuclear Decay

Radioisotope Remaining (%): 100, 50, 25, 12.5, 0

Time: 1 half-life, 2 half-lives, 3 half-lives

● Iodine-131
● Xenon-131

Figure 9 The half-life for the beta decay of iodine-131 is 8.07 days. After one half-life (8.07 days), half of a sample of iodine-131 will have decayed into xenon-131. After two half-lives (16.14 days), three quarters of the sample will have decayed.

Half-life

A nuclear decay rate describes how fast nuclear changes take place in a radioactive substance. Every radioisotope decays at a specific rate that can be expressed as a half-life. A **half-life** is the time required for one half of a sample of a radioisotope to decay. After one half-life, half of the atoms in a radioactive sample have decayed, while the other half remain unchanged. After two half-lives, half of the remaining half decays, leaving one quarter of the original sample unchanged. Figure 9 illustrates the nuclear decay rate of iodine-131. Iodine-131 has a half-life of 8.07 days. After two half-lives, or 16.14 days, the fraction of iodine-131 remaining is one quarter. After three half-lives, or 24.21 days, the fraction of iodine-131 remaining is one half of one quarter, or one eighth.

Half-lives can vary from fractions of a second to billions of years. Figure 10 lists the half-lives of some common radioisotopes. Uranium-238, for instance, has a half-life of 4.5 billion years. This means that in 4.5 billion years, there will be half as much uranium-238 on Earth as there is today. You could also say that 4.5 billion years ago, there was twice as much uranium-238 on Earth as there is today. ⟳ **Unlike chemical reaction rates, which vary with the conditions of a reaction, nuclear decay rates are constant.** Regardless of the temperature, pressure, or surface area of a uranium-238 sample, its half-life is still 4.5 billion years.

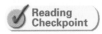 **Reading Checkpoint** *What is a half-life?*

Figure 10 Nuclear decay rates are constant. A given radioisotope decays at a specific rate, or half-life. *Calculating What isotope is produced by the nuclear decay of radon-222?*

Half-Lives and Radiation of Selected Radioisotopes		
Isotope	Half-life	Nuclear Radiation Emitted
Radon-222	3.82 days	α
Iodine-131	8.07 days	β
Thorium-234	24.1 days	β, γ
Radium-226	1620 years	α, γ
Carbon-14	5730 years	β
Thorium-230	75,200 years	α, γ
Uranium-235	7.04×10^8 years	α, γ
Potassium-40	1.28×10^9 years	β, γ
Uranium-238	4.47×10^9 years	α

Nuclear Chemistry **299**

Modeling Half-Life L2

Objective
After completing this activity, students will be able to
• analyze data to calculate the "half-life" of a model radioactive element.

Address Misconceptions

Students may think that a half-life is half the time it takes for a radioactive substance to decay completely. This lab can help dispel this misconception.

Skills Focus Analyzing Data, Calculating, Using Graphs

Prep Time 20 minutes

Materials 100 1-cm squares of wallpaper, large plastic bag, graph paper

Advance Prep Use a paper cutter to cut up the wallpaper quickly.

Class Time 20 minutes

Teaching Tips
• Students can cut up the paper squares themselves.
• Explain to students that, on average, half the remaining squares will be removed each time Step 4 is repeated.
• Ask students: **How does this lab model radioactive decay?** (*Like the wallpaper squares, half the radioactive element decays during each half-life.*)

Expected Outcome Students will need to spill and remove paper squares six to nine times to remove all of the squares.

Analyze and Conclude
1. On average, half the squares will be removed in one spill and three-fourths of the squares will be removed in two spills.
2. Students' graphs should reflect the information in their data tables.
3. One year
Visual, Logical

Download a worksheet on half-life for students to complete, and find additional teacher support from NSTA SciLinks.

Modeling Half-Life

Procedure
1. Put 100 1-cm squares of wallpaper in a large plastic bag. Construct a data table with 2 columns and 9 blank rows. Label the columns Spill Number and Number of Squares Returned.
2. Close the bag and shake it to mix up the squares. Then, spill them onto a flat surface.
3. Remove the squares that are face-side up. Record the number of squares remaining and return them to the bag.
4. Repeat Steps 2 and 3 until there are no squares left to put back into the bag.

Analyze and Conclude
1. **Analyzing Data** How many spills were required to remove half of the squares? To remove three fourths of the squares?
2. **Using Graphs** Graph your results. Plot spill number on the horizontal axis and the number of squares remaining on the vertical axis.
3. **Using Models** If each spill represents one year, what is the half-life of the squares?

Suppose you have a one-gram sample of iridium-182, which undergoes beta decay to form osmium-182. The half-life of iridium-182 is 15 minutes. After 45 minutes, how much iridium-182 will remain in the sample? To solve this problem, you first need to calculate how many half-lives will elapse during the total time of decay.

$$\text{Half-lives elapsed} = \frac{\text{Total time of decay}}{\text{Half-life}} = \frac{45 \text{ min}}{15 \text{ min}} = 3$$

After three half-lives, the amount of iridium-182 has been reduced by half three times.

$$\frac{1}{2} \times \frac{1}{2} \times \frac{1}{2} = \frac{1}{8}$$

So after 45 minutes, $\frac{1}{8} \times 1$ gram, or 0.125 gram, of iridium-182 remains while 0.875 gram of the sample has decayed into osmium-182.

Radioactive Dating

Now suppose you have a sample that was originally iridium-182, but three quarters of it have since decayed into osmium-182. Based on the fraction of iridium-182 left (one quarter), you can calculate the age of the sample to be two half-lives, or 30 minutes old.

The artifacts from Cactus Hill were dated by measuring levels of carbon-14, which has a half-life of 5730 years. Carbon-14 is formed in the upper atmosphere when neutrons produced by cosmic rays collide with nitrogen-14 atoms. The radioactive carbon-14 undergoes beta decay to form nitrogen-14.

$$^{14}_{6}\text{C} \rightarrow ^{14}_{7}\text{N} + ^{0}_{-1}\text{e}$$

Go Online

For: Links on half-life
Visit: www.SciLinks.org
Web Code: ccn-1102

Facts and Figures

Radiocarbon Dating An American chemist, Dr. Willard F. Libby, developed this technique in the late 1940s. Radiocarbon dating is used to date once-living materials. The date when the organism died is the date when it stopped absorbing carbon-14.

Radiocarbon dating cannot be used to date the remains of organisms that died after the 1940s. Starting in the 1940s, the testing of nuclear bombs and use of nuclear reactors has dramatically increased the amount of carbon-14 and other radioisotopes in the environment.

Carbon reacts with oxygen in the atmosphere and forms carbon dioxide. As plants absorb carbon dioxide during photosynthesis, they maintain the same ratio of carbon-14 to carbon-12 as in the atmosphere. Likewise, animals have the same ratio of carbon isotopes as the plants they eat. When a plant or animal dies, however, it can no longer absorb carbon. From this point on, the organism's carbon-14 levels decrease as the radioactive carbon decays. **In radiocarbon dating, the age of an object is determined by comparing the object's carbon-14 levels with carbon-14 levels in the atmosphere.** For example, if the ratio of carbon-14 to carbon-12 in a fossil is half the ratio in the atmosphere, then the organism lived about 5730 years ago.

Because atmospheric carbon-14 levels can change over time, the calculated age of the fossil is not totally accurate. To get a more accurate radiocarbon date, scientists compare the carbon-14 levels in a sample to carbon-14 levels in objects of known age. Such objects might include trees (which can be dated by counting tree rings) or artifacts from a specific historical period.

Radiocarbon dating can be used to date any carbon-containing object less than 50,000 years old, such as the artifact in Figure 11. Objects older than 50,000 years contain too little carbon-14 to be measurable. To date objects thought to be older than 50,000 years, scientists measure the amounts of radioisotopes with longer half-lives than carbon-14. Geologists, for instance, use the half-lives of potassium-40, uranium-235, and uranium-238 to date rock formations. The older the rock, the lower are the levels of the radioisotope present.

Figure 11 Radiocarbon dating has helped archaeologists learn more about ancient civilizations. Excavations in Abydos, a major archaeological site of ancient Egypt, have unearthed fascinating artifacts. This mummy case, containing the remains of a cat, is 1900 years old.

Section 10.2 Assessment

Reviewing Concepts

1. How are nuclear decay rates different from chemical reaction rates?

2. How can scientists determine the age of an object that contains carbon-14?

3. If a radioactive sample has decayed until only one eighth of the original sample remains unchanged, how many half-lives have elapsed?

4. What type of nuclear radiation is emitted when carbon-14 decays?

Critical Thinking

5. **Predicting** Can radiocarbon dating be used to determine the age of dinosaur fossils? Explain. (*Hint:* Dinosaurs roamed Earth more than 65 million years ago.)

6. **Inferring** All of the isotopes of radon have half-lives shorter than four days, yet radon is still found in nature. Explain why all the radon has not already decayed.

7. **Calculating** A certain isotope of technetium has a half-life of six hours. If it is given to a patient as part of a medical procedure, what fraction of the radioisotope remains in the body after one day?

Writing in Science

Explanatory Paragraph Archaeology is the study of past cultures. Explain how a concept in chemistry led to advances in archaeology.

Nuclear Chemistry **301**

Section 10.2 Assessment

1. Unlike chemical reaction rates, nuclear decay rates are constant.

2. The age of an object is determined by comparing the object's carbon-14 levels with carbon-14 levels in the atmosphere.

3. Three half-lives ($\frac{1}{2} \times \frac{1}{2} \times \frac{1}{2} = \frac{1}{8}$) have elapsed.

4. When a carbon-14 nucleus decays, it emits a beta particle.

5. Dinosaur fossils, about 65 million years old, are too old to be radiocarbon dated. Radiocarbon dating can only be used to date objects less than 50,000 years old.

6. Radon isotopes are still found in nature because they are continually formed by the decay of longer-lived radioisotopes.

7. Assuming the technetium is eliminated only by radioactive decay, then Half-Lives elapsed = Total time of decay/Half-Life = 24 hours/6 hours = 4. After four half-lives, the amount has been reduced by half four times. $(\frac{1}{2})^4 = \frac{1}{16}$

Radioactive Dating
Build Science Skills L2

Measuring Ask students to choose a radioactive isotope for dating a hypothetical fossil. Tell students that archaeologists hypothesize that the fossil is about 20,000 years old. Have students look at the half-lives of radioisotopes in this section. Ask, **Which isotope would you recommend that the scientists first try?** (*Carbon-14*) **Why would that isotope be a good choice?** (*It is a good choice because the half-life of carbon-14 is 5370 years. The half-life of radium-226, at 1620 years, is too short. The half-life of thorium-230 is 75,200 years, which is too long. Using either of these could result in a less accurate measurement.*)
Logical, Verbal

3 ASSESS

Evaluate Understanding L2

Randomly ask students to determine the number of particles present after one, two, or three half-lives have passed from a specified initial number of particles.

Reteach L1

Use Figure 10 to review how different radioisotopes may be used to date objects of different ages. Emphasize that some radioisotopes with shorter half-lives are useful for dating young objects while radioisotopes with long half-lives are useful for dating old objects.

Interactive Textbook If your class subscribes to the Interactive Textbook, use it to review key concepts in Section 10.2.

Writing in Science

Half-life is a concept in nuclear chemistry that has led to profound advances in archaeology, the study of past cultures. A half-life is the time required for one half of a sample of a radioisotope to decay. Using radioisotopes such as carbon-14, scientists have been able to accurately date fossils and archaeological sites up to 50,000 years old.

Should Radon Testing in Schools Be Mandatory? L2

Background

Prior to 1984, radon gas was considered a health risk only for workers in uranium mines. Then, in 1984, a nuclear engineer set off an alarm while passing through a radiation monitor at the Limerick Nuclear Power Plant. The engineer, Stan Watras, was leaving work at the time. Since there was no nuclear fuel on site, there was no major source of radiation contamination at the plant. The Health Physics staff at the plant determined that the source of the radiation was Mr. Watras's house in Boyertown, Pennsylvania. The staff took remedial actions to fix Mr. Watras' home. Mr. Watras and his family still live in the house today.

The Watras case put radon testing in the national spotlight. In October of 1988, Congress passed legislation that established a national goal that indoor radon levels not exceed ambient outdoor radon levels (0.2–0.7 pCi/L). A picocurie (Ci) is a unit of radioactivity equal to 0.037 disintegrations per second. The law set aside funds for states to initiate radon testing in schools and workplaces.

Answers

1. The issue that needs to be resolved is whether indoor radon poses a health risk serious enough in schools to warrant mandatory testing.
2. Two reasons why radon testing should be mandatory in all schools is that radon is the second leading cause of lung cancer in the United States and that many classrooms are above the EPA's action level of 4 pCi/L.
3. Answers will vary based on which arguments students choose.

Have students further research issues related to this topic.

---

issues in
SCIENCE

Should Radon Testing in Schools Be Mandatory?

Radon (Rn) is a radioactive element that forms from the nuclear decay of uranium in rocks and soil. A colorless, odorless gas, radon can enter buildings through drains, cracks in the floors and walls, and even the water supply. Indoor radon levels tend to be highest in places that are close to the soil and have little ventilation, such as basements or crawl spaces.

When a person inhales radon-contaminated air, the lungs trap radioactive particles. As these particles decay, radiation is released into the lung tissue. Over time, repeated exposure to high radon levels can result in lung cancer.

The Environmental Protection Agency (EPA) identifies 4 picocuries per liter (pCi/L) of air as the national "action level" for radon. (A picocurie is a unit of radioactivity.) If an indoor space has a radon level of 4 pCi/L or higher, the EPA recommends that steps be taken to reduce it. Such steps might include installing a ventilation system and sealing cracks in the building's foundation

The Viewpoints

Radon Testing in Schools Should Be Mandatory

The EPA estimates that indoor radon exposure contributes to 21,000 lung cancer deaths in the United States each year. After smoking, radon is the second-leading cause of lung cancer.

Students and teachers spend extended periods of time indoors at school. A nationwide survey of radon levels in schools found that nearly one in five schools has at least one classroom with radon exceeding the EPA's action level of 4 pCi/L.

Indoor radon can be easily tested. If elevated radon levels are found, they can be reduced using proven techniques. But without mandatory testing, school administrators may not be aware of the potential risk of radon exposure in their schools.

Radon Testing in Schools Should Not Be Mandatory

The EPA's radon guidelines are based mainly on studies of workers in uranium mines. Radon levels in these mines were far greater than those found in homes or schools. In addition, the miners engaged in tiring labor, resulting in heavy breathing of the surrounding air. Lastly, most of the miners were smokers. The data from these studies are appropriate for predicting the risk of radon exposure for uranium miners—but not for the general public.

The EPA's action level of 4 pCi/L is not universally accepted. In Canada and Europe, for example, radon guidelines are much less strict. Until scientists gather more data about the risk of residential radon exposures, radon testing in schools should not be mandatory.

Research and Decide

1. **Defining the Issue** In your own words, explain the issue that needs to be resolved about indoor radon.

2. **Analyzing the Viewpoints** List two arguments of those who think that radon testing should be mandatory in schools. List two arguments of those who think that radon testing should not be mandatory in schools.

3. **Forming Your Opinion** Should there be mandatory radon testing in schools? Which argument did you find more convincing?

For: More on this issue
Visit: PHSchool.com
Web Code: cch-1100

10.3 Artificial Transmutation

Standard: ICP.7.2

Reading Focus

Key Concepts
- How do artificial transmutations occur?
- How are transuranium elements produced?

Vocabulary
- transmutation
- transuranium elements
- quark

Reading Strategy
Monitoring Your Understanding Preview the Key Concepts, topic headings, vocabulary, and figures in this section. List two things you expect to learn. After reading, state what you learned about each item you listed.

What I Expect to Learn	What I Learned
a. ____?____	b. ____?____
c. ____?____	d. ____?____

During the Middle Ages, a number of people, like the ones shown in Figure 12, were obsessed with the idea of changing lead into gold. For centuries, these early scientists, known as alchemists, tried to use chemical reactions to make gold. But no matter how many recipes they tried, the alchemists only succeeded in making compounds that contained lead. What were they doing wrong?

Nuclear Reactions in the Laboratory

The alchemists were trying to achieve transmutation. **Transmutation** is the conversion of atoms of one element to atoms of another. It involves a nuclear change, not a chemical change.

Nuclear decay is an example of a transmutation that occurs naturally. Transmutations can also be artificial. Scientists can perform artificial transmutations by bombarding atomic nuclei with high-energy particles, such as protons, neutrons, or alpha particles.

Early experiments involving artificial transmutation led to important clues about atomic structure. In 1919, a decade after he discovered the atomic nucleus, Ernest Rutherford performed the first artificial transmutation. Rutherford had been studying the effects of nuclear radiation on various gases. When Rutherford exposed nitrogen gas to alpha particles, he found that some of the alpha particles were absorbed by the nitrogen nuclei. Each newly formed nucleus then ejected a proton, leaving behind the isotope oxygen-17.

$$^{14}_{7}N + {}^{4}_{2}He \rightarrow {}^{17}_{8}O + {}^{1}_{1}H$$

Note that $^{1}_{1}H$ represents a proton. Rutherford's experiment provided evidence that the nucleus contains protons.

Figure 12 This painting of an alchemist's laboratory was made around 1570. The alchemists failed in their attempts to turn lead into gold.

Section Resources

Print
- **Reading and Study Workbook With Math Support,** Section 10.3
- **Transparencies,** Section 10.3

Technology
- **Interactive Textbook,** Section 10.3
- **Presentation Pro CD-ROM,** Section 10.3

---

1 FOCUS

Objectives
10.3.1 Describe and **identify** examples of transmutation.
10.3.2 Describe how transuranium elements are synthesized.
10.3.3 Explain how particle accelerators have been used in scientific research.

Reading Focus

Build Vocabulary

Paraphrase Ask students to write the vocabulary words on a sheet of paper. Instruct students to write a definition, in their own words, for each term as they encounter the term while going through the chapter. After writing their own definition, they should also write a complete sentence with the term.

Reading Strategy

Possible answers: **a.** Examples of artificial transmutation **b.** Rutherford's transmutation of nitrogen-14 into oxygen-17; the synthesis of neptunium-239 **c.** Uses of transuranium elements **d.** Smoke detectors (americium-241); space probes (plutonium-238)

2 INSTRUCT

Nuclear Reactions in the Laboratory

The alchemists of the Middle Ages never succeeded in turning lead into gold. This doesn't mean, however, that it is impossible. Modern scientists, including Glenn Seaborg in 1980, have reportedly turned lead into gold. However, this has only been done with very minute amounts of lead. Challenge students to find out why scientists do not manufacture gold for profit using transmutation. *(The process of using nuclear reactions to change lead into gold is more expensive than the worth of the gold. Currently, it is cheaper to mine gold ore.)*
Verbal

Transuranium Elements

Modeling Transmutation L2

Objective
After completing this activity, students will be able to
- balance equations that describe simple nuclear reactions.

Skills Focus Calculating, **Using Models**

 Prep Time 5 minutes

Class Time 15 minutes

Safety Caution students to avoid dropping beads on the floor where they may lead to slips and falls.

Expected Outcome The products are carbon-13 and oxygen-17.

Analyze and Conclude
1. The missing products were carbon-13 and oxygen-17. The models should show that the total number of protons and neutrons on the left side of the equation is the same as on the right. After counting the number of green beads (protons) in the missing product isotope, its identity can be determined by referring to the periodic table. The mass number of the missing product isotope is the sum of its protons and neutrons.
2. Use the following equation to check students' models.

$$^{27}_{13}\text{Al} + {}^4_2\text{He} \longrightarrow {}^{30}_{14}\text{Si} + {}^1_1\text{H}$$

Visual

Build Reading Literacy L1

Visualize Refer to page **354D** in **Chapter 12**, which provides the guidelines for using visualization.

Have students keep their books closed. Tell them to listen carefully while you read the paragraph about synthesizing neptunium. Ask students to describe how they visualize what happens in the transmutation. Then, ask students to work in pairs and discuss how they visualized the process.
Visual

⊟Quick⟩Lab

Modeling Transmutation

Materials
periodic table, 2 sheets of unlined white paper, 32 green beads, 32 purple beads

Procedure
1. Use the periodic table to complete the following nuclear reaction. Then, write it on one of the sheets of paper.

$$^{10}_5\text{B} + {}^4_2\text{He} \rightarrow {}^A_Z\text{X} + {}^1_1\text{H}$$

2. Count the number of protons and neutrons present in each reactant and product.

3. Using the green beads to represent protons and the purple beads to represent neutrons, make a model of each reactant and product below its symbol on the sheet of paper.

4. Repeat Steps 1 to 3 using the following nuclear reaction and the second sheet of paper.

$$^{14}_7\text{N} + {}^4_2\text{He} \rightarrow {}^A_Z\text{X} + {}^1_1\text{H}$$

Analyze and Conclude
1. **Applying Concepts** What was the missing product in each of the equations? How did you know what the missing product was?

2. **Using Models** Make a model of the nuclear reaction between an alpha particle and an atom of aluminium-27. (*Hint:* One of the two products is a proton.)

Figure 13 In 1977, the National Aeronautics and Space Administration (NASA) launched two identical spacecraft, Voyager 1 and Voyager 2. These spacecraft, which are still exploring the outer solar system, are powered by the alpha decay of plutonium-238. **Inferring** *What isotope is produced by the alpha decay of plutonium-238?*

Transuranium Elements

Elements with atomic numbers greater than 92 (uranium) are called **transuranium elements.** All transuranium elements are radioactive, and they are generally not found in nature. ⊙ **Scientists can synthesize a transuranium element by the artificial transmutation of a lighter element.**

Neptunium was the first transuranium element synthesized. In 1940, scientists at the University of California, Berkeley, bombarded uranium-238 with neutrons, producing uranium-239. The uranium-239 underwent beta decay to form neptunium-239.

$$^{239}_{92}\text{U} \rightarrow {}^{239}_{93}\text{Np} + {}^{\ 0}_{-1}\text{e}$$

Although most transuranium elements have only been produced for research, some are synthesized for industrial or consumer use. For example, americium-241 is a transuranium element used in smoke detectors. As americium-241 decays, it emits alpha radiation. This radiation ionizes the air inside a smoke detector to allow an electric current to flow. When smoke enters the smoke detector, it disrupts the current and the alarm goes off. Another useful transuranium element is plutonium-238. Figure 13 shows a space probe that runs on electrical energy generated by the decay of plutonium-238.

 Reading Checkpoint *What is a transuranium element?*

Customize for Inclusion Students

Gifted
Challenge students to find the names of different types of subatomic particles besides protons, neutrons, and electrons. For example, have them research the six types of quarks. (*The six quarks are often called up, down, charmed, strange, top, and bottom.*) Then, have students find out when they were discovered and what properties are known about them. Have students create a presentation that explains the characteristics and discovery of several subatomic particles. (*Other subatomic particle types or categories include leptons, muons, tau particles, neutrinos, bosons, fermions, gluons, mesons, and baryons.*)

Particle Accelerators

In Rutherford's transmutation experiment, the radioactive element radium was used as a source of alpha particles. However, sometimes transmutations will not occur unless the bombarding particles are moving at extremely high speeds. In order to perform such transmutations, scientists use devices called particle accelerators. In a particle accelerator, charged particles can be accelerated to speeds very close to the speed of light. The fast-moving particles are guided toward a target, where they collide with atomic nuclei. With the help of particle accelerators, scientists have produced more than 3000 different isotopes.

Scientists also conduct collision experiments in order to study nuclear structure. Since the proton, neutron, and electron were discovered, more than 200 different subatomic particles have been detected. According to the current model of the atom, protons and neutrons are made up of even smaller particles called quarks. A **quark** is a subatomic particle theorized to be among the basic units of matter. Both protons and neutrons belong to a class of particles that are made up of three quarks. Six types of quarks are currently thought to exist. Two of these types were discovered at Fermi National Accelerator Laboratory, also known as Fermilab. Figure 14 shows one of the devices used at Fermilab to detect subatomic particles.

Figure 14 This particle detector records subatomic particles produced in the Tevatron, the most powerful particle accelerator in the United States. The Tevatron is located at Fermilab in Batavia, Illinois.

Section 10.3 Assessment

Reviewing Concepts

1. ◆ How do scientists perform artificial transmutations?

2. ◆ How are transuranium elements produced?

3. How does artificial transmutation differ from nuclear decay?

4. Write the equation for the transmutation that occurs when an alpha particle combines with an oxygen-16 atom, emitting a proton.

5. Does fermium-257 undergo nuclear decay? Explain.

Critical Thinking

6. **Predicting** Bombarding a lithium-6 atom with a neutron produces helium-4 and another particle. What is that particle?

7. **Predicting** Curium was first synthesized by bombarding a target isotope with alpha particles, which produced curium-242 and a neutron. What was the target isotope? (*Hint:* Use the symbol $_0^1n$ to represent a neutron.)

8. **Inferring** Why can't the transuranium elements be made by exposing other elements to naturally occurring alpha radiation?

Writing in Science

Summary Write a brief summary of the first artificial transmutation, performed by Ernest Rutherford. (*Hint:* Your summary should describe an example of a nuclear reaction.)

Nuclear Chemistry   **305**

Section 10.3   Assessment

1. By bombarding atomic nuclei with high-energy particles, such as protons, neutrons, or alpha particles

2. By the artificial transmutation of lighter elements

3. Artificial transmutation is a nonnatural process in which a nucleus is bombarded with high-energy particles. Nuclear decay is a natural process in which an unstable nucleus emits charged particles and/or energy.

4. $_8^{16}O + _2^4He \longrightarrow _9^{19}F + _1^1H$

5. Fermium-257, with an atomic number of 100, is a transuranium element and therefore undergoes nuclear decay.

6. Hydrogen-3

7. Plutonium-239

8. Because naturally occurring alpha particles do not have enough energy to be used in the synthesis of transuranium elements. The synthesis of transuranium elements requires high-energy particles.

Particle Accelerators
Build Science Skills   L2

Inferring Ask students to read the first paragraph of Particle Accelerators. Ask, **What evidence supports the claim that most transuranium elements can exist only when atoms are bombarded with particles at very high speeds?** (*Transuranium elements generally do not occur in nature, so the conditions under which they are formed are not likely to be found in nature. Most transuranium elements have been produced only under conditions that can be achieved by using a particle accelerator.*) **Logical**

3 ASSESS
Evaluate Understanding   L2

Ask students to write three completed equations for transmutations. Have students take turns giving the reactants for the equation while another student determines the product with the correct number of protons and neutrons for each transmutation.

Reteach   L1

Have students look at the transmutation equations in the section and ask them to explain how transmutation differs from nuclear decay.

Writing in Science

Rutherford performed the first artificial transmutation while studying the effects of nuclear radiation on gases. After he exposed nitrogen gas to alpha radiation, he observed that some of the alpha particles were temporarily absorbed by the nitrogen nuclei. Each newly formed nucleus then ejected a proton, leaving behind oxygen-17. In this transmutation, nitrogen-14 was converted into oxygen-17.

Interactive Textbook If your class subscribes to the Interactive Textbook, use it to review key concepts in Section 10.3.

Answer to . . .

Figure 13 *Uranium-234. The equation is:*

$$_{94}^{238}Pu \longrightarrow _{92}^{234}U + _2^4He$$

Reading Checkpoint *An element with an atomic number greater than 92*

Nuclear Medicine L2

Background

PET (positron emission tomography) scanning can detect subtle changes in the body's metabolism and chemical reactions. The PET scanner detects radiation produced by a positron-emitting radioisotope injected into the body. Chemical compounds containing radioisotopes of carbon, nitrogen, or oxygen are commonly used as tracers.

Once the tracer enters the body, it travels through the bloodstream to the target organ. When the tracer reaches the target organ, the chemical that it is attached to begins taking part in the chemical reactions. Positrons, the antimatter equivalent of electrons, are released from the tracer and collide with electrons. Each collision annihilates a positron and an electron and releases two gamma rays. The PET scanner detects these gamma rays. The data is fed into a computer and a three-dimensional image is produced of the processes occurring in the target organ.

PET scans are used to evaluate a number of different medical conditions. They can be used to detect cancers, determine the extent to which cancer has spread, and determine the effectiveness of cancer treatment. PET scans can help diagnose brain conditions such as epilepsy and Alzheimer's disease. They can also evaluate cardiac conditions such as heart muscle function and coronary artery disease.

Nuclear Medicine

Exposure to nuclear radiation is often harmful to the human body. However, scientists have also found nuclear radiation to be a powerful tool in the field of medicine.

Because radioisotopes are detectable by their radiation, they can be used as tracers that map out specific locations in the body. For example, the radioisotope iodine-131 is absorbed by the thyroid gland in the throat in the same way that iodine-127 is. If iodine-131 is injected into the body, the radiation it emits will show how well the thyroid gland is functioning.

Radioactive tracers can also be used to pinpoint the location of cancer cells. Cancer cells multiply rapidly and absorb glucose much faster than normal cells. If the glucose molecules are "tagged" with a radioactive tracer, such as flourine-18, the location of the cancer cells can be found by tracking areas of high glucose concentration.

Radioisotopes with short half-lives are chosen for medical uses. These isotopes decay so rapidly that after only a day or two, practically none of the isotope remains.

PET scanner
PET (positron emission tomography) scans use radioactive tracers to examine parts of the body, such as the brain. The patient receives an injection of radioactive tracer. The tracer produces gamma rays that are detected by the scanner.

Tagged glucose is absorbed slowly in the blue areas, indicating normal tissue.

Red color shows greater glucose absorption in possibly cancerous areas.

PET scan of brain
This scan shows the level of activity in different areas of the brain. Glucose tagged with flourine-18 is absorbed more rapidly in areas of high brain activity and by cancer cells. Here, red shows the greatest activity and blue the least.

Positron

Gamma ray *Electron*

Gamma rays

Gamma rays are produced when the tracer emits a positron. A positron is a particle with the mass of an electron but a charge of 1+. The positron is destroyed upon contact with an electron from a nearby atom in the body, and emits two gamma rays in opposite directions.

Gamma-ray detectors

Brain

Atom of tracer isotope

Gamma ray

Producing an image

The scanner detects the gamma rays and produces two-dimensional images like slices through the brain. The scanner's computer then constructs a three-dimensional image based on the scans.

Going Further

- Write a paragraph describing how radioactive tracers are used in medicine. Indicate what qualities make a particular radioisotope useful as a radioactive tracer in the human body.

- Take a Discovery Channel Video Field Trip by watching "Nuclear Medicine."

DISCOVERY CHANNEL SCHOOL
Video Field Trip

Using Models

ACTIVITY

Purpose Students model the radiation detected by a PET scanner.

Materials 500-mL beaker; sponges; shallow pans; food coloring; 1-cm strips of thin and thick cardboard, newspaper, and waxed paper; paper towels

Class Time 20 minutes

Advance Prep Fill the beaker with water and add several drops of food coloring. For each group, prepare a solution-soaked sponge placed flat in a pan.

Procedure Distribute several different strips to students and have them make a pattern on top of the sponge. Tell students to leave some areas of the sponge uncovered. Then, have students gently press the paper towel on top of the sponge for three seconds and remove it, placing the paper towel faceup next to the sponge. Ask, **How does the pattern on the paper towel compare to the pattern of squares on the sponge?** *(They are similar, but not identical. The waxed paper and heavy cardboard completely blocked the absorption of the solution. The newspaper did not block the absorption at all, and the light cardboard partially blocked the solution.)* **If the paper towel were a PET scan, which areas would show the most activity?** *(The areas that absorbed the most colored water.)* **Which areas would show the least?** *(The areas that absorbed the least.)*

Expected Outcome Students will gain a better understanding of how PET images are formed.
Logical, Kinesthetic

Going Further

Doctors can diagnose certain types of cancer by using radioactive tracers, or radioisotopes that are injected into a patient. The nuclear radiation emitted by the radioactive tracer is detected by imaging equipment such as a PET scanner. For a radioactive tracer to be practical, it must be readily absorbed by the organ(s) that doctors wish to study, and it must have a short half-life so as to minimize the patient's exposure to nuclear radiation.
Verbal, Portfolio

 Video Field Trip

Nuclear Medicine

After students have viewed the Video Field Trip, ask them the following questions: **What is nuclear medicine?** *(The use of small amounts of radioactive materials that enable a physician to look inside the body and to treat diseases such as some forms of cancer.)* **What did Marie and Pierre Curie discover?** *(Student answers may include: They discovered radium and polonium.)* **What did**

Irene Curie discover? *(She discovered artificial radioactivity by determining that aluminum remained radioactive after being bombarded with radioactive particles.)* **If radioactive substances are used today to treat certain types of cancer, how was it possible for Marie Curie and Irene Curie to develop a form of cancer by working with radioactive substances?** *(When treating certain types of cancer, only small dosages of radioactivity are used. However, when Marie and Irene Curie did their research, they were in contact with large amounts of radioactive substances for prolonged periods of time.)*

① FOCUS

Objectives

10.4.1 Compare and **contrast** nuclear forces.

10.4.2 Describe the process of nuclear fission.

10.4.3 Explain how nuclear reactors are used to produce energy.

10.4.4 Describe the process of nuclear fusion.

Reading Focus

Build Vocabulary   L2

Word-Part Analysis Remind students that they can use what they know about word parts to figure out the meanings of words. Point out *fission* and *fusion*. Tell students that *-ion* means "the act of" or "the result of an act." Explain that *fiss-* comes from a Latin word meaning "split" and that *fus-* comes from another Latin word meaning "melted."

Reading Strategy   L2

a. Is the splitting of a large nucleus into two smaller fragments **b.** Widely used as an energy source **c.** Is the fusing of two small nuclei into one larger nucleus **d.** Still being researched and developed as an alternate energy source

② INSTRUCT

Nuclear Forces

Use Visuals   L2

Figure 15 Have students carefully examine the illustration. Ask, **Why are there no electric forces between protons and neutrons?** *(Neutrons have no charge.)* **What force is able to overcome the electrostatic forces of repulsion that exist between protons in a nucleus?** *(The strong nuclear force)* **Visual, Logical**

10.4 Fission and Fusion

Standards: ICP.7.3, ICP.7.4, ICP.7.5, ICP.7.6, ICP.7.7, ICP.7.8

Reading Focus

Key Concepts

- Under what conditions does the strong nuclear force overcome electric forces in the nucleus?
- What property of fission makes it so useful?

Vocabulary

- ◆ strong nuclear force
- ◆ fission
- ◆ chain reaction
- ◆ critical mass
- ◆ fusion
- ◆ plasma

Reading Strategy

Comparing and Contrasting Copy the Venn diagram below. As you read, contrast fission and fusion by listing the ways they differ.

Fission   Fusion

a. _?_   releases large amounts of energy   c. _?_

b. _?_   d. _?_

Strong Nuclear Forces

Neutron
Neutron
Proton
Proton

Electric Forces

Neutron
Neutron
Proton
Proton

Figure 15 Two kinds of forces act upon particles in the nucleus. Strong nuclear forces, which are attractive, act on protons and neutrons alike. Electric forces in the nucleus are repulsive, and act only among protons. **Using Models** *What atomic nucleus is represented above?*

Alternative energy sources may someday replace fossil fuels such as coal and oil. One alternative energy source that is widely used today is nuclear energy. Nuclear energy is the energy released by nuclear reactions.

Shortly after the discovery of radioactivity, scientists realized that atomic nuclei contained vast amounts of energy. By the late 1930s, scientists discovered that transmutations involved more than just the conversion of one element into another—they also involved the conversion of mass into energy.

Nuclear Forces

What holds the nucleus together? Remember that the protons in the nucleus are all positively charged, so they tend to repel one another. Clearly, there must be an attractive force that binds the particles of the nucleus. Otherwise, the protons would simply push one another away.

The **strong nuclear force** is the attractive force that binds protons and neutrons together in the nucleus. Because the strong nuclear force does not depend on charge, it acts among protons, among neutrons, and among protons and neutrons. **Over very short distances, the strong nuclear force is much greater than the electric forces among protons.** For example, at distances as short as the width of a proton, the strong nuclear force is more than 100 times greater than the electric force that repels protons. However, the strong nuclear force quickly weakens as protons and neutrons get farther apart. Figure 15 summarizes the forces acting on protons and neutrons in the nucleus.

Section Resources

Print
- **Reading and Study Workbook With Math Support**, Section 10.4
- **Transparencies**, Section 10.4

Technology
- **Interactive Textbook**, Section 10.4
- **Presentation Pro CD-ROM**, Section 10.4
- **Go Online**, NSTA SciLinks, Fission

Strong nuclear forces

Electric force

Strong nuclear forces

Electric forces

The Effect of Size on Nuclear Forces

Electric forces in atomic nuclei depend on the number of protons. The greater the number of protons in a nucleus, the greater is the electric force that repels those protons. So in larger nuclei, the repulsive electric force is stronger than in smaller nuclei.

The effect of size on the strong nuclear force is more complicated. On one hand, the more protons and neutrons there are in a nucleus, the more possibilities there are for strong nuclear force attractions. However, as the size of the nucleus increases, the average distance between protons and neutrons increases. Because the strong nuclear force only acts over short ranges, the possibility of many attractions is never realized in a large nucleus. As a result, the strong nuclear force felt by one proton or neutron in a large nucleus is about the same as in a small nucleus, as shown in Figure 16.

Unstable Nuclei

A nucleus becomes unstable, or radioactive, when the strong nuclear force can no longer overcome the repulsive electric forces among protons. While the strong nuclear force does not increase with the size of the nucleus, the electric forces do. There is, therefore, a point beyond which all elements are radioactive. All nuclei with more than 83 protons are radioactive.

Fission

In 1938, two German chemists, Otto Hahn and Fritz Strassman, performed a series of important transmutation experiments. By bombarding uranium-235 with high-energy neutrons, Hahn and Strassman hoped to produce more massive elements. Instead, their experiments produced isotopes of a smaller element, barium. Unable to explain their data, Hahn and Strassman turned to a colleague for help. In 1939, Lise Meitner, shown in Figure 17, and Otto Frisch, another physicist, offered a groundbreaking explanation for the experiments. The uranium-235 nuclei had been broken into smaller fragments. Hahn and Strassman had demonstrated nuclear fission. **Fission** is the splitting of an atomic nucleus into two smaller parts.

Figure 16 The size of a nucleus affects how strongly it is bound together. **A** In a nucleus containing two protons and two neutrons, the strong nuclear forces easily overcome the electric force between the protons. **B** In a nucleus containing many protons and neutrons, the larger number of electric forces makes the nucleus less stable.

Figure 17 Austrian physicist Lise Meitner (1878–1968), shown here, and Otto Frisch were the first scientists to describe nuclear fission. Meitner correctly predicted that fission releases large amounts of energy.

Fission
Build Reading Literacy L1

Sequence Refer to page **290D** in this chapter, which provides guidelines for using a sequence.

Have students read the text on nuclear fission on pp. 309 and 310. Then, have students do the following:
1. Ask students to make a sketch similar to Figure 18. Tell students that they can use circles to represent the nuclei. Students should use larger circles to represent the uranium nuclei.
2. Have students label and describe what happens as a neutron strikes the uranium-235 nucleus and the steps that follow. Start with the neutron as Step 1. Each following step should be numbered in sequence.
3. Students' sketches should include as much detail as they find from the text, Figure 18, and the caption.
Visual, Portfolio

Integrate Language Arts L2

Tell students that scientists in several countries were instrumental to the understanding of nuclear fission. The English scientist James Chadwick discovered the neutron in 1932. In 1934, Italian scientists led by Enrico Fermi conducted experiments involving the slow-neutron bombardment of uranium. Fermi's results prompted German chemists Otto Hahn and Fritz Strassman, and Austrian physicist Lise Meitner, to further investigate the products formed when uranium is bombarded with neutrons. Meitner and Otto Frisch built on the results of this research and in 1939 described the fission process. Have students write a brief biography of one of the scientists who contributed to the understanding of nuclear fission.
Verbal

Customize for English Language Learners

Cloze Reading
Select and copy an appropriate paragraph from one of the sections, such as the second paragraph on p. 309. Leave the first and last sentences intact, since they are usually the introductory and concluding sentences. For the sentences in the middle, remove key vocabulary words and replace them with a blank. For example, leave blanks for *protons* and *neutrons* in the second sentence of this paragraph, for *proton* in the third sentence, and for *short* in the fourth sentence. Have students read the paragraph and fill in the blanks with the appropriate words. You may create a word bank for students to use when filling in the blanks.

Answer to . . .
Figure 15 *A helium nucleus*

Use Visuals **L1**

Figures 18 and 19 Ask students to look at both figures. Ask, **Why do you think the uranium-236 atom is missing in Figure 19?** *(Uranium-236 is very unstable and does not last long before it splits into two smaller nuclei.)* **What happens to the amount of energy released during a chain reaction?** *(The amount of energy released increases as the chain reaction proceeds.)* **Visual**

Build Math Skills **L1**

Formulas and Equations Ask students to examine the mass-energy equation and determine the units of measurement that *E* is equivalent to. Remind them that the SI units for mass and speed are, respectively, kg and m/s. *(Units of E are equivalent to kg × (m/s)².)* Also ask students to determine what the formula would be for calculating c. *(c = $\sqrt{E/m}$)* **Logical**

Direct students to the **Math Skills** in the **Skills and Reference Handbook** at the end of the student text for additional help.

Download a worksheet on fission for students to complete, and find additional teacher support from NSTA SciLinks.

Figure 18 The fission of uranium-235 yields smaller nuclei, neutrons, and energy. The nuclear equation for this reaction can be written as follows.

$$^{235}_{92}U + ^{1}_{0}n \rightarrow$$

$$^{91}_{36}Kr + ^{142}_{56}Ba + 3^{1}_{0}n + energy$$

Comparing and Contrasting *How does fission differ from nuclear decay?*

Neutron

Krypton-91
$^{91}_{36}Kr$

Energy

$^{235}_{92}U$
Uranium-235

$^{236}_{92}U$
Uranium-236
(very unstable)

$^{142}_{56}Ba$
Barium-142

For: Links on fission
Visit: www.SciLinks.org
Web Code: ccn-1104

Figure 18 illustrates the fission of a uranium-235 nucleus. Notice that one of the products of the reaction is energy. **In nuclear fission, tremendous amounts of energy can be produced from very small amounts of mass.** For example, the nuclear energy released by the fission of 1 kilogram of uranium-235 is equivalent to the chemical energy produced by burning more than 17,000 kilograms of coal.

Converting Mass Into Energy In the nuclear equation shown in Figure 18, the mass numbers on the left equal the mass numbers on the right. Yet when the fission of uranium-235 is carried out, about 0.1 percent of the mass of the reactants is lost during the reaction. This "lost" mass is converted into energy.

In 1905, more than 30 years before the discovery of fission, physicist Albert Einstein had introduced the mass-energy equation. It describes how mass and energy are related.

Mass–Energy Equation
$$E = mc^2$$

In the mass-energy equation, *E* represents energy, *m* represents mass, and *c* represents the speed of light (3.0×10^8 m/s). The conversion of a small amount of mass releases an enormous amount of energy. Likewise, a large amount of energy can be converted into a small amount of mass. The explosion of the first atomic bomb in 1945 offered a powerful demonstration of the mass-energy equation. The bomb contained 5 kilograms of plutonium-239. Fission of the plutonium produced an explosion that was equivalent to 18,600 tons of TNT.

Recall how the law of conservation of mass applied to chemical reactions. In nuclear reactions, however, the energies involved are much larger. To account for the conversion of mass into energy, a modified conservation law is used. According to the law of conservation of mass and energy, the total amount of mass and energy remains constant.

Figure 19 The fission of one nucleus can trigger a chain reaction. The splitting of a uranium-235 nucleus by a neutron yields two or three neutrons, each of which can cause another fission. *Interpreting Diagrams* **Does the fission of uranium-235 always yield the same isotopes as products? Explain.**

The figure shows nuclear fission chain reactions with the following labeled particles: $^{1}_{0}n$, $^{235}_{92}U$, $^{91}_{36}Kr$, $^{93}_{36}Kr$, $^{140}_{56}Ba$, $^{142}_{56}Ba$, $^{94}_{38}Sr$, $^{140}_{54}Xe$, $^{90}_{37}Rb$, $^{144}_{55}Cs$, $^{101}_{42}Mo$, $^{132}_{50}Sn$.

Triggering a Chain Reaction

How fast does a rumor spread? Imagine that you started a rumor by telling it to three of your friends. Then suppose each of those friends told three more friends. If this pattern continued, the rumor would quickly spread to hundreds of people, even though it originally started with just one person, you.

Nuclear fission can follow a similar pattern, in which one reaction leads to a series of others. During the fission of uranium-235, each reactant nucleus splits into two smaller nuclei and releases two or three neutrons. If one of these neutrons is absorbed by another uranium-235 nucleus, another fission can result, releasing more neutrons, as shown in Figure 19. In a **chain reaction,** neutrons released during the splitting of an initial nucleus trigger a series of nuclear fissions.

The speed of a chain reaction can vary. In an uncontrolled chain reaction, all of the released neutrons are free to cause other fissions, resulting in a fast, intense release of energy. Nuclear weapons are designed to produce uncontrolled chain reactions. In a controlled chain reaction, some of the neutrons are absorbed by nonfissionable materials, resulting in only one new fission for each splitting of an atom. The heat from controlled chain reactions can be used to generate electrical energy. Unfortunately, another product of controlled chain reactions is radioactive waste, shown in Figure 20.

In order to sustain a chain reaction, each nucleus that is split must produce, on average, one neutron that causes the fission of another nucleus. This condition corresponds to a specific mass of fissionable material, known as a critical mass. A **critical mass** is the smallest possible mass of a fissionable material that can sustain a chain reaction.

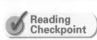 Reading Checkpoint   *What is a chain reaction?*

Figure 20 A crane lowers drums of radioactive waste into a landfill in Hanford, Washington.

Nuclear Chemistry **311**

DK SCIENCE and History

Nuclear Chemistry L2

Enrico Fermi and his research group achieved the first controlled nuclear chain reaction while the United States was fighting World War II. This was the first nuclear reactor. While this reactor was used for research, the main purpose of the reactor was to make plutonium for the atom bomb. After World War II, the U.S. population rose, and the growing population increased the demand for electricity. Scientists saw the potential of nuclear energy to help meet this demand. In 1951, electricity was produced using atomic power for the first time at a reactor in Idaho. The reactor produced enough electricity to light four light bulbs. Today, more than 400 nuclear power plants operate worldwide, with over 100 operating in the United States.

Have students research nuclear power plant safety and write a one-paragraph opinion about whether the benefits of nuclear power generation are worth the risks.
Verbal, Portfolio

Writing in Science

Possible answer: A number of groundbreaking scientific discoveries within the last 100 years have set the stage for nuclear energy. In 1905 (less than ten years after the discovery of radioactivity), Albert Einstein introduced his mass-energy equation, which described how very small amounts of mass could be converted into enormous amounts of energy. In 1938, Otto Hahn and Fritz Strassman performed the first nuclear fission (of uranium). A self-sustaining nuclear chain reaction was achieved just four years later. By 1951, scientists had developed nuclear fission into a promising source of electrical energy.
Verbal

Nuclear Energy from Fission Today, nuclear power plants generate about 20 percent of the electricity in the United States. In a nuclear power plant, controlled fission of uranium-235 occurs in a vessel called a fission reactor.

Unlike power plants that burn fossil fuels, nuclear power plants do not emit air pollutants such as oxides of sulfur and nitrogen. However, nuclear power plants have their own safety and environmental issues. For example, workers in nuclear power plants need to wear protective clothing to reduce their exposure to nuclear radiation. In addition, the fission of uranium-235 produces many radioactive isotopes with half-lives of hundreds or thousands of years. This radioactive waste must be

DK SCIENCE and History

Nuclear Chemistry

Over the last 100 years scientists have uncovered many secrets about the atomic nucleus. Developments have ranged from the synthesis of new elements to the harnessing of nuclear power as a viable energy source.

MARIE AND PIERRE CURIE AT WORK IN THEIR LABORATORY

EQUIPMENT USED BY HAHN AND STRASSMANN

HENRI BECQUEREL

1896 French scientist Antoine Henri Becquerel discovers radioactivity in uranium.

1898 Marie and Pierre Curie discover the radioactive elements radium and polonium. By making radium available to other scientists, the Curies helped advance the study of radioactivity.

1905 Albert Einstein's mass-energy equation, $E = mc^2$, provides the basis for nuclear power.

1932 First atom smasher (subatomic particle accelerator) is used by John Cockcroft and Ernest Walton.

1938 Germans Otto Hahn and Fritz Strassmann produce nuclear fission by bombarding uranium-235 atoms with neutrons.

1890   1910   1930

312 *Chapter 10*

isolated and stored so that it cannot harm people or contaminate the environment while it decays.

Another concern about nuclear power is that the operators of the plant could lose control of the reactor. For instance, if the reactor's cooling system failed, then a meltdown might occur. During a meltdown, the core of the reactor melts and radioactive material may be released. If the structure that houses the reactor is not secure, then the environment can become contaminated. In 1986, one of the reactors at the nuclear power station in Chernobyl, Ukraine, overheated during an experiment. A partial meltdown resulted, and large amounts of radioactive material were released into the atmosphere.

Summary Write a paragraph about the history of nuclear energy based on some of the events in the time line below. (*Hint:* Before you write, use a flowchart to organize the events you wish to include.)

Use Community Resources L2

Ask students to find out what percentage of the power in their state comes from nuclear power plants. Encourage them to use library resources, such as the Internet, to find statistics. If your state does not receive power from nuclear power plants, instruct students to find that information for another state. Ask students to make a diagram and write a brief summary of their findings.
Interpersonal, Portfolio

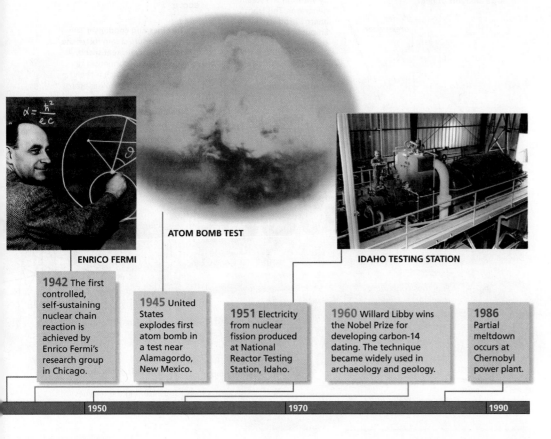

ENRICO FERMI

ATOM BOMB TEST

IDAHO TESTING STATION

1942 The first controlled, self-sustaining nuclear chain reaction is achieved by Enrico Fermi's research group in Chicago.

1945 United States explodes first atom bomb in a test near Alamagordo, New Mexico.

1951 Electricity from nuclear fission produced at National Reactor Testing Station, Idaho.

1960 Willard Libby wins the Nobel Prize for developing carbon-14 dating. The technique became widely used in archaeology and geology.

1986 Partial meltdown occurs at Chernobyl power plant.

1950　　　　　　　1970　　　　　　　1990

Nuclear Chemistry **313**

Nuclear Power Station L2

Background

Uranium-235, the fissionable material used in nuclear power plants, makes up only about 0.7% of all uranium found in nature. In order for a nuclear reactor to operate, about 3% of the uranium in the fuel rods must be uranium-235. Samples of uranium must be enriched so that they contain this higher percentage of uranium-235.

A bundle of fuel rods contains slightly more than the critical mass of uranium-235. Control rods are placed in the bundle in order to control when and how quickly the process of fission occurs.

Interpreting Diagrams In a nuclear power station, water is used to transfer the energy generated in the reactor core. Heat released in the core is absorbed by water in the steam generator. The steam produced is used to drive a turbine; the kinetic energy of the turbine is then converted into electrical energy. Water is also used as a coolant to condense the steam exiting the turbine. The steam condenses into liquid water and is piped back to the steam generator.
Visual

For Enrichment L3

The U.S. Navy uses nuclear reactors to power many different types of ships, ranging from submarines to aircraft carriers. Nuclear power is useful on ships that are at sea for long periods of time because the ships do not have to carry large quantities of fuel or refuel while they are on a mission. Ask students to research how nuclear reactors in ships differ from those in nuclear power stations.
Verbal

HOW It Works

Nuclear Power Station

Since the first nuclear bomb was exploded in 1945, scientists have found ways of utilizing the enormous power of nuclear fission for peaceful purposes. Nuclear power is now a major means of producing electricity. About 20 percent of electricity in the United States is generated this way. Interpreting Diagrams
How is water used in a nuclear power station?

A Reactor core Fission reactions take place in the reactor core, releasing large amounts of heat.

B Steam generator Heat released in the reactor core is absorbed by water in the steam generator. This transfer of energy produces large amounts of high-pressure steam.

Water pressurizer

High-strength protective shielding

Control rods

High-pressure turbine

Pump

Fuel rods containing uranium dioxide

Water

Cooling water exits.

Cooling water enters.

Filter

Pump

Steam condenses.

Condenser

Fission control
The fission reaction within the reactor core is controlled by neutron-absorbing control rods. Because they are still radioactive, the used rods are removed from the reactor core and stored in a pool, as shown above.

C Turbines and condenser The high-pressure steam forces the turbine to rotate at great speed. As it cools, the steam condenses to form liquid water, which is then piped back to the steam generator.

D Electric generator Here the work done by the force turning the turbines produces electrical energy.

Fusion

Another type of nuclear reaction that can release huge amounts of energy is fusion. **Fusion** is a process in which the nuclei of two atoms combine to form a larger nucleus. As in fission, during fusion, a small fraction of the reactant mass is converted into energy.

On any day or night, you can detect the energy released by fusion reactions occurring far away from Earth. The sun and other stars are powered by the fusion of hydrogen into helium. Inside the sun, an estimated 600 million tons of hydrogen undergo fusion each second. About 4 million tons of this matter is converted into energy.

Matter within the sun and other stars exists as plasma. **Plasma** is a state of matter in which atoms have been stripped of their electrons. You can think of plasma as a gas containing two kinds of particles—nuclei and electrons. Although fusion occurs at millions of degrees Celsius, plasma can exist at much lower temperatures. Scientists estimate that more than 99 percent of matter in the universe is plasma.

Fusion may someday provide an efficient and clean source of electricity. Scientists envision fusion reactors fueled by two hydrogen isotopes, deuterium (hydrogen-2) and tritium (hydrogen-3). The fusion of deuterium and tritium produces helium, neutrons, and energy.

$$^{2}_{1}H + ^{3}_{1}H \rightarrow ^{4}_{2}He + ^{1}_{0}n + \text{energy}$$

Scientists face two main problems in designing a fusion reactor. They need to achieve the high temperatures required to start the reaction, and they must contain the plasma.

Figure 21 The Tokamak Fusion Test Reactor at the Princeton Plasma Physics Laboratory in Princeton, New Jersey, was one of the very few fusion reactors that have been built. It was retired in 1997, after 15 years of experimentation.

Section 10.4 Assessment

Reviewing Concepts

1. 🔵 Under what conditions does the strong nuclear force overcome the repulsive effect of electric forces in the nucleus?

2. 🔵 What property of fission makes it a useful reaction?

3. What particles are affected by strong nuclear forces?

4. What must happen in order for a nuclear chain reaction to occur?

5. Why is a cooling system necessary in a nuclear reactor?

6. How do the products of a fusion reaction differ from the products of a fission reaction?

Critical Thinking

7. **Inferring** How does the strong nuclear force affect an atom's electrons? (*Hint:* Think about where the electrons are located in the atom.)

8. **Inferring** Why do fission chain reactions of uranium-235 not occur in underground uranium deposits?

Connecting C Concepts

Fossil Fuels Reread the description of fossil fuels in Section 9.1. Then compare fossil fuel combustion with nuclear fission.

Section 10.4 Assessment

1. Over very short distances, strong nuclear forces are much greater than the electric forces in the nucleus.

2. Tremendous amounts of energy can be produced from very small amounts of mass.

3. Strong nuclear forces act among protons, among neutrons, and among protons and neutrons.

4. Each nucleus that splits must on average produce at least one neutron that results in the fission of another nucleus.

5. A cooling system is necessary in a nuclear reactor to prevent the reactor core from overheating.

6. The products of fusion are less massive nuclei such as helium. The products of fission are more massive nuclei, such as barium or krypton.

7. The strong nuclear force has no effect on an atom's electrons because it acts only over very short distances within the nucleus.

8. Natural deposits of uranium-235 generally do not occur in amounts great enough to reach a critical mass.

Address Misconceptions L2

Students may think that the sun is actually burning because it gives off light and heat. Explain that the light and heat given off by the sun result from nuclear fusion, not combustion. **Verbal**

Build Science Skills L2

Observing Tell students that the sun produces energy by nuclear fusion. Explain that fusion releases very large amounts of energy. Ask, **How do you know that the sun produces large amounts of energy?** (*Students may come up with examples such as, heat, bright sunlight, sunburn, and so on.*) **Logical**

3 ASSESS

Evaluate Understanding L2

Have students write down three characteristics of nuclear fission and fusion. Have students take turns giving a characteristic while the other students identify whether it is typical of fission or fusion.

Reteach L1

Use Figures 18 and 19 to summarize controlled and uncontrolled fission reactions.

Connecting C Concepts

Possible answer: Both fossil fuel combustion and nuclear fission produce heat, which can be used to generate electricity. Fossil fuel combustion is a chemical reaction, the products of which include carbon dioxide, water, carbon monoxide, nitrogen oxides, and soot. Air pollution is one of the main drawbacks of fossil fuel combustion as an energy source. Fission is a nuclear reaction whose products include lighter nuclei and neutrons. Radioactive waste is one of the main drawbacks of fission as an energy source.

Interactive Textbook If your class subscribes to the Interactive Textbook, use it to review key concepts in Section 10.4.

Exploration Lab

Modeling a Chain Reaction

 Exploration Lab

Modeling a Chain Reaction

Modeling a Chain Reaction L2

Objective

After completing this activity, students will be able to

- describe how a nuclear chain reaction occurs
- list some of the factors that affect the rate of nuclear chain reactions.

Skills Focus Observing, Using Models

Prep Time 5 minutes

Class Time 45 minutes

Teaching Tips

- If students have difficulty arranging the dominoes correctly, perform this lab as a demonstration or provide diagrams of the positions of the bases of the dominoes. Students can then place the dominoes directly on the diagram.

Expected Outcome Rearranging the dominoes from a single line to a fan shape in Steps 3 and 4 increased the speed with which they fell. Inserting a metric ruler in Step 5 and adding supporting dominoes in Step 6 prevented some of the dominoes from falling.

In a nuclear fission chain reaction, a nucleus is struck by a neutron, which causes the nucleus to split into two smaller nuclei and to release other neutrons. If these neutrons strike other nuclei, a chain reaction can occur. In this lab, you will model a nuclear fission chain reaction using dominoes.

Problem
How can you make a model of a nuclear fission chain reaction?

Materials
- 20 dominoes
- watch with a second hand, or stopwatch
- metric ruler

Skills Observing, Using Models

Procedure

1. Stand 15 dominoes in a single straight row in such a way that the distance between them is about one half of their height. Knock over the first domino. Measure and record the time it takes for all the dominoes to fall.

2. Repeat Step 1 two more times. Then, average the three time measurements to get a more accurate time.

3. Arrange 15 dominoes as shown below so that each domino will knock over two others. Observe what happens when you knock over the first domino. Measure and record how long it takes for the whole set of dominoes to fall over.

4. Repeat Step 3 two more times. Average the three time measurements to get a more accurate time.

5. Set up 15 dominoes again as you did in Step 3. This time, however, hold a metric ruler on end, in the middle of the arrangement of dominoes, as shown in the photograph on the next page. Knock over the first domino. Observe what happens.

6. Set up 15 dominoes as you did in Step 3, but this time, place 5 additional dominoes behind and at right angles to 5 randomly chosen dominoes for support, as shown below. The 5 supported dominoes represent atoms of a different isotope that must be struck with more energy to undergo fission.

7. Knock over the first domino. Measure and record the time it takes for the dominoes to fall and how many dominoes fall.

8. Repeat Steps 6 and 7 two more times. Then, average the three time measurements to get a more accurate time.

9. Repeat Steps 6 through 8, but this time, place supporting dominoes behind only 3 dominoes.

10. Repeat Steps 6 through 8, but this time, place a supporting domino behind only 1 domino.

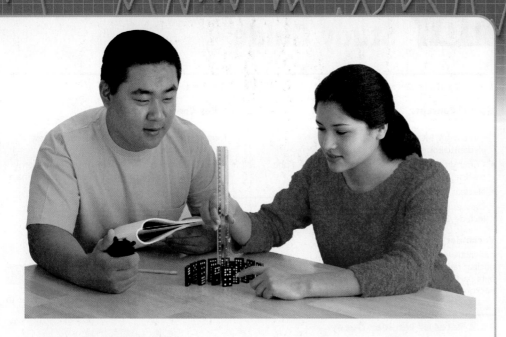

Analyze and Conclude

1. **Calculating** What was the average fall time for the arrangement of dominoes in Steps 1 and 2? In Steps 3 and 4?

2. **Applying Concepts** What type of reaction was modeled in Steps 3 and 4?

3. **Using Models** In your falling-dominoes model of nuclear fission chain reactions, what did a standing domino represent? What did the fall of a domino represent?

4. **Using Models** In your falling-dominoes model of nuclear fission chain reactions, what did the striking of one domino by another represent? What did the metric ruler represent?

5. **Analyzing Data** Before a sample of an easily fissionable isotope is used, it is refined by removing less fissionable isotopes of the same element. On the basis of your observations in Steps 6 through 10, explain why this refinement is necessary.

6. **Inferring** What factors do you think would affect the rate of a nuclear fission chain reaction?

7. **Drawing Conclusions** What do you think would happen to a nuclear fission chain reaction if control rods were not present?

8. **Evaluating and Revising** What are some of the limitations of using falling dominoes to model a nuclear fission chain reaction? Suggest how you might revise this model to make it more representative of a chain reaction.

Go Further Visit the library and find out about the Manhattan Project and how it made history. Use what you have learned from the falling-dominoes model to help you understand the scientific discoveries related to controlled and uncontrolled nuclear chain reactions.

Analyze and Conclude

1. The time should be shorter in Steps 3 and 4.

2. A nuclear chain reaction was modeled in Steps 3 and 4.

3. A standing domino represented the nucleus of an atom. The fall of a domino represented the fission of the nucleus and the release of neutrons.

4. The striking of one domino by another represented the striking of a nucleus of a nearby atom by a neutron. The ruler represented a control rod.

5. Atoms of the less-easily fissionable isotopes can interfere with the development of a chain reaction.

6. The number of neutrons released during fission and the number of other atoms that are nearby and available for the released neutrons to strike affect the rate of the reaction.

7. The reaction would go out of control, perhaps leading to a meltdown or explosion.

8. One limitation of the domino model is that it treats each fission reaction as the same; according to the model, each fission reaction (represented by a single falling domino) leads to exactly two more fissions. In reality, the fission of one nucleus can produce more than two neutrons, each of which may trigger another fission reaction. One way that the model could be revised is to use dominoes of varying sizes and/or colors. The arrangement of dominoes could be modified so that the falling of a larger-sized domino caused more than two smaller-sized dominos to fall. Alternatively, different colored dominoes could be used to represent the differing numbers of neutrons released by each fission reaction (as well as the different product isotopes formed).
Visual, Logical

Go Further

Initiated by the U.S. government during World War II, the Manhattan Project was a large-scale research project that succeeded in developing the first atomic bomb. In their research, students may relate their knowledge of fission chain reactions to Enrico Fermi's experiments with the first nuclear reactor at the University of Chicago in 1942, as well as earlier breakthroughs in nuclear chemistry made by Lise Meitner and Fritz Strassman.
Verbal

Study Guide

Study Tip

Organize New Information
Tell students that learning detail-oriented information is easier when using strategies such as making outlines of a section, making charts of details, making graphic organizers, and making flashcards. Tell students that by using these techniques and reviewing them daily, they can avoid "cramming" for a test.

Thinking Visually

a. Nuclear reactions
b. Fusion
c. Beta particles
d. Gamma rays

Assessment

 If your class subscribes to the Interactive Textbook, your students can go online to access an interactive version of the Student Edition and a self-test.

Reviewing Content

1. b   2. d   3. c
4. d   5. d   6. d
7. b   8. a   9. b
10. a

10.1 Radioactivity

Key Concepts
- During nuclear decay, atoms of one element can change into atoms of a different element altogether.
- Common types of nuclear radiation include alpha particles, beta particles, and gamma rays.
- Nuclear radiation can ionize atoms.
- Devices that are used to detect nuclear radiation include Geiger counters and film badges.

Vocabulary
radioactivity, p. 292; radioisotope, p. 292; nuclear radiation, p. 293; alpha particle, p. 293; beta particle, p. 294; gamma ray, p. 294; background radiation, p. 296

10.2 Rates of Nuclear Decay

Key Concepts
- Unlike chemical reaction rates, which vary with the conditions of a reaction, nuclear decay rates are constant.
- In radiocarbon dating, the age of an object is determined by comparing the object's carbon-14 levels with carbon-14 levels in the atmosphere.

Vocabulary
half-life, p. 299

10.3 Artificial Transmutation

Key Concepts
- Scientists can perform artificial transmutations by bombarding atomic nuclei with high-energy particles such as protons, neutrons, or alpha particles.
- Scientists can synthesize a transuranium element by the artificial transmutation of a lighter element.

Vocabulary
transmutation, p. 303; transuranium elements, p. 304; quark, p. 305

10.4 Fission and Fusion

Key Concepts
- Over very short distances, the strong nuclear force is much greater than the electric forces among protons.
- In nuclear fission, tremendous amounts of energy can be produced from very small amounts of mass.

Vocabulary
strong nuclear force, p. 308; fission, p. 309; chain reaction, p. 311; critical mass, p. 311; fusion, p. 315; plasma, p. 315

Thinking Visually

Concept Map Use information from the chapter to complete the concept map below.

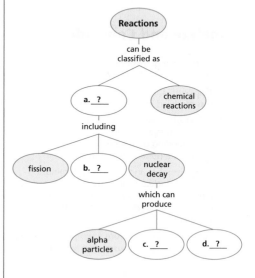

Chapter Resources

Print
- ***Chapter and Unit Tests**, Chapter 10 Test A and Test B
- ***Test Prep Resources**, Chapter 10

Technology
- ***Computer Test Bank**, Chapter Test 10
- ***Interactive Textbook**, Chapter 10
- ***Go Online**, PHSchool.com, Chapter 10

Reviewing Content

Choose the letter that best answers the questions or completes the statement.

1. An alpha particle is identical to
   a. a neutron.   b. a helium nucleus.
   c. an electron.   d. a hydrogen nucleus.

2. When a beta particle is emitted, the mass number of a nucleus
   a. increases by one.   b. decreases by one.
   c. decreases by four. d. remains the same.

3. The most penetrating form of nuclear radiation is
   a. an alpha particle. b. a beta particle.
   c. a gamma ray.   d. an electron.

4. The half-life of cobalt-60 is 5.3 years. What fraction of a sample remains after 21.2 years?
   a. one half   b. one quarter
   c. one eighth   d. one sixteenth

5. Which of the following is a radioisotope commonly used in dating archeological artifacts?
   a. nitrogen-14   b. carbon-12
   c. uranium-235   d. carbon-14

6. Transmutation does not occur in which of these nuclear processes?
   a. nuclear fission   b. nuclear fusion
   c. alpha decay   d. gamma decay

7. Based on its location on the periodic table, an element that is not naturally occurring is
   a. terbium (Tb).   b. curium (Cm).
   c. holmium (Ho).   d. lutetium (Lu).

8. Nuclear particles are held together by
   a. the strong nuclear force.
   b. electrical attraction.
   c. quarks.
   d. electrical repulsion.

9. Nuclear power plants generate electricity from
   a. nuclear fusion.   b. nuclear fission.
   c. combustion.   d. radioactivity.

10. The primary reaction inside stars changes
    a. hydrogen to helium.
    b. helium to hydrogen.
    c. uranium to plutonium.
    d. nitrogen to carbon.

Understanding Concepts

11. How do radioisotopes of an element differ from other isotopes?

12. What is the effect on the mass number and charge of a nucleus when it loses an alpha particle?

13. How do the mass number and charge of a nucleus change when it emits a gamma ray?

14. Which type of radiation—alpha, beta, or gamma—is most dangerous to living things? Explain.

15. Why does a Geiger counter occasionally click even if no artificial radioisotopes are nearby?

16. How does raising the temperature affect the rate of nuclear decay?

17. Why can't carbon-14 be used to determine the age of fossils that are several hundred thousand years old?

18. Write the equation for the transmutation that occurs when an alpha particle combines with a nitrogen-14 atom, emitting a proton.

19. Compare and contrast the processes of fission and fusion.

20. What is necessary to sustain a nuclear chain reaction?

21. Why do nuclear reactions produce more energy per mass of matter than chemical reactions?

22. The diagram below shows a nuclear reactor, including control rods. What is the function of a control rod in a nuclear power plant?

Control rods

Fuel rods

Reactor

Coolant

Nuclear Chemisty **319**

Assessment (continued)

Understanding Concepts

11. Unlike stable isotopes, radioisotopes decay spontaneously by emitting nuclear radiation.

12. The mass number decreases by four; the charge decreases by two.

13. The mass number and charge are unchanged.

14. Gamma rays are more dangerous than alpha particles or beta particles because they can penetrate deep inside the body. However, if alpha particles are inhaled or ingested, they can also be dangerous.

15. The Geiger counter is detecting background radiation.

16. Temperature has no effect on rates of nuclear decay.

17. The amount of carbon-14 remaining after 50,000 years is too low to be easily measured.

18. $^{14}_{7}N + ^{4}_{2}He \longrightarrow ^{17}_{8}O + ^{1}_{1}H$

19. Fission and fusion are both nuclear reactions that convert small amounts of matter into large amounts of energy. In fission, a large nucleus is split into two smaller fragments. In fusion, two light nuclei are fused into a larger nucleus. Unlike nuclear fission, which is used widely as a source of electrical energy, nuclear fusion has yet to be developed into a reliable alternate energy source.

20. In order to sustain a nuclear chain reaction, each fission reaction must on average produce a neutron that subsequently causes another fission.

21. During nuclear reactions, a small amount of matter is converted into a large amount of energy. During chemical reactions, matter is not converted into energy.

22. Control rods regulate the nuclear chain reaction by absorbing neutrons produced by fission reactions that take place in the reactor.

Homework Guide

Section	Questions
10.1	1–3, 11–17, 24–26, 31, 33
10.2	4–5, 27–30
10.3	6–7, 18, 23
10.4	8–10, 19–22, 32

Critical Thinking

23. U-238 to Th-234, alpha; Th-234 to Pa-234, beta and gamma; Pa-234 to U-234, beta and gamma; U-234 to Th-230, alpha; Th-230 to Ra-226, alpha and gamma; Ra-226 to Rn-222, alpha and gamma.

24. Polonium undergoes alpha decay. Bismuth and lead undergo either beta decay or beta decay and gamma decay.

25. Beta radiation or gamma radiation. The plastic or paper wrapped around the film blocks exposure to alpha radiation.

26. Curium-242

Math Skills

27. 12.3 years
28. 22.1 grams
29. 11,460 years (equivalent to two half-lives of carbon-14)

Concepts in Action

30. Radioisotopes used as radioactive tracers have short enough half-lives so as to limit the patient's exposure to nuclear radiation, but long enough half-lives to permit the diagnostic test.

31. Because radon-222 is a gas, it can be ingested by breathing and cause internal radiation exposure. Americium-241 is a solid that cannot be ingested by breathing.

32. Fusion releases more energy than fission, uses a more available fuel source (hydrogen), and does not produce radioactive wastes.

33. Radon is a naturally occurring radioactive gas produced by the nuclear decay of uranium found in rocks and soil. Because it is a gas, radon can seep into a building through cracks and pinholes in the building's foundation. If the basement of the building is not ventilated properly, the radon can continue to accumulate, increasing the risk of radiation exposure.

Your students can independently test their knowledge of the chapter and print out their test results for your files.

Critical Thinking

Use the figure below to answer Questions 23 and 24.

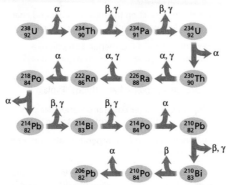

Stable isotope

23. Classifying In the illustrated uranium-238 decay sequence, classify the type of radiation released in each of the transmutations from uranium-238 to radon-222.

24. Making Generalizations Study the sequence of decay from radon-222 to lead-206. Make a generalization as to what type of decay lead, polonium, and bismuth undergo until stable lead-206 is formed.

25. Inferring A film badge consists of a piece of film wrapped in a piece of dark plastic or paper. Doses of what kinds of radiation can be measured with this simple piece of equipment? Explain.

26. Calculating The first sample of californium was made by bombarding a target isotope with alpha particles. In addition to californium-245, the reaction produced a neutron. What was the target isotope?

Math Skills

27. Calculating After 36.9 years, a sample of hydrogen-3 contains one eighth of the amount it contained originally. What is the half-life of the isotope?

28. Calculating The half-life of iron-59 is 44.5 days. After 133.5 days, 2.76 g of iron-59 remains. What was the mass of the original sample?

29. Inferring The beta emissions from a bone that was found buried in a cave indicate that there are 4.6 carbon-14 decays per gram of carbon per minute. A chicken bone from a fast-food restaurant shows 18.4 emissions per gram of carbon per minute. How old is the bone from the cave?

Concepts in Action

30. Inferring Radioisotopes are commonly used in medical tests to diagnose diseases. Do the radioisotopes used for this purpose have long half-lives or short half-lives? Explain.

31. Applying Concepts Americium-241 and radon-222 both emit alpha particles. Americium is found in almost every home as a component of smoke detectors. But radon is considered a health hazard. Why is radon more hazardous?

32. Making Judgments If a fusion power plant could be constructed, why might it be a better source of energy than a fission plant?

33. Writing in Science Write a paragraph explaining how radon gas can collect in buildings. (*Hint:* The first sentence in your paragraph should state the paragraph's main idea.)

Performance-Based Assessment

Evaluating Many transuranium elements were named for the scientists who synthesized them or the location in which they were produced. Choose such a transuranium element, find out how it was created, and evaluate its importance. Write a pamphlet informing your classmates about the element you chose.

Go Online
PHSchool.com

For: Self-grading assessment
Visit: PHSchool.com
Web Code: cca-1100

Performance-Based Assessment

Students will discover that elements with atomic numbers 96 and 99 onwards were named after the scientists who discovered them. Elements with the atomic numbers 95, 97, and 98 were named after the locations in which they were discovered.

Standardized Test Prep for Indiana

 Standards Guide

Question	Standards
3	ICP.7.7
6	ICP.7.6

Test-Taking Tip

Evaluating and Revising

Frequently, a scientifically accurate answer choice may not answer the question that is being asked. Keep these tips in mind:

- Verify what the question is asking.
- Determine if an answer choice is a true statement or not.
- Determine if a true answer choice actually answers the question.
- Be cautious with inserted or deleted words that make a false statement seem accurate.

Practice using these tips in Question 5.

Choose the letter that best answers the question or completes the statement.

1. Which equation correctly shows beta decay?
   (A) $^{210}_{82}Pb \rightarrow {}^{209}_{81}Tl + {}^{0}_{-1}e + \gamma$
   (B) $^{210}_{82}Pb \rightarrow {}^{209}_{83}Bi + {}^{0}_{-1}e + \gamma$
   (C) $^{210}_{82}Pb \rightarrow {}^{210}_{83}Tl + {}^{0}_{-1}e + \gamma$
   (D) $^{210}_{82}Pb \rightarrow {}^{210}_{83}Bi + \gamma$
   (E) $^{210}_{82}Pb \rightarrow {}^{210}_{83}Bi + {}^{0}_{-1}e + \gamma$

2. The half-life of radon-222 is 3.8 days. If a sample currently has 3.1 grams of radon-222, how much radon-222 did this sample have 15.2 days ago?
   (A) 12.4 grams   (B) 47.1 grams
   (C) 49.6 grams   (D) 57.8 grams
   (E) 92.7 grams

3. Radioactive decay of nuclei often involves several decays before a stable nucleus is formed. This is called a decay chain. What stable isotope is formed when radon-222 undergoes a decay chain of four alpha decays followed by four beta decays?
   (A) tungsten-206   (B) platinum-206
   (C) lead-206   (D) tungsten-214
   (E) lead-214

4. Which nucleus balances the following nuclear equation for the fission of uranium-235?
   $$^{235}_{92}U + {}^{1}_{0}n \rightarrow {}^{90}_{38}Sr + {}^{A}_{Z}X + 2{}^{1}_{0}n + \gamma$$
   (A) $^{146}_{54}Xe$ (B) $^{146}_{52}Te$
   (C) $^{144}_{52}Te$ (D) $^{144}_{54}Xe$
   (E) $^{142}_{50}Sn$

5. Uranium-238 is less stable than oxygen-16. What accounts for this difference?
   (A) Uranium is a solid, while oxygen is a gas.
   (B) Unlike oxygen-16, uranium-238 has a nucleus in which repulsive electric forces surpass the strong nuclear forces.
   (C) Oxygen-16 has fewer electrons than uranium-238.
   (D) Uranium-238 has fewer neutrons than oxygen-16.
   (E) Unlike uranium-238, oxygen-16 has a nucleus in which the strong nuclear forces are overcome by repulsive electric forces.

6. The primary source of energy in stars is the fusion of hydrogen into helium. However, another reaction is believed to occur simultaneously. It is called the carbon-nitrogen-oxygen (CNO) cycle. In the diagram below, the symbol $^{0}_{+1}e$ represents a positron. A positron is a particle that has the same mass as an electron but a charge of $1+$.

Which equation describes the CNO cycle?
   (A) $^{1}_{1}H \rightarrow {}^{4}_{2}He + {}^{0}_{+1}e$
   (B) $4{}^{1}_{1}H \rightarrow {}^{4}_{2}He + 2{}^{0}_{+1}e$
   (C) $^{2}_{1}H + {}^{3}_{1}H \rightarrow {}^{4}_{2}He + {}^{1}_{0}n$
   (D) $^{12}_{6}C \rightarrow {}^{12}_{6}C + {}^{4}_{2}He$
   (E) $^{12}_{6}C + {}^{1}_{1}H \rightarrow {}^{12}_{6}C + {}^{4}_{2}He$

Nuclear Chemisty **321**

PHYSICS

The Interactive Textbook, found both online and on CD-ROM, includes the following materials.

Activities and Labs

Worksheets for each activity and lab are available as PDF files with clickable safety symbols.

Colorful Visuals

All art and relevant photographs from the Student Edition can be accessed in the Interactive Textbook.

Self Assessment

Provides additional assessment opportunities and questions:
- Interactive Reading Checkpoint questions
- Interactive Figure caption questions
- Chapter Pretests with hints
- Printable Chapter Assessments
- Standardized Test Prep

My Notes

Students can enter answers for questions or make notes about what they are learning.

References

Provides a drop-down menu of resources:
- Skills and Reference Handbook
- Glossary

Careers

Information on science careers is available through the Career page on www.PHSchool.com.

PHYSICS UNIT PREVIEW

Vasco da Gama Bridge ▶
The Vasco da Gama Bridge spans the water at Lisbon, Portugal. Large ships can pass under the bridge to reach the port.

322

Physics

 Focus on the BIG Ideas

Physicists investigate the laws that govern space, time, forces, motion, matter, and energy. Newton's laws of motion describe the relationship between the forces acting on a body and its motion. The motion of objects is governed by four universal forces: gravitational forces, electromagnetic forces, strong nuclear forces, and weak nuclear forces.

Energy is defined as the ability to do work. The amount of energy in the universe is constant, and energy is conserved within any closed system. However, energy can change between many different forms of kinetic energy and potential energy. The total potential and kinetic energy of all the microscopic particles in an object make up its thermal energy. Heat is the transfer of thermal energy from one object to another because of a temperature difference.

Go Online
PHSchool.com

For students, the PHSchool.com Web site contains interactive data-sharing labs, interactive self-assessments, and science-related links. The PHSchool.com Web site also provides teachers with curriculum support, reference links, a way to create state-specific lesson plans, and instructions on how to create a Web page.

Go Online
 NSTA SciLINKS

NSTA SciLinks provides student worksheets for specific topics with additional teacher support.

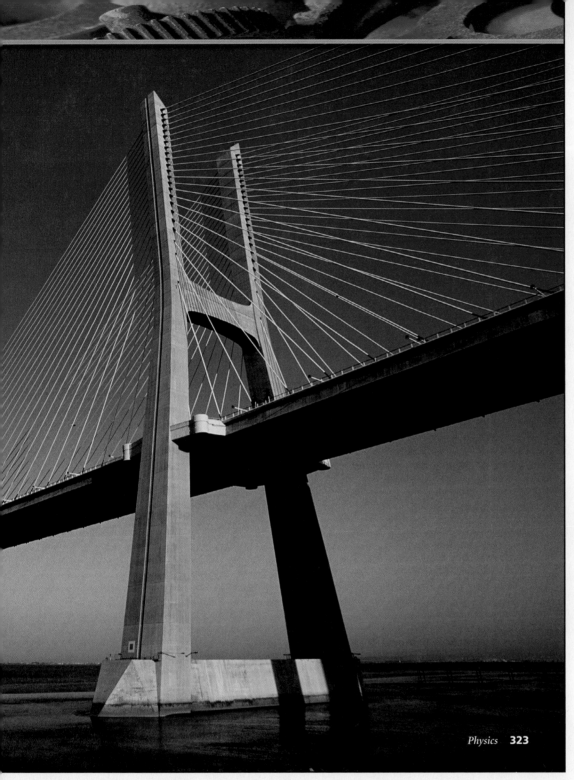

Physics **323**

Use the following videos to help students understand the concepts in each chapter.

Chapter 11 Motion
Charting New Ground
Describes navigation without the benefit of maps and modern technology.

Chapter 12 Forces and Motion
Air Forces
Analyzes the motion of a parachutist.

Chapter 13 Forces in Fluids
Uplifting Experience
Features the forces and machine designs that make flight possible.

Chapter 14 Work, Power, and Machines
Pedal Power
Focuses on how cyclists get the most out of a compound machine.

Chapter 15 Energy
Physics of Fun
Uses the roller coaster to illustrate physics concepts.

Chapter 16 Thermal Energy and Heat
Powered by the Sun
Explores the use of solar energy.

Chapter 17 Mechanical Waves and Sound
Noise!
Focuses on noise pollution reduction.

Chapter 18 The Electromagnetic Spectrum and Light
Finding the Fakes
Shows forensic techniques being used to authenticate paintings.

Chapter 19 Optics
Traveling Light
Describes how fiber optics are used.

Chapter 20 Electricity
Current Computers
Examines how a computer stores, manipulates, and transfers information using miniature circuits.

Chapter 21 Magnetism
Magnetic Viewpoints
Explores the use of magnetic resonance imaging to make detailed images of the body.

Go Online
SCIENCE NEWS

Students can find current information about specific discoveries in science from *Science News*.

Careers in Physics

Physics-related careers require a variety of skills and educational backgrounds. Here are just a few.

Computer Repair Technician

Connection to Chapter 20
Characteristics Independent worker, problem solver
Preparation Courses in electronics, basic understanding of mechanical equipment
Employers Professional and commercial equipment companies, computer and data processing services, computer stores

Aerospace Engineer

Connection to Chapter 13
Characteristics Creative, innovative, problem solver
Preparation Courses in mathematics, science, engineering
Employers Research and testing services, federal government, search and navigation equipment companies, aerospace companies

Camera Operator

Connection to Chapter 19
Characteristics Computer literate, artistic, patient, accurate, detail-oriented, good oral communicator, have good eyesight and hand-eye coordination
Preparation Courses in mathematics, training at a vocational institute, college, or university
Employers Motion picture companies, television stations, production companies

Careers in Physics

Many exciting career opportunities involve physics. Whether you want to become an electrician or an architect, you can put the ideas you read about in this unit to work toward a great career.

Computer Repair Technician
Computer repair technicians repair, maintain, and install mainframes, network servers, and personal computers. They also must be familiar with electronics, the technology that includes components such as electron tubes and photoelectric cells.
Educational requirements
Two-year community or junior college program in computer repair technology

Aerospace Engineer
If you have ever flown in an airplane, you have first-hand experience of the work of aerospace engineers. These professionals understand the principles of flight and are able to design, analyze, model, simulate, and test aircraft, spacecraft, missiles, and rockets. Aerospace engineers often specialize in areas such as propulsion, guidance, or navigation and control.
Educational requirements
Master's degree in physics, aerodynamics, or astronautics

Camera Operator
Lights—Camera—Action—Many motion picture camera operators hear this almost every day. Camera operators use lenses in their cameras and set up lights to photograph scenes. They also adjust the controls on the camera to produce high quality footage.
Educational requirements
High-school diploma

324

HVAC Technician

Connection to Chapter 16
Characteristics Able to troubleshoot, work independently, read and interpret blueprints, and have good hand-eye coordination.
Preparation Basic understanding of heating and cooling system design, understanding of microelectronics
Employers Contracting companies, manufacturers

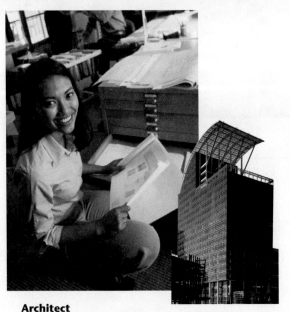

HVAC Technician

HVAC (heating, ventilation, and air conditioning) technicians install, maintain, and repair heating and cooling systems in homes and commercial buildings. HVAC technicians also make sure that ozone-depleting chemicals are not released into the environment.
Educational requirements Two-year community or junior college degree, with courses in mathematics, physics, chemistry, and mechanical drawing; refrigeration handler's license

Architect

Connection to Chapter 12
Characteristics Detail-oriented, artistic, analytical, creative, logical, computer literate, good at oral and written communications, able to work independently or as part of a team, able to conceptualize and understand spatial relationships
Preparation Courses in mathematics and design
Employers Architectural firms, government agencies

Architect

To find out what an architect does, all you have to do is look around you. Architects design all types of buildings, from houses to airport terminals to entire developments. Architects have to be able to predict how a building and its materials will hold up to a variety of forces.
Educational requirements Five-year bachelor of architecture program, three- to four-year master of architecture program for those with a degree in another discipline, internship, and passage of Architect Registration Examination

For: Career links
Visit: PHSchool.com
Web Code: ccb-2000

Electrician

Connection to Chapter 20
Characteristics Safety conscious, have stamina, good hand-eye coordination, ability to read and interpret blueprints
Preparation Courses in electronics
Employers Construction companies, maintenance companies

Electrician

Electricians are responsible for installing, testing, and maintaining electrical systems. They also must adhere to the National Electrical Code and obey state and local building codes to safely install electrical systems.
Educational requirements Four- or five-year apprenticeship program and state license

Physics **325**

Career Teaching Strategy
Have students use help-wanted ads from newspapers and the Internet to research physics-related jobs.

Have students list the available physics-related positions, the qualifications necessary for each job, and the salaries being offered.

Planning Guide

Use these planning tools

Easy Planner
Teacher Express

SECTION OBJECTIVES	STANDARDS		ACTIVITIES and LABS
	NATIONAL	STATE	
11.1 Distance and Displacement, pp. 328–331 ⏱ 1 block or 2 periods **11.1.1 Identify** frames of reference and **describe** how they are used to measure motion. **11.1.2 Identify** appropriate SI units for measuring distances. **11.1.3 Distinguish** between distance and displacement. **11.1.4 Calculate** displacement using vector addition.	A-1, A-2, B-4	ICP.1.1	**SE** Inquiry Activity: How Does a Ramp Affect a Rolling Marble? p. 327 **L2** **SE** Quick Lab: Comparing Distance and Displacement, p. 330 **L2** **TE** Teacher Demo: Frames of Reference, p. 329 **L2** **LM** Investigation 11A: Measuring Distance and Displacement **L2**
11.2 Speed and Velocity, pp. 332–337 ⏱ 1 block or 2 periods **11.2.1 Identify** appropriate SI units for measuring speed. **11.2.2 Compare** and **contrast** average speed and instantaneous speed. **11.2.3 Interpret** distance-time graphs. **11.2.4 Calculate** the speed of an object using slopes. **11.2.5 Describe** how velocities combine.	A-1, B-4, E-2, F-1, G-1, G-3	ICP.1.1, ICP.6.6	**SE** Exploration Lab: Investigating the Velocity of a Sinking Marble, p. 349 **L2** **TE** Teacher Demo: Ticker Tape Car, p. 334 **L2** **LM** Investigation 11B: Investigating Free Fall **L1**
11.3 Acceleration, pp. 342–348 ⏱ 1 block or 2 periods **11.3.1 Identify** changes in motion that produce acceleration. **11.3.2 Describe** examples of constant acceleration. **11.3.3 Calculate** the acceleration of an object. **11.3.4 Interpret** speed-time and distance-time graphs. **11.3.5 Classify** acceleration as positive or negative. **11.3.6 Describe** instantaneous acceleration.	A-1, A-2, B-4, D-1	ICP.1.1, ICP.1.2	**TE** Teacher Demo: Pendulum Accelerometer, p. 344 **L2**

RESOURCES
PRINT and TECHNOLOGY

RSW Section 11.1 — **L1**

T Chapter 11 Pretest — **L2**
Section 11.1 — **L2**

P Chapter 11 Pretest — **L2**
Section 11.1 — **L2**

sci_{LINKS} **GO** Comparing frames of reference — **L2**

RSW Section 11.2 — **L1**

RSW Math Skill — **L2**

MSPS Section 11.2 — **L2**

DC Charting New Ground — **L2**

T Section 11.2 — **L2**

P Section 11.2 — **L2**

sci_{LINKS} **GO** Motion — **L2**

PHSchool.com GO Data sharing — **L2**

RSW Section 11.3 — **L1**

MSPS Section 11.3 — **L2**

T Section 11.3 — **L2**

P Section 11.3 — **L2**

sci_{LINKS} **GO** Acceleration — **L2**

SECTION ASSESSMENT

SE Section 11.1 Assessment, p. 331

iT Section 11.1

SE Section 11.2 Assessment, p. 337

iT Section 11.2

SE Section 11.3 Assessment, p. 348

iT Section 11.3

Go Online

Go online for these Internet resources.

PHSchool.com
Web Code: ccd-2110
Web Code: cca-2110

NSTA SCI**LINKS**
Web Code: ccn-2111
Web Code: ccn-2112
Web Code: ccn-2113

Materials for Activities and Labs

Quantities for each group

STUDENT EDITION

Inquiry Activity, p. 327
1-m long wooden board at least 10 cm wide, 6 identical textbooks, stopwatch, marble

Quick Lab, p. 330
graph paper, metric ruler

Exploration Lab, p. 349
clear shampoo, 100-mL graduated cylinder, 2 small marbles, stopwatch, forceps, masking tape, metric ruler, 10-mL graduated cylinder, long glass stirring rod, dropper pipet, graph paper

TEACHER'S EDITION

Teacher Demo, p. 329
tennis ball

Teacher Demo, p. 334
toy car, ticker tape, ticker timer (acceleration timer), masking tape

Build Science Skills, p. 340
handheld GPS receivers, 1 per group

Teacher Demo, p. 344
short pendulum (25 cm), turntable, lab stand, tape

Chapter Assessment

CHAPTER ASSESSMENT

SE Chapter Assessment, pp. 351–352
CUT Chapter 11 Test A, B
CTB Chapter 11
iT Chapter 11
PHSchool.com GO
Web Code: cca-2110

STANDARDIZED TEST PREP

SE Chapter 11, p. 353
TP Diagnose and Prescribe

Interactive Textbook with assessment at PHSchool.com

Before you teach

From the Author

Michael Wysession
Washington University

Big Ideas

Most of physics, and all of science, is concerned with motions. Before students can learn about the how (forces) and why (energy) of motions, they need to be able to describe them.

Space and Time In our local region of the universe, space has three spatial dimensions. Space is closely related to time, which is often considered to be a fourth dimension. In fact, large distances are measured in light-years, which are units of time.

Einstein demonstrated that all motions are relative, so a frame of reference within the three-dimensional space must be chosen. Distances, directions, and displacements are always measured relative to a frame of reference. Displacement is the combination of distance and direction.

Because it is important to describe motion over time, rates such as speed and velocity are often used. Velocity is the combination of speed and direction, analogous to the relation between displacement and distance. Acceleration is another common way to describe motion. Acceleration is the rate at which motion changes. Displacement, velocity, and acceleration are the most common examples of vectors.

Forces and Motion The motions of objects change when forces act upon them. Students need to be able to calculate these motions, and to be able to graph them. When there are no accelerations (no net forces), velocities are constant. These constant velocities plot as straight lines on a speed-time graph. When there are net forces, non-zero accelerations result in non-linear curves on a speed-time graph.

Matter and Energy Objects that appear to be motionless contain atoms that are continuously in motion—vibrating and colliding. Even pure electromagnetic energy such as light is in motion. Many of the following physics chapters explore the relations between matter and energy. In all cases, understanding and measuring how this matter and energy moves is a fundamental part of understanding the laws of the universe.

Physics Refresher

Distance and Displacement 11.1

For one-dimensional motion, the position of an object can be defined by a function $x(t)$. Displacement over a time interval can then be defined as $\Delta x = x_2 - x_1$. In more than one dimension, the displacement can be defined by a single vector function:

$$\mathbf{s}(t) = x(t)\mathbf{i} + y(t)\mathbf{j} + \ldots$$

In this equation, $\mathbf{s}(t)$ is the displacement as a function of time, $\mathbf{i}$ and $\mathbf{j}$ are unit vectors in the horizontal and vertical directions, respectively, and $x(t)$ and $y(t)$ are positions along the horizontal axis and vertical axis as functions of time.

Distance is how far an object travels on a path. Displacement is the straight-line distance from the start point to the end point.

> **Address Misconceptions**
>
> *The location of an object can be described by stating its distance from a given point, ignoring direction.* To describe position fully, you must specify both distance and direction. For a strategy to overcome this misconception, see **Address Misconceptions** on **page 330**.

Speed and Velocity 11.2

Velocity is defined as the rate of change of displacement. This can be expressed by the following differential equation:

$$\mathbf{v}(t) = d\mathbf{s}(t)/dt$$

Taking the derivative of displacement as shown above gives the instantaneous velocity at a point. The magnitude of this vector is the instantaneous speed.

Students may use the equation $\bar{v} = d/t$ to calculate average speed over a time interval, where $\bar{v}$ is the average speed, d is the distance traveled during a time interval, and t is the time interval.

> **Address Misconceptions**
>
> *An object's speed is the same as its velocity.* Velocity is a vector quantity that describes both speed and the direction of motion. For a strategy to overcome this misconception, see **Address Misconceptions** on **page 336**.

Go Online
NSTA PD LiNKS

For: Teaching methods for motion
Visit: www.SciLinks.org/PDLinks
Web Code: ccn-1199

Acceleration 11.3

Address Misconceptions

If an object is accelerating, then the object is speeding up. Acceleration is any change in velocity. This can be an increase in speed, a decrease in speed, or a change in direction. For a strategy to overcome this misconception, see **Address Misconceptions** on **page 343.**

Acceleration is defined as the rate of change of velocity. This can be expressed by the following differential equation:

$$\mathbf{a}(t) = d\mathbf{v}(t)/dt$$

Acceleration, like velocity and displacement, is a vector quantity having both magnitude and direction. Acceleration can be a change in speed, a change in direction, or both.

Taking the derivative of velocity as shown above gives the instantaneous acceleration at a point. For motion along a straight line, students may use the following equation $a = (v_f - v_i)/t$ to calculate average acceleration, where a is the average acceleration, v_f is the final speed, v_i is the initial speed, and t is the time interval. Note that if velocity of an object moving in the positive direction decreases during the time interval, $v_f < v_i$, and the average acceleration is negative.

Graphing Motion 11.2 and 11.3

Speed in one-dimensional motion can be shown on a graph of distance versus time, as shown in Figure A below. Constant speed appears on the graph as a straight line with finite, nonzero slope. The greater the absolute value of the slope, the greater the speed. A horizontal line represents zero velocity.

Acceleration in one-dimensional motion can be shown on a graph of distance versus time, or on a graph of speed versus time, as shown below right in Figure B. On a speed-time graph, constant speed is a horizontal line (with a slope of zero) and constant

acceleration is a straight line with a nonzero slope. On a distance-time graph, constant acceleration appears as a curved line.

Build Reading Literacy

Monitor Your Understanding

Self-Questioning and Self-Adjusting While Reading

Strategy Help students read and understand difficult technical material. This strategy enables students to focus on their own thought processes as they actively question and apply fix-up strategies to improve comprehension. First, present the three steps in the example below, reviewing the fix-up strategies in Step 2. Then, before students begin, assign a section in Chapter 11, such as Section 11.2, pp. 332–337, for them to read. You might want to model the strategy with a paragraph or two before having students practice it on their own.

Example

1. Self-Question Have students read and think about the paragraphs under each heading, stopping often to ask themselves questions such as, "Do I understand this?" "Is this clear?" and "Does this answer my questions about _____?"

2. Identify Trouble Spots and Apply Fix-Up Strategies

• **Reread/Adjust Reading Pace** When students do not understand a paragraph, have them reread it slowly, making sure they understand each sentence before they continue.

• **Clarify** When students encounter a difficult paragraph, suggest they state what they do understand, talk through confusing points or steps in a process, or relate new information to concepts and examples that are already familiar to them.

• **Read Ahead/Use Visuals and Captions** Show students how to use visuals and captions to help clarify a process or a concept. Suggest that they can also read ahead to see whether a process or concept is discussed further as part of another concept.

• **Use Outside Resources** Point out, too, that students should seek assistance from friends, teachers, or other resources. Hearing additional examples or more than one person's explanation often aids comprehension.

3. Self-Check After students read, have them check their understanding by summarizing or retelling the main idea of a paragraph or section.

See p. 329 for a script on how to use the monitor your understanding strategy with students. For additional Build Reading Literacy strategies, see pp. 336 and 343.

▲ Figure A

Figure B ▶

ASSESS PRIOR KNOWLEDGE

Use the Chapter Pretest below to assess students' prior knowledge. As needed, review these Science Concepts and Math Skills with students.

Review Science Concepts

Section 11.1 Review measurement. Remind students that measurements can be expressed in SI units or other units.

Section 11.2 Review graphing of scientific data. Remind students that graphs have different kinds of data on each axis. The slope of a line on a graph is the rise (change in vertical value) divided by the run (change in horizontal value).

Section 11.3 Further review graphing of scientific data. Remind students that data may form a straight line or a curve on a graph. The slope of a curved line at a given point is the slope of the straight line tangent to the graph at that point.

Review Math Skills

Conversion Factors, Averages, Line Graphs, Formulas and Equations, Significant Figures
Students will need to calculate velocity and acceleration and create graphs of motion as a function of time.

Direct students to the **Math Skills** in the **Skills and Reference Handbook** at the end of the student text.

CHAPTER

11 Motion

What is the relationship between displacement, velocity, and acceleration?

Search for an online simulation tool that generates graphs of displacement vs. time and velocity vs. time. Work in a small group to study examples of motion in a straight line using the simulation tool. First, simulate motion at a constant velocity. Then change the settings to simulate motion at a constant acceleration. Take screen-shots of the motion graphs generated and arrange them in a presentation. Use the graphs to describe the history of the motion that you simulated.

Indiana's Academic Standards for Science

MOTION AND ENERGY
ICP.1.1: Measure the motion of objects to understand the relationships between distance, velocity, and acceleration and deepen understanding through graphical analysis of the time dependence of acceleration, velocity and distance; **ICP.1.2:** Describe and apply Newton's three laws of motion. By experimentation, determine the relationships among the variables in Newton's laws and how all three laws relate mass, acceleration and force as a triad of proportional variables, leading to the definitions of momentum and energy.

ELECTRICAL ENERGY PROPAGATION AND MAGNETISM
ICP.6.6: Explain that some objects, called magnets, exert magnetic forces with no direct contact.

The time-lapse photo shows how the position of a gymnast changes from moment to moment.

326 *Chapter 11*

Chapter Pretest

1. How many meters are in 28 km? *(28,000 m)*

2. Convert 35 km/h to a speed in m/s. *(9.7 m/s)*

3. Rearrange the following equation to solve for d: $v = d/t$. *($d = vt$)*

4. Rearrange the following equation to solve for v_f: $a = (v_f - v_i)/t$. *($v_f = at + v_i$)*

5. What are the SI units for distance and time? *(Meters and seconds)*

6. Which of the following describes the slope of a line? *(d)*
   a. rise × run
   b. run/rise
   c. run − rise
   d. rise/run

7. If a graph uses units of meters on the vertical axis and units of seconds on the horizontal axis, what would be the units of the slope of a line on the graph? *(m/s)*

8. Which of the following is true about a curved line on a graph? *(b)*
   a. The slope is the same at every point.
   b. The slope of the line may be different at every point.
   c. The line has no slope.
   d. The slope of the line is zero.

Chapter Preview

11.1 Distance and Displacement

11.2 Speed and Velocity

11.3 Acceleration

Video Field Trip

Charting New Ground

Inquiry Activity

How Does a Ramp Affect a Rolling Marble?

Procedure

1. Form a ramp by placing one end of a 1-meter-long board on a stack of six identical books.

2. Have your partner release a marble at the top of the ramp. Use a stopwatch to measure the time the marble takes to reach the bottom. Record this time.

3. **Predicting** How many books tall would the stack have to be to double the time needed for the marble to reach the ramp's bottom? Record your prediction.

4. Test your prediction. Remove one book from the stack and repeat Step 2. Continue this process until the time needed for the marble to roll down the ramp doubles.

Think About It

1. **Predicting** What would happen to the time needed for the marble to roll down the ramp if the ramp were nearly horizontal?

2. **Formulating Hypotheses** If you keep adding books to the stack, will the time needed for the marble to roll down the ramp decrease indefinitely? Explain your answer.

Motion **327**

Video Field Trip

Charting New Ground

Encourage students to view the Video Field Trip "Charting New Ground."

ENGAGE/EXPLORE

Inquiry Activity

How Does a Ramp Affect a Rolling Marble? L2

Purpose In this activity, students will begin to describe how the steepness of a ramp affects the motion of a rolling marble.

Skills Focus Measuring, Predicting

Prep Time 10 minutes

Materials 1-m long wooden board at least 10 cm wide, 6 identical textbooks, stopwatch, marble

Class Time 20 minutes

Safety Students must wear safety goggles. Ensure that the boards are smooth to prevent splinters.

Teaching Tips
• The boards should not be curved or warped so that the marbles do not roll off the sides of the ramps.

Expected Outcome Students will observe that the marble takes longer to descend when the steepness of the ramp is reduced.

Predicting Students may correctly predict that a height of three books would approximately double the time the marble takes to reach the bottom of the ramp.

Think About It

1. The time needed would be very long because the speed of the marble would be almost zero.

2. When the ramp is vertical, the marble is in free fall and the time required reaches a finite minimum value.

Kinesthetic, Group

11.1 Distance and Displacement

1 FOCUS

Objectives

11.1.1 Identify frames of reference and **describe** how they are used to measure motion.

11.1.2 Identify appropriate SI units for measuring distances.

11.1.3 Distinguish between distance and displacement.

11.1.4 Calculate displacement using vector addition.

Reading Focus

Build Vocabulary **L2**

Vocabulary Knowledge Rating Chart
Before students read the section, have them rate their knowledge of the vocabulary terms for this section in a chart with the following headings: Term, Can Define or Use It, Have Heard or Seen It, Don't Know. After they have read the section, have them return to the chart and update it to reflect any increase in understanding.

Reading Strategy **L2**

a. Answers may vary. Sample answer: Frame of reference may mean the range of distances or area that you are considering in a problem. **b.** Frame of reference is a system of objects that are not moving with respect to one another. Frames of reference are important because they are needed to accurately describe motion.

2 INSTRUCT

Choosing a Frame of Reference

Use Visuals **L1**

Figure 1 Discuss Figure 1 with students after they read the section Choosing a Frame of Reference. Ask, **Describe the motion of the girl in the butterfly's frame of reference.** *(She would appear to bob up and down, exactly opposite the motion of the butterfly as seen from the girl's frame of reference.)* **Describe the motion of the butterfly in the butterfly's frame of reference.** *(The butterfly is at rest in the butterfly's frame of reference.)* **Which one is "really" moving, the butterfly or the girl?** *(It depends on the frame of reference.)*
Visual, Logical

Standard: ICP.1.1

Reading Focus

Key Concepts
- What is needed to describe motion completely?
- How are distance and displacement different?
- How do you add displacements?

Vocabulary
- frame of reference
- relative motion
- distance
- vector
- resultant vector

Reading Strategy
Predicting Copy the table below and write a definition for *frame of reference* in your own words. After you read the section, compare your definition to the scientific definition and explain why the frame of reference is important.

Frame of reference probably means	Frame of reference actually means
a. ?	b. ?

Figure 1 You must choose a frame of reference to tell how fast the butterfly is moving.
Applying Concepts *Identify a good frame of reference to use when describing the butterfly's motion.*

328 *Chapter 11*

On a spring day a butterfly flutters past. First it flies quickly, then slowly, and then it pauses to drink nectar from a flower. The butterfly's path involves a great deal of motion.

How fast is the butterfly moving? Is it flying toward the flower or away from it? These are the kinds of questions you must answer to describe the butterfly's motion. To describe motion, you must state the direction the object is moving as well as how fast the object is moving. You must also tell its location at a certain time.

Choosing a Frame of Reference

How fast is the butterfly in Figure 1 moving? Remember that the butterfly is moving on Earth, but Earth itself is moving as it spins on its axis and revolves around the sun. If you consider this motion, the butterfly is moving very, very fast!

To describe motion accurately and completely, a frame of reference is necessary. The necessary ingredient of a description of motion—a **frame of reference**—is a system of objects that are not moving with respect to one another. The answer to "How fast is the butterfly moving?" depends on which frame of reference you use to measure motion. How do you decide which frame of reference to use when describing the butterfly's movement?

Section Resources

Print
- *Laboratory Manual,* Investigation 11A
- *Reading and Study Workbook With Math Support,* Section 11.1
- *Transparencies,* Chapter Pretest and Section 11.1

Technology
- *Interactive Textbook,* Section 11.1
- *Presentation Pro CD-ROM,* Chapter Pretest and Section 11.1
- *Go Online,* NSTA SciLinks, Comparing frames of reference

Figure 2 To someone riding on a speeding train, others on the train don't seem to be moving.

How Fast Are You Moving? How fast are the train passengers in Figure 2 moving? There are many correct answers because their motion is relative. This means it depends on the frame of reference you choose to measure their motion. **Relative motion** is movement in relation to a frame of reference. For example, as the train moves past a platform, people standing on the platform will see those on the train speeding by. But when the people on the train look at one another, they don't seem to be moving at all.

Which Frame Should You Choose? When you sit on a train and look out a window, a treetop may help you see how fast you are moving relative to the ground. But suppose you get up and walk toward the rear of the train. Looking at a seat or the floor may tell you how fast you are walking relative to the train. However, it doesn't tell you how fast you are moving relative to the ground outside. Choosing a meaningful frame of reference allows you to describe motion in a clear and relevant manner.

Measuring Distance

Distance is the length of a path between two points. When an object moves in a straight line, the distance is the length of the line connecting the object's starting point and its ending point.

It is helpful to express distances in units that are best suited to the motion you are studying. The SI unit for measuring distance is the meter (m). For very large distances, it is more common to make measurements in kilometers (km). One kilometer equals 1000 meters. For instance, it's easier to say that the Mississippi River has a length of 3780 kilometers than 3,780,000 meters. Distances that are smaller than a meter are measured in centimeters (cm). One centimeter is one hundredth of a meter. You might describe the distance a marble rolls, for example, as 6 centimeters rather than 0.06 meter.

Go Online
NSTA *SciLINKS*

For: Links on comparing frames of reference
Visit: www.SciLinks.org
Web Code: ccn-2111

Motion **329**

Measuring Displacements Combining Displacements

Comparing Distance and Displacement **L2**

Objective
After completing this activity, students will be able to
• distinguish between distance and displacement.

 Address Misconceptions

This activity helps address the misconception that the distance an object travels and its displacement are the same. Challenge this misconception by discussing the answers to the Analyze and Conclude questions.

Skills Focus Measuring

Prep Time 10 minutes

Materials graph paper, metric ruler

Class Time 15 minutes

Teaching Tips
• Make sure that students read the metric side of the ruler if their rulers have both metric and English units.

Expected Outcome Students will be able to distinguish between distance, the length traveled between two points, and displacement, the length of the line between two points.

Analyze and Conclude
1. Displacement is always shorter than or equal to the distance because it is a straight line between two points, not always the actual path of motion.
2. The distance would be shorter if the path were more direct. The shortest path would be a diagonal line connecting Start and End, and it would be the same length as the displacement.
3. No, the displacement could not be shorter because it will always be the straight-line distance between the Start and End points.
Visual, Logical

Comparing Distance and Displacement

Procedure
1. Draw a dot at the intersection of two lines near the bottom edge of a sheet of graph paper. Label the dot "Start."
2. Draw a second, similar dot near the top of the paper. Label this dot "End."
3. Draw a path from the Start dot to the End dot. Choose any path that stays on the grid lines.
4. Use a ruler to determine the distance of your path.
5. Use a ruler to determine the displacement from start to end.

Analyze and Conclude
1. **Observing** Which is shorter, the distance or the displacement?
2. **Evaluating and Revising** How could you have made the distance shorter?
3. **Inferring** If you keep the Start and End points the same, is it possible to make the displacement shorter? Explain your answer.

Measuring Displacements

To describe an object's position relative to a given point, you need to know how far away and in what direction the object is from that point. Displacement provides this information. **Distance is the length of the path between two points. Displacement is the direction from the starting point and the length of a straight line from the starting point to the ending point.**

Displacements are sometimes used when giving directions. Telling someone to "Walk 5 blocks" does not ensure they'll end up in the right place. However, saying "Walk 5 blocks north from the bus stop" will get the person to the right place. Accurate directions give the direction from a starting point as well as the distance.

Think about the motion of a roller coaster car. If you measure the path along which the car has traveled, you are describing distance. The direction from the starting point to the car and the length of the straight line from the starting point to the car describe displacement. After completing one trip around the track, the roller coaster car's displacement is zero.

Combining Displacements

Displacement is an example of a vector. A **vector** is a quantity that has magnitude and direction. The magnitude can be size, length, or amount. Arrows on a graph or map are used to represent vectors. The length of the arrow shows the magnitude of the vector. Vector addition is the combining of vector magnitudes and directions. **Add displacements using vector addition.**

Displacement Along a Straight Line When two displacements, represented by two vectors, have the same direction, you can add their magnitudes. In Figure 3A, the magnitudes of the car's displacements are 4 kilometers and 2 kilometers. The total magnitude of the displacement is 6 kilometers. If two displacements are in opposite directions, the magnitudes subtract from each other, as shown in Figure 3B. Because the car's displacements (4 kilometers and 2 kilometers) are in opposite directions, the magnitude of the total displacement is 2 kilometers.

Figure 3 When motion is in a straight line, vectors add and subtract easily. **A** Add the magnitudes of two displacement vectors that have the same direction. **B** Two displacement vectors with opposite directions are subtracted from each other.

4 km + 2 km = 6 km

4 km − 2 km = 2 km

Displacement That Isn't Along a Straight Path

When two or more displacement vectors have different directions, they may be combined by graphing. Figure 4 shows vectors representing the movement of a boy walking from his home to school. He starts by walking 1 block east. Then he turns a corner and walks 1 block north. He turns once again and walks 2 blocks east. For the last part of his trip to school, he walks 3 blocks north. The lengths of the vectors representing this path are 1 block, 1 block, 2 blocks, and 3 blocks.

The boy walked a total distance of 7 blocks. You can determine this distance by adding the magnitudes of each vector along his path.

The vector in red is called the **resultant vector,** which is the vector sum of two or more vectors. In this case, it shows the displacement. The resultant vector points directly from the starting point to the ending point. If you place a sheet of paper on the figure and mark the length of the resultant vector, you see that it equals the length of 5 blocks. Vector addition, then, shows that the boy's displacement is 5 blocks approximately northeast, while the distance he walked is 7 blocks.

Figure 4 Measuring the resultant vector (the diagonal red line) shows that the displacement from the boy's home to his school is two blocks less than the distance he actually traveled.

Section 11.1 Assessment

Reviewing Concepts

1. 🔵 What is a frame of reference? How is it used to measure motion?

2. 🔵 How are distance and displacement similar and different?

3. 🔵 How are displacements combined?

4. A girl who is watching a plane fly tells her friend that the plane isn't moving at all. Describe a frame of reference in which the girl's description would be true.

Critical Thinking

5. **Using Analogies** Is displacement more like the length of a rope that is pulled tight or the length of a coiled rope? Explain.

6. **Making Judgments** Would you measure the height of a building in meters? Give reasons for your answer.

7. **Problem Solving** Should your directions to a friend for traveling from one city to another include displacements or distances? Explain.

8. **Inferring** The resultant vector of two particular displacement vectors does not equal the sum of the magnitudes of the individual vectors. Describe the directions of the two vectors.

Writing in Science

Compare-Contrast Paragraph Write a paragraph describing how the distance you travel from home to school is different from your displacement from home to school. (*Hint:* Make a simple sketch similar to Figure 4 and refer to it as you write.)

Motion **331**

---

1 FOCUS

Objectives

11.2.1 Identify appropriate SI units for measuring speed.

11.2.2 Compare and **contrast** average speed and instantaneous speed.

11.2.3 Interpret distance-time graphs.

11.2.4 Calculate the speed of an object using slopes.

11.2.5 Describe how velocities combine.

Reading Focus

Build Vocabulary **L2**

Venn Diagram Have students draw a Venn diagram to show how the key terms of the section are related to each other. Student diagrams should show circles labeled Speed and Direction. The area in which the circles overlap should be labeled Velocity.

Reading Strategy **L2**

Answers may vary. Sample answers are shown below.
a. Average speed is distance divided by time. **b.** I could use this to calculate various speeds, like the average speed at which I travel getting to school. **c.** Instantaneous speed is different from average speed **d.** You can't use a single speedometer reading to determine how long a trip will take. **e.** Velocity is not the same as speed. **f.** This could be useful in giving directions or in describing the path that you take on a walk.

2 INSTRUCT

Speed

Build Science Skills **L2**

Forming Operational Definitions An operational definition limits the meaning of a term to what is observed or measured in a particular situation. Ask, **What is an operational definition of speed for a skater on a circular track?** (Sample answer: The amount of time it takes to circle the track one time, the number of times the skater could circle the track one time) **What is an operational definition for a person walking down a street?** (Sample answer: The number of meters traveled each second)
Verbal, Logical

11.2 Speed and Velocity

Standard: ICP.1.1

Reading Focus

Key Concepts

- How are instantaneous speed and average speed different?
- How can you find the speed from a distance-time graph?
- How are speed and velocity different?
- How do velocities add?

Vocabulary

- ◆ speed
- ◆ average speed
- ◆ instantaneous speed
- ◆ velocity

Reading Strategy

Monitoring Your Understanding After you have finished reading this section, copy the table below. Identify several things you have learned that are relevant to your life. Explain why they are relevant to you.

What Is Relevant	Why It Is Relevant
a. ?	b. ?
c. ?	d. ?
e. ?	f. ?

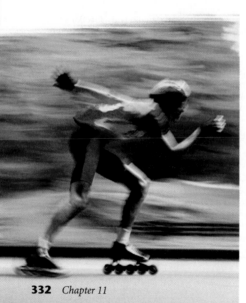

Figure 5 The speed of an in-line skater is usually described in meters per second. The speed of a car is usually described in kilometers per hour.

Look out a window for a few minutes, and you will see things in motion. Some things are moving slowly. Perhaps you see a leaf floating through the air. Other things, such as a car or a bird, are moving fast. The growth rate of trees and grass is so slow that their motion cannot be detected with the unaided eye. The differences among these types of motion can be described in terms of speed.

Speed

To describe the speed of a car, you might say it is moving at 45 kilometers per hour. **Speed** is the ratio of the distance an object moves to the amount of time the object moves. The SI unit of speed is meters per second (m/s). However, just as with distances, you need to choose units that make the most sense for the motion you are describing. The in-line skater in Figure 5 may travel 2 meters in one second. The speed would be expressed as 2 m/s. A car might travel 80 kilometers in one hour. Its speed would be expressed as 80 km/h.

Two ways to express the speed of an object are average speed and instantaneous speed. **Average speed is computed for the entire duration of a trip, and instantaneous speed is measured at a particular instant.** In different situations, either one or both of these measurements may be a useful way to describe speed.

332 *Chapter 11*

Section Resources

Print

- **Laboratory Manual,** Investigation 11B
- **Reading and Study Workbook With Math Support,** Section 11.2 and **Math Skill:** Interpreting a Distance-Time Graph
- **Math Skills and Problem Solving Workbook,** Section 11.2
- **Transparencies,** Section 11.2

Technology

- **Interactive Textbook,** Section 11.2
- **Presentation Pro CD-ROM,** Section 11.2
- **Go Online,** NSTA SciLinks, Motion; PHSchool.com, Data sharing

Average Speed Describing the speed of a hiker isn't as easy as describing constant speed along a straight line. A hiker may travel slowly along rocky areas but then travel quickly when going downhill. Sometimes it is useful to know how fast something moves for an entire trip. **Average speed,** $\bar{v}$, is the total distance traveled, d, divided by the time, t, it takes to travel that distance. This can be written as an equation:

For: Links on motion
Visit: www.SciLinks.org
Web Code: ccn-2112

Average Speed

$$\text{Average speed} = \frac{\text{Total distance}}{\text{Total time}}, \text{ or } \bar{v} = \frac{d}{t}$$

During the time an object is moving, its speed may change, but this equation tells you the average speed over the entire trip.

 Math Skills

Calculating Average Speed
While traveling on vacation, you measure the times and distances traveled. You travel 35 kilometers in 0.4 hour, followed by 53 kilometers in 0.6 hour. What is your average speed?

1 **Read and Understand**
What information are you given?

Total Distance (d) = 35 km + 53 km = 88 km

Total Time (t) = 0.4 h + 0.6 h = 1.0 h

2 **Plan and Solve**
What unknown are you trying to calculate?

Average Speed $(\bar{v})$ = ?

What formula contains the given quantities and the unknown?

$$\bar{v} = \frac{d}{t}$$

Replace each variable with its known value.

$$\bar{v} = \frac{88 \text{ km}}{1 \text{ h}} = 88 \text{ km/h}$$

3 **Look Back and Check**
Is your answer reasonable?

Yes, 88 km/h is a typical highway speed.

 Math Practice

1. A person jogs 4.0 kilometers in 32 minutes, then 2.0 kilometers in 22 minutes, and finally 1.0 kilometer in 16 minutes. What is the jogger's average speed in kilometers per minute?

2. A train travels 190 kilometers in 3.0 hours, and then 120 kilometers in 2.0 hours. What is its average speed?

 Go Online
PLANETDIARY

For: Activity on the movement of Earth's plates
Visit: PHSchool.com
Web Code: ccc-2112

 Math Practice

Solutions L2

1. $\bar{v}$ = (4.0 km + 2.0 km + 1.0 km)/ (32 min + 22 min + 16 min) = (7.0 km)/(70 min) = 0.10 km/min
2. $\bar{v}$ = (190 km + 120 km)/(3.0 h + 2.0 h) = (310 km)/(5.0 h) = 62 km/h
Logical

For Extra Help L1
Remind students that all the values they plug into the equation must have appropriate units. They may have to convert some of the given units. Also remind students that the equation can be rearranged to solve for other variables. Show them how to rearrange to solve for d or t. **Logical`**

Direct students to the **Math Skills** in the **Skills and Reference Handbook** at the end of the student text for additional help.

Additional Problems

1. A car travels 85 km from Town A to Town B, then 45 km from Town B to Town C. The total trip took 1.5 hours. What was the average speed of the car? *(87 km/h)*
2. A bicyclist travels for 1.5 hours at an average speed of 32 km/h. How far does the bicyclist travel in that time? *(48 km)*
Logical, Portfolio

Use Community Resources L2

Have students contact their local or state department of transportation to find out about laws or guidelines for the assignments of speed limits. They may ask, "Are there specific maximum speed limits for residential areas?" or "What is the maximum speed limit for highways outside of city limits?" They may also ask the department representative what other factors are used in determining speed limits.
Interpersonal, Portfolio

Customize for English Language Learners

Create a Word Wall
Students can relate the concepts in this section to the vocabulary words by creating a word wall. Write the words *speed, average speed, instantaneous speed,* and *velocity* on the board. Then, as students work through the section, ask them to define each word in their own terms. Discuss their definitions and write acceptable definitions on the board next to each word. Students may also draw a graph or paste a magazine picture next to the corresponding word.

Download a worksheet on motion for students to complete, and find additional teacher support from NSTA SciLinks.

Graphing Motion

Ticker Tape Car L2

Purpose Students observe a technique that visually records motion.

Materials toy car, ticker tape, ticker timer (acceleration timer), masking tape

Procedure Place the car and the ticker on the ground in an open area. Thread the ticker tape through the ticker, then attach the ticker tape to the car with masking tape. Before you perform the demonstration, show the setup to the students and explain how the ticker works (the ticker marks the ticker tape at regular time intervals). Ask, **How will the marks appear on the tape when the car is moving at a constant speed?** *(The marks will be evenly spaced.)* Start the ticker and give the car a quick push. Turn off the ticker and cut off the used portion of the ticker tape. Have the students gather around the ticker tape and relate the marks on the ticker tape to the motion of the car that they observed.

Expected Outcome At first, the marks on the tape will be unevenly spaced (getting farther apart) because the car is accelerating. As the car slows down, the marks will get closer together again. When the car is at rest, many marks will be superimposed. If possible, demonstrate the car moving at a constant speed. When the car is moving at constant speed, the marks will be evenly spaced on the ticker tape. As an alternative, you can use probeware to plot the car's motion on a computer or graphing calculator, and then relate the graphs to the motion of the car.
Kinesthetic, Logical

Build Science Skills L2

Analyzing Data Use Figures 7A and 7B to demonstrate that speed is shown by the slope of the line on a distance-time graph. For Figure 7A, calculate the slope of the line on the board:

slope = rise/run = $(y_2 - y_1)/(x_2 - x_1)$
= $(350\ m - 100\ m)/(14\ s - 4\ s)$
= $(250\ m)/(10\ s)$
= $25\ m/s$

Then, have students calculate the speed represented by the three distinct portions on the graph in Figure 7C. *(25 m/s, 0 m/s, 37.5 m/s)*
Visual, Logical

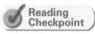

Instantaneous Speed Average speed is useful because it lets you know how long a trip will take. Sometimes however, such as when driving on the highway, you need to know how fast you are going at a particular moment. The car's speedometer gives your instantaneous speed. **Instantaneous speed,** *v*, is the rate at which an object is moving at a given moment in time. For example, you could describe the instantaneous speed of the car in Figure 6 as 55 km/h.

Reading Checkpoint *What does a car's speedometer measure?*

Figure 6 The speedometer in a car measures the car's instantaneous speed. Note the scale markings are given both in km/h and miles per hour, mph.

Graphing Motion

A distance-time graph is a good way to describe motion. Figure 7 shows distance-time graphs for the motion of three cars. Recall that slope is the change in the vertical axis value divided by the change in the horizontal axis value. On these graphs, the slope is the change in the distance divided by the change in time. ◗ **The slope of a line on a distance-time graph is speed.** In Figure 7A, the car travels 500.0 meters in 20.0 seconds, or 25.0 meters per second. In Figure 7B, another car travels 250.0 meters in 20.0 seconds at a constant speed. The slope of the line is 250.0 meters divided by 20.0 seconds, or 12.5 meters per second. Notice that the line for the car traveling at a higher speed is steeper. A steeper slope on a distance-time graph indicates a higher speed.

Figure 7C shows the motion of a car that is not traveling at a constant speed. This car travels 200.0 meters in the first 8.0 seconds. It then stops for 4.0 seconds, as indicated by the horizontal part of the line. Next the car travels 300.0 meters in 8.0 seconds. The times when the car is gradually increasing or decreasing its speed are shown by the curved parts of the line. The slope of the straight portions of the line represent periods of constant speed. Note that the car's speed is 25 meters per second during the first part of its trip and 38 meters per second during the last part of its trip.

Figure 7 The slope of the line on a distance–time graph indicates the speed of the object. **Using Graphs** *If the car in Figure 7A required less time to travel a given distance, how would the slope change?*

A

Constant High Speed

B
Constant Low Speed

C

Varying Speed

Facts and Figures

Speed Records According to the Guinness World Records, the fastest human sprinter is Tim Montgomery, who set a record of 100 m in 9.78 s in 2002. Fred Rompelberg set a record for the fastest speed on a bicycle when he rode 268.831 km/h (167.043 mph) in 1995. In 1972, the fastest recorded wind speed was clocked at 333 km/h (207 mph) in Thule, Greenland. The fastest speed in the universe is the speed of light. Light travels in a vacuum at 3.00×10^8 m/s (186,000 miles/second).

Measuring Distance and Speed

Every car has a speedometer, which measures the car's speed, and an odometer, which measures the distance it has traveled. These devices work by counting the number of times the car's wheels turn (to give distance) and their rate of turning (speed).

Interpreting Diagrams *What is the purpose of the worm gears?*

Digital Odometer Some cars have a magnetic sensor that detects turns of the transmission shaft. The signal is transmitted to a computer, which calculates and displays the car's distance traveled.

Coil spring *This spring holds the pointer at zero when the car and the magnet are at rest.*

Cable *A cable linked to the transmission rotates at a rate directly proportional to the road speed.*

Pointer *The pointer is attached to the drag cup. The faster the magnet spins, the greater the angle the drag cup turns. The higher speed is shown by the pointer.*

Worm gears *The worm gears reduce the cable's rotational speed and move the odometer dials.*

Drag cup *The drag cup turns from its resting position through an angle that increases with the magnet's spin rate.*

Dial

Measurement *For each full turn of the worm gear the odometer moves up one digit, indicating that the car has traveled one tenth of a mile.*

Odometer

Magnet *The magnet is attached to the shaft. As the shaft spins the magnet, a magnetic field exerts force on the drag cup.*

Motion **335**

HOW It Works

Measuring Distance and Speed L2

The speedometer is an important part of any car. Knowing the speed of the car is important for following safety cautions on road signs.

By law, all cars must have a working odometer. It is against the law to change odometer readings or to operate a car in which the odometer is not working. The law prevents people from "rolling back" the odometers in order to increase the resale value of the car.

Interpreting Diagrams The worm gears convert the rotation of the cable into a much slower rotation that turns the odometer. The worm gears also change the direction of rotation so the shafts can be positioned to align with the odometer.
Logical, Visual

For Enrichment L3

Have students use a library or the Internet to research how speeds are measured on ships, airplanes, or spacecraft. Have them write a paragraph explaining their findings.
Verbal, Portfolio

Answer to . . .

Figure 7 *The slope of the line would increase.*

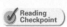 *Instantaneous speed*

Velocity

Compare and Contrast Refer to page **226D** in **Chapter 8**, which provides guidelines for comparing and contrasting.

Have students compare and contrast speed and velocity. Ask students, **How are speed and velocity similar?** *(They both measure how fast something is moving.)* **How are speed and velocity different?** *(Velocity includes the direction of motion, while speed does not.)* **Is velocity more like distance or displacement? Why?** *(Velocity is more like displacement. Both velocity and displacement are vectors, including magnitude and direction.)*
Logical

Address Misconceptions `L2`

Students may think that an object's speed and its velocity are the same thing. On the board, draw a picture of an oval racetrack. Have students imagine a racecar traveling at a constant speed of 120 km/h around the track. Point to a place on the track where the car would be moving to the right. Ask students, **What is the speed of the racecar at this point?** *(120 km/h)* **In what direction is the racecar traveling at this point?** *(To the right)* **What is the velocity of the racecar at this point?** *(120 km/h to the right)* Now point to a point on the track where the car would be moving to the left. Ask students, **What is the speed of the racecar at this point?** *(120 km/h)* **In what direction is the racecar traveling at this point?** *(To the left)* **What is the velocity of the racecar at this point?** *(120 km/h to the left)* The speeds are the same at each point, but the velocities are different because the racecar is traveling in different directions.
Verbal, Visual

Figure 8 A cheetah's speed may be as fast as 90 km/h. To describe the cheetah's velocity, you must also know the direction in which it is moving.

Velocity

The cheetah is the fastest land animal in the world. Suppose a cheetah, running at 90 kilometers per hour, is 30 meters from an antelope that is standing still. How long will it be before the cheetah reaches the antelope? Do you have enough information to answer the question? The answer is no. Sometimes knowing only the speed of an object isn't enough. You also need to know the direction of the object's motion. Together, the speed and direction in which an object is moving are called **velocity**. To determine how long it will be before the cheetah reaches the antelope, you need to know the cheetah's velocity, not just its speed. ◯ **Velocity is a description of both speed and direction of motion. Velocity is a vector.**

Figure 8 shows a cheetah in motion. If you have ever seen a video of a cheetah chasing its prey, you know that a cheetah can change speed and direction very quickly. To represent the cheetah's motion, you could use velocity vectors. You would need vectors of varying lengths, each vector corresponding to the cheetah's velocity at a particular instant. A longer vector would represent a faster speed, and a shorter one would show a slower speed. The vectors would also point in different directions to represent the cheetah's direction at any moment.

A change in velocity can be the result of a change in speed, a change in direction, or both. The sailboat in Figure 9 moves in a straight line (constant direction) at a constant speed. The sailboat can be described as moving with uniform motion, which is another way of saying it has constant velocity. The sailboat may change its velocity simply by speeding up or slowing down. However, the sailboat's velocity also changes if it changes its direction. It may continue to move at a constant speed, but the change of direction is a change in velocity.

Figure 9 As the sailboat's direction changes, its velocity also changes, even if its speed stays the same. **Inferring** *If the sailboat slows down at the same time that it changes direction, how will its velocity be changed?*

336 *Chapter 11*

Combining Velocities

Sometimes the motion of an object involves more than one velocity. 🔵 **Two or more velocities add by vector addition.** The velocity of the river relative to the riverbank (X) and the velocity of the boat relative to the river (Y) in Figure 10A combine. They yield the velocity of the boat relative to the riverbank (Z). This velocity is 17 kilometers per hour downstream.

In Figure 10B, the relative velocities of the current (X) and the boat (Y) are at right angles to each other. Adding these velocity vectors yields a resultant velocity of the boat relative to the riverbank of 13 km/h (Z). Note that this velocity is at an angle to the riverbank.

Figure 10 Vector addition is used when motion involves more than one velocity. **A** The velocity of the boat in the reference frame of the riverbank (17 km/h) is a combination of the relative velocities of the boat and the river. **B** You can determine the resultant velocity of the boat relative to the riverbank (13 km/h) by measuring from the tail of one vector to the head of the other.

Section 11.2 Assessment

Reviewing Concepts

1. 🔵 What does velocity describe?
2. 🔵 What shows the speed on a distance-time graph?
3. 🔵 What is the difference between average speed and instantaneous speed?
4. 🔵 How can two or more velocities be combined?

Critical Thinking

5. **Applying Concepts** Does a car's speedometer show instantaneous speed, average speed, or velocity? Explain.
6. **Designing Experiments** Describe an experiment you could perform to determine the average speed of a toy car rolling down an incline.

7. **Applying Concepts** Explain why the slope on a distance-time graph is speed. (*Hint:* Use the definition of *speed* on page 332 and the graphs in Figure 7.)

Math Practice

8. An Olympic swimmer swims 50.0 meters in 23.1 seconds. What is his average speed?

9. A plane's average speed between two cities is 600 km/h. If the trip takes 2.5 hours, how far does the plane fly? (*Hint:* Use the average speed formula in the form $d = \bar{v}t$.)

Motion **337**

Combining Velocities
Use Visuals `L1`

Figure 10 Figure 10B shows two velocity vectors at right angles combining to form a single vector. You can use this opportunity to show students how to find the magnitude of resultant vectors.

Start by reminding students of the Pythagorean theorem:

$$a^2 + b^2 = c^2$$

for right triangles in which a and b are the legs and c is the hypotenuse. In this case, a is the speed of the boat, b is the speed of the river, and c is the resulting combined speed.
Do the following calculation on the board:

$$c = \sqrt{a^2 + b^2}$$
$$= \sqrt{(12\ km/h)^2 + (5\ km/h)^2}$$
$$= \sqrt{144\ km^2/h^2 + 25\ km^2/h^2}$$
$$= \sqrt{169\ km^2/h^2}$$
$$= 13\ km/h$$

When you have finished the calculation, point out that the result agrees with the speed shown in Figure 10B.
Visual, Logical

3 ASSESS

Evaluate Understanding `L2`

Ask students to write a paragraph describing how they could measure the average speed of a racecar on a racetrack. Also have them draw the velocity vectors at several locations for a racecar traveling at a constant speed around a circular track.

Reteach `L1`

Use the graphs in Figure 7 to reteach the concepts in the section.

Solutions `L2`
8. $\bar{v} = (50.0\ m)/(23.1\ s) = 2.16\ m/s$
9. $d = \bar{v}t = (600\ km/h)(2.5\ h) = 1500\ km$

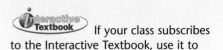 If your class subscribes to the Interactive Textbook, use it to review key concepts in Section 11.2.

> **Answer to . . .**
>
> **Figure 9** *Both the magnitude and direction of the velocity will change.*

Section 11.2 Assessment

1. Velocity describes both speed and direction of motion.
2. The slope of a line on a distance-time graph is equal to speed.
3. Average speed is calculated for the entire duration of a trip, whereas instantaneous speed is determined at a single moment.
4. Two or more velocities can be combined by vector addition.
5. A speedometer measures speed at the current moment, so it shows instantaneous speed, not average speed. Because a speedometer does not show direction it does not show velocity.
6. Students may describe how they could use a stopwatch to measure the time for the car to travel down the incline. The average speed would be calculated by dividing the distance traveled by the total time.
7. Slope is equal to the change in vertical value divided by the change in horizontal value. On a distance-time graph, the change in vertical value is a distance and the change in horizontal value is a time. Therefore, the slope is distance divided by time, which equals average speed.

CONCEPTS in Action

Navigation at Sea L2

Background

Before the invention of the compass, the most reliable source of information for navigators was the stars. Celestial navigation was useful not only at sea, but also in open deserts where there were few landmarks. The simplest examples of celestial navigation are the sighting of north using Polaris, the pole star, and crude approximations of east and west using sunrise and sunset. Early navigators at sea also often simply followed coastlines or tracked well-known ocean currents to keep from losing their way. The Polynesians were masters of navigation in the open sea, traveling long distances to pinpoint tiny islands in the South Pacific. The Polynesians are believed to have used the migratory paths of birds and the directions of waves as navigational clues.

Navigation at Sea

For centuries, crossing the oceans was extremely perilous. There are few landmarks at sea to guide the sailor, and methods of measuring direction, speed, and distance were crude and often inaccurate.

The invention of the magnetic compass brought major advancement in navigation in the early 1100s. Although the compass allowed a sailor to maintain an accurate course, it did nothing to tell him where he actually was. For this, a frame of reference was needed, and the one adopted was the system of latitude and longitude. This system measures location in degrees north or south of the equator, and degrees east or west of Greenwich, England. Using a device called a sextant, latitude in the northern hemisphere was relatively easy to determine. Finding longitude was more difficult. The solution was to combine celestial observation and the use of a highly accurate sea-going clock that kept track of the time at a fixed location on Earth.

Sextant
This instrument was once an essential aid to navigation. With it, a sailor could accurately measure the angles of celestial bodies above the horizon. To take a reading, the observer looks through the telescope and moves the sextant's arm until an image of a star or the sun lines up with the horizon. The angle is then read off the scale.

Sun's rays

Rotating mirror

Fixed mirror

Telescope

Eyepiece

Movable arm

Scale

Magnetic compass
The magnetic compass contains a magnetized needle which, due to the Earth's magnetic field, points roughly toward the North Pole.

Finding location

Regular calculations of latitude and longitude have been the cornerstone of ocean navigation for about 300 years. A sextant and an accurate sea-going clock were needed to calculate both.

Determining latitude
To determine latitude is to find out how far north or south you are from the equator. In the northern hemisphere, latitude is measured with reference to Polaris. Using a sextant, you measure the angle of Polaris above the horizon, and this gives you your latitude, expressed in degrees. If Polaris is directly overhead, you must be at the North Pole (90° north latitude); if it is on the horizon, you must be at the equator (0°).

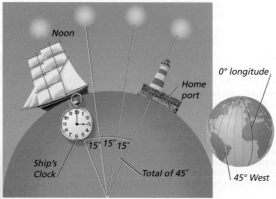

Determining longitude
To determine longitude is to find out how far east or west you are from Greenwich, England. To do this, while you are still in your home port, you set your sea-going clock for noon when the sun is at its highest point. Then, while you are at sea, you check the clock again when the sun is at its highest point. If the clock says 3 P.M., then you must have traveled 3 hours west of the port. Since the sun moves 15° per hour, 3 hours corresponds to 45° west.

Observing Have students go out on a clear night and locate Polaris, the pole star. Students may do this on their own, or you may have a class field trip. If you go as a group, also take a few pairs of binoculars and a telescope, if available. With a basic pair of binoculars, students can see many more stars, as well as many interesting celestial sights such as star clusters, the moons of Jupiter, and craters on Earth's moon. Teach students how to use the two stars at the end of the Big Dipper to locate Polaris. Then, follow the line from these two stars "up" away from the dipper (in the direction of the opening in the dipper; the actual direction will depend on the position of the dipper). The first bright star in the line is Polaris. Have students use a protractor and a ruler or other straight object to estimate Polaris' angle of elevation above the horizon. This angle should be equal to the latitude at which you are observing. Have students compare their estimates to the actual latitude.
Visual, Group, Portfolio

Build Science Skills L2

Measuring

Purpose After doing this activity, students will be able to use a handheld GPS receiver to find coordinates, mark waypoints, and navigate to a location.

Materials handheld GPS receivers, 1 per group

Advance Prep Clear data from all the GPS receivers. Set all receivers so they are using the same units for coordinates. If you are unfamiliar with operating a GPS receiver, review the manual and practice marking a few waypoints (waypoints are locations that you store in the memory of a GPS unit). Find several locations on the school grounds and write down the GPS coordinates for those locations (students will return to these locations in the activity).

Class Time 30 minutes

Procedure

1. Start by showing the class the basics of operating the GPS receiver. You may do this outdoors, or if you are in the classroom, put the receiver in simulator mode. Show students how to tell how strong the signals are, how to read the coordinates of their location, and how to mark a waypoint.

2. Start all groups at a single point. Have them acquire the coordinates at that location and mark a waypoint. Assign each group a different location and give them the coordinates (but do not tell them where the location is). Then, have them use the receivers to find their assigned locations. You may have them use the navigation feature of the receiver to find the location, or they may just use the coordinates. Have them mark a waypoint when they reach the location.

3. After they have found their location, have the group return and describe the location to you. Verify that it is close to the location that you intended. Check each group's receiver to see if their marked waypoints have the correct coordinates.

CONCEPTS in Action

Modern navigation

Today's sea navigators are fortunate by comparison with their predecessors. Instead of having to make complex calculations involving times and sextant angles, they can buy a global positioning system receiver. This modern receiver not only provides quick and accurate readings of latitude and longitude, but it also displays the ship's position on a digital chart.

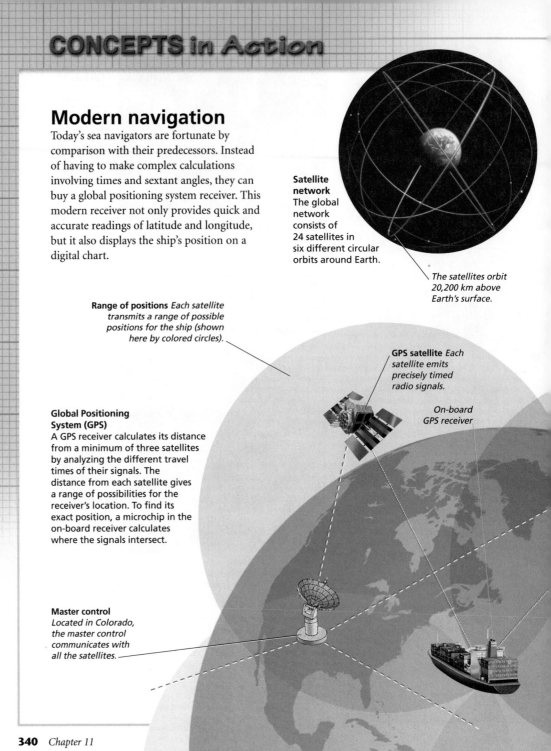

Satellite network The global network consists of 24 satellites in six different circular orbits around Earth.

The satellites orbit 20,200 km above Earth's surface.

Range of positions *Each satellite transmits a range of possible positions for the ship (shown here by colored circles).*

GPS satellite *Each satellite emits precisely timed radio signals.*

On-board GPS receiver

Global Positioning System (GPS)
A GPS receiver calculates its distance from a minimum of three satellites by analyzing the different travel times of their signals. The distance from each satellite gives a range of possibilities for the receiver's location. To find its exact position, a microchip in the on-board receiver calculates where the signals intersect.

Master control
Located in Colorado, the master control communicates with all the satellites.

Charting a course
A navigator normally keeps a record of the ship's movements on a chart. Positions obtained by GPS or other means are plotted on the chart, which can also be used to work out a compass bearing or a course for the next part of the voyage.

Nautical dividers
Divers are used for making chart measurements.

Transparent compass

Ship's position

GPS receiver
Today, receivers are made in a range of sizes down to handheld models. They usually give a position accurate to 100 meters, but enhanced units are accurate within 10 meters.

Coast

Open sea

Using radar
A radar set displays nearby land, boats, and other surface objects. It is useful for both navigation and collision avoidance, especially in foggy conditions.

Going Further

- Research the term *knots*, which is used for measuring a ship's speed. Write a paragraph to explain how speed was originally estimated on a ship by using knots.
- Take a Discovery Channel Video Field Trip by watching "Charting New Ground."

DISCOVERY CHANNEL SCHOOL
Video Field Trip

Expected Outcome Students may have trouble finding the locations at first. The GPS receivers may have varying degrees of accuracy, depending on the receiver and the outside conditions. Also, students may be confused if the axes of the coordinates do not align with the boundaries of the area. However, students should get used to operating the receiver and following the coordinates. Note that due to inaccuracies in GPS data and to differences in individual receivers, the locations that students find might not align perfectly with the locations that you found initially.
Kinesthetic, Group, Logical

Going Further

Students' paragraphs should describe how early navigators measured the speed of a ship by throwing a log or wooden panel overboard. The log or panel was tied with a rope that had knots tied at regular intervals. The speed of the ship (relative to the water) could be measured by counting the number of knots that passed over the edge of the ship in a certain time interval. Knots are still used as units of speed in navigation, although they are measured with more precise instruments. 1 knot = 1 nautical mile per hour = 6076 feet per hour = 1.15 mph.
Verbal

Video Field Trip
Charting New Ground

After students have viewed the Video Field Trip, ask them the following questions: **What was the shape of Earth according to the ancient Greeks? What Earth dimension did they calculate using this shape?** *(They knew Earth was a sphere, and calculated its circumference.)* **What does latitude measure? Longitude?** *(Latitude measures how far north or south a location is.*

Longitude measures how far east or west a location is.) **What did navigators notice about how high the sun rose at noon in northern regions? How could this be used to determine the position of their ships?** *(Navigators noticed that in northern regions the sun remained low in the sky even in the middle of the summer. The height of the sun at noon told navigators how far north they were. Some students may note that when the sun is low in the sky at noon in the Southern Hemisphere, this would indicate how far south you are.)* **How did**

navigators know how far west they were from their homeport in the 1700s? *(The ship's clock would be set at the same time as the clock in the navigator's homeport. As the ship traveled west, the sun was lower in the sky when the clock read noon.)* **List two modern technologies that are now used in making maps.** *(Student answers may include aerial photography, satellites, and computers.)*

1 FOCUS

Objectives

11.3.1 Identify changes in motion that produce acceleration.

11.3.2 Describe examples of constant acceleration.

11.3.3 Calculate the acceleration of an object.

11.3.4 Interpret speed-time and distance-time graphs.

11.3.5 Classify acceleration as positive or negative.

11.3.6 Describe instantaneous acceleration.

Reading Focus

Build Vocabulary **L2**

Word Forms Point out other forms of the terms or parts of the terms. For example, in this section, explain that *linear* contains the word *line* and means, "in a straight line," or more generally, "having to do with lines." Then have students predict what *nonlinear* might mean. *(It means not in a straight line or having to do with lines that are not straight.)*

Reading Strategy **L2**

a. Speed (or direction)
b. Direction (or speed)
c. m/s^2

2 INSTRUCT

What is Acceleration?

Use Visuals **L1**

Figure 11 Use the example of a bouncing basketball to introduce acceleration. Ask, **As the ball falls from the girl's hand, how does its speed change?** *(Its speed increases.)* **What happens to the speed of the ball as the ball rises from the ground back to her hand?** *(The speed decreases.)* **At what points does the ball have zero velocity?** *(When it touches the girl's hand and when it touches the floor)* **How does the velocity of the ball change when it bounces on the floor?** *(The speed quickly drops to zero, then quickly increases again. The ball also changes direction.)* **Visual, Logical**

11.3 Acceleration

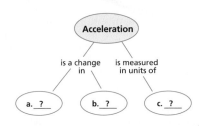

Standards: ICP.1.1, ICP.1.2

Reading Focus

Key Concepts

- How are changes in velocity described?
- How can you calculate acceleration?
- How does a speed-time graph indicate acceleration?
- What is instantaneous acceleration?

Vocabulary

- acceleration
- free fall
- constant acceleration
- linear graph
- nonlinear graph

Reading Strategy

Summarizing Read the section on acceleration. Then copy and complete the concept map below to organize what you know about acceleration.

```
              Acceleration

    is a change          is measured
        in               in units of

  a.  ?       b.  ?          c.  ?
```

Figure 11 The basketball constantly changes velocity as it rises and falls.

A basketball constantly changes velocity during a game. The player in Figure 11 dribbles the ball down the court, and the ball speeds up as it falls and slows down as it rises. As she passes the ball, it flies through the air and suddenly stops when a teammate catches it. The velocity of the ball increases again as it is thrown toward the basket.

But the rate at which velocity changes is also important. Imagine a basketball player running down the court and slowly coming to a stop. Now imagine the player running down the court and stopping suddenly. If the player stops slowly, his or her velocity changes slowly. If the player stops suddenly, his or her velocity changes quickly. The ball handler's teammates must position themselves to assist the drive or to take a pass. Opposing team members want to prevent the ball handler from reaching the basket. Each player must anticipate the ball handler's motion.

Velocity changes frequently, not only in a basketball game, but throughout our physical world. Describing changes in velocity, and how fast they occur, is a necessary part of describing motion.

What Is Acceleration?

The rate at which velocity changes is called **acceleration**. Recall that velocity is a combination of speed and direction. ⟳ **Acceleration can be described as changes in speed, changes in direction, or changes in both. Acceleration is a vector.**

342 Chapter 11

⏱ Section Resources

Print

- **Reading and Study Workbook With Math Support,** Section 11.3
- **Math Skills and Problem Solving Workbook,** Section 11.3
- **Transparencies,** Section 11.3

Technology

- **Interactive Textbook,** Section 11.3
- **Presentation Pro CD-ROM,** Section 11.3
- **Go Online,** NSTA SciLinks, Acceleration

Changes in Speed We often use the word *acceleration* to describe situations in which the speed of an object is increasing. A television newscaster describing the liftoff of a rocket-launched space shuttle, for example, might exclaim, "That shuttle is really accelerating!" We understand that the newscaster is describing the spacecraft's quickly increasing speed as it clears its launch pad and rises through the atmosphere. Scientifically, however, acceleration applies to any change in an object's velocity. This change may be either an increase or a decrease in speed. Acceleration can be caused by positive (increasing) change in speed or by negative (decreasing) change in speed.

For example, suppose that you are sitting on a bus waiting at a stoplight. The light turns green and the bus moves forward. You feel the acceleration as you are pushed back against your seat. The acceleration is the result of an increase in the speed of the bus. As the bus moves down the street at a constant speed, its acceleration is zero. You no longer feel pushed toward your seat. When the bus approaches another stoplight, it begins to slow down. Again, its speed is changing, so the bus is accelerating. You feel pulled away from your seat. Acceleration results from increases or decreases in speed. As the bus slows to a stop, it experiences negative acceleration, also known as deceleration. Deceleration is an acceleration that slows an object's speed.

An example of acceleration due to change in speed is **free fall,** the movement of an object toward Earth solely because of gravity. Recall that the unit for velocity is meters per second. The unit for acceleration, then, is meters per second per second. This unit is typically written as meters per second squared (m/s^2). Objects falling near Earth's surface accelerate downward at a rate of 9.8 m/s^2. Each second an object is in free fall, its velocity increases downward by 9.8 meters per second. Imagine the stone in Figure 12 falling from the mouth of the well. After 1 second, the stone will be falling at about 9.8 m/s. After 2 seconds, the stone will be going faster by 9.8 m/s. Its speed will now be downward at 19.6 m/s. The change in the stone's speed is 9.8 m/s^2, the acceleration due to gravity.

t = 0 s
v = 0 m/s

t = 1 s
v = 9.8 m/s

t = 2 s
v = 19.6 m/s

t = 3 s
v = 29.4 m/s

Figure 12 The velocity of an object in free fall increases 9.8 m/s each second.

Motion **343**

Pendulum Accelerometer **L2**

Purpose Students observe how the displacement of a pendulum can be used as evidence of acceleration, and how a pendulum can show that acceleration is taking place during uniform circular motion.

Materials short pendulum (25 cm), turntable, lab stand, tape

Advance Prep Place the lab stand on the outer edge of the turntable. The stand should be tall enough to hold the pendulum so that it doesn't touch the turntable. Tape the base of the stand to the turntable.

Procedure Tell students that a pendulum can be used to provide evidence of acceleration. Acceleration causes displacement of the pendulum. Demonstrate this by walking forward and backward while holding a pendulum in one hand held in front of you. You will have to accelerate slightly as you walk; otherwise, the pendulum will start swinging. Ask students to describe the position of the pendulum when you stand still, walk forward, change direction, and walk backward. Show students the turntable, and tie the pendulum to the lab stand. Ask students to predict how the pendulum will be displaced when the turntable is spinning. Start the turntable spinning, and have students compare the observed displacement of the pendulum to their predictions.

Expected Outcome When you are holding the pendulum, the pendulum will be displaced toward you when you are walking forward and away from you when you are walking backward. When the turntable is spinning, the pendulum will be displaced away from the center of the turntable. This demonstrates that acceleration is taking place during uniform circular motion. The acceleration in this case is purely a change in direction.
Kinesthetic, Visual

Figure 13 When you ride on a carousel, you accelerate because of the changing direction.

Changes in Direction Acceleration isn't always the result of changes in speed. You can accelerate even if your speed is constant. You experience this type of acceleration if you ride a bicycle around a curve. Although you may have a constant speed, your change in direction means you are accelerating. You also may have experienced this type of acceleration if you have ridden on a carousel like the one in Figure 13. A horse on the carousel is traveling at a constant speed, but it is accelerating because its direction is constantly changing.

Changes in Speed and Direction Sometimes motion is characterized by changes in both speed and direction at the same time. You experience this type of motion if you ride on a roller coaster like the one in Figure 14. The roller coaster ride starts out slowly as the cars travel up the steeply inclined rails. The cars reach the top of the incline. Suddenly they plummet toward the ground and then whip around a curve. You are thrown backward, forward, and sideways as your velocity increases, decreases, and changes direction. Your acceleration is constantly changing because of changes in the speed and direction of the cars of the roller coaster.

Similarly, passengers in a car moving at the posted speed limit along a winding road experience rapidly changing acceleration. The car may enter a long curve at the same time that it slows to maintain a safe interval behind another car. The car is accelerating both because it is changing direction and because its speed is decreasing.

Figure 14 A roller coaster produces acceleration due to changes in both speed and direction. Applying Concepts *Describe the acceleration occuring at this instant on the rollercoaster ride.*

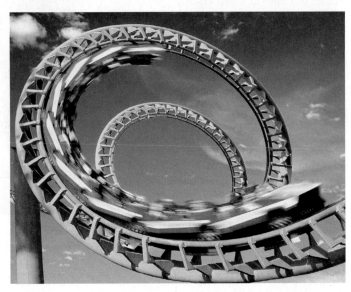

Constant Acceleration The velocity of an object moving in a straight line changes at a constant rate when the object is experiencing constant acceleration. **Constant acceleration** is a steady change in velocity. That is, the velocity of the object changes by the same amount each second. An example of constant acceleration is illustrated by the jet airplane shown in Figure 15. The airplane's acceleration may be constant during a portion of its takeoff.

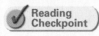 **Reading Checkpoint** *What is constant acceleration?*

Calculating Acceleration

Acceleration is the rate at which velocity changes. **You calculate acceleration for straight-line motion by dividing the change in velocity by the total time.** If a is the acceleration, v_i is the initial velocity, v_f is the final velocity, and t is total time, then this equation can be written as follows.

Acceleration

$$\text{Acceleration} = \frac{\text{Change in velocity}}{\text{Total time}} = \frac{(v_f - v_i)}{t}$$

Notice in this formula that velocity is in the numerator and time is in the denominator. If the velocity increases, the numerator is positive and thus the acceleration is also positive. For example, if you are coasting downhill on a bicycle, your velocity increases and your acceleration is positive. If the velocity decreases, then the numerator is negative and the acceleration is also negative. For example, if you continue coasting after you reach the bottom of the hill, your velocity decreases and your acceleration is negative.

Remember that acceleration and velocity are both vector quantities. Thus, if an object moving at constant speed changes its direction of travel, there is still acceleration. In other words, the acceleration can occur even if the speed is constant. Think about a car moving at a constant speed as it rounds a curve. Because its direction is changing, the car is accelerating.

To determine a change in velocity, subtract one velocity vector from another. If the motion is in a straight line, however, the velocity can be treated as speed. You can then find acceleration from the change in speed divided by the time.

Figure 15 Constant acceleration during takeoff results in changes to an aircraft's velocity that are in a constant direction.

For: Links on acceleration
Visit: www.SciLinks.org
Web Code: ccn-2113

Motion **345**

Solutions

1. $a = (v_f - v_i)/t = (0 \text{ m/s} - 10 \text{ m/s})/20 \text{ s}$
$= -0.5 \text{ m/s}^2$

2. $(v_f - v_i) = at = (9.0 \text{ m/s}^2)(4.0 \text{ s}) = 36 \text{ m/s}$

3. $v_i = 0$; $v_f = at = (9.8 \text{ m/s}^2)(2.0 \text{ s}) = 2.0 \times 10^1 \text{ m/s}$

4. $v_f = 0$; $v_i = -at = -(9.8 \text{ m/s}^2)(2.5 \text{ s})$
$= -25 \text{ m/s}$ (the minus sign indicates that the velocity is in the direction opposite the acceleration)
Logical

For Extra Help   L1

Students may have difficulty rearranging the equation to solve for other variables, especially for v_i or v_f. Write the procedure clearly on the board and describe each step. For example, to solve for v_f,
1) multiply both sides of the equation by t, then 2) cancel the t/t on the right side of the equation, then 3) add v_i to both sides of the equation. Afterwards, have students work in pairs and demonstrate the procedure for each other for the different variables. When you feel they understand the process, they can begin to solve problems that include numbers.
Logical

Direct students to the **Math Skills** in the **Skills and Reference Handbook** at the end of the student text for additional help.

Additional Problems

1. A sprinter accelerates from the starting block to a speed of 8.0 m/s in 4.0 s. What is the magnitude of the sprinter's acceleration? *(2.0 m/s²)*
2. A car is traveling at 14 m/s. Stepping on the gas pedal causes the car to accelerate at 2.0 m/s². How long does the driver have to step on the pedal to reach a speed of 18 m/s? *(2.0 s)*
Logical, Portfolio

1. A car traveling at 10 m/s starts to decelerate steadily. It comes to a complete stop in 20 seconds. What is its acceleration?

2. An airplane travels down a runway for 4.0 seconds with an acceleration of 9.0 m/s². What is its change in velocity during this time?

3. A child drops a ball from a bridge. The ball strikes the water under the bridge 2.0 seconds later. What is the velocity of the ball when it strikes the water?

4. A boy throws a rock straight up into the air. It reaches the highest point of its flight after 2.5 seconds. How fast was the rock going when it left the boy's hand?

Math Skills

Calculating Acceleration

A ball rolls down a ramp, starting from rest. After 2 seconds, its velocity is 6 meters per second. What is the acceleration of the ball?

1   **Read and Understand**

What information are you given?

> **Time** = 2 s
>
> **Starting velocity** = 0 m/s
>
> **Ending velocity** = 6 m/s

2   **Plan and Solve**

What unknown are you trying to calculate?

> **Acceleration** = ?

What formula contains the given quantities and the unknown?

$$a = \frac{(v_f - v_i)}{t}$$

Replace each variable with its known value.

$$\text{Acceleration} = \frac{(6 \text{ m/s} - 0 \text{ m/s})}{2 \text{ s}}$$

$$= 3 \text{ m/s}^2 \text{ down the ramp}$$

3   **Look Back and Check**

Is your answer reasonable?

Objects in free fall accelerate at a rate of 9.8 m/s². The ramp is not very steep. An acceleration of 3 m/s² seems reasonable.

Graphs of Accelerated Motion

You can use a graph to calculate acceleration. For example, consider a downhill skier who is moving in a straight line. After traveling down the hill for 1 second, the skier's speed is 4 meters per second. In the next second the speed increases by an additional 4 meters per second, so the skier's acceleration is 4 m/s². Figure 16 is a graph of the skier's speed.
⊜ **The slope of a speed-time graph is acceleration.** This slope is change in speed divided by change in time.

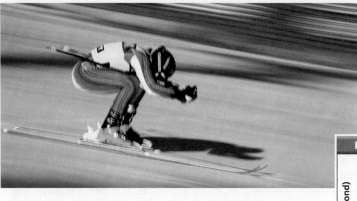

Speed-Time Graphs The skier's speed increased at a constant rate because the skier was moving down the hill with constant acceleration. Constant acceleration is represented on a speed–time graph by a straight line. The graph in Figure 16 is an example of a **linear graph,** in which the displayed data form straight-line parts. The slope of the line is the acceleration.

Constant negative acceleration decreases speed. A speed-time graph of the motion of a bicycle slowing to a stop is shown in Figure 17. The horizontal line segment represents constant speed. The line segment sloping downward represents the bicycle slowing down. The change in speed is negative, so the slope of the line is negative.

Figure 16 The slope of a speed-time graph indicates acceleration. A positive slope shows that the skier's acceleration is positive.

Figure 17 The horizontal part of the graph shows a biker's constant speed. The part of the graph with negative slope shows negative acceleration as the mountain biker slows to a stop.

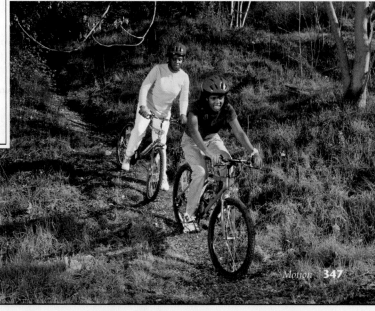

Motion **347**

Finding Slope on a Graph Remind students that the slope of a line on a graph is found by dividing the difference of two points on the vertical axis by the corresponding points on the horizontal axis. The two points used to find the slope should be chosen as far apart on the line as possible.

Have students calculate the slope of the line on the graph in Figure 16. Tell them also to include the units in their calculation. *(4 m/s²)* Now have them calculate the slope of the line between 10 and 20 seconds on the graph in Figure 17. *(0.5 m/s²)*
Logical

Direct students to the **Math Skills** in the **Skills and Reference Handbook** at the end of the student text for additional help.

Use Visuals L1

Figure 17 Ask students the following questions about the speed-time graph in Figure 17. **What are the units on the vertical axis?** *(m/s)* **What are the units on the horizontal axis?** *(s)* **What would be the units of the slope of a line on this graph?** *(m/s/s, or m/s²)* Remind students that the bike represents the motion of a mountain biker in the photograph. Ask students, **Is the bike moving at time zero?** *(Yes)* **How fast is it moving at that time?** *(5 m/s)* **What happens to the bike after 10 seconds?** *(It starts to slow down.)* **How would you describe the acceleration of the bike from that point on?** *(The acceleration is constant and negative.)*
Visual, Logical

Instantaneous Acceleration

Integrate Math `L2`

Differential calculus is the branch of mathematics that physicists use when considering instantaneous quantities, such as instantaneous speed or instantaneous acceleration. When you use calculus to determine acceleration, you can take the difference in velocities over smaller and smaller time intervals until the time interval becomes, in effect, infinitely small. The slope of a curved line is equal to the slope of a line drawn tangent to a point on the plotted curve. Graphically, this is like finding the slope of a line connecting two points on a speed-time graph, but then moving the points closer and closer together until you have the slope of a line tangent to the curve at a single point on the graph. In this case, the slope of the line represents the instantaneous acceleration at that point.

Logical, Visual

3 ASSESS

Evaluate Understanding `L2`

Ask students to sketch a speed-time graph of a car starting from rest, accelerating up to the speed limit, maintaining that speed, then slowing again to a stop.

Reteach `L1`

Use the graphs on page 347 to reteach the concepts in the section. Ask students to identify which kind of acceleration cannot be shown on the graphs.
(A change in direction)

Solutions `L2`

8. $a = (v_f - v_i)/t =$
$(25 \text{ m/s} - 0 \text{ m/s})/(30.0 \text{ s}) =$
0.83 m/s^2
9. $a = (v_f - v_i)/t =$
$(30.0 \text{ m/s} - 25 \text{ m/s})/(10.0 \text{ s}) =$
0.50 m/s^2

Interactive Textbook If your class subscribes to the Interactive Textbook, use it to review key concepts in Section 11.3.

Acceleration Over Time

Figure 18 A distance-time graph of accelerated motion is a curve.

Distance-Time Graphs Accelerated motion is represented by a curved line on a distance-time graph. In a **nonlinear graph,** a curve connects the data points that are plotted. Figure 18 is a distance-time graph. The data in this graph are for a ball dropped from rest toward the ground.

Compare the slope of the curve during the first second to the slope of the curve during the fourth second. Notice that the slope is much greater during the fourth second than it is during the first second. Because the slope represents the speed of the ball, an increasing slope means that the speed is increasing. An increasing speed means that the ball is accelerating.

Instantaneous Acceleration

Acceleration is rarely constant, and motion is rarely in a straight line. A skateboarder moving along a half-pipe changes speed and direction. As a result, her acceleration changes. At each moment she is accelerating, but her instantaneous acceleration is always changing. **Instantaneous acceleration is how fast a velocity is changing at a specific instant.**

Acceleration involves a change in velocity or direction or both, so the vector of the skateboarder's acceleration can point in any direction. The vector's length depends on how fast she is changing her velocity. At every moment she has an instantaneous acceleration, even if she is standing still and the acceleration vector is zero.

Section 11.3 Assessment

Reviewing Concepts

1. Describe three types of changes in velocity.
2. What is the equation for acceleration?
3. What shows acceleration on a speed-time graph?
4. Define instantaneous acceleration.

Critical Thinking

5. **Comparing and Contrasting** How are deceleration and acceleration related?
6. **Applying Concepts** Two trains leave a station at the same time. Train A travels at a constant speed of 16 m/s. Train B starts at 8.0 m/s but accelerates constantly at 1.0 m/s². After 10.0 seconds, which train has the greater speed?

7. **Inferring** Suppose you plot the distance traveled by an object at various times and you discover that the graph is not a straight line. What does this indicate about the object's acceleration?

Math Practice

8. A train moves from rest to a speed of 25 m/s in 30.0 seconds. What is the magnitude of its acceleration?
9. A car traveling at a speed of 25 m/s increases its speed to 30.0 m/s in 10.0 seconds. What is the magnitude of its acceleration?

348 *Chapter 11*

Section 11.3 Assessment

1. Changes in velocity can be described as changes in speed, changes in direction, or changes in both (or, an increase in speed, a decrease in speed, or a change in direction).
2. $a = (v_f - v_i)/t$
3. The slope of the line on a speed-time graph gives the acceleration.

4. Instantaneous acceleration is how fast the velocity is changing at a specific instant.
5. Deceleration is a special case of acceleration in which the speed of an object is decreasing.
6. Train B ($v = v_0 + at = 8.0 \text{ m/s} + (1.0 \text{ m/s}^2)(10.0 \text{ s}) = 8.0 \text{ m/s} + 10.0 \text{ m/s} = 18 \text{ m/s}$)
7. The graph indicates that the object is accelerating.

Investigating the Velocity of a Sinking Marble

In this lab, you will graph the motion of a marble falling through shampoo.

Problem
What does a distance-time graph look like for a marble falling through shampoo?

Materials
- clear shampoo
- 100-mL graduated cylinder
- 2 small marbles
- stopwatch
- forceps
- masking tape
- metric ruler
- 10-mL graduated cylinder
- long glass stirring rod
- dropper pipet
- graph paper

Skills
Measuring, Observing, Using Tables and Graphs

Procedure

1. On a separate sheet of paper, make a copy of the data table shown.

Data Table		
Distance (mm)	First Marble Time (s)	Second Marble Time (s)

2. Wrap a small amount of masking tape around the tips of the forceps. This will allow you to grip the marble with them.

3. Measure the distance between the 10-mL gradations on the 100-mL graduated cylinder. Record the new distance in the first row of your data table.

4. Multiply this distance by 2 and write the result in the second row. For the third row, multiply the distance by 3. Continue until you have written distances in 10 rows.

5. Slowly pour 100 mL of clear shampoo into the 100-mL graduated cylinder.

6. Be ready to observe the marble as it falls through the shampoo. Grasp the marble with the forceps and hold the marble just above the shampoo-filled graduated cylinder.

7. Say "Go!" as you drop the marble into the shampoo. At the same moment, your partner should start the stopwatch.

8. Each time the lower edge of the marble reaches a 10-mL mark on the cylinder, say "Now." Your partner should note and record the time on the stopwatch.

9. Continue calling out "Now" each time the marble reaches a 10-mL mark until it comes to rest on the bottom of the cylinder. Say "Stop!"

10. Use the 10-mL graduated cylinder to add about 8 mL of water to the 100-mL graduated cylinder. Use the glass stirring rod to mix the water and shampoo gently but thoroughly.

11. With the dropper pipet, remove enough liquid from the graduated cylinder to decrease the volume to 100 mL.

12. Repeat Steps 6 through 9 using another marble.

13. Wash all supplies as instructed by your teacher.

Analyze and Conclude

1. **Using Tables and Graphs** Use the data you collected to make a distance-time graph for each of the two marbles.

2. **Observing** Explain the motion of the marbles as they fell through the shampoo. How did you show this motion on your graphs?

3. **Inferring** Based on your graphs, were the marbles accelerating? Explain your answers.

4. **Calculating** Use your data table to calculate the average speed of each marble.

For: Data sharing
Visit: PHSchool.com
Web Code: ccd-2110

Investigating the Velocity of a Sinking Marble
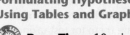 L2

Objective
After completing this activity, students will be able to
- use a distance-time graph to determine speed and acceleration.

Skills Focus
Observing, Formulating Hypotheses, Using Tables and Graphs

 Prep Time 10 minutes

Alternative Materials Corn syrup or mild laundry detergent can be used in place of shampoo.

Class Time 40 minutes

Safety Have students wear safety goggles to ensure shampoo does not enter their eyes.

Teaching Tips
- Tell students to pour the shampoo into the graduated cylinder so that as little as possible sticks to the side.

Expected Outcome The marble falls more quickly through diluted shampoo than through undiluted shampoo.

Sample Data

Students should see that the marbles have a nearly constant speed until they near the bottom of the graduated cylinder, where they begin to slow, but students' results will depend on their own data and the data on the site.

Analyze and Conclude

1. The graph should be a nearly straight line for both marbles. The graph for the second marble will be steeper.

2. At first, the marbles fell at a nearly constant velocity, which is shown as a straight line on the distance-time graph. The second marble fell faster than the first marble. As the marbles approached the bottom of the cylinder, the viscosity of the shampoo caused them to slow down.

3. Answers will depend on the viscosity of the shampoo. In most cases, the marble did not accelerate because of the resistance from the viscous shampoo.

4. The speeds will depend on the type of shampoo used. Typical speeds are 2.5 mm/s and 6.0 mm/s for marbles falling in shampoo and diluted shampoo, respectively.

Logical, Kinesthetic

Study Guide

Study Tip

Schedule Study Time
Tell students to get into the habit of studying each day. They should set aside a block of time for reviewing their science notes. Tell students that focused daily study will reinforce what they learn in class and prepare them for test taking.

Thinking Visually

a. Velocity
b. Distance
c. Direction
d. Changes in both speed and direction

11.1 Distance and Displacement

Key Concepts
- To describe motion accurately and completely, a frame of reference is needed.
- Distance is the length of the path between two points. Displacement is the direction from the starting point and the length of a straight line from the starting point to the ending point.
- Add displacements by using vector addition.

Vocabulary
frame of reference, *p. 328*
relative motion, *p. 329*
distance, *p. 329*
vector, *p. 330*
resultant vector, *p. 331*

11.2 Speed and Velocity

Key Concepts
- Average speed is computed for the entire duration of a trip, and instantaneous speed is measured at a particular instant.
- Average speed = $\dfrac{\text{Total distance}}{\text{Total time}}$
- The slope of a line on a distance-time graph is speed.
- Velocity is a description of both speed and direction of motion. Velocity is a vector.
- Two or more velocities add by vector addition.

Vocabulary
speed, *p. 332*
average speed, *p. 333*
instantaneous speed, *p. 334*
velocity, *p. 336*

11.3 Acceleration

Key Concepts
- Acceleration can be described as changes in speed, changes in direction, or changes in both. Acceleration is a vector.
- You calculate acceleration by dividing the change in velocity by the total time.

$$\text{Acceleration} = \frac{v_f - v_i}{t}$$

- The slope of a speed-time graph is the acceleration.
- Instantaneous acceleration is how fast a velocity is changing at a specific instant.

Vocabulary
acceleration, *p. 342*
free fall, *p. 343*
constant acceleration, *p. 345*
linear graph, *p. 347*
nonlinear graph, *p. 348*

Thinking Visually

Concept Map Copy the concept map below onto a sheet of paper. Use information from the chapter to complete the concept map.

 ## Chapter Resources

Print
- *Chapter and Unit Tests,* Chapter 11 Test A and Test B
- *Test Prep Resources,* Chapter 11

Technology
- *Computer Test Bank,* Chapter Test 11
- *Interactive Textbook,* Chapter 11
- *Go Online,* PHSchool.com, Chapter 11

Assessment

Reviewing Content

Choose the letter that best answers the question or completes the statement.

1. Motion is described with respect to a
 a. graph.   **b.** displacement.
 c. slope.   **d.** frame of reference.

2. Displacement is distance combined with
 a. direction.   **b.** speed.
 c. velocity.   **d.** magnitude.

3. Displacement vectors of 3 m and 5 m in the same direction combine to make a displacement vector that is
 a. 2 m.   **b.** 0 m.
 c. 8 m.   **d.** 15 m.

4. Average speed is the total distance divided by the
 a. average distance.
 b. average acceleration.
 c. total time.
 d. slope.

5. The slope of a distance-time graph is equal to the
 a. speed.   **b.** acceleration.
 c. displacement.   **d.** motion.

6. Velocity is
 a. the slope of a linear graph.
 b. acceleration divided by displacement.
 c. speed with direction.
 d. the same in all reference frames.

7. Two or more velocities can be combined by
 a. graphing the slope.
 b. using vector addition.
 c. calculating the instantaneous speed.
 d. determining the rate.

8. A ball just dropped is an example of
 a. constant speed.
 b. instantaneous speed.
 c. combining displacements.
 d. free fall.

9. Acceleration is equal to
 a. distance divided by time.
 b. change in speed divided by time.
 c. the slope of a distance-time graph.
 d. change in speed multiplied by time.

10. The rate at which velocity is changing at a given instant is described by
 a. instantaneous acceleration.
 b. average speed.
 c. constant speed.
 d. vector addition.

Understanding Concepts

11. Why is it necessary to choose a single frame of reference when measuring motion?

12. For what kinds of distances would you choose to make measurements in millimeters? In kilometers?

13. Light from a star travels to Earth in a straight line at a constant speed of almost 300,000 km/s. What is the acceleration of the light?

14. If two displacement vectors add to yield a total displacement of zero, what do you know about the two displacements?

15. How will the total distance traveled by a car in 2 hours be affected if the average speed is doubled?

16. How do you know that a speedometer tells you the instantaneous speed of a car?

17. On a distance-time graph, what would the curve describing constant speed look like?

18. A spider is crawling on a wall. First it crawls 1 meter up, then 1 meter to the left, and then 1 meter down. What is its total displacement?

19. A jogger travels 8.0 kilometers in 1.25 hours. What is the jogger's average speed?

20. You see a lightning bolt in the sky. You hear a clap of thunder 3 seconds later. The sound travels at a speed of 330 m/s. How far away was the lightning? (*Hint:* Assume you see lightning instantly.)

21. If a river current is 8.0 m/s, and a boat is traveling 10.0 m/s upstream, what is the boat's speed relative to the riverbank?

22. If an object is moving with constant velocity, what do you know about its acceleration?

23. If the plotted points on a speed-time graph do not form a straight line, what do you know about the object's acceleration?

24. Explain a situation in which you can accelerate even though your speed doesn't change.

Assessment

If your class subscribes to the Interactive Textbook, your students can go online to access an interactive version of the Student Edition and a self-test.

Reviewing Content

1. d   **2.** a   **3.** c
4. c   **5.** a   **6.** c
7. b   **8.** d   **9.** b
10. a

Understanding Concepts

11. The motion appears to be different in different frames of reference.

12. Very small distances would be measured in millimeters. Very large distances would be measured in kilometers.

13. It has zero acceleration.

14. They are equal in length and opposite in direction.

15. The total distance would double.

16. A speedometer tells how fast an object is moving at a particular instant in time, which is the same as its instantaneous speed.

17. The curve of an object moving at constant speed would be a straight line on a distance-time graph.

18. 1 meter to the left

19. 6.4 km/h

20. 990 meters

21. 2.0 m/s

22. Acceleration is the change in velocity divided by the total time. If there is no change in velocity, then the acceleration is zero.

23. The object's acceleration is not constant.

24. Possible answer: moving in a circular motion with constant speed

Homework Guide

Section	Questions
11.1	1–3, 11–12, 14, 18–19, 35
11.2	4–7, 15–17, 20–21, 25–27, 29–30, 34
11.3	8–10, 13, 22–24, 28, 31–33

Assessment (continued)

Critical Thinking

25. The velocities of 2 m/s forward and 2 m/s backwards cancel. An observer standing nearby would see the newspaper drop vertically to the ground.
26. Students' experiments should include measuring the track and measuring the time for the train to go around the track. They should also mention calculating the speed from these measurements.
27. The raft could be moving with a constant speed because the speed during each measured interval is the same.
28. 1400 m/s

Math Skills

29. For the first 10 seconds, the person is walking at a constant rate. For the next 10 seconds, the person is standing still.
30. 1.5 m/s
31. 0.75 m/s^2

Concepts in Action

32. The ship's final velocity is 600 m/s, less than its velocity in problem 28.
33. At each moment, the falling ball has an instantaneous acceleration that is the same as its constant downward acceleration of 9.8 m/s^2. The ball bouncing on the floor has a changing acceleration each time it hits the ground.
34. 5 km/h
35. Descriptions will vary but should include the up-and-down dribbling motion of the ball, the movement of the player down the court, and the projectile motion of the ball after it is shot toward the basket.

Your students can independently test their knowledge of the chapter and print out their results for your files.

Critical Thinking

25. Applying Concepts A girl moves at 2 m/s delivering newspapers. She throws a newspaper directly behind her at 2 m/s. In the frame of reference of someone standing nearby, what is the motion of the newspaper?

26. Designing an Experiment Design an experiment to measure the speed of a toy train going around a circular track.

27. Analyzing Data A raft floats downstream. After 1 minute it has moved 50.0 meters. After 2 minutes it has moved 100.0 meters. After 3 minutes it has moved 150.0 meters. Could the raft's speed be constant? Explain.

28. Problem Solving A rocket ship is moving through space at 1000 m/s. It accelerates in the same direction at 4 m/s^2. What is its speed after 100 seconds?

Math Skills

Use the following graph to answer Questions 29 and 30.

A Record of Typical Motion

29. Using Graphs The graph above shows the motion for a person walking down a street. Describe the history of the motion.

30. Using Graphs How fast is the person walking during the first 10 seconds?

31. Calculating A car starts from rest and increases its speed to 15 m/s in 20 seconds. What is the car's acceleration?

Concepts in Action

32. Predicting The propulsion system of the rocket ship described in problem 28 is tested. Its rockets are fired and the ship accelerates from rest at 5 m/s^2 for 2 minutes. How does the ship's final velocity compare with the ship's initial velocity in problem 28?

33. Comparing and Contrasting Compare the case of a rubber ball falling through the air and a rubber ball bouncing up and down on a hard floor. For which of these cases is the instantaneous acceleration always the same as the constant acceleration?

34. Calculating Two trains on parallel tracks are traveling in the same direction. One train starts 10 km behind the other. It overtakes the first train in 2 hours. What is the relative speed of the second train with respect to the first train?

35. Writing in Science Write a paragraph explaining how different reference frames affect descriptions of motion in the following scenario. A basketball player dribbles down the court at a constant speed and then shoots the ball into the basket. Describe the motion of the ball from the reference frame of a camera mounted directly behind the basket. Then, describe the motion of the ball from the reference frame of the basketball player. (*Hint:* Sketch displacement versus time graphs of the ball's motion based on each reference frame.)

Performance-Based Assessment

Creating a Table Use a table to present the distances and displacements between familiar places. In a third column include the average speed at which you travel between these places. Be sure to list the places in pairs, such as home and school, a park and the library, or your bed and front door. Estimate the displacement if you can't measure it.

For: Self-grading assessment
Visit: PHSchool.com
Web Code: cca-2110

Performance-Based Assessment

Students' tables should include several pairs of locations. In most cases, the distance traveled should be greater than the magnitude of the displacement between the locations. Students should use distance and time units appropriate to each pair of locations. Make sure the values for average speeds are realistic.

Standardized Test Prep for Indiana

Question	Standards
1	ICP.1.1
2	ICP.1.1
3	ICP.1.1
4	ICP.1.1
5	ICP.1.1

Test-Taking Tip

When answering a question with a graph, keep these tips in mind:

- Read the question thoroughly to identify what the question is asking.
- Study the name of the graph, if applicable. This may help you identify what information is available from the graph.
- Carefully examine the graph and take note of the axes labels.
- Identify the scale of the axes.
- Recall information, equations, definitions, relationships, and so forth that may be required to interpret the graph. For example, the slope of a distance-time graph is the speed of the object.
- Once you have chosen your answer, check it against the graph.

Determining Distance

The graph above depicts motion in a straight line. During which time periods does acceleration occur?

(A) 0 s–2 s only
(B) 0 s–2 s and 6 s–8 s only
(C) 16 s–18 s only
(D) 0 s–2 s, 6 s–8 s, and 16 s–18 s only
(E) Acceleration occurs during the entire time period shown.

(Answer: D)

1. A delivery truck driver's round-trip route from the warehouse takes her 3 km east, then 1 km north, then 3 km west, and then 1 km south. Which of the following statements is FALSE?
   (A) The displacement of the round trip is zero.
   (B) The distance of the round trip is 8 km.
   (C) After driving 3 km east, the magnitude of the distance and displacement are the same.
   (D) After driving 3 km east and 1 km north, the magnitude of the distance and displacement are the same.
   (E) none of the above

2. A runner completes a 10.0-km race in exactly 30 minutes. What is the runner's average speed in km/h? (60 minutes = 1 hour)
   (A) 30.0 km/h   (B) 20.0 km/h
   (C) 15.0 km/h   (D) 10.0 km/h
   (E) 5.00 km/h

3. Which of the following is NOT a vector quantity?
   (A) velocity
   (B) displacement
   (C) distance
   (D) acceleration
   (E) none of the above

4. Based on the speed-time graph shown at the left, what is the acceleration during the first 2 seconds?
   (A) 1 m/s^2
   (B) 2 m/s^2
   (C) 4 m/s^2
   (D) 5 m/s^2
   (E) 10 m/s^2

5. A race car drives around a circular race track at constant speed. Which of the following statements is TRUE?
   (A) A speed-time graph of the car's motion would be a horizontal line.
   (B) A distance-time graph of the car's motion would be a straight line with a positive slope.
   (C) The velocity of the car is constantly changing.
   (D) The car is constantly accelerating.
   (E) all of the above

Planning Guide

SECTION OBJECTIVES	STANDARDS		ACTIVITIES and LABS
	NATIONAL	STATE	
12.1 Forces, pp. 356–362 🕐 1 block or 2 periods **12.1.1 Describe** examples of force and **identify** appropriate SI units used to measure force. **12.1.2 Explain** how the motion of an object is affected when balanced and unbalanced forces act on it. **12.1.3 Compare** and **contrast** the four kinds of friction. **12.1.4 Describe** how Earth's gravity and air resistance affect falling objects. **12.1.5 Describe** the path of a projectile and **identify** the forces that produce projectile motion.	A-1, A-2, B-4, G-1	ICP.1.3	**SE** Inquiry Activity: What Starts an Object Moving? p. 355 **L2** **SE** Quick Lab: Observing the Effects of Friction, p. 360 **L2** **TE** Build Science Skills: Measuring, p. 357 **L2**
12.2 Newton's First and Second Laws of Motion, pp. 363–369 🕐 1 block or 2 periods **12.2.1 Describe** Newton's first law of motion and its relation to inertia. **12.2.2 Describe** Newton's second law of motion and use it to **calculate** acceleration, force, and mass values. **12.2.3 Relate** the mass of an object to its weight.	A-1, A-2, B-4, F-1, G-1, G-2, G-3	ICP.1.2, ICP.1.3	**SE** Quick Lab: Investigating Inertia, p. 365 **L2** **TE** Teacher Demo: Force and Acceleration, p. 365 **L2** **TE** Teacher Demo: Newton's Second Law of Motion, p. 367 **L2** **LM** Investigation 12A: Investigating Gravitational Acceleration and Fluid Resistance **L2** **LM** Investigation 12B: Testing Galileo's Hypothesis **L1**
12.3 Newton's Third Law of Motion and Momentum, pp. 372–377 🕐 1 block or 2 periods **12.3.1 Explain** how action and reaction forces are related according to Newton's third law of motion. **12.3.2 Calculate** the momentum of an object and **describe** what happens when momentum is conserved during a collision.	B-4, G-1, G-2, G-3	ICP.1.2	**SE** Exploration Lab: Investigating a Balloon Jet, p. 383 **L2** **TE** Build Science Skills: Predicting, p. 373 **L2** **TE** Teacher Demo: Momentum, p. 374 **L2**
12.4 Universal Forces, pp. 378–382 🕐 1 block or 2 periods **12.4.1 Identify** the forms of electromagnetic force that can both attract and repel. **12.4.2 Identify** and **describe** the universal forces acting within the nucleus. **12.4.3 Define** Newton's law of universal gravitation and **describe** the factors affecting gravitational force. **12.4.4 Describe** centripetal force and the type of motion it produces.	A-1, A-2, B-1, B-4, E-2, G-1, G-2, G-3	ICP.1.2, ICP.1.3, ICP.6.6	**SE** Quick Lab: Investigating Force and Distance, p. 380 **L2** **TE** Teacher Demo: Nuclear Forces, p. 379 **L2**

RESOURCES PRINT and TECHNOLOGY

RSW Section 12.1 **L1**

T Chapter 12 Pretest **L2**
Section 12.1 **L2**

P Chapter 12 Pretest **L2**
Section 12.1 **L2**

NSTA SCiLINKS **GO** Forces **L2**

SECTION ASSESSMENT

SE Section 12.1 Assessment, p. 362

iT Section 12.1

RSW Section 12.2 **L1**

RSW Math Skill **L2**

MSPS Section 12.2 **L2**

Discovery SCHOOL **DC** Air Forces **L2**

T Section 12.2 **L2**

P Section 12.2 **L2**

NSTA SCiLINKS **GO** Mass **L2**

SE Section 12.2 Assessment, p. 369

iT Section 12.2

PLM Lab 4: Investigating a Balloon Jet **L2**

RSW Section 12.3 **L1**

MSPS Section 12.3 **L2**

T Section 12.3 **L2**

P Section 12.3 **L2**

NSTA SCiLINKS **GO** Newton's laws **L2**

SE Section 12.3 Assessment, p. 377

iT Section 12.3

RSW Section 12.4 **L1**

T Section 12.4 **L2**

P Section 12.4 **L2**

NSTA SCiLINKS **GO** Gravity **L2**

SE Section 12.4 Assessment, p. 382

iT Section 12.4

Go Online

Go online for these Internet resources.

PHSchool.com
Web Code: cca-2120

NSTA SCiLINKS
Web Code: ccn-2121
Web Code: ccn-2122
Web Code: ccn-2123
Web Code: ccn-2124

Materials for Activities and Labs

Quantities for each group

STUDENT EDITION

Inquiry Activity, p. 355
5 pennies

Quick Lab, p. 360
2 rubber erasers, sticky notes, scissors, metric ruler

Quick Lab, p. 364
index card, coin

Quick Lab, p. 380
balloon, bubble solution, bubble wand

Exploration Lab, p. 383
string (3 m in length), drinking straw, 4 long balloons, masking tape, stopwatch, meter stick, 2 threaded nuts, 2 chairs

TEACHER'S EDITION

Build Science Skills, p. 357
5-N spring scale, centimeter ruler, book, string, 5 objects (such as books) weighing from 1 to 5 newtons

Teacher Demo, p. 365
2 identical toy cars (or dynamics carts), 2 student volunteers, identical floor surface for each car

Teacher Demo, p. 367
wind-up toy car, 3 metal washers, tape

Build Science Skills, p. 370
sheet of paper, stopwatch, auditorium stage

Build Science Skills, p. 373
soccer ball, several heavy books

Teacher Demo, p. 374
water-filled balloons, pillow

Teacher Demo, p. 379
2 magnetic toy train cars or any 2 magnets, wide adhesive tape on a roll (or rubber band)

Chapter Assessment

CHAPTER ASSESSMENT

SE Chapter Assessment, pp. 385–386
CUT Chapter 12 Test A, B
CTB Chapter 12
iT Chapter 12
PHSchool.com GO
Web Code: cca-2120

STANDARDIZED TEST PREP

SE Chapter 12, p. 387
TP Diagnose and Prescribe

Interactive Textbook with assessment at PHSchool.com

Before you teach

From the Author

Michael Wysession
Washington University

Big Ideas

There are four distinct forces in our universe: gravitational, electromagnetic, and strong and weak nuclear forces. At the time of the big bang, these four forces were likely unified as a single force, but they fragmented as the universe expanded and cooled.

Space and Time Gravity is the most important force over large distances, and is responsible for large-scale motions in space. Gravity is the weakest of all the forces, but because it acts between all matter and because it decays at a moderate rate with distance, it is the most dominant force over large distances.

The strong and weak nuclear forces act between atomic particles. The strong force holds the nuclei of atoms together. The weak force is responsible for radioactive decay. These forces are immense at subatomic distances, but decay rapidly with distance.

The electromagnetic force is best known for effects such as electricity and magnetism. However, it also provides most of the everyday "forces" in our lives. Hold something up, and the electrons around the atoms of your hand are repelling the electrons around the atoms of the object you are holding. Pushing, pulling, hitting, and holding all result from the repelling electromagnetic forces supplied by the electrons on the outsides of the atoms of objects.

Forces and Motion The most important equation in all of science is likely $F = ma$, which says that when you push on an object, it accelerates. Push on a massive object, and it accelerates slowly. Push harder, and it accelerates faster. The most prevalent force on our planet's surface is the gravitational pull of Earth's mass. As a result, the most prevalent kind of motion is downward acceleration (i.e., things fall downhill).

Matter and Energy As Einstein showed, gravity is better viewed as a distortion of the fabric of space by matter. Very massive objects, like black holes and galaxies, create very large "warping" of the spatial dimensions of space. This explains why light from distant galaxies is bent around intervening galaxies.

Physics Refresher

Forces 12.1

A force, which can be simply defined as any push or pull, is the cause of acceleration (change in velocity). Force is a vector, that is, it has magnitude and direction. The SI unit of force is the newton (N), the amount of force that produces an acceleration of 1 m/s² on a 1 kg mass.

If all forces on an object are combined and the net force is zero, the object does not accelerate. If the net force is not zero, velocity remains constant.

> **Address Misconceptions**
>
> *Some students may incorrectly think that only animate objects can exert a force. However, gravity is inanimate, as are many other forces. For a strategy to overcome this misconception, see* **Address Misconceptions** *on* **page 358.**

Friction 12.1

Friction is the opposing force that touching objects experience as they move past one another. Static friction is the force of resistance to motion when two contacting surfaces are stationary. Kinetic friction (which includes sliding, rolling, and fluid friction) is the force of resistance that opposes the relative motion of two contacting surfaces moving past one another.

Laws of Motion 12.2 and 12.3

Newton's first law of motion says that an object at rest will remain at rest, and an object in motion will continue in motion with constant velocity unless it experiences a net force.

Newton's second law of motion says that an object's acceleration is directly proportional to the net force acting on it and

A Mass = 1 shopping cart **B** Mass = 8 shopping carts

Force

Acceleration

Force

Acceleration

Acceleration depends on force and mass.

Go Online PD Links
NSTA

For: Teaching methods for forces and motion
Visit: www.SciLinks.org/PDLinks
Web Code: ccn-1299

inversely proportional to its mass $(a = F/m, F = ma)$. One application is the measurement of weight. Weight, W, is a force, while the gravity, g, is the acceleration $(W = mg)$. On Earth's surface, g is approximately 9.8 m/s^2.

In the 1680s, Newton related the laws in his book *Philosophiae Naturalis Principia Mathematica*. He stated that force is proportional to change in momentum. Mathematically, this law is $F = m \times v$. A change in velocity is the same as acceleration, so this equation became $F = ma$.

Newton's third law of motion says that, when object A exerts a force on object B, object B exerts a force on object A that is equal in magnitude and opposite in direction.

Universal Forces 12.4

Three of the four universal forces are electromagnetic, strong nuclear, and weak nuclear. The range and relative strengths of the universal forces are summarized in the table below.

Universal Force Characteristics

Force	Relative Strength	Range
Strong nuclear	1	~10^{-15} m
Electromagnetic	10^{-2}	$\propto \frac{1}{r^2}$
Weak nuclear	10^{-13}	$< 10^{-18}$ m
Gravitational	10^{-38}	$\propto \frac{1}{r^2}$

The electromagnetic force consists of both the electric force and the magnetic force. These forces are found in regions in which there are electric and magnetic fields. Michael Faraday discovered that a changing magnetic field produces an electric field, and James Clerk Maxwell illustrated that a changing electric field produces a magnetic field.

Address Misconceptions

Some students may think that objects become positively charged because they have gained protons. What takes place is electron (not proton) transfer. Electrons have a negative charge. For a strategy to overcome this misconception, see **Address Misconceptions** on **page 379.**

The nucleus of an atom is held together by attractions among protons and neutrons called the strong nuclear force and the weak nuclear force. The strong nuclear force is greater than the electric repulsion of the protons' positive forces and therefore overcomes that repulsion, holding them together. The attraction due to the strong force, however, occurs over a very short distance, less than 3×10^{-15} m, or about three protons' width. The weak nuclear force is stronger than gravitational force.

Build Reading Literacy

Visualize

Forming Mental Pictures

Strategy Help students understand and recall complex text by forming mental pictures as they read. In some cases, visual elements of the text can aid students in visualizing; in other cases students must rely solely on text descriptions. Choose several paragraphs from Chapter 12, such as the four on p. 358. If possible, include at least one paragraph that has an accompanying figure and at least one other paragraph that refers to concepts or events that are not illustrated in visual elements, such as diagrams, charts, graphs, or photographs.

Example

1. Have students keep their books closed. Tell them to listen while you read and to visualize, or form mental pictures of, each object or action you read about.
2. Then, read a paragraph or so aloud, pausing frequently to demonstrate, by thinking aloud, how to visualize each thing described. When reading complex or technical text, pausing after each phrase will often be appropriate.
3. Tell students to continue visualizing. Slowly and clearly, read on. Then, select a logical stopping point and discuss with students the images they visualized.
4. If there is an accompanying figure, have students open to it and see how it compares with their visualizing. Point out that visuals in the text help readers picture what they are reading.
5. Have students work with partners to practice by taking turns reading and visualizing aloud. Tell them to expand on visuals that appear in the text and to describe their own mental images of ideas or events that are not shown in visuals.

See p. 368 for a script on how to use the visualize strategy with students. For additional Build Reading Literacy strategies, see pp. 357, 372, and 378.

ASSESS PRIOR KNOWLEDGE

Use the Chapter Pretest below to assess students' prior knowledge. As needed, review these Science Concepts and Math Skills with students.

Review Science Concepts

Section 12.1 Review with students what motion is and how it is measured. Encourage students to describe what a force is and what it can do.

Section 12.2 Ask students to review algebraic equations and exponents. Suggest that they observe physical forces in their everyday lives and be prepared to discuss how they think these forces affect motion.

Section 12.3 Encourage students to review the concepts of mass and velocity, making sure they do not confuse mass with weight or velocity with speed. Reinforce that mass and weight are not the same and that speed with direction is velocity.

Section 12.4 Review models of the atom if this concept has been covered. Remind students of their prior knowledge of gravitational force and forces that act between magnets and charged particles.

Review Math Skills

Formulas and Equations, Exponents, and Line Graphs
Students will need to work with equations and exponents to solve problems using Newton's second law of motion.

Direct students to the **Math Skills** in the **Skills and Reference Handbook** at the end of the student text.

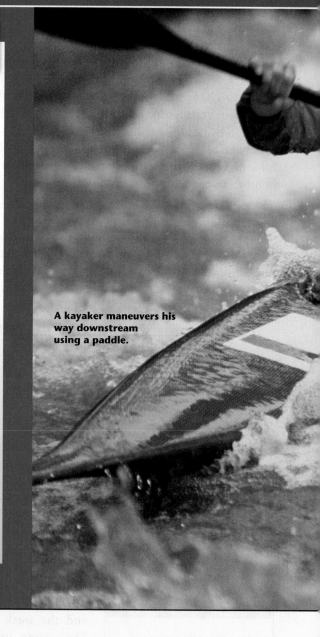

CHAPTER

12 Forces and Motion

21st Century Learning
Information and Media Literacy

What forces are in a car crash?
When a car is in a collision, the forces on the car and on the people inside can be dangerously unbalanced. Go online and research video simulations of car crashes. Pick a crash simulation that you can use as a basis for a video presentation about forces. Plan to show the video during your presentation, and to pause it in at least three places to identify and describe both the balanced and unbalanced forces at that moment.

Indiana's Academic Standards for Science

MOTION AND ENERGY OF MACROSCOPIC OBJECTS
ICP.1.2: Describe and apply Newton's three laws of motion. By experimentation, determine the relationships among the variables in Newton's laws and how all three laws relate mass, acceleration and force as a triad of proportional variables, leading to the definitions of momentum and energy; ICP.1.3: Describe how Newton's law of universal gravitation, together with the laws of motion, explains the motions of objects on earth and of the moon, planets and stars.

ELECTRICAL ENERGY PROPAGATION AND MAGNETISM
ICP.6.6: Explain that some objects, called magnets, exert magnetic forces with no direct contact.

A kayaker maneuvers his way downstream using a paddle.

354 *Chapter 12*

Chapter Pretest

1. What is relative motion? *(Relative motion is movement in relation to a frame of reference.)*

2. What is the difference between distance and displacement? *(Distance is the length of a path between two points. Displacement is the direction from the starting point and the length of a straight line from the starting point to the ending point.)*

3. How is average speed calculated? *(Total distance is divided by total time.)*

4. On a distance-time graph, what does the slope represent? *(The slope represents the speed.)*

5. What is velocity? *(Velocity is speed with direction.)*

6. How is acceleration related to velocity? *(Acceleration is change in velocity, that is, any change in speed, direction, or both.)*

7. A backpack falls out of an open window. The backpack starts from rest and hits the ground 1.0 second later with a velocity of 9.8 m/s. What is the average acceleration of the backpack? *(c)*
 a. 9.8 m/s   b. 9.8 m
 c. 9.8 m/s^2 d. All of the above

8. How are mass and weight different? *(Mass is a measure of inertia. Weight is the measure of the force of gravity acting on an object.)*

Chapter Preview

Video Field Trip

Air Forces

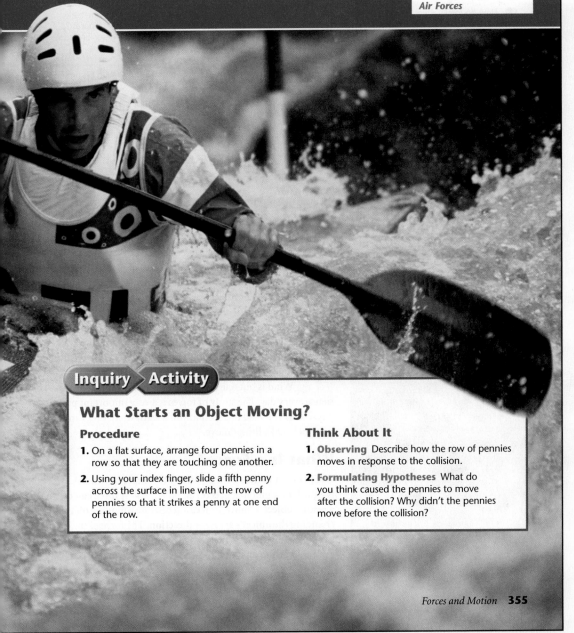

Inquiry ⟩ Activity

What Starts an Object Moving?

Procedure

1. On a flat surface, arrange four pennies in a row so that they are touching one another.

2. Using your index finger, slide a fifth penny across the surface in line with the row of pennies so that it strikes a penny at one end of the row.

Think About It

1. **Observing** Describe how the row of pennies moves in response to the collision.

2. **Formulating Hypotheses** What do you think caused the pennies to move after the collision? Why didn't the pennies move before the collision?

Forces and Motion **355**

Video Field Trip

Air Forces

Encourage students to view the Video Field Trip "Air Forces."

ENGAGE/EXPLORE

Inquiry ⟩ Activity

What Starts an Object Moving?   L2

Purpose
In this activity, students begin to use the concept of force to explain movement.

 Address Misconceptions

Students may hold the misconception that only a moving object can exert force. To help dispel this misconception, after completing this activity ask students what caused the penny on the end of the row to move. Each penny exerts a force on the next, although only the last penny in the row moves.

Skills Focus Observing, Formulating Hypotheses

Prep Time 5 minutes

Materials 5 pennies

Advance Prep Checkers or game chips can be substituted for pennies.

Class Time 10 minutes

Safety Students should wear safety goggles. Caution students not to observe from a position in which the pennies move toward them.

Teaching Tips
• If students are having difficulty striking the row of coins head-on, they can tape a pair of rulers to the table on either side of the row of coins to create a linear track for the coins to travel along.

Expected Outcome As the row of coins is struck, the moving coin will stop at the head of the row while the coin at the far end of the row will move away.

Think About It
1. Only the coin at the far end of the row moved away.
2. During the collision, a force was transferred from one coin to the next in the row. Because no horizontal force was acting on the coins before the collision, they did not move at that time. Students may not articulate the abstract concept of a force well at this stage. Although students can reasonably be expected to start developing this concept, they may not express it in formally correct scientific language at this stage.
Visual

1 FOCUS

Objectives

12.1.1 Describe examples of force and **identify** appropriate SI units used to measure force.

12.1.2 Explain how the motion of an object is affected when balanced and unbalanced forces act on it.

12.1.3 Compare and **contrast** the four kinds of friction.

12.1.4 Describe how Earth's gravity and air resistance affect falling objects.

12.1.5 Describe the path of a projectile and **identify** the forces that produce projectile motion.

Reading Focus

Build Vocabulary   **L2**

LINCS Have students use the LINCS strategy to learn and review the terms *force, friction, air resistance,* and *gravity.* In LINCS exercises, students **L**ist the parts that they know (list the word and its definition on an index card). **I**magine a picture (create a mental image of the term's meaning and describe the image using real words). **N**ote a sound-alike word (think of a familiar word that sounds like the term or part of it). **C**onnect the terms (make up a short story about each term's meaning that uses the sound-alike word). **S**elf-test (have them quiz themselves).

Reading Strategy   **L2**

a. Yes **b.** No motion **c.** Yes
d. No motion **e.** Yes **f.** No motion
g. Yes **h.** No motion **i.** No **j.** Potted tree accelerates

2 INSTRUCT

What Is a Force?

Use Visuals   **L1**

Figure 1 Emphasize that the wind acts as a force because it pushes against the man. Ask, **In what ways can the force of the wind alter the man's motion?** *(It can change the speed or direction of motion.)* **Will these changes cause the man to accelerate?** *(Yes)*
Visual

12.1 Forces

Standard: ICP.1.3

Reading Focus

Key Concepts

- How do forces affect the motion of an object?
- What are the four main types of friction?
- How do gravity and air resistance affect a falling object?
- In what direction does Earth's gravity act?
- Why does a projectile follow a curved path?

Vocabulary

- force
- newton
- net force
- friction
- static friction
- sliding friction
- rolling friction
- fluid friction
- air resistance
- gravity
- terminal velocity
- projectile motion

Reading Strategy

Relating Text and Visuals Copy the table below. As you read, look carefully at Figures 2, 3, and 5. Complete the table by describing the forces and motion shown in each figure.

Figure	Is Net Force 0?	Effect on Motion
2A	a. ___?___	b. ___?___
2B	c. ___?___	d. ___?___
3	e. ___?___	f. ___?___
5A	g. ___?___	h. ___?___
5B	i. ___?___	j. ___?___

Figure 1 The wind pushes against the man and his umbrella. The push from the wind is a force.

A powerful storm is approaching. The weather forecast calls for gale-force winds. Many people in the city decide to leave work early in order to get home before things get worse. As shown in Figure 1, a man pushes ahead into a strong wind and shields himself from the driving rain with an umbrella. The strong wind makes it very difficult for him to hold onto his umbrella. To keep the umbrella from being pulled from his hands, he tightly squeezes the umbrella handle. Elsewhere, a store owner attempts to bring in a folding sign that hasn't blown away because it is chained to a pole.

Wind is but one example of the many forces you experience every day. The study of forces is a very important part of physics. As you read this section you'll learn what forces are and how they make things move.

What Is a Force?

The man out in the storm is battling the forces of wind. A **force** is a push or a pull that acts on an object. **A force can cause a resting object to move, or it can accelerate a moving object by changing the object's speed or direction.** The force of the wind pushing against the man slows his speed. A strong gust could even change the direction in which he was moving.

356 *Chapter 12*

Section Resources

Print

- **Reading and Study Workbook With Math Support,** Section 12.1
- **Transparencies,** Chapter Pretest and Section 12.1

Technology

- **Interactive Textbook,** Section 12.1
- **Presentation Pro CD-ROM,** Chapter Pretest and Section 12.1
- **Go Online,** NSTA SciLinks, Forces

Measuring Force Forces are often easy to measure. In fact, if you've ever shopped at a grocery store, you may have measured forces using a spring scale like the one shown in Figure 2. The stretch of the spring in the scale depends on the amount of weight (a type of force) acting on it. As more fruit is placed on the scale, the spring is stretched farther and the scale reading increases.

Units of Force Force is measured in newtons, abbreviated as N. One **newton** is the force that causes a 1-kilogram mass to accelerate at a rate of 1 meter per second each second (1 m/s²). In fact, 1 newton is equal to 1 kilogram-meter per second squared ($1 N = 1 kg\cdot m/s^2$). The newton is named after Sir Isaac Newton (1642–1727), the English scientist who explained how force, mass, and acceleration are related. You'll learn more about forces and mass in the next section.

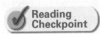 *What amount of force accelerates a 1-kilogram mass at 1 m/s²?*

Representing Force You can use an arrow to represent the direction and strength of a force. The direction of the arrow represents the direction of the force. The length of the arrow represents the strength, or magnitude, of the force.

In Figure 2, the force arrows represent the weight of the items on the scale. Both arrows point down because weight always acts downward. The lengths of the arrows show you that more weight acts on the scale in Figure 2B than the one in Figure 2A.

Combining Forces

Have you ever helped to push a car that has run out of gas? If you have, you were taking advantage of the fact that forces can be combined. The individual force of each person's push adds with the others into a larger force that allows you to move the car.

You can combine force arrows to show the result of how forces combine. That is, forces in the same direction add together and forces in opposite directions subtract from one another. The **net force** is the overall force acting on an object after all the forces are combined.

Figure 2 The downward force arrows represent the weight (a type of force) on the scales. The dial indicator gives a visual measure of the weight. **Calculating** *What is the approximate weight difference between the two scale readings?*

Forces and Motion **357**

Build Science Skills

L2

Measuring

Purpose Students learn to measure force and sketch force arrows.

Materials 5-N spring scale, centimeter ruler, book, string, 5 objects (such as books) weighing from 1 to 5 newtons

Class Time 30 minutes

Procedure Have students pull each object at a slow, constant speed across a flat surface using the spring scale. They may need to attach the scale to the object using string. Students should record the force required to pull each object. Next, have them draw force arrows for each object. The arrows should be drawn to scale using a scale factor of 1 centimeter per newton of force.

Expected Outcome Students will draw scaled force arrows for each object. **Logical**

Combining Forces
Build Reading Literacy L1

Identify Main Ideas/Details Refer to page 98D in **Chapter 4**, which provides the guidelines for identifying main ideas and details.

Ask students to explain the main concept in the first two short paragraphs under the head Combining Forces on p. 357. *(Forces can be combined.)* Encourage students to illustrate the main idea with a diagram. Ask, **What would be the effect on the direction of the net force if some of the people push the car forward while others push it backwards?** *(The net force would be in the direction of the people who were pushing with a greater force.)*
Logical, Portfolio

Customize for English Language Learners

Illustrate Content
You may assist English language learners by using diagrams, illustrations, or other visuals to explain the content of the lesson. Students may also benefit from keeping a "picture dictionary" with their own visuals to illustrate important concepts. For example, students may include diagrams to illustrate how forces

combine and to show the meaning of *balanced force* and *unbalanced force*. This strategy can be especially helpful for students who are in the beginning stages of learning English. Students who have a greater mastery of English may also benefit from sharing their picture dictionaries with each other and explaining the concepts for which they have included visuals.

Answer to . . .

Figure 2 *The difference in weight between the two scale readings is about 3 pounds.*

 The amount of force that accelerates 1 kg at 1 m/s² is one newton.

Integrate Health **L2**

Figure 3 illustrates a group exercise (tug of war). Emphasize to students the value of regular exercise. According to the American Academy of Family Physicians, regular exercise reduces risk of some serious diseases including heart disease, diabetes, and obesity. Exercise also enhances flexibility so that body movement is easier. Regular exercise helps to relieve stress, increase energy and endurance, and—because it raises the rate at which the body burns calories—maintain a healthy weight.

Ask students to hypothesize why a person with normal (not high) blood pressure and a normal body weight is at lower risk for heart disease. *(That person's heart does not have to do extra work.)*
Verbal, Logical

Address Misconceptions **L2**

Some students may think that only people and animals can exert a force. You may dispel this fallacy by pointing out that moving automobiles or other moving vehicles are not living organisms. In addition, explain that the force of gravity is also inanimate. You could also use figures in the text to show that there are many examples all around students of forces that are not animate.
Visual, Logical

Use Visuals **L1**

Figure 4 Emphasize that the arrows in Figure 4 help students understand how forces combine. Tell students that the length of the arrows represents magnitude (size) of force. Ask, **When two arrows directly oppose one another and are different in size, what will be the direction of the net force?** *(The direction of the net force will be the same as the direction of the longer arrow.)* **How is the net force determined when two forces act in the same direction on an object?** *(The forces are added. The direction is the same as the forces.)* **Which of the combinations of forces shown in the figure would cause an object to move?** *(Only the unbalanced forces shown in A and B would cause the object to move.)*
Visual

Figure 3 In this tug of war, the two groups pull with equal forces in opposite directions. The forces combine by subtracting from each other.
Interpreting Photos *What is the net force acting on the rope?*

A Adding forces

B Subtracting forces

C Equal and opposite forces

 = 0

Figure 4 Forces can add together or subtract from one another. **A** Two forces acting in the same direction add together. **B** Forces in opposite directions subtract from each other. **C** Forces that are equal in size and opposite in direction result in no net force.

Balanced Forces Sometimes, the net force acting on an object is zero. Look at the tug of war in Figure 3. Each group pulls on the rope with the same amount of force, but they pull in opposite directions. Neither group wins the tug of war because the forces on the rope are balanced. Balanced forces are forces that combine to produce a net force of zero. **When the forces on an object are balanced, the net force is zero and there is no change in the object's motion.**

Examples of balanced forces are common. For example, imagine two people locked in an arm wrestling match. Although neither person's arm may be moving, a pair of equal and opposite balanced forces are acting. An unlimited number of individual forces can act on an object and still produce a net force of zero. As shown in Figure 3, the individual force exerted by each person still results in a zero net force on the rope.

Unbalanced Forces Often, the forces on an object are unbalanced. If you push hard against the side of a book that is resting on a table, the book will begin to move. This is an example of an unbalanced force. An unbalanced force is a force that results when the net force acting on an object is not equal to zero. **When an unbalanced force acts on an object, the object accelerates.**

Forces acting in opposite directions can also combine to produce an unbalanced force. When a team of people win a tug of war, they win by pulling with a greater force than the losing team. The two unequal forces act in opposite directions but combine to produce an unbalanced net force. The net force equals the size of the larger force minus the size of the smaller force. This unbalanced force causes the rope, the winning team, and the losing team to accelerate in the direction of the unbalanced force. Figure 4 shows several examples of how forces combine.

Reading Checkpoint *What is the net force of a pair of balanced forces?*

Facts and Figures

Virtual Reality Forces A knowledge of balanced and unbalanced forces is important for virtual reality applications. Sensors detect the direction and magnitude of force exerted on an object by a user. The system then provides resistive force feedback to the user that corresponds to the desired virtual material. For example, the resistive force can be increased to simulate a stiff material such as hard rubber. The resistive force can be decreased to simulate a soft material such as a cloth.

Friction

All moving objects are subject to **friction,** a force that opposes the motion of objects that touch as they move past each other. Without friction, the world would be a very different place. In a frictionless world, every surface would be more slippery than a sheet of ice. Your food would slide off your fork. Walking would be impossible. Cars would slide around helplessly with their wheels spinning.

Friction acts at the surface where objects are in contact. Note that "in contact" includes solid objects that are directly touching one another as well as objects moving through a liquid or a gas. **There are four main types of friction: static friction, sliding friction, rolling friction, and fluid friction.**

Static Friction Imagine trying to push a large potted tree across a patio. Although you apply force to the pot by pushing on it, you can't get the pot to move. As shown in Figure 5A, the force of static friction opposes your push. **Static friction** is the friction force that acts on objects that are not moving. Static friction always acts in the direction opposite to that of the applied force.

You experience static friction every time you take a step. As you push off with each step, static friction between the ground and your shoe keeps your shoe from sliding.

Sliding Friction With the help of a friend, you push on the pot with enough force to overcome the static friction. The pot slides across the patio as shown in Figure 5B. Once the pot is moving, static friction no longer acts on it. Instead, a smaller friction force called sliding friction acts on the sliding pot. **Sliding friction** is a force that opposes the direction of motion of an object as it slides over a surface. Because sliding friction is less than static friction, less force is needed to keep an object moving than to start it moving.

For: Links on forces
Visit: www.SciLinks.org
Web Code: ccn-2121

Figure 5 Different types of friction act on moving and nonmoving objects. **A** Static friction acts opposite the direction of the force you apply to move the plant. The potted tree does not move. **B** When you push with more force, the potted tree begins to slide. Sliding friction acts to oppose the direction of motion.

Forces and Motion **359**

Friction
Use Community Resources
L2

Ask a civil engineer to visit your class and talk about the effects of friction between road surfaces and the tires of a moving car. Have the engineer emphasize the necessity of friction in controlling a car. Suggest that the engineer explain to the students what happens when a car hydroplanes because of lack of friction between the tires and the surface of the road. Encourage students to ask questions about how engineers take friction into account when designing roads and bridges.
Interpersonal

Download a worksheet on forces for students to complete, and find additional teacher support from NSTA SciLinks.

Answer to . . .

Figure 3 *The net force on the rope is zero.*

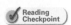 *The net force is zero.*

Quick Lab

Observing the Effects Of Friction **L2**

Objective
After completing this activity, students will be able to
• describe the effect of friction on motion.

Skills Focus Observing, Drawing Conclusions

 Prep Time 5 minutes

Materials 2 rubber erasers, sticky notes, scissors, metric ruler

Class Time 10 minutes

Teaching Tips
• Have students construct data tables in which to record their observations.
• You may need to show students how to arrange the erasers so that the ruler will strike both of them at the same time.
• Tell students to repeat the experiment if an eraser flips over or falls off the table.

Expected Outcome Students will observe that the sticky note increases the distance that the eraser slides.

Analyze and Conclude
1. The eraser with the sticky note attached slid farther.
2. The sticky note enabled one eraser to slide farther by reducing friction.
3. Friction produces a force that opposes motion. The greater the friction between two surfaces, the stronger that force is.
4. The erasers would slide farther if the force of friction were reduced by coating the erasers or the tabletop with a smoother material, or if the erasers were struck more firmly, providing a greater force in the direction of motion.
Logical

For Enrichment **L3**

Students can use a spring scale to pull a mass across surfaces that provide more or less friction, to observe the difference between the forces required to overcome static and sliding friction. In general, more force is required to overcome static friction and begin sliding than to continue sliding at constant velocity.
Kinesthetic

Quick Lab

Observing the Effects of Friction

Procedure

1. Attach a sticky note to the widest side of a rectangular eraser. The note must cover the entire side of the eraser. Trim off excess paper with scissors.

2. Place the eraser from Step 1 note-side down, next to a second eraser so that one end of each eraser extends 2 cm over the edge of a table.

3. Use a ruler to strike both erasers firmly and evenly at the same time. Record the distance each eraser slides.

4. Repeat Steps 2 and 3 two more times. Calculate and record the average distance each eraser slides.

Analyze and Conclude

1. **Observing** Which eraser slid farther?

2. **Formulating Hypotheses** Why did the erasers slide different distances?

3. **Drawing Conclusions** How does friction affect the motion of a sliding object?

4. **Revising** What could you do to make the erasers slide even farther?

Rolling Friction When a round object rolls across a flat floor, both the object and the floor are bent slightly out of shape. This change in shape at the point of rolling contact is the cause of **rolling friction,** the friction force that acts on rolling objects. For a given set of materials, the force of rolling friction is about 100 to 1000 times less than the force of static or sliding friction. Because of this, professional movers often use wheeled dollies to move heavy objects.

Ball bearings like those shown in Figure 6 are often used to reduce friction in machines. A ball bearing is made up of a set of round balls located between two smooth surfaces. The balls roll as the surfaces move past each other. Friction is greatly reduced between the surfaces because rolling friction replaces sliding friction. Inline skates, skateboards, bicycles, and automobiles are just a few of the many machines that use ball bearings.

Fluid Friction Friction also acts on a submarine moving through water and on an airplane flying through air. Water and a mixture of gases such as air are known as fluids. The force of **fluid friction** opposes the motion of an object through a fluid. You feel fluid friction when stirring thick cake batter. The motion of the spoon through the batter is slowed by fluid friction. Fluid friction increases as the speed of the object moving through the fluid increases. Thus the faster you stir, the greater the friction is.

Fluid friction acting on an object moving through the air is known as **air resistance.** At higher speeds, air resistance can become a significant force. For this reason, bicyclists and speed skaters often wear slick racing suits to reduce air resistance.

Reading Checkpoint *What are two common examples of fluid friction?*

Figure 6 Ball bearings in these wheels greatly reduce friction by replacing sliding friction with rolling friction.

Facts and Figures

Friction and Tennis You may mention to the students that, if they have ever played tennis on a clay court, they may have discovered that clay courts are covered with a layer of fine sand. The sand granules act as ball bearings for a short distance and then cause the player to slide. Ask, **With clay courts, what types of friction is the player experiencing?**

(The player first experiences rolling friction when the sand granules are still rolling. The player then experiences sliding friction when the granules stop rolling and start sliding. The sliding friction is actually occurring between the grains of sand and the surface below the sand, as the sand sticks to the shoes of the player.)

Gravity

Why do leaves fall to the ground? The answer is gravity. **Gravity** is a force that acts between any two masses. Gravity is an attractive force, that is, it pulls objects together. Earth's gravitational force exerts a force of attraction on every other object that is near Earth. That includes you—the force of Earth's gravity holds you on the ground. Note that the force of gravity does not require objects to be in contact for it to act on them. Unlike friction, gravity can act over large distances.

🌐 **Earth's gravity acts downward toward the center of Earth.** Fortunately, an upward force usually balances the downward force of gravity. What forces act on the boulder in Figure 7? Gravity pulls down on the boulder. An upward force supplied by the supporting rock acts upward and balances the downward gravitational force. Because the forces on the boulder are balanced, it remains at rest as it has for thousands of years.

Falling Objects What forces affect the motion of a dollar bill dropped from the top of a tall building? Both gravity and air resistance affect the motion of a falling object. 🌐 **Gravity causes objects to accelerate downward, whereas air resistance acts in the direction opposite to the motion and reduces acceleration.**

In Figure 8, a flying squirrel has jumped from a tree and is falling toward the ground. As you can see, the squirrel has positioned its body parallel to Earth's surface and spread its arms and legs. By doing this, the squirrel creates a very large surface area. The large area maximizes the force of air resistance acting to slow the squirrel's downward acceleration. Because of the squirrel's slower downward acceleration, it is able to travel farther through the air than would otherwise be possible.

As objects fall to the ground, they accelerate and gain speed. With increasing speed comes increasing air resistance. If an object falls for a long time, the upward force of air resistance becomes equal to the downward force of gravity. At this point, the forces acting on the object are balanced. Acceleration is zero and the object continues falling at a constant velocity. **Terminal velocity** is the constant velocity of a falling object when the force of air resistance equals the force of gravity. Read the Concepts in Action pages later in this chapter to learn how sky divers reach terminal velocity.

Figure 7 Earth exerts an attractive, downward force on this boulder.
Inferring **Because the boulder is at rest, what do you know about the net force acting on it?**

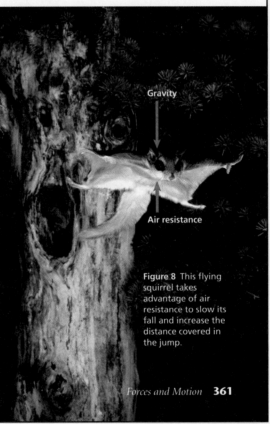

Figure 8 This flying squirrel takes advantage of air resistance to slow its fall and increase the distance covered in the jump.

Forces and Motion **361**

Gravity

Address Misconceptions L2

Students may think that no forces are acting on an object at rest. Help students see that this is false. Reinforce that resting objects have no *net force* acting on them. Show students that anything that has weight has at least two forces on it (if it is not in free fall). Forces of gravity pull the object downward toward Earth, and a reaction force pushes against that object, in accordance with Newton's third law of motion. Ask students to explain why a book which has weight (a type of force) rests on a desk without moving.
Visual, Logical

Use Visuals L1

Figure 8 The spread-out wings of the flying squirrel increase the air resistance that opposes the force of gravity, slowing the squirrel's fall. Have students examine the two force arrows in the figure. Ask, **What is the direction of the net force acting on the squirrel?** *(Downward)* **Why is the squirrel able to increase the distance covered when it jumps if the air resistance increases?** *(Because the squirrel's downward acceleration is slowed by the increased air resistance, the squirrel has more time to travel through the air. The squirrel's forward speed is not noticeably changed by the increased air resistance, and thus it travels a greater horizontal distance because it falls through the air a greater period of time.)*
Visual

Facts and Figures

Flying Squirrels Southern flying squirrels are found mostly from southern Ontario to the Gulf Coast. The length of an adult squirrel, including the tail, is about 23 to 25 cm, and its weight is usually between 55 and 110 g. Its fur is long, soft, and silky. On each side of the squirrel's body is a gliding membrane between the wrist of the front leg and the ankle of the hind leg. When the front and hind legs are extended, the membranes help the squirrel to glide in a motion that appears to be flying, giving the animal the name "flying squirrel." The tail acts as a rudder and helps to stabilize the squirrel as it glides.

Answer to . . .

Figure 7 *The net force on the boulder is zero.*

 Answers may include stirring cake batter and air resistance.

Projectile Motion
Use Visuals **L1**

Figure 9 Have students read the text under Projectile Motion. Then, ask questions to reinforce the idea that projectile motion is the result of the initial horizontal velocity and the vertical force of gravity. Ask, **Why does the yellow ball in Figure 9B continue downward at the same rate as the blue and green balls in Figure 9A?** *(They all accelerate downward by the force of gravity, approximately 9.8 m/s².)* **Why does the yellow ball (in 9B) continue horizontally?** *(The ball's initial horizontal velocity is not affected by the downward force of gravity.)* **Visual, Logical**

3 ASSESS
Evaluate
Understanding **L2**

Have students write a review question and its answer for each objective at the beginning of this section. Students should also be able to discuss the section objectives.

Reteach **L1**

Have students use Figure 4 to summarize the concepts of balanced and unbalanced forces. Use Figures 5 and 8 to review friction, gravity, and air resistance.

Connecting ⊂ Concepts

Students' sketches should show constant horizontal velocity, steadily increasing downward velocity, and constant downward acceleration.

Interactive Textbook If your class subscribes to the Interactive Textbook, use it to review key concepts in Section 12.1.

Figure 9 Gravity acts on falling objects. **A** Although their masses are different, the blue and green balls fall at the same rate. **B** The yellow ball is a projectile, following a curved path. **Applying Concepts** *What forces act on each of the falling balls?*

Projectile Motion

When you throw a ball forward, you'll notice that it actually follows a curved path. This curved path is an example of **projectile motion,** the motion of a falling object (projectile) after it is given an initial forward velocity. Air resistance and gravity are the only forces acting on a projectile.

Figure 9 shows the motion of two balls released at the same time. Figure 9A shows that balls of different mass fall at the same rate. In Figure 9B the curved path of the yellow ball is the result of the force of gravity and the initial horizontal velocity. ⊂ **The combination of an initial forward velocity and the downward vertical force of gravity causes the ball to follow a curved path.** The two balls fall with the same acceleration and strike the ground at the same time.

Section 12.1 Assessment

Reviewing Concepts

1. ⊂ How is the motion of an object affected when a force acts on it?
2. ⊂ List the four types of friction.
3. ⊂ How does air resistance affect the acceleration of a falling object?
4. ⊂ Earth's gravitational force acts in what direction?
5. ⊂ Describe why a projectile follows a curved path.

Critical Thinking

6. **Comparing and Contrasting** Compare the strengths of static, sliding, and rolling friction.

7. **Applying Concepts** Explain why falling leaves often do not fall in a straight-line path to the ground.
8. **Predicting** Two coins are knocked off a table at the same time by different forces. Which coin will hit the floor first?

Connecting ⊂ Concepts

Velocity and Acceleration Make sketches of Figures 9A and 9B. Use them to relate the concepts of velocity and acceleration from Section 11.3 to falling objects. Add velocity and acceleration arrows at three locations on each sketch.

Answer to . . .

Figure 9 *Forces acting on both of the falling balls are air resistance and gravity. In addition, the projectile in Figure 9B was briefly acted on by the force that gave it its initial horizontal velocity.*

Section 12.1 Assessment

1. A force can set an object at rest into motion, or it can accelerate a moving object by changing its speed or direction.
2. Static friction, sliding friction, rolling friction, and fluid friction
3. It acts opposite the direction of motion and slows the acceleration of a falling object.
4. Downward toward the center of Earth

5. The combination of initial horizontal velocity and downward vertical force causes a projectile to follow a curved path.
6. The force of static friction is greater than that of sliding friction. The force of sliding friction is generally greater than that of rolling friction.
7. Varying air resistance acting on the leaf results in a fluttering motion.
8. Both coins hit the ground at the same time.

12.2 Newton's First and Second Laws of Motion

Standards: ICP.1.2, ICP.1.3

Reading Focus

Key Concepts
- How does Newton's first law relate change in motion to a zero net force?
- How does Newton's second law relate force, mass, and acceleration?
- How are weight and mass related?

Vocabulary
- inertia
- mass
- weight

Reading Strategy
Building Vocabulary Copy the table below. Then as you read the section, write a definition for each vocabulary term in your own words.

Vocabulary	Definition
Inertia	a. ___?___
b. ___?___	c. ___?___
d. ___?___	e. ___?___

Why do some cars accelerate faster than others? How does an ice skater glide far across the ice after pushing off only once? The answers to these questions involve the concepts of mass and inertia.

Aristotle, Galileo, and Newton

Modern scientists understand the relationships between force and motion. However, it took about 2000 years to develop this understanding.

Aristotle The ancient Greek scientist and philosopher Aristotle (384 B.C.–322 B.C.) made many scientific discoveries through careful observation and logical reasoning. He was not always correct. Aristotle incorrectly proposed that force is required to keep an object moving at constant speed. This error held back progess in the study of motion for almost two thousand years.

Galileo Italian scientist Galileo Galilei (1564–1642) experimented to find out about the world. By rolling balls down wooden ramps, he studied how gravity produces constant acceleration. Galileo concluded that moving objects that were not subjected to friction or any other force would continue to move indefinitely. Galileo's portrait and the title page from the book that presented his work are shown in Figure 10.

Figure 10 Galileo's work helped correct misconceptions about force and motion that had been widely held since Aristotle's time.

Section Resources

Print
- *Lab Manual,* Investigations 12A and 12B
- *Reading and Study Workbook With Math Support,* Section 12.2 and **Math Skill:** Calculating Acceleration
- *Math Skills and Problem Solving Workbook,* Section 12.2
- *Transparencies,* Section 12.2

Technology
- *Interactive Textbook,* Section 12.2
- *Presentation Pro CD-ROM,* Section 12.2
- *Go Online,* NSTA SciLinks, Mass

---

1 FOCUS

Objectives
12.2.1 Describe Newton's first law of motion and its relation to inertia.

12.2.2 Describe Newton's second law of motion and use it to **calculate** acceleration, force, and mass values.

12.2.3 Relate the mass of an object to its weight.

Reading Focus

Build Vocabulary
Vocabulary Rating Chart Have students make a four-column chart with the headings Term, Can Define or Use It, Have Heard or Seen It, and Don't Know. Have them put inertia, mass, and weight in the first column, rating their knowledge of each term by putting a checkmark in one of the other columns. Give students a purpose for reading by asking them to check their expectations as they read. Ask them to make another chart after they have read the section.

Reading Strategy
a. The tendency of an object to resist a change in its motion **b.** Mass **c.** The amount of matter an object contains as measured by its inertia **d.** Weight **e.** The force of gravity acting on an object

2 INSTRUCT

Aristotle, Galileo, and Newton
Integrate Social Studies
Aristotle did not correctly explain why an object falls toward Earth. Later, Galileo's observations led him to confirm that Earth is one of many planets, all governed by the same laws of gravity. Galileo prepared the way for Isaac Newton, whose laws are presented in this chapter. To demonstrate these ideas, have students further research the ideas Aristotle and Newton had on gravity. Then, drop an object to the floor, and have student volunteers play the roles of "Aristotle" and "Newton" and debate what caused the object to fall.
Verbal, Interpersonal

Build Science Skills L2

Inferring Before studying Newton's first law of motion, have students look at Figures 12A and 12B. Ask, **What would have happened to the test dummy if the air bag had not deployed and the dummy had not been wearing a seatbelt?** *(Students should infer from the photos that the dummy's forward motion continues after the crash, and that the dummy might have gone through the windshield.)* **Visual, Logical**

Newton's First Law of Motion
Use Visuals L1

Figures 12A and 12B Have students examine Figures 12A and 12B. Ask, **What is the effect of inertia on the car?** *(Inertia causes the mass of the car to continue forward, crushing the front of the car.)* **What effect does inertia have on the dummy?** *(After the car stops, the dummy continues to move forward until it is stopped by the air bag and seatbelt.)* **How is the mass of a passenger related to the passenger's inertia?** *(Passengers with greater mass have more inertia. It is harder to stop the forward motion of passengers with greater mass.)* **Visual, Logical**

Investigating Inertia L2

Objective
After completing this activity, students will be able to
• use the concept of inertia to explain the movement of objects.

 Address Misconceptions

This lab can help to correct the misconception that inertia refers to the tendency of objects to resist motion, rather than the tendency to resist a change in motion. Use student answers to Question 1 as the basis of a discussion about the nature of inertia.

Skills Focus Observing, Formulating Hypotheses

Prep Time 5 minutes

Materials index card, coin

Advance Prep Checkers may be substituted for coins.

Class Time 5 minutes

Figure 11 Isaac Newton published his work on force and motion in the book entitled *Principia*.

Newton In 1665, the plague broke out in London, forcing Isaac Newton to leave Trinity College in Cambridge, England, where he was a student. Over the next two years, Newton built on the work of scientists such as Galileo. He published his results many years later in a book entitled *Principia*. In this important work, Newton first had to define mass and force. He then introduced his laws of motion. Newton's portrait and the title page of *Principia* are shown in Figure 11.

Newton's First Law of Motion

Newton summarized his study of force and motion in several laws of motion. ◑ **According to Newton's first law of motion, the state of motion of an object does not change as long as the net force acting on the object is zero.** Thus, unless an unbalanced force acts, an object at rest remains at rest, and an object in motion remains in motion with the same speed and direction. For example, a soccer ball resting on the grass remains motionless until a force is applied to it in the form of a kick. The kicked ball begins rolling. Because friction between the grass and the ball acts on the ball as it rolls, the ball slows. The force of friction slows the ball and brings it to a stop.

Newton's first law of motion is sometimes called the law of inertia (in UR shuh). **Inertia** is the tendency of an object to resist a change in its motion. In other words, an object at rest tends to remain at rest, and an object in motion tends to remain in motion with the same direction and speed. Note that as the soccer ball sat motionless in the grass, the forces acting on it were balanced. The ball remained at rest until an unbalanced force acted on it. The ball has inertia.

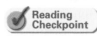 **Reading Checkpoint** *How does a zero net force affect an object's motion?*

Figure 12

A This crash sequence illustrates inertia—the tendency of an object in motion to remain in motion.

B At impact, the air bag deploys. Note that the test dummy continues its forward motion as the collision begins to slow the car.

Expected Outcome Fast changes in the movement of the card can occur with little effect on the movement of the coin. When the card moves slowly, it carries the coin along.

Analyze and Conclude
1. In Step 1, the inertia of the coin resisted acceleration by the card. The force of friction was not strong enough to hold the coin in place on the accelerating card. In Step 2, the acceleration of the card was not as great. Therefore, the force of friction was strong enough to hold the coin in place on the card. In Step 3, the situation was identical to that in Step 2 at first. However, when the card suddenly stopped moving, the inertia of the coin was great enough to keep it moving in the same direction, in spite of the force of friction.

2. If the mass of the coin were greater, its inertia also would be greater. Therefore, the coin would again have resisted acceleration in Step 1 and moved with the card in Step 2 if the card was not moving too quickly. In Step 3, the coin would have continued moving longer after the card stopped moving. **Logical**

Think about what happens if you are in a moving car that is involved in a front-end collision. The collision makes the car stop suddenly. What happens to you? Because you have inertia, you continue moving forward. The series of photos in Figure 12 shows you how dangerous a front-end collision can be. If a seat belt and airbag had not restrained the test dummy, it would have crashed into the steering wheel and windshield with great force. The seat belt and airbag work by exerting force against the body of the dummy, opposing its forward motion.

Newton's Second Law of Motion

How do unbalanced forces affect the motion of an object? An unbalanced force causes an object's velocity to change. In other words, the object accelerates. For example, you apply a net force to a ball when you throw it. The harder you throw, the more the ball accelerates. In fact, the acceleration of the ball is directly proportional to the net force acting on it. If you double the force, the acceleration of the ball doubles as well. Newton also learned that the acceleration of an object depends upon its mass. **Mass** is a measure of the inertia of an object and depends on the amount of matter the object contains.

👉 According to Newton's second law of motion, the acceleration of an object is equal to the net force acting on it divided by the object's mass. Thus, doubling the mass of an object cuts its acceleration in half. Newton was able to put these ideas into a single formula.

Newton's Second Law

$$\text{Acceleration} = \frac{\text{Net force}}{\text{Mass}}, \quad \text{or} \quad a = \frac{F}{m}$$

C As the car comes to a stop, the air bag prevents the test dummy from striking the steering wheel.

D **Interpreting Photographs** What objects and devices absorb the energy of the crash?

Forces and Motion **365**

HOW It Works

Crash-Test Dummies `L2`

Defining the way a body will respond to a crash is difficult because different parts of the human body behave in different ways in a crash. For that reason, developing a crash-test dummy that behaves like a human body in a crash has been difficult.

Early automotive crash test dummies were based on dummies used in aerospace. Because head, spine, and neck injuries can be life-threatening, dummies' heads, necks, and spines were a major focus of research. In 1973, dummies were improved. Injuries to lower extremities are rarely fatal, but they can reduce a person's quality of life. Further research and development of crash-test dummies will focus on lower extremities.

Interpreting Diagrams Forces from both the seatbelt and the air bag slow the dummy's movement.
Visual

For Enrichment `L3`

Have students research the methods used by the National Highway Traffic Safety Administration (NHTSA) to test a vehicle's crash worthiness and its likelihood of rolling over. Also have students create tables explaining the meaning of the star rating system used by the NHTSA. Select a method for students to use to present their findings to the class.
Logical

Use Community Resources `L2`

Arrange for a police officer to speak to your class about seatbelt safety laws. Have the officer reinforce the importance of seatbelts in preventing injury. The police department may have a video that could visually reinforce the concept of seatbelt safety and its relationship to Newton's first law of motion in sudden stops.
Logical, Visual

 HOW It Works

Crash-Test Dummies

Dummies are used in simulated car crashes to study what might happen to passengers in a real crash. They are fitted with a range of measuring devices that track the motion of the dummies throughout the crash. By analyzing the data, scientists learn how injuries occur and how they can be prevented. **Interpreting Diagrams** *What forces act on the crash-test dummy to slow its forward movement?*

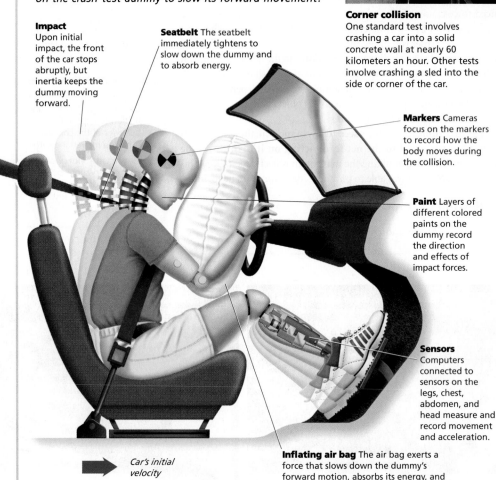

Impact
Upon initial impact, the front of the car stops abruptly, but inertia keeps the dummy moving forward.

Seatbelt The seatbelt immediately tightens to slow down the dummy and to absorb energy.

Corner collision
One standard test involves crashing a car into a solid concrete wall at nearly 60 kilometers an hour. Other tests involve crashing a sled into the side or corner of the car.

Markers Cameras focus on the markers to record how the body moves during the collision.

Paint Layers of different colored paints on the dummy record the direction and effects of impact forces.

Sensors Computers connected to sensors on the legs, chest, abdomen, and head measure and record movement and acceleration.

Car's initial velocity

Inflating air bag The air bag exerts a force that slows down the dummy's forward motion, absorbs its energy, and prevents it from hitting the steering wheel.

366 *Chapter 12*

Facts and Figures

Bike Helmets You may help your students understand that Newton's first law of motion is a reason for wearing helmets when cycling. During an accident, the foam padding in a helmet is deformed, absorbing the energy of the impact. Explain that each year, almost 400,000 children ages 14 and under are treated in emergency rooms for bicycle-related injuries. Head injuries account for more than two thirds of bicycle-related hospital admissions and more than half of bicycle-related deaths. If each child wore a bicycle helmet, between 39,000 and 45,000 head injuries, and between 18,000 and 55,000 scalp and face injuries could be prevented annually.

The acceleration of an object is always in the same direction as the net force. In using the formula for Newton's second law, it is helpful to realize that the units N/kg and m/s² are equivalent. The Math Skills box reinforces this relationship.

Note that Newton's second law also applies when a net force acts in the direction opposite to the object's motion. In this case, the force produces a deceleration that reduces the speed. This is the principle used by automobile seat belts. In a collision, the seat belt applies a force that opposes a passenger's forward motion. This force decelerates the passenger in order to prevent serious injury.

  Math Skills

Newton's Second Law

An automobile with a mass of 1000 kilograms accelerates when the traffic light turns green. If the net force on the car is 4000 newtons, what is the car's acceleration?

1 Read and Understand

What information are you given?

Mass, m = 1000 kg

Force, F = 4000 N (in the forward direction)

2 Plan and Solve

What unknown are you trying to calculate?

Acceleration, a = ?

What formula contains the given quantities and the unknown?

$$\text{Acceleration} = \frac{\text{Net force}}{\text{Mass}}, a = \frac{F}{m}$$

Replace each variable with its known value and solve.

$$a = \frac{4000\ \text{N}}{1000\ \text{kg}} = \frac{4\ \text{N}}{\text{kg}} = \frac{4\ \frac{\text{kg}\cdot\text{m}}{\text{s}^2}}{\text{kg}} = 4\ \text{m/s}^2$$

a = 4 m/s² in the forward direction

3 Look Back and Check

Is your answer reasonable?

Powerful sports cars can accelerate at 6 m/s² or more. Thus, a smaller acceleration of 4 m/s² seems reasonable.

 Math Practice

1. A boy pushes forward a cart of groceries with a total mass of 40.0 kg. What is the acceleration of the cart if the net force on the cart is 60.0 N?

2. What is the upward acceleration of a helicopter with a mass of 5000 kg if a force of 10,000 N acts on it in an upward direction?

3. An automobile with a mass of 1200 kg accelerates at a rate of 3.0 m/s² in the forward direction. What is the net force acting on the automobile? (*Hint:* Solve the acceleration formula for force.)

4. A 25-N force accelerates a boy in a wheelchair at 0.5 m/s² What is the mass of the boy and the wheelchair? (*Hint:* Solve Newton's second law for mass.)

 Teacher Demo

Newton's Second Law of Motion L2

Purpose Students observe that acceleration is inversely proportional to mass. ($a = F/m$)

Materials wind-up toy car, 3 metal washers, tape

Procedure Have students wind the toy car completely and observe its motion along a flat surface. Next, have them tape metal washers to the car, wind it, and watch its motion along the flat surface again.

Expected Outcome Students will notice that the car's acceleration decreases because of the increased mass. **Visual**

 Math Practice

Solutions L2
1. $a = F/m = 60.0\ \text{N}/40.0\ \text{kg} = 1.50\ \text{m/s}^2$
2. $a = F/m = 10,000\ \text{N}/5000\ \text{kg} = 2\ \text{m/s}^2$
3. $a = F/m$; $F = ma = 1200\ \text{kg} \times 3.0\ \text{m/s}^2 = 3600\ \text{N}$
4. $a = F/m$; $m = F/a = 25\ \text{N}/0.50\ \text{m/s}^2 = 50\ \text{kg}$
Logical

For Extra Help L1

Remind students that they first need to solve the equation $a = F/m$ for the unknown. Also ask students to identify all the known and unknown variables before using the equation. **Logical**

Direct students to the **Math Skills** in the **Skills and Reference Handbook** at the end of the student text for additional help.

Additional Problems

1. A 20-N net force acts on an object with a mass of 2.0 kg. What is the object's acceleration? (*10 m/s²*)
2. A box has a mass of 150 kg. If a net force of 3000 N acts on the box, what is the box's acceleration? (*20 m/s²*)
3. What is the acceleration of a 1000 kg car subject to a 500 N net force? (*0.5 m/s²*)
Logical, Portfolio

Use Visuals   L1

Figure 13 Use this figure to be sure that students understand the equation *F* = *ma* before asking the following question about the mass-acceleration ratio. Ask, **Why would one cart accelerate eight times as fast as the chain of eight carts with the same force applied in each case? Explain using the second-law equation.** *(If the force remains the same in the equation* F = ma, *then as mass increases, the acceleration has to decrease in proportion to the increase in mass.)* **How would the force have to change in order to have the same acceleration for eight carts as for one cart?** *(The force would have to be eight times greater.)* **How would another force directed to the left on the cart affect the cart's acceleration?** *(The acceleration would depend on the net force acting on the cart. The net force would be the force acting to the right minus the force acting to the left.)*
Visual

Build Reading Literacy   L1

Visualize Refer to page **354D** in **Chapter 12,** which provides the guidelines for visualizing.

Tell students that forming a mental image of concepts they are learning helps them remember new concepts. For example, this section discusses weight in newtons, but students may think of weight in terms of pounds. Help students to visualize that the pound equals 4.448 newtons. Tell them, that in approximate weights, $\frac{1}{4}$ pound is slightly more than one newton. Encourage students to think of something the size of a pound, such as a pound of butter. If the butter is divided into four sticks, each stick is slightly more than the weight of one newton. Likewise, a quarter-pound hamburger could be called a "newton" burger.
Visual

Go Online
NSTA SciLINKS

Download a worksheet on mass for students to complete, and find additional teacher support from NSTA SciLinks.

Force   Force

Acceleration   Acceleration

Figure 13 Acceleration depends directly on force and inversely on mass. Neglecting friction, when the same force acts, the single cart accelerates eight times faster than the chain of eight carts. **Predicting** *How would the acceleration of a chain of two carts compare with the acceleration of a single cart if the same force acted on both?*

Go Online
NSTA SciLINKS

For: Links on mass
Visit: www.SciLinks.org
Web Code: ccn-2122

The shopping carts in Figure 13 further illustrate Newton's second law. What happens if you push on a single shopping cart? The unbalanced force causes the cart to accelerate. What happens when you push with the same force on a chain of eight shopping carts? The acceleration of the chain of carts is much less than that of the single cart. The chain of carts accelerates less because it has more mass.

Weight and Mass

Do you sometimes talk about weight and mass as if they were the same thing? Although related to each other, mass and weight are not the same. **Weight** is the force of gravity acting on an object. An object's weight is the product of the object's mass and acceleration due to gravity acting on it.

> **Weight Formula**
> Weight = Mass × Acceleration due to gravity
> $$W = mg$$

The weight formula is basically Newton's second law. However, weight (*W*) is substituted for force (*F*) and acceleration due to gravity (*g*) is substitutued for acceleration (*a*). In other words, *W* = *mg* is a different form of $a = \frac{F}{M}$, that is when the equation is solved for force, *F* = *ma*. The value of *g* in the formula is 9.8 m/s².

In using the weight formula or Newton's second-law formula, make sure you use the correct units. The force (*F* or *W*) should be in newtons, the acceleration (*a* or *g*) in meters per second squared, and the mass (*m*) in kilograms. The following example shows how to use the weight formula.

If an astronaut has a mass of 112 kilograms, what is his weight on Earth where the acceleration due to gravity is 9.8 m/s²?

Weight = Mass × Acceleration due to gravity

= 112 kg × 9.8 m/s²

= 1100 kg·m/s² = 1100 N

A Astronaut on Earth
Mass = 88.0 kg; Weight = 863 N

B Astronaut on Moon
Mass = 88.0 kg; Weight = 141 N

Figure 14 Weight is a measure of the force of gravity acting on an object. **A** An astronaut with a mass of 88 kg weighs 863 N on Earth. **B** An astronaut with a mass of 88 kg weighs 141 N on the moon. **Calculating** *If the same astronaut stood on Mars where the acceleration due to gravity is about 3.7 m/s², how much would the astronaut weigh?*

If you study the weight formula, you'll see that mass and weight are proportional. Doubling the mass of an object also doubles the object's weight. ⊂⊃ **Mass is a measure of the inertia of an object; weight is a measure of the force of gravity acting on an object.** Consider the same astronaut shown on Earth and on the moon in Figure 14. On the moon, the acceleration due to gravity is only about one sixth that on Earth. Thus, the astronaut weighs only about one sixth as much on the moon as on Earth. In both locations, the mass of the astronaut is the same.

Section 12.2 Assessment

Reviewing Concepts

1. ⊂⊃ State Newton's first law of motion in your own words.
2. ⊂⊃ What equation states Newton's second law of motion?
3. ⊂⊃ How is mass different from weight?

Critical Thinking

4. **Applying Concepts** Describe several examples of Newton's first and second laws that you observe during a normal day.
5. **Making Judgments** A steel ball is the same size as a wooden ball, but weighs twice as much. If both balls are dropped from an airplane, which of them will reach terminal velocity more quickly? Explain.

Math Practice

6. During a test crash, an air bag inflates to stop a dummy's forward motion. The dummy's mass is 75 kg. If the net force on the dummy is 825 N toward the rear of the car, what is the dummy's deceleration?

7. A bicycle takes 8.0 seconds to accelerate at a constant rate from rest to a speed of 4.0 m/s. If the mass of the bicycle and rider together is 85 kg, what is the net force acting on the bicycle? (*Hint:* First calculate the acceleration.)

Forces and Motion **369**

Section 12.2 Assessment

1. Students should paraphrase the following: According to Newton's first law of motion, the state of motion of an object does not change as long as the net force acting on the object is zero.
2. $a = F/m$
3. Mass is a measure of the inertia of an object; weight is a measure of the force of gravity acting on an object.

4. Students should cite examples in which objects at rest remain at rest or tend to continue moving (first law) and in which a net force acting on an object causes a change in the object's state of motion (second law).
5. The heavier steel ball will take longer to reach terminal velocity. A greater speed is needed to produce the air resistance required to balance the steel ball's greater weight. The steel ball must fall for a longer period of time in order to reach this greater speed.

3 ASSESS

Evaluate Understanding L2

Have students work in pairs to write three math problems (with solutions) based on Newton's second law, $a = F/m$. Then have them do the same for the weight equation, $W = mg$. Ask students to present their problems and solutions in class.

Reteach L1

Use Figure 12 to review inertia and its relationship to Newton's first law of motion. Use Figure 13 to review Newton's second law of motion. Use Figure 14 to review how Newton's second law is related to the weight formula.

Math Practice

Solutions L2

6. $a = F/m = 825$ N/75 kg $= 11$ m/s², toward the rear of the car
7. $a = \delta v/t = (4.0$ m/s)/(8.0 s) $= 0.50$ m/s²; $F = ma = 85$ kg x 0.50 m/s² $= 43$ N

Interactive Textbook If your class subscribes to the Interactive Textbook, use it to review key concepts in Section 12.2.

Answer to . . .

Figure 13 *The two-cart chain would accelerate at half the rate of the single cart.*

Figure 14 *330 N*

Terminal Speed
Background

The skydiver's weight, the gravitational force downward, is constant and is calculated with the formula $W = mg$. The variable g is 9.8 m/s/s, usually written 9.8 m/s^2. The opposing drag force, D, from the air, continues to increase until terminal velocity is reached. The drag force depends on the shape and position of the skydiver. Drag is calculated from a complex formula.

The skydiver's net force is weight minus drag, $W - D$. Using net force $W - D$ for F, acceleration is found as follows: $a = F/m = (W - D)/m$.

When weight equals drag, $W - D$ becomes zero; therefore, acceleration becomes zero. The skydiver stops accelerating and reaches maximum velocity, which is called terminal velocity.

Build Science Skills

Observing

Purpose Students investigate air resistance and its effect on the rate of acceleration.

Materials sheet of paper, stopwatch, auditorium stage

Class Time 25 minutes

Procedure Have one student drop the flat sheet of paper from the auditorium stage while another times the paper's descent with the stopwatch. A third student can record the time.

Repeat the experiment, but this time have the student crumple the sheet of paper. Compare the descent times. Ask, **What variables remained constant and what variables changed?** *(Air resistance changed. Weight (mass) and acceleration due to gravity, g, remained the same.)* **Why are the times different?** *(A greater air resistance force acts on the flat sheet, causing it to fall more slowly.)* **If both the flat and crumpled sheets were dropped in a vacuum where there is no air resistance, what would happen?** *(The time it takes the sheet to fall would be the same.)*

Expected Outcome The increased force of air resistance acting on the flat sheet causes it to fall more slowly than the crumpled sheet.
Visual, Logical

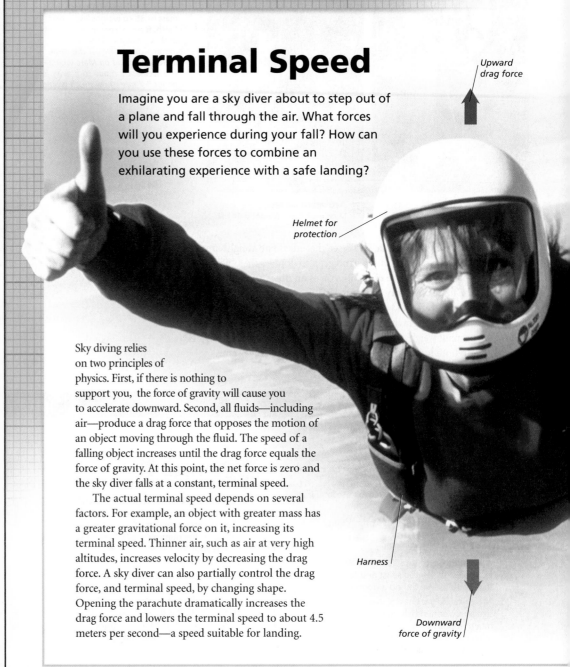

CONCEPTS in Action

Terminal Speed

Imagine you are a sky diver about to step out of a plane and fall through the air. What forces will you experience during your fall? How can you use these forces to combine an exhilarating experience with a safe landing?

Upward drag force

Helmet for protection

Sky diving relies on two principles of physics. First, if there is nothing to support you, the force of gravity will cause you to accelerate downward. Second, all fluids—including air—produce a drag force that opposes the motion of an object moving through the fluid. The speed of a falling object increases until the drag force equals the force of gravity. At this point, the net force is zero and the sky diver falls at a constant, terminal speed.

The actual terminal speed depends on several factors. For example, an object with greater mass has a greater gravitational force on it, increasing its terminal speed. Thinner air, such as air at very high altitudes, increases velocity by decreasing the drag force. A sky diver can also partially control the drag force, and terminal speed, by changing shape. Opening the parachute dramatically increases the drag force and lowers the terminal speed to about 4.5 meters per second—a speed suitable for landing.

Harness

Downward force of gravity

370 *Chapter 12*

The Sky Diving Sequence

No matter what the starting altitude, any sky dive consists of the same basic stages, starting with the jump from the plane.

Altimeter showing altitude

1 Jumping out Upon jumping, the sky diver begins accelerating at a rate of 9.8 meters per second per second in free fall. Within a few seconds she will reach maximum speed.

Parachute

2 Falling freely Sky divers usually jump from a height of about 3000 meters and fall freely for about 45 seconds before opening the parachute. The top speed reached, known as terminal speed, is about 52 meters per second. Falling from very high altitudes, where the air is thinner and the drag force is less, can produce higher terminal speeds.

3 Slowing the fall Usually the parachute is fully open by the time the sky diver is 300 meters above the ground. The parachute causes rapid deceleration and allows the sky diver to make a steady descent, using the control lines to steer.

Sky diver lands standing up

4 Landing The sky diver pulls down on the control lines to achieve a safe and steady low-speed landing.

Going Further

- Research the development and use of the parachute and prepare a poster presentation of your findings. Be sure to include a development time line listing names and dates of significant contributions and advances.

- Take a Discovery Channel Video Field Trip by watching "Air Forces."

DISCOVERY CHANNEL SCHOOL Video Field Trip

Students may think that objects in a vacuum fall at a constant speed. Help them to realize that objects accelerate as they fall. Earth's gravitational acceleration in a vacuum is approximately 9.8 m/s/s, meaning that the velocity increases 9.8 m/s every second, or 9.8 m/s^2, as the object falls.

Without a vacuum, however, air resistance increases as the object falls until the object reaches terminal velocity. Reinforce that all objects in a vacuum accelerate at the same rate, but that they do not fall at a constant speed until they reach terminal velocity.
Logical

Going Further

Student poster presentations may include references to Leonardo da Vinci, Fauste Veranzio, and Joseph and Jacques Montgolfier.
Visual, Verbal

DISCOVERY CHANNEL SCHOOL Video Field Trip

Air Forces

After students have viewed the Video Field Trip, ask them the following questions: **What is the net force on the skydiver just before stepping out of the plane? Explain your answer.** (*Zero. The force of gravity is balanced by the force the aircraft exerts so that the skydiver is not yet accelerating.*) **How do the force of gravity and air resistance compare as the skydiver is falling and gaining speed? Explain your answer.** (*The force of gravity is greater than the* air resistance because the gravitational force is downward and the air resistance is upward, resulting in a net force downward.) **How does the force of air resistance change as the skydiver gains speed while falling?** (*The air resistance increases.*) **What happens to the skydiver's speed when the force of air resistance becomes equal to the force of gravity? Explain your answer.** (*The skydiver's speed stays the same. Gravity and air resistance balance each other. Because the net force is zero, there is no acceleration.*) **How does the force of air resistance change when the skydiver's parachute opens?** (*It suddenly increases.*)

1 FOCUS

Objectives

12.3.1 Explain how action and reaction forces are related according to Newton's third law of motion.

12.3.2 Calculate the momentum of an object and **describe** what happens when momentum is conserved during a collision.

Reading Focus

Build Vocabulary   L2

Paraphrase Have students work with a partner to write an explanation in their own words for the law of conservation of momentum. They may do so by reading this section and by using what they have already learned about mass, inertia, and velocity. Have student groups read their explanation aloud. Encourage other students to react to the explanation they hear.

Reading Strategy   L2

a. kg•m/s **b.** Mass (or velocity)
c. Velocity (or mass)

Build Reading Literacy   L1

Relate Text and Visuals Refer to page **190D** in **Chapter 7**, which provides the guidelines for relating text and visuals.

Ask questions that will help students understand how the visuals help clarify and extend concepts presented in the text. Point out Figure 15. Ask, **Describe the forces created when the bumper car strikes another car.** *(There is a force from each car toward the other car.)* **If a moving car hits a car at rest, will the car at rest exert a force on the moving car? Explain your answer.** *(Yes, according to Newton's third law, the car at rest exerts an equal and opposite force on the moving car.)*
Visual, Verbal

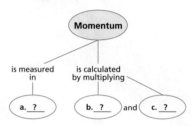

12.3 Newton's Third Law of Motion and Momentum

 Standard: ICP.1.2

Reading Focus

Key Concepts
- What is Newton's third law of motion?
- What is needed for an object to have a large momentum?
- How is momentum conserved?

Vocabulary
- momentum
- law of conservation of momentum

Reading Strategy
Summarizing Read the section on momentum. Then copy and complete the concept map below to organize what you know about momentum.

```
                    Momentum
                   /        \
          is measured      is calculated
              in           by multiplying
              |            /           \
          a. _?_      b. _?_   and   c. _?_
```

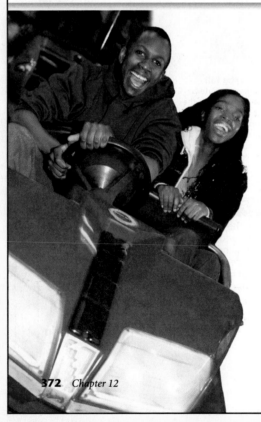

Think physics the next time you go to an amusement park. There is no better place than an amusement park to see Newton's laws in action. As you experience sudden starts, stops, changes in direction, and possibly even free fall, you can be sure that the laws of physics control your motion. The bumper cars in Figure 15 illustrate momentum and Newton's third law of motion, the subjects of this section.

If you have ever driven a bumper car, you know your goal is to slam into another car head on. When you collide with the other car, you do so with enough force to jolt the other driver almost out of the seat. There are two parts to this collision, however—the collision also causes your own car to rebound sharply. Newton's third law of motion explains the behavior of the bumper cars during a collision.

Figure 15 When this bumper car collides with another car, two forces are exerted. Each car in the collision exerts a force on the other.

 ## Section Resources

Print
- *Reading and Study Workbook With Math Support*, Section 12.3
- *Math Skills and Problem Solving Workbook*, Section 12.3
- *Transparencies*, Section 12.3

Technology
- *Probeware Lab Manual*, Lab 4
- *Interactive Textbook*, Section 12.3
- *Presentation Pro CD-ROM*, Section 12.3
- *Go Online*, NSTA SciLinks, Newton's laws

Newton's Third Law

A force cannot exist alone. Forces always exist in pairs. **According to Newton's third law of motion, whenever one object exerts a force on a second object, the second object exerts an equal and opposite force on the first object.** These two forces are called action and reaction forces.

Action and Reaction Forces The force your bumper car exerts on the other car is the action force. The force the other car exerts on your car is the reaction force. These two forces are equal in size and opposite in direction.

Pressing your hand against a wall also produces a pair of forces. As you press against the wall, your hand exerts a force on the wall. This is the action force. The wall exerts an equal and opposite force against your hand. This is the reaction force.

A similar situation occurs when you use a hammer to drive a nail into a piece of wood. When the hammer strikes the nail, it applies a force to the nail. This action force drives the nail into the piece of wood. Is there a reaction force? According to Newton's third law there must be an equal and opposite reaction force. The nail supplies the reaction force by exerting an equal and opposite force on the hammer. It is this reaction force that brings the motion of the hammer to a stop.

Action-Reaction Forces and Motion
Can you determine the action and reaction forces occurring in Figure 16? The swimmer uses her arms to push against the water and create an action force. The action force causes the water to move in the direction of the action force. However, the water also exerts its equal and opposite reaction force on the swimmer. The reaction force acts on the swimmer and pushes her forward through the water.

Unlike the swimmer in Figure 16, not all action and reaction forces produce motion. Pushing against the wall with your hand is an example of an action-reaction force pair that does not result in motion.

Action-Reaction Forces Do Not Cancel You may be wondering why the action and reaction forces acting on the swimmer in Figure 16 do not cancel each other and produce a net force of zero. The reason is that the action and reaction forces do not act on the same object. The action force acts on the water, and the reaction force acts on the swimmer. Only when equal and opposite forces act on the same object do they result in a net force of zero.

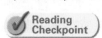 *Why don't action and reaction forces cancel each other out?*

Go Online
NSTA SciLINKS

For: Links on Newton's laws
Visit: www.SciLinks.org
Web Code: ccn-2123

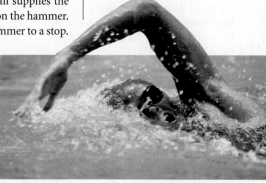

Figure 16 Action-reaction forces propel the swimmer through the water. The swimmer pushes against the water, and the water pushes the swimmer ahead.
Comparing and Contrasting
Describe the magnitude and direction of the action and reaction forces acting on the swimmer.

---

2 INSTRUCT

Newton's Third Law
Build Science Skills **L2**

Predicting

Purpose Students use Newton's third law of motion to predict the effect of objects that hit against one another.

Materials soccer ball, several heavy books

Class Time 15 minutes

Procedure Ask students to use Newton's third law to predict the outcome of each activity before performing it. First, have students lift several heavy books above their heads and notice the downward force they feel against their hands. Next, place a soccer ball against a wall. Have a student kick the ball gently. The student should notice the opposing force he or she feels against his or her foot. Afterwards, have students discuss the origin of the forces they felt in each activity.

Expected Outcome Students will realize that the force they exerted on the books and ball caused an equal and opposite force against them.
Visual, Logical

Go Online

NSTA SciLINKS

Download a worksheet on Newton's laws for students to complete, and find additional teacher support from NSTA SciLinks.

Customize for English Language Learners

Use Interaction
One of the best ways to teach science content and language to all students, including English language learners, is to encourage verbal interaction, such as that which occurs in a group. You may help English language learners by using group activities in this section, as the section lends itself well to activities involving action-reaction forces. Since all force involves action-reaction, you may start with activities that make the concept easy to learn. For example, demonstrate that standing on the floor results in a reaction force of the floor, which is actually pushing back. Encourage students to work in groups to list other action-reaction forces.

Answer to . . .

Figure 16 *The action force is the force the swimmer exerts on the water. The equal and opposite reaction force is the force the water exerts on the swimmer.*

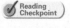 *They do not cancel each other out because they act on different objects.*

Momentum

Momentum

L2

Purpose Students observe that force is related to the time during which an object's momentum changes.

Materials water-filled balloons, pillow

Procedure Before beginning the demonstration, explain to students that force can be written as a function of momentum and time: $F = m \times a = m \times (v/t) = (m \times v)/t$. Therefore, $F \times t = m \times v$, where momentum is $m \times v$, and $F \times t$ is the quantity known as impulse. Point out that force has an inverse relationship to time in the equation. Therefore, the longer the time period over which momentum change occurs, the smaller the force will be.

Take students outdoors to a paved area. Drop a water-filled balloon to the ground and let it burst on the pavement. Next, drop a water-filled balloon so that it lands on the pillow without bursting.

Safety Caution students to stand a safe distance away from you when you drop the balloons.

Expected Outcome Students should realize that when the balloon stops quickly, the momentum change occurs over a short time. This results in a large force acting on the balloon—the large force breaks the balloon. When the balloon lands on the pillow, its momentum change occurs over a much longer period of time. The balloon doesn't burst because the force acting on it is much less.
Visual, Logical

FYI

The coverage of momentum in this text is limited to linear momentum—angular momentum and conservation are not covered. Momentum is a vector quantity, having both magnitude and direction.

Momentum

Imagine a loaded shopping cart and a small glass marble are both slowly rolling toward you at the same speed. The marble is easier to stop. Intuitively, you know that a loaded shopping cart is harder to stop because it has a greater mass. If the marble were moving 100 times faster than the shopping cart, which would be easier to stop? **Momentum** is the product of an object's mass and its velocity. An object with large momentum is hard to stop. **An object has a large momentum if the product of its mass and velocity is large.** The momentum for any object at rest is zero. A huge rocket such as the space shuttle has zero momentum as it sits on the launch pad. A small 1-kilogram meteor traveling at the very high speed of 20 kilometers per second has a very large momentum.

DK SCIENCE and History

Amusement Park Rides

For more than one hundred years, engineers have been designing rides that subject riders to jarring motions, large accelerations, terrifying heights, soakings, or free falls.

Acceleration *Riders experience an acceleration toward the loop's center as they move around it.*

Start turret, 13 meters above the ground

LOOPING GRAVITY RAILWAY

Maximum height *The first Ferris wheel is 80.5 m tall.*

Wood-paneled car *Each car has a mass of 13 tons and holds as many as 60 people.*

The ride *Passengers move at a speed of about 0.5 m/s.*

FERRIS WHEEL

1846 The first railway to turn its passengers upside down opens at a park in Paris, France.

1884 The first true roller coaster in America appears at Coney Island, New York.

1893 The George Ferris Giant Wheel, named after the inventor, debuts at the Columbian Exposition in Chicago. A ride costs 50 cents.

1900 Trolley companies build amusement parks to encourage weekend travel.

1845   1875   1905

374 *Chapter 12*

You can calculate momentum by multiplying an object's mass (in kilograms) and its velocity (in meters per second).

Momentum Formula

$$\text{Momentum} = \text{Mass} \times \text{Velocity}$$

Momentum is measured in units of kilogram-meters per second.

Which has more momentum, a 0.046-kilogram golf ball with a speed of 60.0 meters per second, or a 7.0-kilogram bowling ball with a speed of 6.0 meters per second?

$$\text{Momentum}_{\text{golf ball}} = 0.046 \text{ kg} \times 60.0 \text{ m/s} = 2.8 \text{ kg} \cdot \text{m/s}$$

$$\text{Momentum}_{\text{bowling ball}} = 7.0 \text{ kg} \times 6.0 \text{ m/s} = 42 \text{ kg} \cdot \text{m/s}$$

The bowling ball has considerably more momentum than the golf ball.

Writing in Science

Explain a Sequence Write a paragraph about one of the amusement park rides shown on the time line. Describe the motion of the ride using Newton's laws of motion. (*Hint:* Before you write, use a diagram to analyze the forces acting on the ride at a particular moment.)

Roller coaster *This version, about three kilometers long, catapults riders to about 25 m/s in the first 4 seconds.*

THEME PARK

Sun wheel, a modern twist on the Ferris wheel.

Rubber bumper *This prolongs the time of impact and decreases the force of the collisions.*

Sharp drop *Riders reach a maximum speed of about 25 m/s during the drop.*

BUMPER CAR

FREE FALL RIDE

1928 The first fully steerable bumper car is invented.

1934 The first wild mouse coaster, with sharp turns and abrupt drops, is built in Germany.

1955 The first cartoon-themed amusement park opens in Anaheim, California.

1963 The world's first log-in-water ride is an instant success at a park in Texas. Similar rides are soon being built around the world.

1996 A free-fall ride with a drop of 46 meters opens in Maryland.

1935   1965   1995

Forces and Motion **375**

DK SCIENCE and History

Amusement Park Rides
L2

Have students read about the amusement park inventions shown in the timeline. Then, ask them what other science-related events they would add to the timeline. Suggestions may include these events: Orville and Wilbur Wright's first flight at Kitty Hawk, North Carolina, in 1903; Henry Ford's initial Model-T production in 1908; the opening of the 50-mile Panama Canal in 1914; or Charles Lindbergh's $33\frac{1}{2}$-hour, non-stop flight in a monoplane from New York to Paris in 1927. Then, ask students how all of the events in the timeline affected both science and society, including those events that students have added. **Verbal**

Build Math Skills
L1

Equations and Formulas Many students have difficulty relating the description of a relationship given in the text with the equation used to solve problems. Have students read Momentum. Ask them to use the description from the text to write the momentum equation (Momentum = Mass × Velocity). Once they have written the equation, have them practice solving the equation for each of the three possible unknowns: momentum, mass, and velocity. Tell them that it is important to practice working with the units (kg•m/s). Refer students to the text samples on this page.
Logical, Portfolio

Direct students to the **Math Skills** in the **Skills and Reference Handbook** at the end of the student text for additional help.

Writing in Science

Explanations describing the forces and resulting motion that occur as a sequence of events will vary depending on which amusement park ride is chosen. Paragraphs should discuss forces, acceleration, and momentum.
Verbal, Portfolio

Conservation of Momentum
Use Visuals

Figure 17 To help teach conservation of momentum, point out to students that each car's momentum is written on the car, and its velocity is written above the car. Ask students to describe the motion in 17A before and after the collision. *(The blue car, going in the same direction as the green car, but faster, catches the green car and collides with it. After the collision, part of the momentum from the blue car is transferred to the green car, but the total momentum is still the same.)* Ask, **What is the momentum of the blue car and the green car before and after the collision in 17A?** *(Before the collision, the blue car's momentum is 300,000 kg•m/s and the green car's momentum is 150,000 kg•m/s. After the collision, the blue car's momentum is 150,000 kg•m/s and the green car's momentum is 300,000 kg•m/s.)* **What is the sum of the momentum before and after the collision?** *(The total momentum is 450,000 kg•m/s before and after the collision.)* **How does this show conservation of momentum?** *(The total momentum doesn't change.)* Repeat the above questions for Figures 17B and 17C.
Visual, Logical

For: Activity on momentum
Visit: PHSchool.com
Web Code: ccp-2123

Students can interact with simulations of momentum and conservation of momentum online.

A Both cars moving.

Before collision
10 m/s →
Momentum = 300,000 kg·m/s
5 m/s →
Momentum = 150,000 kg·m/s
Momentum before collision = 450,000 kg·m/s

Cars bounce off each other.
After collision
5 m/s →
Momentum = 150,000 kg·m/s
10 m/s →
Momentum = 300,000 kg·m/s
Momentum after collision = 450,000 kg·m/s

B One car moving.

Before collision
10 m/s →
Momentum = 300,000 kg·m/s
0 m/s
Momentum = 0
Momentum before collision = 300,000 kg·m/s

Cars bounce off each other.
After collision
0 m/s
Momentum = 0
10 m/s →
Momentum = 300,000 kg·m/s
Momentum after collision = 300,000 kg·m/s

C One car moving.

Before collision
10 m/s →
Momentum = 300,000 kg·m/s
0 m/s
Momentum = 0
Momentum before collision = 300,000 kg·m/s

Cars couple.
After collision
5 m/s →
Momentum = 300,000 kg·m/s
Momentum after collision = 300,000 kg·m/s

Figure 17 The different collisions between equal-mass train cars are shown above. In each collision, the total momentum of the train cars does not change—momentum is conserved. **Calculating** *What is the mass of each train car?*

Go Online
active art

For: Activity on momentum
Visit: PHSchool.com
Web Code: ccp-2123

Conservation of Momentum

What happens to momentum when objects collide? Look at the collisions in Figure 17. Under certain conditions, collisions obey the law of conservation of momentum. In physics, the word *conservation* means that something has a constant value. That is, conservation of momentum means that momentum does not increase or decrease.

Imagine two trains colliding as shown in Figure 17A. If the two cars are part of a closed system, then momentum is conserved. A closed system means other objects and forces cannot enter or leave a system. Objects within the system, however, can exert forces on one another. According to the **law of conservation of momentum,** if no net force acts on a system, then the total momentum of the system does not change.

Thus, if we consider the two train cars as a closed system, the cars can exert forces on each other. But overall, the total momentum of the system is conserved. ⬤ **In a closed system, the loss of momentum of one object equals the gain in momentum of another object—momentum is conserved.**

Data ▶ Analysis

Momentum

A class studied the speed and momentum of a 0.25-kilogram ball dropped from a bridge. The graph shows the momentum of the ball from the time it was dropped until the time it hit the river flowing below the bridge.

1. **Applying Concepts** At what time did the ball have zero momentum? Describe this point in the ball's motion.

2. **Using Graphs** At what time did the ball have the greatest momentum? What was the peak momentum value?

3. **Calculating** What is the ball's speed after 1.25 seconds? (*Hint:* Use the graph and the momentum formula.)

Momentum of a 0.25-kg Ball

Three different closed systems are shown in Figure 17. Each system consists of two train cars with the same mass that collide. In Figures 17A and 17B, the train cars collide and then bounce apart. In Figure 17C, the cars collide and then join together. Examine the momentum of each train car before and after the collision. Note that the total momentum before and after each collision does not change. The momentum is conserved.

Section 12.3 Assessment

Reviewing Concepts

1. 💬 Using Newton's third law, explain what is meant by action and reaction pairs of forces.

2. 💬 State in your own words the formula for momentum.

3. 💬 What is a necessary condition for the conservation of momentum?

4. If an eagle and a bumblebee are traveling at 8 km/hr, which has more momentum? Explain.

Critical Thinking

5. **Applying Concepts** A friend tells you that a rowboat is propelled forward by the force of its oars against the water. First, explain whether the statement is correct, and then identify the action and reaction forces.

6. **Inferring** Explain how Newton's third law of motion is at work when you walk.

7. **Applying Concepts** Explain in terms of Newton's third law why someone who tries to jump from a canoe to a riverbank may fall into the water.

Writing in Science

Explanatory Paragraph Write a paragraph explaining why it is impossible to identify a single isolated force. State in your first sentence the main idea of Newton's third law of motion.

Forces and Motion **377**

Section 12.3 Assessment

1. Whenever one object exerts a force on a second object, the second object exerts an equal and opposite force on the first object.
2. Momentum = Mass × Velocity
3. The objects involved must be part of a closed system.
4. Because the speeds are equal, the eagle's greater mass gives it more momentum.
5. It is incorrect because it is the force of the water against the oars that propels the boat forward. The oars pushing against the water is the action force, and the water pushing back against the oars is the reaction force.
6. As you walk, you bend your foot and push off against the ground. This action force produces the reaction force of the ground pushing against your shoe. The reaction force pushes you forward.
7. When you jump, you push against the canoe. However, the canoe also moves in the opposite direction of your jump. Because the canoe moves away, it produces a smaller reaction force on you. This small reaction force is not strong enough to propel you to the riverbank.

12.4 Universal Forces

Standards: ICP.1.3, ICP.6.6

1 FOCUS

Objectives

12.4.1 Identify the forms of electromagnetic force that can both attract and repel.

12.4.2 Identify and **describe** the universal forces acting within the nucleus.

12.4.3 Define Newton's law of universal gravitation and **describe** the factors affecting gravitational force.

12.4.4 Describe centripetal force and the type of motion it produces.

Reading Focus

Build Vocabulary   **L2**

Compare-Contrast Table Have students each make a table similar to the table on p. 378. Have students use *electromagnetic force, nuclear forces,* and *gravitational force* as the entries under the heading Force. For Relative Strength, have students use words such *as weak, weaker, weakest, strong, stronger,* and *strongest.* Suggest that students make this table as they read in order to help them learn the section's content.

Reading Strategy   **L2**

a. Neutrons and protons b. Very short (decreases rapidly beyond the diameter of a few protons) c. Very strong (100 times stronger than electrical repulsion force at that distance) d. All particles e. Short f. Weaker than the strong nuclear force.

2 INSTRUCT

Electromagnetic Forces

Build Reading Literacy   **L1**

Relate Cause and Effect Refer to page **260D** in **Chapter 9**, which provides the guidelines on relating cause and effect.

Encourage students to make a list of cause-and-effect relationships as they read about electromagnetic forces. Then, have students compare their lists. Students may list the behavior of charged objects when they approach one another, the clinging of clothes that have become charged, and the repulsion or attraction of magnetic poles. **Verbal, Logical**

Reading Focus

Key Concepts

- What force can attract and repel?
- What force holds the nucleus together?
- What is Newton's law of universal gravitation?

Vocabulary

- electromagnetic force
- strong nuclear force ◆ weak nuclear force ◆ gravitational force ◆ centripetal force

Reading Strategy

Comparing and Contrasting Copy the table below. After reading the section, compare the two universal nuclear forces by completing the table.

Force	Acts on Which Particles?	Acts Over What Distance?	Relative Strength
Strong nuclear	a. ?	b. ?	c. ?
Weak nuclear	d. ?	e. ?	f. ?

If you could travel to a distant planet in another galaxy, what would you expect to find? The scene shown in Figure 18 is one possibility. Although this world looks so different from the one you know, some things on this distant planet would be familiar—the forces.

Observations of planets, stars, and galaxies strongly suggest four different forces exist throughout the universe. These forces are known as universal forces. The four universal forces are the electromagnetic, strong nuclear, weak nuclear, and gravitational. All the universal forces act over a distance between particles of matter, which means that the particles need not be in contact in order to affect one another. In addition, each of these forces is affected by the distance between the particles of matter.

Figure 18 An artist's depiction of a planet's surface shows a world very different from Earth. Regardless of location, however, certain universal forces are present.

378 *Chapter 12*

Electromagnetic Forces

Electric and magnetic force are two different aspects of the electromagnetic force. **Electromagnetic force** is associated with charged particles. **Electric force and magnetic force are the only forces that can both attract and repel.** To understand electric and magnetic forces, recall what you learned about charged particles in Chapter 4.

Section Resources

Print
- *Reading and Study Workbook With Math Support,* Section 12.4
- *Transparencies,* Section 12.4

Technology
- *Interactive Textbook,* Section 12.4
- *Presentation Pro CD-ROM,* Section 12.4
- *Go Online,* NSTA SciLinks, Gravity

Electric Forces Electric forces act between charged objects or particles such as electrons and protons. Objects with opposite charges—positive and negative—attract one another. Objects with like charges repel one another. Figure 19 shows that clothes often cling together when they are removed from a dryer. Some clothes, such as cotton socks, lose electrons easily and become positively charged. Other clothes, such as polyester shirts, gain electrons easily and become negatively charged. Because the oppositely charged particles attract one another, the clothes cling together.

Magnetic Forces Magnetic forces act on certain metals, on the poles of magnets, and on moving charges. Magnets have two poles, north and south, that attract each other. Two poles that are alike repel each other. If you have handled magnets, you know that when opposite magnetic poles are brought close, they almost seem to jump together. On the other hand, when two similar poles approach each other, you can feel them pushing apart.

Figure 20 shows a child's wooden train set whose cars are linked with magnets. Each car has a north pole on one end and a south pole on the other. Children quickly learn that if a train car won't stick to the one in front of it, the car must be turned around.

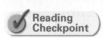 **Reading Checkpoint** *What type of force acts between particles with the same electrical charge?*

Nuclear Forces

Think about the nucleus of an atom, with its protons crammed into an incredibly small space. Because protons are positively charged, you would expect that an electric force of repulsion would break the nucleus apart. Scientists believe the nucleus would fly apart if there were not another, much stronger, attractive force holding the protons within the nucleus.

👁 **Two forces, the strong nuclear force and the weak nuclear force, act within the nucleus to hold it together.** The strong nuclear force overcomes the electric force of repulsion that acts among the protons in the nucleus. The weak nuclear force is involved in certain types of radioactive processes.

Strong Nuclear Force The **strong nuclear force** is a powerful force of attraction that acts only on the neutrons and protons in the nucleus, holding them together. The range over which the strong nuclear forces acts is approximately equal to the diameter of a proton (10^{-15} m). Although this force acts over only extremely short distances, it is 100 times stronger than the electric force of repulsion at these distances.

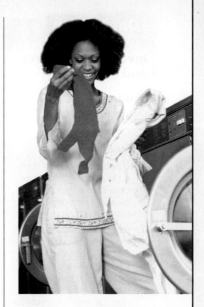

Figure 19 Clothes often acquire electric charges in the dryer. Clothes with opposite charges tend to cling together.

Figure 20 A magnetic force of attraction holds the two train cars together.
Applying Concepts *How are the two magnetic poles of the magnets related?*

Forces and Motion **379**

Gravitational Force

Investigating Force and Distance   **L2**

Objective
After completing this activity, students will be able to
• describe how the force of electrostatic attraction is affected by distance.

Skills Focus Observing, Formulating Hypotheses

 Prep Time 5 minutes

Advance Prep Select a day when the relative humidity is moderate or low to perform this lab.

Class Time 5 minutes

Teaching Tips
• Demonstrate how to charge the balloon and hold it above the bubble.
• Some hair products will interfere with the balloon. In this case, have students rub the balloon against their clothes.

Expected Outcome The bubbles will be attracted to the charged balloon. The force of this attraction will increase as students bring the balloon closer to the bubbles.

Analyze and Conclude
1. There is very little electrical interaction between objects that are far apart. As the distance is decreased, the attraction between the two objects becomes stronger.
2. If the balloon were brought closer to the bubble, the force of attraction would increase and the bubble would move upwards toward the balloon.
Visual, Logical

Investigating Force and Distance

Materials
balloon, bubble solution, bubble wand

Procedure
1. Inflate a balloon and then make a knot in its neck to close it. Rub the balloon back and forth against your hair to charge it.
2. Blow several bubbles into the air and hold the charged balloon above them. Observe how the distance between the balloon and the bubbles affects the speed at which the bubbles fall. **CAUTION** *Quickly wipe up any spilled bubble solution to avoid slips and falls.*
3. Try to temporarily suspend a bubble in the air without touching it with the balloon.

Analyze and Conclude
1. **Drawing Conclusions** How does the distance between two objects affect the force of attraction between them?
2. **Predicting** If a bubble were suspended below the balloon, what do you think would happen when you moved the balloon closer to the bubble?

Weak Nuclear Force The other powerful force in the nucleus is the weak nuclear force. As the name implies, the weak force is weaker in strength than the strong nuclear force. The **weak nuclear force** is an attractive force that acts only over a short range. The short range over which the weak nuclear force acts, about 10^{-18} meters, is less than the range of the strong nuclear force.

Gravitational Force

Gravity, the weakest universal force, is so much a part of your life that you probably take it for granted. You know from experience that objects fall toward Earth. It was Newton who discovered that gravity affects all objects in the universe. The same force acting on a falling apple is also acting on the moon to keep it in its orbit.

Gravitational force involves much more than just Earth's gravitational field. **Gravitational force** is an attractive force that acts between any two masses. ⬤ **Newton's law of universal gravitation states that every object in the universe attracts every other object.**

Thus, Earth exerts a force on an apple, and the apple exerts an equal force on Earth. You exert a gravitational force on your textbook, and your textbook exerts an equal gravitational force on you. The reason you don't notice gravity pulling your textbook toward you is that your mass and the mass of the textbook are so small. It takes a huge mass such as Earth's to exert a large gravitational force. The attractive force of gravity acting between two objects is shown in Figure 21.

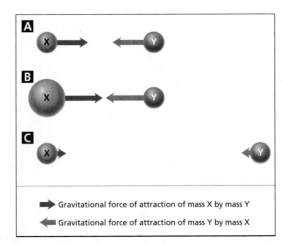

Figure 21 Gravitational force depends upon mass and distance. **A** Two masses, X and Y, attract each other. **B** The larger mass of X results in a larger gravitational force. **C** Increasing the distance between the masses significantly reduces the gravitational force.

Facts and Figures

Law of Universal Gravitation Newton came to the conclusion that any two objects in the universe exert a gravitational force of attraction on each other. The force is directed along a line joining the objects' centers. Newton concluded that the gravitational attraction *(G)* is proportional to the product of the objects' masses *(m₁ and m₂)* and inversely proportional to the square of the distance *(d)* between them. That equation is

$F = G(m_1 m_2 / d^2)$. Because the value of G is very small, the gravitational force is only significant if one or both objects has a large mass and the distance between the objects is not very large. Earth's gravitational acceleration g is related to the equation of universal gravitation by the expression $g = g(m_e / d^2)$, where m_e is Earth's mass. In this case, the equation for universal gravitation reduces to the familiar equation $F = mg$.

Gravity Acts Over Large Distances The gravitational force between two objects is proportional to their masses and decreases rapidly as the distance between the masses increases. The greater the mass of the objects, the greater is the gravitational force. Gravitational force decreases with the square of the distance between the objects. As shown in Figures 21A and 21C, if the distance between masses doubles, the force of gravity is only one fourth as strong.

Gravity is the weakest universal force, but it is the most effective force over long distances. Gravity holds you on Earth. It keeps the moon in orbit around Earth, the planets in orbit around the sun, and the stars in orbit in their galaxies. The sun's mass is about 300,000 times the mass of Earth, so the sun's gravitational force is much stronger than that of Earth. The influence of the sun's gravitational force extends well beyond Earth. Pluto, which is almost 40 times farther from the sun than Earth is, has its orbit determined by the gravitational pull of the sun.

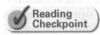
Reading Checkpoint *What factors affect gravitational force?*

The Earth, Moon, and Tides How is the moon kept in orbit around Earth? Recall that the moon has inertia, so according to Newton's first law, it should continue to move along a straight path until acted upon by a force. That force is Earth's gravitational force, which acts continuously to pull the moon toward it, as shown in Figure 22.

Earth's gravitational attraction keeps the moon in an elliptical orbit around Earth. It works in much the same way that a string tied to an eraser allows you to twirl the eraser in a circle over your head. As you twirl the eraser, the string exerts a centripetal force on the eraser. A **centripetal force** is a center-directed force that continuously changes the direction of an object to make it move around the center. This center-directed force causes a continuous change in the direction of the eraser. In a similar way, the center-directed force of Earth's gravity pulls the moon into an elliptical orbit around Earth.

If you have spent time at the seashore, you have probably noticed that the level of the tide changes throughout the day. The gravitational pull from the moon produces two bulges in Earth's oceans. One bulge is on the side of Earth closest to the moon. The other bulge is on the side of Earth farthest from the moon. Earth rotates once per day beneath theses two bulges. This rotation results in two high and two low tides per day on Earth.

Go Online
NSTA *SciLinks*

For: Links on gravity
Visit: www.SciLinks.org
Web Code: ccn-2124

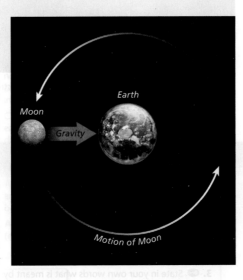

Figure 22 The moon's inertia and the gravitational pull of Earth result in an elliptical orbit. The gravitational pull of the moon is the primary cause of Earth's ocean tides.

Forces and Motion **381**

Build Science Skills L2

Observing Take students outside. Tie a string around an eraser, as described in the second paragraph of The Earth, Moon, and Tides. Ask a volunteer to twirl the eraser over his or her head. **CAUTION** *Make sure the students observing this demo stand far away from the student twirling the eraser.* Have students observe that the eraser follows a circular orbit. Remind students that inertia causes an object to resist change in motion. Explain that this means that the eraser would travel in a straight path if a force did not pull it into an orbit. Ask the volunteer to slowly twirl the eraser and then let go of the string. Have students observe what happens. Ask, **What force kept the eraser moving in a circular orbit?** *(The centripetal force from the string kept the eraser moving in a circular orbit.)* **What proof do you have that a centripetal force was acting on the twirling eraser to change its motion?** *(As soon as the string was released, the eraser moved in a straight line path.)* **As the eraser is twirled at a constant speed, is it accelerating? Explain your answer.** *(Yes, acceleration occurs because the eraser is constantly changing direction.)*
Visual, Logical

Use Visuals L1

Figure 22 Use Figure 22 to reinforce the concept of centripetal force and inertia, as discussed in Build Science Skills. Help students to see that gravitational pull is the centripetal (center-directed) force in planetary orbits. Ask, **What is the direction of the moon's velocity in Figure 22?** *(The moon's velocity is tangent to its elliptical path. At the instant shown, the direction of the moon's velocity is straight down toward the bottom of the page.)*
Visual, Logical

Go Online
NSTA *SciLinks*

Download a worksheet on gravity for students to complete, and find additional teacher support from NSTA SciLinks.

Answer to . . .

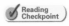
Reading Checkpoint *Mass and distance*

Forces and Motion **381**

ASSESS PRIOR KNOWLEDGE

Use the Chapter Pretest below to assess students' prior knowledge. As needed, review these Science Concepts and Math Skills with students.

Review Science Concepts

Section 13.1 Review force and area and their related SI units. Remind students that force does not always result in motion. Encourage students to review rules for significant figures in answers involving division.

Section 13.2 Review balanced and unbalanced forces, net force, and weight. Encourage students to review Newton's laws of motion.

Section 13.3 Review with students the concepts of force, pressure, mass, weight, and density. Emphasize the similarities and differences between these concepts to help prevent confusion about buoyancy.

Review Math Skills

Formulas and Equations, Conversion Factors, Significant Figures Students will need to calculate and convert pressures and express answers with the correct number of significant figures.

Direct students to **Math Skills** in the **Skills and Reference Handbook** at the end of the student text.

CHAPTER

13 Forces in Fluids

21st Century Learning
Creativity and Intellectual Curiosity

What are some useful applications of air pressure?
A number of common technologies—including aerosol cans, drinking straws, and fire extinguishers—function by making use of a difference in gas pressure. Use the library or Internet to identify some other devices that make use of a pressurized gas. Choose one device and then create a multimedia presentation that explains how the device works. Your presentation should describe in detail the role of gas pressure in the operation if the device.

A kite is held aloft by the forces of the wind.

388 Chapter 13

Chapter Pretest

1. If two forces act in opposite directions on an object, how do you determine the net force on the object? *(Subtract the smaller force from the larger force.)*
2. What effect do balanced forces have on the motion of an object? *(The forces cause no change in the object's motion.)*
3. What effect do unbalanced forces have on the motion of an object? *(The object's speed increases in the direction of the greater force.)*

4. Which units could you use to describe the area of a chalkboard? *(b)*
   a. Meters (m)
   b. Square meters (m²)
   c. Cubic meters (m³)
5. Which of the following defines weight? *(b)*
   a. The amount of matter in an object
   b. The force due to gravity acting on an object
   c. The same as mass

6. A tennis ball has a volume of 125 cm³ and a mass of 57 g. What is the ball's average density? *(Hint: density = mass/volume) (Ball's density = 0.46 g/cm³)*
7. The distance between a home and school is 6.35 km. What is this distance in meters? *(6350 m)*
8. Which of Newton's laws describes action-reaction forces? *(Newton's third law)*

Chapter Preview

13.1 **Fluid Pressure**

13.2 **Forces and Pressure in Fluids**

13.3 **Buoyancy**

Discovery CHANNEL SCHOOL
Video Field Trip
Uplifting Experience

Inquiry > Activity

What Makes Something Sink or Float?

Procedure

1. **Predicting** Record your prediction of whether a wooden toothpick and a piece of clay will float in water.

2. To test your predictions, fill a bowl almost to its rim with water.

3. Place a wooden toothpick in the water. Shape a piece of clay into a cup and place it in the water. Record your observations.

4. Remove the clay from the water, dry it with a paper towel, and then tightly roll it into a small ball. Place the ball of clay in the water and record your observations.

Think About It

1. **Evaluating** Which of your predictions were correct?

2. **Observing** What effect did rolling the clay into a ball have on its ability to float?

3. **Formulating Hypotheses** What property of the clay did you change by rolling it into a small ball? Explain how this change affected the clay's ability to float.

Forces in Fluids **389**

Discovery CHANNEL SCHOOL
Video Field Trip
Uplifting Experience

Encourage students to view the Video Field Trip "Uplifting Experience."

ENGAGE/EXPLORE

Inquiry > Activity

What Makes Something Sink or Float? **L2**

Purpose In this activity, students begin to describe the effect of density on buoyancy.

⚑ **Address Misconceptions**

Students may hold the misconception that weight, rather than density, determines buoyancy. To help dispel this misconception, ask students whether larger pieces of wood and clay would have behaved in the same way as the small pieces observed in this activity.

Skills Focus Observing, Formulating Hypotheses

🕐 **Prep Time** 5 minutes

Materials small, plastic bowl; wooden toothpick; piece of modeling clay; paper towel; water

Class Time 15 minutes

Safety Students should wear safety goggles whenever they work in the laboratory.

Expected Outcome The toothpick and cup-shaped piece of clay will float. Rolled-up clay will sink.

Think About It
1. Students can be expected to predict correctly that the toothpick will float, but may be uncertain about whether the clay will float.
2. Rolling the clay into a ball caused it to sink.
3. Students may recognize that rolling the clay into a ball increases the density of the clay cup, but most will not be able to state at this stage that the density increases because the air enclosed in the clay cup is excluded when the clay is rolled up.
Visual, Logical

1 FOCUS

Objectives

13.1.1 Describe and **calculate** pressure.

13.1.2 Identify appropriate SI units for measuring pressure.

13.1.3 Describe the relationship between water depth and the pressure it exerts.

13.1.4 Describe how forces from pressure are distributed at a given level in a fluid.

13.1.5 Explain how altitude affects air pressure.

Reading Focus

Build Vocabulary   `L2`

LINCS Have students: **L**ist the words or parts of words that they know (for example, *press*, part of *pressure*). **I**magine a picture that creates a mental image of each term's meaning and describe the image in words (such as a column of water exerting force on a square unit area). **N**ote a reminding "sound-alike" word. **C**onnect the terms. (Make up a short story that includes the meanings of the terms.) **S**elf-test. (Quiz themselves.)

Reading Strategy   `L2`

a. Definitions will vary and may involve the scientific or the nonscientific definition of pressure. **b.** Pressure is the amount of force per unit area. Students should contrast the scientific definition with the common definition.

2 INSTRUCT

Pressure

Use Visuals   `L1`

Figure 1 Emphasize that pressure is affected by force and area. Ask, **If the weight is the same in both cases, why is the pressure not the same?** *(Pressure is the amount of force (weight) per unit area, not simply the amount of force.)* Ask, **Why is there greater pressure when the seat is smaller?** *(The pressure formula, P = F/A, shows that pressure is inversely proportional to the area on which the force is exerted. Thus, with a smaller surface area, the bicycle seat produces a greater pressure.)* **Visual**

13.1 Fluid Pressure

Reading Focus

Key Concepts

- How is pressure calculated?
- How does water pressure change with depth?
- How is pressure distributed at a given level in a fluid?
- How does air pressure change with altitude?

Vocabulary

- ◆ pressure
- ◆ pascal
- ◆ fluid

Reading Strategy

Using Prior Knowledge Before reading the section, copy the table below. In it, write the common definition of the word *pressure*. After you have read the section, write the scientific definition of *pressure* and contrast it to your original definition.

Meanings of *Pressure*		
Common definition	a.	?
Scientific definition	b.	?

Why is a theater seat so much more comfortable than a bicycle seat? One of the main reasons any seat is comfortable is the pressure it exerts on your body. As you read this chapter, you'll learn about pressure, and how fluids such as air and water can exert and transmit pressure.

Pressure

The comfort of the plush theater seats shown in Figure 1 is related to **pressure**—the result of a force distributed over an area. A theater seat's large padded seat and back offer a larger area to support your weight than a bicycle seat does. Thus, the theater seat exerts less pressure on you and is more comfortable than the bicycle seat.

Many other everyday situations also involve pressure. A sharp pencil easily pokes a hole through a sheet of paper, whereas the eraser end of the pencil does not. Why is this? The reason is the same—pressure.

Figure 1 Because the theater seat exerts a supporting force over a larger area, it is more comfortable than the bicycle seat. **Comparing and Contrasting** *What force acts on both seats?*

390 *Chapter 13*

 Section Resources

Print

- *Reading and Study Workbook With Math Support,* Section 13.1 and **Math Skill:** Graphing Air Pressure Data
- *Math Skills and Problem Solving Workbook,* Section 13.1
- *Transparencies,* Chapter Pretest and Section 13.1

Technology

- *Interactive Textbook,* Section 13.1
- *Presentation Pro CD-ROM,* Chapter Pretest and Section 13.1

The pencil point has a much smaller area than the eraser, so it exerts much greater pressure than the eraser. The greater pressure exerted by the pencil point allows it to pierce the paper easily.

👉 **To calculate pressure, divide the force by the area over which the force acts.**

Pressure

$$\text{Pressure} = \frac{\text{Force}}{\text{Area}}$$

In the formula, force should be in newtons (N) and area should be in square meters (m^2). The resulting unit, newtons per square meter (N/m^2), is the SI unit of pressure, also known as a **pascal** (Pa). The pascal is named for French scientist Blaise Pascal (1623–1662). Pressures are often stated in units of kilopascals (kPa). Note that 1 kPa is 1000 Pa.

Consider a box with a weight of 2700 newtons resting on the ground. If the area of the box touching the ground is 1.5 square meters, what pressure does the box exert on the ground?

$$\text{Pressure} = \frac{\text{Force}}{\text{Area}} = \frac{2700 \text{ N}}{1.5 \text{ m}^2} = 1800 \text{ N/m}^2 = 1800 \text{ Pa} = 1.8 \text{ kPa}$$

Pressure in Fluids

A **fluid** is a substance that assumes the shape of its container. Both liquids and gases are fluids. Water, oil, gasoline, air, and helium are fluids. The particles that make up liquids and gases are shown in Figure 2.

Just as a person sitting in a seat exerts force and pressure, so does a fluid. Imagine a glass filled with water. The water flows to take the same shape as that of the glass. Because the water is in contact with the walls and bottom of the glass, it exerts pressure on these surfaces. The amount of pressure exerted depends on several factors.

Have you ever noticed what happens to the pressure exerted on your body as you swim downward in a pool? 👉 **Water pressure increases as depth increases. The pressure in a fluid at any given depth is constant, and it is exerted equally in all directions.** Surprisingly, the shape of a container and the area of its bottom surface do not affect fluid pressure. For a fluid that is not moving, depth and the type of fluid are the two factors that determine the pressure the fluid exerts.

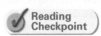 **Reading Checkpoint** *How is fluid pressure related to fluid depth?*

Figure 2 Both liquids and gases can flow and take on the shape of their containers. **A** Particles in a liquid are tightly packed together but are able to slide past one another. **B** Particles in a gas are far apart and travel in straight lines until they collide with another particle or object. **Inferring** *Based on the illustrations, can a gas be compressed into a smaller space?*

Forces in Fluids **391**

 Teacher **Demo**

Relating Cause and Effect **L2**

Purpose Students observe the effect different areas make in determining pressure.

🚩 **Address Misconceptions**

Students may mistakenly think that pressure is the same as force. Challenge this misconception by asking students to discuss the difference between pressure and force in this demo.

Materials 1 shoe with large-area heel, 1 shoe with small-area heel (both shoes must fit the same student),1 square of vinyl tile

Procedure Ask the student to put on both shoes and step on the vinyl tile. Have the student stand on one foot at a time on the tile. Have all of the other students observe the indentations made in the tile.

Expected Outcome The small-heeled shoe creates a deeper indentation in the tile. The deeper indentation is caused by the greater pressure exerted by the small-heeled shoe.
Visual, Logical

Pressure in Fluids
Build Math Skills **L1**

Data Tables and Line Graphs Have students create a data table with various values of water pressure and area. (Water pressure increases by about 1kg/cm^2 per 10 m of water.) Then, have them calculate the force for each pressure. They can use the data to create pressure/force and pressure/area line graphs.
Logical

Direct students to the **Math Skills** in the **Skills and Reference Handbook** at the end of the student text for additional help.

Answer to . . .

Figure 1 *The weight of the person acts on each seat.*

Figure 2 *Yes. The space between gas particles allows a gas to be compressed into a smaller volume.*

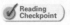 **Reading Checkpoint** *Fluid pressure increases as fluid depth increases.*

Forces in Fluids **391**

Planetary Atmospheres L2

Answers
1. Venus, 9120 kPa
2. Nitrogen
3. Mercury, 10^{-15} bar; Earth, 1 bar; Venus, 90.0 bar; Mars, 0.0070 bar
4. Pressure = Force/Area; Force = Pressure × Area; Force = 9120 kPa × 2.00 m^2 = 9.12 × 10^6 N/m^2 × 2.00 m^2 = 2.00 × 10^7 N
5. The helium-filled balloon would have the smallest volume on Venus because Venus has the greatest atmospheric pressure and the helium inside the balloon is compressible.

For Extra Help L1

Discuss scientific notation to help students read the atmospheric pressures in the table. Ask students to rewrite all the pressure values using scientific notation. Reinforce that atmospheric percentages could be understood by using a pie chart. Remind students to use the equation $F = PA$ when solving for force in newtons. **Logical**

Air Pressure and the Atmosphere
Build Reading Literacy L1

Anticipation Guide Refer to page 388D in this chapter, which provides the guidelines for an anticipation guide.

Students should anticipate what will occur as a result of the principle's application. Display the following questions on the board or with an overhead projector before students read the text on pp. 392–393. Discuss student responses, then have them read the text. Ask students which of the following statements are true:
1. Air pressure increases as altitude increases. *(False)*
2. When your altitude increases, the pressure inside your ears equalizes with atmospheric pressure. *(True)*
3. When inside air pressure has equalized with atmospheric pressure, the balanced forces result in a net force of zero. *(True)*
4. Atmospheric pressure is exerting a large force on your body as you read this. *(True)*
After students have read the text, revisit the questions. **Verbal**

Data Analysis

Planetary Atmospheres

The layer of gases surrounding a planet is known as its atmosphere. All of the planets in our solar system have some form of atmosphere. The weight of an atmosphere creates atmospheric pressure at the planet's surface.

The table at the right gives data about the atmospheric composition and pressure for several of the planets.

1. **Interpreting Tables** Which planet listed in the table has the greatest atmospheric pressure?
2. **Interpreting Tables** What chemical substance exists in all but one of the atmospheres?

Planetary Atmospheres

Planet	Composition of Atmosphere	Atmospheric Pressure (kPa)
Mercury	Mixture of helium, sodium, and oxygen	10^{-12}
Earth	77% nitrogen, 21% oxygen, 1% argon	101.3
Venus	96% carbon dioxide, 3.5% nitrogen	9120
Mars	95% carbon dioxide, 2.7% nitrogen, 1.6% argon	0.71

3. **Converting Units** The bar is another unit of pressure (1 bar = 101.3 kPa). Convert each of the given pressures into bars.
4. **Using Formulas** How much force is exerted on a 2.00-square-meter area of Venus's surface?
5. **Predicting** On which planet would a helium-filled balloon have the smallest volume?

Figure 3 This Pascal vase is made up of several oddly shaped vases that are connected to one another at their base. **Drawing Conclusions** *What can you conclude from the fact that all of the fluid levels are the same?*

As you just learned, fluid pressure is determined by the type of fluid and its depth. Thus the amount of fluid, measured in terms of volume or weight, does not affect pressure. To prove this, imagine a large lake and a bathtub. Although they contain very different amounts of water, the pressure at a depth of 25 centimeters is the same in both the lake and the bathtub.

Note that each of the connected vases in Figure 3 contains a different amount of liquid. Yet, the liquid levels are all the same. Why is this? It is because pressure depends on depth, not amount. If the pressure at the bottom of all the vases were not the same, the water would flow until the pressures equalized.

Air Pressure and the Atmosphere
You live at the bottom of a vast ocean of fluid. Unlike fish, however, you live in an ocean of air. Air is a mixture of gases that make up Earth's atmosphere. Just as ocean water exerts pressure, so does Earth's atmosphere. The weight of Earth's atmosphere exerts a pressure of about 101 kPa at sea level.

Just as water pressure in a beaker increases with depth, air pressure increases with the depth of the atmosphere. Instead of saying they are at a certain depth in the atmosphere, however, people refer to their altitude above sea level. **Air pressure decreases as the altitude increases.**

Facts and Figures

Conversions for Pressure
Some conversion factors are:
- 1 Pa = 1 N/m^2
- 1 bar = 10^5 Pa
- 1 atm = 1.013 × 10^5 Pa
- 1 atm = 760 mm Hg

In other words, one bar is the force of 100,000 pascals, or 100,000 newtons acting on one square meter. Because one bar is a large measurement, a millibar (1 millibar = 0.001 bar = 100 Pa) is sometimes used to report air pressure. However, the millibar is often replaced with the term hectopascals (hPa), which is also equal to 100 pascals. To convert between inches of mercury, millibars, and hectopascals, use the relation that 0.02953 inches of mercury is equal to one millibar and equal to one hectopascal.

Have your ears ever popped while you were riding in an elevator, flying in a plane, or driving up to the mountains? In situations such as these, the outside air pressure changes more quickly than your ears can adjust. This creates a difference in pressure between the inside of your ear and the air outside. These unbalanced pressures equalize when air passes through a small tube within your ear. This is the popping sensation you feel.

You may be surprised to learn that as you read this, the atmosphere is exerting more than 1000 newtons of force on the top of your head. As shown in Figure 4, this is enough force to crush a can! Why then aren't you crushed by air pressure? Fortunately, the inside of your body also exerts pressure. You are not crushed like the can in Figure 4 because the pressure inside your body balances the air pressure outside. The balanced forces cancel, resulting in a net force of zero.

Figure 4 This series of photos (1–4) illustrates that the atmosphere can exert enough force to crush a metal can. A can containing a small amount of water is heated until the water boils. Then the can is capped, the hot plate is switched off, and the can is allowed to cool. As the can cools, the pressure inside the can becomes less than the pressure outside the can. The difference in pressure crushes the can.

Section 13.1 Assessment

Reviewing Concepts

1. What must you know to calculate pressure?
2. What is the relationship between the depth of water and the pressure it exerts?
3. How is pressure distributed at a given level in a fluid?
4. How does the pressure exerted by the atmosphere change as altitude increases?
5. Why don't you feel the pressure exerted by the atmosphere?

Critical Thinking

6. **Inferring** Some deep-sea fish have been known to explode as they are brought to the ocean's surface. How do pressure changes cause this to happen?

7. **Applying Concepts** A 500-N student stands on one foot. A 750-N student stands on two feet. If both students wear the same size shoe, which exerts the greater pressure?

Math Practice

8. A circus performer on a pair of stilts exerts a pressure of 32 kPa on the ground. If the performer stands on one stilt, what pressure does the stilt exert on the ground?

9. A book with a weight of 12 N rests on its back cover. If the back cover measures 21 cm by 28 cm, how much pressure does the book exert?

Forces in Fluids **393**

Build Science Skills L2

Controlling Variables Have students think about ways the demonstration shown in Figure 4 could be changed. Ask, **What are the variables in this demonstration?** *(The variables are the amount of water in the can, atmospheric pressure, and the temperature of the hot plate.)* **Which of these variables can be easily controlled?** *(Amount of water in the can and temperature of the hot plate)* **What are some possible effects of changing the controllable variables?** *(Increasing the amount of water will increase the time required to boil the water. Increasing the temperature of the hot plate will decrease the time needed to boil the water.)* **Logical, Visual**

3 ASSESS

Evaluate Understanding L2

Using the equation, $P = F/A$, have students work in pairs to write three math problems (with solutions) based on the pressure equation used in this section. Remember that even incorrectly worded problems are useful, as students can be asked to identify and correct the errors.

Reteach L1

Review the definitions of a fluid and pressure. Use Figure 3 to discuss how pressure in fluids is affected by depth and altitude.

Math Practice

Solutions L2

8. The pressure exerted when standing on one stilt is twice the pressure exerted when on two stilts.
Pressure = 2 × 32 kPa = 64 kPa
9. Pressure = Force/Area
Pressure = 12 N/(0.21 m × 0.28 m) = 12 N/0.0588 m² = 2.0 × 10² N/m² = 2.0 × 10² Pa

Interactive Textbook If your class subscribes to the Interactive Textbook, use it to review key concepts in Section 13.1.

Answer to . . .

Figure 3 *The pressure at the bottom of each vase section is the same. If the pressures differed, the fluid would flow and the levels would not be equal.*

Forces in Fluids **393**

Section 13.1 Assessment

1. Force and area are needed to calculate pressure.
2. Water pressure increases as depth increases.
3. At a given depth, pressure is constant and exerted equally in all directions.
4. Atmospheric pressure decreases as altitude above sea level increases.
5. You cannot feel atmospheric pressure acting on your body because the pressure inside your body balances the pressure outside.

6. Deep-sea fish have high internal body pressures in order to counteract the extreme water pressure that exists where they live. When the fish is suddenly brought to the surface, where the pressure is much less, its internal pressure can cause it to rupture or explode.
7. The 500-N student exerts greater pressure on area A than a 750-N student does on area 2A. (500 N/A > 750 N/2A).

13.2 Forces and Pressure in Fluids

1 FOCUS

Objectives

13.2.1 Describe how pressure is transmitted in a fluid according to Pascal's principle.

13.2.2 Explain how a hydraulic system works to change a force.

13.2.3 Explain how the speed and pressure of a fluid are related according to Bernoulli's principle.

Reading Focus

Build Vocabulary   L2

Word-Part Analysis Ask students what words they know that have the key word parts *hydro-* or *hydr-*. (*Hydrogen, hydrate, hydroelectric*) Explain that *hydraulic* contains the word parts *hydro-* or *hydr-*, which come from the Greek *hydor* ("water"). *Hydraulic* is also made of the word part *aulos* ("tube," "pipe").

Reading Strategy   L2

a. Students will most likely predict that the foam balls will be blown apart from one another. Check that students provide reasons for their prediction. **b.** Reasons will likely include the force the air exerts on the foam balls as it blows past them.

2 INSTRUCT

Transmitting Pressure in a Fluid

Teacher ▸ **Demo**

Pascal's Principle   L2

Purpose Students will observe the effects of Pascal's principle.

Materials 2 syringes (10 cc and 60 cc), 20 cm clear plastic tubing (4.8 mm ID), food coloring, water, 150-mL beaker, stirring rod

Procedure Attach the ends of the tubes to the syringes. Fill the system with water until the syringes are half full. Insert the plungers. Have students watch the water levels as you push first one plunger, then the other.

Expected Outcome Students will relate water level in the syringes to Pascal's principle. **Visual, Logical**

Reading Focus

Key Concepts
- 👁 How does Pascal's principle describe the transmission of pressure through a fluid?
- 👁 How does a hydraulic system work?
- 👁 How is the speed of a fluid related to the pressure within the fluid?

Vocabulary
- ◆ hydraulic system
- ◆ lift

Reading Strategy

Predicting Copy the table below. Then imagine two small foam balls hanging from strings at the same height with about three centimeters of space between them. Before you read the section, write a prediction about what will happen to the balls when you blow air through the space between them. Identify your reasons. After you have read the section, check the accuracy of your prediction.

Prediction	a._____ ?
Reason for prediction	b._____ ?

Suppose your teacher held a table tennis ball on an upward-pointing hair dryer. He then asked you to predict what would happen when the hair dryer was turned on and the ball was released. Did you predict that the ball would be blown up and away? If you did, you were wrong!

As shown in Figure 5, when the hair dryer was turned on, the table tennis ball was not blown away. Instead, it was lifted up and suspended in the air stream above the hair dryer. Suppose your teacher then made the ball bob in the air stream by gently moving the hair dryer up and down. How was that possible? Read on to learn how fluids are able to transmit pressure and how moving fluids produce the pressure changes and forces that explain this demonstration.

Transmitting Pressure in a Fluid

As you learned in the previous section, a fluid exerts pressure equally in all directions at a given depth. You also know that the amount of pressure exerted by a fluid depends on the type of fluid and its depth. Apply these two concepts in the following thought experiment. Imagine a two-liter plastic soda bottle completely filled with water, with its cap tightly screwed on. The bottle is sitting upright on a table. Can you visualize and describe how the pressure forces act against the inside of the bottle?

Figure 5 The fast-moving stream of air from the blow dryer creates a column of low-pressure air. The table tennis ball is suspended in an area of low pressure.

Section Resources

Print
- *Laboratory Manual,* Investigation 13B
- *Reading and Study Workbook With Math Support,* Section 13.2
- *Transparencies,* Section 13.2

Technology
- *Interactive Textbook,* Section 13.2
- *Presentation Pro CD-ROM,* Section 13.2
- *Go Online,* NSTA SciLinks, Bernoulli's principle

Pascal's Principle The pressure forces acting on the bottle are shown in Figure 6A. Note that at any given depth, equal pressures act against the inside of the bottle. Note also that the pressure increases with depth. Now imagine what happens to the pressure inside the bottle if you tightly squeeze it at the middle. Will the pressure be greater at the point where you squeeze?

The pressure inside the squeezed bottle is shown in Figure 6B. Note that the pressure increases with depth, as it did before the bottle was squeezed. More important, note that the pressure increases equally throughout the water, not just at the point where you squeeze. Pascal discovered this phenomenon in the 1600s. His observation led to a general principle. **According to Pascal's principle, a change in pressure at any point in a fluid is transmitted equally and unchanged in all directions throughout the fluid.**

Hydraulic Systems Hydraulics is the science of applying Pascal's principle. The dump truck in Figure 7A makes use of a hydraulic lift system. A **hydraulic system** is a device that uses pressurized fluid acting on pistons of different sizes to change a force.

Look at the diagram of a hydraulic system shown in Figure 7B. An input force is applied to the small piston, which pushes against the fluid sealed in the hydraulic system. Applying Pascal's principle, you know that the pressure produced by the small piston is transmitted through the fluid to the large piston. Thus, the pressure on both pistons is the same.

However, the pressure pushing against the large piston acts on a much larger area, which is the key to how the system works. **In a hydraulic lift system, an increased output force is produced because a constant fluid pressure is exerted on the larger area of the output piston.** This large output force is used to lift and dump the load. The amount the input force is increased depends on the areas of the pistons. If the large piston has eight times the area of the small piston, then the output force is eight times greater than the input force. Why is this? Recall that force is equal to the product of pressure and area. Because the pressure on each piston is the same, the difference in forces is directly related to the difference in areas.

Force   Force

Figure 6 A change in pressure at any point in a fluid is transmitted equally and unchanged in all directions throughout the fluid. **A** Note that the forces exerted against the walls of the container are equal at a given depth. **B** When squeezed, the pressure is transmitted equally throughout the fluid.

Figure 7 **A** The truck uses hydraulic-powered struts to lift its load and dump it on the ground. **B** The larger area of the output piston produces the increased force used to lift the load.

Output force

Large piston

Small piston

Hydraulic fluid

Input force

Forces in Fluids **395**

Bernoulli's Principle
Integrate Earth Science   **L2**

Hurricane Damage Bernoulli's principle explains some of the devastating effects of a hurricane. When the high-speed winds of the hurricane pass over a building, the pressure quickly decreases. The difference in pressure between the inner and outer surfaces of the structure results in a strong upward force that can lift the roof off the building.
Verbal

Build Science Skills **L2**

Applying Concepts Divide the class into small groups. Provide each group with one of the following phenomena, and have them discuss how Bernoulli's principle applies to the situation.
(1) Wind speed increases as it flows over a mountain. *(Air pressure over mountains decreases.)* (2) Wind blows faster when it passes between high buildings in a city. *(Air pressure is lower between the buildings.)* (3) The upward draft of a fire in a chimney is better on a windy day. *(Decreased pressure above the chimney forces the smoke upward.)*
Logical, Portfolio, Group

Go Online
NSTA SciLINKS

Download a worksheet on Bernoulli's principle for students to complete, and find additional teacher support from NSTA SciLinks.

Figure 8 The airplane wing changes the flow pattern of the air it passes through. Note how air flowing over the top of the wing is diverted up and over the wing's curved surface.
Comparing and Contrasting *How does the flow of air over the top of the wing (green arrows) compare with the flow of air under the wing (blue arrows)?*

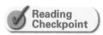
Go Online
NSTA SciLINKS

For: Links on Bernoulli's principle
Visit: www.SciLinks.org
Web Code: ccn-2132

Bernoulli's Principle

Try this simple experiment. Pick up a single sheet of paper and hold its top corners using both of your hands. Now position the paper directly in front of your mouth and blow as hard as you can over the top surface of the paper. Even though you are blowing over its top, the far end of the paper lifts upward.

The Swiss scientist Daniel Bernoulli (1700–1782) discovered the reason why the sheet of paper behaves as it does. ● **According to Bernoulli's principle, as the speed of a fluid increases, the pressure within the fluid decreases.** As the air blows across the top of the paper, the pressure exerted by the air decreases. Because the air below the paper is nearly motionless, it exerts a greater pressure. The difference in pressure forces the paper upward.

Bernoulli's principle explains the table tennis ball demonstration discussed earlier. The air from the dryer strikes the bottom of the ball and lifts it into the air. The pressure in this fast-moving air stream, however, is less than the pressure in the surrounding air. If the ball moves sideways out of the air stream, it encounters higher-pressure, slower-moving air. The higher-pressure air forces the ball back into the air stream coming from the hair dryer.

Bernoulli's principle has many applications in industry and explains many things in nature as well.

✓ **Reading Checkpoint** *How is a fluid's speed related to the pressure it exerts?*

Wings and Lift The ability of birds and airplanes to fly is largely explained by Bernoulli's principle. As shown in Figure 8, the air traveling over the top of an airplane wing moves faster than the air passing underneath. This creates a low-pressure area above the wing. The pressure difference between the top and the bottom of the wing creates an upward force known as **lift.** The lift created in this way is a large part of what keeps the airplane aloft.

Facts and Figures

Fluid Flow in Pipes Imagine water flowing from one pipe into another pipe with a smaller cross-sectional area. The amount of mass flowing through each pipe must be the same (conservation of mass). Thus, the water will flow faster in the smaller pipe in order to maintain the same mass flow rate.

The product of the area and average velocity in pipe 1 equals the product of the area and average velocity in pipe 2, $A_1v_1 = A_2v_2$. As area increases, velocity decreases, and vice versa. Holding your finger partly over the end of a hose is an example of increased velocity due to decreased area.

The wings of birds produce lift in much the same way as an air-plane wing. Unlike airplane wings, birds can flap their wings to produce forward movement and some lift.

Sometimes wings are used to create a downward force. Race cars often have an upside-down wing known as a spoiler mounted on the rear of the car. The downward force created by the spoiler pushes the tires down onto the road, giving the car better traction. Increased traction allows the car to go around corners at higher speeds.

Spray Bottles Figure 9 shows the design of a typical hose-end sprayer. This type of sprayer is often used to apply fertilizers and pesticides to lawns, plants, and trees. A concentrated solution of the chemical that is to be sprayed is placed in the solution chamber. The sprayer is then attached to a garden hose.

As water streams through the sprayer, it passes over the top of a small tube that reaches down into the solution chamber. The fast-moving water creates a low-pressure area at the top of the tube. The pressure difference between the solution chamber and the tube forces the concentrated solution up the tube. The solution then mixes with the water and is sprayed out of the end of the sprayer.

Figure 9 The design of a hose-end sprayer is based on Bernoulli's principle. Pressure differences draw the concentrated solution up into the fast-moving water stream.

1 Water moves through sprayer at high speed (low pressure).

2 Water and fertilizer mix here.

3 Mixture sprays out tip.

Concentrated fertilizer solution (atmospheric pressure)

Section 13.2 Assessment

Reviewing Concepts

1. ◯ Describe Pascal's principle in your own words.

2. ◯ How is a hydraulic system able to increase force?

3. ◯ How are fluid speed and fluid pressure related?

4. How does an airplane wing produce lift?

Critical Thinking

5. **Predicting** Water is nearly incompressible. Air is easily compressed. Predict what will happen when an air-filled balloon is pulled to the bottom of a swimming pool.

6. **Applying Concepts** The area of an output piston is 25 times greater than the area of the input piston. If the input force is 40 newtons, what is the output force?

7. **Relating Cause and Effect** Two table tennis balls are suspended from strings so they hang at the same height with a small space between them. When a hair dryer is used to blow air between the two balls, the balls come together and touch. Explain why this occurs.

8. **Inferring** When cars pass one another in opposite directions on the highway, they tend to be forced together. Use Bernoulli's principle to explain why this happens.

Connecting Concepts

Net Force Review unbalanced forces in Section 12.1 and their relation to net force. Relate Bernoulli's principle to air flowing over an airplane wing and the creation of a net upward force.

Forces in Fluids **397**

3 ASSESS

Evaluate Understanding L2

Ask students at random to use either Bernoulli's principle or Pascal's principle to explain the operation of the following: sprayer (atomizer), airplane lift, and hydraulic jack.

Reteach L1

Use Figure 7 to review Pascal's principle and the application of constant fluid pressure in a hydraulic system. Use Figure 8 to summarize Bernoulli's principle, discussing how fast-moving air creates an area of lower pressure and results in lift.

Connecting Concepts

The pressure difference acting on the wing due to Bernoulli's principle results in different forces acting on the top and bottom of the wing. These forces are unbalanced (do not add to zero), resulting in a net upward force known as lift.

Interactive Textbook If your class subscribes to the Interactive Textbook, use it to review key concepts in Section 13.2.

Answer to . . .

Figure 8 *The air flowing over the top of the wing moves faster than the air flowing under the wing.*

 Reading Checkpoint *As the speed of a fluid increases, the pressure within the fluid decreases.*

Section 13.2 Assessment

1. A change in pressure at any point in a fluid is transmitted equally and unchanged in all directions throughout the fluid.
2. The increased output force is produced because the fluid pressure is exerted on the larger area of the output piston.
3. As the speed of a fluid increases, the pressure within the fluid decreases.
4. Lift of a wing is largely explained by Bernoulli's principle. Air traveling faster over the top of the wing produces an area of reduced pressure. The resulting pressure difference between the top and bottom of the wing produces lift.
5. The water pressure increases with increasing depth in the pool, causing the air-filled balloon to be compressed.
6. Area of output piston/Area of input piston = 25; Input force = Output force/25 = 50 N/25 = 2 N; Output force = Input force × 25; Output force = 40 N × 25 = 1000 N
7. The moving air between the balls has a lower pressure than the surrounding, nonmoving air. The pressure difference forces the balls together.
8. Each moving car pulls a layer of air with it as it moves. When the cars pass, these two areas of moving, lower-pressure air meet, producing a pressure difference, which forces the cars toward each other.

CONCEPTS
— in Action —

Airplane Motion L2
Background

The motion of an airplane is determined by the relationship of the four forces acting on it: thrust, drag, lift, and the plane's weight. When the plane cruises, all of the forces are balanced. The plane's horizontal movement is determined by thrust and drag. If thrust is greater than drag, the plane accelerates. If drag is greater than thrust, the plane slows down. The plane's vertical movement is determined by the plane's weight and lift. If lift is greater than weight, the plane rises. If weight is greater than lift, the plane falls.

The weight and thrust of an airplane are fixed quantities. The weight depends on the plane's mass, and the thrust depends on the plane's propulsion system. The lift and drag, however, change according to many factors. For example, both lift and drag increase as the square of the plane's velocity. If the plane's speed doubles, lift and drag quadruple. Also, lift and drag are directly proportional to air density. Because air density decreases with increased altitude, a plane experiences less lift the higher it goes. This explains why planes have a maximum height, known as a *flight ceiling*, at which they can travel.

Airplane Motion

Four forces act on an airplane in flight. They are thrust, drag, lift, and weight. Lift and drag are known as aerodynamic forces because they result entirely from the plane's movement through the air.

Of the aerodynamic forces, lift is the least familiar. One source of lift is Bernoulli's principle. According to Bernoulli's principle, the pressure of a fluid such as air decreases as its speed increases. Because the air moving over the top of an airplane wing moves faster than the air moving beneath the wing, it creates a pressure difference that lifts the wing and hence the plane. Another source of lift is the slant of the wing. As the wing moves through the air, the wing forces air downward. According to Newton's third law of motion, this action must have a reaction. The reaction force also exerts an upward force on the wing.

Thrust

Flight controls
In addition to the engines, the pilot has control over a number of other parts of the airplane that affect its motion through the air. These include the spoilers and flaps, and other parts of the wings and tail. These parts affect yaw (turning to left or right), pitch (tilting from back to front) and roll (one wing tilting up, and the other down).

Rudder controls yaw.

Flap affects lift and drag.

Elevator controls pitch.

Aileron controls roll.

Spoiler increases drag.

YAW   PITCH   ROLL

398 *Chapter 13*

Air flow around wing

The movement of an airplane wing through the air causes air passing over the top of the wing first to be accelerated upward (upwash) and then rapidly downward (downwash). Overall, the wing produces a downward movement of the air, and the wing itself is pushed upward. The air flowing over the top of the wing has the lowest pressure. The result is an overall pressure difference that pushes the wing up.

Initial upwash

Downwash along wing

More air moves downward (to fill void)

Fast-moving, low-pressure air

Air below wing under pressure

Lift due to pressure imbalance

Direction in which the plane is traveling

Engine generates thrust.

Lift

Wing generates lift.

Drag

Weight

Four forces acting on a plane

The engine produces thrust, which pushes the plane forward. Thrust is opposed by drag (air resistance), which increases with the airplane's speed. The thrust must create enough speed to generate lift. Lift is the upward force on the airplane caused by movement of its wings through the air. For the plane to become airborne, the lift must exceed the plane's weight.

Going Further

- Research the development of airplane engines since the early 1900s. Prepare a poster to present your findings. Include information on engine type, power or thrust produced, and a description of the plane the engine was used in.

- Take a Discovery Channel Video Field Trip by watching "Uplifting Experience."

DISCOVERY CHANNEL **SCHOOL** Video Field Trip

Designing Experiments

Purpose Students demonstrate Bernoulli's principle.

ACTIVITY

Materials clear straw, 1000-mL beaker or jar, several drops of dark food coloring, water

Class Time 45 minutes

Procedure Divide students into groups of two, and provide each group with the materials. Ask them to think about how the materials could be used to demonstrate Bernoulli's principle. Each group should develop a hypothesis, write a plan, and carry out their experiment. Afterwards, have each group of students write a description of their experiment, including an explanation of the results.

Expected Outcome Students will probably place the straw in a beaker filled with colored water. By blowing across the top of the straw, their partner will see the level of the water in the straw rise because of Bernoulli's principle.
Visual, Kinesthetic, Logical

Going Further

Poster presentations will vary considerably, but might include the development of vee, inline, radial, turboprop, and jet engines.
Visual

DISCOVERY CHANNEL **SCHOOL**

Video Field Trip

Uplifting Experience

After students have viewed the Video Field Trip, ask them the following questions: **When you hold your hand with its front tilted slightly upward out of a car window, why do you feel an upward force?** *(You feel your hand pushed upward because it deflects air downward. The upward force can also be explained in terms of air flowing faster over the top of your hand and slower along the bottom.)* **How can the forces keeping an airplane in the air be explained in** terms of how fast air moves around the wings? *(The air moves faster over the top of the wings than under the bottom. This action produces lower pressure above the wings than below the wings, giving an upward net force.)* **How does the lift, or upward force on the plane, depend on the air speed of the plane?** *(The faster the plane moves the greater the lift. Students may note that this is why a plane must reach a particular take-off speed to be able to leave the ground.)* **What is the name of the shape and design that allows air to flow smoothly around a wing or other object moving through the air?** *(Streamlining)*

1 FOCUS

Objectives

13.3.1 Explain the effect of buoyancy on the apparent weight of an object.

13.3.2 Explain the relationship between the volume of fluid displaced by an object and buoyant force acting on the object according to Archimedes' principle.

13.3.3 Describe the relationship among object density, fluid density, and whether an object sinks or floats in a fluid.

13.3.4 Describe the relationship among object weight, buoyant force, and whether an object sinks or floats in a fluid.

Reading Focus

Build Vocabulary   L2

Word Forms Students benefit from knowing related forms of a key word tied to lesson concepts (for example, *buoyancy* and *buoyant*). Have students find the meaning of the root word *buoy* and build on it as they read p. 400.

Reading Strategy   L2

a. Archimedes' Principle: The buoyant force on an object is equal to the weight of fluid it displaces.

b. Density and Buoyancy: Objects less dense than the fluid they are in float. Objects denser than the fluid they are in sink. When the buoyant force is equal to the weight, the object floats or is suspended. When the buoyant force is less than the weight, the object sinks.

2 INSTRUCT

Buoyant Force

Use Visuals   L1

Figure 10 Remind students that pressure is exerted equally in all directions at a given level. Ask, **Why are the forces acting on the ball not all the same magnitude?** (*Different parts of the ball are at different depths. Water pressure increases as depth increases.*) **What determines the direction of the forces acting on the ball?** (*The forces are always perpendicular to the surface of the ball.*) **Visual, Logical**

13.3 Buoyancy

Reading Focus

Key Concepts

- What is the effect of buoyancy on the apparent weight of an object?
- How can you determine if an object will float or sink in a fluid?

Vocabulary

- buoyancy
- buoyant force
- Archimedes' principle

Reading Strategy

Summarizing Copy the table below. As you read about buoyancy, write a brief summary of the text following each green heading. Your summary should include only the most important information.

Section 13.3 Buoyancy
Buoyant Force Buoyant force is the apparent loss of weight of an object submerged in a fluid.
a.   ?
b.   ?

Have you ever stood in a pool and tried lifting a friend who was submerged in the water? If you have, you may recall how surprisingly easy your friend was to lift. Or perhaps you have gone swimming in a lake or bay where the very salty water made it easy to float on the surface. What forces make these two situations possible? In this section you'll learn the answers to these questions.

Buoyant Force

You are easily able to lift a friend submerged in water because of buoyancy. **Buoyancy** is the ability of a fluid to exert an upward force on an object placed in it. **Buoyancy results in the apparent loss of weight of an object in a fluid.** In fact, every object in a fluid experiences buoyancy. When an object is submerged in water, the water exerts an upward force on the object, making it easier to lift. This upward force, which acts in the opposite direction of gravity, is called a **buoyant force.**

How is a buoyant force produced? To answer this question, examine the forces pressure exert on the submerged object in Figure 10. Because water pressure increases with depth, the forces pushing up on the bottom of the object are greater than the forces from pressure pushing down on the top of the object. All of the other non-vertical forces cancel one another out. The result is a net upward force—the buoyant force.

Figure 10 The forces from pressure acting on the bottom of this golf ball are greater than those acting on the top. This produces a net force—called the buoyant force—that acts upward on the ball.

Section Resources

Print

- *Laboratory Manual*, Investigation 13A
- *Reading and Study Workbook With Math Support*, Section 13.3
- *Transparencies*, Section 13.3

Technology

- *Probeware Lab Manual*, Lab 5
- *Interactive Textbook*, Section 13.3
- *Presentation Pro CD-ROM*, Section 13.3
- *Go Online*, NSTA SciLinks, Buoyancy

Archimedes' Principle

Archimedes, an ancient Greek mathematician who died in 212 B.C., is credited with an important discovery that bears his name. According to **Archimedes' principle,** the buoyant force on an object is equal to the weight of the fluid displaced by the object.

When an object is submerged, it pushes aside, or displaces, a volume of fluid equal to its own volume. When an object floats on the surface of a fluid, it does not displace its entire volume. The floating object does, however, displace a volume equal to the volume of the part of the object that is submerged.

Density and Buoyancy

Density and buoyancy are closely related. Recall that density is the ratio of an object's mass to its volume. Densities are often expressed in the non-SI units of grams per cubic centimeter (g/cm^3). Water, for example, has a density of $1 \ g/cm^3$, whereas steel has a density of $7.8 \ g/cm^3$.

 If an object is less dense than the fluid it is in, it will float. If the object is more dense than the fluid it is in, it will sink. Different fluids can also float or sink in one another. Oil, for example, floats on water because oil is less dense than water.

You can also determine if an object will float by analyzing the forces acting on it. As you can see in Figure 11, two forces act on every object in a fluid—weight and the buoyant force. The force of gravity, equal to the object's weight, acts downward on the object. The buoyant force, equal to the weight of the volume of displaced fluid, acts upward on the object. **When the buoyant force is equal to the weight, an object floats or is suspended. When the buoyant force is less than the weight, the object sinks.**

Figure 11 The weight and buoyant force determines if an object sinks or floats. **A** The metal cube sinks because its weight is greater than the buoyant force. **B** Equal forces acting on this submerged cube allow it to be suspended in the fluid. **C** The partially submerged wood cube floats at a depth where the buoyant force and weight are equal.

Forces in Fluids **401**

Changing Buoyancy

Procedure

1. Fill a plastic bottle with water up to its neck. Squeeze a dropper pipet's bulb and draw water into the pipet until it is about half full. Insert the pipet, bulb end up, into the bottle. The pipet should float at the water's surface.

2. Add water to the bottle until it is full. Tightly twist the cap onto the bottle. Trap as little air as possible in the bottle.

3. Observe what happens to the pipet as you squeeze, hold, and then release the bottle.

Analyze and Conclude

1. **Applying Concepts** Describe the changes in pressure during Step 3.

2. **Inferring** How did the volume of the air trapped inside the pipet change when the bottle was squeezed?

3. **Drawing Conclusions** Explain how squeezing and releasing the bottle caused the pipet to move up and down in the water.

Changing Buoyancy [L2]

Objective
After completing this lab, students will be able to
- describe the effect of a pressure change within a fluid system.

🚩 **Address Misconceptions**

Students may have the misconception that only movement of a fluid produces pressure. To help dispel this misconception, ask students if there is any pressure at all inside the bottle when it is not being squeezed. If they answer that there is not, ask what prevents the pressure of the atmosphere from collapsing the bottle.

Skills Focus Observing, Inferring

⏱ **Prep Time** 5 minutes

Materials clear plastic bottle with screw cap, dropper pipet, water

Advance Prep Provide long specimen forceps, if possible, so students can retrieve sunken dropper pipets without having to empty their bottles completely.

Class Time 20 minutes

Safety Caution students to wipe up any spilled water immediately.

Teaching Tips
- If the pipet sinks, tell students to remove it from the bottle, squeeze out some of the water, and return the pipet to the bottle.

Expected Outcome Squeezing the bottle causes the pipet to sink. When the bottle is released, the pipet rises.

Analyze and Conclude
1. The pressure increased when the bottle was squeezed, and returned to its original value when the bottle was released.
2. Squeezing the bottle caused the air bubble to become smaller.
3. When the air bubble in the pipet shrank, more water entered, increasing the mass and density of the pipet and its contents. This increase caused the pipet to sink. These changes were reversed when the bottle was released: The pressure was reduced, allowing the air bubble to enlarge, pushing water out of the pipet and increasing the buoyancy of the pipet.
Logical

Build Reading Literacy L1

Visualize Refer to page **354D** at the beginning of **Chapter 12**, which provides the guidelines for visualizing.

Encourage students to visualize the concepts of objects suspended or sinking in water. For example, suggest that they imagine themselves floating on a raft in a pool. Then, have them think what would happen if a friend also got on the raft. Would the raft continue to float, or would it sink further in the water? Encourage students to think about the weight and buoyant force on the raft. **Visual, Logical**

DK HOW It Works

Submarine L2

Submarines carry compressed air to use in the ballast tanks. At a constant temperature, the volume of a gas is inversely proportional to the pressure. The pressure of the compressed gas is therefore very high. Submarines have different methods that can be used for rising to the surface. One way is to blow the compressed, high-pressure air into the ballast tanks. Another method is to drive the submarine to the surface. This is done by positioning the diving planes so that the submarine's forward movement causes it to surface. The submarine then forces seawater out of the ballast tanks using low-pressure air.

Interpreting Diagrams Neglecting changes in the density of seawater, the buoyant force acting on the submerged submarine is constant and described by Archimedes' principle. By altering the submarine's weight relative to the constant buoyant force, the submarine is able to rise or drive.
Logical

For Enrichment L3

Students who need more of a challenge may design and construct a simple model submarine and present it to the class as an illustration of Archimedes' principle.
Verbal, Logical, Portfolio

Suspended An object that has the same density as the fluid it is submerged in will be suspended (it will float at any level) in the fluid. The buoyant force acting on the suspended object exactly equals the object's weight. Submarines and some fish are able to suspend themselves in water partly by adjusting their density. To learn more about submarines, read the How It Works box below.

Sinking If the shape of a ship's hull allows it to float, what causes a ship to sink? As you know, when the ship's weight becomes greater than the buoyant force acting on it, the ship will sink. This may occur when the ship damages its hull and takes on water. As water enters the hull, the ship displaces less water and the buoyant force decreases. If the damage is not fixed, the ship will eventually sink.

DK HOW It Works

Submarine

According to Archimedes' principle, the buoyant force on an object is equal to the weight of the fluid displaced by the object. Whereas the weight of an object acts downward, the buoyant force acts upward. **Interpreting Diagrams**
When diving and surfacing, how do submarines make use of Archimedes' principle?

Steering a submarine
The crew alters the buoyancy of the submarine to make it rise or sink. To steer the submarine through the water, crewmen also use the propeller and the rudder, and adjust the angle of the diving planes.

A **Negative buoyancy** As long as it remains submerged, a submarine experiences a constant buoyant force. To overcome the buoyant force so the submarine can dive—that is, to achieve negative buoyancy—its weight must increase. This is done by flooding the ballast tanks, replacing air with water.

402   *Chapter 13*

Facts and Figures

Archimedes Archimedes was born in the third century B.C., in Syracuse, a Greek city-state on the island of Sicily. He is considered by many to be one of the greatest mathematicians of all time. One of his most useful mathematical accomplishments was the discovery of the formula for a sphere's surface area ($S = 4\pi r^2$). He also discovered that the volume of a sphere is two-thirds the volume of a cylinder with the same radius. His discovery of the buoyant force on an object (Archimedes' principle) was set forth in the first of two books known as *On Floating Bodies*. Archimedes is also known for inventing a device, now known as Archimedes' screw, for easily raising water.

Floating You may be wondering why a piece of steel sinks, whereas a huge steel ship floats. A heavy steel ship floats because of the shape of its hull. The hull is shaped so that it displaces a large volume of water, creating a large buoyant force. The buoyant force created by the ship's hull is large enough to counteract the ship's tremendous weight.

Objects also float more easily in dense fluids. Why is this? As you know, the buoyant force acting on the object equals the weight of the volume of the fluid it displaces. For a given displacement, the denser the fluid is, the greater is the weight displaced. This greater displaced weight results in a greater buoyant force. This is why it is easier for a person to float in very salty water. The dense salty water produces a larger buoyant force when displaced by the person's body.

For: Links on buoyancy
Visit: www.SciLinks.org
Web Code: ccn-2133

B **Neutral buoyancy** Once the submarine's ballast tanks hold enough water for the submarine's weight to equal the buoyant force, the submarine is said to have neutral buoyancy. It now has no tendency to rise or sink.

Diving planes angled upward

Air being pumped into ballast tanks

Diving planes horizontal

Rear diving planes angled downward

Ballast tanks emptying of water

SUBMARINE RISING

Diving planes horizontal

SUBMARINE FLOATING LEVEL

Ballast tanks partially filled with water

C **Positive buoyancy** To rise again, the submarine's weight must be decreased. Air is pumped into the ballast tanks to force the water out. The buoyant force acting on the submarine now exceeds the submarine's weight. With positive buoyancy, the submarine rises.

Forces in Fluids **403**

Facts and Figures

Densities Why does ice float in water? Why does a balloon filled with helium rise in air? Their densities answer these questions. When the densities of two objects are compared, the one with lower density will float or rise above the one with higher density.

The density of ice is about 920 kg/m³, while the density of fresh water (at 4°C) is approximately 1,000 kg/m³. Therefore, ice will float on water. In addition, the density of helium is approximately 0.178 kg/m³, while the density of air (at sea level) is about 1.293 kg/m³. Therefore, a balloon filled with helium will rise in the air.

Teacher **Demo**

Volume Measurement   L2

Purpose Students observe an easy way to measure the volume of a solid object.

Materials small steel ball or irregularly shaped object, 500-mL beaker, 100-mL beaker, water

Procedure Have a student set the 100-mL beaker beside and under the spout of the 500-mL beaker. Then, have the student overfill the 500-mL beaker with water until some of the water spills into the 100-mL beaker. Empty the water out of the 100-mL beaker and return it to its position below the 500-mL beaker. Then, carefully add the steel ball or other object into the 500-mL beaker.

Expected Outcome The water that is displaced by the steel ball will pour into the smaller beaker. The volume of that displaced water equals the volume of the steel ball. **Visual, Logical**

Build Science Skills   L2

Inferring Have students consider the explanation of *floating*. Ask, **How could the shape of a hull cause greater displacement of water?** *(Lead students to realize that it is density—mass divided by volume—that determines floating. If the volume is greater, the density is less because the same amount of mass is divided over a greater volume. An aluminum canoe is an example. If the same amount of aluminum were shaped into a cube, it would sink because it would be denser than the water. However, in the shape of a canoe, the volume becomes much greater, making the density much less and allowing it to float.)* **Logical**

Integrate Social Studies   L2

Ask students to use the Internet to research ship museums. These museums often preserve and restore these vessels. Have students write a paragraph about the restoration of a particular ship at one of the museums. **Verbal, Portfolio**

Download a worksheet on buoyancy for students to complete, and find additional teacher support from NSTA SciLinks.

Use Community Resources `L2`

Arrange for a submarine or ship crew member or a commercial diver to visit your class to discuss experiences related to buoyancy. Encourage students to write questions in advance. You may want to ask the students to write a paper for their portfolio on what they learned from the guest. **Verbal, Portfolio**

3 ASSESS

Evaluate Understanding `L2`

Ask students to explain the relationship among buoyant force, weight of fluid displaced, and the apparent weight of floating objects.

Reteach `L1`

Use Figure 11 and How It Works illustrations to review buoyancy, Archimedes' principle, and the way a submarine dives and rises.

Writing in Science

The paragraph should state that the weight of the sunken object is greater than the buoyant force acting on it, and that the weight of the floating object is equal to the buoyant force acting on it.

 Interactive Textbook If your class subscribes to the Interactive Textbook, use it to review key concepts in Section 13.3.

Figure 12 The exposed green and red stripes on the ship's hull indicate that the ship is riding high in the water.
Applying Concepts *How will the ship's level in the water change if it takes on additional cargo?*

The ability of a huge steel ship to float in water can also be explained in terms of density. As you know, a solid piece of steel sinks in water. A ship's shape, however, allows it to displace a very large volume of water relative to its weight. That is, the ship's shape increases its volume and decreases its density. As long as the ship's effective density is less than that of water, the ship floats.

The heavier the ship, the more water it must displace in order to float. The relationship between weight and the level a ship rides at in the water can be seen in Figure 12. If the cargo ship were completely loaded, it would need to displace more water in order to float.

Why do some balloons float in air whereas others do not? The answer has to do with density differences. Helium and hot air are both less dense than normal-temperature air. When a balloon is filled with either helium or hot air, a buoyant force from the displaced normal-temperature air acts on the balloon. If the size of the buoyant force is large enough, the balloon rises into the air.

Section 13.3 Assessment

Reviewing Concepts

1. How does buoyancy affect the apparent weight of an object in a fluid?

2. What determines if an object will float or sink in a fluid?

3. How does Archimedes' principle relate the buoyant force acting on an object and the volume of fluid displaced by the object?

4. How is the density of a floating object related to the density of the fluid it is floating in?

Critical Thinking

5. **Applying Concepts** An empty oil tanker displaces enough water to support its weight. Why doesn't the tanker sink when loaded with thousands of tons of oil?

6. **Inferring** A small object is able to float at any level when placed in water. What does this observation tell you about the object's density?

7. **Applying Concepts** A 350-N block of wood is thrown into a lake, where it floats. What is the buoyant force acting on it?

Writing in Science

Compare and Contrast Paragraph Write a paragraph comparing the forces acting on an object that floats in water and an object that sinks in water. Be sure to describe the relative sizes of the forces acting on each object. (*Hint:* Before you write, review the forces shown in Figure 11.)

Answer to . . .

Figure 12 *The ship will float at a lower level in the water if it takes on additional weight.*

Section 13.3 Assessment

1. Buoyancy results in the apparent loss of weight of an object in a fluid.
2. Floating: If an object is less dense than the fluid it is in, it will float. If the buoyant force is equal to the weight of the object, the object will float or be suspended. Sinking: If an object is more dense than the fluid it is in, it will sink. If the buoyant force is less than the weight of the object, the object will sink.
3. The buoyant force acting on an object is equal to the weight of fluid displaced by the object.
4. Floating objects have a density that is less than that of the fluid in which they are floating.
5. As the tanker is loaded with oil, its increased weight causes it to displace more water. This increased water displacement results in a greater buoyant force, which supports the loaded tanker.
6. The density of the object must be equal to the density of the water.
7. 350 N

Determining Buoyant Force

In this lab, you will analyze recorded data to determine the buoyant forces acting on objects.

Problem
How does the buoyant force determine whether an object sinks?

Materials
string, rock, spring scale, can, plastic tub, sponge, paper towels, 100-g standard mass, wooden block tied to a fishing weight, 250-mL graduated cylinder

 For the probeware version of this lab, see the Probeware Lab Manual, Lab 5.

Skills
Measuring, Calculating

Procedure

1. Make a copy of the data table shown.

2. Tie one end of the string around the rock. Tie the other end to the spring scale. Suspend the rock from the spring scale and measure and record its weight in air in your data table.

3. Place the can in an upright position in the plastic tub. Completely fill the can with water. Wipe up any water that spills into the tub. **CAUTION** *Wipe up any water that spills on the floor to avoid slips and falls.*

4. Lower the rock into the water until it is completely submerged. Record in your data table the apparent weight in water of the submerged rock. Remove the rock from the can.

5. Without spilling any water, carefully remove the can from the tub. Pour the water from the tub into the graduated cylinder. Record the volume of displaced water in your data table.

6. Repeat Steps 2 through 5, first with the 100-g standard mass and then with the wooden block that is tied to a fishing weight.

7. To determine the buoyant force on each object, subtract its apparent weight in water from its weight in air. Record these values.

8. Calculate the weight of the water each object displaces. (*Hint:* 1.0 mL of water has a weight of 0.0098 N.) Record these weights.

Analyze and Conclude

1. **Observing** What force is responsible for the difference between the weight of each object in the air and its apparent weight in water?

2. **Analyzing Data** How is the buoyant force related to the weight of water displaced?

3. **Forming Operational Definitions** Define buoyant force and describe two ways you can measure it or calculate it.

4. **Drawing Conclusions** Explain what causes an object to sink or to float, using the terms *buoyancy, weight, force, density,* and *gravity*.

Data Table

Object	Weight in Air (N)	Apparent Weight in Water (N)	Buoyant Force (weight in air – apparent weight in water, N)	Volume of Displaced Water (mL)	Weight of Displaced Water (N)
Rock					
100-g standard mass					
Wood block with fishing weight					

Determining Buoyant Force L2

Objective
After completing this lab, students will be able to
- define the buoyant force as the difference between an object's weight in air and its apparent weight in water.
- state that the buoyant force on an object floating in water is equal to the weight of the water the object displaces.

Skills Focus Measuring, Calculating

 Prep Time 10 minutes

Advance Prep If possible, supply a standard mass with a hook for ease of weighing. Attach enough mass to the wooden block to ensure that it will exert a measurable force on the spring scale when the block is in water.

Class Time 30 minutes

Teaching Tips
- Ask students why it was necessary to attach a weight to the wooden block. Explain that the weight is necessary to ensure that the wooden block will exert a measurable force on the spring scale when the block is in water.
- In Step 3, instruct students to overfill the can so some water pours over the top edge.

Expected Outcome The buoyant force on each object is equal to the weight of the water it displaces.

Analyze and Conclude
1. The difference is equal to the buoyant force that the water exerts on the object.
2. They are equal.
3. The buoyant force on an object is equal to the difference between its weight in air and its apparent weight in water. It is also equal to the weight of the water the object displaces.
4. An object will float when the upward force of buoyancy is greater than or equal to the downward force of gravity (the weight of the object). For the buoyant force to counteract the gravitational force, the object must weigh as much as or less than the volume of water it displaces. For this reason, floating objects have low densities.
Verbal, Logical

 Probeware Lab Manual Versions of this lab for use with probeware available from Pasco, Texas Instruments, and Vernier are in the Probeware Manual.

Sample Data Table

Object	Weight in Air (N)	Apparent Weight in Water (N)	Buoyant Force (weight in air – apparent weight in water, N)	Volume of Displaced Water (mL)	Weight of Displaced Water (N)
Rock	0.3	0.2	0.1	5.0	0.049
100-g standard mass	1.0	0.75	0.25	10.0	0.098
Wood block with fishing weight	1.8	1.5	0.3	25.0	0.24

Study Guide

Study Tip

Focused Study

Chapters can be understood more easily with short, focused blocks of studying. There are several important principles to learn in the chapter (Pascal's, Bernoulli's, and Archimedes'). Trying to learn all of the principles at once is more likely to cause confusion.

Thinking Visually

a. Liquids (or gases) **b.** Gases (or liquids) **c.** Pressure = Force/Area **d.** Depth **e.** Altitude (or speed) **f.** Speed (or altitude) **g.** Pascals

13.1 Fluid Pressure

Key Concepts

- Pressure = $\dfrac{\text{Force}}{\text{Area}}$
- Water pressure increases as depth increases.
- The pressure in a fluid at any given depth is constant and is exerted equally in all directions.
- Air pressure decreases as altitude increases.

Vocabulary

pressure, *p. 390*
pascal, *p. 391*
fluid, *p. 391*

13.2 Forces and Pressure in Fluids

Key Concepts

- According to Pascal's principle, a change in pressure at any point in a fluid is transmitted equally and unchanged in all directions throughout the fluid.
- In a hydraulic lift system, an increased output force is produced by a constant fluid pressure exerted on the larger area of the output piston.
- According to Bernoulli's principle, as the speed of a fluid increases, the pressure within the fluid decreases.

Vocabulary

hydraulic system, *p. 395*
lift, *p. 396*

13.3 Buoyancy

Key Concepts

- Buoyancy results in the apparent loss of weight of an object in a fluid.
- If an object is less dense than the fluid it is in, it will float. If the object is more dense than the fluid it is in, it will sink.
- When the buoyant force is equal to the weight, an object floats or is suspended. When the buoyant force is less than the weight, the object sinks.

Vocabulary

buoyancy, *p. 400*
buoyant force, *p. 400*
Archimedes' principle, *p. 401*

Thinking Visually

Use the information from the chapter to complete the concept map below.

Chapter Resources

Print
- ***Chapter and Unit Tests***, Chapter 13 Test A and Test B
- ***Test Prep Resources***, Chapter 13

Technology
- ***Computer Test Bank***, Chapter Test 13
- ***Interactive Textbook***, Chapter 13
- ***Go Online***, PHSchool.com, Chapter 13

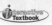
Reviewing Content

*Choose the letter that best answers the question or
completes the statement.*

1. A resting object exerts pressure equal to
   a. its mass times its contact area.
   b. its weight times its contact area.
   c. its mass divided by its contact area.
   d. its weight divided by its contact area.

2. Compared to the pressure exerted by a brick
standing on its end, the pressure exerted by a
brick resting on its side is
   a. the same.   **b.** less.
   c. more.   **d.** twice as much.

3. The amount of water pressure you experience
while swimming in a pool depends on
   a. your buoyancy.
   b. the area of the pool.
   c. the volume of water in the pool.
   d. how deep you are in the water.

4. Which of the following is NOT true about the SI
unit of pressure?
   a. It is used for fluids only.
   b. It is called a pascal.
   c. It is equal to one newton per square meter.
   d. It represents force per unit area.

5. Blaise Pascal discovered that changes in pressure
   a. are transmitted equally throughout a fluid.
   b. increase with depth of fluid.
   c. decrease with depth of fluid.
   d. depend on area.

6. In a hydraulic lift system, the output force is
greater than the input force because
   a. a larger pressure acts on the output piston.
   b. a larger pressure acts on the input piston.
   c. the fluid pressure acts on areas of
   different sizes.
   d. of Bernoulli's principle.

7. Which of the following is NOT true about
Bernoulli's principle?
   a. The pressure within a moving fluid is
   greater than the pressure within a
   nonmoving fluid.
   b. As a fluid's speed increases, the pressure
   within it decreases.
   c. When a moving fluid slows, the pressure
   within it increases.
   d. It helps explain the lift of an airplane.

8. The buoyant force acting on a submerged object
is equal to
   a. the object's mass.
   b. the object's volume.
   c. the mass of the fluid displaced by the object.
   d. the weight of the fluid displaced by
   the object.

9. A partially submerged object floats when
   a. the object's weight is equal to the
   buoyant force.
   b. the object's mass is equal to the
   buoyant force.
   c. the object's weight is greater than
   the buoyant force.
   d. the buoyant force is downward.

10. A submarine changes depth by altering its
   a. speed.   **b.** density.
   c. total area.   **d.** shape.

Understanding Concepts

11. How is pressure different from force?

12. What are two characteristics of fluids?

13. State Archimedes' principle in your own words.

14. What two forces determine whether an object
floats or sinks?

15. Why is it easier to float in salt water than in
fresh water?

16. Why do helium-filled balloons rise in air?

17. Explain how a hydraulic lift operates.

18. Why is it easier to pull a submerged boat anchor
to the surface than it is to lift it onto the boat?

19. Three different liquids and two equal-size cubes
are placed in a beaker as shown. Which of the
objects has the greater buoyant force acting on it?

Forces in Fluids **407**

Assessment

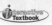 If your class subscribes to
the Interactive Textbook, your students
can go online to access an interactive
version of the Student Edition and a
self-test.

Reviewing Content

1. d   **2.** b   **3.** d
4. a   **5.** a   **6.** c
7. a   **8.** d   **9.** a
10. b

Understanding Concepts

11. A force is a push or pull, whereas
pressure is force per unit area.
12. Fluids flow and take on the shape of
their containers.
13. The buoyant force on an object is
equal to the weight of the fluid
displaced by the object.
14. Weight and buoyant force
15. Salt water has a greater density and
creates a greater buoyant force when
displaced.
16. A helium-filled balloon is less dense
than air, thus it rises (floats).
17. An input force to the input piston
creates pressure within the hydraulic fluid.
This fluid pressure is applied to the greater
surface area of the output piston, creating
a larger output force.
18. The buoyant force acting on the
anchor submerged in the water is much
greater than the buoyant force when
the anchor is submerged in air.
19. The cube at the bottom has a
greater buoyant force acting on it.

 Homework Guide

Section	Questions
13.1	1–4, 11–12, 16, 20, 24, 26, 28–29
13.2	5–7, 17, 23, 27, 30–31
13.3	8–10, 13–15, 18–19, 21–22, 25

Critical Thinking

20. The weight of the rescuer is spread over a greater area, thus reducing the pressure acting on the ice. The reduced pressure makes it less likely that the rescuer will break through the ice.

21. Any experiment that will safely allow students to determine if the density of each gas is less than that of air is acceptable. Answers may include filling a balloon with each gas and observing whether it rises in the air.

22. The buoyant force provided by the water lessens the impact and weight acting on the weakened muscles.

23. Drawings should show that the inclined roofline of a house can cause the air flowing over the roof to speed up, much like the air flow over an airplane wing. The low-pressure, fast-moving air creates a pressure difference between the inside and outside of the house. This pressure difference can cause a house to explode.

Math Skills

24. 10 cm^3
25. 0.098 N
26. 520,000 Pa
27. 370,000 Pa

Concepts in Action

28. In general, the pressure at 200 m is four times greater than the pressure at 50 m. At any depth, the pressure on the bottom of the submarine is greater than the pressure on the top of the submarine.

29. The capped can will be crushed because the pressure outside the can is much greater than the pressure inside the can. The uncapped can will not be crushed because the pressure inside and outside the can is equal.

30. Pressing the brake pedal produces increased pressure in the hydraulic fluid. The increased fluid pressure acts on the larger-sized piston located at the brake, producing a larger force. This larger force is applied to the brake pad and is used to stop the car.

31. Explanations should discuss how the wing shapes cause air flowing over their tops to travel faster, thus creating an area of decreased pressure. The pressure difference between the top and bottom wing surfaces creates lift.

Critical Thinking

20. Applying Concepts In order to save someone who has fallen through the ice of a frozen lake, rescuers often reach the victim by crawling across the ice on their stomachs. Explain why the rescuers use this technique.

21. Designing an Experiment Your lab has two pressurized gas cylinders, each containing a different gas. Describe an experiment that could be used to determine whether each gas is less dense than air.

22. Applying Concepts For patients with muscles weakened due to injury, physical therapists recommend exercising in a swimming pool. Why is pool exercise preferred to exercise in a gym?

23. Using Models The high-speed winds of a hurricane sometimes cause houses to explode. Use a drawing to model the pressures acting on the house. Explain the areas of high and low pressure using Bernoulli's principle.

Math Skills

Use the illustration to answer Questions 24 and 25. The results of adding a small stone to a beaker that was filled to the brim with water is shown below.

24. Converting Units What is the volume of the stone in cm^3? (*Hint:* 1.0 mL = 1.0 cm^3)

25. Calculating If 1.0 cm^3 equals 1.0 mL, and 1.0 cm^3 of water has a mass of 1.0 g, calculate the buoyant force acting on the stone.

---

26. Using Formulas A 520-N ballet dancer is balanced on the toe of her shoe. If the toe has an area of 0.0010 m^2, what pressure does she exert on the floor?

27. Using Formulas A small hydraulic jack exerts a force of 2200 N. If the area of the jack's output piston is 0.0060 m^2, what is the pressure of the hydraulic fluid inside the jack?

Concepts in Action

28. Comparing and Contrasting Water exerts pressure on all sides of a submerged submarine. Compare and contrast the pressures acting on the submarine at a depth of 50 m to the pressures at a depth of 200 m.

29. Predicting An empty metal can is capped, attached to weights, and thrown into a deep ocean trench. A second, identical metal can is left uncapped, attached to weights, and thrown into the same trench. Both cans sink. Predict what will happen to each can and explain your reasons.

30. Applying Concepts When a driver presses on the brake pedal of a car, the car is easily brought to a stop. Explain how the car's hydraulic braking system transmits and increases the force applied to the brake pedal.

31. Writing in Science Explain how airplane wings and the wings of birds affect the air flowing over them to produce lift.

Performance-Based Assessment

Using Models Use what you have learned from this chapter to make a model boat out of a 10-cm-square piece of foil. Test your model boat in a tank of water to see how many pennies it can support before sinking. Compare the performance of your boat with those of your classmates. Suggest several design improvements based on your results.

For: Self-grading assessment
Visit: PHSchool.com
Web Code: cca-2130

Performance-Based Assessment

Student model boat designs and results will vary. In general, boat shapes displacing the most water per unit depth submerged below the water line will support more pennies.

Your students can independently test their knowledge of the chapter and print out their test results for your files.

Standardized Test Prep for Indiana

Choose the letter that best answers the question or completes the statement.

1. During a storm, the wind exerts a 150-N force on a window that measures 1.00 m by 0.50 m. The outside air pressure is 101 kPa. What pressure, in pascals, does the wind exert on the window?
   (A) 75 Pa   (B) 150 Pa
   (C) 1.5×10^3 Pa   (D) 3.0×10^2 Pa
   (E) 3.0×10^5 kPa

2. Two identical beakers are both half filled with a liquid. Beaker A contains water and Beaker B contains a liquid that is denser than water. Which of the following is FALSE?
   (A) The pressure at the bottom of Beaker B is greater than that at the bottom of Beaker A.
   (B) The pressure within each fluid is exerted equally in all directions.
   (C) The mass of fluid in Beaker B is greater than the mass of fluid in Beaker A.
   (D) The mass of fluid in Beaker A is greater than the mass of fluid in Beaker B.
   (E) The volume of fluid in Beaker B is equal to the volume of fluid in Beaker A.

3. When air is blown between two balls suspended from strings, the balls come together and touch. This is explained by
   (A) Archimedes' principle.
   (B) Pascal's principle.
   (C) the Pauli exclusion principle.
   (D) Bernoulli's principle.
   (E) the hydraulic principle.

4. In a hydraulic system, the area of the output piston is three times larger than the area of the input piston. How is the output force related to the input force?
   (A) It is nine times smaller.
   (B) It is three times smaller.
   (C) They are both zero.
   (D) It is three times larger.
   (E) It is nine times larger.

Questions 5 and 6 refer to the diagram of an unknown substance in a beaker of water shown below.

5. How are the weight of the unknown object and the buoyant force acting on it related?
   (A) They are the same.
   (B) They are both equal to zero.
   (C) The weight is less than the buoyant force.
   (D) The buoyant force is more than the weight.
   (E) The weight is more than the buoyant force.

6. Which of the following is TRUE?
   (A) Forces from pressure act equally on all sides of the cube.
   (B) The unknown substance has a density greater than 1.0 g/cm^3.
   (C) The buoyant force equals the pressure.
   (D) The buoyant force is more than the weight.
   (E) The weight is equal to the buoyant force.

Forces in Fluids **409**

Standardized Test Prep for Indiana

1. D   2. D   3. D
4. D   5. E   6. B

 Standards Guide

Question	Standards
1	ICP.3.2

Planning Guide

SECTION OBJECTIVES	STANDARDS		ACTIVITIES and LABS
	NATIONAL	STATE	
14.1 Work and Power, pp. 412–416 🕐 1 block or 2 periods **14.1.1 Describe** the conditions that must exist for a force to do work on an object. **14.1.2 Calculate** the work done on an object. **14.1.3 Describe** and **calculate** power. **14.1.4 Compare** the units of watts and horsepower as they relate to power.	A-1, A-2, B-4, G-1, G-2, G-3		**SE** Inquiry Activity: How Do Ramps Help You Raise Objects? p. 411 **L2** **TE** Teacher Demo: Work, p. 413 **L2**
14.2 Work and Machines, pp. 417–420 🕐 1 block or 2 periods **14.2.1 Describe** what a machine is and how it makes work easier to do. **14.2.2 Relate** the work input to a machine to the work output of the machine.			
14.3 Mechanical Advantage and Efficiency, pp. 421–426 🕐 1 block or 2 periods **14.3.1 Compare** a machine's actual mechanical advantage to its ideal mechanical advantage. **14.3.2 Calculate** the ideal and actual mechanical advantages of various machines. **14.3.3 Explain** why the efficiency of a machine is always less than 100%. **14.3.4 Calculate** a machine's efficiency.	A-1, A-2, G-1, G-2, G-3		**SE** Quick Lab: Using Friction to Change Mechanical Advantage, p. 424 **L2** **SE** Consumer Lab: Determining Mechanical Advantage, pp. 438–439 **L2** **TE** Teacher Demo: Mechanical Advantage, p. 423 **L2**
14.4 Simple Machines, pp. 427–435 🕐 1 block or 2 periods **14.4.1 Name, describe,** and **give an example** of each of the six types of simple machines. **14.4.2 Describe** how to determine the ideal mechanical advantage of each type of simple machine. **14.4.3 Define** and **identify** compound machines.	A-1, A-2		**SE** Quick Lab: Comparing Lever Arms, p. 429 **L2** **TE** Teacher Demo: Inclined Planes, p. 430 **L2** **LM** Investigation 14A: Comparing the Mechanical Advantage of Levers **L2** **LM** Investigation 14B: Comparing Pulleys **L1**

RESOURCES
PRINT and TECHNOLOGY

SECTION ASSESSMENT

RESOURCES PRINT and TECHNOLOGY		SECTION ASSESSMENT
RSW Section 14.1	L1	**SE** Section 14.1 Assessment, p. 416
RSW Math Skill	L2	
MSPS Section 14.1	L2	**iT** Section 14.1
T Chapter 14 Pretest	L2	
Section 14.1	L2	
P Chapter 14 Pretest	L2	
Section 14.1	L2	
SCLINKS **GO** Work	L2	
RSW Section 14.2	L1	**SE** Section 14.2 Assessment, p. 420
T Section 14.2	L2	
P Section 14.2	L2	**iT** Section 14.2
SCLINKS **GO** Machines	L2	
RSW Section 14.3	L1	**SE** Section 14.3 Assessment, p. 426
MSPS Section 14.3	L2	
T Section 14.3	L2	**iT** Section 14.3
P Section 14.3	L2	
SCLINKS **GO** Mechanical advantage	L2	
PHSchool.com GO Data Sharing	L2	
RSW Section 14.4	L1	**SE** Section 14.4 Assessment, p. 435
MSPS Section 14.4	L2	
DC Pedal Power	L2	**iT** Section 14.4
T Section 14.4	L2	
P Section 14.4	L2	
SCLINKS **GO** Simple machines	L2	

Go Online

Go online for these Internet resources.

PHSchool.com

Web Code: ccd-2140
Web Code: cca-2140

NSTA *SCLINKS*

Web Code: ccn-2141
Web Code: ccn-2142
Web Code: ccn-2143
Web Code: ccn-2144

Materials for Activities and Labs

Quantities for each group

STUDENT EDITION

Inquiry Activity, p. 411
6 textbooks, 2 boards (1 long, 1 short), meter stick, spring scale, lab cart

Quick Lab, p. 424
6 books, board, 3 different kinds of shoes, 1-kg mass, spring scale

Quick Lab, p. 429
pencil, masking tape, spring scale, 500-g mass, meter stick

Consumer Lab, pp. 438–439
board with 2 nails, 4 thread spools (3 with different diameters), rubber band, masking tape, multispeed bicycle (1 or more per class), meter stick, thick leather glove

TEACHER'S EDITION

Teacher Demo, p. 413
a rigid object

Teacher Demo, p. 423
1 pulley, 10-N spring scale, 500-g mass, string

Teacher Demo, p. 430
long board, heavy box, small stepladder, spring scale

Build Science Skills, p. 437
1 bicycle with gears similar to that shown on pp. 436–437

Chapter Assessment

CHAPTER ASSESSMENT

SE	Chapter Assessment, pp. 441–442
CUT	Chapter 14 Test A, B
CTB	Chapter 14
iT	Chapter 14
PHSchool.com GO	
	Web Code: cca-2140

STANDARDIZED TEST PREP

SE	Chapter 14, p. 443
TP	Diagnose and Prescribe

Interactive Textbook with assessment at PHSchool.com

Before you teach

From the Author

Michael Wysession
Washington University

Big Ideas

This chapter ties together two fundamental aspects of physics: force and energy. Force applied over a distance to move an object equals work, and work is equal to the transfer of energy to that object by the action of a force.

Space and Time When an object is moved through space and time, we can quantify the results of that force. Moving the object against opposing forces (like friction or gravity) requires energy. The amount of energy expended (called work) is equal to the product of the force and the distance moved by the action of a force.

It is also helpful to know the rate at which energy is expended to move an object. Power is the rate at which energy is transferred to a system. Power is measured in watts, which are units of energy per time.

Forces and Motion Machines change the way forces are applied in order to do work. Some machines increase the distance over which an input force acts, allowing for smaller input forces. Some machines decrease the distance over which an input force acts, thus requiring larger input forces. Some machines change the direction of the force.

There are only a few types of simple machines: the pulley, wheel and axle, inclined plane, lever, screw, and wedge. Most machines in daily life are compound machines, which are combinations of two or more—and often many—simple machines.

Matter and Energy There is always an energy cost when doing work and using machines. Because of friction, the amount of energy applied to a system is always more than the amount of energy produced by the system. The missing energy goes into heat, or thermal energy, due to friction. The efficiency of a machine is the ratio of the work output to the work input.

Physics Refresher

Work 14.1

In physics, a force does work on an object if components of the force act in the direction of the object's movement. Work done (W) is defined as a product of the force or component of the force (F) and the distance moved (d) in the direction of the force. In equation form, Work $= (F \cos \theta)(d)$. Note that when the component of force is perpendicular to the direction, $\cos \theta$ is zero, and the work done is zero. Likewise, when the force is in the direction of motion, $\cos \theta = 1$, and work done is

Address Misconceptions

Some students may think that any force on an object multiplied by the distance the object moves is work. However, work done by a force is defined as a product of the force and the displacement in the direction of the force. For a strategy to overcome this misconception, see **Address Misconceptions** on **page 413.**

maximized. In this chapter, students consider only force in the direction of movement. The equation for work, then, is $W = F \times d$. The SI unit for work is newton-meter (N·m), or joule (J).

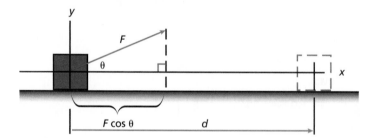

Power 14.1

Power is the rate at which the work is done. The equation for power is $P = W/\Delta t$, where P = power, W = work, and Δt = difference in time. Substituting the definition of work into the equation for power yields another useful relationship.

Address Misconceptions

Some students may think that power is the same as force. However, power is the rate at which work is done. For a strategy to overcome this misconception, see **Address Misconceptions** on **page 414.**

$$P = W/\Delta t = Fd/\Delta t = Fv$$

For: Teaching methods for work, power, and machines
Visit: www.SciLinks.org/PDLinks
Web Code: ccn-1499

In this equation, v = velocity. The SI unit for power is watt (W), described as 1 joule per second (1 J/s). Horsepower (hp) is another unit of power, where 1 hp = 746 W.

Work and Machines 14.2 and 14.4

Simple machines, whether a lever, a wheel and axle, an inclined plane, a wedge, a screw, or a pulley, take advantage of the inverse relationship of force and distance in the work equation, $W = Fd$. For example, the same work is done to lift a load whether a ramp is used or not. If a ramp is used, the distance through which the force is applied increases and the amount of force required decreases. If friction is neglected, the product Fd is constant and equals the work done (W) whether the ramp is used or not.

Mechanical Advantage 14.3

Mechanical advantage is a ratio of output force to input force (f_{out}/f_{in}) or input distance to output distance (d_{in}/d_{out}). The ratio d_{in}/d_{out} ignores the friction acting on the machine and is used to calculate ideal mechanical advantage (IMA). Because friction opposes the input force, the input force must increase to yield a desired output force. This results in the decreased mechanical advantage of any actual machine. In contrast, the ratio (f_{out}/f_{in})

Input distance

Output distance

Ramp

is the actual mechanical advantage (AMA).

Efficiency 14.3

Work is a measure of energy transfer. Therefore, if a machine were frictionless, then the input work would equal the output work, with 100% of the energy transferred. Because real machines are always subject to friction, the efficiency of real machines is always less than 100%. Friction dissipates energy in the form of heat and sound. The efficiency of a machine is a measure of how much work the machine puts out compared to how much work is put in. The ratio of work output to work input defines the ideal efficiency of a machine.

$$\text{Efficiency} = (\text{Work}_{out}/\text{Work}_{in})(100\%)$$

Build Reading Literacy

Think Aloud

Verbalize Thought Processes While Reading

Strategy Model cognitive and metacognitive processes that students can use to build meaning, self-correct, and monitor their own comprehension. Choose part of a section from Chapter 14, such as What Is Work? on pp. 412–413, and preview it. As you do so, imagine that you are reading these paragraphs for the first time, just as your students will be. Make a copy of the section, and on it write comments and questions that you can use as "think-aloud" models.

Example

1. Read several paragraphs aloud and have your students follow along silently. Have them listen to how you pause to check your own comprehension and to determine meaning at trouble spots. You might model some of the following strategies aloud as you read:

• Make a prediction, then revise or verify it.
• Describe mental pictures as they form.
• Connect new information with prior knowledge or related ideas; share an analogy.
• Verbalize confusing points and work out steps to clarify their meanings; adjust your reading pace if needed.

2. Select a logical stopping point. Then, have students read the next paragraph silently and apply similar strategies internally. Afterward, ask students to share the strategies they used. Repeat this step several times.

3. Have students work in pairs, taking turns applying think-aloud strategies to the next several paragraphs.

See p. 414 for a script on how to use the think-aloud strategy with students. For additional Build Reading Literacy strategies, see pp. 418, 422, and 431.

ASSESS PRIOR KNOWLEDGE

Use the Chapter Pretest below to assess students' prior knowledge. As needed, review these Science Concepts and Math Skills with students.

Review Science Concepts

Section 14.1 Review Newton's first and second laws. Encourage students to review the definition of force and the units used to represent it. Remind students how to break down a force vector into two component vectors at right angles to each other.

Section 14.2 Review the vector characteristics of force—magnitude and direction.

Section 14.3 Have students recall what they've learned about friction.

Section 14.4 Review geometric relationships related to circles and triangles. Tell students to keep these relationships in mind as they learn about simple machines.

Review Math Skills

Formulas and Equations Students will need to work with ratios and proportions, percents and decimals, and formulas and equations in order to solve equations related to mechanical advantage and efficiency.

Direct students to the **Math Skills** in the **Skills and Reference Handbook** at the end of the student text.

CHAPTER 14

Work, Power, and Machines

21st Century Learning

Problem Identification, Formulation, and Solution

How can you improve the efficiency of a machine?

Look for some examples of simple machines in your school or at home. Form a small group and discuss with your classmates how these machines make it easier to do work. Discuss possible ways to increase the efficiency of one of these machines. Work with your group to produce a short video about your ideas. In the video, offer suggestions on how to maximize the work that can be done by the machine.

This powerful strip-mining shovel is able to remove tons of earth in a single load of its bucket.

Chapter Pretest

1. According to Newton's first law, if no net force acts on an object, the object continues in motion with constant _____ . *(a)*
   a. velocity   **b.** force   **c.** acceleration

2. A horizontal force on an object can be broken down into these components: 5 N north and 5 N east. If no other forces act on the object, in what direction will the object move? *(Northeast)*

3. Newton's second law states that the net force acting on an object equals the product of what two variables? *(Mass and acceleration)*

4. A machine produces an output force of 12.3 N when an input of 8.6 N is applied. What is the ratio of the machine's output force to its input force? *(1.4)*

5. A person exerts 22 N on a box. If a frictional force of 3 N opposes this force, what is the net force acting on the box? *(19 N)*

6. A machine has an output force of 57.3 N when a force of 32.6 N is used to operate the machine. What is the percentage increase of the force? *(176%)*

7. A small wheel has a radius of 32 cm, and a large wheel has a diameter of 128 cm. What is the ratio of the diameters of the large wheel to the small wheel? *(b)*
   a. 4   **b.** 2   **c.** 0.25   **d.** 0.5

Chapter Preview

DISCOVERY SCHOOL
Video Field Trip
Pedal Power

Inquiry > Activity

How Do Ramps Help You Raise Objects?

Procedure

1. Make a stack of five books.

2. Make a ramp by leaning a short board against the top of the book stack. Place a sixth book against the bottom edge of the board to keep the ramp from sliding down.

3. Measure and record the height and length of the ramp.

4. Use a spring scale to pull a laboratory cart up the ramp at constant speed. Record the force indicated on the spring scale.

5. Repeat Steps 2 through 4 using a longer board.

Think About It

1. **Comparing and Contrasting** Which ramp required a greater force to pull the cart? Which ramp required the cart to travel a greater distance?

2. **Predicting** How do you think the force needed to pull the cart would change if the cart accelerated up the length of the ramp?

3. **Formulating Hypotheses** Explain why a box that is too heavy to lift can often be pushed up a ramp.

Work, Power, and Machines **411**

DISCOVERY SCHOOL

Video Field Trip
Pedal Power

Encourage students to view the Video Field Trip "Pedal Power."

ENGAGE/EXPLORE

Inquiry > Activity

How Do Ramps Help You Raise Objects?   **L2**

Purpose In this activity, students begin to develop the idea that simple machines can reduce the force needed to accomplish a task by exerting a smaller force over a greater distance.

🚩 **Address Misconceptions**

Students may think that a ramp can reduce the amount of work done to accomplish a task. This lab can help to dispel that misconception. Use Question 1 as the basis of a discussion to point out that a longer ramp reduces the force required, but increases the distance over which the force must be applied. The work done by forces lifting the object is the same.

Skills Focus Formulating Hypotheses

⏱ **Prep Time** 15 minutes

Materials 6 textbooks, 2 boards (1 long, 1 short), meter stick, spring scale, lab cart

Class Time 20 minutes

Safety Sand the boards to remove any rough areas. Warn students to beware of splinters. Students should wear safety goggles.

Teaching Tips
- Depending on the range of your spring scales, you may need to place a mass in the cart to produce a measurable reading on the scale.
- The spring scale must be pulled parallel to the ramp so the force being measured is equal to and opposite the force of friction.

Expected Outcome Switching to the longer ramp reduces the force needed to raise the cart and increases the distance over which the force is applied.

Think About It
1. The shorter ramp; the longer ramp
2. A greater force would be needed to accelerate the cart up the ramp.
3. A heavy box can be pushed up a long ramp with less force than would be needed to lift the box because the ramp distributes the work done over a longer path.
Logical

14.1 Work and Power

1 FOCUS

Objectives

14.1.1 Describe the conditions that must exist for a force to do work on an object.

14.1.2 Calculate the work done on an object.

14.1.3 Describe and **calculate** power.

14.1.4 Compare the units of watts and horsepower as they relate to power.

Reading Focus

Build Vocabulary   L2

Table Encourage students to make a table to help them remember the definitions of *work* and *power*. These terms should go in the first column. Then, have students write the corresponding units, *joule* and *watt* (with *horsepower* in parentheses) in the second column, on the same row with the proper term. The third column is used for definitions of *work* and *power*.
Verbal

Reading Strategy   L2

a. Up **b.** None **c.** No **d.** Horizontal
e. Horizontal **f.** Yes **g.** Diagonal
h. Horizontal **i.** Yes **j.** Up
k. Horizontal **l.** No

2 INSTRUCT

What Is Work?

Build Science Skills   L2

Interpreting Photographs Tell students to imagine the action that occurs after the time shown in the photo. Ask, **Is work done on the weights when they are lowered, or dropped to the ground?** *(Yes)* **What force acts on and does work on the weights as they are lowered or dropped?** *(Gravity)*
Logical, Visual

Reading Focus

Key Concepts

- When does a force do work?
- How are work and power related?

Vocabulary

- work
- joule
- power
- watt
- horsepower

Reading Strategy

Relating Text and Visuals Copy the table shown at the right. As you read, look carefully at Figures 1 and 2 and read their captions. Complete the table by describing the work shown in each figure.

Figure	Direction of Force	Direction of Motion	Is Work Done?
1	a. ?	b. ?	c. ?
2A	d. ?	e. ?	f. ?
2B	g. ?	h. ?	i. ?
2C	j. ?	k. ?	l. ?

Figure 1 The weight lifter applies a large force to hold the barbell over his head. However, because the barbell is motionless, no work is done on the barbell. **Applying Concepts** *Did the weight lifter do work on the barbell to lift it over his head?*

Y ou are already familiar with the everyday meaning of work. Working at an after-school job, doing yard work at home, and completing your homework may all be common events in your life. In science, however, "work" means something very different.

Look at the weight lifter shown in Figure 1. He is exerting a large force in order to hold the heavy barbell over his head. You can tell from the look on his face that holding up the weight is hard work. However, a scientist would tell you that at this instant the weight lifter is actually doing no work on the nonmoving barbell. Read on to learn about the work that was done to lift the barbell overhead.

What Is Work?

Recall that an object begins moving only when an unbalanced force acts on it. In science, **work** is the product of force and distance. Work is done when a force acts on an object in the direction the object moves. For example, work is done by the weight lifter when he exerts an upward force to raise the barbell over his head.

Work Requires Motion Though it may seem surprising, the weight lifter in Figure 1 does no work on the barbell as he holds it over his head. Why is that? Because although force is applied to the barbell, the force does not cause the barbell to move. **For a force to do work on an object, some of the force must act in the same direction as the object moves. If there is no movement, no work is done.**

412 *Chapter 14*

Section Resources

Print
- *Reading and Study Workbook With Math Support,* Section 14.1 and **Math Skill:** Calculating Work and Power
- *Math Skills and Problem Solving Workbook,* Section 14.1
- *Transparencies,* Chapter Pretest and Section 14.1

Technology
- *Interactive Textbook,* Section 14.1
- *Presentation Pro CD-ROM,* Chapter Pretest and Section 14.1
- *Go Online,* NSTA SciLinks, Work

Force

Direction of motion

A Force and motion in same direction

This force does no work.

This force does work.

Force

Direction of motion

B Part of force in direction of motion

Force

Direction of motion

C Lifting force not in direction of motion

Work Depends on Direction The amount of work done on an object, if any, depends on the direction of the force and the direction of the movement. For example, though you would never do this, imagine pulling a suitcase as shown in Figure 2A. Note that all of the force acts in the same direction as the suitcase moves—all of the force does work on the suitcase.

A force does not have to act entirely in the direction of movement to do work. Look at the forces and direction of motion shown as the suitcase is pulled in Figure 2B. The force acts upward and to the right along the handle, whereas the suitcase moves only to the right along the ground. Figure 2B shows that there is a horizontal portion of the force acting in the direction of motion. Only the horizontal part of the applied force—the part in the direction of movement—does work.

👀 **Any part of a force that does not act in the direction of motion does no work on an object.** As shown in Figure 2C, the vertical lifting force does not act in the direction of motion. Thus, this vertical force does no work on the suitcase.

Calculating Work

Although the weight lifter in Figure 1 does no work while holding the barbell over his head, he did do work in lifting the barbell to the overhead position. The work done is calculated by multiplying the constant force acting in the direction of motion by the distance that the object moves.

Work

$$\text{Work} = \text{Force} \times \text{Distance}$$

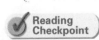 *How do you calculate work?*

Figure 2 The work done on an object depends on the size of the force acting in the direction of motion and on the distance the object moves. **A** When force and motion are in the same direction, the work done is maximized. **B** Only the horizontal part of the force does work to move the suitcase to the right. **C** Because the lifting force is not in the direction the suitcase moves, the force does no work on the suitcase.

Go Online

NSTA *SciLINKS*

For: Links on work
Visit: www.SciLinks.org
Web Code: ccn-2141

Work, Power, and Machines **413**

Some students may think that any force acting on an object multiplied by the distance the object moves is work. To overcome this misconception, have a student walk across the room carrying a book. Explain that the force used to hold the book up does no work on the book because that force is not in the direction that the book moves. **Kinesthetic**

Calculating Work

Teacher ▶ Demo

Work L2

Purpose Students observe how work requires movement of an object in the direction of the applied force.

Materials a rigid object

Procedure Move the object in different ways as students describe the force acting on the object, the motion of the object, and whether work is done on the object. First, drop the object. *(The force is gravity acting downward; force and motion are in the same direction, so work is done.)* Next, press the object against the wall. *(Force is from the person pushing the object toward the wall; there is no motion; there is no work because there is no movement in the direction of force.)* Finally, push the object across a desk. *(Forces are the person pushing horizontally and gravity acting downward; there is only horizontal motion; there is work only in the horizontal direction.)*

Expected Outcome Students should see how the relationship between force and displacement determines whether work is done. **Visual, Logical**

Go Online

NSTA *SciLINKS*

Download a worksheet on work for students to complete, and find additional teacher support from NSTA SciLinks.

Answer to . . .

Figure 1 *Yes*

 Work = Force × Distance

Work, Power, and Machines **413**

Build Reading Literacy L1

Think Aloud Refer to page 410D in this chapter, which provides guidelines for thinking aloud.

Set the example for this strategy by verbalizing your own thought processes while reading aloud Units of Work. Encourage student volunteers to read Using the Work Formula while quietly verbalizing their thought processes. Then, have a class discussion about the advantages students found in staying focused on a logical thought process when reading in this manner.
Intrapersonal, Auditory

What Is Power?

Address Misconceptions L2

Some students may think that power is the same as force. To overcome this misconception, have students think about the time needed for a person to push a heavy box across the room. Now imagine the person pushing the box across the floor in half the time. Point out that although this requires increased force and power, the two quantities are not the same. Increased force (in newtons) is needed to move the box at a faster rate, and more power (in watts) is required because the increased force was applied over a shorter period of time.
Logical

Build Science Skills L2

Applying Concepts Review with students the equations for both work and power. Ask, **Since *P* 5 *W*/*t* 5 *Fd*/*t* and since *d*/*t* 5 *v*, would *P* 5 *Fv*?** *(Yes, P = W/t = Fd/t = Fv.)* Ask, **If you use a snow blower and know the velocity of the expelled snow (in m/s) and the power output of the snow blower (in watts), can you calculate the force applied to the snow (in newtons?)** *(Yes, if you assume all the power is used for propelling the snow. If you know two of the three variables, P, F, or v, you can calculate the third. It is important, though, to use the correct units.)*
Logical

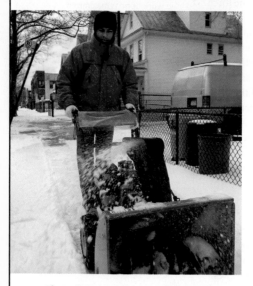

Figure 3 Power is the rate of doing work. Because the snow blower can remove more snow in less time, it requires more power than hand shoveling does.
Comparing and Contrasting *What is the source of power in each of the above photos?*

Units of Work When using SI units in the work formula, the force is in newtons, and distance is in meters. The product of force and distance results in the units of newton-meters, also known as joules. The **joule** (J) is the SI unit of work. When a force of 1 newton moves an object 1 meter in the direction of the force, 1 joule of work is done. The joule is named after James Prescott Joule (1818–1889), a British scientist famous for researching the relationship between work and heat.

Using the Work Formula It is easy to calculate the work done by a weight lifter who lifts a 1600-newton barbell over his head. Assume that the barbell is lifted to a height of 2.0 meters. To use the work formula, simply substitute the correct values into the formula and multiply.

$$\text{Work} = \text{Force} \times \text{Distance}$$

$$\text{Work} = 1600 \text{ N} \times 2.0 \text{ m}$$

$$\text{Work} = 3200 \text{ N·m} = 3200 \text{ J}$$

What Is Power?

Often people are not just concerned about getting work done. They want it done fast, and that requires power. Power, like work, has a precise meaning in science.

Power is the rate of doing work. ⏺ **Doing work at a faster rate requires more power. To increase power, you can increase the amount of work done in a given time, or you can do a given amount of work in less time.**

Figure 3 shows an example of what a difference in power means when performing a task such as snow removal. Work is required to move snow from one location to another. As you can see in Figure 3, a person using a shovel and a person using a snow blower can both do the work needed to remove the snow. Clearly, the snow blower can do the job much faster. The fact that the snow blower can do more work in less time means that it has more power.

You may have noticed that the size of the engine used by a machine is often an indication of its power. For example, compare the snow blower's small engine with the engine used by a truck pushing a snowplow. The truck's powerful engine allows it to remove snow at a very fast rate.

Reading Checkpoint *How does doing work at a faster rate affect the power required?*

Facts and Figures

Cassini-Huygens Spacecraft In 1997, NASA launched the Cassini-Huygens spacecraft on a mission to investigate Saturn, Venus, and Jupiter. The craft was loaded with instruments and cameras to help it complete this task. The Cassini spacecraft is the largest ever built and weighs nearly 5650 kg (6 tons). During launch, over 55 million joules of work were required for each kilometer that the spacecraft was lifted.

Calculating Power

You can calculate power by dividing the amount of work done by the time needed to do the work.

> **Power**
> $$\text{Power} = \frac{\text{Work}}{\text{Time}}$$

When using SI units in the power formula, work is in joules (J) and time is in seconds (s). The SI unit of power is the **watt** (W), which is equal to one joule per second. Thus, a 40-watt light bulb requires 40 joules each second that it is lit. This amount of power is also approximately equal to lifting your textbook a height of one meter in half a second.

  Math Skills

Calculating Power

You exert a vertical force of 72 newtons to lift a box to a height of 1.0 meter in a time of 2.0 seconds. How much power is used to lift the box?

1 Read and Understand

What information are you given?

> Force = 72 N   Distance = 1.0 m
>
> Time = 2.0 s

2 Plan and Solve

What formula contains the given quantities and the unknown?

$$\text{Power} = \frac{\text{Work}}{\text{Time}} = \frac{\text{Force} \times \text{Distance}}{\text{Time}}$$

Replace each variable with its known value and solve.

$$\text{Power} = \frac{72\ \text{N} \times 1.0\ \text{m}}{2.0\ \text{s}} = 36\ \text{J/s} = 36\ \text{W}$$

3 Look Back and Check

Is your answer reasonable?

36 watts is not a lot of power, which seems reasonable considering the box was lifted slowly, through a height of only 1 meter.

Math Practice

1. Your family is moving to a new apartment. While lifting a box 1.5 m straight up to put it on a truck, you exert an upward force of 200 N for 1.0 s. How much power is required to do this?

2. You lift a book from the floor to a bookshelf 1.0 m above the ground. How much power is used if the upward force is 15.0 N and you do the work in 2.0 s?

3. You apply a horizontal force of 10.0 N to pull a wheeled suitcase at a constant speed of 0.5 m/s across flat ground. How much power is used? (*Hint:* The suitcase moves 0.5 m/s. Consider how much work the force does each second and how work is related to power.)

 Math Practice

Solutions

1. Work = Force × Distance
= 200 N × 1.5 m = 300 J
Power = Work/Time
= 300 J/1.0 s = 300 W
2. Work = Force × Distance
= 15.0 N × 1.0 m = 15 J
Power = Work/Time
= 15 J/2.0 s = 7.5 W
3. Work = Force × Distance
= 10.0 N × 0.5 m = 5 J
Power = Work/Time
= 5 J/1.0 s = 5 W
Logical

For Extra Help   **L1**

Help students to learn 1 W = 1 J/s by relating the units to the variables in the power formula: Power = Work/Time. Have them write these units in their journals along with the work equation.
Logical, Visual

Direct students to the **Math Skills** in the **Skills and Reference Handbook** at the end of the student text for additional help.

Additional Problems

1. A student rows a boat across a still pond, doing 3600 J of work on the oars in 60 seconds. What is the student's power output? (Power = Work/Time = 3600 J/60 s = 60 J/s = 60 W)
2. A truck pulls a trailer at a constant velocity for 100 m while exerting a force of 480 newtons for 1 minute (60 seconds). Calculate the power. (*Hint:* First calculate the work.) (Work = Force × Distance = 480 N × 100 m = 48,000 J; Power = Work/Time = 48,000 J/60 s = 800 J/s = 800 W)
Logical

> **Answer to . . .**
>
> **Figure 3** *The woman provides the power needed to shovel the snow, whereas the gas-powered engine provides the power needed by the snow blower.*
>
> 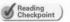 Reading Checkpoint   *Doing work at a faster rate requires more power.*

James Watt and Horsepower

Use Visuals L1

Figure 4 Ask students how the power that could be delivered by the 4 hp engine and the 4 work horses compares. *(Both can do roughly the same amount of work. See FYI note below.)* Then, remind them that 1 hp = 746 watts. Ask them to convert the 4 hp to power in watts. *(4 hp × 746 W/hp = 2984 W)* Then, relate the power of 1 hp to moving a stack of CDs. Because 1 newton is approximately equal to the weight of one compact disc in its case, 1 hp is enough power to move about 2,500 compact discs 1 meter in 1 second. **Visual**

FYI

Watt's horsepower value was based upon strong dray horses, which are about 50% more powerful than an average horse.

3 ASSESS

Evaluate Understanding L2

Have student work in pairs to write out two questions and answers about work and power. Then, ask students to form groups of four and quiz one another. Randomly select students to present their question and answer to the rest of the class.

Reteach L1

Use Figure 2 and its caption to summarize the key concepts related to work. Discuss how the force component in the direction of the motion and the force component not in the direction of the motion affect the work done.

Solutions
7. Work = Force × Distance
= 25 N × 1.5 m = 38 J
8. Power = Work/Time
= 100 J/2 s = 50 W

Interactive Textbook If your class subscribes to the Interactive Textbook, use it to review key concepts in Section 14.1.

Figure 4 Although the horse-drawn plow and the gasoline-powered engine get their power from different sources, both are capable of doing work at a rate of about four horsepower.

James Watt and Horsepower

Besides the watt, another common unit of power is the horsepower. One **horsepower** (hp) is equal to about 746 watts. The horsepower was first defined by Scottish scientist James Watt (1736–1819). Watt was looking for a way to compare the power outputs of steam engines he had designed. Horses were a logical choice for comparison as they were the most commonly used source of power in the 1700s. Watt did not want to exaggerate the power of his steam engines. Thus, after many experiments, he defined the horsepower based on the power output of a very strong horse. Figure 4 shows a comparison of two equivalent power sources.

Section 14.1 Assessment

Reviewing Concepts
1. What conditions must exist in order for a force to do work on an object?
2. What formula relates work and power?
3. How much work is done when a vertical force acts on an object moving horizontally?

Critical Thinking
4. **Applying Concepts** A desk exerts an upward force to support a computer resting on it. Does this force do work? Explain.
5. **Predicting** Two cars have the same weight, but one of the cars has an engine that provides twice the power of the other. Which car can make it to the top of a mountain pass first? Which car does more work to reach the pass?

6. **Comparing and Contrasting** You carry two heavy bags of groceries upstairs to your kitchen. Will you do more work on the bags if you carry them up one at a time? Explain.

Math Practice
7. How much work does a 25-newton force do to lift a potted plant from the floor to a shelf 1.5 meters high?
8. You lift a large bag of flour from the floor to a 1-meter-high counter, doing 100 joules of work in 2 seconds. How much power do you use to lift the bag of flour?

Section 14.1 Assessment

1. Some of the force must act in the same direction as the object moves.
2. Power = Work/Time
3. No work is done.
4. The supporting force does no work because the object it acts on (the computer) does not move.

5. The car with the more powerful engine will reach the top first. Both cars do the same amount of work to reach the top.
6. Carrying one bag at a time uses only half the force, but requires that the force be applied through twice the distance. The work done is the same in both cases.

14.2 Work and Machines

Reading Focus

Key Concepts

- How do machines make work easier?

- How are work input and work output related for a machine?

Vocabulary

- machine
- input distance
- output force
- work output
- input force
- work input
- output distance

Reading Strategy

Summarizing Copy the table shown. As you read, complete the table for each machine. After you read, write a sentence summarizing the idea that your table illustrates.

Machine	Increases or Decreases Input Force	Increases or Decreases Input Distance
Tire jack	a. ___?___	b. ___?___
Lug wrench	c. ___?___	d. ___?___
Rowing oar	e. ___?___	f. ___?___
Summary:	g. _____?_____	

Two good friends, each one wearing her most glamorous dress, are on their way to a school dance when disaster strikes. Their car gets a flat tire! To fix it, they'll have to remove the flat tire and put on the spare tire. But won't loosening the lug nuts and lifting the car off of the ground require more force than they can exert just using their hands? How can they change the tire?

As shown in Figure 5, machines come to the rescue. Fortunately, all cars come with the tools designed to help you change a tire. With the help of a lug wrench and jack, which are actually simple machines, they'll have no problem changing the tire. Read on to learn how a car jack and a lug wrench alter forces to make changing a tire a relatively easy task.

Machines Do Work

A **machine** is a device that changes a force. When using the jack, you apply a force to the jack handle. The jack changes this force and applies a much stronger force to lift the car. Because the jack increases the force you exert, it is a machine. Machines make work easier to do. They change the size of a force needed, the direction of a force, or the distance over which a force acts. Both the lug wrench and the jack allow a single person to apply enough force to accomplish tasks they would normally not be able to.

Figure 5 All cars come equipped with simple machines designed to make changing a tire a fairly easy task.
Inferring *Does the jack used to lift the car increase or decrease the force applied to it?*

Work, Power, and Machines **417**

Section Resources

Print
- *Reading and Study Workbook With Math Support,* Section 14.2
- *Transparencies,* Section 14.2

Technology
- *Interactive Textbook,* Section 14.2
- *Presentation Pro CD-ROM,* Section 14.2
- *Go Online,* NSTA SciLinks, Machines

---

1 FOCUS

Objectives

14.2.1 Describe what a machine is and how it makes work easier to do.

14.2.2 Relate the work input to a machine to the work output of the machine.

Reading Focus

Build Vocabulary L2

Paraphrase Paraphrasing can help students grasp the meaning of vocabulary terms. Encourage students to make a table with three columns. Ask them to write *machine, input distance, output force, work output, input force, work input,* and *output distance* in the first column; paraphrased meanings in the second column, and textbook definitions in the third column. Have students use the paraphrased terms to gain a better understanding of the text's definitions.

Reading Strategy L2

a. Decreases b. Increases c. Decreases d. Increases e. Increases f. Decreases g. Machines that decrease the applied force increase the distance the force is applied through and vice versa.

2 INSTRUCT

Machines Do Work

Address Misconceptions L2

Some students may think that all objects have a certain amount of force. For example, they may think that a moving object has force that allows it to move, and when the force runs out, the object stops moving. Challenge this misconception by relating it to machines. A machine needs an input force in order to perform work. The force is not already within the machine or a property of the machine.
Logical

Answer to . . .

Figure 5 *The jack increases the force applied to it.*

Build Reading Literacy L1

Relate Cause and Effect Refer to page **260D** in **Chapter 9**, which provides the guidelines for relating cause and effect.

Use Figure 6 to help students identify the cause-and-effect relationship between work done on and work done by a machine. *(The overall cause is the input work, and the overall effect is the output work.)* Show them also that the output force exerted (the force to lift the car) is greater than the input force, while the output distance (the distance the car is lifted) is less than the input distance. To be sure students understand the concepts, ask, **What is the input force in this example?** *(The force applied to the jack handle)* **What is the input distance?** *(The distance the jack handle moves through)* **What is the output force in this example?** *(It is the force exerted on the car.)* **What is the output distance?** *(It is the distance the car was lifted.)* **Logical, Visual**

Download a worksheet on machines for students to complete, and find additional teacher support from NSTA SciLinks.

Figure 6 Turning the jack handle allows the man to raise the car. The distance moved by the handle is much greater than the distance the car is raised.
Comparing and Contrasting *How does the force exerted on the jack handle compare with the force exerted by the jack on the car?*

Increasing Force

How is a machine able to increase a force? Study what is happening in Figure 6. Each complete rotation of the jack handle applies a small force over a large distance. However, each rotation lifts the car only a very short distance. Thus a small force exerted over a large distance becomes a large force exerted over a short distance.

Raising a car using a machine such as a jack is similar to moving a stack of books by picking them up one at a time. Lifting the books one at a time takes less force. But there's a tradeoff—the total distance traveled is much greater. If a machine increases the distance over which you exert a force, then it decreases the amount of force you need to exert.

Increasing Distance

Some machines decrease the applied force, but increase the distance over which the force is exerted. Look at the rowing shell in Figure 7. Each oar operates as a machine that pushes the boat through the water. The arrows show how pulling the end of each oar through a small distance moves the end of the oar in the water through a large distance. Increasing the distance the oar travels through the water helps you go fast. But again, there is a tradeoff. The increased travel of the oar through the water requires you to exert a greater force. A machine that decreases the distance through which you exert a force increases the amount of force required.

Changing Direction

Some machines change the direction of the applied force. An example is shown in Figure 7. Pulling back on the handle of the oar causes its other end to move in the opposite direction. So not only can machines change the amount of force and the distance the force acts through, but they can also change the direction of the force.

 Reading Checkpoint *Give an example of a machine that changes the direction of an applied force.*

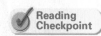

For: Links on machines
Visit: www.SciLinks.org
Web Code: ccn-2142

418 *Chapter 14*

Customize for Inclusion Students

Hearing Impaired

Reinforce the lesson's content by providing a variety of visual examples. Be sure to spend time on all of the visual examples provided in the text. In addition, you may wish to provide other illustrations of machines that increase force, increase distance, or change direction. Label the illustrations so that students make the connection between the concept in the text and the visual example.

Work Input and Work Output

To row the boat in Figure 7, the rower pulls back on each oar handle and the other end of each oar pushes against the water. Work is done on the oars (the machine) by pulling on them, and the oars do work on the water to move the boat. Recall from Chapter 12 that friction acts against the motion of any object. 🔵 **Because of friction, the work done by a machine is always less than the work done on the machine.**

Work Input to a Machine The force you exert on a machine is called the **input force.** The distance the input force acts through is known as the **input distance.** The work done by the input force acting through the input distance is called the **work input.** The work input equals the input force multiplied by the input distance.

Each oar in Figure 7 is a machine. For the oar, the input force is the force exerted on the handle and the input distance is the distance the handle moves. The work input is the work you do to move the handle. You can increase the work input by increasing the input distance, increasing the input force, or increasing both at once.

Figure 7 The oars of the boat act as machines that increase the distance over which the force acts. **Predicting** *If the oar is pushed farther away from the boat, how will the force needed to pull the oar through the water change?*

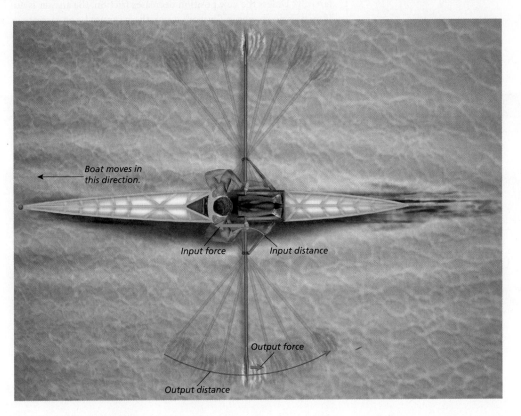

Boat moves in this direction.

Input force   Input distance

Output force

Output distance

Work, Power, and Machines **419**

Figure 7 Have students look carefully at this figure to understand the relationships between input force, output force, distance, and mechanical advantage. Ask, **What is the input distance?** *(The input distance is the length of the path along which the oar handle moves. The path forms an arc.)* **How does the input distance compare to the output distance?** *(It is less.)* **What does this tell you about the mechanical advantage of the rowing setup?** *(The IMA is less than 1.)* **Visual, Logical**

Build Science Skills   L2

Calculating Using Figure 7, explain that, ignoring friction, if the rower uses 800 N of force to pull an oar's handle a distance of 0.5 m and the distance that the oar moves through in the water is 2 m, the force pushing against the water would be 200 N. Ask students to verify these values with calculations. *(Ignoring friction, $W_{in} = W_{out}$; $F_{in}d_{in} = F_{out}d_{out}$; 800 N $\times$ 0.5 m = 200 N $\times$ 2 m)* **Visual, Logical**

Facts and Figures

Perpetual Motion Machines Because of friction, building a machine that produces more energy than it uses is impossible. Nevertheless, each year, the United States Patent and Trademark Office receives applications for alleged perpetual motion machines. The office responds by requesting a working model. Three categories of perpetual motion machines are (1) those that create energy, (2) those that violate the rule that states, "the work done by a machine is always less than the work done on the machine," and (3) those that can run forever without requiring additional energy.

Answer to . . .

Figure 6 *The force exerted on the jack handle is much less than the force exerted by the jack on the car.*

Figure 7 *The required input force would increase.*

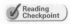 **Reading Checkpoint** *A jack changes the direction of the applied force because the input force is circular and the output force is vertical. Other examples include a crowbar, a seesaw, and a pulley.*

3 ASSESS

Evaluate Understanding `L2`

Show students a pair of scissors or other simple mechanical device and ask them to identify the input force, distance, and work and the output force, distance, and work.

Reteach `L1`

Use Figure 7 to emphasize the relationship between input force, distance, and work and output force, distance, and work. Remind students that output work is always less than input work due to friction.

Connecting ⊂ Concepts

The end of the oar in the water applies an action force to the water. According to Newton's third law, the water pushes back on the oar with an opposite reaction force. This reaction force propels the boat through the water. Fluid friction acts on the oar as it moves through the water, slowing its motion.

Interactive Textbook If your class subscribes to the Interactive Textbook, use it to review key concepts in Section 14.2.

Answer to . . .

Figure 8 *The movement of the water indicates that a force is acting on it.*

Figure 9 *The different areas are designed to accommodate different sized nuts and allow differing amounts of force to be used to crack a nut.*

Figure 8 The output work of the oars results from the oars pushing against the water so that the water pushes back against the oars.
Observing *What evidence can you see in the photo that a force is acting on the water?*

Work Output of a Machine The force that is exerted by a machine is called the **output force**. The distance the output force is exerted through is the **output distance**. The **work output** of a machine is the output force multiplied by the output distance. Look back at Figure 7 one more time to see the output force, distance, and work for the oars. How are the input work and output work related? Although nearly equal, the output work is less than the input work because of friction. All machines use some amount of input work to overcome friction.

As the rowers pull on one end of each oar, the other ends push against the water as shown in Figure 8. The force of the oar on the water causes an equal and opposite reaction force to be exerted by the water on the oar. It is this reaction force that propels the boat through the water.

Can you increase the work output of the oar by positioning it differently? Unless the new position decreases friction, the answer is no. If there is no change in the work input, there cannot be an increase in the work output. The only way to increase the work output is to increase the amount of work you put into the machine. You cannot get more work out of a machine than you put into it!

Section 14.2 Assessment

Reviewing Concepts

1. 🔵 How can using a machine make a task easier to perform?
2. 🔵 How does the work done on a machine compare to the work done by a machine?
3. What changes can a machine make to a force?
4. A machine produces a larger force than you exert to operate the machine. How does the input distance of the machine compare to its output distance?
5. You do 200 J of work pulling the oars of a rowboat. What can you say about the amount of work the oars do to move the boat? Explain.
6. How can you increase the work output of a machine?

Critical Thinking

7. **Inferring** When you swing a baseball bat, how does the output distance the end of the bat moves compare with the distance you move your hands through? Why might this difference be useful?
8. **Applying Concepts** An advertisement for a new type of wrench claims it reduces the force needed to tighten a bolt. If the advertisement is correct, what do you know to be true about the input distance?

Connecting ⊂ Concepts

Forces Recall what you learned about forces in Chapter 12. Explain how friction and Newton's third law of motion influence the movement of the oar as it is pulled by the rower shown in Figure 7.

Section 14.2   Assessment

1. Machines make work easier to do by altering the size of force needed, the direction of a force, or the distance over which a force acts.
2. Because of friction, the work done by a machine is always less than the work done on the machine.
3. Size of force; direction of force; distance through which a force acts

4. Because the output force is greater than the input force, the input distance must be greater than the output distance.
5. Less than 200 J of work are done to move the boat because some of the input work is lost to friction forces.
6. Increase the work input to the machine, or reduce any friction that limits work output.

7. The output distance is much greater than the input distance. The high speed of the bat end helps the batted ball to also acquire a high speed (and travel far).
8. If the input force is decreased, then the input distance must be increased.

14.3 Mechanical Advantage and Efficiency

Reading Focus

Key Concepts
- How does the actual mechanical advantage of a machine compare to its ideal mechanical advantage?
- Why is the efficiency of a machine always less than 100 percent?

Vocabulary
- mechanical advantage
- actual mechanical advantage
- ideal mechanical advantage
- efficiency

Reading Strategy
Building Vocabulary Copy the table below. Then as you read the section, write a definition for each vocabulary term in your own words.

Vocabulary	Definition	
Mechanical advantage	a.	?
b. ?	c.	?
d. ?	e.	?
f. ?	g.	?

T ry cracking a walnut by squeezing it in your hand. You'll find that you can't apply enough force to break the shell. Next try cracking the shell using a nutcracker. A nutcracker, which is a type of machine, is shown in Figure 9. If you squeeze the nutcracker near its pivot end, you still won't be able to crack the nut. When you squeeze the ends of the handles, however, a fairly small force cracks the shell apart. In this section you'll learn why a machine like the nutcracker is so sensitive to the location of the input force.

Mechanical Advantage

The relation of input force used to operate a machine and the output force exerted by the machine depends on the type of machine and how it is used. Thus the location of the nut in the nutcracker affects the force the nutcracker is able to exert.

The **mechanical advantage** of a machine is the number of times that the machine increases an input force. Suppose a nut is in the nutcracker at position A in Figure 9. In this position the nutcracker exerts a force on the nut about seven times greater than the force you exert on the nutcracker. In position A the nutcracker's mechanical advantage is about 7. However, if the nut is moved to position B, the mechanical advantage decreases to about 3.

Figure 9 A nutcracker is a machine capable of converting the input force applied to it into a larger force capable of cracking a nut. Because it increases force, the nutcracker has a mechanical advantage greater than 1.
Inferring *What might be the reason that the nutcracker has two different areas (A and B) to use for nut cracking?*

Work, Power, and Machines **421**

Section Resources

Print
- *Reading and Study Workbook With Math Support,* Section 14.3
- *Math Skills and Problem Solving Workbook,* Section 14.3
- *Transparencies,* Section 14.3

Technology
- *Interactive Textbook,* Section 14.3
- *Presentation Pro CD-ROM,* Section 14.3
- *Go Online,* NSTA SciLinks, Mechanical advantage; PHSchool.com, Data sharing

1 FOCUS

Objectives
14.3.1 Compare a machine's actual mechanical advantage to its ideal mechanical advantage.

14.3.2 Calculate the ideal and actual mechanical advantages of various machines.

14.3.3 Explain why the efficiency of a machine is always less than 100%.

14.3.4 Calculate a machine's efficiency.

Reading Focus

Build Vocabulary   L2
Vocabulary Knowledge Rating Chart Have students make a four-column chart with the headings Term, Can Define/Use It, Have Heard/Seen It, and Don't Know. Have them put vocabulary terms in the first column, rating their knowledge of each term by putting a checkmark in one of the other columns. Ask students what they expect this section will be about based on their understanding of the terms. Have them check those expectations as they read. Ask students to create another chart after they have read the section.

Reading Strategy
a. The number of times a machine increases force **b.** Actual mechanical advantage **c.** Ratio of output force to input force **d.** Ideal mechanical advantage **e.** The mechanical advantage of a machine if there were no friction **f.** Efficiency **g.** Percentage of work input that becomes work output

2 INSTRUCT

Mechanical Advantage

Use Visuals   L1
Figure 9 Draw a sketch of the nutcracker on the board and ask students where the input force and the output force are for each position. Label the input and output arms for each position and return to the diagram when teaching ideal mechanical advantage.
Visual, Logical

Build Reading Literacy L1

Active Comprehension Refer to page 498D in **Chapter 17**, which provides the guidelines for active comprehension.

Ask a student volunteer to read aloud the paragraphs at the top of pages 422 and 423 about actual and ideal mechanical advantage. Then, ask the class, **What more would you like to know about mechanical advantage?** Write students' questions on the board. Have students consider the questions as they finish reading. Allow time for discussion.
Verbal, Intrapersonal

Download a worksheet on mechanical advantage for students to complete, and find additional teacher support from NSTA SciLinks.

DK SCIENCE and History

Innovations of the Industrial Revolution L2

Have students read about the innovations of the Industrial Revolution. Then, ask them what general events they remember from history, social studies, literature, or other classes that they would add to the time line. Write these events on the board. Suggestions could be events such as the Declaration of Independence in 1776, the beginning of the U.S. Civil War in 1861, and the opening of the Panama Canal in 1914. Ask students how all events in the time line affected both science and society, including those you have added. Discuss any other scientific innovations, inventions, or discoveries that could be added to the time line.
Verbal

Writing in Science

Explanations will vary depending on which invention is chosen, but all students should correctly identify the simple machines involved in the invention's operation. Explanations should describe the proper sequence of events in the invention's motion and may mention input and output forces and distances.
Verbal, Logical

For: Links on mechanical advantage
Visit: www.SciLinks.org
Web Code: ccn-2143

Actual Mechanical Advantage The mechanical advantage determined by measuring the actual forces acting on a machine is the actual mechanical advantage. The **actual mechanical advantage** (AMA) equals the ratio of the output force to the input force.

Actual Mechanical Advantage

$$\text{Actual mechanical advantage} = \frac{\text{Output force}}{\text{Input force}}$$

A loading ramp is a machine used to move heavy items into a truck. For instance, a long inclined ramp decreases the input force needed to lift a refrigerator into a truck. The mechanical advantage of a ramp with a rough surface is less than that of a similar smooth ramp because a greater force is needed to overcome friction.

DK SCIENCE and History

Innovations of the Industrial Revolution

From the 1700s to the early 1900s, a stream of new machines and other inventions changed patterns of work and commerce forever.

Chimney

Boiler

Seed-free cotton collects here.

Threads are interwoven here.

Waste material

COTTON GIN

POWER LOOM

STEPHENSON'S ROCKET

1765 James Watt modifies the existing Newcomen steam engine to create a more efficient machine.

1793 Eli Whitney's cotton gin efficiently and quickly separates harvested cotton fiber from seeds. The process makes cotton manufacturing easier, and cotton farming profitable.

1807 The *Clermont*, Robert Fulton's river steamboat, makes its maiden voyage on the Hudson River.

1813 Francis Lowell and Paul Moody create the first power loom in America, based on an English design.

1829 Stephenson's Rocket, an early steam locomotive, wins a competition for locomotive speed in England.

| 1750 | 1775 | 1800 | 1825 |

422 Chapter 14

Customize for English Language Learners

Use Personal Experience
ELL students can benefit by relating examples from their lives to material presented in the text. Encourage students to name machines they have used that increased mechanical advantage. You may review the examples of the nutcracker and the loading ramp. Students may also sketch an illustration or find a magazine photo of machines that increase mechanical advantage.

Ideal Mechanical Advantage What can be done to increase the actual mechanical advantage of a ramp? One way is to reduce the friction of the ramp. In fact, if any machine were frictionless, its mechanical advantage would be the maximum possible value. The **ideal mechanical advantage** (IMA) of a machine is the mechanical advantage in the absence of friction. ▶ **Because friction is always present, the actual mechanical advantage of a machine is always less than the ideal mechanical advantage.** Because friction reduces mechanical advantage, engineers often design machines that use low-friction materials and lubricants.

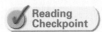
Reading Checkpoint *How does increased friction affect the actual mechanical advantage of a machine?*

Writing in Science

Explanatory Paragraph
Study the photo of one of the inventions shown in the time line. Write a paragraph in which you identify the simple machines used in the device and explain how these machines are used in the operation of the device.

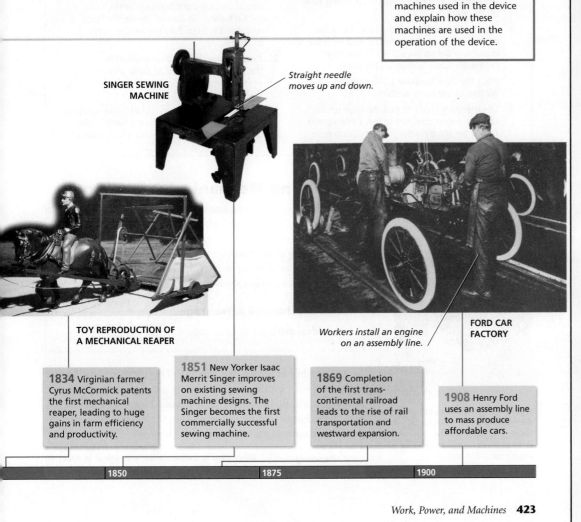

SINGER SEWING MACHINE

Straight needle moves up and down.

TOY REPRODUCTION OF A MECHANICAL REAPER

Workers install an engine on an assembly line.

FORD CAR FACTORY

1834 Virginian farmer Cyrus McCormick patents the first mechanical reaper, leading to huge gains in farm efficiency and productivity.

1851 New Yorker Isaac Merrit Singer improves on existing sewing machine designs. The Singer becomes the first commercially successful sewing machine.

1869 Completion of the first transcontinental railroad leads to the rise of rail transportation and westward expansion.

1908 Henry Ford uses an assembly line to mass produce affordable cars.

1850   1875   1900

Work, Power, and Machines **423**

Teacher Demo

Mechanical Advantage **L2**

Purpose Students learn about the concept of mechanical advantage.

Materials 1 pulley, 10-N spring scale, 500-g mass, string

Procedure Configure the pulley as shown in Figure 19A, p. 432. Attach the 500-g mass to one end of the string, and attach the spring scale to the other end of the string. Have students watch the scale as you use it to lift the mass. Show them that the force required equals the weight of the 500-g mass. Next, configure the pulley as shown in Figure 19B, p. 432. Demonstrate that the force needed to lift the 500-g mass is equal to half the weight of the mass. Explain to students that half the force was required because the mass is supported by two lengths of the string.

Expected Outcome Students should observe that the mechanical advantage using a fixed pulley is 1, and the mechanical advantage of a moveable pulley is 2.
Visual, Group

Build Science Skills **L2**

Designing Experiments Encourage students to work in teams to design and conduct experiments to test mechanical advantage. Suggest that they begin by brainstorming about possible simple machines they can test. For example, they could test a pair of pliers. Next, students should write a hypothesis and a plan for their experiment. All student plans should be approved by the teacher before they can be performed. Have students present their findings to the class.
Logical, Visual

Answer to . . .

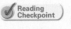
Reading Checkpoint *Increased friction would decrease a machine's actual mechanical advantage.*

Calculating Mechanical Advantage

Using Friction to Change Mechanical Advantage L2

Objective
After completing this activity, students will be able to
- explain how friction affects mechanical advantage and the force needed to perform work.

Address Misconceptions

Students may not think of friction as a force. Measuring a force that depends on friction can help to dispel this misconception.

Skills Focus Measuring, Drawing Conclusions

Prep Time 15 minutes

Advance Prep Provide smooth, splinter-free boards. Ask students to provide sneakers, slippers, and other footwear that vary in the friction they provide against a floor. All the shoes should be similar in weight.

Class Time 15 minutes

Safety Make certain that boards are free of rough or splintering edges.

Teaching Tips
- The spring scale must be pulled parallel to the board, as shown in the photo.

Ask, **How does friction affect the input force needed to accomplish a task?** *(Friction increases the force needed.)* **What work is accomplished by the force needed to overcome friction?** *(The additional force results in heating.)*

Expected Outcome Shoes with smoother soles will produce less friction, require less force, and provide more mechanical advantage.

Analyze and Conclude
1. Check students' answers.
2. Shoes with smoother soles that produce less friction will require less force and provide more mechanical advantage.
3. The shoe with the sole that provides the most traction required the most force. The additional force resulted in heating of the shoe and the ramp.

Visual, Logical, Group

Using Friction to Change Mechanical Advantage

Materials
6 books, board, 3 different kinds of shoes, 1-kilogram mass, spring scale

Procedure
1. Create a stack of five books. Make a ramp by leaning the end of a board against the top of the stack. Place a sixth book at the bottom of the ramp to keep the board from sliding down off the stack of books.
2. Attach the spring scale to a shoe. Place the mass in the shoe. Suspend the shoe with the mass from the spring scale. Observe and record the force reading on the scale.
3. Place the shoe containing the mass on the bottom of the ramp as shown.
4. Use the spring scale to pull the shoe up the ramp at a slow constant speed. Observe and record the force reading on the spring scale.
5. **Predicting** Record your prediction of the force needed to pull the mass up the ramp in each of the other shoes. Investigate your predictions by repeating Steps 2 through 4 for each shoe.

Analyze and Conclude
1. **Calculating** Determine and record the actual mechanical advantage of the ramp for each shoe. To do this, divide the force measured in Step 2 by the force measured in Step 4.
2. **Comparing** Which shoe resulted in the largest mechanical advantage? The smallest mechanical advantage? Explain these results.
3. **Drawing Conclusions** Which shoe required the most force to pull it up the ramp? What did this additional force accomplish? Explain.

Figure 10 The cable supporting the gondola forms an inclined plane, a type of machine. The inclined plane is used to move people up to the top of the mountain.

Calculating Mechanical Advantage

Ideal mechanical advantage is easier to measure than actual mechanical advantage because it depends only on the locations of the forces and the distances over which they act. To calculate the ideal mechanical advantage of any machine, divide the input distance by the output distance. Remember that the effects of friction are neglected when calculating ideal mechanical advantage.

Ideal Mechanical Advantage

$$\text{Ideal mechanical advantage} = \frac{\text{Input distance}}{\text{Output distance}}$$

The gondola in Figure 10 makes use of the inclined plane formed by its supporting cable to more easily move people uphill. The increased horizontal distance (input distance) is greater than the vertical gain in height (output distance). Thus the inclined cable gives the gondola a mechanical advantage greater than 1.

 What two quantities must you know in order to calculate ideal mechanical advantage?

Math Skills

Calculating IMA

A woman drives her car up onto wheel ramps to perform some repairs. If she drives a distance of 1.8 meters along the ramp to raise the car 0.3 meter, what is the ideal mechanical advantage (IMA) of the wheel ramps?

1 Read and Understand

What information are you given?

Input distance = 1.8 m

Output distance = 0.3 m

2 Plan and Solve

What unknown are you trying to calculate?

IMA = ?

What formula contains the given quantities and the unknown?

$$IMA = \frac{Input\ distance}{Output\ distance}$$

Replace each variable with its known value and solve.

$$IMA = \frac{1.8\ \cancel{m}}{0.3\ \cancel{m}} = 6$$

3 Look Back and Check

Is your answer reasonable?

The IMA must be greater than 1 because the input distance is greater than the output distance. The calculated IMA of 6 seems reasonable.

Math Practice

1. A student working in a grocery store after school pushes several grocery carts together along a ramp. The ramp is 3 meters long and rises 0.5 meter. What is the ideal mechanical advantage of the ramp?

2. A construction worker moves a crowbar through a distance of 0.50 m to lift a load 0.05 m off of the ground. What is the IMA of the crowbar?

3. The IMA of a simple machine is 2.5. If the output distance of the machine is 1.0 m, what is the input distance?

Efficiency

Because some of the work input to a machine is always used to overcome friction, the work output of a machine is always less than the work input. The percentage of the work input that becomes work output is the **efficiency** of a machine. **Because there is always some friction, the efficiency of any machine is always less than 100 percent.**

> **Efficiency**
>
> $$Efficiency = \frac{Work\ output}{Work\ input} \times 100\%$$

Facts and Figures

Building the Egyptian Pyramids The mystery of how the pyramids of Giza were constructed still causes disagreement among scientists. The largest pyramid, known as the Great Pyramid, was originally about 147 m high. It was constructed using stone blocks, each having a mass of about 2200 kg. A prominent theory suggests that the ancient Egyptians built huge earthen ramps for hauling the blocks. However, the Egyptians would have needed very long ramps in order to do this. For example, a mechanical advantage of 20 would require ramps almost 3 km long.

Math Practice

Solutions   **L2**

1. IMA = Input distance/Output distance; IMA = 3 m/0.5 m = 6
2. IMA = Input distance/Output distance; IMA = 0.50 m/0.05 m = 10
3. Input distance = (IMA)(Output distance); Input distance = (2.5)(1.0 m) = 2.5 m
Logical

For Extra Help **L1**

Write the formula for IMA on the board and review the algebra skills needed to solve the formula for any one of the three variables. **Logical**

Direct students to the **Math Skills** in the **Skills and Reference Handbook** at the end of the student text for additional help.

Additional Problems

1. If you exert 100 N on a jack to lift a 10,000 N car, what would be the jack's actual mechanical advantage? (AMA = Output force/Input force = 10,000 N/100 N = 100)
2. What is the ideal mechanical advantage of a 5-m-long ramp that rises 1 m off the ground at its end? (IMA = Input distance/Output distance = 5 m/1 m = 5)
Logical, Portfolio

Efficiency

Address Misconceptions **L2**

Some students may think that machines put out more work than people put in. In actuality, friction causes the work output of a machine to always be less than work input. Help students overcome this misconception by asking them to think about a hypothetical, perfect machine. Point out that even the slightest friction would decrease work output, and the efficiency would be less than 100%. Reinforce that although machines change forces, some of the input force is always lost to friction. **Logical**

> **Answer to . . .**
>
> 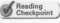 *You must know both the input distance and the output distance to calculate ideal mechanical advantage.*

Build Math Skills **L1**

Ratios and Proportions Reinforce the fact that no machine can be 100% efficient by having students relate that fact to the efficiency equation given on p. 425. Ask, **What is the maximum value the ratio (fraction) work output to work input can have?** *(The value must be < 1.)* **If a machine is 50% efficient, what is the value of the ratio (fraction) work output to work input?** $(\frac{1}{2})$
Logical

Direct students to the **Math Skills** in the **Skills and Reference Handbook** at the end of the student text for additional help.

3 ASSESS

Evaluate Understanding **L2**

Have students write a paragraph explaining ideal and actual mechanical advantage and how they are related to efficiency. Have students read their paragraph in class and ask the class to critique it.

Reteach **L1**

Bring in a nutcracker similar to the one in Figure 9 and use it to demonstrate the concept of mechanical advantage.

Solutions

8. Efficiency = (Work output/Work input) × 100% = (800 J/1000 J) × 100% = 80%

9. Efficiency = (Work output/Work input) × 100%, Work output = (Efficiency × Work input)/100% = (40% × 1000 J)/100% = 400 J

If your class subscribes to the Interactive Textbook, use it to review key concepts in Section 14.3.

Figure 11 The flow pattern of a smoke trail is analyzed by computers to determine the fluid friction forces (air resistance) acting on the vehicle. Engineers use these test data to optimize a vehicle's shape for maximum fuel efficiency.

Efficiency is usually expressed as a percentage. For example, if the efficiency of a machine is 75 percent, then you know that 75 percent of the work input becomes work output. If a machine requires 10.0 J of work input to operate, then the work output is 75% of 10.0 J.

$$\text{Work output} = \frac{\text{Work input} \times \text{Efficiency}}{100\%}$$

$$\text{Work output} = \frac{10.0 \text{ J} \times 75\%}{100\%} = 7.5 \text{ J}$$

Reducing friction increases the efficiency of a machine. Automobiles, for example, are designed so their wheels roll on bearings that contain many small steel rollers. Recall that rolling friction is less than sliding friction. Thus, the roller bearings reduce the friction of the rotating wheels. To further reduce the rolling friction, the roller bearings are also lubricated with grease.

As shown in Figure 11, the shapes of many cars are designed to minimize air resistance. The lower the air resistance, the more easily a car passes through the air. At highway speeds, more than 50% of the output work of the engine is used to overcome air resistance. Streamlining the car's body reduces the amount of work the engine must do to move the car at any speed.

Section 14.3 Assessment

Reviewing Concepts

1. Why is the actual mechanical advantage of a machine always less than its ideal mechanical advantage?

2. Why can no machine be 100% efficient?

3. You test a machine and find that it exerts a force of 5 N for each 1 N of force you exert operating the machine. What is the actual mechanical advantage of the machine?

4. How can two machines appear identical and yet not have the same actual mechanical advantage?

5. What information would you use to calculate the efficiency of a machine?

Critical Thinking

6. Making Generalizations When is the ideal mechanical advantage of a machine greater than 1?

7. Applying Concepts Suppose you are an inventor in 1900. You are constructing a bicycle of your own design. What could you do to ensure your bicycle efficiently changes the work input into forward motion?

Math Practice

8. You have just designed a machine that uses 1000 J of work from a motor for every 800 J of useful work the machine supplies. What is the efficiency of your machine?

9. If a machine has an efficiency of 40%, and you do 1000 J of work on the machine, what will be the work output of the machine?

Section 14.3 Assessment

1. The presence of friction results in the actual mechanical advantage of a machine always being less than its ideal mechanical advantage.

2. Because there is always some friction, the efficiency of any machine is always less than 100%.

3. Actual mechanical advantage = Output force/Input force = 5 N/1 N = 5

4. If the amount of friction acting on the machines differs, then the actual mechanical advantage of the machines will also differ.

5. Efficiency is calculated from work input and work output.

6. The IMA of a machine is greater than 1 whenever the output force is greater than the input force.

7. Answers will vary but should include the importance of keeping friction to a minimum.

14.4 Simple Machines

Reading Focus

Key Concepts

- What are the six types of simple machines?
- What determines the mechanical advantage of the six types of simple machines?

Vocabulary

- lever
- fulcrum
- input arm
- output arm
- wheel and axle
- inclined plane
- wedge
- screw
- pulley
- compound machine

Reading Strategy

Summarizing After reading the section on levers, complete the concept map below to organize what you know about first-class levers. Construct and complete similar concept maps for second- and third-class levers.

First-class lever

IMA range is **a. ?**

fulcrum is located **b. ?**

examples include **c. ?**

---

1 FOCUS

Objectives

14.4.1 Name, describe, and **give an example** of each of the six types of simple machines.

14.4.2 Describe how to determine the ideal mechanical advantage of each type of simple machine.

14.4.3 Define and **identify** compound machines.

Reading Focus

Build Vocabulary   L2

Concept Maps Have students expand on the concept maps used in the Reading Strategy by adding definitions for *fulcrum, IMA, input arm,* and *output arm* on the same page as the concept map.

Reading Strategy   L2

a. less than 1 to greater than 1
b. between the input force and the output force c. seesaw, scissors, tongs

2 INSTRUCT

Address Misconceptions   L2

Some students may think that the greater a machine's mechanical advantage, the faster the machine can complete the task. Remind students that other factors, such as friction, may influence whether the machine decreases the time required to complete a task. Also, reinforce that although the input force required by the machine may be decreased, there is a corresponding increase in the distance the force is applied over. Thus, decreased force does not necessarily mean the task can be completed more quickly.
Logical

What can you say about the workings of the strange contraption shown in Figure 12? Notice that a series of devices are arranged so that output of one device acts as the input of the next.

Many mechanical devices are combinations of two or more of the six different simple machines. **The six types of simple machines are the lever, the wheel and axle, the inclined plane, the wedge, the screw, and the pulley.** As you'll learn, you can tell a lot about a simple machine by its appearance. For several machines, you can even calculate the ideal mechanical advantage based solely on the locations of the forces involved.

Figure 12 The idea for this labor-saving auto jack comes from Rube Goldberg (1883–1970), a sculptor, author, and Pulitzer Prize-winning cartoonist.

Work, Power, and Machines **427**

⏱ Section Resources

Print

- ***Laboratory Manual,*** Investigations 14A and 14B
- ***Reading and Study Workbook With Math Support,*** Section 14.4
- ***Math Skills and Problem Solving Workbook,*** Section 14.4
- ***Transparencies,*** Section 14.4

Technology

- ***Interactive Textbook,*** Section 14.4
- ***Presentation Pro CD-ROM,*** Section 14.4
- ***Go Online,*** NSTA SciLinks, Simple machines

Levers

Use Visuals

Figure 13 Point out to students the arrows designating input force and output force in the sketches. The locations of these arrows relative to the fulcrum illustrate the difference between the three classes of levers. Ask, **In which figure is the input force located between the fulcrum and the output force?** *(Figure 13C)* **What type of lever is this?** *(Third-class lever)* Then, help students relate each sketch to its accompanying photo.
Visual

Integrate Social Studies

For thousands of years, levers have been used for digging, cultivating land, and moving heavy objects. People in India and Egypt used levers to perform important tasks as long ago as 1500 B.C. Weighing scales that made use of levers were used around 5000 B.C. in Egypt. These scales functioned by placing weights at one end of a beam, and the object being weighed at the other end. This type of scale is similar to those used today in many doctors' offices.
Verbal

Use Community Resources

Arrange for a mechanical engineer to visit the classroom to discuss important ways in which levers (and other simple machines) are used in machinery. Ask the engineer to bring examples to class that illustrate how simple machines function. Encourage students, with the help of the engineer, to measure the dimensions of some of the simple machines brought to class and calculate mechanical advantage.
Interpersonal, Portfolio

Figure 13

Three Classes of Levers

A First-Class Lever

The screwdriver is being used as a first-class lever with a mechanical advantage greater than 1. (Diagram is not drawn to scale.)

B Second-Class Lever

The wheelbarrow has its output force located between the input force and the fulcrum. (Diagram is not drawn to scale.)

C Third-Class Lever

The output distance of the broom is greater than the input distance the hands move through. (Diagram is not drawn to scale.)

Levers

Suppose you need to pry the lid off a can of paint. How can you make the task easier? A common solution is to slip the flat end of a screwdriver under the lid of the paint can and then to pry the lid off by pushing down on the screwdriver. This is an example of a **lever,** a rigid bar that is free to move around a fixed point. The fixed point the bar rotates around is the **fulcrum.** Levers are classified into three categories based on the locations of the input force, the output force, and the fulcrum.

The **input arm** of a lever is the distance between the input force and the fulcrum. The **output arm** is the distance between the output force and the fulcrum. ◯ **To calculate the ideal mechanical advantage of any lever, divide the input arm by the output arm.**

First-Class Levers Figure 13A shows a screwdriver being used as a first-class lever to open a paint can. The fulcrum in this case is actually the inside edge of the paint can. The position of the fulcrum identifies a first-class lever—the fulcrum of a first-class lever is always located between the input force and the output force.

Depending on the location of the fulcrum, the mechanical advantage of a first-class lever can be greater than 1, equal to 1, or less than 1. Examples of first-class levers include a seesaw, scissors, and tongs.

428 Chapter 14

⌐ Customize for Inclusion Students ¬

Gifted
Have students create a computer graphics presentation that compares the different classes of levers. The presentations should include photographs of various objects that are levers. Each object should have the input force, output force, and fulcrum labeled.

Second-Class Levers In a second-class lever the output force is located between the input force and the fulcrum. The wheelbarrow shown in Figure 13B is a second-class lever.

When you lift the handles of a wheelbarrow, it rotates around its fulcrum. Parts of the wheelbarrow near the fulcrum move through a smaller distance than those closer to the handle. Thus the input distance your hands move to lift the wheelbarrow is larger than the output distance the wheelbarrow moves to lift its load. The increased input distance means it takes less force from you to lift the load. The mechanical advantage of a second-class lever is always greater than 1.

Third-Class Lever The input force of a third-class lever is located between the fulcrum and the output force. As shown in Figure 13C, the output distance over which the third-class lever exerts its force is always larger than the input distance you move the lever through. Because of this, the mechanical advantage of a third-class lever is always less than 1. Baseball bats, hockey sticks, and golf clubs are all third-class levers.

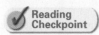 **Reading Checkpoint** *Which classes of levers can have a mechanical advantage less than 1?*

For: Links on simple machines
Visit: www.SciLinks.org
Web Code: ccn-2144

 Quick Lab

Comparing Lever Arms

Materials
pencil, masking tape, spring scale, 500-g mass, meter stick

Procedure

1. Construct a data table with columns labeled Output Force, Output Arm, Input Force, Input Arm, and Mechanical Advantage.

2. Suspend the 500-g mass from the spring scale. Observe the force on the scale and record it as the output force.

3. Tape a pencil parallel to and near the edge of a table as shown. Tape the 500-g mass to the meter stick so it's centered on the 10-cm mark.

4. Position the 20-cm mark of the meter stick on the pencil as shown. Record the distance from the pencil to the center of the mass as the output arm.

5. Attach the spring scale at the 90-cm mark of the meter stick. Record the distance from the pencil to this mark as the input arm.

6. Pull straight down on the spring scale so the 500-g mass is lifted off of the table. Record the force on the spring scale as the input force.

7. Repeat Steps 5 and 6 with the spring scale located at the 80-cm, 70-cm, 60-cm, and 50-cm marks on the meter stick.

Analyze and Conclude

1. **Calculating** Calculate and record the mechanical advantage of the lever for each input arm.

2. **Using Graphs** Plot a graph of mechanical advantage versus the length of the input arm.

3. **Analyzing Data** How does changing the input arm affect the mechanical advantage?

Quick Lab

Comparing Lever Arms   L2

Objective
After completing this activity, students will be able to
• describe the relationship between the input arm length and the mechanical advantage of a lever.

Skills Focus   Analyzing Data

 Prep Time 10 minutes

Class Time 20 minutes

Safety Students should wear safety goggles.

Teaching Tips
• Ask students to identify the fulcrum and the input and output arms and forces as they work.

Expected Outcome Graphs will indicate that the mechanical advantage is roughly proportional to the length of the input arm.

Analyze and Conclude
1. Student data should indicate that the mechanical advantage is roughly proportional to the length of the input arm.
2. Students should construct graphs that reflect a direct proportion between mechanical advantage and the length of the input arm.
3. The mechanical advantage is proportional to the length of the input arm.
Logical, Visual

For Enrichment   L3

Have students determine and compare the ideal mechanical advantage of several tools that involve levers, such as scissors, metal-cutting shears, bolt cutters, a crowbar, and tire irons. **Logical, Visual**

Download a worksheet on simple machines for students to complete, and find additional teacher support from NSTA SciLinks.

Answer to . . .

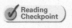 **Reading Checkpoint** *First- and third-class levers can have a mechanical advantage less than 1.*

Wheel and Axle
Build Science Skills L2

Observing Have students first read the text about wheels and axles. Then ask, **Name some mechanical devices you have observed that you think use the wheel-and-axle principle.** *(Possible answers: cranks, wrenches, screwdrivers, clocks, bicycles, steering wheels and axles, automobile wheels with tires and their shafts, and any other rotating wheel and shaft run by a belt or by gears)*
Logical, Visual

Inclined Planes

 Teacher > **Demo**

Inclined Planes L2

Purpose Students gain appreciation for inclined-plane MA.

Materials long board, heavy box, small stepladder, spring scale

Procedure With a student's help, put one end of the board on the floor and the other end on the lowest step of the stepladder. Measure the height of that step from the floor, and record it on the board as "output distance." Measure the distance along the board, and record it on the board as "input distance." Calculate the IMA for the setup. *(IMA = input distance/output distance)* Now pull the box up along the board using the spring scale and record the force required. Repeat this process using two other steps on the ladder.

Ask students to compare the force required to the IMA of the board used as a ramp. *(The greater the IMA, the less force required.)* Then, write the equation *Fd = W* on the board, and remind students that distance and force have an inverse relationship: as one increases the other decreases.

Expected Outcome The lowest step will give the largest mechanical advantage, because the divisor in the MA equation is the smallest. Students experience and comprehend that the greater the mechanical advantage, the less input force is needed to accomplish the work.
Visual, Group

Figure 14 A wheel and axle is a type of simple machine consisting of two disks or cylinders with different radii. **A** The steering mechanism used in a car is a wheel and axle. **B** When turning a screw with a screwdriver, the input force is applied to the larger-radius handle and the screw is turned by the smaller-radius shaft.

Figure 15 This long and winding road acts like a type of simple machine known as an inclined plane. Applying Concepts *As the road becomes steeper, how does its mechanical advantage change?*

Wheel and Axle

Are you excited about "getting behind the wheel" of a car in a few years? To be scientifically correct, you'll actually be getting behind a wheel and axle, a type of simple machine. A **wheel and axle** is a simple machine that consists of two disks or cylinders, each one with a different radius. A steering wheel, as shown in Figure 14A, consists of a large wheel attached to a narrow axle.

The outer disk is the wheel and the inner cylinder is the axle. The wheel and the axle rotate together as a unit. In a car, the steering wheel the driver turns is the wheel, and the shaft that rotates with it is the axle.

Depending on the purpose of the machine, the input force can be exerted on the wheel or the axle. ○ **To calculate the ideal mechanical advantage of the wheel and axle, divide the radius (or diameter) where the input force is exerted by the radius (or diameter) where the output force is exerted.** Though it may not appear so, a wheel and axle is similar to a lever, with the center of the two cylinders acting as the fulcrum.

A wheel and axle machine can have a mechanical advantage greater than 1 or less than 1. For a steering wheel, the driver applies force to the larger radius of the wheel. Because the input distance is larger than the output distance, a steering wheel has a mechanical advantage greater than 1.

Inclined Planes

Imagine how hard it would be to walk straight up the side of a steep hill. By following the gentler slope of a winding trail, it is easier to walk up the hill. Why is that so? It is because the required input force is decreased when the input distance is greater than the output distance. Remember, however, that although it is easier to reach the top of a hill using the trail, you'll have to walk a longer distance. As shown in Figure 15, switchback roads are often used to make steep mountain passes easier for automobiles to climb.

430 *Chapter 14*

Facts and Figures

The Earliest Wheels An early use of wheels is depicted in a rock drawing from ancient Sumeria, now part of southern Iraq. The pictograph, dating from 3500 B.C., shows wheels under a sled used for transporting objects.

Gently sloping trails and roads are also a type of simple machine—an inclined plane. An **inclined plane** is a slanted surface along which a force moves an object to a different elevation. The ramp that makes a refrigerator easier to lift into a truck is an inclined plane. So are the wheelchair ramps used in front of buildings. The distance along the ramp is its input distance, whereas the change in height of the ramp is its output distance. ◉ **The ideal mechanical advantage of an inclined plane is the distance along the inclined plane divided by its change in height.** For example, a 6-meter-long ramp that gains 1 meter of height has an ideal mechanical advantage of 6.

Wedges and Screws

Wedges and screws are similar to inclined planes because both involve sloping surfaces. A key difference, however, is that wedges and screws have sloping surfaces that move.

Wedges A **wedge** is a V-shaped object whose sides are two inclined planes sloped toward each other. Figure 16 shows a type of wedge often used to split wood. A sledgehammer drives the wedge into the log. As the wedge is driven in, its sloping sides push the wood on either side a small distance apart. This gives a wedge a mechanical advantage greater than 1. The thinner a wedge is relative to its length, the less the wedge separates the wood fibers as it moves through the log. ◉ **A thin wedge of a given length has a greater ideal mechanical advantage than a thick wedge of the same length.** Other examples of wedges are a knife blade, which cuts best when its edge is sharp, and a zipper, which uses a wedge to separate and join the zipper's teeth.

Screws A **screw,** as shown in Figure 17, is an inclined plane wrapped around a cylinder. For two screws of the same length, the one whose threads are closer together moves forward less for each turn of the screw. ◉ **Screws with threads that are closer together have a greater ideal mechanical advantage.**

The thread on a screw is usually measured in threads per inch or threads per centimeter. A screw with fewer threads per inch takes fewer turns to drive into a piece of wood or other material. But the smaller mechanical advantage of the screw requires you to exert a greater input force in order to drive it in. Other common examples of the screw include nuts, which have the threads on the inside, and bolts.

Reading Checkpoint *How is a screw similar to an inclined plane?*

Input Force

Output Force

Figure 16 The wedge being used to split the log consists of two inclined planes that slope toward each other. The inclined planes force the wood fibers apart as the wedge is driven into the log.
Relating Cause and Effect
What is the cause of the forces, exerted by the wedge, that split the log apart?

Figure 17 A screw is a simple machine made up of an inclined plane wrapped around a cylinder.

Work, Power, and Machines **431**

Work, Power, and Machines **431**

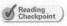

Pulleys

Use Visuals L1

Figure 19 Tell students to look at all three sketches in Figure 19. Ask, **What is the mechanical advantage of the pulley in 19A?** *(MA = 1)* **What is the MA in 19B?** *(MA = 2)* **What is the MA in 19C?** *(MA = 4)* Remind students that MA is the output force divided by the input force. Ask, **Does an MA of 4 mean that the pulley exerts 4 N of force for every 1 N of force put into it?** *(Yes)*
Visual, Logical

Build Science Skills L2

Predicting Have students look at Figure 19C. Ask, **What would happen to the mechanical advantage of the pulley system if two more pulleys were added?** *(The mechanical advantage would change from 4 to 8 because each pulley adds two load-carrying rope sections to the system.)*
Logical, Visual

FYI

A pulley is an important tool used in rescue operations. Various types are used, depending on the emergency. Pulley systems (block and tackle) can be attached to fire trucks, the beams of buildings, or other anchor points and used to lower or raise objects or people. A type of pulley known as a snatch block has one sheave, or groove, and an opening on one side of the pulley's shell. A rope is threaded through the opening so that the pulley or the object can be pulled to the side. Other pulleys are attached to pivots to provide greater flexibility of movement.

Figure 18 A worker watches as a pulley moves a large fabricated part through a factory.
Interpreting Photos *Based on what can be seen in the photograph, what is the approximate mechanical advantage of the pulley being used?*

Pulleys

A construction worker needs to lift a load of roofing materials onto the roof where he is working. Because it is easier and safer, he uses a pulley system to lift the load. The pulley system allows him to pull with less force than is needed to lift the load directly upward.

A **pulley** is a simple machine that consists of a rope that fits into a groove in a wheel. Pulleys produce an output force that is different in size, direction, or both, from that of the input force. **The ideal mechanical advantage of a pulley or pulley system is equal to the number of rope sections supporting the load being lifted.** Part of a pulley system is shown in Figure 18.

Fixed Pulleys A fixed pulley is a wheel attached in a fixed location. Fixed pulleys are only able to rotate in place. The direction of the exerted force is changed by a fixed pulley, but the size of the force is not. If you use the fixed pulley shown in Figure 19A, the rope or chain lifts the load up as far as you pull down the rope. Thus, the ideal mechanical advantage of a fixed pulley is always 1. Assuming friction forces are small, the input force and output force will be the same. Examples of fixed pulleys include the pulley at the top of a flagpole and the pulleys used to pull up blinds.

Figure 19
Three Types of Pulleys

A Fixed Pulley

A fixed pulley changes only the direction of the input force.

B Movable Pulley

Movable pulleys change both the direction and the size of the input force.

C Pulley System

Pulley systems are made up of both fixed and movable pulleys.

Facts and Figures

Checks on Mechanical Advantage As the mechanical advantage of a pulley system increases, the distance that a load can be lifted per unit length of input distance moved through decreases proportionally. For example, a single pulley with an MA of 2 and a 44.5 N input force can lift an 89 N weight 15 cm when 30 cm of rope is pulled. By contrast, a double pulley system with twice the MA (4) and a 44.5 N input force can lift a 178 N weight. However, pulling 30 cm of rope will lift the weight only 7.5 cm (half the distance as the single pulley). Another limit to lifting ability is friction, which increases as more pulleys are added to the system. Friction reduces the ideal mechanical advantage to a lesser actual mechanical advantage.

Pulley System Performance

A shipyard has many different pulleys and pulley systems in use. The pulleys are used to move large, heavy, fabricated ship sections through the manufacturing process. During an annual safety and performance inspection of three of the company's systems, a facility engineer collected the data shown in the graph. The data give the measured output forces for a range of given input forces.

1. **Using Graphs** What system requires the smallest input force to lift a 2500-N load?

2. **Calculating** Determine the actual mechanical advantage for each of the systems for a 2000-N input force.

3. **Applying Concepts** Which of the three systems shown in the graph consists of a single fixed pulley? Explain how you know.

Performance of Three Pulley Systems

4. **Inferring** Describe what happens to system B's output force as the input force increases above 4000 N. How does this affect the mechanical advantage of the system at higher loads? Offer a possible cause for the performance shown in the graph.

5. **Applying Concepts** Using the mechanical advantage value from Question 2, determine the output force of system A for an input force of 8000 N.

Movable Pulley As you can see in Figure 19B, a movable pulley is attached to the object being moved rather than to a fixed location. If you are pulling up on the rope on the right with a force of 10 newtons, then both sections of the rope pull up with the same force of 10 newtons. Thus, the pulley exerts a 20-newton output force from a 10-newton input force. The movable pulley in Figure 19B has a mechanical advantage of 2. Movable pulleys are used to reduce the input force needed to lift a heavy object. Sailors use movable pulleys to pull in sails, and skyscraper window washers stand on platforms suspended by movable pulleys.

Pulley System By combining fixed and movable pulleys into a pulley system, a large mechanical advantage can be achieved. The mechanical advantage that results depends on how the pulleys are arranged. The pulley system shown in Figure 19C has four segments of supporting rope. Ignoring friction, each one of the four segments supplies a lifting force as strong as the force you exert on the rope. Thus the output force is four times stronger than the input force. The pulley system has a mechanical advantage of 4. Using pulley systems in combination with other simple machines, large cranes are able to lift railroad locomotives!

How is it possible to achieve a large mechanical advantage using pulleys?

For: Activity on types of pulleys
Visit: PHSchool.com
Web Code: ccp-2144

Work, Power, and Machines **433**

Pulley System Performance   L2

Answers
1. C
2. A: AMA = Output force/input force = 2000 N/2000 N = 1; B: AMA = Output force/input force = 4000 N/2000 N = 2; C: AMA = Output force/input force = 16,000 N/2000 N = 8
3. System A could be a fixed pulley because it has a mechanical advantage of 1.
4. The output force begins to decrease relative to the required input force. At higher loads the mechanical advantage is decreased. Increased friction at higher loads could be a cause.
5. 8000 N

For Extra Help   L1

Remind students that straight lines on a line graph indicate that the horizontal/vertical (x/y) ratio remains constant. Show that lines A and C remain straight and that B remains straight until it gets to 4000 N of input force.

For A, output force equals input force at any point. (A's MA = 1.) For B, output force is 2 times input force at any point until 4000 N. (B's MA = 2 for forces < 4000 N) For C, the output force is eight times the input force at any point. (C's MA = 8.)
Logical

Go Online
active art

For: Activity on types of pulleys
Visit: PHSchool.com
Web Code: ccp-2144

Students can learn more about different types of pulleys online.

Answer to . . .

Figure 18 *There appear to be seven rope segments supporting the load, thus the mechanical advantage of the pulley system is 7.*

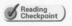 *By having several pulleys with numerous rope segments supporting the load, a large mechanical advantage can be achieved.*

DK HOW It Works

Elevator **L2**

Around 1800, people used ropes made from plant fibers, along with steam and hydraulic power, to lift heavy loads. In 1853, Elisha Graves Otis introduced safety features that made it possible for passengers to ride in elevators. Electric motors were not used in elevator operation until the latter part of the nineteenth century.

Interpreting Diagrams It balances the weight of the elevator.
Visual

For Enrichment **L3**

Students may research and give presentations to the class concerning new developments in various types of elevators. (*Hint:* Use "elevators" as an Internet search term to find helpful government sites on the subject.)
Verbal, Portfolio

DK HOW It Works

Elevator

Skyscrapers are vital to the economies of large cities with limited area for buildings. Stacking one floor on top of another produces a lot of floor space for offices. However, skyscrapers would be impractical without elevators. Elevators allow people to be transported hundreds of feet in the air. The cable elevator is the most popular type today. Interpreting Diagrams ***What is the purpose of the counterweight?***

Elevator motor
The elevator motor is needed to accelerate the car and compensate for the varying load.

Motor

Sheave (pulley)

Cables

Car empty *The motor is needed to lower the car.*

Counterweight

Car half full *When the weights are balanced, the work done by the motor is minimized.*

Car full *The motor is needed to raise the car.*

Governor *This device regulates the speed of the car.*

Motor

Sheave *A pulley carries the cables attached to the car and the counterweight.*

Steel cables

Counterweight *The counterweight is made of cast iron, or concrete in a steel frame.*

Outer shaft doors

Elevator car *As the motor turns the sheave, the car moves up or down the shaft on guide rails.*

Safety brakes *The brakes slow the car if it moves too fast.*

Guide rails

Shock absorber *This piston stops the car if it falls.*

ELEVATOR SHAFT

434 *Chapter 14*

Compound Machines

Look closely at a pair of scissors. You'll notice they consist of a couple of simple machines. The edges are sharpened like wedges. The blades and the handles together function as levers. In fact, most of the machines you use every day are actually a combination of simple machines working together. A **compound machine** is a combination of two or more simple machines that operate together. Many familiar compound machines, such as a car, a washing machine, or a clock, are combinations of hundreds or thousands of simple machines.

Look at the complex mechanisms of the watch shown in Figure 20. How do these simple machines interact to accomplish their task of keeping time? In a compound machine, the output force of one simple machine becomes the input force for another machine. Inside the watch, a complex series of gears is designed so that one gear drives the next. Each gear acts as a continuous lever. These gears help keep accurate track of days, hours, minutes, and seconds.

Figure 20 The complex workings of this watch consist of a series of machines. The output of one machine acts as the driving input for the next machine in the series.

Compound Machines
Use Visuals L1

Figure 20 Encourage students to look closely at the workings of the watch in Figure 20. Ask, **What type of simple machine do you see functioning as gears?** *(Wheel and axle)*
Visual

3 ASSESS

Evaluate Understanding L2

Ask students to identify simple machines in their everyday lives, making sure to name a machine for each of the six types. As a class, see how many different examples you can name.

Reteach L1

Bring in examples of each type of simple machine and demonstrate to the class how to use each one. Ask students to identify the input and output forces for each machine.

Writing in Science

Student paragraphs will vary, but should properly identify how the output of one machine acts as the input to the next machine in the series.

Interactive Textbook If your class subscribes to the Interactive Textbook, use it to review key concepts in Section 14.4.

Section 14.4 Assessment

Reviewing Concepts

1. Name six kinds of simple machines. Give an example of each.

2. Describe how to determine the ideal mechanical advantage of each type of simple machine.

3. How are the lever and the wheel and axle related to each other?

4. What is the ideal mechanical advantage of a ramp if its length is 4.0 m and its higher end is 0.5 m above its lower end?

5. Tightening a screw with a larger spacing between its threads requires fewer turns of a screwdriver than tightening a screw with smaller thread spacing. What is a disadvantage of the screw with larger thread spacing?

6. What class or classes of lever always have a mechanical advantage greater than 1?

Critical Thinking

7. **Making Generalizations** If you want to pry the lid off a paint can, will it require less force to use a long screwdriver or a short screwdriver? Explain.

8. **Calculating** When the pedals of a bicycle move through a distance of 0.25 m, the rear wheel of the bicycle moves 1.0 m. What is the ideal mechanical advantage of the bicycle?

9. **Applying Concepts** Explain why it could be useful for the mechanical advantage of a bicycle to be less than 1.

Writing in Science

Steps in a Process Write a paragraph describing the series of events that occur in the operation of a complex machine that you have used today.

Work, Power, and Machines **435**

Section 14.4 Assessment

1. Examples include: lever (crow bar), wheel and axle (screwdriver), inclined plane (ramp), wedge (axe), screw (machine screw), pulley (flag-raising pulley)

2. For each machine, IMA = Input distance/Output distance: lever (Input arm/Output arm), wheel and axle (Input radius/Output radius), inclined plane (Distance along plane/Change in height), wedge (Distance along wedge/Change in wedge thickness), screw (Distance screw is rotated through/Distance screw advances), pulley (Number of rope segments supporting the load)

3. A wheel and axle is like a lever in which the fulcrum is located at the center of the two concentric rotating cylinders.

4. IMA = Input distance/Output distance = 4.0 m/0.5 m = 8

5. The screw with the greater thread spacing has a smaller mechanical advantage, making it harder to turn.

6. Second-class levers

7. A long screwdriver requires less force to pry the lid off of the paint can because it has a longer input distance and a greater mechanical advantage.

8. IMA = Input distance/Output distance = 0.25 m/1 m = .25

9. A mechanical advantage less than 1 means the rider does not have to pedal much in order to make the bike travel a large distance over the ground.

Gearing Up for Better Bikes

Background

Using gears to change speed is not a new idea. In a 1784 patent, James Watt described a "two-speed transmission." Although mechanics at that time were quite simple, wheels, axles, pulleys, and drive belts were already in use.

Until the mid-1800s, British patents were issued to agricultural machinery that had only two speeds. However, in the 1850s, patent requests began to arrive for three-speed systems.

Eventually, derailleur systems were developed. One of these systems is used on a bicycle with gears. As the text explains, "derailleurs are used to move the chain from one sprocket to another." Therefore, derailleurs make it possible for gears to change.

When comparing the output gear rotation to the input gear rotation, the ratio of the diameters or number of gear teeth of the gears determines the relative speeds. In other words, if the input gear has twice the diameter or twice the number of gear teeth of that of the output gear, the input gear would have half the speed of the output gear.

Gearing Up for Better Bikes

The different gears on a bike allow you to change the distance the bike moves for each turn of the pedals. Cyclists use a low gear to climb hills and to accelerate. In a low gear, the chain connects a small front gear to a large back gear. A high gear is used for speed on level roads or for going downhill. In a high gear, the chain connects a large front gear to a small back gear.

Sprockets, or cogs

Derailleur Gears

The chain connecting the front chainwheel to the rear wheel sprocket serves as a belt to make the wheel turn faster than your feet. Wheel sprockets of various sizes are used to obtain different speeds. Derailleurs are used to move the chain from one sprocket to another.

Rear derailleur *The guide pulley feeds the chain to the selected rear wheel sprocket. The tension pulley uses a spring to keep the entire chain assembly tight.*

Freewheels *These allow the bike to roll forward without the cyclist pedaling. When the bike is pedaled forward, a ratchet engages to drive the rear wheel.*

Guide pulley

Chain *The chain needs to be the correct width to operate smoothly over the sprockets and chainwheels, and the correct length for optimum shifting performance.*

Tension pulley

436 *Chapter 14*

Bicycle gear ratios
The lowest gear ratio on the bike might be a front chainwheel with 13 teeth and a rear gear with 52 teeth. In this case, the rear wheel will turn once for every four turns of the chainwheel. Working up through the gears gradually changes this ratio, allowing the bike to travel farther with every turn of the pedals.

DISTANCE

RATIOS

Back gear — Front gear

Low gear

Middle gear

High gear

Distance traveled in one turn of the pedals

Front derailleur *The chain passes through this cage as it feeds onto the front chainwheels. By moving from side to side, the front derailleur is able to shift the chain among the chainwheels.*

Spider *The spider is the multi-armed part of the crank.*

Gearless bikes
Before the bicycle chain was invented, bicycle pedals were fixed to the axle of the front wheel. Today's track racers are also gearless (and brakeless), but only for the sake of fairness. This means that all of the bikes have the same mechanical advantage.

Chainwheels *These are also called chainrings or front sprockets. The larger the chainwheel, the higher the gear is.*

Crank *The crank connects the pedal to the front chainwheel.*

Going Further

- Write an instruction manual to explain how a new cyclist can make the best use of gear ratios. Use terms from this feature to describe which gear ratios are best for different situations and why.
- Take a Discovery Channel Video Field Trip by watching "Pedal Power."

DISCOVERY CHANNEL SCHOOL
Video Field Trip

Work, Power, and Machines **437**

Inferring

Purpose Students observe how the number of teeth on gears affects gear ratios.

Materials 1 bicycle with gears similar to that shown on pp. 436–437

Class Time 30 minutes

Procedure Point out the different gears on the bicycle. Have students work in pairs to count the number of teeth on each gear. One student can count as the other student records the numbers. Then, have the students calculate the different gear ratios for the bicycle and identify which is the highest and which is the lowest. Ask, **What does the gear ratio mean in terms of the pedal and wheel revolutions?** *(A high gear ratio means more wheel revolutions for each turn of the pedals.)* **Would a high or low gear ratio be good for climbing hills?** *(Low gear ratio)* **Would a high or low gear ratio be good for traveling along level ground?** *(High gear ratio)*

Safety Caution students to keep hands and clothing away from the chain and the gears.

Expected Outcome Students understand the relationship between number of gear teeth and gear ratios.
Logical, Visual

Going Further

Student instruction manuals will vary, but should discuss why low gears are good for hills and why high gears are good for flat roads. Manuals should also discuss how to properly select a high or low gear using the front and rear derailleurs.
Verbal, Logical

Video Field Trip
Pedal Power

After students have viewed the Video Field Trip, ask them the following questions: **Why did early bicycle riders have to deal with being high above the ground while riding?** *(The early bicycles were designed with a very large front wheel, placing the rider high above the ground.)* **What properties must a bicycle frame have in order to be useful in long distance bicycle races such as the Tour de France?**

(The bicycle frame must be sturdy, reliable, and lightweight.) **Why is the ability to move through the air with as little resistance from the wind as possible important to the movement of a racing bike?** *(Most of the energy the rider expends; 70% to 95% is used just to overcome wind.)* **In long distance bicycle races, one cyclist on the team may ride in front of another cyclist on the team for most of the race. How does this action help the second cyclist?** *(This reduces the amount of energy the second cyclist must expend to keep moving.)*

Study Tip

Keep a Calendar
Encourage students to keep an assignment calendar and a "to do" list. Recommend that students take time each day to plan when they will work on each assignment, putting items from the "to do" list onto the calendar. Remind students to consider deadlines and to allow a realistic amount of time for each assignment.

Thinking Visually

a. watts
b. work
c. joules
d. force
e. newtons
f. meters

14.1 Work and Power

🔵 Key Concepts

- Work = Force × Distance. Work is done on an object when a force acts in the same direction as the object moves.
- Power = Work ÷ Time. Power is the rate of doing work. Doing work faster requires more power.

Vocabulary

work, p. 412	watt, p. 415
joule, p. 414	horsepower, p. 416
power, p. 414	

14.2 Work and Machines

🔵 Key Concepts

- Machines make work easier by changing the force needed, the direction of the force, or the distance over which the force acts.
- Work output (done by a machine) is always less than the work input (done on the machine).

Vocabulary

machine, p. 417	output force, p. 420
input force, p. 419	output distance, p. 420
input distance, p. 419	work output, p. 420
work input, p. 419	

14.3 Mechanical Advantage and Efficiency

🔵 Key Concepts

- Friction is present in all machines. Because of friction, the actual mechanical advantage is always less than the ideal mechanical advantage.

- Actual mechanical advantage = $\dfrac{\text{Output force}}{\text{Input force}}$

- Ideal mechanical advantage = $\dfrac{\text{Input distance}}{\text{Output distance}}$

- Efficiency = $\dfrac{\text{Work output}}{\text{Work input}} \times 100\%$

- Because of friction, the efficiency of any machine is always less than 100 percent.

Vocabulary

mechanical advantage, p. 421	ideal mechanical advantage, p. 423
actual mechanical advantage, p. 422	efficiency, p. 425

14.4 Simple Machines

🔵 Key Concept

- The six types of simple machines are the lever, the wheel and axle, the inclined plane, the wedge, the screw, and the pulley.

Vocabulary

lever, p. 428	wedge, p. 431
fulcrum, p. 428	screw, p. 431
input arm, p. 428	pulley, p. 432
output arm, p. 428	compound machine, p. 435
wheel and axle, p. 430	
inclined plane, p. 431	

Thinking Visually

Concept Map Use information from the chapter to complete the concept map below.

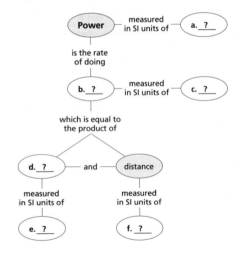

⏱ Chapter Resources

Print
- **Chapter and Unit Tests,** Chapter 14 Test A and Test B
- **Test Prep Resources,** Chapter 14

Technology
- **Computer Test Bank,** Chapter Test 14
- **Interactive Textbook,** Chapter 14
- **Go Online,** PHSchool.com, Chapter 14

Reviewing Content

Choose the letter that best describes the question or completes the statement.

1. Work is the product of
  a. speed and force. **b.** force and distance.
  c. power and force. **d.** motion and force.

2. Which of the following is a unit of work?
  a. joule **b.** watt
  c. horsepower **d.** newton

3. How much work, in N•m, is done when a 10.0-N force moves an object 2.5 m?
  a. 0.25 N•m **b.** 2.5 N•m
  c. 25 N•m **d.** 4.0 N•m

4. Power is equal to work divided by
  a. time.
  b. force.
  c. distance.
  d. mechanical advantage.

5. If a machine has a mechanical advantage much larger than 1, its output force is
  a. much larger than its input force.
  b. much less than its input force.
  c. about the same as its input force.
  d. in the same direction as its input force.

6. How is the work output of a machine related to its work input?
  a. always less **b.** always greater
  c. always equal **d.** always zero

7. A machine with a 5-N input force and a 25-N output force has a mechanical advantage of
  a. 2. **b.** 5.
  c. 20. **d.** 125.

8. The mechanical advantage of a pulley system depends upon
  a. the diameter of the pulley wheels.
  b. the length of the rope.
  c. the number of sections of rope.
  d. the direction of the input force.

9. A screw can be considered a type of
  a. lever. **b.** inclined plane.
  c. pulley. **d.** compound machine.

10. Which is not a simple machine?
  a. wedge **b.** screw
  c. lever **d.** fulcrum

Understanding Concepts

11. Does an athlete do work on a trophy as she lifts it overhead? Is work done on the trophy as she stands still holding the trophy overhead? Explain.

12. What is the scientific definition of power?

Questions 13–15 refer to the illustration below.

13. Identify the position of the fulcrum.

14. If $X = 3.0$ cm and $Y = 15.0$ cm, what is the ideal mechanical advantage of the pliers?

15. If the output force is 50.0 N and the input force is 12.5 N, what is the actual mechanical advantage of the pliers?

16. A machine you designed has input and output arms that pivot around a fulcrum. When the input arm is pushed down through a short distance, the output arm moves down through a longer distance. Is the output force less than, equal to, or greater than the input force?

17. A machine has an efficiency of 60%. What happens to 60% of the work put into the machine, and what happens to the other 40%?

18. Identify the simple machines in a pair of scissors.

19. Why would you use a single fixed pulley to lift a box if the pulley's mechanical advantage is 1?

20. What determines the class of a lever?

21. Is a screw with fewer or more threads per centimeter easier to drive into a piece of wood? Explain.

Work, Power, and Machines **441**

Assessment

 If your class subscribes to the Interactive Textbook, your students can go online to access an interactive version of the Student Edition and a self-test.

Reviewing Content

1. b **2.** a **3.** c
4. a **5.** a **6.** a
7. b **8.** c **9.** b
10. d

Understanding Concepts

11. Yes; no; Work is done as force is used to lift the trophy up through a distance. No work is done when a force is used to hold the trophy motionless overhead.
12. Power is the rate of doing work.
13. B
14. 5
15. 4
16. Less than
17. 60% of the work input becomes work output, while the other 40% of work input is lost to friction.
18. Two levers and two wedges
19. You would use a single fixed pulley whenever you want to change the required direction of input force.
20. The locations of the input force, output force, and fulcrum determine the class of a lever.
21. The greater the number of threads per centimeter a screw has, the greater its mechanical advantage is and the easier it is to drive in a piece of wood.

Homework Guide

Section	Questions
14.1	1–4, 11–12, 28–29, 32
14.2	6, 16, 34
14.3	5, 7, 17, 27
14.4	8–10, 13–16, 18–26, 30–31, 33

Chapter 14

Critical Thinking

22. Examples will vary but may include a rowing oar, golf club, or baseball bat. Machines with a mechanical advantage less than 1 are useful when an increased output distance is advantageous.

23. The ramp has an IMA of 5 and the pulley system has an IMA of 4. The ramp requires a greater input distance but a smaller force to lift the load.

24. Friction occurs where objects are in contact as they move past one another. For a pulley, friction primarily occurs as the rope moves around the pulley and as the pulley rotates around its axis.

25. Steel bolt (screw), iron nail (wedge), screwdriver (wheel and axle)

Math Skills

26. 3
27. 29 N
28. 100 J
29. 60,000 J

Concepts in Action

30. A screwdriver used to drive a screw into a board acts as a wheel and axle. The length of the screwdriver does not affect its mechanical advantage when used as a wheel and axle. As a wheel and axle, the wide handle provides a greater mechanical advantage than the narrow handle does.

31. A faucet handle is a wheel and axle. The output force is larger than the input force.

32. Walking up the stairs requires 100 W of power, whereas the elevator requires 1000 W of power (both assuming 1000 N of force acting over a distance of 20 m). The elevator reaches the fifth floor 10 times faster than walking up the stairs.

33. Friction causes the work output to be less than the work input in each simple machine. The loss of useful work in each simple machine is additive, and sums to the total loss of useful work.

34. The lower gear increases the distance you pedal (increases input distance), but does so by making it easier to pedal (decreases input force needed to produce the output force required to climb the hill).

Critical Thinking

22 Applying Concepts Give an example of a useful machine you have seen that has a mechanical advantage less than 1. State how the machine is useful in terms of changing forces, distances, or directions.

23. Comparing and Contrasting A ramp 20 m long and 4 m high is used to lift a heavy box. A pulley system with 4 rope sections supporting the load is used to lift an identical box to a height of 4 m. Assume that friction can be ignored. Compare and contrast the input force and input distance needed to lift each box.

24. Generalizing In a pulley system, where is there likely to be friction that reduces the efficiency?

25. Classifying Classify each of these items as a type of simple machine: a steel bolt, an iron nail, and a screwdriver.

Math Skills

Use the illustration below to answer Questions 26 and 27.

26. Using Equations The figure above shows the distances from the fulcrum to the input and output forces of a lever. Use these distances to calculate the ideal mechanical advantage of the lever.

27. Using Equations If the actual mechanical advantage is 2.9 and the input force is 10.0 N, what is the output force?

28. Using Equations How much work does a 50-N force do when lifting a box 2 meters?

29. Calculating How much work does a 1-kW motor do in one minute?

Concepts in Action

30. Applying Concepts Which would be the better choice for driving a screw into a board, a long screwdriver with a narrow handle, or a short screwdriver with a wide handle? Explain.

31. Classifying What type of simple machine is a water faucet handle? Is the output force larger or smaller than the input force?

32. Comparing and Contrasting A man weighing 1000 newtons walks from the ground floor to the fifth floor of a building, gaining 20 meters of height in 200 seconds. The next day he returns to the building, but this time uses the elevator. The elevator takes 20 seconds to reach the fifth floor. Compare and contrast the power and time requirements to reach the fifth floor.

33. Relating Cause and Effect In a bicycle, the output of one simple machine is the input of another. Why might you expect the efficiency of the bicycle to be less than the efficiency of each of the simple machines that is part of it?

34. Writing in Science Explain why you might shift into a lower gear to climb a hill on a bike. Your explanation should include a discussion of the input force and distance.

Performance-Based Assessment

Using Models Imagine you have a younger brother who weighs half as much as you do. Design a seesaw you could use together. Create a model of your seesaw design and label it to show the distances that you and your brother must sit from the fulcrum. Explain why you chose the fulcrum position as you did.

For: Self-grading assessment
Visit: PHSchool.com
Web Code: cca-2140

Performance-Based Assessment

Student seesaw design will vary depending on the weights of the two people. Review student sketches for accuracy of fulcrum position. The product (Weight × Distance to fulcrum) should be the same on each side of the fulcrum.

Your students can independently test their knowledge of the chapter and print out their test results for your files.

Choose the letter that best answers the question or completes the statement.

1. An applied force acts upward on a moving wooden crate as shown below. Which of the following statements is TRUE?
(A) The power used to move the crate is 150 W.
(B) The force does no work on the crate.
(C) The force does 150 J of work on the crate.
(D) The force does 66 J of work on the crate.
(E) The force accelerates the crate.

100-N applied force

Direction of motion

Speed = 1.5 m/s

2. A machine is used to lift boxes in a warehouse. Which change will increase the power of the machine?
(A) decreasing the distance the boxes are lifted
(B) decreasing the force exerted by the machine
(C) increasing the friction inside the machine
(D) decreasing the time it takes to lift the boxes
(E) decreasing the work done by the machine

3. Which statement is NEVER true for a machine?
(A) The output force is greater than the input force.
(B) The machine changes a force.
(C) The machine changes the direction of a force.
(D) The machine changes the distance over which a force acts.
(E) The work output equals the work input.

4. Which of the following will increase the actual mechanical advantage of a machine?
(A) decreasing the output force
(B) decreasing the friction
(C) increasing the input force
(D) decreasing the time required
(E) increasing the time required

5. The diagram below represents a first-class lever. Which point(s) could be the fulcrum for this lever?
(A) A only
(B) B only
(C) C only
(D) A or C only
(E) A, B, or C only

A   B   C

6. What information is required to calculate the actual mechanical advantage of a lever?
(A) input arm and output arm
(B) input distance and output distance
(C) input force and output force
(D) Work input and work output
(E) internal friction

Work, Power, and Machines **443**

Planning Guide

SECTION OBJECTIVES	STANDARDS		ACTIVITIES and LABS
	NATIONAL	STATE	
15.1 Energy and Its Forms, pp. 446–452 ⏱ 1 block or 2 periods **15.1.1 Describe** the relationship between work and energy. **15.1.2 Relate** kinetic energy to mass and speed and **calculate** these quantities. **15.1.3 Analyze** how potential energy is related to an object's position and **give examples** of gravitational and elastic potential energy. **15.1.4 Solve equations** that relate an object's gravitational potential energy to its mass and height. **15.1.5 Give examples** of the major forms of energy and **explain** how each is produced.	A-1, A-2, B-1, B-3, B-4, B-5, B-6	ICP.1.4, ICP.5.7, ICP.6.7, ICP.7.4, ICP.7.5	**SE** Inquiry Activity: How Can Energy Change Form? p. 445 **L2** **SE** Quick Lab: Investigating Elastic Potential Energy, p. 450 **L2** **TE** Teacher Demo: Burning a Peanut, p. 451 **L2** **LM** Investigation 15A: Determining the Effect of Mass on Kinetic Energy **L2**
15.2 Energy Conversion and Conservation, pp. 453–459 ⏱ 1 block or 2 periods **15.2.1 Describe** conversions of energy from one form to another. **15.2.2 State** and **apply** the law of conservation of energy. **15.2.3 Analyze** how energy is conserved in conversions between kinetic energy and potential energy and **solve equations** that equate initial energy to final energy. **15.2.4 Describe** the relationship between energy and mass and **calculate** how much energy is equivalent to a given mass.	A-1, A-2, B-5, G-1, G-2, G-3	ICP.1.4, ICP.4.1	**SE** Quick Lab: Exploring Energy Conversion, p. 454 **L2** **SE** Application Lab: Investigating a Spring Clip, p. 467 **L2** **TE** Teacher Demo: Energy in a Pendulum, p. 456 **L2** **LM** Investigation 15B: Determining the Kinetic Energy of a Pendulum **L1**
15.3 Energy Resources, pp. 462–466 ⏱ 1 block or 2 periods **15.3.1 Classify** energy resources as renewable or nonrenewable. **15.3.2 Evaluate** benefits and drawbacks of different energy sources. **15.3.3 Describe** ways to conserve energy resources.	A-1, A-2, B-5, D-1, F-2, F-3, F-4	ICP.1.4, ICP.8.1, ICP.8.2, ICP.8.3, ICP.8.4, ICP.8.5, ICP.8.6, ICP.8.7	**TE** Teacher Demo: Simple Solar Cell, p. 464 **L2**

RESOURCES
PRINT and TECHNOLOGY

RSW Section 15.1 **L1**

RSW Math Skill **L2**

MSPS Section 15.1 **L2**

T Chapter 15 Pretest **L2**

Section 15.1 **L2**

P Chapter 15 Pretest **L2**

Section 15.1 **L2**

SCiLINKS GO Potential and kinetic energy **L2**

PLM Lab 6: Investigating a Spring Clip **L2**

RSW Section 15.2 **L1**

MSPS Section 15.2 **L2**

DC Physics of Fun **L2**

T Section 15.2 **L2**

P Section 15.2 **L2**

SCiLINKS GO Energy **L2**

PHSchool.com GO Data sharing **L2**

RSW Section 15.3 **L1**

MSPS Section 15.3 **L2**

T Section 15.3 **L2**

P Section 15.3 **L2**

SCIENCE NEWS GO Energy and energy resources **L2**

SECTION ASSESSMENT

SE Section 15.1 Assessment, p. 452

iT Section 15.1

SE Section 15.2 Assessment, p. 459

iT Section 15.2

SE Section 15.3 Assessment, p. 466

iT Section 15.3

Go Online

Go online for these Internet resources.

PHSchool.com
Web Code: ccd-2150
Web Code: cca-2150

SCIENCE NEWS
Web Code: cce-2153

NSTA SCiLINKS
Web Code: ccn-2151
Web Code: ccn-2152

Materials for Activities and Labs

Quantities for each group

STUDENT EDITION

Inquiry Activity, p. 445
flashlight, solar calculator, wind-up toy; other items may be substituted if the three listed in the Procedure are not available. Alternatives include a wind-up alarm clock, electric alarm clock, jack-in-the-box, radio, or CD player.

Quick Lab, p. 450
basketball, tennis ball, meter stick

Quick Lab, p. 454
small steel ball of known mass, box lined with soft modeling clay, meter stick, graph paper

Application Lab, p. 467
clamp, spring clip, masking tape, metric ruler, 50-newton spring scale, graph paper

TEACHER'S EDITION

Teacher Demo, p. 451
peanut, paper clip, pliers, pan of water, matches, safety goggles

Teacher Demo, p. 456
pendulum bob and string, hook at top of board, chalk (or marker), level

Build Science Skills, p. 461
flexible track (like the bendable tracks used for toy cars), steel balls, books or wooden supports

Teacher Demo, p. 464
small solar array, small motor with fan, direct sunlight or bright light source

Chapter Assessment

CHAPTER ASSESSMENT

SE Chapter Assessment, pp. 469–470

CUT Chapter 15 Test A
Chapter 15 Test B

CTB Chapter 15

iT Chapter 15

PHSchool.com GO
Web Code: cca-2150

STANDARDIZED TEST PREP
SE Chapter 15, p. 471
TP Diagnose and Prescribe

Interactive Textbook with assessment at PHSchool.com

Before you teach

From the Author

Michael Wysession
Washington University

Big Ideas

Energy is continuously converting between many different forms. During these conversions, energy is never created or destroyed, and the total energy of a closed system is always constant. "The Conservation of Energy" is the underlying law of the universe.

Space and Time Most types of energy can be divided into two classes: energy of location (potential energy) and energy of motion (kinetic energy). Potential energy is the capacity to do work. An object can be given potential energy by moving it against an opposing force, like lifting it up against the force of gravity or pushing it into a compressing spring. Drop the object or release the spring, and work is done as the potential energy converts to kinetic energy.

Chemical energy can also be thought of as a kind of potential energy. Energy is required to bring atoms together to form chemical bonds. When these bonds are broken, energy is released.

Forces and Motion Kinetic energy is energy of motion. The most common type of KE is the motion of macroscopic objects. Kinetic energy is calculated as one half of the product of the mass of the object times the square of the object's velocity.

There are other forms of energy that involve motions, however. Thermal energy, or heat, is a measure of the vigor of motions of the atoms of a material. Electrical energy includes the motions of electrons through a conducting material. Electromagnetic energy involves the motion of electromagnetic waves (like light).

Matter and Energy As Einstein showed through the famous equation $E = mc^2$, mass is a form of energy. Because "c^2" is enormous, when mass is destroyed, it converts into a great deal of energy. Two types of nuclear energy, fission and fusion, can be used as sources of human energy needs. Nonrenewable energy sources are mined from the ground, and include uranium (nuclear fission), oil, gas, and coal. Renewable energy sources are derived from the sun, and include solar, wind, hydroelectric, and biomass.

Physics Refresher

Mechanical Energy 15.1

The total mechanical energy in a system is the sum of all kinetic energy and potential energy in the system. Kinetic energy is the energy that an object has due to its motion. Potential energy is the energy due to the relative position of objects in a system or due to the shape of an object (e.g., when an object is stretched or compressed).

The translational kinetic energy (kinetic energy due to motion in one direction) of an object is defined as follows:

$$KE = \tfrac{1}{2}mv^2$$

In this equation, m is mass and v is velocity. Because the velocity is squared, kinetic energy is always positive. There are also other types of kinetic energy, such as vibrational kinetic energy.

Gravitational potential energy is the energy an object has due to its position in a gravitational field. Near Earth's surface, gravitational potential energy can be calculated with the following formula:

$$PE = mgh$$

In this equation, m is mass, g is the acceleration due to gravity, and h is the height relative to an arbitrary zero point.

Elastic potential energy is the energy an object has when it is stretched or compressed. It can also be the energy contained in a system of objects connected by a spring or springs.

Other Forms of Energy 15.1

The total mechanical energy of a system is the sum of kinetic energy and potential energy. However, the objects in a system may also contain energy that (ideally) does not play a role in the behavior of the system on a large scale. These forms of energy are called nonmechanical energy or internal energy. Many forms of internal energy turn out to be kinetic energy or potential energy when viewed at small scales.

> **⚑ Address Misconceptions**
>
> *Students may mistakenly think that an object at rest has no energy.* This is true of kinetic energy, but not of other forms of energy. For a strategy to overcome this misconception, see **Address Misconceptions** on **page 448**.

Go Online

NSTA PD Links

For: Teaching methods for energy
Visit: www.SciLinks.org/PDLinks
Web Code: ccn-1599

Energy Conversions 15.2

Energy often changes from one form to another. A classic example is the energy in a pendulum. When a pendulum bob is at its maximum displacement, the mechanical energy in the system is all in the form of gravitational potential energy. As the pendulum bob falls, the potential energy is converted to kinetic energy. When the pendulum bob swings through its lowest point, the mechanical energy in the system is all in the form of kinetic energy. As the pendulum bob rises on the other side, this kinetic energy is converted back to gravitational potential energy. Energy slowly escapes the system as it is converted to thermal energy (due to friction and air resistance).

$E = PE$

$E = PE + KE$

$E = KE$

Conservation of Energy 15.2 and 15.3

Address Misconceptions

Students may incorrectly think that energy is truly lost in many energy transformations. In an energy transformation, some energy may be converted to non-mechanical forms of energy and some energy may leave the system, but total energy is always conserved. For a strategy to overcome this misconception, see **Address Misconceptions** on page 457.

The law of conservation of energy states that energy cannot be created or destroyed. Note that the law does not specify that *mechanical* energy is conserved, or that the total energy in a system is always the same. In all real systems, energy leaks out of the system, often in the form of thermal energy due to friction. Because mass and energy are equivalent, the law of conservation of energy is sometimes stated more generally as the law of conservation of mass and energy.

Energy conservation, as an economic or environmental issue, should not be confused with the law of conservation of energy. Energy conservation has to do with preservation of energy resources that can be harnessed and distributed for human use.

Build Reading Literacy

Directed Reading/Thinking Activity (DRTA)

Predict, Read, Confirm, Revise Predictions

Strategy Help students develop their own reading and thinking processes by setting their own purposes for reading. Select a section of Chapter 15 for students to read, such as Section 15.1, pp. 446–452. Before modeling the strategy with students, divide the targeted section into approximately four equal portions. Present the steps per the example below.

Example

1. Preview Tell students to survey the section by analyzing the titles, headings, visual elements, and boldfaced type. Have students also read the introductory and concluding paragraphs.
2. Predict/Generate Questions Ask students to hypothesize and predict what they will learn, and to formulate their own "teacher-type" questions to be answered; that is, of the type that a teacher might ask. List students' responses on the board.
3. Read/Evaluate and Refine Predictions Have students read a portion of the section. Pause afterward for students to evaluate their predictions. Discuss any answers they learned to their questions, and any prior misconceptions that were clarified. Ask students to formulate refined predictions and questions based on the new information.
4. Repeat the process for the remaining text portions.

See p. 455 for a script on how to use the directed reading/thinking activity (DRTA) strategy with students. For additional Build Reading Literacy strategies, see pp. 446 and 464.

ASSESS PRIOR KNOWLEDGE

Use the Chapter Pretest below to assess students' prior knowledge. As needed, review these Science Concepts and Math Skills with students.

Review Science Concepts

Section 15.1 Review the concept of work. Remind students that work equals force times distance, and that there must be movement in order for work to be done. Review speed and velocity. Review mass and weight. Remind students that weight is a force.

Section 15.2 Review friction and air resistance. Ask students to consider how friction affects the temperature of objects. Review conservation of momentum. Students will learn that energy is also a conserved quantity.

Section 15.3 Review power and efficiency. Remind students that work out does not always equal work in.

Review Math Skills

Scientific Notation, Multiplying and Dividing Exponents, Formulas and Equations, Squares and Square Roots Students will need these skills to solve problems involving kinetic energy, potential energy, and conservation of mechanical energy.

Direct students to the **Math Skills** in the **Skills and Reference Handbook** at the end of the student text.

CHAPTER
15 Energy

What is the most effective energy resource for your state?

In Section 15.3, you will learn about various energy resources used around the world. Work in a small group to research effective energy resources in your state. Identify the pros and cons of each energy source, and develop an overall energy strategy for your state. Post your group's strategy and research on a Web page, and create an online discussion board to invite feedback from state residents. Use the feedback to help troubleshoot and refine your proposed energy strategy.

Indiana's Academic Standards for Science

MOTION AND ENERGY OF MACROSCOPIC OBJECTS
ICP.1.4: Describe the kinetic and potential energies of macroscopic objects, and use measurements to develop an understanding of these forms of energy.

ENERGY TRANSPORT
ICP.4.1: Using conservation of energy, calculate the thermal energy released or absorbed by an object and distinguish between exothermic and endothermic changes.

CHEMICAL ENERGY, REACTIONS, AND BONDING
ICP.5.7: Explain that in exothermic chemical reactions chemical energy is converted into other forms such as thermal, electrical, light, and sound energy.

ELECTRICAL ENERGY PROPAGATION AND MAGNETISM
ICP.6.7: Using the examples of motors and generators, explain that electrical energy can be transformed into mechanical energy and vice versa.

Also covered: ICP.7.4, ICP.7.5, ICP.8.1, ICP.8.2, ICP.8.3, ICP.8.4, ICP.8.5, ICP.8.6, ICP.8.7

444 *Chapter 15*

This frog converts one form of energy into another as it leaps into the air.

Chapter Pretest

1. How much work is done when a weightlifter holds a barbell motionless over his head? *(No work is done.)*
2. Calculate the work done on a 2-N mass when it is lifted to a height of 2 m. *(4 J)*
3. Calculate the average speed of a bicycle that travels 100 m in 20 s. *(5 m/s)*

4. Is weight a force? What is the formula for calculating weight? *(Yes. W = mg)*
5. How does the temperature of an object change when it is acted on by friction? *(The temperature increases.)*
6. True or False: In a closed system, the loss of momentum of one object equals the gain in momentum of another object. *(True)*

7. How is power related to work? *(Power is the rate at which work is done.)*
8. True or False: The amount of work done on a machine (work in) always equals the amount of work done by the machine (work out). *(False)*

Chapter Preview

15.1 Energy and Its Forms

15.2 Energy Conversion and Conservation

15.3 Energy Resources

Discovery
CHANNEL
SCHOOL

Video Field Trip

Physics of Fun

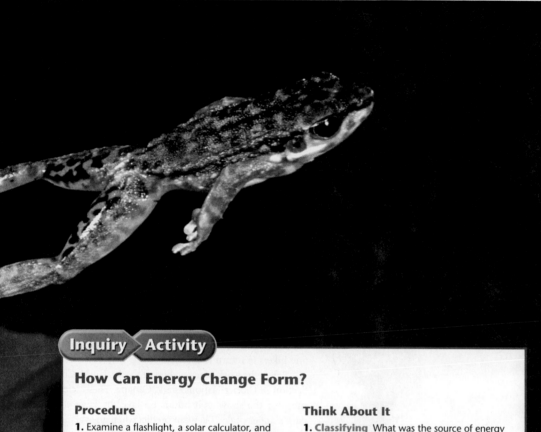

Inquiry Activity

How Can Energy Change Form?

Procedure

1. Examine a flashlight, a solar calculator, and a wind-up toy. Determine how each object operates.

2. Record the name of each object, the source of the energy that it requires, and the kind of energy it produces. For example, does the object require or produce electricity or light?

Think About It

1. **Classifying** What was the source of energy for each object?

2. **Inferring** What form of energy did each object produce?

3. **Drawing Conclusions** How did energy change form in each object? For example, did any of the objects convert light into another form of energy?

Discovery
CHANNEL
SCHOOL

Video Field Trip

Physics of Fun

Encourage students to view the Video Field Trip "Physics of Fun."

Inquiry Activity

How Can Energy Change Form?   **L2**

Purpose
In this activity, students begin to distinguish different types of energy and describe energy transformations.

Skills Focus Observing, Inferring, Formulating Hypotheses

 Prep Time 5 minutes

Materials
flashlight, solar calculator, wind-up toy; other items may be substituted if the three listed in the Procedure are not available.

Class Time 20 minutes

Teaching Tips
• Have students construct data tables to record their observations.
• Encourage students to focus on the idea that energy can change forms, rather than on correctly naming different types of energy.

Expected Outcome Students will identify the energy transformations that occur in various devices.

Think About It
1. At this stage, students may identify the energy source for a battery-powered flashlight as "electricity," rather than chemical energy. Similarly, they may fail to recognize that light, rather than "electricity," is the energy source for a solar calculator. A wind-up toy requires a form of mechanical energy (elastic potential energy).

2. At this stage, students can reasonably be expected to distinguish devices that produce mechanical, electrical, chemical energy, or light. A wind-up toy produces mechanical energy, a flashlight produces light, and a solar calculator produces electrical energy.

3. Students should be able to describe the energy conversion that each device performs. For example, they may say that a flashlight converts electrical energy to light, a wind-up toy converts one source of mechanical energy into another example of mechanical energy, and a solar calculator converts light into electrical energy.

Logical

1 FOCUS

Objectives

15.1.1 Describe the relationship between work and energy.

15.1.2 Relate kinetic energy to mass and speed and **calculate** these quantities.

15.1.3 Analyze how potential energy is related to an object's position and **give examples** of gravitational and elastic potential energy.

15.1.4 Solve equations that relate an object's gravitational potential energy to its mass and height.

15.1.5 Give examples of the major forms of energy and **explain** how each is produced.

Reading Focus

Build Vocabulary   L2

Separating Compound Terms
Almost all the vocabulary terms for this section are compound terms of the form *(modifier) + energy*. Have students list the word or words modifying *energy* in each term. For each modifier, have them state or guess its meaning. After they have read the section, have them check to see if their guesses were correct.

Reading Strategy   L2

a. kinetic energy
b. the energy of motion
c. gravitational potential energy
d. elastic potential energy

2 INSTRUCT

Build Reading Literacy   L1

Outline Refer to page **156D** in **Chapter 6**, which provides the guidelines for an outline.

Have students create an outline of the section (pp. 446–452). Outlines should follow the head structure used in the section. Major headings are shown in green, and subheadings are shown in blue. Ask, **Based on your outline, what are two types of potential energy?** *(Gravitational and elastic)* **List three other forms of energy.** *(Answers may include kinetic energy, mechanical energy, thermal energy, chemical energy, electrical energy, electromagnetic energy, or nuclear energy.)*
Verbal, Logical

15.1 Energy and Its Forms

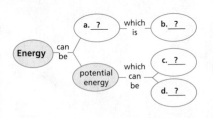

Standards: ICP.1.4, ICP.5.7, ICP.6.7, ICP.7.4, ICP.7.5

Reading Focus

Key Concepts
- How are energy and work related?
- What factors does the kinetic energy of an object depend on?
- How is gravitational potential energy determined?
- What are the major forms of energy?

Vocabulary
- energy
- kinetic energy
- potential energy
- gravitational potential energy
- elastic potential energy
- mechanical energy
- thermal energy
- chemical energy
- electrical energy
- electromagnetic energy
- nuclear energy

Reading Strategy
Building Vocabulary Copy the partially completed concept map below. Then, as you read, complete it with vocabulary terms and definitions from this section.

The road that winds through the mountain valley was closed. Skiers were banned from the area. The sound of artillery fire echoed from the mountains. It seemed out of place in this picturesque scene of snow-covered peaks surrounding the valley. A moment of quiet followed the blast. Suddenly, the snow broke loose with a menacing roar. Tumbling down the mountainside, the snow buried everything in its path. You can see in Figure 1 the enormous mass of accumulated snow that had hung above the valley. After the avalanche, the valley was quiet again. It is safe for skiers and hikers to return to the area.

This is the work of researchers at the Avalanche Control Section in Glacier National Park, Canada. These scientists monitor the snow as it builds up layer by layer on the park's upper peaks. They can predict when an avalanche is about to happen. With well-timed artillery shots, they make the avalanche happen at a time when the released energy cannot harm anyone.

Figure 1 In an avalanche, a mass of loose snow, soil, or rock suddenly gives way and slides down the side of a mountain.

446 *Chapter 15*

Section Resources

Print
- *Laboratory Manual,* Investigation 15A
- *Reading and Study Workbook With Math Support,* Section 15.1 and **Math Skill:** Calculating Potential Energy
- *Math Skills and Problem Solving Workbook,* Section 15.1
- *Transparencies,* Chapter Pretest and Section 15.1

Technology
- *Interactive Textbook,* Section 15.1
- *Presentation Pro CD-ROM,* Chapter Pretest and Section 15.1
- *Go Online,* NSTA SciLinks, Potential and kinetic energy

Energy and Work

Where did the energy of the avalanche come from? Where did it go? Energy is known by the changes it causes. You can hear the roar of an avalanche and see the movement of the snow. Sound and motion are examples of energy in action. In order to define energy, you need to return to the definition of a related topic, work. Recall that work is done when a force moves an object through a distance. **Energy** is the ability to do work. In other words, energy is transferred by a force moving an object through a distance.

Work and energy are closely related. When work is done on an object, energy is transferred to that object. ◯ **Work is a transfer of energy.** Both work and energy are typically measured in joules (J). Recall that 1 joule equals 1 newton-meter, the work done when an object is moved 1 meter by a 1-newton force. Although energy can take many different forms, it can always be measured in joules.

Think about the work and energy involved in doing something as simple as carrying your backpack up a flight of stairs. You do work on the backpack by lifting it against the force of gravity. This work requires energy. The energy to do the work comes from your muscles. Your muscles receive energy from the food you eat. The energy contained in your food comes from plants that have used the energy of sunlight, or animals that have eaten such plants. Figure 2 shows some of the many forms of energy.

Kinetic Energy

Many forms of energy can be classified into two general types: kinetic energy and potential energy. The energy of motion is called **kinetic energy.** The word kinetic comes from the Greek word *kinetos,* meaning "moving."

◯ **The kinetic energy of any moving object depends upon its mass and speed.** To calculate the kinetic energy of an object in joules, multiply $\frac{1}{2}$ by the object's mass (m) in kilograms and the square of its speed (v) in meters per second.

> **Kinetic Energy**
> $$\text{Kinetic energy (KE)} = \frac{1}{2}mv^2$$

Notice that doubling the mass in the formula would double the kinetic energy. However, doubling the speed would quadruple the kinetic energy, since kinetic energy is proportional to the square of an object's speed.

Figure 2 Energy has many different forms. **A** The sun gives off energy in the form of heat and light. **B** Plants convert sunlight into food that we can process and eat. **C** People convert food energy into muscle movement.
Applying Concepts *How did the skiers in the photo obtain the energy to climb the mountain slope?*

Energy **447**

Energy and Work
Integrate Health   L2

The energy in food is often measured in units of Calories. A food Calorie is actually equal to 1 kcal, or 1000 conventional calories. A conventional calorie is the amount of energy required to raise the temperature of 1 gram of water by 1°C. A conventional calorie is equivalent to 4.184 J, so a food Calorie is equivalent to 4184 J.

The number of Calories in a food item is the amount of chemical energy that can be obtained from complete combustion of the food. Some of this energy is lost as heat when you digest the food. Once the food is digested, the remaining energy is available for you to do work. However, if you don't use all of the energy you get from food to do work, the extra energy may be stored in fat molecules. To avoid gaining fat, you should burn about as many food Calories as you take in each day.

Ask students, **If you ate a sandwich that provided you with a net of 450 Calories of energy, how many joules of work would you be able to do with that energy?** *(If your body were 100% efficient, about 1.9 million joules.)*

Ask students, **List some ways that your body uses energy.** *(Answers may include: walking, lifting, breathing, maintaining body temperature, digesting food)* You may also encourage students to look for Calorie information on food labels and to keep a tally of how many Calories they consume over the course of a day.
Logical, Portfolio

Kinetic Energy
Build Science Skills   L2

Inferring Ask, Why would tripling the speed at which a car is moving have a greater effect on its kinetic energy than tripling its mass? *(Kinetic energy is directly proportional to mass, but it is proportional to the square of the object's speed. Tripling the mass would triple the kinetic energy, but tripling the velocity would make the kinetic energy nine times greater.)*
Logical

Answer to . . .

Figure 2 *They obtained energy from the food they ate.*

Math Practice

Solutions L2

1. $KE = \frac{1}{2}mv^2 =$
$(0.50)(70.0 \text{ kg})(2.0 \text{ m/s})^2 = 140 \text{ J}$
2. $KE = \frac{1}{2}mv^2 =$
$(0.50)(1400 \text{ kg})(25 \text{ m/s})^2 = 440,000 \text{ J}$
3. Rearranging the KE formula to
solve for v, $v = \sqrt{2(\text{KE})/m} =$
$\sqrt{2(18,000 \text{ J})/50.0 \text{ kg}} = 27 \text{ m/s}$
Logical

For Extra Help L1

Help students solve for speed, v. First,
show students how to rearrange the
equation to solve for v^2.
$$v^2 = 2(\text{KE})/m$$
Then, remind students to take the
square root of both sides to solve for v.
$$v = \sqrt{2(\text{KE})/m}$$
Logical
Direct students to the **Math Skills** in
the **Skills and Reference Handbook**
at the end of the student text for
additional help.

Additional Problems

1. What is the kinetic energy of a
70.0-kg man walking at a speed of
4.0 m/s? *(560 J; Emphasize that this is
not twice, but four times the kinetic energy
of the man walking at 2 m/s in Math
Practice Question 1.)*
2. A bicycle and rider with a combined
mass of 150 kg have 300 J of kinetic
energy while coasting. What is the speed
of the bicycle? *(2 m/s)* **Logical, Portfolio**

Potential Energy

Address Misconceptions L2

Students may think that an object at
rest has no energy. While a stationary
object has no kinetic energy, it can have
potential energy if there are forces acting
on it. If it is being pulled on by the force
of gravity, it has gravitational potential
energy. For example, a person sitting in
a dunk tank has gravitational potential
energy. As soon as the seat under him is
pulled away, the force of gravity is no
longer balanced by the opposing force of
the seat. Work is done on the person as
he falls into the water. Recall that energy
is the ability to do work. Because work is
done as the person falls, you know
energy must have been present. **Logical**

Math Practice

1. A 70.0-kilogram man is walking
at a speed of 2.0 m/s. What is
his kinetic energy?

2. A 1400-kilogram car is moving at
a speed of 25 m/s. How much
kinetic energy does the car have?

3. A 50.0-kilogram cheetah has a
kinetic energy of 18,000 J. How
fast is the cheetah running?
(*Hint:* Rearrange the equation to
solve for *v*.)

Figure 3 When this musician
pulls the string of her cello to one
side, the string is stretched and
gains potential energy.

Math Skills

Calculating Kinetic Energy
A 0.10-kilogram bird is flying at a constant speed of 8.0 m/s. What
is the bird's kinetic energy?

 Read and Understand
What information are you given?

> **Mass,** $m = 0.10$ kg   **Speed,** $v = 8.0$ m/s

What unknown are you trying to calculate?

> **Kinetic energy of the bird, KE**

2 Plan and Solve
*What equation contains the given quantities and
the unknown?*

$$KE = \frac{1}{2}mv^2$$

Substitute the known values in the formula for KE.

$$KE = \frac{1}{2}(0.10 \text{ kg})(8.0 \text{ m/s})^2$$

$$= 3.2 \text{ kg·m}^2/\text{s}^2 = 3.2 \text{ J}$$

3 Look Back and Check
Is your answer reasonable?

It seems reasonable because the bird has a low mass, so it
would not have much kinetic energy.

Potential Energy

Potential energy is energy that is stored as a result of position or
shape. The musician in Figure 3 adds energy to the cello string by
plucking it. The energy is stored in the stretched string when the
musician pulls it to one side. Then she releases the string and allows
it to vibrate. The stored energy is converted into kinetic energy. You
can also store energy just by picking up a book and holding it in the
air. Let go of the book and that stored energy will turn into the kinetic
energy of motion as the book falls to the floor. Plucking a string and
lifting a book are two examples of stored energy—energy with the
potential to do work. Two forms of potential energy are gravitational
potential energy and elastic potential energy.

Gravitational Potential Energy When you lift your gym bag up to the top seat of the bleachers, you do work to increase the potential energy of your bag. Potential energy that depends upon an object's height is called **gravitational potential energy.** This type of potential energy increases when an object is raised to a higher level.

The diver shown in Figure 4 is standing motionless at the end of a diving board, so she has no kinetic energy. But she does have energy—gravitational potential energy. She gained this potential energy by doing work—by climbing up the steps to the diving board. As always, the work done equals force (her weight) multiplied by distance (the height she climbs). You can use this work to calculate how much potential energy is gained.

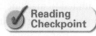 An object's gravitational potential energy depends on its mass, its height, and the acceleration due to gravity. The gravitational potential energy an object gains is equal to its weight (mg) multiplied by its height (h).

Gravitational Potential Energy

Potential energy (PE) = mgh

To calculate gravitational potential energy in joules, the mass of the object is expressed in kilograms and the height of the object is expressed in meters. The acceleration due to gravity, g, has a value in SI units of 9.8 m/s^2 on Earth. Note that height is measured from the ground or floor or some other reference level. Therefore, gravitational potential energy is measured relative to that same reference level.

Gravitational potential energy is directly related to the mass of the object and its height relative to a reference level. Thus, doubling either the mass of the object or its height doubles its gravitational potential energy.

Suppose the diver at the top of a 10.0-meter-high diving platform has a mass of 50.0 kilograms. You can calculate her potential energy relative to the ground as follows.

$$PE = mgh$$
$$= (50.0 \text{ kg})(9.8 \text{ m/s}^2)(10.0 \text{ m})$$
$$= 4900 \text{ kg} \cdot \text{m}^2/\text{s}^2 = 4900 \text{ J}$$

If, instead, the diver was standing on the ground, her height above the ground would be zero. Therefore, her gravitational potential energy relative to the ground would also be zero.

 Reading Checkpoint *What is gravitational potential energy?*

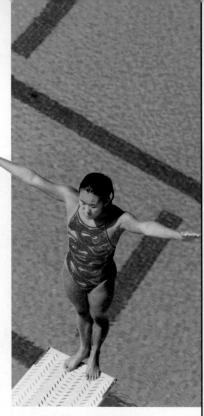

Figure 4 This diver has gravitational potential energy as she stands at the end of a diving board. **Predicting** *How would the diver's potential energy change if she stood on a platform twice as high as the one shown in the photo?*

For: Links on potential and kinetic energy

Visit: www.SciLinks.org

Web Code: ccn-2151

Energy **449**

Figure 5 A compressed bicycle shock absorber and a wound-up toy robot both have elastic potential energy.

Quick Lab

Investigating Elastic Potential Energy **L2**

Objective
After completing this activity, students will be able to
- describe the energy conversions that occur when a small ball is dropped while on top of a large ball.
- apply the law of conservation of energy to practical situations.

⚑ Address Misconceptions

Students may think that the height of a ball's bounce is a fixed, inherent characteristic of the ball. This lab can help students overcome this misconception.

Skills Focus Observing, Inferring

🕐 **Prep Time** 5 minutes

Advance Prep Do the lab outdoors or in the gym because the tennis ball will bounce very high in Step 3. Any two highly elastic balls will work, as long as one has more mass and is considerably larger than the other.

Class Time 15 minutes

Safety Students should stand clear of the balls in Step 3.

Teaching Tips
- In Step 3, students should hold the basketball in one hand and balance the tennis ball with the other hand.

Expected Outcome The tennis ball should bounce about four times higher in Step 3 than it does alone.

Analyze and Conclude
1. It may bounce to a height of 60 to 80 cm in Step 2 and approximately 3 m in Step 3.
2. The mechanical energy after the bounce is less than the initial mechanical energy because the ball does not rise to the height from which it was dropped. Just before and just after the bounce, the gravitational potential energy is zero, so the difference in energy must be due to a difference in kinetic energy.
3. The tennis ball bounced much higher in Step 3 than it did in Step 2 and Step 1 for two reasons. First, the tennis ball had more kinetic energy in Step 3 than it did in Step 2 because it received some elastic potential energy from the basketball.

Quick Lab

Investigating Elastic Potential Energy

Materials basketball, tennis ball, meter stick

Procedure
1. Drop the basketball from a height of 1 m. Use a meter stick to measure how high it bounces. Record your result.
2. Repeat Step 1 with the tennis ball.
3. Place the tennis ball on top of the basketball and drop both together from a height of 1 m. Record your observations.

Analyze and Conclude
1. **Observing** How high did the tennis ball bounce in Steps 2 and 3?
2. **Applying Concepts** From your observations of Step 2, how can you prove that the kinetic energy of the tennis ball just after a bounce is less than it was just before the bounce?
3. **Drawing Conclusions** Use the concepts of kinetic and potential energy to explain your observations of the tennis ball in Step 3.

Elastic Potential Energy The potential energy of an object that is stretched or compressed is known as **elastic potential energy.** Something is said to be elastic if it springs back to its original shape after it is stretched or compressed. Think back to the last time you stretched a rubber band between your fingers. By stretching the rubber band, you did work on it. Just like the musician did with her cello string, the energy you added was stored in the rubber band as potential energy. If you've ever broken a stretched rubber band, you may have felt a painful snap on your hand. The rubber band's elastic potential energy was converted into kinetic energy.

Elastic potential energy can also be stored in objects that are compressed, such as springs. Drop a slice of bread on the floor and it does not bounce noticeably. Why doesn't it? The bread is not very elastic. Drop a basketball on the floor and the basketball bounces back up. The compressed air in the ball forces the ball to spring back into shape after hitting the ground, propelling the ball back up. Other examples of elastic potential energy are shown in Figure 5.

Forms of Energy

All energy can be considered to be kinetic energy, potential energy, or the energy in fields such as those produced by electromagnetic waves. Some familiar examples are the chemical energy in fireworks, electrical energy in lightning bolts, and nuclear energy within the sun. 🔑 **The major forms of energy are mechanical energy, thermal energy, chemical energy, electrical energy, electromagnetic energy, and nuclear energy.** Each of these forms of energy can be converted into other forms of energy.

Mechanical Energy The energy associated with the motion and position of everyday objects is **mechanical energy.** Don't be confused by the name, however. Mechanical energy is not limited to machines. Mechanical energy is the sum of an object's potential energy and kinetic energy. Speeding trains, bouncing balls, and sprinting athletes all have mechanical energy.

Second, the mass of the tennis ball is much smaller than the mass of the basketball. Therefore, the tennis ball reached a greater velocity and bounced higher than it did in Step 2 and higher than the basketball did in Step 1.
Kinesthetic, Visual

For Enrichment **L3**

Students can use resources in the library or on the Internet to research the slingshot effect, which uses the gravitational potential energy of space probes as they pass by planets to accelerate the probes toward their targets. This effect is based on a principle similar to one used in this lab.
Verbal

Mechanical energy does not include thermal energy, chemical energy, or other forms of energy associated with the motion or the arrangement of atoms or molecules. Most of these other forms of energy do involve kinetic or potential energy, but on an atomic scale. However, the mechanical energy of a speeding train and a sprinting athlete comes from the chemical energy of the train's fuel and the sprinter's body cells.

Thermal Energy Almost all of the matter around you contains atoms. These particles are always in random motion and thus have kinetic energy. The total potential and kinetic energy related to the motion of all the microscopic particles in an object make up its **thermal energy.** When an object's atoms move faster, its thermal energy increases and the object becomes warmer. As Figure 6 shows, when objects are hot enough, they can emit visible light.

Chemical Energy The campers in Figure 7 are toasting marshmallows over a campfire. The source of energy for the fire is the energy stored in wood. When the wood is burned, energy is released and heats the marshmallows as well as the area around the campfire. The energy stored in wood is chemical energy. **Chemical energy** is the energy stored in chemical bonds. When bonds are broken, the released energy can do work. All chemical compounds, including fuels such as coal and gasoline, store energy. For example, cars can use the chemical energy stored in gasoline to move about. The gasoline is burned in the car's engine and some of its chemical energy is converted into mechanical energy to move the car.

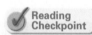 **Reading Checkpoint** *What is chemical energy?*

Figure 6 Energy occurs in many forms. This molten metal is extremely hot. It contains a great deal of thermal energy.
*Observing **What other kinds of energy are evident in this photograph?***

Figure 7 This family is using the chemical energy of burning wood to produce thermal energy for heating marshmallows.

Energy **451**

Forms of Energy

Teacher ▶ **Demo**

Burning a Peanut   L2

Purpose To demonstrate that food contains chemical energy.

Materials peanut, paper clip, pliers, pan of water, matches, safety goggles

Safety Prior to conducting this demonstration, ask if there are any students with peanut allergies. As an alternative to a peanut, another nut could be used. Wear safety goggles and keep a fire extinguisher close at hand.

Procedure Make a small loop at one end of the paper clip to hold the peanut. Hold the other end of the paper clip with pliers. Place the peanut in the loop and hold it over the pan of water. Light the match and hold it to the peanut until the peanut starts to burn. The pan of water will catch and extinguish any pieces of the peanut that fall.

Expected Outcome The peanut should burn steadily for about a minute. This demonstrates that even a single peanut contains a large amount of chemical energy. You may make this demonstration quantitative by holding the peanut under a beaker containing 25 mL of water. You can measure the temperature change of the water and calculate the amount of energy released from the peanut.
Visual

FYI

Students may benefit from understanding that sound is a form of energy. When energy leaves a system during energy transfers, part of the energy is usually lost as sound. Students will study mechanical waves and sound in Chapter 17.

Answer to . . .

Figure 6 *Kinetic energy, gravitational potential energy, electromagnetic energy*

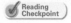 **Reading Checkpoint** *The energy stored in chemical bonds*

Build Science Skills `L2`

Classifying Ask students to classify the following types of energy as kinetic energy or potential energy when considered at an atomic or subatomic scale: thermal energy *(Kinetic)*, chemical energy *(Potential)*, nuclear energy *(Potential)*
Logical, Visual

3 ASSESS

Evaluate Understanding `L2`

Ask students to list at least two kinds of energy in the objects in each of the following examples:
A car driving *(Kinetic energy, chemical energy)*
A car battery *(Chemical energy, electrical energy)*
An apple falling *(Kinetic energy, gravitational potential energy, chemical energy)*
A spring-loaded mouse trap *(Elastic potential energy when set, kinetic energy when sprung)*

All of the above objects also have thermal energy, electromagnetic energy, and nuclear energy.

Reteach `L1`

Review Figures 3–8. For each figure, discuss the type of energy that the figure illustrates.

Solutions `L2`
8. PE = *mgh* =
(60.0 kg)(9.8 m/s^2)(74.8 m) = 44,000 J
9. KE = $\frac{1}{2}mv^2$ =

(0.50)(0.145 kg)(30.0 m/s)^2 = 65.3 J

 Interactive Textbook If your class subscribes to the Interactive Textbook, use it to review key concepts in Section 15.1.

Figure 8 Two major forms of energy are electrical energy and electromagnetic energy. **A** Lightning bolts transfer electric charge. **B** Galaxies are giant structures in space that typically contain billions of stars. The stars give off enormous amounts of electromagnetic energy.

Electrical Energy Many devices you use every day use electricity, or electrical energy. **Electrical energy** is the energy associated with electric charges. Electric charges can exert forces that do work. Batteries, which convert chemical energy to electrical energy, are used to operate portable CD players, flashlights, and calculators. Electrical energy also occurs in nature. The powerful bolts of lightning shown in Figure 8A are produced by electrical energy.

Electromagnetic Energy The sun radiates electromagnetic energy into space and is the source, either directly or indirectly, of most of the world's energy supplies. **Electromagnetic energy** is a form of energy that travels through space in the form of waves. Visible light and X-rays are examples of electromagnetic energy. Because electromagnetic waves can travel long distances through air and space, they are often used for communication. The glowing galaxy in Figure 8B is emitting electromagnetic energy of many kinds.

Nuclear Energy The nucleus of an atom is held together by strong and weak nuclear forces, which can store an enormous amount of potential energy. The energy stored in atomic nuclei is known as **nuclear energy.** A nuclear power plant uses nuclear fission reactions to generate electricity. Nuclear fission is a process that releases energy by splitting nuclei apart. A second type of nuclear reaction, nuclear fusion, releases energy when less massive nuclei combine to form a more massive nucleus. The heat and light of the sun are produced by the fusion of hydrogen nuclei into helium nuclei.

Section 15.1 Assessment

Reviewing Concepts
1. Describe the relationship between work and energy.
2. How is the kinetic energy of an object determined?
3. What factors determine the gravitational potential energy of an object?
4. Give an example of each of the major forms of energy.
5. When you heat a pot of water over a flame, what form of energy is added to the water?

Critical Thinking
6. **Applying Concepts** What kind of energy is represented by an archer stretching a bow string?

7. **Applying Concepts** Can an object have both kinetic energy and potential energy at the same time? Explain.

Math Practice

8. A 60.0-kg person walks from the ground to the roof of a 74.8-m-tall building. How much gravitational potential energy does she have at the top of the building?
9. A pitcher throws a 0.145-kg baseball at a velocity of 30.0 m/s. How much kinetic energy does the ball have?

Section 15.1 Assessment

1. Energy is the ability to do work, and work is the transfer of energy.
2. By multiplying half an object's mass by the square of its speed
3. Its mass, the acceleration due to gravity, and its height relative to a reference level
4. Sample answers include a bouncing ball for mechanical energy, molten steel or fire for thermal energy, wood or gasoline for chemical energy, CD players or lightning for electrical energy, light for electromagnetic energy, and nuclear power plants for nuclear energy.
5. Thermal energy
6. Elastic potential energy
7. Yes. Kinetic energy and potential energy are not mutually exclusive. For example, a falling object has both kinetic energy and gravitational potential energy.

15.2 Energy Conversion and Conservation

Standards: ICP.1.4, ICP.4.1

Reading Focus

Key Concepts

- Can energy be converted from one form into another?
- What is the law of conservation of energy?
- What energy conversion takes place as an object falls toward Earth?
- How are energy and mass related?

Vocabulary

- energy conversion

Reading Strategy

Relating Cause and Effect Copy the flow-chart below. As you read, complete the chart to explain an energy conversion. Make two similar charts for pendulums and pole vaults.

Gull lifts oyster, increasing oyster's gravitational potential energy. → a. ___?___ → b. ___?___

---

1 FOCUS

Objectives

15.2.1 Describe conversions of energy from one form to another.

15.2.2 State and **apply** the law of conservation of energy.

15.2.3 Analyze how energy is conserved in conversions between kinetic energy and potential energy and **solve equations** that equate initial energy to final energy.

15.2.4 Describe the relationship between energy and mass and **calculate** how much energy is equivalent to a given mass.

Reading Focus

Build Vocabulary L2

Paraphrasing Tell students that *conversion* means *a change from one form or state to another.* Prompt students to describe other situations where conversions take place, such as converting money from one currency to another or converting from one unit of measure to another. For each example, identify the previous form or state and the new form or state.

Reading Strategy L2

a. The gull drops the oyster, and the oyster's gravitational potential energy is converted into kinetic energy as the oyster falls. (Air resistance can be ignored.)
b. The oyster strikes a rock and breaks. Kinetic energy is converted into work (breaking the shell) and thermal energy. The kinetic energy and gravitational potential energy of the oyster are now zero.
c. Pull pendulum up (work converted to PE).
d. Pendulum swings down (PE converts to KE).
e. Pendulum swings up (KE converts into gravitational PE).
f. Pole-vaulter sprints (work increases KE).
g. Pole bends (KE converts to elastic PE).
h. Pole-vaulter accelerates up (PE converts to KE).

On October 9, 1992, people from Kentucky to New York reported seeing a bright streak of white light shooting across the night sky. Most observers, having seen "shooting stars" before, expected this one to quickly burn out and disappear. However, that did not happen. The shooting star, or meteor, continued streaking across the sky. After a few seconds, pieces of the meteor broke off, creating a series of smaller streaks of light. Eventually, the streaks disappeared from view. Although the event was interesting, most witnesses probably soon forgot about it.

However, the meteor was not soon forgotten by the owners of a red automobile in Peekskill, New York. Unfortunately for them, a large chunk of the meteor made it through Earth's atmosphere and struck their parked car. The car was badly damaged, as shown in Figure 9. Luckily, no one was in the car at the time, and so no one was hurt.

As the Peekskill meteor traveled through the atmosphere, some of its kinetic energy was converted into light and heat. The light made the meteor visible in the sky. The heat caused a large portion of the meteor to vaporize in the atmosphere. Upon impact, much of the meteor's remaining kinetic energy went into smashing the metal body of the car.

Figure 9 A meteor crashed into the rear of this car, causing considerable damage.

Energy **453**

Section Resources

Print

- *Laboratory Manual,* Investigation 15B
- *Reading and Study Workbook With Math Support,* Section 15.2
- *Math Skills and Problem Solving Workbook,* Section 15.2
- *Transparencies,* Section 15.2

Technology

- *Probeware Lab Manual,* Lab 6
- *Interactive Textbook,* Section 15.2
- *Presentation Pro CD-ROM,* Section 15.2
- *Go Online,* NSTA SciLinks, Energy; PHSchool.com, Data sharing

2 INSTRUCT

Energy Conversion

Exploring Energy Conversion   L2

Objective

After completing this activity, students will be able to
- describe the relationship between kinetic energy and velocity.

Address Misconceptions

Students may intuitively understand that faster objects have more kinetic energy than slower objects, but may hold the misconception that kinetic energy is roughly proportional to velocity. The strong effect of height—and therefore velocity—on crater diameter can help students overcome this misconception.

Skills Focus Observing, Inferring, Calculating

 Prep Time 20 minutes

Advance Prep Boxes should be large enough for students to drop the balls into the boxes without missing them. A box about the size of a shoebox should be sufficient. Tell students the mass of the ball.

Class Time 25 minutes

Teaching Tips
- Have students construct data tables to record their observations.
- Remind students to measure the height of the ball from the surface of the clay, not from the floor or tabletop.
- Remind students to convert measurements to meters and kilograms in order to calculate energy in joules for Question 2.

Expected Outcome Students will observe that an increase in height will produce a larger crater.

Analyze and Conclude
1. Increasing the height increases the crater diameter.
2. Energies depend on the mass of the ball. $PE_{60\ cm} = 2 \times PE_{30\ cm}$ and $PE_{90\ cm} = 3 \times PE_{30\ cm}$.
3. Increasing kinetic energy results in a crater with a larger diameter.
Kinesthetic, Logical

Figure 10 Energy is converted from one form to another as this match is lit.
Applying Concepts *What energy conversions take place when you turn on a battery-powered portable radio?*

Energy Conversion

The Peekskill meteor clearly shows that energy can change forms. **Energy can be converted from one form to another.** The process of changing energy from one form to another is **energy conversion.**

Not all energy conversions are as dramatic as the Peekskill meteor. Energy conversions are constantly taking place all around you, often without you noticing. Wind-up toys store elastic potential energy in a compressed spring. When the spring unwinds, potential energy is converted into the kinetic energy of the toy's moving parts. Light bulbs convert electrical energy into thermal energy and electromagnetic energy.

In some cases, energy is converted from one form into another in a series of steps. The striking of the match shown in Figure 10 is a good example. In lighting a match, your muscles use chemical energy moving your hand to strike the match against a rough area on the matchbox. Friction between the match and the matchbox converts some of the match's kinetic energy into thermal energy. The thermal energy triggers a chemical reaction on the match tip, releasing some of the match's stored chemical energy. The stored chemical energy is then converted into thermal energy and electromagnetic energy in the flame.

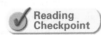 *What energy conversions occur in lighting a match?*

Quick Lab

Exploring Energy Conversion

Materials

small steel ball of known mass, box lined with soft modeling clay, meter stick, graph paper

Procedure

1. Construct a data table with 3 blank rows and 5 columns labeled Mass, Height, Diameter, Potential Energy, and Kinetic Energy.
2. Drop the ball into the box of clay from a height of 30 cm. Record this height.
3. Measure and record the diameter of the crater that the ball formed.
4. Repeat Steps 2 and 3, dropping the ball from 60 cm and 90 cm.
5. Graph your data. Plot the crater diameter on the vertical axis and height on the horizontal axis.

Analyze and Conclude

1. **Using Graphs** According to your graph, how are crater diameter and the height of the ball related?
2. **Calculating** For each height, calculate and record the initial potential energy of the ball.
3. **Drawing Conclusions** How are kinetic energy and crater diameter related? (*Hint:* The ball's kinetic energy when it hits the clay equals the potential energy it started with, *mgh*.)

Customize for Inclusion

Hearing Impaired

Clues about energy and energy transfers are often in the form of sounds. For example, you may be able to tell how fast a train is moving by how loud it sounds, how hard a baseball player hits the ball by the sound of the crack of the bat, or how angry someone is by the volume of one's voice. However, sounds are not the only clues to energy and energy transfers. Invite hearing-impaired students to consider and share what kinds of information they observe that tell them about how much energy people and objects have, and about energy transfers. For example, they may use visual clues such as light given off by the coil in a toaster to tell that the coil is hot.

Figure 11 Although speed skaters slide quickly over smooth ice, they are still slowed down by friction with the air and the surface of the ice.
Inferring What are two ways that skaters can reduce friction?

Conservation of Energy

When energy changes from one form to another, the total energy remains unchanged even though many energy conversions may occur. This is one of the most important concepts in science, the law of conservation of energy. **The law of conservation of energy states that energy cannot be created or destroyed.** According to the law of conservation of energy, energy can be converted from one form to another. However, in a closed system, the amount of energy present at the beginning of a process is the same as the amount of energy at the end. (In a closed system, nothing can enter or leave.)

You know that if you stop pedaling when you're riding a bike on a flat path, the bike will eventually come to a stop. The moving bike had kinetic energy. Where did the bike's kinetic energy go? The bike slowed down and stopped because of frictional forces acting over a distance. The work done by friction changes kinetic energy into thermal energy.

As a bicycle moves, it encounters friction with the ground and the air. Such friction causes a continual conversion of kinetic energy into thermal energy. Thus, as the bicycle slows, it gains thermal energy. So do the ground and the air. When the energy lost to frictional forces is accounted for, energy is conserved overall.

Recall that friction within machinery reduces efficiency. Friction is a major cause of energy consumption in cars and factories. All moving parts are subject to friction.

You can reduce friction but you can't avoid it. Friction is everywhere. Even the skaters in Figure 11 are subject to friction. Recall that objects moving through the air are slowed by air resistance. In many cases, most of a falling object's potential energy is converted into thermal energy because of air resistance.

You can ignore the effects of friction in many everyday situations. A marble dropped from one meter above the ground, for example, encounters so little air resistance that it can be ignored.

For: Links on energy
Visit: www.SciLinks.org
Web Code: ccn-2152

Energy **455**

Energy Conversions

Energy in a Pendulum L2

Purpose Students use the law of conservation of energy to predict and explain the motion of a pendulum.

Materials pendulum bob and string, hook at top of board, chalk (or marker), level

Procedure Tie the string to the pendulum bob and hang the pendulum in front of the board. The pendulum should reach at least 2/3 of the way down the board. When the pendulum is at rest, draw a vertical line directly behind the pendulum string. Use the level to draw a long horizontal line about 15 cm above the pendulum bob. Displace the pendulum to one side so that it is even with the horizontal line. Ask students to predict how high the pendulum will swing on the other side. Release the pendulum bob.

Let the pendulum swing until it no longer reaches the height of the horizontal line. Have students discuss what may have happened to the mechanical energy that was lost from the system.

Now have a student come to the board and hold a pencil at the intersection of the vertical line and the horizontal line. The pencil should be sticking straight out with the eraser against the board. The pencil will shorten the length of the pendulum in the second half of the pendulum's motion. Make sure the student holding the pencil is clear of the pendulum's path. Hold the pendulum bob as before and again ask students to predict how high the pendulum will swing on the other side. Release the pendulum bob, and observe.

Expected Outcome In both cases, the pendulum should initially rise to the height of the horizontal line. Discuss with students how this demonstrates the conservation of energy. After the pendulum swings for a while, it no longer rises to the height of the horizontal line because some of the kinetic energy is converted to thermal energy due to air resistance and friction at the support. Point out to students that total energy is still conserved, although mechanical energy is not.

Kinesthetic, Logical

Figure 12 Some gulls use energy conversion to obtain food by dropping oysters onto rocks. **Applying Concepts** *Where is the oyster's potential energy greatest? Where is its kinetic energy greatest?*

Figure 13 Pendulum clocks use pendulums to maintain accurate time.

Energy Conversions

One of the most common energy conversions is between potential energy and kinetic energy. **The gravitational potential energy of an object is converted to the kinetic energy of motion as the object falls.** That's what happens when an avalanche brings tons of snow from the top of a mountain to the valley floor. Similarly, when you release a compressed spring, the elastic potential energy of the spring is converted into kinetic energy as the spring expands. Conversions between kinetic and potential energy can happen in both directions, that is, from kinetic to potential energy, or from potential to kinetic energy.

Some gulls use energy conversion to obtain food. Oysters are a food source for gulls. However, it is difficult for a gull to break open an oyster's hard shell with its beak. Unfortunately for the oyster, gulls have learned a clever way to use gravitational potential energy, as shown in Figure 12. A hungry gull picks up an oyster and flies high into the air directly over some rocks. The gull does work on the oyster by raising it against the force of gravity, thereby increasing the oyster's potential energy. While over the rocks, the gull lets the oyster fall. As the oyster falls, its gravitational potential energy is converted into kinetic energy. The oyster picks up speed until it hits the rocks. The impact breaks open the shell. The gull then swoops down to enjoy its meal.

Energy Conversion in Pendulums At the lake, you grab a rope hanging from a tree branch. With a yell, you swing down toward the lake, and pick up speed until you land with a giant splash. A rope swing is an example of a pendulum. A pendulum consists of a weight swinging back and forth from a rope or string.

Pendulums were used in the first truly accurate clocks. The Dutch scientist Christiaan Huygens (1629–1695) made the first pendulum clock in 1656. Pendulum clocks such as the one shown in Figure 13 make use of the fact that the time it takes for a pendulum to swing back and forth once is precisely related to its length.

Kinetic energy and potential energy undergo constant conversion as a pendulum swings. At the highest point in its swing, the pendulum is momentarily motionless as it changes direction. At this point, the weight at the end of the pendulum has zero kinetic energy and maximum potential energy.

As the pendulum swings downward, potential energy is converted to kinetic energy. At the bottom of the swing, the pendulum has maximum kinetic energy and zero potential energy. The pendulum then moves upward again, repeating the process. Eventually, frictional forces slow down the pendulum. In a clock, a spring mechanism or hanging weights provide energy to keep the pendulum swinging despite the effects of friction.

Energy Conversion in the Pole Vault

The pole vault is a difficult track and field event that requires a combination of speed, strength, timing, and energy conversion. In the pole vault, an athlete uses a flexible pole to propel himself over a high bar. Look at the pole-vaulter's jump in Figure 14 and think about how energy changes during the jump.

In order to start the jump with as much kinetic energy as possible, the pole-vaulter sprints down the runway as fast as he can. At the end of his sprint, he plants the end of a long pole at the base of the high bar and propels himself into the air. The pole-vaulter's kinetic energy is partially converted into elastic potential energy as the pole bends. The pole springs back into shape, propelling the pole-vaulter upward, hopefully high enough to clear the bar.

As the pole-vaulter soars, his kinetic energy decreases while he gains gravitational potential energy. Once the highest point has been reached, his gravitational potential energy begins to convert back to kinetic energy. The pole-vaulter picks up speed as he falls back to the ground.

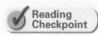 **Reading Checkpoint** *What energy changes occur in a pole vault?*

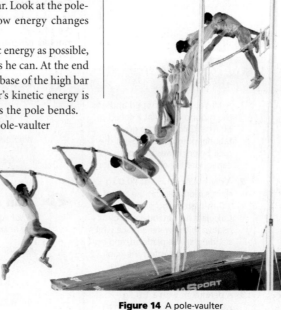

Figure 14 A pole-vaulter converts kinetic energy into potential energy in order to propel himself high into the air. **Applying Concepts** *At which point does a pole-vaulter have the most gravitational potential energy?*

Energy Conversion Calculations

When friction is small enough to be ignored, and no mechanical energy is added to a system, then the system's mechanical energy does not change. Recall that mechanical energy is the total kinetic and potential energy of an object.

$$\text{Mechanical energy} = \text{KE} + \text{PE}$$

You can apply the law of conservation of energy to any mechanical process. A mechanical process can be any action, such as the motion of a pendulum, water falling in a waterfall, or a diver propelled by a diving board. In all of these processes, if friction can be neglected, the mechanical energy at the beginning equals the mechanical energy at the end. That is, total mechanical energy remains constant. This equality can be stated as follows.

Conservation of Mechanical Energy

$$(\text{KE} + \text{PE})_{\text{beginning}} = (\text{KE} + \text{PE})_{\text{end}}$$

The Math Skills box on the following page shows how the conservation of mechanical energy equation can be used.

Energy **457**

Math Practice

Solutions
L2

1. $(PE)_{beginning} = (KE)_{end} = \frac{1}{2}mv^2 =$
(0.50)(10 kg)(60 m/s)^2 =
18,000 J
2. $(PE)_{beginning} = mgh =$
(70.0 kg)(9.8 m/s^2)(3.0 m) = 2100 J;
At the beginning, KE = 0 and at the
end, PE = 0, so $(PE)_{beginning} = (KE)_{end}$
$= \frac{1}{2}mv^2$; Substituting the known values,
2100 J = (0.5)(70.0 kg)(v^2);
Solving for v, $v = \sqrt{(2)(2100 \text{ J})/70.0 \text{ kg}}$
= 7.7 m/s
3. $(PE)_{beginning} = mgh =$
(1.0 kg)(9.8 m/s^2)(0.04 m) = 0.4 J;
at the beginning, KE = 0; at the lowest
point, PE = 0; therefore
$(PE)_{beginning} = (KE)_{end} = 0.4$ J
Logical

For Extra Help
L1

For most simple conservation of
mechanical energy problems, the
calculations depend on some form of
the equation PE = KE, or $mgh = \frac{1}{2}mv^2$.
If students are having difficulty with a
particular problem, help them rearrange
the equation to separate known and
unknown variables before plugging in
numbers.
Logical

Direct students to the **Math Skills** in
the **Skills and Reference Handbook**
at the end of the student text for
additional help.

Additional Problems

1. If you throw a baseball straight up
with a speed of 5 m/s, what will be the
speed of the ball when it comes back to
your hand? Ignore air resistance. *(5 m/s)*
2. A 1000-kg car is coasting at 10 m/s
toward a hill that is 10 m high. Will the
car make it to the top of the hill if the
driver does not step on the gas pedal?
*(No. Initial KE =50,000 J. At a height of
10 m, PE would be about 100,000 J.
The car could only reach a height of 5 m,
ignoring friction.)*
Logical, Portfolio

Math Practice

1. A 10-kg rock is dropped and hits
the ground below at a speed of
60 m/s. Calculate the gravitational potential energy of the
rock before it was dropped. You
can ignore the effects of friction.

2. A diver with a mass of 70.0 kg
stands motionless at the top of a
3.0-m-high diving platform.
Calculate his potential energy
relative to the water surface while
standing on the platform, and his
speed when he enters the pool.
*(Hint: Assume the diver's initial
vertical speed after diving is zero.)*

3. A pendulum with a 1.0-kg
weight is set in motion from a
position 0.04 m above the lowest
point on the path of the weight.
What is the kinetic energy of the
pendulum at the lowest point?
(Hint: Assume there is no friction.)

Math Skills

Conservation of Mechanical Energy
At a construction site, a 1.50-kg brick is dropped from rest and hits
the ground at a speed of 26.0 m/s. Assuming air resistance can be
ignored, calculate the gravitational potential energy of the brick
before it was dropped.

1 ### Read and Understand
What information are you given?

> **Mass,** $m = 1.50 \text{ kg}$ **Final speed,** $v = 26.0$ m/s

What unknown are you trying to calculate?

> **Gravitational potential energy of the brick
> before it was dropped, PE**

2 ### Plan and Solve
*What equations or formulas contain the given quantities and
the unknown?*

*Because the brick falls without air resistance, the
conservation of mechanical energy equation can be used.*

$$(KE + PE)_{beginning} = (KE + PE)_{end}$$

You will also need to use the formula for kinetic energy (KE).

$$KE = \frac{1}{2}mv^2$$

*Note that the KE at the beginning is zero because the brick
has not yet begun to fall. Also, when the brick hits the
ground, its potential energy is zero. Substitute these values
into the conservation of energy formula.*

$$(PE)_{beginning} = (KE)_{end}$$

Substitute the formula for KE.

$$PE = KE = \frac{1}{2}mv^2$$

Substitute the known values and calculate the PE.

$$PE = \frac{1}{2}(1.50 \text{ kg})(26.0 \text{ m/s})^2 = 507 \text{ kg·m}^2/\text{s}^2 = 507 \text{ J}$$

3 ### Look Back and Check
Is your answer reasonable?

Check the answer by finding the initial height of the brick,
using PE = 507 J = *mgh*. Substituting in *m* and *g* gives
h = 34.5 m. This is a reasonable height for an object in
free fall to reach a speed of 26.0 m/s.

Facts and Figures

Quantization of Energy $E = mc^2$, Einstein's
equation showing the equivalence of mass and
energy, is probably the most famous equation
in physics today. However, Max Planck's
equation, $E = h\nu$, is also important. In this
equation, *E* is energy, *h* is a constant called
Planck's constant (6.63 × 10^{-34} J•s), and ν
(the Greek letter "nu") is frequency. This
equation encapsulates the idea that energy
exists in discrete packets, called quanta.

Planck proposed this equation in 1900 to
help explain blackbody radiation. Einstein
provided further experimental support for this
equation in 1905 when he used it to explain
the photoelectric effect. The photoelectric
effect is a result of the fact that light, like all
forms of energy, comes in discrete packets.
Light quanta are also called photons. Students
will learn more about photons in Chapter 18.

Energy and Mass

Physicist Albert Einstein (1879–1955), shown in Figure 15, developed his special theory of relativity in 1905. This theory included the now-famous equation $E = mc^2$. In Einstein's equation, E is energy, m is mass, and c is the speed of light. This seemingly ordinary equation has surprising consequences. ⬤ **Einstein's equation, $E = mc^2$, says that energy and mass are equivalent and can be converted into each other.** In other words, energy is released as matter is destroyed, and matter can be created from energy.

Notice that the speed of light is squared in Einstein's equation. The speed of light is an extremely large number, 3.0×10^8 meters per second. Thus, a tiny amount of matter can produce an enormous amount of energy. Suppose 1 gram of matter were entirely converted into energy.

$$E = mc^2 = (10^{-3}\ \text{kg}) \times (3 \times 10^8\ \text{m/s}) \times (3 \times 10^8\ \text{m/s})$$

$$= 9 \times 10^{13}\ \text{kg·m}^2/\text{s}^2 = 9 \times 10^{13}\ \text{J}$$

In comparison, 1 gram of TNT produces only 2931 joules of energy. In nuclear fission and fusion reactions, however, large amounts of energy are released by the destruction of very small amounts of matter. Therefore, the law of conservation of energy has been modified to say that mass and energy together are always conserved.

Figure 15 Albert Einstein made important contributions to many areas of physics. His theory of special relativity showed that energy and mass are equivalent.

Section 15.2 Assessment

Reviewing Concepts

1. ⬤ Describe how energy can be converted from one form to another in a wind-up toy.
2. ⬤ What does the law of conservation of energy state?
3. ⬤ As an object falls in free fall, what energy change is taking place?
4. ⬤ What did Einstein conclude about the relationship between energy and mass?
5. What type of energy change results when friction slows down an object?
6. Describe the energy of a playground swing at its highest position.

Critical Thinking

7. **Inferring** Why does a bouncing ball rise to a lower height with each bounce? What energy conversion is taking place?

8. **Applying Concepts** To begin a dive, a diver jumps into the air and then lands on the diving board, causing it to bend. What type of energy conversions occur as the board springs back and propels the diver up into the air?

Math ◆ Practice

9. A 0.15-kg ball is thrown into the air and rises to a height of 20.0 m. How much kinetic energy did the ball initially have?
10. A 125-g steel ball with a kinetic energy of 0.25 J rolls along a horizontal track. How high up an inclined track will the ball roll if friction can be ignored?

Energy **459**

Section 15.2 Assessment

1. Elastic potential energy stored in the wound-up spring is converted to kinetic energy as the spring unwinds and the toy moves.
2. Energy cannot be created or destroyed.
3. Gravitational potential energy is converted into kinetic energy as the object falls.
4. Energy and mass are equivalent, and can be converted into one another.
5. Friction causes the conversion of kinetic energy to thermal energy.

6. The swing has maximum gravitational potential energy and no kinetic energy at its highest position.
7. Friction within the ball, between the ball and the ground, and between the ball and the air converts kinetic energy into thermal energy. Each bounce has less kinetic energy.
8. The elastic potential energy of the board is converted into both kinetic energy and gravitational potential energy (because the diver's height increases while the diver is still in contact with the board).

Energy and Mass
Build Science Skills L2

Calculating Have students use Einstein's mass-energy equation to calculate the energy equivalence of an electron ($m = 9.1 \times 10^{-31}$ kg) and of their own body. *(For an electron: $E = mc^2 = (9.1 \times 10^{-31}$ kg$)(3.0 \times 10^8$ m/s$)^2 = 8.2 \times 10^{-14}$ J; for a 50-kg student: $E = mc^2 = (50$ kg$)(3 \times 10^8$ m/s$)^2 = 5 \times 10^{18}$ J)*
Logical, Portfolio

3 ASSESS

Evaluate Understanding L2

Ask students to describe systems or situations in which energy conversions are taking place. They may use examples from the section or new examples. For each system, they should identify at least two forms of energy. They should also describe how energy is lost from the system, and say what form the energy takes after it has left the system.

Reteach L1

Review Figures 10–14. For each figure, discuss the energy conversions that are taking place. Identify what forms of energy are present before, during, and after the events shown in each figure.

Math ◆ Practice

Solutions L2

9. The ball's potential energy at the beginning and kinetic energy at its maximum height are zero. Using the conservation of energy formula, $(KE)_{beginning} = (PE)_{end}$, $(KE)_{beginning} = mgh = (0.15$ kg$)(9.8$ m/s$^2)(20.0$ m$) = 29$ J
10. The ball's initial potential energy and its kinetic energy at the maximum height along the track are zero. Using the conservation of energy formula, $(KE)_{beginning} = (PE)_{end} = mgh$, solve for h. $h = KE/mg = 0.25$ J$/(0.125$ kg $\times 9.8$ m/s$^2) = 0.20$ m

Interactive Textbook If your class subscribes to the Interactive Textbook, use it to review key concepts in Section 15.2.

Roller Coasters L2

Background

Most historians believe that roller coasters developed from ice slides used for recreation in sixteenth-century Russia. Some of these slides were over 70 feet high and stretched for hundreds of feet. Wheeled roller coasters became popular in France during the nineteenth century. Roller coasters became popular in the United States during the early twentieth century, epitomized by the many coasters at New York's Coney Island amusement park. Roller coasters had a resurgence in popularity in the 1960s, when many large wooden coasters were built, and in the 1970s, when many steel looping coasters were created. Today's largest and fastest roller coasters are made of steel. Some have vertical drops of over 300 feet and reach speeds of over 100 miles per hour. But many people still enjoy the rattle and creak of wooden coasters, too.

Roller Coasters

A roller coaster is a train powered by gravity. An initial store of potential energy is released dramatically during the ride.

A roller coaster's first hill, called the lift hill, is the highest point of the ride. As the coaster plunges down the first drop, its potential energy is converted into kinetic energy, the energy of motion. Later, some of this kinetic energy is converted back into potential energy as the coaster's speed decreases during a climb. Over the course of the ride, the coaster's total mechanical energy (potential plus kinetic energy) gradually decreases. This change occurs due to friction from the rails and the air, which causes the coaster's mechanical energy to be converted into heat. By the end of the ride, all the potential energy created on the lift hill has been lost as heat.

As it falls, the coaster converts potential energy into kinetic energy.

Releasing energy

A roller coaster goes through a series of exchanges between potential and kinetic energy.

A cable *pulls cars to the top of the lift hill. During the climb, the coaster builds up potential energy.*

Potential energy *rapidly turns into kinetic energy during the first plunge.*

Kinetic energy *reaches a maximum as the coaster reaches the bottom of the first hill.*

The second loop *has a lower peak than the first because the coaster's energy is reduced by friction.*

Design and safety

The job of a roller coaster designer is to make sure that a ride is terrifying but safe. Some people are concerned that designers are providing riders with greater thrills at the expense of their safety. Safety experts say that the risk of injury is small, but it is important to pay attention to restrictions regarding height and medical conditions.

Coaster forces
During a ride, you are kept in your seat by the safety bar and by the force of the seat pushing on you. The coaster also exerts large forces on the track, which must be inspected daily for structural damage.

Acceleration
An early loop ride at Coney Island subjected riders to about 12 g's (12 times the acceleration due to gravity). For safety reasons, most modern rides do not exceed 5 g's.

Going Further

- Select an amusement park ride that you enjoy. Use library or Internet resources to discover the principles of physics that allow this ride to work. Write a paragraph or draw a diagram explaining what you have learned.
- Take a Discovery Channel Video Field Trip by watching "Physics of Fun."

DISCOVERY CHANNEL SCHOOL
Video Field Trip

Energy **461**

DISCOVERY CHANNEL SCHOOL
Video Field Trip
Physics of Fun

After students have viewed the Video Field Trip, ask them the following questions: **How does a roller coaster get to the top of the first hill?** *(It is pulled up by a chain and motor mechanism.)* **How does the roller coaster continue to move after the first hill?** *(By gravity. Students' answers may also include that potential energy is converted to kinetic energy as the roller coaster's height decreases, and back again to potential energy on the next hill.)*

When does the roller coaster have the most potential energy? *(At the tops of hills. Students may additionally comment that the potential energy is greatest at the top of the first hill.)* **What happens to the roller coaster's potential energy as it goes down a hill?** *(It is converted into kinetic energy.)* **Why are the frames of modern roller coasters made out of steel, instead of the wooden frames that were once used?** *(Steel can support the stronger forces produced by the roller coaster. Also, it can be shaped into many different forms.)*

1 FOCUS

Objectives

15.3.1 Classify energy resources as renewable or nonrenewable.

15.3.2 Evaluate benefits and drawbacks of different energy sources.

15.3.3 Describe ways to conserve energy resources.

Reading Focus

Build Vocabulary **L2**

Word-Part Analysis Ask students what words they know that contain the key word parts *geo-* and *bio-*. *(Answers may include geology, geometry; biology, biography.)* Ask them to give a definition of each word part. *(geo- means "Earth" and bio- means "life.")*

Reading Strategy **L2**

a. Nonrenewable energy resources include oil, natural gas, and coal. They exist in limited quantities.
b. Renewable energy resources include hydroelectric, solar, geothermal, wind, biomass, and nuclear fusion.
c. Energy resources can be conserved by reducing energy needs and by increasing energy efficiency.

2 INSTRUCT

Nonrenewable Energy Resources

Use Visuals **L1**

Figure 16 Have students examine Figure 16. Ask, **What energy resource is being extracted in the figure?** *(Crude oil)* **Does it require energy to pump crude oil from underground and to process crude oil into more useful forms of fuel, such as gasoline?** *(Yes)* **If it requires energy to pump and process oil, then how can oil be a useful source of energy?** *(The amount of energy that the oil provides is greater than the energy required to extract it.)* **Of the forms of energy that you learned in Section 1, what form of energy does the oil contain?** *(Chemical energy)*
Visual, Logical

15.3 Energy Resources

Standards: ICP.8.1, ICP.8.2, ICP.8.3, ICP.8.4, ICP.8.5, ICP.8.6, ICP.8.7

Reading Focus

Key Concepts

- What are the major nonrenewable and renewable sources of energy?
- How can energy resources be conserved?

Vocabulary

- nonrenewable energy resources
- fossil fuels
- renewable energy resources
- hydroelectric energy
- solar energy
- geothermal energy
- biomass energy
- energy conservation

Reading Strategy

Identifying Main Ideas Copy the table below. As you read, write the main idea for each heading.

Heading	Main Idea
Nonrenewable energy resources	a. ___?___
Renewable energy resources	b. ___?___
Conserving energy resources	c. ___?___

Figure 16 Crude oil is pumped out of the ground or ocean floor. It is then refined and turned into gasoline, fuel oil, and other oil products.

From the alarm clock that wakes you up each morning to the light that you turn off before you sleep, you depend on energy resources to operate many different devices to get you through each day. Energy resources can be classified as either renewable or nonrenewable.

Nonrenewable Energy Resources

Nonrenewable energy resources exist in limited quantities and, once used, cannot be replaced except over the course of millions of years. **Nonrenewable energy resources include oil, natural gas, coal, and uranium.** Such resources are currently being used much faster than they can be replaced, creating concern about how long they will last.

Oil, natural gas, and coal are known as **fossil fuels** because they were formed underground from the remains of once-living organisms. Currently, fossil fuels account for the great majority of the world's energy use. These fuels are not distributed evenly throughout the world. For example, about 60 percent of known oil supplies are located in a small area in the Middle East. The United States has just 2 percent of the world's oil supplies but about 25 percent of the world's coal supplies. Fossil fuels are relatively inexpensive and are usually readily available, but their use creates pollution.

462 Chapter 15

Section Resources

Print

- **Reading and Study Workbook With Math Support,** Section 15.3
- **Math Skills and Problem Solving Workbook,** Section 15.3
- **Transparencies,** Section 15.3

Technology

- **Interactive Textbook,** Section 15.3
- **Presentation Pro CD-ROM,** Section 15.3
- **Go Online,** Science News, Energy and energy resources

Renewable Energy Resources

Renewable energy resources are resources that can be replaced in a relatively short period of time. Most renewable energy resources originate either directly or indirectly from the sun. The sun and Earth are constantly releasing large amounts of energy. This energy can be used for generating electric power, heating buildings or other purposes. ⬤ **Renewable energy resources include hydroelectric, solar, geothermal, wind, biomass, and, possibly in the future, nuclear fusion.** The challenge for engineers and scientists is to find efficient ways to make these energy resources inexpensive and convenient.

Hydroelectric Energy Energy obtained from flowing water is known as **hydroelectric energy.** Hydroelectric energy is an indirect form of solar energy. Energy from the sun causes evaporation of water, which later falls back to Earth as precipitation. The water from this precipitation often collects to form rivers. As river water flows downhill, its gravitational potential energy is converted into kinetic energy. This kinetic energy can be used to turn turbines that are connected to electric generators in a power plant, such as the one shown in Figure 17. The major advantages of hydroelectric energy include its low cost to produce and lack of pollution. Dams, however, cause a variety of environmental problems. For example, dams hamper the run of fish upriver for spawning. Also, in the United States, many of the most suitable sites for hydroelectric plants are already in use.

Figure 17 Hoover Dam was built across the Colorado River on the Arizona-Nevada border. This 221-meter-tall structure can generate over 2 million kilowatts of power. *Applying Concepts* **What type of energy conversion is involved in a hydroelectric plant?**

World Energy Use

Which energy resources are most commonly used around the world? How is energy use changing over time? The table shows total world energy use in 2000 and 2007. Energy use can be measured in British thermal units, or Btu (1 Btu = 1055 J). Note that petroleum includes oil and related fuels.

1. **Using Tables** What was the world's largest source of energy in 2000? In 2007?
2. **Analyzing Data** In general, how did usage change from 2000 to 2007?
3. **Graphing** Make a circle graph of world energy use by source for the year 2007.

World Energy Use ($\times 10^{15}$ Btu)		
Source	2000	2007
Petroleum	155.52	173.87
Coal	92.37	132.47
Natural gas	90.95	111.21
Hydroelectric power	26.73	29.64
Nuclear fission	25.65	27.06
Other	2.99	5.32

4. **Analyzing Data** What percentage of world energy use in 2007 was accounted for by fossil fuels?
5. **Predicting** How might total world energy use be different in 2020? Explain.

Energy **463**

Renewable Energy Resources

Integrate Earth Science ⬛L2

While hydroelectric power itself is a clean and renewable resource, hydroelectric dams block the regular flow of rivers, flooding areas upstream to create large reservoirs. Dam construction often receives public support not only because it provides power, but also because it creates lakes that provide recreational opportunities. The reservoir creates a new aquatic ecosystem, but it also destroys the ecosystem that was there for a long time before the dam was built. Have students use a library or the Internet to research the effects of dams on landscapes and ecosystems. Have them write a report arguing for or against the construction of large dams. **Verbal, Portfolio**

Data Analysis

World Energy Use ⬛L2

1. Petroleum in both years
2. Each type of energy use increased between 2000 and 2007.
3. Students' circle graphs should reflect the following approximate percentages of world energy use by source: petroleum (36%), coal (28%), natural gas (23%), hydroelectric power (6%), nuclear fission (6%), other (1%).
4. Approximately 87%
5. Based on the trend between 2000 and 2007, students will likely predict that total world energy use will be significantly higher in 2020 than it was in 2007. They may also predict that the percentage of energy resources in the "other" category (which includes most renewable energy resources) will increase by 2020.
Logical

For Extra Help ⬛L1

Tell students to scan the data vertically to answer Question 1 and horizontally to answer Question 2. For Questions 3 and 4, review the calculation of percentages. Tell students that they must first find the total world energy use for the year 2007 by adding all the numbers in the right-hand column. **Logical**

Answer to . . .

Figure 17 *Gravitational potential energy to kinetic energy and kinetic energy to electric energy*

Simple Solar Cell   L2

Purpose Demonstrate energy conversions and renewable resources.

Materials small solar array, small motor with fan, direct sunlight or bright light source

Procedure Attach the wires from the motor to the solar array. Place the solar array in direct sunlight or under a bright light source.

Expected Outcome The motor will spin and the fan blades will rotate. Ask students to describe the energy transformations, starting with the light and ending with the motion of the blades. *(Electromagnetic energy from light is converted to electrical energy in the solar cell. The motor converts this electrical energy into kinetic energy, which turns the fan.)*
Kinesthetic, Logical

Use Community Resources   L2

Have students contact the local electric company and ask what kind of power plant(s) it uses. Have students ask if the company uses any renewable energy resources, such as wind, solar, or geothermal energy.
Interpersonal, Portfolio

Build Reading Literacy   L1

Compare and Contrast Refer to page 226D in **Chapter 8**, which provides the guidelines for comparing and contrasting.

Have students compare and contrast renewable energy resources. Ask, **How are all renewable energy sources similar?** *(They can be replaced in a short time; most originate from the sun; most are nonpolluting.)* Ask, **Which renewable energy sources are derived from the kinetic energy of natural materials?** *(Hydroelectric, wind)*
Logical

Science News provides students with current information on energy and energy resources.

Figure 18 Solar and geothermal energy plants use renewable resources to generate electricity. **A** A concentrating solar power (CSP) plant uses solar cells to convert sunlight into electricity. **B** A geothermal plant in California uses Earth's thermal energy to generate electricity. **Comparing and Contrasting** *What are some similarities and differences between solar energy and geothermal energy?*

Go Online
SCIENCE NEWS®

For: Articles on energy and energy resources
Visit: PHSchool.com
Web Code: cce-2153

Solar Energy The amount of energy from the sun that reaches Earth in one hour is more than the amount of energy used by the world's population in a year. Sunlight that is converted into usable energy is called **solar energy.** Passive solar designs use sunlight to heat a building without using machinery. Sunlight passing through the windows of a house may be absorbed by walls that then radiate thermal energy to warm the house.

In an active solar energy system, sunlight heats flat collection plates through which water flows. The heated water may be used directly, or it may be used to heat the house. Sunlight can also be converted into electrical energy by solar cells, also known as photovoltaic cells, like those shown in Figure 18A. Concentrating solar power (CSP) plants use mirrors to focus sunlight to produce electricity.

The benefits of solar energy depend on the climate. Solar energy is nonpolluting, but for areas where cloudy days are frequent, solar energy is less practical.

Geothermal Energy **Geothermal energy** is thermal energy beneath Earth's surface. In some regions, especially near volcanoes, geothermal energy is used to generate electicity. The geothermal power plant in Figure 18B pumps water into the ground, where it turns into steam. The steam is then used to drive electric generators. Geothermal energy is nonpolluting, but is not widely available.

Other Renewable Resources Sunlight causes plants to grow, converting electromagnetic energy into chemical energy. The chemical energy stored in living things is called **biomass energy.** Biomass can be converted directly into thermal energy. For example, many people around the world burn wood or peat to heat their homes or for cooking. Also, agricultural wastes such as corn stalks can be converted into a high-energy alcohol fuel that can be added to gasoline for cars.

Wind energy is another renewable energy source. Wind turbines convert the kinetic energy of wind into electrical energy. Wind energy is actually a form of solar energy. Energy from the sun causes uneven heating of air, which, in turn, causes differences in air pressure. Winds blow from areas of higher pressure to areas of lower pressure.

A form of hydrogen is also the most likely raw material for another future source of energy, nuclear fusion. The process of fusion will probably produce little pollution or radioactive waste. Scientists have been working on sustained fusion for years, but many challenges remain.

Reading Checkpoint   *What is biomass energy?*

Facts and Figures

Extreme Solar Energy The British-American physicist Freeman Dyson is famous for his inventive ideas related to the Search for Extraterrestrial Intelligence (SETI). In 1959, Dyson proposed a theoretical device, now called a Dyson sphere, that an advanced civilization could use to capture nearly all of the energy radiated from a star.

Dyson believed that while a moderately technological civilization like our own is limited to the energy resources found on our home planet, a highly advanced technological civilization (particularly one capable of interstellar travel) would have more extreme energy needs. Therefore, they would eventually come up with a device similar to the Dyson sphere. Dyson suggested that scientists searching for extraterrestrial life should look for evidence of Dyson spheres because they would be sure signs of an advanced civilization.

DK HOW It Works

Wind Turbine

Wind turbines convert the kinetic energy in the horizontal movement of wind into rotational energy of the turbine's rotor shaft. Rotational energy is then converted into electrical energy using an electric generator. The output of a wind turbine depends on the turbine's size and the wind's speed. **Interpreting Diagrams** *What is the purpose of the gearbox?*

Wind farm
Enormous wind farms like this one in California can generate as much power as a large power plant (without any air pollution).

Blades The shape and angle of the blades are designed to extract as much energy as possible from the horizontal movement of the wind.

Gearbox The rotor shaft itself rotates fairly slowly at about 20–30 revolutions per minute. The gearbox converts this to a rotation some 50 times faster—about 1500 revolutions per minute.

Generator The shaft from the gearbox enters the generator, which converts the kinetic energy of the shaft into electrical energy.

The anemometer measures wind speed.

Wind vane

Rotor shaft

Direction of rotation

Wind direction

A yaw ring changes the direction of the turbine.

Electrical energy passes to the local grid.

Yaw drive mechanism

Control unit This computer-operated unit controls the yaw drive mechanism, ensuring that the turbine always faces directly into the wind.

Energy **465**

DK HOW It Works

Wind Turbine `L2`

Humans have used wind as a source of power for many centuries. Perhaps the earliest example is the use of sails to power ships. Windmills were used in the Middle East and China to pump water or grind grains as early as 500 A.D. The earliest windmills turned on a vertical axis, rather than a horizontal axis as most do today. Windmills played an important role in the development of the American West, as they provided power to pump water from underground sources to support livestock and crops. The use of wind turbines to generate electricity developed in tandem with the increasing use of electricity in the late nineteenth and early twentieth centuries. Today, wind provides less than one % of the electric power used in the United States. However, proponents of wind power estimate that wind could provide up to ten times our current total use of electricity.

Wind power is essentially a type of solar power because wind is driven by uneven heating of air near Earth's surface by the sun. This also means that wind is a free and renewable resource. Because there are no chemical or nuclear reactions involved in generating electricity from wind, wind power produces no pollution.

Interpreting Diagrams The purpose of the gearbox is to increase the rotational speed of the shaft.
Logical

For Enrichment `L3`

The most extensive wind resources on Earth are found over the oceans. Have students research large offshore wind farms currently in use or in development. They may write a report or prepare a presentation for the class about their findings.
Verbal, Portfolio

Answer to . . .

Figure 18 *Both solar energy and geothermal energy are renewable energy resources that are nonpolluting and can be used to produce electricity or heat. The source of solar energy is the sun, while that of geothermal energy is heat from Earth. The factors that influence their availability differ as well.*

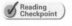 *The chemical energy stored in living things*

Conserving Energy Resources

Address Misconceptions L2

Some students may think that energy comes from a specific source, such as food or a power company. Point out that objects always have some gravitational potential energy (with respect to some reference point), and that any moving object has kinetic energy. The forms of energy discussed in this section can be harnessed and distributed on a large scale, often by converting them to electrical energy. **Verbal**

Build Science Skills L2

Analyzing Data Have students examine a monthly electricity bill to find the energy usage. Show students that kW-h = power × time = (work/time) × time = work. Explain that work has the same units as energy. Ask students to convert the usage from kilowatt-hours to joules (1 kW-h = 1000 W-h × 3600 s/h = 3.6×10^6 J). **Logical, Portfolio**

3 ASSESS

Evaluate Understanding L2

Ask students to state the fundamental difference between renewable and nonrenewable energy resources and then list at least three examples of each.

Reteach L1

Have each student review an energy resource. Have them work in pairs and discuss the pros and cons of the resource that they reviewed.

 Writing in Science

Encourage students to use a library or the Internet to research energy conservation and alternative energy resources.

Interactive Textbook If your class subscribes to the Interactive Textbook, use it to review key concepts in Section 15.3.

Answer to . . .

Figure 19 *By reducing the total number of vehicles*

Figure 19 Mass transportation systems include buses, trains, and streetcars such as the one shown here. Inferring *How can the use of mass transportation save energy?*

Conserving Energy Resources

Fossil fuel supplies may become increasingly scarce and expensive in the future. An important way to make these energy resources last longer is to use them more slowly. ⬤ **Energy resources can be conserved by reducing energy needs and by increasing the efficiency of energy use.** Finding ways to use less energy or to use energy more efficiently is known as **energy conservation.**

It's easy to forget that the energy you use often comes at the expense of resources that are being used up forever. People can reduce the use of these resources by making energy-saving decisions, for example turning off lights when they are not being used. Because conventional cars consume an enormous amount of energy, the decisions that people make about transportation are very important. Walking or biking on short trips and carpooling can save considerable energy. Using mass transportation, such as the streetcar shown in Figure 19, can also reduce energy use.

Making appliances, cars, and even light bulbs more energy efficient is a way of reducing energy use while still enjoying its benefits. Much has already been done to make appliances more energy efficient. Light bulbs have been developed that provide superior lighting at a lower energy cost. The technology for further improvement, including more fuel-efficient cars, is already known in many cases. However, the initial cost of energy efficiency can be an obstacle for manufacturers and for consumers. Energy-efficient purchases often cost more initially, but can save money in fuel costs over time.

Section 15.3 Assessment

Reviewing Concepts

1. List the major nonrenewable and renewable sources of energy.

2. What could be done to make present energy resources last longer?

3. Why are coal, oil, and natural gas called fossil fuels?

Critical Thinking

4. **Applying Concepts** You are looking for the best place to build a hydroelectric plant along a river. Would you locate the plant along a steep or flat section of the river? Explain.

5. **Comparing and Contrasting** How are passive and active solar energy systems different?

6. **Applying Concepts** Describe three ways that you used energy resources today.

Writing in Science

Writing to Persuade Suppose you are an energy planner who is concerned about the possibility of future shortages of electricity. Write a paragraph describing one or two proposals that you think would help to avoid this potential problem.

Section 15.3   Assessment

1. Nonrenewable: oil, natural gas, coal, and uranium; Renewable: solar, hydroelectric, wind, biomass, geothermal, and possibly nuclear fusion in the future

2. Use nonrenewable energy resources more slowly by reducing energy use and increasing energy efficiency.

3. They are each made from remains of ancient organisms.

4. Steep, because the faster moving water has more kinetic energy and thus can generate more power

5. Passive solar systems convert sunlight to thermal energy without the use of machinery. Active solar systems use machinery to convert sunlight into thermal energy or electricity.

6. Student answers may include turning on an electric light, listening to the radio, taking a shower, using a computer, and so forth.

Investigating a Spring Clip

There are many ways to use potential energy. A spring clip is a device used to hold weights on a barbell. The spring clip stores energy when you compress it. In this lab, you will determine how the distance you compress a spring clip is related to the force you apply and to the spring's potential energy.

Problem
How does the force you apply to a spring clip affect its elastic potential energy?

Materials
- clamp
- spring clip
- masking tape
- metric ruler
- 50-newton spring scale
- graph paper

 For the probeware version of this lab, see the Probeware Lab Manual, Lab 6.

Skills
Measuring, Using Tables and Graphs

Procedure

1. Make a data table with three columns. Label the columns Force (N), Position of Handle (cm), and Total Distance Moved (cm).

2. Using the clamp, firmly attach one handle of the spring clip to a tabletop, with the other handle facing up and away from the table as shown. **CAUTION** *Be careful not to pinch your fingers with the clamp or spring clip.*

3. Remove the plastic cover from the upper handle of the spring clip. Hook the spring scale to the spring clip handle as shown and use masking tape to secure it. Have your teacher check your setup for safety before proceeding.

4. Have a classmate hold the ruler next to the spring clip as shown. Record the starting position of the handle. (The reading on the spring scale should be zero.)

5. Slowly pull the spring scale down at a right angle to the upper handle until the upper handle moves 0.1 cm. Record the force and the position of the upper handle. Slowly release the scale back to the starting position.

6. Repeat Step 5, this time pulling the handle 0.2 cm from the starting position.

7. Repeat Step 5 a few more times, pulling the handle 0.1 cm farther each time. Continue until the spring scale reaches its maximum force.

8. Calculate the total distance the handle moved each time you pulled it and record these values in your data table. Graph your data. Place distance on the horizontal axis and force on the vertical axis.

Analyze and Conclude

1. **Using Graphs** What is the approximate relationship between the total distance you compressed the spring clip and the force you applied to it?

2. **Classifying** What type of energy transfer did you use to compress the spring clip? What type of energy did the spring clip gain when it was compressed?

3. **Drawing Conclusions** What relationship exists between the distance the spring clip was compressed and its potential energy? (*Hint:* The elastic potential energy of the spring clip equals the work done on it.)

For: Data sharing
Visit: PHSchool.com
Web Code: ccd-2150

 Probeware Lab Manual Versions of this lab for use with probeware available from Pasco, Texas Instruments, and Vernier are in the Probeware Lab Manual.

 Application Lab

Investigating a Spring Clip   L2

Objective
After completing this activity, students will be able to
- describe the relationship between an applied force and the resulting change in elastic potential energy.

Skills Focus Observing, Measuring, Using Tables and Graphs

Prep Time 15 minutes

Advance Prep Spring clips can be purchased from department or sporting-goods stores. C-clamps can be purchased from hardware stores.

Class Time 45 minutes

Safety Students should wear safety goggles. Check students' setups in Step 2 to make sure that the spring clip is securely clamped to the table and will not come loose when compressed. Masking tape placed as shown in the photograph will prevent the spring scale from becoming a projectile if a student accidentally releases it.

Teaching Tips
- Make sure that students do not exceed the limits of the spring scale. If it is stretched too far, it may not work properly in the future.

Expected Outcome There should be a linear relationship between force and distance. As distance increases, force increases.

Analyze and Conclude
1. As the distance increased, the force increased. The relationship between force and distance is directly proportional.
2. Students did work to compress the spring clip. This action increased the elastic potential energy of the spring clip.
3. The greater the distance the spring clip was compressed, the greater its elastic potential energy.
Kinesthetic, Logical

Students should see a direct relationship between applied force and elastic potential energy, but their results will depend on their own data and the data on the site.

Study Guide

Study Tip

Take Control
Tell students to make a list of all the things they need to do. Suggest that they divide their workload into manageable chunks.

Thinking Visually

a. Electrical
b. The energy associated with electric charges
c. Chemical
d. Possible answers include wood, gasoline, food items, and so forth.
e. Energy that travels through space in the form of waves
f. Possible answers include visible light and X-rays.
g. The energy stored in atomic nuclei
h. The total kinetic and potential energy related to the motion of all the microscopic particles in an object
i. Possible answers include molten metal and fire.

Assessment

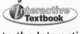 If your class subscribes to the Interactive Textbook, your students can go online to access an interactive version of the Student Edition and a self-test.

Reviewing Content

1. a   2. b   3. a
4. d   5. c   6. d
7. a   8. b   9. c
10. c

15.1 Energy and Its Forms

Key Concepts
- Work is the transfer of energy.
- The kinetic energy of any moving object depends on its mass and speed.
- An object's gravitational potential energy depends on its mass, its height, and the acceleration due to gravity.
- The major forms of energy are mechanical energy, thermal energy, chemical energy, electrical energy, electromagnetic energy, and nuclear energy.

Vocabulary
energy, p. 447
kinetic energy, p. 447
potential energy, p. 448
gravitational potential energy, p. 449
elastic potential energy, p. 450
mechanical energy, p. 450
thermal energy, p. 451
chemical energy, p. 451
electrical energy, p. 452
electromagnetic energy, p. 452
nuclear energy, p. 452

15.2 Energy Conversion and Conservation

Key Concepts
- Energy can be converted from one form to another.
- The law of conservation of energy states that energy cannot be created or destroyed.
- The gravitational potential energy of an object is converted to the kinetic energy of motion as the object falls.
- Einstein's equation shows that energy and mass are equivalent, and can be converted into each other.

Vocabulary
energy conversion, p. 454

15.3 Energy Resources

Key Concepts
- Nonrenewable energy resources include oil, natural gas, coal, and uranium.
- Renewable energy resources include hydroelectric, solar, geothermal, wind, biomass, and, possibly in the future, nuclear fusion.
- Energy resources can be conserved by reducing our energy needs and by increasing the efficiency of energy use.

Vocabulary
nonrenewable energy resources, p. 462
fossil fuels, p. 462
renewable energy resources, p. 463
hydroelectric energy, p. 463
solar energy, p. 464
geothermal energy, p. 464
biomass energy, p. 464
energy conservation, p. 466

Thinking Visually

Comparing and Contrasting Copy the partially completed table below. Complete it to compare the major forms of energy.

Form of Energy	Definition	Example
Mechanical	Energy of motion and position of everyday objects	Bouncing ball
a. ___?___	b. ___?___	Lightning
c. ___?___	Energy stored in chemical bonds	d. ___?___
Electromagnetic	e. ___?___	f. ___?___
Nuclear	g. ___?___	Fission
Thermal	h. ___?___	i. ___?___

 ## Chapter Resources

Print
- *Chapter and Unit Tests,* Chapter 15 Test A and Test B
- *Test Prep Resources,* Chapter 15

Technology
- *Computer Test Bank,* Chapter Test 15
- *Interactive Textbook,* Chapter 15
- *Go Online,* PHSchool.com, Chapter 15

Interactive Textbook with
assessment at PHSchool.com

Reviewing Content

Choose the letter that best answers the question or completes the statement.

1. The energy of a moving object is
   a. kinetic energy. b. potential energy.
   c. chemical energy. d. nuclear energy.

2. If the speed of an object doubles, its kinetic energy
   a. doubles. b. quadruples.
   c. stays the same. d. is halved.

3. An example of an object having elastic potential energy is
   a. a stretched spring. b. books on a shelf.
   c. a moving arrow. d. a falling oyster.

4. An example of electromagnetic energy is
   a. a falling rock. b. a stretched spring.
   c. a speeding train. d. sunlight.

5. Energy stored in the bonds between atoms is called
   a. kinetic energy. b. mechanical energy.
   c. chemical energy. d. thermal energy.

6. Mechanical energy is
   a. found in machinery only.
   b. usually measured at the atomic level.
   c. the sum of the chemical and thermal energy of an object.
   d. the sum of the kinetic and potential energy of an object.

7. An example of the conversion of gravitational potential energy into kinetic energy is
   a. a falling raindrop.
   b. a gasoline-powered engine.
   c. striking a match.
   d. a hockey puck sliding on ice.

8. The law of conservation of energy states that
   a. energy cannot be converted from one form to another.
   b. energy cannot be created or destroyed.
   c. energy resources must be used efficiently.
   d. energy is constantly being lost to friction.

9. Which of the following energy resources accounts for most of the world's present energy use?
   a. uranium b. solar energy
   c. fossil fuels d. wind energy

10. Most renewable energy originates from
    a. fossil fuels. b. the ground.
    c. the sun. d. uranium.

Understanding Concepts

11. What is energy?

12. How are kinetic energy and potential energy different?

13. How does the potential energy of an object change when its height is tripled?

14. Look at the graphs below. One of the graphs is a plot of kinetic energy vs. mass for a set of objects with different masses, all moving at the same speed. The other graph is a plot of kinetic energy vs. speed for a set of objects with the same mass, all moving at different speeds. Identify each graph and explain how can you tell which graph is which.

15. What happens to the atoms of an object if its thermal energy is increased?

16. Explain the energy conversions that occur as a basketball falls, hits the ground, and bounces back up. Ignore frictional forces.

17. What force is acting when the kinetic energy of a moving object is converted into thermal energy?

18. Explain how energy is converted as a pendulum swings.

19. Is mechanical energy always conserved? Explain why or why not.

20. Explain the meaning and the importance of the formula $E = mc^2$.

21. Why are coal, oil, and natural gas considered to be nonrenewable energy resources?

22. What is the source of geothermal energy?

Energy **469**

Homework Guide

Section	Questions
15.1	1–6, 11–15, 23–24, 26–29, 32
15.2	7–8, 16–20, 25, 30–31, 33
15.3	9–10, 21–22, 34–36

Understanding Concepts

11. Energy is the ability to do work.
12. Kinetic energy is the energy of motion of a moving object. Potential energy is energy stored due to the position or shape of an object.
13. Its potential energy is also tripled because potential energy is proportional to an object's height relative to a reference level.
14. Graph A is the kinetic energy vs. mass plot because kinetic energy is directly proportional to mass. Graph B is the kinetic energy vs. speed plot because kinetic energy is proportional to the square of speed.
15. The object's atoms move faster.
16. Gravitational potential energy is converted into kinetic energy as the ball falls. The kinetic energy is converted into elastic potential energy when the ball hits the ground and is compressed. The elastic potential energy is converted back into kinetic energy as the ball springs back into shape and is propelled upward. Finally, the ball's kinetic energy is converted into gravitational potential energy as the ball rises.
17. Friction
18. The point from which the pendulum weight is released is its maximum height, and this position has maximum potential energy. As the pendulum swings downward, gravitational potential energy is converted into kinetic energy. At the bottom of the swing, the pendulum reaches its maximum kinetic energy. Relative to this height, it has zero potential energy. The pendulum then moves upward, and its kinetic energy is converted back into gravitational potential energy. As the result of friction resistance, some energy is also converted into thermal energy during each swing.
19. No. Mechanical energy is not conserved when friction exists.
20. This formula shows that energy and mass are equivalent, and that energy can be converted into mass and mass can be converted into energy. A tiny amount of mass is equivalent to a large amount of energy.
21. They are all fossil fuels that formed over millions of years and cannot be quickly replaced.
22. Geothermal energy comes from the heat below Earth's surface.

Chapter 15

Critical Thinking

23. KE = $1/2 mv^2$ =
$(0.500)(100.0 \text{ kg})(10,000 \text{ m/s})^2$ =
5.00×10^9 J

24. Step 1: Use the scale to find the mass of the ball. Step 2: Put the ball on top of a vertically oriented compressed spring. Step 3: Release the spring and measure how high the ball is propelled into the air. Step 4: Use the equation for gravitational potential energy to find the energy of the ball at its peak. Step 5: Apply the law of conservation of energy. The gravitational potential energy of the ball equals the elastic potential energy of the spring.

25. $(KE + PE)_{150m} = (KE + PE)_{63m}$
$KE_{150m} = 0$; PE_{150m} =
$(0.15 \text{ kg})(9.8 \text{ m/s}^2)(150 \text{ m}) = 220$ J;
$PE_{63m} = (0.15 \text{ kg})(9.8 \text{ m/s}^2)(63 \text{ m}) = 93$ J
$(0 + 220 \text{ J}) = (KE_{63m} + 93 \text{ J})$
$KE_{63m} = 220 \text{ J} - 93 \text{ J} = 130$ J

Math Skills

26. KE = $1/2 mv^2$; units for KE are $kg \bullet (m/s)^2 = kg \bullet m^2/s^2$
PE = mgh; units for PE are $kg \bullet (m/s^2) \bullet m = kg \bullet m^2/s^2$
Note that 1 $kg \bullet m/s^2$ is a newton, so the units for KE and PE are newton-meters, or joules.

27. Ball 1, 32.0 J; Ball 2, 1.00 J; Ball 3, 24.0 J

28. Ball 2, with a gravitational potential energy of 197 J

29. Ball 2, with a kinetic energy of 197 J

Concepts in Action

30. The graph of kinetic energy should start high and gradually decrease as the ball reaches its maximum height. Then, the curve should rise again until the ball hits the ground. The potential energy graph should be the reverse, with maximum values when kinetic energy is lowest and a value of zero when the ball is on the ground.

31. The frictional force of the air is converting the gravitational potential energy into thermal energy.

32. PE = mgh =
$(200.0 \text{ kg})(9.8 \text{ m/s}^2)(3.00 \text{ m}) = 5900$ J

33. At the top of the loop, the car's gravitational potential energy is a maximum and its kinetic energy is a minimum. As the car moves downward, it picks up speed as gravitational potential energy is converted into kinetic energy. The car's kinetic energy is highest and gravitational potential energy is lowest at the bottom of the loop.

Critical Thinking

23. Calculating A small meteoroid is approaching Earth. It has a mass of 100.0 kg and a speed of 10.0 km/s. How much kinetic energy does the meteoroid have? (*Hint:* 1 km = 1000 m)

24. Designing an Experiment Design an experiment to find out how much elastic potential energy is in a compressed spring. In addition to the spring, you may use a small metal ball, a ruler, and a scale for measuring mass.

25. Calculating A 0.15-kg ball is dropped from the top of a 150-m building. What is the kinetic energy of the ball when it passes the sixteenth floor at a height of 63 m? (Ignore air resistance.)

Math Skills

26. Converting Units Using mass in kg, velocity in m/s, and height in m, show that the formulas for kinetic energy and gravitational potential energy result in energy values with the same units. What is the energy unit called?

Questions 27–29 refer to the data in the table below.

Three balls are thrown vertically into the air from different heights above the ground. The data for each ball are shown in the table below.

Data Table			
Object	Mass (kg)	Initial Upward Speed (m/s)	Initial Height Above Ground (m)
Ball 1	1.00	8.00	15.00
Ball 2	2.00	1.00	10.00
Ball 3	3.00	4.00	5.00

27. Calculating How much kinetic energy does each ball have when it is thrown?

28. Analyzing Data Which ball has the greatest gravitational potential energy when it reaches its maximum height? (*Hint:* Find the total energy for each ball.)

29. Predicting Which ball hits the ground with the most kinetic energy?

Concepts in Action

30. Using Graphs A soccer ball is kicked from the ground into the air. Describe two graphs that show how the potential energy and kinetic energy change between the time the ball is kicked and when it lands. (*Hint:* Make time the *x*-axis.)

31. Inferring When a falling object reaches a speed called terminal velocity, its speed no longer increases. The object is losing gravitational potential energy but not gaining kinetic energy. Since energy must be conserved, where must the gravitational potential energy be going?

32. Calculating Suppose a 200.0-kilogram dolphin is lifted in the air to be placed into an aquarium tank. How much energy is needed to lift the dolphin 3.00 meters into the air?

33. Applying Concepts How is energy converted as a car moves between the top and the bottom of a roller coaster loop?

34. Making Judgments What are some advantages and disadvantages of solar energy?

35. Applying Concepts How can electricity be obtained from the wind?

36. Writing in Science Using your own words, write a brief summary of the law of conservation of energy. Include an example from your everyday life.

Performance-Based Assessment

Applying Concepts Identify one practical way that your family or school could reduce energy use. Find out how much energy is currently being used for the purpose you choose, and estimate how much energy your suggestion could save. Write a brief summary of your recommendations.

For: Self-grading assessment
Visit: PHSchool.com
Web Code: cca-2150

---

34. Advantages include lack of noise and lack of pollution. A disadvantage is its dependence on the availability of the sun. Solar energy is not available at night, unless it has been stored from the daytime. Some regions do not have enough sunny days to make solar energy practical.

35. The kinetic energy of the wind can be used to turn the arms of a turbine, which can generate electricity when connected to a generator.

36. Students should state the law of conservation of energy in their own words. Their example should either account for the thermal energy lost due to friction or focus on an example where friction is negligible.

Test-Taking Tip

Avoiding Careless Mistakes
Students often make mistakes when they fail to examine a test question and possible answers thoroughly. Read the question carefully and underline key words that may change the meaning of the question, such as *not, except, excluding,* and so on. After choosing an answer, reread the question to check your selection.

Which statement about work and energy is NOT correct?

(A) Both can be expressed in joules.
(B) Energy is the ability to do work.
(C) Work done is always equal to energy input.
(D) Energy input is always greater than work output.
(E) Energy is transferred in order to accomplish work.

(Answer: C)

Choose the letter that best answers the question or completes the statement.

1. Which form of energy does a plant store when light is transformed during photosynthesis?
   (A) chemical energy
   (B) thermal energy
   (C) mechanical energy
   (D) electrical energy
   (E) nuclear energy

2. Which of the following is NOT an example of kinetic energy being converted to potential energy?
   (A) a basketball player jumping for a rebound
   (B) releasing a compressed spring
   (C) squeezing a rubber ball
   (D) pulling a sled up a hill
   (E) a swing moving upward

3. A 50.0-kg wolf is running at 10.0 m/sec. What is the wolf's kinetic energy?
   (A) 5 J   (B) 500 J
   (C) 5000 J   (D) 250 J
   (E) 2500 J

4. Friction causes kinetic energy to be converted into
   (A) potential energy.
   (B) thermal energy.
   (C) mechanical energy.
   (D) electrical energy.
   (E) chemical energy.

5. Which of the following is NOT considered a renewable energy resource?
   (A) geothermal energy
   (B) biomass
   (C) hydroelectric energy
   (D) uranium
   (E) wind energy

Use the figure below to answer Questions 6 and 7.

A pendulum weight is released in position A. The weight moves through positions B, C, D, and E.

6. At which location(s) does the pendulum have maximum potential energy?
   (A) A and B
   (B) B and D
   (C) C only
   (D) D and E
   (E) A and E

7. At which location(s) does the pendulum have maximum kinetic energy?
   (A) A and B
   (B) B and D
   (C) C only
   (D) D and E
   (E) A and E

Energy **471**

Standards Guide

Question	Standards
1	ICP.1.4
2	ICP.1.4
3	ICP.8.2
4	ICP.1.4
5	ICP.1.4

Performance-Based Assessment

Students should focus on a specific energy conservation measure, such as replacing incandescent light bulbs with a more efficient alternative. They can estimate daily energy use of an electrical device by multiplying the device's power rating in watts by the approximate number of hours the device is used each day. If they choose an option related to space heating or cooling, they should also consider seasonal variations in use.

Go Online
PHSchool.com

Your students can independently test their knowledge of the chapter and print out their results for your files.

SECTION OBJECTIVES	STANDARDS		ACTIVITIES and LABS
	NATIONAL	STATE	
16.1 Thermal Energy and Matter, pp. 474–478 🕐 1 block or 2 periods **16.1.1 Explain** how heat and work transfer energy. **16.1.2 Relate** thermal energy to the motion of particles that make up a material. **16.1.3 Relate** temperature to thermal energy and to thermal expansion. **16.1.4 Calculate** thermal energy, temperature change, or mass using the specific heat equation. **16.1.5 Describe** how a calorimeter operates and **calculate** thermal energy changes or specific heat using calorimetry measurements.	A-1, A-2, B-2, B-5, G-1, G-2, G-3	ICP.3.3	**SE** Inquiry Activity: What Happens When Hot and Cold Liquids Mix? p. 473 **L2** **SE** Quick Lab: Cooling Air, p. 476 **L2** **SE** Design Your Own Lab: Using Specific Heat to Analyze Metals, p. 493 **L2** **TE** Teacher Demo: Calorimetry, p. 478 **L2**
16.2 Heat and Thermodynamics, pp. 479–483 🕐 1 block or 2 periods **16.2.1 Describe** conduction, convection, and radiation and **identify** which of these is occurring in a given situation. **16.2.2 Classify** materials as thermal conductors or thermal insulators. **16.2.3 Apply** the law of conservation of energy to conversions between thermal energy and other forms of energy. **16.2.4 Apply** the second law of thermodynamics in situations where thermal energy moves from cooler to warmer objects. **16.2.5 State** the third law of thermodynamics.	A-1, A-2, B-2, B-5, B-6, D-1, G-1, G-2, G-3	ICP.3.3, ICP.4.2, ICP.8.3, ICP.8.4	**SE** Quick Lab: Observing Convection, p. 481 **L2** **TE** Teacher Demo: Conductors and Insulators, p. 480 **L2** **TE** Build Science Skills: Applying Concepts, p. 482 **L2** **LM** Investigation 16A: Determining the Effect of Surface Area on Heat Transfer **L2** **LM** Investigation 16B: Explaining How a Flame Can Boil Water in a Paper Cup **L1**
16.3 Using Heat, pp. 486–492 🕐 1 block or 2 periods **16.3.1 Describe** heat engines and **explain** how heat engines convert thermal energy into mechanical energy. **16.3.2 Describe** how the different types of heating systems operate. **16.3.3 Describe** how cooling systems, such as refrigerators and air conditioners, operate. **16.3.4 Evaluate** benefits and drawbacks of different heating and cooling systems.	A-1, B-3, B-5, F-4, G-1, G-2, G-3	ICP.3.3, ICP.8.3, ICP.8.4	**TE** Teacher Demo: Cooling by Evaporation, p. 490 **L2**

RESOURCES PRINT and TECHNOLOGY	SECTION ASSESSMENT
PLM Lab 7: Using Specific Heat to Analyze Metals **L2**	**SE** Section 16.1 Assessment, p. 478
RSW Section 16.1 **L1**	**iT** Section 16.1
RSW Math Skill **L2**	
MSPS Section 16.1 **L2**	
T Chapter 16 Pretest **L2**	
Section 16.1 **L2**	
P Chapter 16 Pretest **L2**	
Section 16.1 **L2**	
SCiLINKS **GO** Specific heat **L2**	
RSW Section 16.2 **L1**	**SE** Section 16.2 Assessment, p. 483
DC Powered by the Sun **L2**	**iT** Section 16.2
T Section 16.2 **L2**	
P Section 16.2 **L2**	
SCiLINKS **GO** Thermodynamics **L2**	
RSW Section 16.3 **L1**	**SE** Section 16.3 Assessment, p. 492
MSPS Section 16.3 **L2**	**iT** Section 16.3
T Section 16.3 **L2**	
P Section 16.3 **L2**	
SCIENCE NEWS **GO** Heat **L2**	

Go Online

Go online for these Internet resources.

PHSchool.com
Web Code: cca-2160

SCIENCE NEWS®
Web Code: cce-2163

NSTA *SCiLINKS*
Web Code: ccn-2161
Web Code: ccn-2162

Materials for Activities and Labs

Quantities for each group

STUDENT EDITION

Inquiry Activity, p. 473
2 plastic foam cups, glass stirring rod, thermometer, 2 100-mL graduated cylinders

Quick Lab, p. 476
round balloon, 2-L plastic bottle, metric tape measure, plastic bucket, ice

Quick Lab, p. 481
100-mL beaker, cold water, dropper pipet, hot water, food coloring, paper towel

Design Your Own Lab, p. 493
10 steel bolts, balance, 50-cm length of string, clamp, ring stand, boiling water bath (shared with class), thermometer, 500-mL graduated cylinder, ice water, foam cup with lid, aluminum nails, crushed can

TEACHER'S EDITION

Teacher Demo, p. 478
plastic foam cup with lid, thermometer, water, iron bolt (~75 g)

Teacher Demo, p. 480
a block of wood, an aluminum pie plate, a metal spoon, a plastic spoon, a silk or cotton handkerchief, a metal screwdriver

Build Science Skills, p. 482
putty (enough to make 1 golf ball-sized ball per student), table or desktop

Build Science Skills, p. 484
a box with black interior, a box with white interior, clear plastic wrap, 2 beakers, 2 thermometers

Teacher Demo, p. 490
paper towels, water, tape, hand-held or electric fan, thermometer

Chapter Assessment

CHAPTER ASSESSMENT

SE Chapter Assessment, pp. 495–496
CUT Chapter 16 Test A, B
CTB Chapter 16
iT Chapter 16
PHSchool.com GO
Web Code: cca-2160

STANDARDIZED TEST PREP

SE Chapter 16, p. 497
TP Diagnose and Prescribe

Interactive Textbook with assessment at PHSchool.com

Before you teach

From the Author

Michael Wysession
Washington University

Big Ideas

Thermal energy, temperature, and heat are all related, but they describe very different quantities. Every object (including a student!) has a great amount of thermal energy, which is the sum of the kinetic and potential energies related to the motion of all of the particles in the object. An object's temperature is determined by the level of kinetic energy of its particles. Heat is thermal energy that is transferred from one object to another.

Space and Time At all levels of the universe (atoms, planets, galaxies), thermal energy naturally flows from hot regions to cold regions. This law is often referred to as entropy. The implication of entropy is that energy in the universe will eventually dissipate so that, far in the future, stars will no longer be able to form.

There is a limit to how cold an object can get, called absolute zero. The temperature of empty space is actually a few degrees above absolute zero, due to the presence of microwave energy left over from the big bang.

Forces and Motion Thermal energy flows from hot regions to cold regions in three ways: by radiation, by conduction, and by convection. With radiation, electromagnetic waves radiate away from a hot region. Conduction involves the propagation of heat through matter by collisions between particles. With convection, the particles in a material move, carrying thermal energy with them. In the presence of gravity, convection involves the flow of hot material up and cold material down. Large-scale motions on and within Earth are caused by convection: flow of air in the atmosphere, water in the ocean, and rock and metal within the mantle and core.

Matter and Energy When the thermal energy of matter increases, its temperature increases in relation to a particular material's specific heat. Most matter expands when it becomes hotter, a process called thermal expansion. Heat engines and heat pumps use thermal properties of liquids and gases to do work. Heat engines rely on the expansion of gases when they combust or are heated. Heat pumps rely upon the absorption of heat by liquids when they vaporize.

Physics Refresher

Thermal Energy and Temperature 16.1

The internal energy of an object is the total energy of atoms and molecules within it. This text uses the term *thermal energy* instead of *internal energy*. Thermal energy may include the average potential energy of interacting atoms as well as average kinetic energy. Average kinetic energy generally increases as the temperature increases, and there is a close relation between average kinetic energy and temperature. The precise relation depends on the material. For a monatomic gas, the average kinetic energy per atom of gas at absolute temperature T is given by

$$KE_{avg} = \frac{3}{2} kT,$$

where k is Boltzmann's constant. For a diatomic gas, the moving particles are molecules having an average kinetic energy $\frac{5}{2} kT$ per molecule. In solids and liquids this relationship can be more complex.

Transfer of Thermal Energy 16.2

Convection transfers thermal energy by the motion of the particles in a fluid from one place to another. A fluid that is heated expands, becoming less dense than the surrounding fluid. The difference in densities causes the warm, less dense fluid to rise and the cooler, denser fluid to sink.

In conduction, the particle collisions transfer thermal energy on average from particles with greater kinetic energy to particles with lower kinetic energy.

> ⚑ **Address Misconceptions**
>
> *Students may assume that the phrase* heat transfer *shows that heat is a moving substance.* Heat is a transfer of thermal energy that may or may not involve a movement of particles. For a strategy to overcome this misconception, see **Address Misconceptions** on **page 475**.

Direction of thermal energy transfer

T_{High} T_{Low}

Conduction

Radiation transfers energy by means of electromagnetic waves, which can travel through empty space. Absorption of radiation by matter increases the matter's thermal energy, while emission of radiation decreases the thermal energy of the matter.

Thermodynamics 16.2 and 16.3

Address Misconceptions

Students may assume that all of the energy added to a system by heating it will increase the system's thermal energy. Heat may also be converted into work or internal energy (in a phase change). For a strategy to overcome this misconception, see **Address Misconceptions** on **page 482**.

In addition to the three laws of thermodynamics is the so-called "zeroth" law, which states that if an object is in thermal equilibrium with two other objects, those two objects are in thermal equilibrium with each other. This condition allows a definition of a temperature scale, which assigns the same temperature to all three objects.

In the operation of a heat engine, all of the energy can be accounted for using the first law of thermodynamics. But the energy that must be given up is considered waste energy if it cannot spontaneously be transferred back to the high-temperature source. The measure of the increased disorder that results from making energy less useable is called entropy. Another statement of the second law is that the total entropy for the system and its surroundings spontaneously increases for all macroscopic processes.

Entropy changes take place in all matter, but these changes become smaller as the temperature of matter decreases. The temperature at which no entropy change (that is, no change in the disorder of the system) would occur is defined as absolute zero. This is one way of expressing the third law of thermodynamics.

Uses of Heat 16.3

In many types of heat engines, a quantity of matter (water and steam in a steam engine, a gasoline-air mixture in a gasoline engine) is heated. The three common features of all heat engines are 1) energy is transferred to the chamber by heat from a region at a higher temperature, 2) work is done in the chamber, and 3) thermal energy is transferred from the chamber to a region of lower temperature. In a refrigerator, the process is reversed: Work is done to transfer thermal energy from a region at a cooler temperature to a region at a high temperature.

Go Online
NSTA PD LINKS

For: Teaching methods for thermal energy and heat
Visit: www.SciLinks.org/PDLinks
Web Code: ccn-1699

Build Reading Literacy

Make Inferences

Reading Between the Lines

Strategy Help students fill in information not found in the text by drawing on prior knowledge and using context clues. To use this strategy, students must identify their prior knowledge, recognize clues in the text, and make connections between their prior knowledge and text clues to make an inference.

Choose a passage such as the last two paragraphs on p. 474. The passage should contain concepts that the author refers to but does not explain completely. You may wish to photocopy the paragraphs and highlight examples for your own reference prior to oral reading.

Example

1. Read aloud or have students read aloud a portion of the chosen text. Point out an example of the author's referring to something without explaining it completely. Tell students that texts often do not define everything because they assume that the reader has a certain amount of background knowledge.
2. Model this strategy by thinking aloud. First, mention facts you already know that are directly related to the subject, either from your own experience or from what you have read about it previously in the text.
3. Next, read text clues aloud and point out what those clues tell about the concept.
4. Then, explain what you understand about the text by combining your prior knowledge and text clues.
5. Have students read the next paragraph or two silently, applying the strategies to make an inference. Discuss their inferences.
6. Repeat this process, having students work with partners to find other opportunities to make inferences in the chapter.

See p. 475 for a script on how to use the make inferences strategy with students. For additional Build Reading Literacy strategies, see pp. 480 and 486.

ASSESS PRIOR KNOWLEDGE

Use the Chapter Pretest below to assess students' prior knowledge. As needed, review these Science Concepts and Math Skills with students.

Review Science Concepts

Section 16.1 Review work, kinetic energy, and thermal energy. Remind students of the Celsius and Kelvin temperature scales used in science. Review how matter consists of atoms, ions, and molecules.

Section 16.2 Review efficiency of machines and the law of conservation of energy. Remind students of the definition of absolute zero.

Section 16.3 Review the states of matter. Review chemical energy and energy conversions.

Review Math Skills

Scientific Notation, Calculating with Significant Figures, Formulas and Equations Students will need to manipulate 4-variable formulas to calculate specific heat.

Direct students to the **Math Skills** in the **Skills and Reference Handbook** at the end of the student text.

CHAPTER

16 Thermal Energy and Heat

21st Century Learning
Accountability and Adaptability

What is thermal pollution and how can it be reduced?

Research thermal pollution on the Internet. Find out why all heat engines produce thermal pollution, and identify sources of thermal pollution in your area. Use this information to post a comment to a local blog or an online news article about the environment. Explain thermal pollution in a way that the general public will understand, and suggest how individuals and organizations can help reduce thermal pollution.

Indiana's Academic Standards for Science

PROPERTIES OF MATTER
ICP.3.3: Understand how thermal energy (the microscopic motions of the atoms and/or molecules) is related to the macroscopic concept of temperature. Examine the differences in these concepts by measuring the temperature changes, and determining specific heat capacity, of water as it is heated or cooled.

ENERGY TRANSPORT
ICP.4.2: Differentiate between conduction, convection, and radiation and identify them as types of energy transfer.

SOCIETY (ENERGY PRODUCTION, ENVIRONMENT, ECONOMICS)
ICP.8.3: Describe the benefits and risks of the development of renewable forms of energy such as solar energy, wind-energy, geothermal energy, fusion energy and biofuels; ICP.8.4: Describe how efficient use of renewable and non-renewable energy sources is essential to maintaining an acceptable environment.

Chapter Pretest

1. True or False: Degrees Celsius and kelvins are units of temperature. *(True)*

2. What kind of energy is released when bonds between atoms are broken? *(Chemical energy)*

3. True or False: Thermal energy is the total potential and kinetic energy of the microscopic particles in an object. *(True)*

4. The change of state from liquid to gas is called _____. *(vaporization)*

5. Which of the following is the energy of a moving object? *(d)*
   a. Mechanical energy
   b. Chemical energy
   c. Potential energy
   d. Kinetic energy

6. The principle that energy cannot be created or destroyed is known as the law of

_____.

(conservation of energy)

7. Define work. *(Work is a transfer of energy.)*

8. If the input work for a simple machine is 21.0 J, and the output work is 7.0 J, the efficiency of the machine is

_____. *(c)*

   a. 3.0%
   b. 0.33%
   c. 33%
   d. 30%

Chapter Preview

16.1 **Thermal Energy and Matter**

16.2 **Heat and Thermodynamics**

16.3 **Using Heat**

DISCOVERY SCHOOL

Video Field Trip

Powered by the Sun

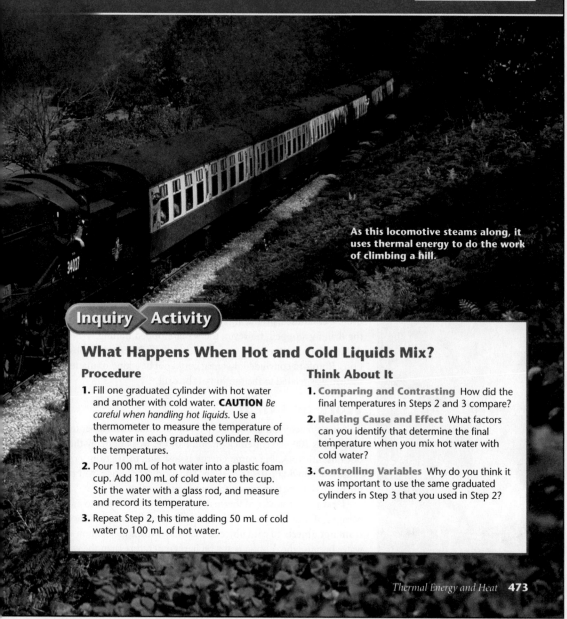

As this locomotive steams along, it uses thermal energy to do the work of climbing a hill.

Inquiry Activity

What Happens When Hot and Cold Liquids Mix?

Procedure

1. Fill one graduated cylinder with hot water and another with cold water. **CAUTION** *Be careful when handling hot liquids.* Use a thermometer to measure the temperature of the water in each graduated cylinder. Record the temperatures.

2. Pour 100 mL of hot water into a plastic foam cup. Add 100 mL of cold water to the cup. Stir the water with a glass rod, and measure and record its temperature.

3. Repeat Step 2, this time adding 50 mL of cold water to 100 mL of hot water.

Think About It

1. **Comparing and Contrasting** How did the final temperatures in Steps 2 and 3 compare?

2. **Relating Cause and Effect** What factors can you identify that determine the final temperature when you mix hot water with cold water?

3. **Controlling Variables** Why do you think it was important to use the same graduated cylinders in Step 3 that you used in Step 2?

Thermal Energy and Heat **473**

DISCOVERY SCHOOL

Video Field Trip

Powered by the Sun

Encourage students to view the Video Field Trip "Powered by the Sun."

ENGAGE/EXPLORE

Inquiry Activity

What Happens When Hot and Cold Liquids Mix? L2

Purpose Students recognize that the final temperature of a mixture depends on the masses and temperatures of the substances that are mixed.

 Address Misconceptions

Students may think that because the temperature of the cold water added is the same for both mixtures, the final temperature should be similar. To help remedy this misconception, ask what else may affect the final temperature.

Skills Focus Observing, Inferring, Measuring

Prep Time 15 minutes

Materials 2 plastic foam cups, glass stirring rod, thermometer, 2 100-mL graduated cylinders

Class Time 20 minutes

Safety Students should use tongs or wear heat-resistant gloves when handling hot glassware. Use non-mercury thermometers.

Teaching Tips

• Hot and cold tap water should be sufficient to show the desired results. Water could be cooled in a freezer to increase the temperature difference.

• Students should stir the mixtures before measuring the temperature.

• Students should do the first trial rapidly so that the water temperatures are the same for both trials.

Expected Outcome The cup that received 100 mL of cold water will be cooler.

Think About It

1. The mixture to which 50 mL of cold water was added had a higher temperature.

2. Students may cite the temperatures and "amounts" of water added. They may also say that energy or heat changed the temperature of the water.

3. Using the same source of hot and cold water ensures that the temperatures used will be close to the same in both trials.

Logical, Group

1 FOCUS

Objectives

16.1.1 Explain how heat and work transfer energy.

16.1.2 Relate thermal energy to the motion of particles that make up a material.

16.1.3 Relate temperature to thermal energy and to thermal expansion.

16.1.4 Calculate thermal energy, temperature change, or mass using the specific heat equation.

16.1.5 Describe how a calorimeter operates and **calculate** thermal energy changes or specific heat using calorimetry measurements.

Reading Focus

Build Vocabulary L2

Concept Map Have students construct a concept map of the vocabulary terms in this section. Instruct students to place the terms in ovals and connect the ovals with lines on which linking words are placed. Students should place the main concept (Thermal Energy and Matter) at the top. As they move away from the main concept, the content should become more specific.

Reading Strategy L2

Sample answers: **a.** A pitcher of juice **b.** Why did Rumford conclude that heat is not a form of matter? **c.** The brass was hot enough to make water boil only during drilling, so the heat must be related to the motion of the drill. **d.** How is specific heat related to temperature? **e.** The lower a material's specific heat, the more its temperature rises when a given amount of energy is absorbed by a given mass.

2 INSTRUCT

Work and Heat

FYI

It is common usage to talk about heat flowing. More precisely, it is thermal energy that flows. It is always correct to use "heat" as a verb; using "heat" as a noun should be avoided.

16.1 Thermal Energy and Matter

 Standard: ICP.3.3

Reading Focus

Key Concepts

- In what direction does heat flow spontaneously?
- What is the temperature of an object related to?
- What two variables is thermal energy related to?
- What causes thermal expansion?
- How is a change in temperature related to specific heat?
- On what principle does a calorimeter operate?

Vocabulary

- heat
- temperature
- absolute zero
- thermal expansion
- specific heat
- calorimeter

Reading Strategy

Previewing Copy the table below. Before you read, preview the figures in this section and add two more questions to the table. As you read, write answers to your questions.

Questions About Thermal Energy and Matter	Answers
Which has more thermal energy, a cup of tea or a pitcher of juice?	a. ?
b. ?	c. ?
d. ?	e. ?

Figure 1 Count Rumford supervised the drilling of brass cannons in a factory in Bavaria. From his observations, Rumford concluded that heat is not a form of matter.

In the 1700s, most scientists thought heat was a fluid called *caloric* that flowed between objects. In 1798, the American-born scientist Benjamin Thompson (1753–1814), also known as Count Rumford, challenged this concept of heat. Rumford managed a factory that made cannons. Figure 1 shows how a brass cylinder was drilled to make the cannon barrel. Water was used to cool the brass so that it did not melt. Rumford observed that the brass became hot as long as the drilling continued, producing enough heat to boil the water. Soon after the drilling stopped, however, the water stopped boiling. When the drilling resumed, the water again came to a boil. Based on his observations, Rumford concluded that heat could not be a kind of matter, but instead was related to the motion of the drill.

Work and Heat

A drill is a machine that does work on the cannon. Remember that no machine is 100 percent efficient. Some of the work done by the drill does useful work, but some energy is lost due to friction. Friction causes the moving parts to heat up. The more work done by the drill, the more that friction causes the cannon to heat up.

Heat is the transfer of thermal energy from one object to another because of a temperature difference. **Heat flows spontaneously from hot objects to cold objects.** Heat flows from the cannon to the water because the cannon is at a higher temperature than the water.

 Section Resources

Print

- **Reading and Study Workbook With Math Support,** Section 16.1 and **Math Skill:** Calculating with Specific Heat
- **Math Skills and Problem Solving Workbook,** Section 16.1
- **Transparencies,** Chapter Pretest and Section 16.1

Technology

- **Probeware Lab Manual,** Lab 7
- **Interactive Textbook,** Section 16.1
- **Presentation Pro CD-ROM,** Chapter Pretest and Section 16.1
- **Go Online,** NSTA SciLinks, Specific heat

Temperature

How do you know something is hot? You might use a thermometer to measure its temperature. **Temperature** is a measure of how hot or cold an object is compared to a reference point. Recall that on the Celsius scale, the reference points are the freezing and boiling points of water. On the Kelvin scale, another reference point is **absolute zero**, which is defined as a temperature of 0 kelvins.

🔵 **Temperature is related to the average kinetic energy of the particles in an object due to their random motions through space.** As an object heats up, its particles move faster, on average. As a result, the average kinetic energy of the particles, and the temperature, must increase.

Why does heat flow from a high to a low temperature? One way that heat flows is by the transfer of energy in collisions. On average, high-energy particles lose energy, and low-energy particles gain energy in collisions. Overall, collisions transfer thermal energy from hot to cold objects.

Thermal Energy

Recall that thermal energy is the total potential and kinetic energy related to the motion of all the particles in an object. 🔵 **Thermal energy depends on the mass, temperature, and phase (solid, liquid, or gas) of an object.**

Thermal energy, unlike temperature, depends on mass. Suppose you compare a cup of tea and a teapot full of tea. Both are at the same temperature, so the average kinetic energy of the particles is the same in both containers. However, there is more thermal energy in the teapot because it contains more particles.

Now consider how thermal energy varies with temperature. You can do this by comparing a cup of hot tea with a cup of cold tea. In both cases, the tea has the same mass, and the same number of particles. But the average kinetic energy of particles is higher in the hot tea, so it also has greater thermal energy than the cold tea.

Figure 2 shows the particles in a cup of hot tea and in a pitcher of lemonade. The tea is at a higher temperature because its particles move a little faster, on average. But they are only moving slightly faster, and the pitcher of lemonade has many more particles than the tea. As it turns out, the pitcher of lemonade has more thermal energy than the cup of hot tea.

 What is thermal energy?

Figure 2 Thermal energy depends on mass and temperature. **A** The tea is at a higher temperature than the lemonade because its particles have a higher average kinetic energy. **B** The lemonade is at a lower temperature, but it has more thermal energy because it has many more particles. **Inferring** *In which liquid are water particles moving faster, on average?*

Thermal Energy and Heat **475**

Thermal Contraction and Expansion

Cooling Air L2

Objective
After completing this activity, students will be able to
- describe the effect of temperature on the volume of a gas.

Skills Focus Measuring, Comparing and Contrasting

 Prep Time 20 minutes

Materials round balloon, 2-L plastic bottle, metric tape measure, plastic bucket, ice

Advance Prep The circumference of the balloon can be found by wrapping a string around the balloon and then measuring the length of the string.

Class Time 20 minutes

Safety Students should wear safety goggles and lab aprons and must wipe up any spills immediately to avoid falls.

Teaching Tips
- Students can calculate the volume of the balloon from its circumference by approximating the shape of the balloon as a sphere and using the equation $C = 2\pi r$ to find the radius. The volume is then given by $V = \frac{4}{3}\pi r^3$. Make sure students include the bottle to determine the total volume of the enclosed air.

Expected Outcome The balloon contracts as the air in the bottle cools.

Analyze and Conclude
1. The volume decreased when cool.
2. Cooling the air inside the bottle and balloon reduced the kinetic energy of its particles, and therefore the pressure on the balloon, causing it to contract.
Visual, Logical

Specific Heat
Build Science Skills L2
Analyzing Data Have students examine the specific heat values in Figure 3. Ask, **Which substance requires nearly 1 J of energy to raise the temperature of 1 g by 1°C?** *(Air)* **What amount of energy would be required to raise the temperature of 2.00 g of water by 1.00°C?** *(4.18 × 2.00 = 8.36 J)* **Logical**

 Quick Lab

Cooling Air
Procedure
1. Inflate a round balloon and then stretch its opening over the mouth of a 2-L bottle. Use a tape measure to measure and record the balloon's circumference.
2. Put a dozen ice cubes into a plastic bucket. Add cold water to the bucket to a depth of 15 cm. Submerge the bottom of the bottle in the ice water and tape the bottle in place.
3. After 10 minutes, measure and record the circumference of the balloon.

Analyze and Conclude
1. **Observing** How did the volume of air in the balloon change?
2. **Inferring** Explain why the air behaved as it did.

Thermal Contraction and Expansion

If you take a balloon outside on a cold winter day, it shrinks. Can you explain why? As temperature decreases, the particles that make up the air inside the balloon move more slowly, on average. Slower particles collide less often and exert less force, so gas pressure decreases and the balloon contracts. This is called thermal contraction.

If you bring the balloon inside, it expands. **Thermal expansion** is an increase in the volume of a material due to a temperature increase. **Thermal expansion occurs when particles of matter move farther apart as temperature increases.** Gases expand more than liquids and liquids usually expand more than solids. A gas expands more easily than a liquid or a solid because the forces of attraction among particles in a gas are weaker.

Thermal expansion is used in glass thermometers. As temperature increases, the alcohol in the tube expands and its height increases. The increase in height is proportional to the increase in temperature. In an oven thermometer, a strip of brass and a strip of steel are bonded together and wound up in a coil. As the coil heats up, the two metals expand at different rates, and the coil unwinds. This causes the needle to rotate on the temperature scale.

Reading Checkpoint *What is thermal expansion?*

Specific Heat

When a car is heated by the sun, the temperature of the metal door increases more than the temperature of the plastic bumper. Do you know why? One reason is that the iron in the door has a lower specific heat than the plastic in the bumper. **Specific heat** is the amount of heat needed to raise the temperature of one gram of a material by one degree Celsius. If equal masses of iron and plastic absorb the same heat, the iron's temperature rises more. **The lower a material's specific heat, the more its temperature rises when a given amount of energy is absorbed by a given mass.**

Specific heat is often measured in joules per gram per degree Celsius, or J/g•°C. Figure 3 gives specific heats for a few common materials. It takes 4.18 joules of energy to raise the temperature of 1.00 gram of water by 1.00 degree Celsius. How much energy is needed to heat 2.00 grams of water to the same temperature? You would have to add twice as much energy, or 8.36 joules.

Specific Heats of Selected Materials	
Material (at 100 kPa)	Specific Heat (J/g•°C)
Water	4.18
Plastic (polypropylene)	1.84–2.09
Air	1.01
Iron	0.449
Silver	0.235

Figure 3 Specific heat is the heat needed to raise the temperature of 1 gram of material by 1°C. **Analyzing Data** *Which material in the table has the highest specific heat? The lowest?*

Facts and Figures

Thermal Contraction One of the few exceptions to thermal expansion is water near its freezing point. Over most temperature ranges, water increases in volume as its temperature increases, but between 0°C and 4°C water actually contracts as it gets warmer. This unusual behavior occurs because hydrogen bonding between water molecules in ice arranges them in a way that occupies a greater volume than in liquid water. This results in ice being less dense than liquid water. In the winter, when a pond begins to freeze, the denser, warmer water sinks to the bottom, and the cooler, less dense ice floats. This forms a layer of warmer water at the bottom of the pond, in which fish are able to live.

The heat (Q) absorbed by a material equals the product of the mass (m), the specific heat (c), and the change in temperature (ΔT).

Specific Heat

$$Q = m \times c \times \Delta T$$

In this formula, heat is in joules, mass is in grams, specific heat is in J/g•°C, and the temperature change is in degrees Celsius.

Go Online
NSTA SCi LINKS

For: Links on specific heat
Visit: www.SciLinks.org
Web Code: ccn-2161

 Math Skills

Calculating Specific Heat
An iron skillet has a mass of 500.0 grams. The specific heat of iron is 0.449 J/g•°C. How much heat must be absorbed to raise the skillet's temperature by 95.0°C?

 Read and Understand

What information are you given?

Mass of iron, $m = 500.0$ g

Specific heat of iron, $c = 0.449$ J/g•°C

Temperature change, $\Delta T = 95.0$°C

2 **Plan and Solve**

What unknown are you trying to calculate?

Amount of heat needed, $Q = ?$

What formula contains the given quantities and the unknown?

$$Q = m \times c \times \Delta T$$

Replace each variable with its known value.

$$Q = 500.0 \text{ g} \times 0.449 \text{ J/g•°C} \times 95.0°C$$

$$= 21,375 \text{ J} = 21.4 \text{ kJ}$$

 Look Back and Check

Is your answer reasonable?

Round off the data to give a quick estimate.

$Q = 500 \text{ g} \times 0.5 \text{ J/g•°C} \times 100°C = 25$ kJ

This is close to 21.4 kJ, so the answer is reasonable.

 Math Practice

1. How much heat is needed to raise the temperature of 100.0 g of water by 85.0°C?

2. How much heat is absorbed by a 750-g iron skillet when its temperature rises from 25°C to 125°C?

3. In setting up an aquarium, the heater transfers 1200 kJ of heat to 75,000 g of water. What is the increase in the water's temperature? (*Hint:* Rearrange the specific heat formula to solve for ΔT.)

4. To release a diamond from its setting, a jeweler heats a 10.0-g silver ring by adding 23.5 J of heat. How much does the temperature of the silver increase?

5. What mass of water will change its temperature by 3.0°C when 525 J of heat is added to it?

Additional Problems

1. Gold has a specific heat of 0.13 J/g•°C. If a sample of gold with a mass of 250 g undergoes a temperature increase of 4.0°C, how much heat does it absorb? *(130 J)*

2. A piece of iron at a temperature of 145.0°C cools off to a temperature of 45.0°C. If the iron has a mass of 10.0 g and a specific heat of 0.449 J/g•°C, how much heat is given up? *(449 J)*
Logical, Portfolio

Build Math Skills [L1]
Formulas and Equations Students should become familiar with rearrangements of the formula $Q = m \times c \times \Delta T$, so that any one of these quantities can be calculated in terms of the other three. Have students rearrange the equation in order to calculate specific heat $c = Q/(m \times \Delta T)$, mass $m = Q/(c \times \Delta T)$, and temperature $\Delta T = Q/(m \times c)$.
Logical, Portfolio

Direct students to the **Math Skills** in the **Skills and Reference Handbook** at the end of the student text for additional help.

 Math Practice

Solutions [L2]
1. $Q = m \times c \times \Delta T$
= (100.0 g)(4.18 J/g•°C)(85.0°C)
= 35.5 kJ
2. $Q = m \times c \times \Delta T$
= (750 g)(0.449 J/g•°C)(125°C − 25°C)
= (750 g)(0.449 J/g•°C)(100°C) = 34 kJ
3. $\Delta T = Q/(m \times c)$
= 1,200,000 J/(75,000 g $\times$ 4.18 J/g•°C)
= 3.8°C
4. $\Delta T = Q/(m \times c)$
= 23.5 J/(10.0 g $\times$ 0.235 J/g•°C)
= 10.0°C
5. $m = Q/(\Delta T \times c)$
= 525 J/(3.0°C $\times$ 4.18 J/g•°C) = 42 g
Logical

For Extra Help [L1]
Make sure students start by writing out the equation required to solve each problem. Then, check that they are able to solve the equation for the unknown variable using basic algebra skills.
Logical

Go Online
NSTA SCi LINKS

Download a worksheet on specific heat for students to complete, and find additional teacher support from NSTA SciLinks.

Answer to . . .

Figure 3 *Silver has the lowest specific heat. Water has the highest specific heat.*

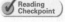 Reading Checkpoint *Thermal expansion is the increase in volume of a material due to a temperature increase.*

Measuring Heat Changes

Calorimetry L2

Purpose Students observe a calorimeter measuring changes in thermal energy.

Materials plastic foam cup with lid, thermometer, water, iron bolt (~75 g)

Procedure Place the iron bolt in a freezer for one hour prior to the demonstration. Fill the cup two-thirds full with room-temperature water and record its temperature. Place the cold iron in the water and cover the cup. After three minutes, record the temperature of the water. Ask what students can infer about the bolt's initial temperature.

Safety Wipe up spills immediately.

Expected Outcome Students should conclude that the bolt was colder than the water. **Visual, Group**

---

3 ASSESS

Evaluate Understanding L2

Ask students to write a summary paragraph relating thermal energy, temperature, and heat.

Reteach L1

Use Figure 2 to summarize key concepts about thermal energy.

Solutions

10. $Q = m \times c \times \Delta T = (1000.0 \text{ g}) \times (0.39 \text{ J/g} \cdot {}^\circ\text{C}) \times (45.0 - 25.0 {}^\circ\text{C})$
$= 7800 \text{ J}$
11. $\Delta T = Q/(m \times c)$
$= 18{,}200 \text{ J}/(100.0 \text{ g})(4.18 \text{ J/g} \cdot {}^\circ\text{C})$
$= 43.5 {}^\circ\text{C}$

 Interactive Textbook If your class subscribes to the Interactive Textbook, use it to review key concepts in in Section 16.1.

Answer to . . .

Figure 4 *The stirrer keeps temperature uniform.*

Figure 4 A calorimeter is used to measure specific heat. A sample to be tested is heated and placed in the calorimeter. The lid is put on and the temperature change is observed.
Hypothesizing *Why does the calorimeter need a stirrer?*

Measuring Heat Changes

A **calorimeter** is an instrument used to measure changes in thermal energy. A calorimeter uses the principle that heat flows from a hotter object to a colder object until both reach the same temperature. According to the law of conservation of energy, the thermal energy released by a test sample is equal to the thermal energy absorbed by its surroundings. The calorimeter is sealed to prevent thermal energy from escaping.

Figure 4 shows how a calorimeter can be used to measure the specific heat of aluminum. A known mass of water is added to the calorimeter. The mass of the sample of aluminum is measured. The aluminum is heated and then placed in the water. The calorimeter is sealed. As the aluminum cools off, the water is stirred to distribute thermal energy evenly. The water heats up until both the aluminum and the water are at the same temperature. The change in temperature of the water is measured. The thermal energy absorbed by the water is calculated using the specific heat equation. Since this same amount of thermal energy was given off by the sample of aluminum, the specific heat of aluminum can be calculated.

Section 16.1 Assessment

Reviewing Concepts

1. In what direction does heat flow on its own spontaneously?
2. How is the temperature of an object related to the average kinetic energy of its particles?
3. Name two variables that affect the thermal energy of an object.
4. What causes thermal expansion of an object when it is heated?
5. How do the temperature increases of different materials depend on their specific heats?
6. What principle explains how a calorimeter is used to measure the specific heat of a sample material?

Critical Thinking

7. **Applying Concepts** Why is it necessary to have regularly spaced gaps between sections of a concrete sidewalk?

8. **Predicting** An iron spoon and silver spoon have the same mass. Which becomes hotter when both are left in hot tea for one minute? (*Hint:* Use the specific heats given in Figure 3.)
9. **Calculating** If it takes 80.0 joules to raise the temperature of a material by 10.0°C, how much heat must be added to cause an additional increase of 20.0°C?

Math Practice

10. The specific heat of copper is 0.39 J/g•°C. How much heat is needed to raise the temperature of 1000.0 g of copper from 25.0°C to 45.0°C?
11. A peanut burned in a calorimeter transfers 18,200 joules to 100.0 g of water. What is the rise in the water's temperature? (*Hint:* Rearrange the specific heat formula to solve for ΔT.)

Section 16.1   Assessment

1. Heat flows spontaneously from hot objects to cold objects.
2. Temperature is related to the average kinetic energy of the particles in an object due to their random motions through space.
3. Mass of the object, temperature
4. Particles of matter tend to move farther apart as temperature increases.
5. The lower a material's specific heat, the more its temperature increases when equal amounts of thermal energy are added to equal masses.

6. A calorimeter uses the principle that heat flows from a hotter object to a colder object until both reach the same temperature.
7. The gaps provide space for concrete slabs to expand into so they do not buckle.
8. Both spoons absorb the same energy and have the same mass. Because silver has a lower specific heat (0.235 J/g•°C) than iron (0.449 J/g•°C), the silver becomes hotter.
9. Doubling the temperature change doubles the energy required, so 160 joules must be added.

16.2 Heat and Thermodynamics

Standard: ICP.4.2

To bake cookies, you put cookie dough on a baking sheet and pop it in the oven. When the timer goes off, you use oven mitts to pull out the baking sheet. Why isn't your bare arm burned by the hot air in the oven? One reason is that air is not a very good conductor of thermal energy.

Conduction

Conduction is the transfer of thermal energy with no overall transfer of matter. Conduction occurs within a material or between materials that are touching. To understand conduction, look at the Newton's cradle in Figure 5. When a ball is pulled back and released, you might expect all of the balls to move to the right after the impact. Instead, most of the kinetic energy is transferred to one ball on the end. Similarly, in conduction, collisions between particles transfer thermal energy, without any overall transfer of matter.

Recall that forces are weak among particles in a gas. Compared to liquids and solids, the particles in gases are farther apart. **Conduction in gases is slower than in liquids and solids because the particles in a gas collide less often.** In most solids, conduction occurs as particles vibrate in place and push on each other. In metals, conduction is faster because some electrons are free to move about. These free electrons collide with one another and with atoms or ions to transfer thermal energy.

Figure 5 Conduction is the transfer of thermal energy without transferring matter. This device, called Newton's cradle, helps to visualize conduction. After one ball strikes the rest, most of the kinetic energy is transferred to one ball on the end.

Thermal Energy and Heat **479**

Section Resources

Print

- *Laboratory Manual,* Investigations 16A and 16B
- *Reading and Study Workbook With Math Support,* Section 16.2
- *Transparencies,* Section 16.2

Technology

- *Interactive Textbook,* Section 16.2
- *Presentation Pro CD-ROM,* Section 16.2
- *Go Online,* NSTA SciLinks, Thermodynamics

Teacher > Demo

Conductors and Insulators   **L2**

Purpose To show the similarities and differences between types of thermal conductors and insulators.

Materials a block of wood, an aluminum pie plate, a metal spoon, a plastic spoon, a silk or cotton handkerchief, a metal screwdriver

Procedure Place the objects on a windowsill that is well-exposed to sunlight. Leave half of each object lying in the sunlight and the other half lying in the shade. Place the screwdriver so that the half of the metal shaft nearest the handle is in the shade. Leave the objects in the sunlight for at least 30 minutes. Have each student pick up each object by the end that has been in shade. Have them note carefully any difference between the temperatures of the two ends of each object.

Safety Remind students that the parts of the objects that have been in sunlight may be very hot.

Expected Outcome The pie plate, the metal spoon, and the shaft of the screwdriver are all metals, and so are good thermal conductors. The parts of these objects that have been in the shade should feel warm. The wood, handkerchief, plastic spoon, and handle of the screwdriver are thermal insulators, and should not feel very warm.
Kinesthetic, Group

Convection
Build Reading Literacy   **L1**

Sequence Refer to page **290D** in **Chapter 10**, which provides the guidelines for a sequence.

Convection involves a sequence of steps. Have students describe the convection of warm air as a sequence of events, starting with "air heated by sunlight." *(The sequence may resemble the following: 1) The temperature of the air increases. 2) The air expands. 3) The less dense air rises while cooler, denser air sinks.)*
Logical

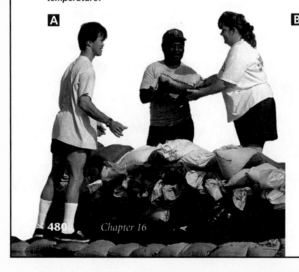

Figure 6 The arrows show how thermal energy is conducted away from the heat source in a metal frying pan. **Predicting** *Would it be safe to touch the handle of the wooden spoon?*

Figure 7 Convection is the transfer of thermal energy by the movement of particles in a fluid. **A** Passing sandbags along a line is like transferring thermal energy by convection. **B** The arrows show convection of air in an oven. **Predicting** *Which part of the oven should have the highest temperature?*

480   *Chapter 16*

Thermal Conductors Figure 6 shows a frying pan on a hot stove. The bottom of the pan heats up first. The metal handle heats up last. You can see that the flames do not directly heat the handle. The handle heats up because the metal is a good thermal conductor.

A **thermal conductor** is a material that conducts thermal energy well. A wire rack in a hot oven can burn you because the metal conducts thermal energy so quickly. Pots and pans often are made of copper or aluminum because these are good conductors.

A thermal conductor doesn't have to be hot. Why does a tile floor feel colder than a wooden floor? Both floors are at room temperature. But the tile feels colder because it is a better conductor and transfers thermal energy rapidly away from your skin.

Thermal Insulators Why is it safe to pick up the wooden spoon shown in Figure 6? Wood heats up slowly because it is a poor conductor of thermal energy. A material that conducts thermal energy poorly is called a **thermal insulator.**

Air is a very good insulator. A double-pane window has an air space contained between two panes of glass. The air slows down conduction to reduce heat loss in winter and to keep heat out of a building in summer. More expensive windows use argon gas, which is an even better insulator than air. Wool garments and plastic foam cups are two more examples of insulators that use trapped air to slow down conduction.

Convection

Convection is the transfer of thermal energy when particles of a fluid move from one place to another. Look at the people building a wall with sandbags in Figure 7A. The moving sandbags are like the particles in a fluid. The wall grows taller as more and more sandbags arrive. In much the same way, particles in a fluid can transfer thermal energy from a hot area to a cold area.

Customize for Inclusion Students

Learning Disabled
Learning-disabled students may process information in different ways, depending on their individual learning preferences and strengths. Some may respond better to visual stimuli, while others may learn best through the aural or kinesthetic modes. In presenting information for these students, involve as many modalities as possible. For example,

teach conduction by placing a stainless steel spoon and a plastic spoon in warm water. Have students observe the spoons and compare the way they feel when they are removed from the water. In similar ways, involve students' aural, visual, and kinesthetic senses to reinforce your explanation of scientific concepts.

Baking instructions sometimes tell you to use the top rack of an oven. Figure 7B shows why the temperature is lower at the top of the oven. When air at the bottom of the oven heats up, it expands and becomes less dense than the surrounding air. Due to the difference in density, the hot air rises. The rising air cools as it moves away from the heat source. As a result, the coolest air is at the top of the oven.

Air circulating in an oven is an example of a convection current. A **convection current** occurs when a fluid circulates in a loop as it alternately heats up and cools down. In a heated room, convection currents help keep the temperature uniform throughout the room. ⬤ Convection currents are important in many natural cycles, such as ocean currents, weather systems, and movements of hot rock in Earth's interior.

Radiation

At a picnic, you might use a charcoal grill to cook food. When you stand to the side of the grill, heat reaches you without convection or conduction. In much the same way, the sun warms you by radiation on a clear day. The space between the sun and Earth has no air to transfer thermal energy. **Radiation** is the transfer of energy by waves moving through space. Heat lamps used in restaurants are a familiar example of radiation.

⬤ **All objects radiate energy. As an object's temperature increases, the rate at which it radiates energy increases.** In Figure 8, the electric heating coil on a stove radiates so much energy that it glows. If you are close to the heating coil, you absorb radiation, which increases your thermal energy. In other words, it warms you up. The farther you are from the heating coil, the less radiation you receive, and the less it warms you.

Reading Checkpoint *What is radiation?*

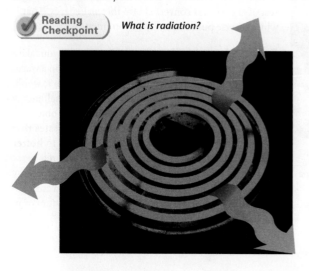

Figure 8 A heating coil on a stove radiates thermal energy. The changing color of the red arrows indicates that the farther you are from the coil, the less radiation you receive.

Thermal Energy and Heat **481**

Observing Convection

Procedure

1. Fill a 100-mL beaker halfway with cold water.
2. Fill a dropper pipet with hot water colored with food coloring. Wipe the pipet with a paper towel so no food coloring is on the outside of the pipet.
3. Insert the tip of the pipet into the cold water, halfway between the surface of the water and the bottom of the beaker.
4. Slowly squeeze the pipet bulb. Observe the water in the beaker from the side.

Analyze and Conclude

1. **Observing** Describe the motion of the colored hot water in the beaker.
2. **Inferring** Explain why the hot water behaved as it did.
3. **Predicting** How would colored cold water move in a beaker of hot water?

Observing Convection L2

Objective
Students will learn to
• use the concept of convection to describe fluid motion.

Skills Focus Observing, Predicting

Prep Time 10 minutes

Advance Prep Provide a 500-mL beaker of hot water with several drops of food coloring.

Class Time 20 minutes

Safety Turn off the hot plate at the start of the activity. Remind students not to touch anything that is hot, to handle glassware carefully, and to wear safety goggles and lab aprons.

Teaching Tips
• Remind students to release the colored water slowly, so that its movement will depend only on its temperature.

Expected Outcome The colored water should float to the top of the beaker.

Analyze and Conclude
1. It rose to the top of the beaker and formed a visible layer there.
2. The warm water rose to the top due to convection.
3. The cold water would sink.
Visual, Logical

Radiation

Address Misconceptions L2

Students may confuse the term *radiation* as it is used here with radiation from nuclear decay. Explain that in both types of radiation, energy spreads outward, or radiates, from a source. But nuclear decay such as alpha decay can also transfer mass. In thermal radiation, the mass of an object does not change because only energy is transferred.
Verbal

Answer to . . .

Figure 6 *Yes, because wood is not a good thermal conductor.*

Figure 7 *Hot air rises and cools, so the highest temperature is at the bottom of the oven, where the heat source is.*

Reading Checkpoint *Radiation is the transfer of energy through space without the help of matter to carry it.*

Thermal Energy and Heat 481

Thermodynamics
Build Science Skills
L2

Applying Concepts

Purpose Students apply the concept of conservation of energy.

Materials putty (enough to make 1 golf ball-sized ball per student), table or desktop

Class Time 10 minutes

Procedure Have students roll putty into balls about the size of a golf ball. Students hold the putty balls 2–3 feet above a table or desk and then drop them, noting the changes that occur.

Expected Outcome The potential energy of the putty ball held above the table will be converted to kinetic energy when the ball is released. Finally, it will stick to the table, and so undergo a decrease in kinetic and potential energy. According to the first law of thermodynamics, none of the energy is lost. Some of the mechanical energy is applied to changing the shape of the putty ball. The rest is converted to increasing the thermal energy of both the putty and the table, though increased thermal energy may not be detectable due to the small amount of energy involved. **Logical**

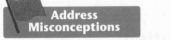

Address Misconceptions **L2**

Students may assume that adding energy to a system by heating it will only increase the system's thermal energy. Explain that work may be done, or internal energy may increase (during a phase change). Sometimes the added heat is mostly used to increase the thermal energy of the system, and little work is done. Demonstrate this effect by placing a sealed bottle of apple juice on a sunny windowsill. Only a small amount of work will be done because of the rigid walls of the bottle, but the temperature of the juice will increase. Work is negligible compared to the amount of energy added to the juice. **Kinesthetic**

Download a worksheet on thermodynamics for students to complete, and find additional teacher support from NSTA SciLinks.

For: Links on thermodynamics
Visit: www.SciLinks.org
Web Code: ccn-2162

Figure 9 You can consider the bicycle pump, the tire, and the air inside of both to be a system. The person does work on the system by pushing on the pump. Some of the work is converted into thermal energy, which heats the air in the pump and the tire.

Thermodynamics

The study of conversions between thermal energy and other forms of energy is called **thermodynamics.** Count Rumford made a good start in this field. But many scientists still believed that heat was a kind of matter. Then in 1845, James Prescott Joule (1818–1889) published his results from a convincing experiment.

Joule carefully measured the energy changes in a system. Recall that a system is any group of objects that interact with one another. Joule's system included a falling weight that turned a paddle wheel in a container of water. As the weight fell, the paddle churned a known mass of water. The water heated up due to friction from the turning paddle. Joule carefully measured the work done by the falling weight. He found that the work almost exactly equaled the thermal energy gained by the water. Joule is often given credit for discovering the first law of thermodynamics. That is the law of conservation of energy applied to work, heat, and thermal energy.

First Law of Thermodynamics Recall that energy cannot be created or destroyed. But energy can be converted into different forms. ◁ **The first law of thermodynamics states that energy is conserved.** If energy is added to a system, it can either increase the thermal energy of the system or do work on the system. But no matter what happens, all of the energy added to the system can be accounted for. Energy is conserved.

Look at the bicycle pump in Figure 9. You can consider the tire, the pump, and the air inside to be a system. The force exerted on the pump does work on the system. Some of this work is useful; it compresses air into the tire. The rest of the work is converted into thermal energy. That is why a bicycle pump heats up as you inflate a tire.

Second Law of Thermodynamics If you take a cold drink from the refrigerator and leave it out in a warm room, will the drink become colder? Of course it won't. You know that the drink will warm up. Thermal energy flows spontaneously only from hotter to colder objects.

◁ **The second law of thermodynamics states that thermal energy can flow from colder objects to hotter objects only if work is done on the system.** A refrigerator, for example, must do work to transfer thermal energy from the cold food compartment to the warm room air. The thermal energy is released by coils at the bottom or in the back of the refrigerator.

Facts and Figures

The "Zeroth" Law of Thermodynamics
In order for a thermometer to give meaningful information, its temperature must be equal to that of the object whose temperature is unknown. This occurs when both objects are in a state of *thermal equilibrium*, or when the thermal energy transferred by heat from the object to the thermometer is equal to the heat from the thermometer to the object. This is the same as saying that there is no net heat transfer between the object and thermometer.

The definition of thermal equilibrium is the basis of what is called the "zeroth" law of thermodynamics—two systems in thermal equilibrium with a third system are in thermal equilibrium with each other. As the name implies, this concept is fundamental to thermodynamics, and the first three laws are dependent on it. The zeroth law was established after the first two laws of thermodynamics had been accepted.

A **heat engine** is any device that converts heat into work. One consequence of the second law of thermodynamics is that the efficiency of a heat engine is always less than 100 percent. The best an engine can do is to convert most of the input energy into useful work. Thermal energy that is not converted into work is called **waste heat.** Waste heat is lost to the surrounding environment. In fact, a heat engine can do work only if some waste heat flows to a colder environment outside the engine.

Spontaneous changes will always make a system less orderly, unless work is done on the system. For example, if you walk long enough, your shoelaces will become untied. But the opposite won't happen; shoelaces don't tie themselves. Disorder in the universe as a whole is always increasing. You can only increase order on a local level. For instance, you can stop and tie your shoelaces. But this requires work. Because work always produces waste heat, you contribute to the disorder of the universe when you stop to tie a shoelace!

Third Law of Thermodynamics The efficiency of a heat engine increases with a greater difference between the high temperature inside and the cold temperature outside the engine. In theory, a heat engine could be 100 percent efficient if the cold outside environment were at absolute zero (0 kelvins). But this would violate the third law of thermodynamics. ⬤ **The third law of thermodynamics states that absolute zero cannot be reached.** Scientists have been able to cool matter almost all of the way to absolute zero. Figure 10 shows the equipment used to produce the record lowest temperature, just 3 billionths of a kelvin above absolute zero!

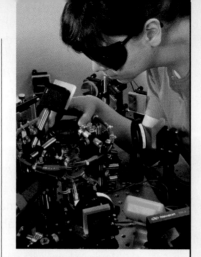

Figure 10 The third law of thermodynamics states that absolute zero cannot be reached. This physicist is adjusting a laser used to cool rubidium atoms to 3 billionths of a kelvin above absolute zero. This record low temperature was produced by a team of scientists at the National Institute of Standards and Technology.

Section 16.2 Assessment

Reviewing Concepts

1. ⬤ Why is conduction in gases slower than conduction in liquids or solids?

2. ⬤ Give three examples of convection currents that occur in natural cycles.

3. ⬤ What happens to radiation from an object as its temperature increases?

4. ⬤ State the first law of thermodynamics.

5. ⬤ In your own words, what is the second law of thermodynamics?

6. ⬤ State the third law of thermodynamics.

7. Why does a metal spoon feel colder than a wooden spoon at room temperature?

8. Why is solar energy transferred to Earth by radiation?

Critical Thinking

9. **Applying Concepts** If your bedroom is cold, you might feel warmer with several thin blankets than with one thick one. Explain why.

10. **Relating Cause and Effect** If every object is radiating constantly, why aren't all objects getting colder?

Connecting C Concepts

Conservation of Energy Review energy conservation in Section 15.2. Describe how the first and the second laws of thermodynamics are consistent with the law of conservation of energy.

Thermal Energy and Heat **483**

Solar Home **L2**
Background

Solar heating for the home can consist of either "passive" systems, which do not use any mechanical device to distribute the fluids heated by the sun, or "active" systems that use fans or pumps to transfer the heated fluids. Although it is not practical to use solar heating systems to completely meet heating needs year round, solar heating systems can reduce the amount of energy used in conventional heating systems, thus reducing heating costs.

Build Science Skills **L2**

Observing

Purpose Students observe how passive solar heating can be used for heating.

Materials a box with black interior, a box with white interior, clear plastic wrap, 2 beakers, 2 thermometers

Class Time 50 minutes preparation, or one class period

Procedure Separate students into groups, each with its own set of materials. Members of each group place one beaker, half full of water, in each of their boxes and cover both boxes with plastic wrap. Both boxes are placed in sunlight for half an hour. Group members then remove the beakers from the boxes, placing a thermometer in each. Finally, all students record the temperature of the water.

Safety Have students wear lab aprons and safety goggles.

Expected Outcome Because the black box absorbs and remits radiation better than the white box, the thermal energy of its walls and interior will be greater. The water will be in thermal equilibrium with the interior of the box. Therefore, the water that had been in the black box will have a higher temperature than the water in the white box.

Kinesthetic, Group

Solar Home

Huge amounts of radiant energy from the sun constantly fall on the surface of our planet. How can this energy be harnessed to help make a home that is warm and comfortable in all seasons?

Heating a home with solar energy means making the best use of available sunlight. To provide warmth, large windows are placed on the south side of the house to trap sunlight, while north-facing walls have good insulation and few windows. On the roof, solar collectors absorb energy from the sun's rays to heat water, while solar panels convert the sun's energy to electrical energy for use in household appliances. High-quality insulation is used in all outside walls to reduce heat lost through convection, conduction, and radiation. But because the sun does not shine continuously, solar-heated homes also use energy from conventional sources to keep the home heated day and night, year-round.

Large area of glass to trap radiant energy from the sun

Automated louvers for cooling when needed

Trees on south and west sides for summer shade

Positioning for sunlight
Windows should face south to trap as much light as possible from the winter sun, with few windows on the west side to reduce overheating in summer.

Summer sun

Winter sun

Evergreens provide a year-round windbreak.

Deciduous trees give summer shade.

Planting trees and shrubs
Trees placed away from the house act as a windbreak to reduce heat loss. Deciduous trees, planted closer, prevent overheating in summer, and allow sunlight to pass through in winter.

Solar panel to generate electricity

Solar collector to heat water

Well-insulated timber-framed walls

Small windows to reduce heat loss

Solar panels

Solar panels use the sun's energy to generate electricity for the home. The panels are made up of a series of linked photovoltaic cells. Light from the sun releases electrons from silicon atoms in the cells, producing an electric current. Rechargeable batteries can store electrical energy to provide power when there is no sunlight.

Sun's rays

Rechargeable battery

Entertainment or communication appliance

Solar panel on roof

Air conditioning system

Lighting

Electric circuit

Cooking appliance

Heating system

Stud frame

Plasterboard

Insulating material

Wall insulation
Wood is a natural insulator, so timber construction reduces heat flow through the walls. Filling the wall cavity with insulating material seals the walls against drafts, and greatly reduces heat loss.

Wood siding

Going Further

- Research solar-heated pools in the library or on the Internet. Make a poster display explaining how solar heating differs from a typical pool heating system. Include diagrams that explain how radiation, absorption, insulation, and convection are used in a solar-heated pool.

- Take a Discovery Channel Video Field Trip by watching "Powered by the Sun."

Discovery CHANNEL SCHOOL
Video Field Trip

Thermal Energy and Heat **485**

Going Further

Student posters should clearly show energy sources and energy transfers in solar-heated and conventionally heated pools. Diagrams should label places where radiation, absorption, and convection occur. For example, absorption occurs in the solar collector and convection occurs in the tubing that carries heated water to the pool. To reduce heat loss in a solar-heated pool, insulating plastic is placed on the water's surface when the pool is not in use.
Visual

Discovery CHANNEL SCHOOL

Video Field Trip
Powered by the Sun

After students have viewed the Video Field Trip, ask them the following questions: **How long is energy from the sun expected to be available?** *(Billions of years)* **Why is it important to make effective use of solar energy?** *(Other sources of energy are being constantly used up.)* **How does the building at the Rocky Mountain Institute manage to produce crops throughout the year?** *(By using a greenhouse with glass walls that let in* sunlight. *Student answers may include that a greenhouse also stays warm inside partly by keeping out the colder air outside.)* **How does the heating system in the Rocky Mountain Institute building produce heat?** *(It converts sunlight into thermal energy.)* **How does this heating system work?** *(Solar panels absorb sunlight and heat a fluid. The fluid is pumped to a very large water tank. Heat from the stored hot fluid is transferred to the water that people use. Students may comment that the water can be heated to between 130°C and 140°C even in the coldest weather.)*

1 FOCUS

Objectives

16.3.1 Describe heat engines and **explain** how heat engines convert thermal energy into mechanical energy.

16.3.2 Describe how the different types of heating systems operate.

16.3.3 Describe how cooling systems, such as refrigerators and air conditioners, operate.

16.3.4 Evaluate benefits and drawbacks of different heating and cooling systems.

Reading Focus

Build Vocabulary **L2**

LINCS Have students: **L**ist the parts of the vocabulary that they know, such as *central, heating, system, heat,* and *pump.* **I**magine what a central heating system might look like and how the terms might fit together. **N**ote a reminding, sound-alike term, such as *central nervous system* or *sound system.* **C**onnect the terms, perhaps in a long sentence or a short story. **S**elf-test (quiz themselves).

Reading Strategy **L2**

a. Piston compresses the fuel-air mixture. b. Ignited mixture expands and pushes the piston. c. Exhaust gases leave the cylinder.

2 INSTRUCT

Heat Engines
Build Reading Literacy **L1**

Relate Cause and Effect Refer to page **260D** in **Chapter 9**, which provides the guidelines for relating cause and effect.

Have students read the paragraphs about the external combustion engine and study the illustration in Figure 11. Ask, **What causes the piston in the cylinder to do work?** *(The expanding steam pushes the piston, causing it to do work.)* **What is the effect of the movement of the slide valve?** *(It traps hot steam in the cylinder and allows cool steam to leave.)* **Logical**

16.3 Using Heat

Standards: ICP.3.3, ICP.8.3, ICP.8.4

Reading Focus

Key Concepts
- What are the two main types of heat engines?
- How do most heating systems distribute thermal energy?
- How does a heat pump reverse the normal flow of heat?

Vocabulary
- external combustion engine
- internal combustion engine
- central heating system
- heat pump
- refrigerant

Reading Strategy
Sequencing Copy the cycle diagram below and complete it as you read to show the sequence of events in a gasoline engine.

Intake stroke: Fuel and air enter cylinder. → Compression stroke: a. ? → Power stroke: b. ? → Exhaust stroke: c. ? →

Steam locomotives were one of the most important early uses of the steam engine. Prior to the locomotive, steam engines provided power for coal mines and mills. But don't think that steam engines are only a thing of the past. In fact, most electric power plants today use steam turbines, a very efficient kind of steam engine.

Heat Engines

Heat engines played a key role in the development of the modern industrial world. **The two main types of heat engines are the external combustion engine and the internal combustion engine.**

External Combustion Engine A steam engine is an **external combustion engine**—an engine that burns fuel outside the engine. Thomas Newcomen developed the first practical steam engine in 1712. His engine was used to pump water out of coal mines. In 1765, James Watt designed an engine that was more efficient, in part because it operated at a higher temperature.

Figure 11 shows one type of steam engine. Hot steam enters the cylinder on the right side. When the valve slides to the left, hot steam is trapped in the cylinder. The steam expands and cools as it pushes the piston to the left. Thus heat is converted into work. The piston moves back and forth as hot steam enters first on one side and then on the other side.

Figure 11 In an external combustion engine, combustion occurs outside of the engine.

Hot steam in

Slide valve

Exhaust steam out

Valve rod

Piston rod

Cylinder

Piston

486 *Chapter 16*

Section Resources

Print
- *Reading and Study Workbook With Math Support,* Section 16.3
- *Math Skills and Problem Solving Workbook,* Section 16.3
- *Transparencies,* Section 16.3

Technology
- *Interactive Textbook,* Section 16.3
- *Presentation Pro CD-ROM,* Section 16.3
- *Go Online,* Science News, Heat

Internal Combustion Engine Most cars use internal combustion engines that burn gasoline. An **internal combustion engine** is a heat engine in which the fuel burns inside the engine. Most internal combustion engines use pistons that move up and down inside cylinders. Each upward or downward motion of a piston is called a stroke. The linear motion of each stroke is converted into rotary motion by the crankshaft. The crankshaft is connected to the transmission, which is linked to the vehicle's wheels through the drive shaft.

Figure 12 shows the sequence of events in one cylinder of a four-stroke engine. In the intake stroke, a mixture of air and gasoline vapor enters the cylinder. Next, in the compression stroke, the piston compresses the gas mixture. At the end of compression, the spark plug ignites the mixture, which heats the gas under pressure. In the power stroke, the hot gas expands and drives the piston down. During the exhaust stroke, gas leaves the cylinder, and the cycle repeats.

Recall that a heat engine must discharge some waste energy in order to do work. In an internal combustion engine, the cooling system and exhaust transfer heat from the engine to the environment. A coolant—usually water and antifreeze—absorbs some thermal energy from the engine and then passes through the radiator. A fan blows air through the radiator, transferring thermal energy to the atmosphere. Without a cooling system, an engine would be damaged by thermal expansion. If you are ever in a car that overheats, stop driving and allow the engine to cool. Otherwise, there is a risk of serious damage to the engine.

Gasoline engines are more efficient than old-fashioned steam engines, but they still are not very efficient. Only about one third of the fuel energy in a gasoline engine is converted to work. Auto makers have tried several ways to make engines more efficient. One design, called a hybrid design, uses a heat engine together with an electric motor. This design is explained in the How It Works box on the next page.

Go Online
active art

For: Activity on four-stroke engines
Visit: PHSchool.com
Web Code: ccp-2163

Figure 12 In an internal combustion engine, fuel is burned inside the engine. Most cars have a four-stroke internal combustion engine. This diagram shows only one of the cylinders during each stroke. **Classifying** *In which of the strokes does the piston do work that can be used by the car?*

| **A** Intake stroke | **B** Compression stroke | **C** Power stroke | **D** Exhaust stroke |

Thermal Energy and Heat **487**

HOW It Works

Hybrid Automobile L2

The hybrid automobile is a result of research that was begun initially to develop an efficient electric car. By combining a small gasoline engine with an electric motor, the hybrid automobile is able to travel longer distances, like a gasoline-powered vehicle, but with reduced fuel consumption and emissions. During regenerative braking, kinetic energy that is normally lost to friction is partially recovered for later use. This can be explained to students in simple terms: It takes work to turn a generator. When the spinning wheels do the work of turning the generator, the wheels lose kinetic energy. In other words, the wheels must slow down.

Interpreting Diagrams Fuel consumption is reduced by using lightweight materials, an aerodynamic design, and high-pressure tires that reduce friction. The use of two engines saves fuel because the small gasoline engine is more efficient than traditional larger engines, and the electric motor is more efficient than a gasoline engine for accelerating at low speeds.
Visual

For Enrichment L3

Interested students can make a multimedia presentation for the class explaining the hybrid automobile. Numerous articles on the subject can be found on the Internet and in science and engineering periodicals.
Verbal, Portfolio

HOW It Works

Hybrid Automobile

Internal combustion engines produce harmful emissions from the combustion of gasoline. Recently, cleaner electric cars have been developed, but these need frequent recharging. Hybrid cars solve these problems by using a combination of smaller gasoline engines and electric motors. **Interpreting Diagrams** *Which features of the hybrid automobile help to reduce fuel consumption?*

A new breed of car
This hybrid car was first produced in 1999. It is light, aerodynamic, and has a small, efficient engine.

Lightweight materials *A small engine and synthetic materials, such as carbon fiber, reduce the car's weight to improve fuel efficiency.*

Aerodynamic body *The teardrop shape reduces air resistance, improving efficiency.*

Battery *The battery stores energy for the electric motor.*

Gasoline engine *This small heat engine is most efficient for cruising at constant speed. It is assisted by the electric motor during acceleration.*

Fuel tank

Electric motor *The electric motor is more efficient than a heat engine for accelerating at low speeds. When the brakes are used, the electric motor acts as a generator, recharging the batteries. This way of generating power is called regenerative braking.*

Transmission *This converts the rotation of shafts in the electric motor and the gas engine into wheel rotation. In this model, both the electric motor and the engine can directly drive the transmission.*

Tires *These tires are inflated to a higher pressure than conventional tires to reduce friction.*

488 *Chapter 16*

Heating Systems

At the start of the industrial revolution, wood-burning fireplaces were the principal method of heating buildings. Rumford was keenly aware of the drawbacks of fireplaces. They were smoky and not very efficient. Too much heat went up the chimney. In 1796, Rumford designed a fireplace that now bears his name. His fireplace was not as deep as standard fireplaces, and it had slanted walls to reflect heat into the room. His improvements were quickly accepted and used throughout England.

Today, fireplaces are often used to supplement central heating systems. A **central heating system** heats many rooms from one central location. The central location of a heating system often is in the basement. The most commonly used energy sources for central heating systems are electrical energy, natural gas, oil, and coal. Heating systems differ in how they transfer thermal energy to the rest of the building. ⬤ **Most heating systems use convection to distribute thermal energy.**

Hot-Water Heating Figure 13 shows the main components of a hot-water heating system. At the boiler, heating oil or natural gas burns and heats the water. The circulating pump carries the hot water to radiators in each room. The hot water transfers thermal energy to the radiator by conduction. As the pipes heat up, they heat the room air by conduction and radiation. Hot air rises and sets up a convection current in each room. After transferring much of its thermal energy to the room, the cooled water returns to the boiler and the cycle begins again.

Temperature is controlled by a thermostat. One kind of thermostat is like a thermometer, with a strip of brass and steel wound up in a coil. When the heating system is on, the coil heats up. The two metals in the coil expand at different rates, and the coil rotates. This trips a switch to turn off the heat. As the room cools, the coil rotates in the opposite direction, until it trips the switch to turn the heat back on.

Steam Heating Steam heating is very similar to hot-water heating except that steam is used instead of hot water. The transfer of heat from the steam-heated radiator to the room still occurs by conduction and radiation. Steam heating often is used in older buildings or when many buildings are heated from one central location.

 Reading Checkpoint *How are fireplaces often used today?*

Figure 13 Within the pipes of this hot-water heating system, the water circulates in a convection current. In each room, the air moves in a convection current. **Relating Cause and Effect** *Why has the water returning to the boiler cooled down?*

Thermal Energy and Heat **489**

Heating Systems

Address Misconceptions L2

Students may think that heating systems are simply energy conversion devices because they can use a variety of energy sources to produce thermal energy. Remind students that the energy required to operate a heating system exceeds the amount of thermal energy distributed by the system, partly because there is always some energy that is lost through exhaust in the original central heating process. In addition, energy is lost through heat transfer processes from pipes and ducts that transfer heated fluids from the central heating system to the various rooms. Even in electric heating, some energy is lost in heating the wires used to transfer electrical energy to the heating coils.
Logical

Use Visuals L1

Figure 13 Point out that the system shown must be well insulated so as to prevent the loss of heat. Have students look at the various parts of the hot-water heating system. Ask, **Where can thermal energy be lost in this system, and by what manner of heat transfer?** *(Energy is lost through the water pipes leading from the boiler to the radiator. Most of this energy is lost by radiation, though some conduction to the air takes place. A good deal of energy is lost by convection from the exhaust vent. A smaller amount of heat is lost through the pipes leading from radiators to the boiler.)*
Visual

Facts and Figures

Heat of Vaporization Although hot-water heating and steam heating systems are similar in structure, steam systems convey more energy for each kilogram of water used. This difference occurs because the phase change that takes place during the boiling process, when liquid water is vaporized to steam, requires a much greater input of energy than is necessary to heat water in a hot-water system. The energy required for this phase change, called the *heat of vaporization,* is equal to 2.26×10^6 J/kg. This amount is more than 500 times as great as the energy required to raise the temperature of a kilogram of liquid water by 1°C (about 4180 J/kg). When steam completely condenses to liquid water, an amount of energy equal to the heat of vaporization is given up. This is why steam heating is effective, and also why steam is so hazardous.

Answer to . . .

Figure 13 *Water returning to the boiler has cooled because it has lost thermal energy in the radiator.*

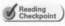 **Reading Checkpoint** *Today, fireplaces are often used to supplement central heating systems.*

Cooling Systems

Cooling by Evaporation L2

Purpose Students observe how evaporation of a liquid can cool its surroundings.

Materials paper towels, water, tape, hand-held or electric fan, thermometer

Procedure Wrap a wet paper towel around the bulb of a thermometer and wait several minutes. Record the thermometer's temperature. Tape the wet paper towel to the thermometer's bulb. Blow air across the paper towel with the fan. Read the thermometer's temperature again.

Safety Clean up any spills immediately. Handle thermometers with care to avoid breakage. Be sure cords are untangled and cannot trip anyone. Do not handle electrical equipment with wet hands.

Expected Outcome Water absorbs energy as it evaporates. This removes energy from the thermometer bulb, so the temperature reading of the thermometer decreases.
Kinesthetic, Visual

Integrate Chemistry L2

Different compounds can be used as refrigerants, just as long as they can be made to evaporate at low temperatures. Among the refrigerants that have this property are certain *chlorofluorocarbons,* or CFCs, which have been used widely in refrigerators and air conditioners. In the 1970s, chlorine atoms released by CFCs were found to react with the layer of atmospheric ozone, which absorbs harmful ultraviolet radiation from the sun. The decomposition of the ozone layer prompted the establishment of the Montreal Accords in 1990 and the eventual replacement of CFCs with less harmful refrigerants.
Verbal, Logical

Science News provides students with current information on heat.

Figure 14 In a forced-air central heating system, the hot air enters the room through a supply vent in the floor. The hot air rises as cooler, denser air in the room sinks. The cooler air returns to the furnace through the return vent. **Inferring** *If the hot air supply vent were located near the ceiling, what would be the warmest part of the room?*

Electric Baseboard Heating An electric baseboard heater uses electrical energy to heat a room. A conductor similar to the heating element in an electric stove is used to convert electrical energy to thermal energy. The hot coil heats the air near it by conduction and radiation. Then convection circulates the warm air to heat the room.

Radiant heaters are similar to electric baseboard heating. They are often sold as small portable units, and are used to supplement a central heating system. These "space heaters" are easy to turn on and off and to direct onto cold toes or other areas where heat is needed most. Sometimes these heaters have a fan that helps to circulate heat.

Forced-Air Heating To maintain even room temperatures, forced-air heating systems use fans to circulate warm air through ducts to the rooms of a building. In a forced-air heating system, shown in Figure 15, convection circulates air in each room. Because the warm air entering the room rises toward the ceiling, the warm-air vents are located near the floor. Cool room air returns to the furnace through floor vents on the other side of the room. One advantage of forced-air heating is that the air is cleaned as it passes through filters located near the furnace.

Reading Checkpoint *How do forced-air heating systems circulate air?*

Cooling Systems

Most cooling systems, such as refrigerators and air conditioners, are heat pumps. A **heat pump** is a device that reverses the normal flow of thermal energy. Heat pumps do this by circulating a refrigerant through tubing. A **refrigerant** is a fluid that vaporizes and condenses inside the tubing of a heat pump. When the refrigerant absorbs heat, it vaporizes, or turns into a gas. When the refrigerant gives off heat, it condenses, or turns back into a liquid.

Recall that thermal energy flows spontaneously from hot objects to cold objects. **Heat pumps must do work on a refrigerant in order to reverse the normal flow of thermal energy.** In this process, a cold area, such as the inside of a refrigerator, becomes even colder.

Go Online
SCIENCE NEWS
For: Articles on heat
Visit: PHSchool.com
Web Code: cce-2163

Data Analysis

What Is the Real Cost of a Washing Machine?

If you ever shop for a new washing machine, you'll notice the bright yellow Energy Guide sticker on each machine. The sticker gives the machine's operating cost per year as estimated by the U.S. Department of Energy. The largest part of the cost for cleaning clothes is heating the water that goes into the washing machine. So a machine that uses less water is more efficient.

1. **Using Graphs** One family uses an electric water heater. What is their cost per year for machine A? For machine D?

2. **Calculating** How much money does this family save each year using machine A compared to using machine D?

3. **Calculating** The price of machine A is $300 more than the price of machine D. If the family uses a machine for 10 years, which

one costs less overall? (*Hint:* Add the price to the operating cost for 10 years.)

4. **Calculating** Another family uses a gas water heater. Which machine should this family choose? Explain your thinking.

5. **Evaluating and Revising** A washing machine advertisement states that the annual cost assumes an electric water heater is used. Why would an advertisement include only this cost?

Comparing Washing Machines

Refrigerators A refrigerator is a heat pump—it transfers thermal energy from the cold food compartment to the warm room. To move heat from a colder to a warmer location, a motor must do work to move refrigerant through tubing inside the refrigerator walls. Could you cool your kitchen on a hot day by leaving the refrigerator door open? It might seem so, but an open refrigerator would actually heat the kitchen! You may have noticed the hot coils underneath or behind the refrigerator. The coils not only release heat absorbed from the food compartment; they also release thermal energy produced by the work the motor does. That is why a refrigerator with an open door adds more heat to the room than it removes.

What is a heat pump?

Temperature in room: 25°C

Temperature inside refrigerator: 3°C

Figure 15 When a refrigerator door is open, some thermal energy from the room enters the refrigerator. But more thermal energy leaves the refrigerator through the coils underneath the food compartment.
Interpreting Photos *Why can't you cool a room by leaving the refrigerator door open?*

Thermal Energy and Heat **491**

Facts and Figures

Water Cooling Although refrigerants are used to reach temperatures below the freezing point of water, water itself has been used for cooling for centuries. Because of its specific heat and heat of vaporization, water can greatly reduce the temperature of hot dry air. Fountains helped to cool the air in courtyards in places like Spain and Italy. In many desert cities, evaporative coolers, in which hot air is drawn through water-soaked pads into houses, are still widely used for air conditioning.

Data Analysis

What Is the Real Cost of a Washing Machine? L2

Answers
1. The annual cost of Brand A is about $10 per year. The annual cost of Brand D is $60 per year.
2. The family saves $50 each year using Brand A.
3. The operating cost of Brand A for 10 years is 10 × $10 = $100. The operating cost of Brand D for 10 years is 10 × $60 = $600. Brand A costs less overall because although the initial price is $300 higher, the machine saves $500 in operating costs.
4. Using a gas water heater, Brand A saves only $20 in operating costs each year. Based only on cost, the family should choose Brand D because it will cost $100 less to own and operate for 10 years.
5. The goal of the advertisement is to convince as many people as possible to buy the machine. Therefore, the advertisement emphasizes the money that could be saved under the best of circumstances (using an electric water heater).

For Extra Help L1

Discuss the basic features of a bar graph. Unlike line graphs, in which one quantity on the horizontal axis corresponds to a unique quantity on the vertical axis, more than one bar can be given for a particular item on the horizontal axis. For instance, in the above graph, each brand has two bars shown: one for electric heaters and one for gas heaters. Similarly, a comparison between results in different years can be shown using several bars. The placement of the bars allows easy comparison of changes on one graph. **Visual**

Answer to . . .

Figure 14 *The ceiling, because warm air entering the room tends to remain near the ceiling*

Figure 15 *The refrigerator gives off more thermal energy than it absorbs.*

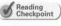 *In a forced-air heating system, fans circulate warm air through ducts to the rooms of a building.*

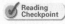 *A heat pump is a device that reverses the normal flow of thermal energy.*

Thermal Energy and Heat **491**

Use Visuals   L1

Figure 16 Stress that evaporation is the key process for cooling in an air conditioner and refrigerator. Most of the work done by the air conditioner motor involves changing the pressure of the refrigerant so that it will evaporate (and so absorb thermal energy) and condense (to give up thermal energy) easily. Ask, **What is the direction of the net flow of thermal energy in an air conditioner?** *(Looking at the red arrows only, thermal energy is transferred from the air inside the room to the outdoor air.)* **Visual**

❸ ASSESS

Evaluate Understanding   L2

Ask students to write two questions each about heating systems and cooling systems. Review the questions for accuracy, and then have students form groups and ask each other their approved questions.

Reteach   L1

Use Figure 12 to review how an internal combustion engine operates during one cycle.

Student flyers should clearly compare four heating systems. Students may choose to show the comparisons using a chart. Possible columns in the chart are efficiency, physical space used per room, environmental concerns, and local climate. Students may choose to compare systems in different climates. In southern states, a benefit of a forced-air heating system is that it combines easily with central air conditioning. Electric baseboard heating is advantageous in regions where electric power is inexpensive.

Interactive Textbook If your class subscribes to the Interactive Textbook, use it to review key concepts in Section 16.3.

Answer to . . .

Figure 16 *The compressor does work by pushing particles of vapor closer together to form a high-pressure vapor. It also does work as it pushes refrigerant through the tubing.*

Warm air out

Condenser coil
Vapor cools to liquid as heat is removed.

Cold air out

Compressor

Warm air in

Expansion valve
Pressure drops, causing liquid refrigerant to become cold.

Evaporator coil
Liquid absorbs heat to become vapor.

Figure 16 In a window air conditioner, outside air is heated as a fan blows it through the condenser coil. Inside the room, a fan draws in warm air through the evaporator coil. The fan blows cooled air out into the room. **Interpreting Diagrams** *What work is done by the compressor?*

Air Conditioners Have you ever been outside on a hot day and stood near a room air conditioner? The air conditioner is actually heating the outdoor air. Near the air conditioner is the last place you'd want to be on a hot day!

Where does the hot air come from? It must come from inside the house. But as you know from the second law of thermodynamics, heat only flows from a lower temperature (indoors) to a higher temperature (outdoors) if work is done on the system.

Figure 16 shows how a room air conditioner operates. The compressor raises the temperature and pressure of the refrigerant, turning it into a hot, high-pressure gas. The temperature of the condenser coil is higher than the outside air temperature, so heat flows spontaneously from the coil to the outside air. A fan increases the rate at which heat flows. As thermal energy is removed from the coil, the refrigerant cools and condenses into a liquid.

The liquid refrigerant then flows through the expansion valve and decreases in temperature. As the cold refrigerant flows through the evaporator coil, it absorbs thermal energy from the warm room air. The fan sends cold air back into the room. The refrigerant becomes a vapor, and the process starts all over again.

Section 16.3 Assessment

Reviewing Concepts

1. 🔘 List the two main types of heat engines.
2. 🔘 How is thermal energy distributed in most heating systems?
3. 🔘 How does a heat pump move thermal energy from a cold area to a warm area?
4. If the efficiency of a gasoline engine is 25 percent, what happens to the missing 75 percent of the energy in the fuel?

Critical Thinking

5. **Predicting** A diesel engine runs at a higher temperature than a gasoline engine. Predict which engine would be more efficient. Explain your answer.

6. **Applying Concepts** Why would it be a mistake to locate a wood-burning stove on the second floor of a two-story house?

Writing in Science

Writing to Persuade Imagine that you are a marketing executive in a company that sells HVAC (heating, ventilation, and air conditioning) equipment. Write a one-page flyer comparing four kinds of heating systems. Organize the flyer so it is easy for customers to see the benefits of each system.

Section 16.3 Assessment

1. External combustion engine, internal combustion engine
2. Most heating systems distribute thermal energy by convection.
3. Heat pumps must do work on a refrigerant in order to reverse the normal flow of heat.
4. The energy that does not do useful work is converted into thermal energy.
5. The maximum efficiency of a heat engine increases with a greater difference between the temperature inside and the temperature outside the engine. A diesel engine is likely to be more efficient, assuming both engines discharge thermal energy into an environment at the same temperature.
6. Convection will carry cool air to the lower level so the lower level will be cooler than the upper level. This is inefficient because if the lower level is comfortable, the upper level will be warmer than necessary.

Using Specific Heat to Analyze Metals

In this lab, you will determine the specific heat of steel and aluminum. Then you will use specific heat to analyze the composition of a metal can.

Problem
How can you use specific heat to determine the composition of a metal can?

Materials
- 10 steel bolts
- balance
- 50-cm length of string
- clamp
- ring stand
- boiling water bath (shared with class)
- thermometer
- 500-mL graduated cylinder
- ice water
- foam cup with lid
- aluminum nails
- crushed can

 For the probeware version of this lab, see the Probeware Lab Manual, Lab 7.

Skills
Calculating, Designing Experiments

Procedure

Part A: Determining Specific Heat

1. Copy the data table shown below.

Data Table		
	Water	Steel Bolt
Mass (g)		
Initial temperature (°C)		
Final temperature (°C)		
Specific heat (J/g•°C)	4.18	

2. Measure and record the mass of 10 steel bolts.

3. Tie the bolts to the string. Use a clamp and ring stand to suspend the bolts in the boiling water bath. **CAUTION** *Be careful not to splash boiling water.* After a few minutes, record the water temperature as the initial temperature of the bolts.

4. Use a graduated cylinder to pour 200 mL of ice water (without ice) into the foam cup. Record the mass and temperature of the ice water. (*Hint:* The density of water is 1 g/mL.)

5. Use the clamp to move the bolts into the cup of ice water. Cover the cup and insert the thermometer through the hole in the cover.

6. Gently swirl the water in the cup. Record the highest temperature as the final temperature for both the water and the steel bolts.

7. Calculate and record the specific heat of steel. (*Hint:* Use the equation $Q = m \times c \times \Delta T$ to calculate the energy the water absorbs.)

8. Repeat Steps 3 through 7 with aluminum nails to determine the specific heat of aluminum. Start by making a new data table. Use a mass of aluminum that is close to the mass you used for the steel bolts.

Part B: Design Your Own Experiment

9. **Designing Experiments** Design an experiment that uses specific heat to identify the metals a can might be made of.

10. Construct a data table in which to record your observations. After your teacher approves your plan, perform your experiment.

Analyze and Conclude

1. **Comparing and Contrasting** Which metal has a higher specific heat, aluminum or steel?

2. **Drawing Conclusions** Was the specific heat of the can closer to the specific heat of steel or of aluminum? What can you conclude about the material in the can?

3. **Evaluating** Did your observations prove what the can was made of? If not, what other information would you need to be sure?

4. **Inferring** The can you used is often called a tin can. The specific heat of tin is 0.23 J/g•°C. Did your data support the idea that the can was made mostly of tin? Explain your answer.

Thermal Energy and Heat **493**

Expected Outcome Students should measure a specific heat for the steel can that is close to that of the steel bolts.

Sample Data Ten bolts with a mass of 100 g will raise the temperature of 200 mL of water by about 5°C. The same mass of aluminum nails will raise the temperature by about 9°C.

Analyze and Conclude
1. The specific heat of aluminum (about 0.90 J/g•°C) is higher than the specific heat of steel (about 0.45 J/g•°C).

2. The specific heat of the can was very close to the specific heat of steel. This is evidence that the can is made mostly of steel.

3. The observations support the idea that the can is made of steel, but do not prove it; other metals may have similar specific heats. A list of the specific heats of various metals for comparison would be helpful, as would other kinds of evidence, such as the densities and chemical properties of the metals.

4. The specific heat of the can is close to that of steel, suggesting that the can is primarily steel.
Logical

Using Specific Heat to Analyze Metals L2

Objective
After completing this lab, students will be able to
- describe how specific heat is determined.

 Address Misconceptions

Students may have the misconception that the temperatures of the metal and water are the only factors that will affect the final temperature of the mixture. To help dispel this misconception, ask them to compare the effects of dropping an ice cube into a lake and into a glass of water.

Skills Focus Calculating, Measuring, Designing Experiments

Prep Time 20 minutes

Advance Prep Crush a steel can for each lab group. Smooth any rough or sharp edges with a file while wearing heavy leather gloves and safety goggles. Puncture the lids of the foam cups to enable students to insert the thermometers. Provide a large beaker of boiling water (with a thermometer in it) on a hot plate for the entire class to use. Provide ring stands, clamps, and 50-cm lengths of string for suspending the bolts in the boiling water bath.

Class Time 45 minutes

Safety Provide only nonmercury thermometers. Students should use tongs or heat-resistant gloves when handling hot objects and liquids. Students should wear safety goggles and lab aprons and should not stir with the thermometers.

Teaching Tips
- Students may need some guidance in using the specific-heat equation.

Questioning Strategies Ask students the following questions. **Why is it important to quickly transfer the bolts into the beaker?** *(Because the bolts are very hot, they will lose thermal energy very quickly as soon as they leave the hot water.)* **Why is it important to swirl the water after adding the hot bolts?** *(This ensures an even temperature and more accurate results.)*

 Probeware Lab Manual
Versions of this lab for use with probeware available from Pasco, Texas Instruments, and Vernier are in the Probeware Lab Manual.

Thermal Energy and Heat 493

Study Guide

Study Tip

Organize New Information
Tell students to organize the information they learn each day. Remind them that doing this helps them to understand better how all of the information is connected.

a. Energy is conserved: Thermal energy added to a system can do work or increase the thermal energy of the system.
b. Heat can flow from an object at lower temperature to an object at higher temperature only if work is done on the system.
c. Third law

Assessment

 If your class subscribes to the Interactive Textbook, your students can go online to access an interactive version of the Student Edition and a self-test.

Reviewing Content

1. d	**2.** b	**3.** a
4. b	**5.** b	**6.** c
7. a	**8.** d	**9.** b
10. a		

Understanding Concepts

11. Heat flows spontaneously from hot to cold objects. In many collisions, more energetic particles tend to transfer thermal energy to less energetic particles.
12. The object that is a better conductor of heat feels cooler to the touch because it conducts heat away from the hand faster.
13. As the temperature of the air in the balloon increases, the particles' average kinetic energy increases. The more energetic particles hit the inside of the balloon with greater force, causing the balloon to expand.

16.1 Thermal Energy and Matter

Key Concepts

- Heat flows spontaneously from hot objects to cold objects.
- Temperature is related to the average kinetic energy of an object's particles due to their random motion through space.
- Thermal energy depends on the mass, temperature, and phase (solid, liquid, or gas) of an object.
- Thermal expansion occurs because particles of matter tend to move farther apart as temperature increases.
- The lower a material's specific heat is, the more its temperature rises when a given amount of energy is absorbed by a given mass.
- A calorimeter uses the principle that heat flows from a hotter object to a colder object until both reach the same temperature.

Vocabulary

heat, *p. 474*
temperature, *p. 475*
absolute zero, *p. 475*
thermal expansion, *p. 476*
specific heat, *p. 476*
calorimeter, *p. 478*

16.2 Heat and Thermodynamics

Key Concepts

- Conduction in gases is slower than in liquids and solids because the particles in a gas collide less often.
- Convection currents are important in many natural cycles, such as ocean currents, weather systems, and movements of hot rock in Earth's interior.
- All objects radiate energy. As an object's temperature increases, the rate at which it radiates energy increases.
- The first law of thermodynamics states that energy is conserved.
- The second law of thermodynamics states that thermal energy can flow from colder objects to hotter objects only if work is done on the system.
- The third law of thermodynamics states that absolute zero cannot be reached.

Vocabulary

conduction, *p. 479*
thermal conductor, *p. 480*
thermal insulator, *p. 480*
convection, *p. 480*
convection current, *p. 481*
radiation, *p. 481*
thermodynamics, *p. 482*
heat engine, *p. 483*
waste heat, *p. 483*

16.3 Using Heat

Key Concepts

- The two main types of heat engines are the external combustion engine and the internal combustion engine.
- Most heating systems use convection to distribute thermal energy.
- Heat pumps must do work on a refrigerant in order to reverse the normal flow of thermal energy.

Vocabulary

external combustion engine, *p. 486*
internal combustion engine, *p. 487*
central heating system, *p. 489*
heat pump, *p. 490*
refrigerant, *p. 490*

Thinking Visually

Concept Map Copy the concept map below onto a sheet of paper. Use the information from the chapter to complete the diagram.

Assessment

Reviewing Content

Choose the letter that best answers the question or completes the statement.

1. When a drill is used to bore a hole in an object,
   a. no useful work is done.
   b. no energy is lost due to friction.
   c. the drill is 100 percent efficient.
   d. friction causes the object to heat up.

2. Why does liquid rise in a thermometer?
   a. convection   **b.** thermal expansion
   c. condensation   **d.** radiation

3. To heat 1 g of water by 1°C requires
   a. 1 calorie.   **b.** 1 Calorie.
   c. 1 joule.   **d.** 1 watt.

4. The best thermal insulators
   a. conduct heat well.   **b.** are gases.
   c. are metals.   **d.** have free electrons.

5. A blow dryer transfers thermal energy mainly by
   a. conduction.   **b.** convection.
   c. radiation.   **d.** specific heat.

6. Which statement is NOT true about radiation?
   a. All objects radiate.
   b. Hot objects radiate faster than cold objects.
   c. Radiation only transfers energy in matter.
   d. The sun's energy reaches Earth by radiation.

7. Energy added to a system
   a. does work or increases thermal energy.
   b. cannot heat the environment.
   c. is converted to radiation.
   d. reduces the kinetic energy of the system.

8. All engines operate at less than 100 percent efficiency because they
   a. absorb heat.   **b.** conduct heat.
   c. burn gasoline. **d.** emit heat.

9. Which occurs just before ignition?
   a. intake stroke   **b.** compression stroke
   c. exhaust stroke   **d.** power stroke

10. Which of the following is a FALSE statement about a heat pump?
   a. It requires no work.
   b. It moves heat from a cold to a hot area.
   c. It uses a refrigerant.
   d. Air conditioners are heat pumps.

Understanding Concepts

11. In what direction does heat flow? Why do particles of matter transfer thermal energy in this direction?

12. How can one object feel warmer than another object if the two objects are at the same temperature?

13. Why does a balloon filled with air expand when it is heated?

14. Power lines sag more between telephone poles in summer than in winter. Explain why this is so.

15. Why does a piece of steel heat up more than an equal mass of plastic when both absorb the same energy?

16. In a calorimeter, what determines how much energy is absorbed by the water?

17. Why are metals generally good thermal conductors?

18. How does sunlight reach an astronaut on the International Space Station?

19. How can the efficiency of a heat engine be improved?

20. What is waste heat?

21. What is the most important difference between an internal combustion engine and an external combustion engine?

22. Why does a heat pump need an external source of energy (such as electrical energy)?

23. Describe convection in a room heated by a radiator.

Thermal Energy and Heat **495**

Assessment (continued)

14. The power lines are warmer in summer and the metal in the wire expands. Because the wires are longer, they sag more.

15. The metal has a lower specific heat than the plastic, so its temperature increases more as thermal energy is absorbed.

16. The energy given off by the test sample determines the energy absorbed by the water, assuming no energy is lost to the surroundings.

17. Metals are good thermal conductors because some of the electrons in the metal are free to move about.

18. Radiation from the sun can travel through space to reach the astronaut.

19. Efficiency can improve if the engine runs at a higher temperature or if the engine discharges heat into a colder environment.

20. Waste heat is thermal energy that is not converted into work.

21. In an internal combustion engine, fuel is burned inside the engine. Combustion occurs outside the engine in an external combustion engine.

22. A heat pump transfers thermal energy from a cool area to a warm area. To do this, work must be done, which requires a source of energy.

23. Warm air rises from the radiator to the ceiling, cools, and then sinks. The radiator heats the cool air, and the cycle repeats.

⏱ Homework Guide

Section	Questions
16.1	1–3, 11–16, 24, 28–30, 32, 36
16.2	4–7, 17–18, 25, 31, 33
16.3	8–10, 19–23, 26–27, 34–35

Critical Thinking

24. You cannot because your hand and forehead are probably at the same temperature, so there is no heat flow to your hand.

25. All three methods tend to transfer thermal energy from hot to cold objects. In conduction, the motion of particles within a material transfers thermal energy. In convection, thermal energy is transferred by motion of a fluid. In radiation, thermal energy is transferred by electromagnetic waves. Radiation is the only way to transfer thermal energy through a vacuum.

26. The engine is less efficient on Venus because it would discharge thermal energy into an environment at a higher temperature.

27. In the first few minutes after the heat comes on, the temperature is highest near the radiators. When the heat shuts off, convection currents have made the room temperature more uniform, but the highest temperature will be near the ceiling.

Math Skills

28. Aluminum has the highest specific heat. The temperature of aluminum rises the least for a given amount of energy added. In the equation $Q = m \times c \times \Delta T$, if Q and m are constant, then c is proportional to $1/\Delta T$. A smaller value for ΔT therefore means a larger value for c.

29. For aluminum, $Q = m \times c \times \Delta T$
$= (1 \text{ g})(0.90 \text{ J/g•°C})(5.6°C) = 5.0 \text{ J}$
For iron, $Q = m \times c \times \Delta T$
$= (1 \text{ g})(0.45 \text{ J/g•°C})(11.1°C) = 5.0 \text{ J}$

30. She should ask how mass and the rise in temperature are related. According to the equation $Q = m \times c \times \Delta T$, if Q and c are constant, an increase in m by a factor of 10 will reduce rather than increase the rise in temperature by a factor of 10.

Concepts in Action

31. Blood flowing toward your heart is colder because the cold environment removes thermal energy from your body's extremities. Blood flowing toward your fingers is warmer because it comes from the body's interior and is more insulated from the cold.

32. A casserole cover keeps thermal energy from escaping and from being lost by evaporation. A calorimeter's insulation keeps thermal energy inside the container. Therefore, most of the thermal energy heats the water, and the temperature change accurately measures the thermal energy released.

Critical Thinking

24. Controlling Variables You can tell if your sister has a low fever by feeling her forehead with your hand. Can you detect your own fever with your hand? Explain why or why not.

25. Comparing and Contrasting How are conduction, convection, and radiation similar to one another? How are they different?

26. Applying Concepts Why would an engine be less efficient on Venus than on Earth? (*Hint:* On Venus, the surface temperature is 460°C.)

27. Predicting Just after a heating system turns on, what part of a room will be warmest? When the heat turns off and the radiators are cold, what part of the room will be warmest? Explain.

Math Skills

Use the following graph to answer Questions 28–30.

Temperature Rise of 1 Gram of Different Materials

Material	Temperature Rise (°C)
Aluminum	5.6
Iron	11.1
Copper	13.0
Tin	21.9

28. Using Graphs The same energy was added to each sample. Which material has the highest specific heat? Explain your answer.

29. Calculating The specific heat of aluminum is 0.90 J/g•°C and of iron is 0.45 J/g•°C. How much energy was absorbed by each 1-gram sample?

30. Posing Questions A friend infers from the graph that the temperature of a 10.0-g sample of iron would rise 110°C. What should she ask before using the graph this way?

Concepts in Action

31. Applying Concepts When you are outside on a cold winter day, which would you expect to be warmer, blood flowing toward your heart or blood flowing toward your fingers? Explain.

32. Using Analogies If you put a cover on a casserole at dinner, it will stay warm longer. In what way can this help you to explain why a calorimeter is more accurate if it is well insulated?

33. Formulating Hypotheses Some recipes say that while a pie is baking, aluminum foil should be put on the edges to keep the crust from burning. Hypothesize how the aluminum foil helps keep the crust from burning.

34. Making Judgments Suppose you try to heat an apartment using a portable heater in one of the rooms. Would a fan be helpful? Explain why or why not.

35. Inferring In a home heated only by solar energy, why is it especially important to have very good insulation?

36. Writing in Science Explain why a school might ask teachers to keep windows closed and the shades down during a heat wave.

Performance-Based Assessment

Making a Computer Presentation Make a computer slideshow presentation about conductors and insulators. Start by identifying various materials around your home as either good conductors or good insulators. Plan the organization of the slideshow. Finish the show with a summary table that classifies all of the materials in your presentation. Present your show to your class.

Go Online
PHSchool.com

For: Self-grading assessment
Visit: PHSchool.com
Web Code: cca-2160

33. Accept all reasonable responses. Students may suggest that the foil reflects radiation that would be absorbed by the crust. The foil may also keep convection currents away from the crust. And because the foil is a good conductor, it may conduct heat away from the crust.

34. The fan would be helpful. It could be used to move warm air toward the rest of the apartment, heating the apartment by convection.

35. At night, the flow of thermal energy out of the home would be greater than during the day because it is colder outside. But this is also when passive solar heating is at a minimum, so it is important to reduce heat loss with insulation.

36. The best way to manage the building temperature is to prevent thermal energy from entering through the windows. The shades keep radiation from entering. Keeping the windows closed prevents convection currents that would bring thermal energy into the classroom.

Standardized Test Prep for Indiana

Test-Taking Tip

Sometimes all the response choices to a test question look similar. For example, they might have the same prefix or suffix. When all of the answer choices are similar, try answering the question BEFORE looking at the answers. Once you have answered the test item yourself, then look for the answer choice that agrees with your answer. Look for words that are correct words, but do not belong with the others.

The transfer of energy by collision of particles in a material occurs through

(A) convection.
(B) conduction.
(C) radiation.
(D) ionization.
(E) insulation.

(Answer: B)

Choose the letter that best answers the question or completes the statement.

1. Which statement describes the direction of spontaneous heat flow?
   (A) Heat flows between two objects at the same temperature.
   (B) Heat flows in a vacuum by conduction.
   (C) Heat flows from an object at high temperature to one at low temperature.
   (D) Heat flows from an object at low temperature to one at high temperature.
   (E) Thermal energy can only be absorbed by cool objects.

2. How are refrigerants used to remove heat in a refrigerator?
   (A) The refrigerant vaporizes as it absorbs heat from the food.
   (B) The refrigerant vaporizes as it supplies heat to the food.
   (C) The refrigerant condenses as it absorbs heat from the food.
   (D) The refrigerant condenses and turns into a liquid, giving off heat to the food.
   (E) The refrigerant condenses and turns into a gas, giving off heat to the food.

3. The table below shows the average high and low temperatures in January and July for two cities at the same latitude. Both cities receive about the same amount of sunlight. Which city is on an island in the ocean and which city is in a desert?
   (A) City A is on an island; City B is in the desert.
   (B) Both cities are in the desert.
   (C) Both cities are on an island.
   (D) City B is on an island; City A is in the desert.
   (E) Not enough information is given.

City Temperatures				
	January High	January Low	July High	July Low
City A	26°C	18°C	28°C	20°C
City B	32°C	10°C	44°C	27°C

4. Which of the following best explains why gases expand more readily than liquids or solids?
   (A) Gases have less density than solids or liquids.
   (B) Gases are lighter than solids or liquids.
   (C) Gases have a higher average kinetic energy than solids or liquids.
   (D) Gas particles have weaker attractive forces than solids or liquids.
   (E) Gases are more compressible than solids or liquids.

5. Which substance will have the greatest increase in temperature when equal masses absorb equal amounts of thermal energy? (Specific heats are given in parentheses.)
   (A) water (4.18 J/g•°C)
   (B) ammonia gas (2.1 J/g•°C)
   (C) ethyl alcohol (2.43 J/g•°C)
   (D) aluminum (0.90 J/g•°C)
   (E) lead (0.46 J/g•°C)

6. Which of the following illustrates the first law of thermodynamics?
   (A) Refrigerators make objects colder.
   (B) A bicycle pump gets warm when used.
   (C) Stoves radiate energy.
   (D) Soft drinks served with ice melt the ice.
   (E) Absolute zero cannot be reached.

Thermal Energy and Heat **497**

Performance-Based Assessment

Students' presentations should integrate research from sources outside the textbook. Presentations should be clearly organized and the list of materials should be correctly classified. The summary table could rank the conductors and insulators and provide additional information such as applications in the home, at school, or in the community. Extra credit should be given for creative visual display of information.

Your students can independently test their knowledge of the chapter and print out their test results for your files.

Planning Guide

SECTION OBJECTIVES	STANDARDS		ACTIVITIES and LABS
	NATIONAL	STATE	
17.1 Mechanical Waves, pp. 500–503 🕐 1 block or 2 periods **17.1.1 Define** mechanical waves and **relate** waves to energy. **17.1.2 Describe** transverse, longitudinal, and surface waves and **discuss** how they are produced. **17.1.3 Identify** examples of transverse and longitudinal waves. **17.1.4 Analyze** the motion of a medium as each kind of mechanical wave passes through it.	A-1, A-2, B-6	ICP.2.3	**SE** Inquiry Activity: How Does a Disturbance Produce Waves? p. 499 **L2** **SE** Quick Lab: Observing Waves in a Medium, p. 502 **L2** **TE** Teacher Demo: Wave Dance, p. 501 **L2**
17.2 Properties of Mechanical Waves, pp. 504–507 🕐 1 block or 2 periods **17.2.1 Define** frequency, period, wavelength, and wave speed and **describe** these properties for different kinds of waves. **17.2.2 Solve equations** relating wave speed to wavelength and frequency or period. **17.2.3 Describe** how to measure amplitude and **relate** amplitude to the energy of a wave.	A-1, A-2, B-6	ICP.2.1, ICP.2.2, ICP.2.3, ICP.2.4	**SE** Quick Lab: Comparing Frequency and Wave Speed, p. 505 **L2**
17.3 Behavior of Waves, pp. 508–512 🕐 1 block or 2 periods **17.3.1 Describe** how reflection, refraction, diffraction, and interference affect waves. **17.3.2 State a rule** that explains refraction of a wave as it passes from one medium to another. **17.3.3 Identify** factors that affect the amount of refraction, diffraction, or interference. **17.3.4 Distinguish** between constructive and destructive interference and **explain** how standing waves form.	B-6	ICP.2.4	**TE** Teacher Demo: Water-Wave Reflections, p. 508 **L2** **TE** Teacher Demo: Standing Waves, p. 512 **L2**
17.4 Sound and Hearing, pp. 514–521 🕐 1 block or 2 periods **17.4.1 Describe** the properties of sound waves and **explain** how sound is produced and reproduced. **17.4.2 Describe** how sound waves behave in applications such as ultrasound and music. **17.4.3 Explain** how relative motion determines the frequency of sound an observer hears. **17.4.4 Analyze** the functions of the main regions of the human ear.	A-1, A-2, B-6, C-6, E-2, F-1, F-2, F-5, G-1	ICP.2.1, ICP.2.2, ICP.2.3	**SE** Exploration Lab: Investigating Sound Waves, pp. 524–525 **L2** **TE** Build Science Skills: Observing, p. 515 **L2** **LM** Investigation 17A: Comparing the Speed of Sound **L2** **LM** Investigation 17B: Comparing Sound Conduction **L1**

RESOURCES PRINT and TECHNOLOGY

RSW Section 17.1 **L1**

🖳 **T** Chapter 17 Pretest **L2**

　Section 17.1 **L2**

💿 **P** Chapter 17 Pretest **L2**

　Section 17.1 **L2**

🔵 *SCiLINKS* **GO** Vibrations and waves **L2**

RSW Section 17.2 **L1**

RSW Math Skill **L2**

MSPS Section 17.2 **L2**

🖳 **T** Section 17.2 **L2**

💿 **P** Section 17.2 **L2**

🔵 *SCiLINKS* **GO** Wave properties **L2**

RSW Section 17.3 **L1**

🖳 **T** Section 17.3 **L2**

💿 **P** Section 17.3 **L2**

🔵 *SCiLINKS* **GO** Diffraction and interference **L2**

RSW Section 17.4 **L1**

DISCOVERY SCHOOL **DC** Noise! **L2**

🖳 **T** Section 17.4 **L2**

💿 **P** Section 17.4 **L2**

SCIENCE NEWS **GO** Sound **L2**

SECTION ASSESSMENT

SE Section 17.1 Assessment, p. 503

🔵 **iT** Section 17.1

SE Section 17.2 Assessment, p. 507

🔵 **iT** Section 17.2

SE Section 17.3 Assessment, p. 512

🔵 **iT** Section 17.3

SE Section 17.4 Assessment, p. 521

🔵 **iT** Section 17.4

Go Online

Go online for these Internet resources.

PHSchool.com
　Web Code: cch-2173
　Web Code: cca-2170

 SCiLINKS
　Web Code: ccn-2171
　Web Code: ccn-2172
　Web Code: ccn-2173

SCIENCE NEWS
　Web Code: cce-2174

Materials for Activities and Labs

Quantities for each group

STUDENT EDITION

Inquiry Activity, p. 499
dropper pipet; wide, flat-bottomed container; meter stick

Quick Lab, p. 502
large, clear container; food coloring; ruler; droppers (optional)

Quick Lab, p. 505
3-m rope, tape measure, stopwatch

Exploration Lab, pp. 524–525
meter stick, 2 cardboard tubes, scissors or scalpel, 2 rubber bands, wax paper, balloon, small mirror, transparent tape, flashlight

TEACHER'S EDITION

Teacher Demo, p. 501
10 chairs, 10 students, space to move around

Teacher Demo, p. 508
clear bowl, water, overhead projector

Teacher Demo, p. 512
long, soft, heavy rope, such as a jump rope

Build Science Skills, p. 515
set of tuning forks of similar construction

Build Science Skills, p. 522
tuning fork hammer, 2 tuning forks with the same frequency (about 400 Hz), stethoscope

Chapter Assessment

CHAPTER ASSESSMENT

SE　Chapter Assessment, pp. 527–528

CUT　Chapter 17 Test A, B

CTB　Chapter 17

iT　Chapter 17

PHSchool.com GO
Web Code: cca-2170

STANDARDIZED TEST PREP

SE　Chapter 17, p. 529

TP　Diagnose and Prescribe

Interactive Textbook with assessment at PHSchool.com

Before you teach

From the Author

Sophia Yancopoulos
Manhattan College

Big Ideas

Later chapters will build on the basics of mechanical waves, so it's important that students get the wave types, properties, and behaviors under their belts. For waves traveling at a given speed, it can be shown that wavelength is inversely proportional to frequency. This is easily derived from the equation distance equals velocity times time because "distance" is equal to wavelength, and "time" for the passage of one wave is its period, which is inversely proportional to frequency. The most important idea is that when an object moves, the object itself moves from point A to point B. A wave, however, is different. A wave is the disturbance in a medium. Although the medium moves somewhat as the wave travels, what moves from point A to point B in this case is the disturbance.

Matter and Energy A mechanical wave is defined as a disturbance in matter that carries energy from one place to another. It takes energy to create any kind of wave, but a mechanical wave, unlike an electromagnetic wave, cannot travel without a medium.

Forces and Motion The behavior of a wave—whether this behavior is refraction, reflection, diffraction, or interference—depends on the medium through which it travels, as well as on the wave type. Sound waves, for example, can be manipulated in various ways, or even cancelled. Discussing technological applications that students are probably familiar with may be a good way to generate interest. Be as concrete and visual as possible, since the subject of electromagnetic waves builds on this information, and is far less easily grasped.

Physics Refresher

Mechanical Waves 17.1

Electromagnetic waves are not mechanical waves. For many years, physicists tried to develop a mechanical understanding of electromagnetic waves, searching without success for proof of the "ether," a medium for these waves. Physicists now know that electromagnetic waves do not require a medium.

For a medium to transmit a mechanical wave, the medium must be elastic. For example, when a gas is compressed in a cylinder with a piston, the piston springs back when released. Gases are elastic under compression, so they will transmit compression waves. Gases have almost no tensile strength, so a gas will not transmit a transverse wave. A steel bar will transmit both longitudinal and transverse waves.

> ⚑ **Address Misconceptions**
>
> *Students may mistakenly think that waves are part of the medium that travel with the waves.* However, waves carry energy through a medium, but the medium usually has no net movement. For a strategy to overcome this misconception, see **Address Misconceptions** on **page 502**.

Properties of Mechanical Waves 17.2

The period of a wave, measured in seconds, equals $\frac{1}{\text{Frequency}}$. In symbols, the wave equation can be written as $v = \lambda \times f$, where v is the wave speed, λ is the wavelength, and f is the frequency. Amplitude, the maximum distance the medium is displaced from its rest position, is a measure of wave energy. As amplitude increases, the wave energy increases. The relationship is not linear. For most waves, energy is proportional to $(\text{amplitude})^2$.

Behavior of Waves 17.3

Reflection and refraction occur at the boundary between two mediums. Part or all of the wave is reflected. Part of the wave may pass through, but its speed and direction may change. The reflected wave always has the same speed and frequency as the original wave. The refracted wave will have the same frequency but different speed and wavelength. Refraction is a behavior of all waves. Earthquake waves are refracted as they pass through different layers inside of Earth. By studying the patterns and kinds of earthquake waves received around the world, geologists are able to infer the interior structure of Earth.

For: Teaching methods for mechanical waves and sounds
Visit: www.SciLinks.org/PDLinks
Web Code: ccn-1799

When a wave moves past an obstacle or passes through a narrow opening, it diffracts, or bends in such a way as to recreate the form (in frequency and amplitude) that the wave had before encountering the obstacle or opening. Diffraction, as shown below, depends on how the size of the opening compares to the wavelength. The larger the opening, the greater the amount of signal that can pass through it unimpeded. The smaller the opening, the more the wave has to bend to reconstruct its original form.

Diffraction at a large opening

Diffraction at a small opening

Sound and Hearing 17.4

Address Misconceptions

Some students think that sound waves can push a dust particle away from a speaker or blow out a candle flame. Generally, there is no net transport of matter by a wave. For a strategy to overcome this misconception, see **Address Misconceptions** on **page 518**.

The three aspects of any sound are its source, the transference of energy from this source, and the detection of the sound. The transference of sound energy takes the form of longitudinal waves. Sound waves are longitudinal waves in matter. Fluids, such as air and water, can only transmit longitudinal waves. If the frequency of a sound wave is above the range of human hearing, it is called ultrasound. If the frequency of a sound wave is below the range of human hearing, it is called infrasound.

The unit of intensity level, the decibel or dB, was named after Alexander Graham Bell. Intensity can also be expressed in units of watts per square meter. Here are some intensities of sounds expressed in W/m^2.

Sound	Intensity Level (dB)	Intensity (W/m^2)
Threshold of hearing	0	1×10^{-12}
Whisper	20	1×10^{-10}
Normal conversation	65	3×10^{-6}
Street noise	70	1×10^{-5}
Rock concert	120	1
Threshold of pain	120	1

Build Reading Literacy

Active Comprehension

Engaging Interest in a Topic

Strategy Stimulate students' interest in a topic prior to reading. As with the KWL strategy, students generate questions based on their curiosity. Interest is thus translated into a purpose for reading. Looking for answers to the questions during reading helps keep students engaged in what they are reading. Before students begin reading, choose an opening paragraph from one of the sections in Chapter 17, for example, the first paragraph on p. 500.

Example

1. Have a student read the opening paragraph.
2. Ask the group, "What more would you like to know about _____?" (for example, mechanical waves). Make a list of student responses.
3. Tell students to read the remainder of the section, keeping the questions in mind as they read.
4. After reading, you may discuss the extent to which each question was answered by the text. Ask students also to comment on any new information they learned that was surprising.
5. Have students work in small groups, applying the active comprehension strategy to the reading of each section of the chapter.

See p. 509 for a script on how to use the active comprehension strategy with students. For additional Build Reading Literacy strategies, see pp. 503, 507, and 516.

ASSESS PRIOR KNOWLEDGE

Use the Chapter Pretest below to assess students' prior knowledge. As needed, review these Science Concepts and Math Skills with students.

Review Science Concepts

Section 17.1 Waves carry energy, so review the concept of energy and energy conversions with students.

Section 17.2 Remind students of the unit of time (seconds, s). Review what it means to say something is moving. Remind students how to measure and calculate speed (distance/time).

Section 17.3 Review velocity and displacement, which help with understanding interference and refraction. Remind students that energy is the ability to do work and that waves carry energy.

Section 17.4 Since the speed of sound depends on temperature and density, review how density and temperature are related to solids, liquids, and gases.

Review Math Skills

Formulas and Equations, Percents and Decimals Students will need to manipulate equations to solve for the unknown. They also may need practice working with decimal fractions. Review what is meant by powers of ten.

Direct students to **Math Skills** in the **Skills and Reference Handbook** at the end of the student text.

CHAPTER
17 Mechanical Waves and Sound

21st Century Learning
Information and Media Literacy

What are some useful applications of refraction?

One interesting example of wave behavior is refraction, which is the bending of a wave as it enters a new medium at an angle. Do Internet research on refraction and find out about some of the useful applications of this behavior. Create a multimedia presentation on refraction that includes text, diagrams, and photos, and deliver the presentation to the class.

Indiana's Academic Standards for Science

MECHANICAL ENERGY AND PROPAGATION OF ENERGY BY WAVES
ICP.2.1: Identify properties of objects that vibrate, using Newton's laws to understand the motion. Understand that vibrating objects can give rise to mechanical waves; **ICP.2.2:** Identify properties of waves including frequency, wavelength, amplitude, energy, and wave speed; **ICP.2.3:** Describe how energy is propagated by waves without the transfer of mass using examples such as water waves, earthquakes, and sound waves; **ICP.2.4:** Apply the properties of waves to wave phenomena including reflection, and refraction, as well as the transmission and loss of energy.

Ocean waves, like all mechanical waves, carry energy through a medium.

498 Chapter 17

Chapter Pretest

1. What is energy? *(Ability to do work)*
2. What is mechanical energy? *(Energy due to the motion or position of an object)*
3. True or False: Displacements in opposite directions add together. *(False. Displacements in opposite directions subtract.)*
4. How is speed calculated? *(Distance/time)*
5. What are the standard units of distance and time? *(Meters and seconds)*

6. Which is longer, 0.25 m or 25 m? *(25 m)*
7. What happens to the spacing of the particles within a solid or liquid as the temperature increases? *(The particles move farther apart.)*
8. What happens to the speed of the particles in a solid, liquid, or gas as the temperature is increased? *(The particles move faster.)*

9. If a car takes 2 hrs to travel 100 km, what is its average speed? *(b)*
   a. 25 km/h
   b. 50 km/h
   c. 75 km/h
   d. 100 km/h

Chapter Preview

DISCOVERY CHANNEL SCHOOL

Video Field Trip

Noise!

How Does a Disturbance Produce Waves?

Procedure

1. Fill a clear plastic container and a dropper pipet with water.

2. Observe the surface of the water by looking down at an angle into the container. Use the dropper pipet to release a drop of water from a height of about 3 cm above the surface of the water.

3. Repeat Step 2 with a drop released from each of these heights: 10, 20, 50, and 70 cm.

Think About It

1. **Observing** Which drop produced the highest waves?

2. **Making Generalizations** In general, how would you expect the distance a drop falls to affect the wave it produces? Explain your answer.

3. **Formulating Hypotheses** Why does the distance a drop falls affect the height of the waves it produces? Explain your answer.

Mechanical Waves and Sound **499**

DISCOVERY CHANNEL SCHOOL

Video Field Trip

Noise!

Encourage students to view the Video Field Trip "Noise!"

ENGAGE/EXPLORE

Inquiry Activity

How Does a Disturbance Produce Waves? **L2**

Purpose In this activity, students begin to understand that the height or amplitude of a wave depends on the wave's energy.

Skills Focus Observing, Comparing and Contrasting

 Prep Time 15 Minutes

Materials dropper pipet; wide, flat-bottomed container; meter stick

Advance Prep Distribute empty containers and fill them from a gallon jug once they are in place at the lab stations.

Class Time 10 minutes

Teaching Tips
• Instruct students to look at the surface of the water diagonally, rather than horizontally or vertically.

Expected Outcome The height (amplitude) of the wave will increase as the height from which the water is dropped increases.

Think About It
1. The drop that fell from 70 cm produced the highest waves.
2. The greater the distance a drop falls, the more kinetic energy it will have, and the larger the wave it will produce.
3. The greater the height from which a drop falls, the more energy it has because it accelerated to a greater speed than a drop that fell a shorter distance. Therefore, it transfers more energy to the surface of the water, producing higher waves.
Visual, Logical

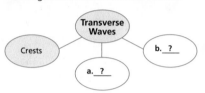

1 FOCUS

Objectives

17.1.1 **Define** mechanical waves and **relate** waves to energy.

17.1.2 **Describe** transverse, longitudinal, and surface waves and **discuss** how they are produced.

17.1.3 **Identify** examples of transverse and longitudinal waves.

17.1.4 **Analyze** the motion of a medium as each kind of mechanical wave passes through it.

Reading Focus

Build Vocabulary   L2

Paraphrase This section contains several words that may not be familiar to students: *medium, crest, trough, transverse, longitudinal, compression,* and *rarefaction.* Have students paraphrase these words using words they know. For example, they might construct a sentence such as, "In other words, a *medium* is the stuff carrying the wave."

Reading Strategy   L2

a. Troughs **b.** Rest position; Longitudinal Wave: Compressions, Rarefactions, Rest position, Direction; Surface Wave: Circular motion that returns to same position, Direction of wave

2 INSTRUCT

What Are Mechanical Waves?

Build Science Skills   L2

Inferring Have students look at Figure 1. Ask, **What happens to the swimmers in the pool as a wave passes?** *(The swimmers move up and down and back and forth.)* **What kind of energy do the swimmers have as they bob up and down?** *(Kinetic)* **From where do they get this energy?** *(From the wave)*
Logical, Visual

17.1 Mechanical Waves

Standard: ICP.2.3

Reading Focus

Key Concepts

- What causes mechanical waves?
- What are the three main types of mechanical waves?

Vocabulary

- mechanical wave
- medium
- crest
- trough
- transverse wave
- compression
- rarefaction
- longitudinal wave
- surface wave

Reading Strategy

Previewing Copy the web diagram below. Use Figure 2 to complete the diagram. Then use Figures 3 and 4 to make similar diagrams for longitudinal waves and surface waves.

Transverse Waves — Crests — a. ? — b. ?

Have you ever gone to a wave pool at an amusement park? You can hear the laughter and screams as wave after wave passes by, giving the people a wild ride. It's obvious that waves are moving through the water, but you may not realize that the screams and laughter are also carried by waves. In this chapter, you will learn about the different kinds of mechanical waves, including sound waves.

What Are Mechanical Waves?

A **mechanical wave** is a disturbance in matter that carries energy from one place to another. Recall that energy is the ability to do work. In a wave pool, each wave carries energy across the pool. You can see the effects of a wave's energy when the wave lifts people in the water.

Figure 1 In a wave pool, the waves carry energy across the pool.

Mechanical waves require matter to travel through. The material through which a wave travels is called a **medium.** Solids, liquids, and gases all can act as mediums. In a wave pool, waves travel along the surface of the water. Water is the medium. Waves travel through a rope when you shake one end of it. In that case, the medium is the rope.

A mechanical wave is created when a source of energy causes a vibration to travel through a medium. A vibration is a repeating back-and-forth motion. When you shake a rope, you add energy at one end. The wave that results is a vibration that carries energy along the rope.

500 *Chapter 17*

Section Resources

Print
- *Reading and Study Workbook With Math Support,* Section 17.1
- *Transparencies,* Chapter Pretest and Section 17.1

Technology
- *Interactive Textbook,* Section 17.1
- *Presentation Pro CD-ROM,* Chapter Pretest and Section 17.1
- *Go Online,* NSTA SciLinks, Vibrations and waves

Types of Mechanical Waves

Mechanical waves are classified by the way they move through a medium. ⬤ **The three main types of mechanical waves are transverse waves, longitudinal waves, and surface waves.**

Transverse Waves When you shake one end of a rope up and down, the vibration causes a wave. Figure 2 shows a wave in a rope at three points in time. Before the wave starts, every point on the rope is in its rest position, represented by the dashed line. The highest point of the wave above the rest position is the **crest.** The lowest point below the rest position is the **trough** (TRAWF). You can see from the ribbon attached to the rope that crests and troughs are not fixed points on a wave. In Figure 2A, the ribbon is at a crest. In Figure 2C, the ribbon is at a trough. The motion of a single point on the rope is like the motion of a yo-yo. The point vibrates up and down between a maximum and minimum height.

Notice that the wave carries energy from left to right, in a direction perpendicular to the up-and-down motion of the rope. This is a transverse wave. A **transverse wave** is a wave that causes the medium to vibrate at right angles to the direction in which the wave travels.

Have you ever shaken crumbs off a picnic blanket? This is another example of a transverse wave. Shaking one end of the blanket up and down sends a transverse wave through the blanket. The up and down motion of the blanket helps to shake off the crumbs.

Go Online
NSTA *SciLINKS*

For: Links on vibrations and waves
Visit: www.SciLinks.org
Web Code: ccn-2171

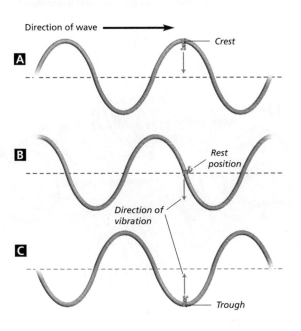

Direction of wave ⟶

A Crest

B Rest position

Direction of vibration

C Trough

Figure 2 A transverse wave causes the medium to vibrate in a direction perpendicular to the direction in which the wave travels. In the wave shown here, each point on the rope vibrates up and down between a maximum and minimum height. **A** The ribbon is at a crest. **B** The ribbon is at the rest position. **C** The ribbon is at a trough.
Comparing and Contrasting How does the direction of the wave compare with the direction in which the ribbon moves?

Mechanical Waves and Sound **501**

Customize for English Language Learners

Simplify the Presentation
In English, one word may have several different meanings. For that reason, students who are learning English may have additional difficulty grasping the scientific meanings of such words.

Identify the multiple-meaning words in this section, such as *wave, matter,* and *medium.* Discuss with students the different meanings of each word and then explain which meaning is used in this section.

Observing Waves in a Medium   **L2**

Objective
After completing this activity, students will be able to
• describe a mechanical wave as a passage of energy through a medium, with no net movement of the medium.

Address Misconceptions

This lab can dispel the misconception that waves are parts of the medium that travel with the wave.

Skills Focus Inferring

Prep Time 15 minutes

Materials large, clear container; food coloring; ruler; droppers (optional)

Advance Prep Dilute food coloring with water. Use droppers to drop colored water into the container.

Class Time 15 minutes

Safety Students should wear a laboratory apron to avoid stains.

Teaching Tips
• Instruct students to observe the wave and the drop from the side.

Expected Outcome The drop of food coloring sits on the bottom of the container as the water wave moves back and forth. Some small currents disturb the food coloring.

Analyze and Conclude
1. The wave moved. The food coloring stayed in place on the bottom.
2. Students may hypothesize that water at the bottom is not disturbed by a surface wave, or that the disturbance depends on the depth of the water.
Visual, Logical

For Enrichment   **L3**

Float bits of cork on the water. Generate waves and observe the motion of the cork bits. Students should observe up-and-down motion and also side-to-side motion of the cork bits. Students should vary the depths of the water to see if this affects the results.
Visual

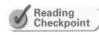

Observing Waves in a Medium

Procedure

1. Fill a large, clear, square or rectangular container halfway with water. Add a drop of food coloring in the center of the container.

2. At the side of the container, submerge a ruler length-wise. Move the ruler up and down to make waves.

3. Observe and record how the waves and the food coloring move.

Analyze and Conclude

1. **Comparing and Contrasting** Compare the movement of the waves with the movement of the food coloring.

2. **Formulating Hypotheses** Generate one or more hypotheses to explain the observed motion of the food coloring.

Figure 3 A longitudinal wave causes the medium to vibrate in a direction parallel to the direction in which the wave travels. Each point on the spring vibrates back and forth about its rest position. **A** When the end of the spring is pushed, a compression starts to move along the spring. **B** When the end of the spring is pulled, a rarefaction follows the compression along the spring.

Longitudinal Waves Figure 3 shows a wave in a spring toy at two points in time. To start the wave, add energy to the spring by pushing and pulling the end of the spring. The wave carries energy along the spring from left to right. You can see in Figure 3A that when the wave starts, some of the coils are closer together than they would be in the rest position. An area where the particles in a medium are spaced close together is called a **compression** (kum PRESH un). As the compression moves to the right in Figure 3B, coils behind it are spread out more than they were in the rest position. An area where the particles in a medium are spread out is called a **rarefaction** (rehr uh FAK shun).

Look at the ribbon tied to one of the coils. The ribbon is first in a compression and then in a rarefaction. However, the ribbon and the coil it is tied to do not move along the spring. As compressions and rarefactions travel along the spring toward the right, each coil vibrates back and forth around its rest position. In this wave, the vibration is a back-and-forth motion of the coil that is parallel to, or in the same direction as, the direction in which the wave moves. This is a longitudinal wave. A **longitudinal wave** (lawn juh TOO duh nul) is a wave in which the vibration of the medium is parallel to the direction the wave travels.

Waves in springs are not the only kind of longitudinal waves. P waves (originally called primary waves) are longitudinal waves produced by earthquakes. Because P waves can travel through Earth, scientists can use these waves to map Earth's unseen interior.

Reading Checkpoint   *What are compressions and rarefactions?*

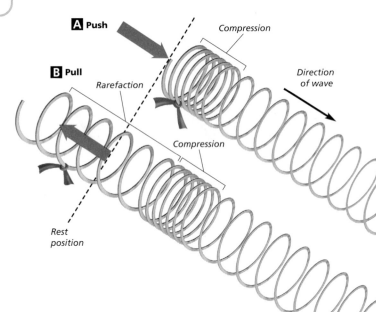

A Push

B Pull

Compression

Rarefaction

Direction of wave

Compression

Rest position

Facts and Figures

Surfing Surfing originated in Polynesia and was developed in Hawaii. Native Hawaiians rode long, heavy, carved wooden surfboards. Surfing is possible because of the properties of waves as they enter shallower water. The speed of a wave in shallow water depends on the depth of the water. As a wave approaches the shore, it slows down. In shallow water with a sloping bottom, the front portion of the wave is in shallower water and moving slower than

the rear portion, so the back of the wave catches up with the front. This causes the wave to "break." Surfers ride the breaking wave as the surfboard slides down the steep front of the wave. Modern surfboards are made from a foam core covered with plastic resin. These lighter and smaller surfboards are much easier to handle than the heavy wooden boards used by early Hawaiians.

Surface Waves If you ask people to describe waves, most likely they will describe ocean waves before they think of the waves that travel in a rope or a spring. Ocean waves are the most familiar kind of surface waves. A **surface wave** is a wave that travels along a surface separating two media.

The ocean wave in Figure 4 travels at the surface between water and air. The floating fishing bobber helps to visualize the motion of the medium as the wave carries energy from left to right. When a crest passes the bobber, the bobber moves up. When a trough passes, the bobber moves down. This up-and-down motion, like the motion of a transverse wave, is perpendicular to the direction in which the wave travels. But the bobber also is pushed back and forth by the surface wave. This back-and-forth motion, like the motion of a longitudinal wave, is parallel to the direction in which the wave travels. When these two motions combine in deep water, the bobber moves in a circle.

If you watched the bobber for ten minutes, it would not move closer to shore. Most waves do not transport matter from one place to another. But when ocean waves approach the shore, they behave differently. Perhaps you have seen seaweed washed ashore by breaking waves. As a wave enters shallow water, it topples over on itself because friction with the shore slows down the bottom of the wave. The top of the wave continues forward at its original speed. As a result, the wave carries the medium, along with anything floating in it, toward the shore.

Wave direction ➡

Figure 4 As the ocean wave moves to the right, the bobber moves in a circle, returning to its original position. **Making Generalizations** *If these were breaking waves near the shore, what would happen to the bobber over time?*

Section 17.1 Assessment

Reviewing Concepts

1. 🔊 Describe how mechanical waves are produced.
2. 🔊 List the three main types of mechanical waves.
3. For each type of wave, compare the vibration of the medium to the direction of the wave.
4. Name one example of each type of wave.

Critical Thinking

5. **Comparing and Contrasting** How are transverse and longitudinal waves similar? How are they different?

6. **Applying Concepts** A spring hangs from the ceiling. Describe how a single coil moves as a longitudal wave passes through the spring.
7. **Interpreting Diagrams** In Figure 4, why is the first position of the bobber the same as the fifth position of the bobber?

Connecting ⊂ Concepts

Energy Review potential and kinetic energy in Section 15.1. Then, describe the energy changes in a single coil of a spring as longitudinal waves pass through it.

Mechanical Waves and Sound **503**

■ FOCUS

Objectives

17.2.1 Define frequency, period, wavelength, and wave speed and **describe** these properties for different kinds of waves.

17.2.2 Solve equations relating wave speed to wavelength and frequency or period.

17.2.3 Describe how to measure amplitude and **relate** amplitude to the energy of a wave.

Reading Focus

Build Vocabulary **L2**

Word Forms The term amplitude contains the root *ampl-*, which comes from the Latin *amplus*. Have students think of other English words that contain *ampl- (amplify, ample)*. What do these words have in common? *(All have to do with largeness or fullness.)*

Reading Strategy **L2**

a. The time required for one cycle **b.** The number of complete cycles in a given time **c.** The distance between a point on a wave and the same point on the next cycle of the wave **d.** The maximum displacement of a medium from its rest position

■ INSTRUCT

Frequency and Period

Use Visuals **L1**

Figure 5 Have students compare the number of complete cycles per second in Figures 5A and 5B. Ask, **What happens to the frequency when the number of cycles per second increases?** *(It increases.)* **If a wave has a frequency of 0.5 Hz, how many cycles per second is it vibrating?** *(It is vibrating at one-half cycle per second.)* **What is the period of a 0.5-Hz wave?** *(2 seconds)*
Logical

17.2 Properties of Mechanical Waves

 Standards: ICP.2.1, ICP.2.2, ICP.2.3, ICP.2.4

Reading Focus

Key Concepts

- What determines the frequency of a wave?
- How are frequency, wavelength, and speed related?
- How is the amplitude of a wave related to the wave's energy?

Vocabulary

- ◆ periodic motion
- ◆ period
- ◆ frequency
- ◆ hertz
- ◆ wavelength
- ◆ amplitude

Reading Strategy

Building Vocabulary Copy and expand the table below. As you read, write a definition in your own words for each term.

Vocabulary Term	Definition
Period	a. ___?___
Frequency	b. ___?___
Wavelength	c. ___?___
Amplitude	d. ___?___

A Frequency = 1.0 hertz
One cycle per second

Rest position

B Frequency = 2.0 hertz
Two cycles per second

Figure 5 Frequency is the number of complete cycles in a given time. **A** A wave vibrating at one cycle per second has a frequency of 1.0 Hz. **B** A wave vibrating at two cycles per second has a frequency of 2.0 Hz.

Will it be a good day for surfing? You might not think that a surfer would check the Internet to find out. But some Web sites now update ocean wave data every hour. Of course, fishing boats and naval vessels also need this information. Usually, the properties used to describe waves are period, frequency, wavelength, speed, and amplitude.

Frequency and Period

How do surfers know when the next wave is coming? If they count the time between two successive crests, the next crest usually will come after this same time interval. Any motion that repeats at regular time intervals is called **periodic motion.** The time required for one cycle, a complete motion that returns to its starting point, is called the **period.** For an ocean wave, the period is the time between two successive crests.

Any periodic motion has a **frequency,** which is the number of complete cycles in a given time. For a wave, the frequency is the number of wave cycles that pass a point in a given time. Frequency is measured in cycles per second, or **hertz** (Hz).

A wave's frequency equals the frequency of the vibrating source producing the wave. The rope in Figure 5A is shaken with a frequency of one vibration per second, so the wave frequency is one cycle per second, or 1 hertz. In Figure 5B, the vibration is twice as fast, so the frequency is two cycles per second, or 2 hertz.

 Section Resources

Print
- ***Reading and Study Workbook With Math Support,*** Section 17.2 and **Math Skill:** Calculating Wave Properties
- ***Math Skills and Problem Solving Workbook,*** Section 17.2
- ***Transparencies,*** Section 17.2

Technology
- ***Interactive Textbook,*** Section 17.2
- ***Presentation Pro CD-ROM,*** Section 17.2
- ***Go Online,*** NSTA SciLinks, Wave properties

Quick Lab

Comparing Frequency and Wave Speed

Materials
3-m rope, tape measure, stopwatch

Procedure

1. Tie one end of the rope to a chair. Shake the other end to send waves down the rope.
2. With a partner, measure the time it takes your hand to move back and forth ten times. Then, measure and record the distance from your hand to the chair and the time it takes a wave crest to travel this distance.
3. Repeat Step 2, but this time shake the rope more rapidly. Record your data.

Analyze and Conclude

1. **Calculating** What was the frequency of the waves in Steps 2 and 3? (*Hint:* Divide 10 waves by the time it took to make them.)
2. **Calculating** What was the wave speed in Steps 2 and 3? (*Hint:* Divide distance by time.)
3. **Drawing Conclusions** How was wave speed affected by increasing the frequency?

Wavelength

Wavelength is the distance between a point on one wave and the same point on the next cycle of the wave. For a transverse wave, wavelength is measured between adjacent crests or between adjacent troughs. For a longitudinal wave, wavelength is the distance between adjacent compressions or rarefactions. Notice in Figure 6 that when wavelength is shorter, crests are closer together. They must occur more frequently. ⊙ **Increasing the frequency of a wave decreases its wavelength.**

 Reading Checkpoint *What is wavelength?*

Wave Speed

Recall that the speed of an object equals distance divided by time. To calculate a swimmer's speed, for example, you can measure the length of one lap in a pool and the time it takes to swim one lap. This is like measuring the wavelength (one lap) and period (time to swim one lap) of the swimmer's motion. In much the same way, you can calculate the speed of a wave by dividing its wavelength by its period. You can also calculate wave speed by multiplying wavelength by frequency.

Speed of Waves

$$\text{Speed} = \text{Wavelength} \times \text{Frequency}$$

When the wavelength is in meters and the frequency is in hertz, the units for speed are meters per second. If you know any two of the values in this formula, you can solve for the third value.

A

Long wavelength

Rest position

B

Short wavelength

Figure 6 Wavelength can be measured from any point on a wave to the same point on the next cycle of the wave. **A** The wavelength of a transverse wave equals the distance from crest to crest or from trough to trough. **B** The wavelength of this wave is half the wavelength of the wave in A. **Inferring** *Which wave has a greater frequency?*

Mechanical Waves and Sound **505**

Customize for Inclusion Students

Visually Impaired
Tie a weight (such as a washer or fishing weight) to a string, and attach the string to a pendulum clamp on a ring stand so that it hangs vertically and is free to swing. Allow students to touch the pendulum and make it swing. By holding their hand in the right place, they can feel the weight touch their hand as it completes each cycle. Students can compare the periods and frequencies of pendulums with different lengths (lengths of 1 m, 25 cm, and 6.25 cm should produce frequencies of about 0.5 Hz, 1 Hz, and 2 Hz, respectively).

Wavelength
Build Science Skills   L2

Measuring Have students use a small ruler to measure the wavelength of each wave in Figure 6 and verify that the wavelength measured does not depend on which two corresponding points are used. **Visual, Logical**

Wave Speed

 Quick Lab

Comparing Frequency and Wave Speed   L2

Objective
After completing this activity, students will be able to
• distinguish between wave frequency and wave speed.

Skills Focus Measuring, Comparing and Contrasting

Prep Time 10 minutes

Class Time 20 minutes

Teaching Tips
• Have students practice before doing timed trials.
• Using a longer rope gives more clear-cut results.

Expected Outcome Neither the amplitude nor the frequency affects the speed of propagation of a wave.

Analyze and Conclude
1. Answers will depend on student data. Answers of one to five waves per second are reasonable.
2. Answers will depend on student data but should be expressed in units of m/s.
3. The wave frequency had no effect on the wave speed. **Logical**

For Enrichment   L3

Students can time the speed of waves in various other solid media, such as wires and monofilament fishing line, and attempt to determine the properties of materials that affect the speed of wave transmission. **Kinesthetic**

Answer to . . .

Figure 6 *The frequency of B is greater than the frequency of A.*

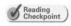 **Reading Checkpoint** *Wavelength is the distance between one point on a wave and the same point on the next cycle of the wave.*

Mechanical Waves and Sound **505**

Math **Practice**

Solutions **L2**

1. The speed is 2.0 m × 2.0 Hz = 4.0 m/s.
2. The speed is 0.1 m × 4 Hz = 0.4 m/s.
3. The speed is 10 cm/0.2 s = 50 cm/s.
4. The wavelength is (5 km/s)/10 Hz = 0.5 km.
Logical

For Extra Help **L1**

Have students write the equation required to solve each problem first. Then, check that they recognize what they know and don't know in the equation. **Logical**

Direct students to the **Math Skills** in the **Skills and Reference Handbook** at the end of the student text for additional help.

Additional Problems

1. The waves in a pool have a wavelength of 0.20 m and a frequency of 2.8 Hz. What is the speed of these waves? *(0.56 m/s)*
2. A student moves the end of a soft spring back and forth to make waves. The waves travel at 1.8 m/s and have a wavelength of 1.2 m. What is the frequency of these waves? *(1.5 Hz)*
Logical, Portfolio

Build Science Skills **L2**

Inferring Physics includes many relationships similar to the wave equation. Students need to develop a sense of how each variable relates to the others. Ask, **If the speed of a wave decreases, but the frequency stays the same, what happens to the wavelength?** *(The wavelength must decrease.)*
Logical

 Address Misconceptions **L2**

Students are sometimes unable to distinguish between the transverse motion of the medium and motion of the wave and think that waves with a higher frequency will move faster. In many mediums, mechanical waves move at approximately the same speed for a wide range of frequencies. To reinforce this idea, have students shake the end of the rope at several frequencies. They can confirm that this doesn't affect the wave speed. **Logical**

 Math **Practice**

1. A wave on a rope has a wavelength of 2.0 m and a frequency of 2.0 Hz. What is the speed of the wave?

2. A motorboat is tied to a dock with its motor running. The spinning propeller makes a surface wave in the water with a frequency of 4 Hz and a wavelength of 0.1 m. What is the speed of the wave?

3. What is the speed of a wave in a spring if it has a wavelength of 10 cm and a period of 0.2 s? (*Hint:* Use the equation Speed = $\frac{\text{Wavelength}}{\text{Period}}$.)

4. What is the wavelength of an earthquake wave if it has a speed of 5 km/s and a frequency of 10 Hz?

 Go Online

For: Links on wave properties
Visit: www.SciLinks.org
Web Code: ccn-2172

 Math **Skills**

Speed of Mechanical Waves
One end of a rope is vibrated to produce a wave with a wavelength of 0.25 meters. The frequency of the wave is 3.0 hertz. What is the speed of the wave?

1 ### Read and Understand
What information are you given?

Wavelength = 0.25 m

Frequency = 3.0 Hz

2 ### Plan and Solve
What unknown are you trying to calculate?

Speed = ?

What formula contains the given quantities and the unknown?

Speed = Wavelength × Frequency

Replace each variable with its known value.
(*Hint:* $1Hz = \frac{1}{s}$)

Speed = 0.25 m × 3.0 Hz

= 0.25 m × 3.0 $\frac{1}{s}$

Speed = 0.75 m/s

3 ### Look Back and Check
Is your answer reasonable?

Because the frequency is 3.0 hertz, the wave should travel a distance of 3 wavelengths in 1 second. This distance is 0.75 meters, which agrees with the calculated speed of 0.75 m/s.

The speed of a wave can change if it enters a new medium or if variables such as pressure and temperature change. However, for many kinds of waves, the speed of the waves is roughly constant for a range of different frequencies. **If you assume that waves are traveling at a constant speed, then wavelength is inversely proportional to frequency.** What does this mean for two waves with different frequencies? The wave with the lower frequency has a longer wavelength.

 Go Online

Download a worksheet on wave properties for students to complete, and find additional teacher support from NSTA SciLinks.

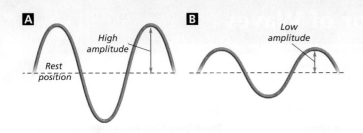

A
High amplitude
Rest position

B
Low amplitude

Amplitude

If you drop a pebble into a pond, the wave is not very high. If you do a "cannonball" jump into the water, you know the wave will be much higher. These two waves have different amplitudes. The **amplitude** (AM pluh tood) of a wave is the maximum displacement of the medium from its rest position.

Figure 7 shows the amplitudes of two transverse waves in a rope. The amplitude of a transverse wave is the distance from the rest position to a crest or a trough. It takes more energy to produce a wave with higher crests and deeper troughs. 🌐 **The more energy a wave has, the greater is its amplitude.**

How do you measure the amplitude of a longitudinal wave? In this case, the amplitude is the maximum displacement of a point from its rest position. The more energy the wave has, the more the medium will be compressed or displaced.

Go Online
PLANETDIARY

For: Activity on tsunamis
Visit: PHSchool.com
Web Code: ccc-2172

Section 17.2 Assessment

Reviewing Concepts

1. 🌐 How is the vibration of the source related to a wave's frequency?
2. 🌐 How is wavelength related to frequency for waves moving at a constant speed?
3. 🌐 How is the energy of a wave related to its amplitude?
4. Describe two ways you could measure the wavelength of a longitudinal wave.
5. Describe how you measure the amplitude of a transverse wave.

Critical Thinking

6. **Applying Concepts** If a wave's period doubles, how does the wave's frequency change? (*Hint:* Period = $\frac{1}{\text{Frequency}}$)

7. **Designing Experiments** Describe an experiment to measure the frequency of a longitudinal wave in a spring.
8. **Predicting** If you double the frequency of a wave, what is the effect on its wavelength (assuming speed does not change)?

Math Practice

9. A wave on a rope has a frequency of 3.3 Hz and a wavelength of 1.2 m. What is the speed of the wave?
10. A spring toy vibrates at 2 Hz to produce a wave. What is the period of the wave?

Mechanical Waves and Sound **507**

Amplitude
Use Visuals L1

Figure 7 The two waves shown have different amplitudes, but the same wavelength and frequency. Ask, **If you were shaking the ropes, how would what you would feel in Figure 7A differ from what you feel in Figure 7B?** (*"My hand would shake harder in A than B."*) Explain that wave A delivers more energy than wave B. **Visual, Logical**

Build Reading Literacy L1

Outline Refer to page **156D** in **Chapter 6**, which provides the guidelines for an outline.

Have students outline the section, leaving room for notes. Then, they should scan through each heading and try to find the main idea. **Logical**

3 ASSESS

Evaluate Understanding L2

Have students create cards of vocabulary terms and definitions, and then work in pairs to match them.

Reteach L1

Use Figure 7 to review the section's key concepts. Ask students to describe the frequency and wavelength of the waves.

Math Practice

Solutions
9. The speed is 1.2 m × 3.3 Hz = 4.0 m/s.
10. The period is 1/2 Hz = 0.5 s.

 Interactive Textbook If your class subscribes to the Interactive Textbook, use it to review key concepts in Section 17.2.

Section 17.2 Assessment

1. A wave's frequency equals the frequency of the vibrating source.
2. Wavelength is inversely proportional to frequency for waves moving at a given speed.
3. The more energy a wave has, the greater is its amplitude.
4. The wavelength could be found by measuring the distance between adjacent compressions or adjacent rarefactions. The wavelength also could be calculated by measuring the wave speed and frequency.
5. The amplitude equals the distance from the rest position to a crest or trough.
6. The frequency is one half as great.
7. Put a ribbon on the spring. Set up a mechanical device to vibrate the spring back and forth in periodic motion. Measure the time it takes for the ribbon to vibrate back and forth 20 times. Divide the measured time into 20 cycles to calculate the frequency in Hz. Repeat the procedure for several trials and average the results.
8. Doubling the frequency will halve the wavelength.

Go Online
PLANETDIARY

Find links to additional activities and have students monitor phenomena that affect Earth and its residents.

Answer to . . .

Figure 7 *The wave in A*

1 FOCUS

Objectives

17.3.1 Describe how reflection, refraction, diffraction, and interference affect waves.

17.3.2 State a rule that explains refraction of a wave as it passes from one medium to another.

17.3.3 Identify factors that affect the amount of refraction, diffraction, or interference.

17.3.4 Distinguish between constructive and destructive interference and **explain** how standing waves form.

Reading Focus

Build Vocabulary L2

Concept Map Have students build a concept map using the terms in this section. Students should write Behavior of Waves in an oval at the top and connect it with linking words to ovals containing vocabulary terms.

Reading Strategy L2

a. A wave reflected at a fixed boundary is inverted but has the same speed and frequency. **b.** Refraction occurs because one side of a wave front moves more slowly than the other side. **c.** The larger the wavelength, the more a wave diffracts. **d.** It can be constructive or destructive. **e.** It forms only for multiples of one-half wavelength.

2 INSTRUCT

Reflection

Teacher Demo

Water-Wave Reflections L2

Purpose Students will observe surface wave reflections.

Materials clear bowl, water, overhead projector

Procedure Fill the bowl with water and place it on the overhead projector. Make gentle waves with a finger.

Expected Outcome Surface waves can be observed reflecting off the side of the bowl. **Visual**

17.3 Behavior of Waves

 Standard: ICP.2.4

Reading Focus

Key Concepts

- How does reflection change a wave?
- What causes the refraction of a wave when it enters a new medium?
- What factors affect the amount of diffraction of a wave?
- What are two types of interference?
- What wavelengths will produce a standing wave?

Vocabulary

- reflection
- refraction
- diffraction
- interference
- constructive interference
- destructive interference
- standing wave
- node
- antinode

Reading Strategy

Identifying Main Ideas Copy and expand the table below. As you read, write the main idea of each topic.

Topic	Main Idea
Reflection	a. _____?
Refraction	b. _____?
Diffraction	c. _____?
Interference	d. _____?
Standing waves	e. _____?

Have you ever noticed bright lines like those shown in Figure 8 dancing on the bottom of a pool? These lines are produced when light shines through waves on the surface of the water. The lines don't seem to have a pattern because there are so many waves interacting. Imagine following just one of these waves. What will happen when it strikes the side of the pool? When it encounters another wave or an obstacle like a person? As the waves crisscross back and forth, many interactions can occur, including reflection, refraction, diffraction, and interference.

Figure 8 The ripples visible on the bottom of the pool are caused by light shining through surface waves.

Reflection

The next time you are in a pool, try to observe ripples as they hit the side of the pool. **Reflection** occurs when a wave bounces off a surface that it cannot pass through. The reflection of a wave is like the reflection of a ball thrown at a wall. The ball cannot go through the wall, so it bounces back.

If you send a transverse wave down a rope attached to a wall, the wave reflects when it hits the wall. **Reflection does not change the speed or frequency of a wave, but the wave can be flipped upside down.** If reflection occurs at a fixed boundary, then the reflected wave will be upside down compared to the original wave.

508 *Chapter 17*

Section Resources

Print
- *Reading and Study Workbook With Math Support*, Section 17.3
- *Transparencies*, Section 17.3

Technology
- *Interactive Textbook*, Section 17.3
- *Presentation Pro CD-ROM*, Section 17.3
- *Go Online*, NSTA SciLinks, Diffraction and interference

Refraction

Refraction is the bending of a wave as it enters a new medium at an angle. Imagine pushing a lawnmower from grass onto gravel, as shown in Figure 9. The direction of the lawnmower changes because one wheel enters the gravel before the other one does. The wheel on the gravel slows down, but the other wheel is still moving at a faster speed on the grass. The speed difference between the two wheels causes the lawnmower to change direction. Refraction changes the direction of a wave in much the same way. ◯ When a wave enters a medium at an angle, refraction occurs because one side of the wave moves more slowly than the other side.

Figure 10 shows the refraction of an ocean wave as it flows into a shallow area. The shallower water can be considered a new medium. The lines on the photograph show the changing direction of the wave. These lines, called wave fronts, are parallel to the crests of the wave.

Notice that the wave fronts approach the shore at an angle. The left side of each wave enters shallower water before the right side does. As the left side of the wave slows down, the wave bends toward the left.

If a wave front is parallel to the shoreline, the wave enters the shallower water all at once. The wave will slow down but it will not change direction. Refraction of the wave occurs only when the two sides of a wave travel at different speeds.

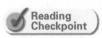 **Reading Checkpoint** *What is refraction?*

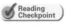
Figure 9 A lawnmower turns when it is pushed at an angle from the grass onto the gravel. **Relating Cause and Effect** *Explain why the lawnmower straightens out after both wheels are on the gravel.*

Grass   Gravel

Left wheel is still rolling faster on grass.

Direction changes.

Mower pivots because the right wheel moves more slowly when it reaches gravel.

Figure 10 As an ocean wave approaches the shore at an angle, the wave bends, or refracts, because one side of each wave front slows down before the other side does.

Mechanical Waves and Sound **509**

Diffraction

Use Visuals   `L1`

Figure 11 Emphasize to students that both pictures are showing the same phenomena, diffraction. Point out the similarities between the two images. Ask, **What would the diffraction pattern look like if one of the barriers were removed in Figure 11A?** *(The waves would still spread out behind the other barrier. This would look like half of the diffraction pattern in Figure 11B.)*
Visual, Logical

Interference

Address Misconceptions   `L2`

Students sometimes make an analogy between pulses and particles traveling toward each other and assume that when two pulses meet in the center of a long spring, they bounce or reflect as if they were solid objects. Use a long, soft spring and a jump rope to demonstrate two differently sized and shaped pulses approaching each other so that students can see that they pass through each other.
Verbal

Go Online NSTA SciLINKS

Download a worksheet on diffraction and interference for students to complete, and find additional teacher support from NSTA SciLinks.

Figure 11 A Mechanical waves, like the water waves shown here, diffract as they move past an obstacle or through an opening. **A** This wave diffracts, or spreads out, after it passes through a narrow opening. **B** Diffraction also occurs when a wave encounters an obstacle.

Go Online NSTA SciLINKS

For: Links on diffraction and interference
Visit: www.SciLinks.org
Web Code: ccn-2173

Diffraction

Diffraction (dih FRAK shun) is the bending of a wave as it moves around an obstacle or passes through a narrow opening. Figure 11A shows how water waves spread out as they pass through a narrow opening. The pattern produced is very similar to the circular ripples you see when a pebble is tossed into a pond. Diffraction also occurs when waves bend around an obstacle, as shown in Figure 11B.

A wave diffracts more if its wavelength is large compared to the size of an opening or obstacle. If the wavelength is small compared to the opening or obstacle, the wave bends very little. The larger the wavelength is compared to the size to the opening or obstacle, the more the wave diffracts.

 Reading Checkpoint   *What is diffraction?*

Interference

If two balls collide, they cannot continue on their original paths as if they had never met. But waves can occupy the same region of space and then continue on. **Interference** occurs when two or more waves overlap and combine together. **Two types of interference are constructive interference and destructive interference.** The displacements of waves combine to increase amplitude in constructive interference and to decrease amplitude in destructive interference.

Facts and Figures

The First Known Seismoscope Earthquakes travel through Earth as longitudinal waves, transverse waves, and surface waves. Surface waves are the most destructive and are the waves that people feel during an earthquake. The world's first earthquake wave detector was invented in 132 A.D. by Zhang Heng, a scientist in the Han Dynasty in China. It was sensitive enough to detect small surface waves. The device had eight dragons arranged in a circle. Each dragon's mouth held a brass ball. When an earthquake wave passed, a brass ball would fall, indicating the direction of the wave. One day a ball fell, indicating that an earthquake had occurred, although no one had felt an earthquake. A few days later, couriers arrived, reporting an earthquake in Lung-Hsi, about 640 km away.

Constructive Interference Imagine a child being pushed on a swing by her mother. If the mother times her pushes correctly, she will push on the swing just as the child starts to move forward. Then the mother's effort is maximized and the child gets a boost to go higher. In the same way, the amplitudes of two waves can add together. **Constructive interference** occurs when two or more waves combine to produce a wave with a larger displacement.

What happens if you and a friend send waves with equal frequencies toward each other on a jump rope? Figure 12A shows how constructive interference produces a wave with an increased amplitude. The crests of waves 1 and 2 combine to make a higher crest in wave 3. At the point where two troughs meet, wave 3 has a lower trough.

Destructive Interference What happens if the mother has bad timing while pushing on the swing? Instead of working to boost her daughter upward, some of her effort is wasted, and the girl will not swing as high. In much the same way, destructive interference can reduce the amplitude of a wave. **Destructive interference** occurs when two or more waves combine to produce a wave with a smaller displacements.

In Figure 12B, two waves with the same frequency meet, but this time the crest of wave 1 meets the trough of wave 2. The resulting wave 3 has a crest at this point, but it is lower than the crest of wave 1. Destructive interference produces a wave with a reduced amplitude.

For: Activity on interference
Visit: PHSchool.com
Web Code: ccp-2173

Figure 12 Two waves with equal frequencies travel in opposite directions. The motions are graphed here to make it easier to see how the waves combine. **A** When a crest meets a crest, the result is a wave with an increased amplitude. **B** When a crest meets a trough, the result is a wave with a reduced amplitude.
Making Generalizations How is the amplitude of wave 3 related to the amplitudes of waves 1 and 2?

A Constructive Interference

B Destructive Interference

Use Visuals L1
Figure 12 Have students examine the figure carefully. Note that the two waves are moving in opposite directions. In Figure 12A, the crests line up with crests and the troughs line up with troughs. In Figure 12B, the crests line up with troughs and the troughs with crests. Ask, **In Figure 12A, what would wave 3 look like if wave 1 and wave 2 had the same amplitude?** *(The amplitude of wave 3 would be twice that of wave 1 or 2.)* **In Figure 12B, what would wave 3 look like if wave 1 and wave 2 had the same amplitude?** *(Wave 3 would have zero amplitude.)* Point out to students that even in the case of two waves with the same amplitude, the waves do not entirely cancel. After they pass through each other, they continue on in their original form.
Visual, Logical

Build Science Skills L2
Using Tables and Graphs Give students dimensions for the horizontal axis of the grid in Figure 12, such as each increment equals 10 cm. Ask students to determine the wavelength of waves 1 and 2 in Figures 12A and 12B. *(The wavelength of each of the waves equals 60 cm.)* Ask, **Do waves 1 and 2 in Figure 12B have the same wavelength?** *(Yes)* **If each graph grid represents a time period of 10 seconds, what is the period and frequency of wave 1 in Figure 12A?** *(Period = 6 s; frequency = 1/6 Hz)*

For: Activity on interference
Visit: PHSchool.com
Web Code: ccp-2173

Students can interact with simulations of constructive and destructive interference online.

Answer to . . .

Figure 12 *The amplitude of wave 3 equals the sum of the amplitudes of waves 1 and 2 for constructive interference. For destructive interference, it's the difference of the amplitudes.*

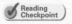 *Diffraction is the bending of a wave when it encounters an obstacle or a narrow opening.*

Mechanical Waves and Sound 511

Standing Waves

Standing Waves L2

Purpose Students will observe different standing waves.

Materials long, soft, heavy rope, such as a jump rope

Class Time 10 minutes

Procedure Tie one end of the rope to a chair or other firm support. Hold the other end of the rope so that it is suspended in air. Start with the rope hanging in an arc. Make standing waves by shaking the rope at different frequencies. Ask students to estimate the wavelength as you increase the frequency and produce more nodes. *(As the frequency increases, the wavelength decreases.)*

Expected Outcome The length of the rope must be an integral number of half wavelengths for a standing wave to occur. **Kinesthetic, Visual**

---

3 ASSESS

Evaluate Understanding L2

Have students write three review questions for this section.

Reteach L1

Use Figures 9–13 as examples that illustrate the key concepts of the section.

Students will need to first decide how the time between photographs compares with the period of the wave. If the five photographs occur during one half period of the wave, the sequence will show the person starting at a maximum crest and moving downward to a minimum trough. No circular motion should result because the lateral motions caused by the two waves should cancel.

Interactive Textbook If your class subscribes to the Interactive Textbook, use it to review key concepts in Section 17.3.

Answer to . . .

Figure 13 *The upper photograph has waves with a longer wavelength.*

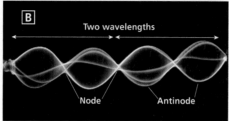

Figure 13 These photos show standing waves for two different frequencies. **A** One wavelength equals the length of the cord. **B** Two wavelengths equal the length of the cord. *Interpreting Photos In which photo do the waves have a longer wavelength?*

Standing Waves

If you tie one end of a rope to a chair and shake the other end, waves travel up the rope, reflect off the chair, and travel back down the rope. Interference occurs as the incoming waves pass through the reflected waves. At certain frequencies, interference between a wave and its reflection can produce a standing wave. A **standing wave** is a wave that appears to stay in one place—it does not seem to move through the medium.

You can observe a standing wave if you pluck a guitar string or any elastic cord. Only certain points on the wave, called nodes, are stationary. A **node** is a point on a standing wave that has no displacement from the rest position. At the nodes, there is complete destructive interference between the incoming and reflected waves. An **antinode** is a point where a crest or trough occurs midway between two nodes.

Why does a standing wave happen only at particular frequencies? **A standing wave forms only if half a wavelength or a multiple of half a wavelength fits exactly into the length of a vibrating cord.** In Figure 13A, the wavelength equals the length of the cord. In Figure 13B, the wavelength is halved. You can adjust the wavelength by changing the frequency of the waves. Once you find a frequency that produces a standing wave, doubling or tripling the frequency will also produce a standing wave.

Section 17.3 Assessment

Reviewing Concepts

1. How is a wave changed by reflection?
2. What causes refraction when a wave enters a medium at an angle?
3. What determines how much a wave diffracts when it encounters an opening or an obstacle?
4. List the types of interference.
5. At what wavelengths can a standing wave form in an elastic cord?

Critical Thinking

6. **Comparing and Contrasting** How does the frequency of a reflected wave compare to the frequency of the incoming wave?

7. **Comparing and Contrasting** How are diffraction and refraction similar? How are they different?

8. **Applying Concepts** What is the amplitude of the wave that results when two identical waves interfere constructively?

Writing in Science

Explain a Sequence Imagine you are floating in a wave pool. The crest of one wave hits you from the left just as the crest of another hits you from the right. The two waves are otherwise identical. A friend takes a series of five photos starting when the crests hit you. Write a paragraph describing the photos.

Section 17.3   Assessment

1. The reflected wave is upside down compared to the original wave.
2. Refraction occurs because the entire wave does not enter the new medium at the same time. One side of a wave front entering the new medium undergoes a speed change before the rest of the wave front does, resulting in the change in direction.
3. The larger the wavelength of a wave compared to the size of the obstacle or opening, the more the wave diffracts.
4. Destructive, constructive
5. A standing wave forms only if half a wavelength or a multiple of half a wavelength fits exactly into the length of the vibrating object.
6. The frequencies are equal. Reflection does not change the frequency of a wave.
7. Diffraction and refraction both involve the bending of waves. Refraction occurs when a wave enters a new medium at an angle, while diffraction occurs when a wave encounters an obstacle or a narrow opening.
8. The amplitude of the resulting wave is double the amplitude of the two interfering waves.

Are Regulations Needed to Protect Whales from Noise Pollution?

Researchers have known for decades that humpback whales sing complicated songs. Their songs can be as long as 30 minutes, and a whale may repeat the song for two or more hours. Songs can be heard at distances of hundreds of kilometers. There is evidence that whales use variations in the songs to tell other whales about the location of food and predators. Only the male humpbacks sing, which has led some researchers to think that songs are also used to attract a mate.

The whale songs may be threatened by noise pollution. In the past 50 years, ocean noise has increased due to human activity. Goods are transported across the ocean in larger ships than ever before. Large ships use bigger engines. They produce low-frequency noise by stirring up air bubbles with their propellers. Unfortunately, whales also use low-frequency sound in their songs, perhaps because these sounds carry farther than high-frequency sounds in the ocean. Propeller noise from large ships is loud enough to interfere with whale songs at a distance of 20 kilometers.

The Viewpoints

Regulations Are Needed to Reduce Noise Pollution From Large Ships

Whales use their songs in ways that affect their survival—eating, mating, and avoiding predators. Studies often focus on the effects of noise from a single ship, but in routes taken by ocean freighters, noise from many ships combines to produce a higher volume. Ocean freighters often travel near whale migration routes, so even noise that affects whales at a distance of 20 kilometers may have an impact on whale survival. If regulations are delayed until research can prove that noise pollution affects whales, it may be too late to help the whales. Many kinds of whales are on the endangered species list, so it is important to err on the side of safety.

Regulations Are Not Needed to Reduce Noise Pollution From Large Ships

Whale songs can be lengthy and are often repeated, so the effect of noise from ships is limited because ships quickly move out of an area. One study showed that whales changed the rhythm and tempo of their songs in response to noise from large ships, but there was no evidence that the communication was less effective. Also, it is expensive to modify ship propellers to reduce low-frequency noise. If less-developed countries cannot afford to modify ships, regulations will not be effective in reducing ocean noise levels.

Research and Decide

1. **Defining the Issue** In your own words, describe the major issue that needs to be resolved about ocean noise pollution.

2. **Analyzing the Viewpoints** List three arguments for those who think regulations should require large ships to reduce noise pollution. List three arguments for those who think regulations are not necessary.

3. **Forming Your Opinion** Explain which argument you find most convincing.

For: More on this issue
Visit: PHSchool.com
Web Code: cch-2173

Are Regulations Needed to Protect Whales from Noise Pollution? **L2**

Background

In the United States, whales fall under the Marine Mammal Protection Act of 1972 (MMPA). This act makes it illegal for any person residing in the United States to kill, hunt, injure, or harass any species of marine mammal. The act includes noise pollution. Ocean noise may result from military testing, sonar, assembling and dismantling of drilling rigs, seismic testing, marine commerce, and proposed experiments using 195-dB pulses to measure the temper-ature in the North Atlantic. Low-frequency sonar produces 235-dB pulses. Oil tankers continuously produce low-frequency sounds of 177 dB at 500 Hz in all the shipping lanes of the world. Seismic oil-exploration pulses are 210 dB. For comparison, the call of a gray whale is 185 dB.

Since light does not penetrate very far in ocean water, whales use sound to find their way around, locate food, and understand their environment. Sound travels five times faster in water than in air and is transmitted more efficiently. Some sounds can travel for hundreds of kilometers.

Whales are thought to hear in the range of 40 Hz to 150 kHz, depending on the species. However, the upper and lower limits are inferred for many whales. Research into large whale hearing is limited by the large size and behaviors of these animals.

Go Online
PHSchool.com

Have students further research the issues related to this topic.

Answers

1. The issue is: Should regulations be passed to limit noise from large ships?

2. For Regulation: Whales depend on communication for breeding and locating food resources. Noise that affects whales at a short distance may still have an impact on behavior. Because many species are endangered, it is wise to err on the safe side of the issue. Against Regulation: Whale songs can be lengthy and are often repeated, so there are several opportunities for a message to get through. Whales may modify songs in response to noise pollution, but there's no evidence it makes communication less effective. Reducing noise of large ships may not be feasible in less developed countries, which makes regulations ineffective.

3. Students should support their decision by referring to the arguments in Question 2.

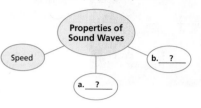

1 FOCUS

Objectives

17.4.1 Describe the properties of sound waves and **explain** how sound is produced and reproduced.

17.4.2 Describe how sound waves behave in applications such as ultrasound and music.

17.4.3 Explain how relative motion determines the frequency of sound an observer hears.

17.4.4 Analyze the functions of the main regions of the human ear.

Reading Focus

Build Vocabulary `L2`

Paraphrase Some terms in this section, such as *intensity, decibel,* and *resonance,* may be unfamiliar to students. Have students create a definition in their own words for these or other difficult words.

Reading Strategy `L2`

a. Intensity and loudness **b.** Frequency and pitch

2 INSTRUCT

Properties of Sound Waves

Use Community Resources `L2`

Invite members of the school band or orchestra or a community band or orchestra to demonstrate musical instruments for the class. Allow students to pose questions to the musicians, such as "How is the pitch of your instrument changed?" or "How do you increase the volume of sound coming from your instrument?"
Musical, Visual

17.4 Sound and Hearing

 Standards: ICP.2.1, ICP.2.3

Reading Focus

Key Concepts
- What properties explain the behavior of sound?
- How is ultrasound used?
- How does frequency of sound change for a moving source?
- What are the functions of the three main regions of the ear?
- How is sound recorded?
- How do musical instruments vary pitch?

Vocabulary
- sound waves
- intensity
- decibel
- loudness
- pitch
- sonar
- Doppler effect
- resonance

Reading Strategy

Using Prior Knowledge Copy the web diagram below. Before you read, add properties you already know about. Then add details about each property as you read.

```
        Properties of
        Sound Waves
   Speed            b. __?__
        a. __?__
```

Take a moment to listen. Even in a quiet room you can usually hear many different sounds. You might hear someone opening a book, people talking in the hall, cars and trucks driving outside, and maybe even an airplane flying overhead. You can identify sounds without seeing them because sound waves carry information to your ears.

Properties of Sound Waves

Sound waves are longitudinal waves—compressions and rarefactions that travel through a medium. Have you ever stopped to question why sounds can hurt your ears? Why there is a delay before you hear an echo down a long, empty hallway at school? **Many behaviors of sound can be explained using a few properties—speed, intensity and loudness, and frequency and pitch.**

Speed Why is there a delay when you hear an echo? It takes time for sound to travel from place to place. In dry air at 20°C, the speed of sound is 342 meters per second. That's more than ten times faster than your speed in a car on a highway!

Figure 14 shows how the speed of sound varies in different media. In general, sound waves travel fastest in solids, slower in liquids, and slowest in gases. This is partly due to the fact that particles in a solid tend to be closer together than particles in a liquid or a gas. The speed of sound depends on many factors, including the density of the medium and how elastic the medium is.

Figure 14 The speed of sound is shown here for a variety of materials.
Making Generalizations *How does temperature affect the speed of sound?*

Speed of Sound	
Medium (at 1 atm)	Speed (m/s)
Dry air, 0°C	331
Dry air, 20°C	342
Fresh water, 0°C	1401
Fresh water, 30°C	1509
Salt water, 0°C	1449
Salt water, 30°C	1546
Lead, 25°C	1210
Cast iron, 25°C	4480
Aluminum, 25°C	5000
Borosilicate glass, 25°C	5170

514 *Chapter 17*

 ## Section Resources

Print
- *Laboratory Manual,* Investigations 17A and 17B
- *Reading and Study Workbook With Math Support,* Section 17.4
- *Transparencies,* Section 17.4

Technology
- *Interactive Textbook,* Section 17.4
- *Presentation Pro CD-ROM,* Section 17.4
- *Go Online, Science News,* Sound

Intensity and Loudness Intensity is the rate at which a wave's energy flows through a given area. Sound intensity depends on both the wave's amplitude and the distance from the sound source. If someone whispers in your ear, the sound intensity may be greater than when someone shouts at you from the other end of a field.

Sound intensity levels are measured in units called decibels. The **decibel** (dB) is a unit that compares the intensity of different sounds. The decibel scale is based on powers of ten. For every 10-decibel increase, the sound intensity increases tenfold. Figure 15 shows the intensity levels of some common sounds. A 0-decibel sound can just barely be heard. A 20-decibel sound has 100 times more energy per second than a 0-decibel sound. A 30-decibel sound delivers 1000 times more energy per second than a 0-decibel sound.

Unlike intensity, loudness is subjective—it is subject to a person's interpretation. **Loudness** is a physical response to the intensity of sound, modified by physical factors. The loudness you hear depends, of course, on sound intensity. As intensity increases, loudness increases. But loudness also depends on factors such as the health of your ears and how your brain interprets the information in sound waves.

Frequency and Pitch Try plucking a stretched rubber band. Then, stretch the rubber band farther and pluck again. You should be able to see the vibration become faster as you hear the sound frequency become higher. The frequency of a sound wave depends on how fast the source of the sound is vibrating.

The size of a musical instrument tells you something about the frequencies it can produce. The trumpet in Figure 16 can produce higher frequencies than the French horn. Both instruments produce different frequencies by changing the length of tubing through which air moves. The air in the tubing forms a standing wave. The longer the tubing, the longer is the wavelength of the standing wave, and the lower is the frequency of the note produced.

Pitch is the frequency of a sound as you perceive it. Pitch does depend upon a wave's frequency. High-frequency sounds have a high pitch, and low-frequency sounds have a low pitch. But pitch, like loudness, also depends on other factors such as your age and the health of your ears.

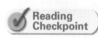 **Reading Checkpoint** *What is loudness?*

Sound Intensity Level	
Sound	Intensity Level (decibels)
Threshold of human hearing	0
Whisper	15–20
Normal conversation	40–50
Street noise	60–70
Inside a bus	90–100
Operating heavy machinery	80–120
Rock concert (in audience)	110–120
Threshold of pain	120
Jet plane (taking off)	120–160

Figure 15 Lengthy exposure to sounds more intense than 90 decibels can cause hearing damage. *Analyzing Data Which sounds are potentially dangerous?*

Figure 16 The French horn can produce lower notes than the trumpet because it can make a longer tube for a standing wave.

French Horn

Trumpet

Mechanical Waves and Sound **515**

Ultrasound

Build Reading Literacy L1

SQ3R Refer to page 530D in Chapter 18, which provides the guidelines for SQ3R (Study, Question, Read, Recite, Review).

Teach this independent study skill as a whole-class exercise. Direct students to survey Section 17.4 and list the headings: Speed, Intensity and Loudness, Frequency, Pitch, and so on. As they survey, have students write one question for each heading, such as "What is one common application for ultrasound?" Then, have students write answers to the questions as they read the section. After reading, have students recite the questions and answers, explaining that vocalizing in your own words helps you retain what you learned.
Auditory, Group

The Doppler Effect

Use Visuals L1

Figure 18 Point out that the ambulance was in a different place when each circular wave was emitted. Reproduce this diagram on the board and number the waves 1 through 6, starting with the largest wave. Ask, **In the figure, where was the ambulance when wave 1 was emitted?** *(At the center of that wave)* **Where was the ambulance when the other waves were emitted?** *(At the center of each wave, moving to the right)*
Visual, Logical

Go Online
PLANETDIARY

Find links to additional activities and have students monitor phenomena that affect Earth and its residents.

Figure 17 Ultrasound can be used to make images of the heart, which help doctors diagnose disease.

Go Online
PLANETDIARY

For: Activity on sonar and marine mammals
Visit: PHSchool.com
Web Code: ccc-2174

Ultrasound

Most people hear sounds between 20 hertz and 20,000 hertz. Infrasound is sound at frequencies lower than most people can hear, and ultrasound is sound at frequencies higher than most people hear. **Ultrasound is used in a variety of applications, including sonar and ultrasound imaging.**

Sonar is a technique for determining the distance to an object under water. Sonar stands for *sound navigation and ranging.* The distance to the object is calculated using the speed of sound in water and the time that the sound wave takes to reach an object and the echo takes to return.

Ultrasound imaging is an important medical technique. Figure 17 shows an image of the heart made by sending ultrasound pulses into a patient. A pulse is a very short burst of a wave. Each ultrasound pulse is short—about $\frac{1}{8000}$ of a second—so that it doesn't interfere with the reflected pulse. Computer software uses the reflected pulses to make a detailed map of structures and organs inside the body.

The Doppler Effect

Perhaps you have heard the pitch of a siren change as it passed you. This is the **Doppler effect**—a change in sound frequency caused by motion of the sound source, motion of the listener, or both. The Doppler effect was discovered by the Austrian scientist Christian Doppler (1803–1853).

As a source of sound approaches, an observer hears a higher frequency. When the sound source moves away, the observer hears a lower frequency. Figure 18 shows a single frequency emitted by the ambulance siren. As the ambulance moves toward observer B, the wave fronts bunch together. Observer B hears a higher frequency than the frequency of the source. For observer A, however, the wave fronts are spread out, and the frequency is lower than the source frequency.

Figure 18 Observer A hears a lower-pitch sound than observer B because the wave fronts are farther apart for observer A. **Inferring** *What can you infer about the pitch the ambulance driver hears?*

Observer A (decreased frequency)

Observer B (increased frequency)

Facts and Figures

Diffraction of Sound All sound waves are diffracted when they pass by an obstacle or through an opening. The human voice has a range of approximately 70 to 400 Hz. This corresponds to wavelengths between 4.9 m and 0.86 m. Recall that the amount of diffraction depends on the wavelength of the wave compared to the size of the opening or obstacle. Because sound waves have wavelengths approximately the same size as the width of a doorway or a window opening, the sound of a person's voice easily diffracts from room to room.

Hearing and the Ear

Can you feel sound waves with your hand at this very moment? Probably you can't. But suppose you hold a balloon. Then your hand can feel sounds because the balloon membrane vibrates. Just like the balloon, your ear has a membrane that vibrates when sound waves strike it.

Your ear is a complex system that consists of three main regions—the outer ear, the middle ear, and the inner ear—as shown in Figure 19. ◉ **The outer ear gathers and focuses sound into the middle ear, which receives and amplifies the vibrations. The inner ear uses nerve endings to sense vibrations and send signals to the brain.**

For: Articles on sound
Visit: PHSchool.com
Web Code: cce-2174

Figure 19
The Anatomy of the Ear

Outer Ear The part of the ear you can see funnels sound waves down the ear canal, a tunnel about 2.5 cm long. There, sound waves strike the eardrum, a tightly stretched membrane between the outer and middle ear. The eardrum vibrates at the same frequency as the sound waves striking it.

Middle Ear The middle ear contains three tiny bones—the hammer, the anvil, and the stirrup. When the eardrum vibrates, the hammer vibrates at the same frequency. The hammer strikes the anvil, which in turn moves the stirrup back and forth. The three bones act as a lever system to amplify the motion of the eardrum.

Inner Ear Vibrations from the stirrup travel into the cochlea, a spiral-shaped canal filled with fluid. The inside of the cochlea is lined with thousands of nerve cells with tiny hair-like projections. As the fluid in the cochlea vibrates, the projections sway back and forth and send electrical impulses to the brain.

Outer Ear · Middle Ear · Inner Ear

Hammer
Anvil
Cochlea
Auditory nerve
Eardrum
Stirrup
Ear canal

Hearing and the Ear

Use Visuals   L1

Figure 19 This figure contains a lot of information and is worth some extra time. Point out important features of the diagram for students. The outer ear is made up of the visible, sound-collecting part (the pinna) and the ear canal. The pinna gathers and reflects sound waves down the canal. Ask, **How do sounds get to the eardrum?** *(Through the air in the ear canal)* **What is the stirrup?** *(One of the small bones in the middle ear)* **What does the stirrup do?** *(It transfers vibrations into the cochlea.)* **What is the function of the auditory nerves?** *(To transmit nerve impulses to the brain)* **Visual, Logical**

Science News provides students with current information on sound.

Answer to . . .

Figure 18 *The frequency for the driver is unchanged because the driver has no motion relative to the siren.*

How Sound Is Reproduced

Address Misconceptions L2

Students sometimes think that sound waves can push a dust particle away from a speaker or blow out a candle flame placed in front of a speaker. However, sound waves would actually make the dust particle or candle flame vibrate back and forth in a direction parallel to the direction in which the wave is moving.
Verbal

SCIENCE and History

Sound Recording L2

Edison, who was slightly deaf, discovered he could feel the vibrations in a telephone speaker with his finger. If a loudspeaker is available, have students gently touch the surface of the speaker grille as music is being played. They should easily be able to detect the vibrations. Ask, **What is causing the vibrations?** *(Sound waves striking the grille)* Students can also hold a book in front of their face, sing a note or speak loudly, and feel the vibrations in the book. Ask, **What is causing the vibrations of the book?** *(Sound waves in air striking the book)* Edison also noticed that a paper telegraph tape, when pulled through a telegraph machine at high speed, made sounds that resembled a human voice. He put these two ideas together and designed the first phonograph.

Over the years since, inventors have constructed many other types of recording devices. Today, there are several different digital audio compression technologies available in addition to MP3. Only time will tell if one becomes the preferred standard.
Logical, Kinesthetic

Writing in Science

Students should compare and contrast the new technology with a previous technology. To be persuasive, their writing must use facts to support benefits claimed for the new technology.
Logical

How Sound Is Reproduced

Sound has been reproduced in many ways, from old-fashioned records to modern digital technologies. But no matter how sound is recorded or stored, in the end it must be converted back into sound waves by loudspeakers. **Sound is recorded by converting sound waves into electronic signals that can be processed and stored. Sound is reproduced by converting electronic signals back into sound waves.**

A modern speaker produces sound waves in much the same way that a drum does. A drum skin vibrates up and down like a trampoline. As the drum vibrates, it sends a series of compressions and rarefactions through the air across the room. They carry energy to your ears in the form of sound waves.

SCIENCE and History

Sound Recording

Recording technology has come a long way since Thomas Edison made the first sound recording of the human voice at his New Jersey laboratory in 1877.

Metal cylinder *This is wrapped with a layer of tinfoil.*

Mouthpiece *The mouthpiece records sounds as scratches on the tinfoil.*

Hand crank

PHONOGRAPH

Funnel *The funnel is used for recording and playback.*

Horn *The horn channels sounds from an iron diaphragm.*

Steel needle

GRAMOPHONE

As wire recording gives way to magnetic tape, portable reel-to-reel recorders, like this 1950s model, become very popular.

REEL-TO-REEL RECORDER

1877 American inventor Thomas Edison records his voice on a tinfoil cylinder phonograph.

1885 The wax-coated cylinder is introduced as an improvement on Edison's first design.

1887 German-born American Emile Berliner invents the Gramophone, which stores sounds as grooves in the wax surface of a flat disc.

1900 Danish inventor Valdemar Poulsen unveils a magnetic recording device, called the Telegraphone.

1928 Tape with a magnetic coating is developed in Germany. Further refinements and a 1930s tape recorder called the Magnetophone make reel-to-reel recording popular.

1875 — 1900 — 1925

518 *Chapter 17*

Facts and Figures

Sound Reproduction The first audio recordings were made by purely mechanical action. The singer or instrumentalist sang or played into a funnel-shaped tube that led directly to a cork diaphragm. The diaphragm was attached through a series of levers to a needle that would carve a groove into a wax cylinder or disk. Since there was no way to duplicate a recording, the orchestra or performer would be required to play the composition over and over for hours as up to 10 individual recordings were made at a time. Ensembles of musicians made recordings in a small room. One wall of the room was the opening of the huge recording tube. In an interesting historical twist, several contemporary musicians have started to use this old technology to record their compositions.

In a speaker, an electronic signal causes a magnet to vibrate. The magnet is attached to a membrane. The vibrating membrane sends sound waves through the air. Larger-diameter speakers, like a large bass drum, are better at reproducing lower frequencies of sound. Smaller-diameter speakers, like a small bongo drum, are better for reproducing higher frequencies of sound.

When a singer sings into a microphone, the reverse process happens. Sound waves from the singer's voice vibrate a membrane inside the microphone. The membrane causes a magnet to vibrate, which produces an electronic signal in the microphone wires. The energy of sound waves has been converted into an electronic signal that can be processed and stored.

Writing in Science

Writing to Persuade
Research one type of recording technology. Write a product review as if you lived at the time it was invented. Persuade people that this technology is much better than previously available technologies.

Integrate Social Studies L2

Thomas Edison is generally credited as the inventor of the phonograph, which he publicly demonstrated in 1877. He did not pursue the invention at first. Alexander Graham Bell, his cousin Chester Bell, and C. S. Tainter made improvements to Edison's design to improve the sound quality. They called their device the graphophone. The Bells and Tainter offered to combine their patents and designs with Edison's work, but Edison rejected the offer. Instead, he developed an improved machine similar to the graphophone. Edison's new system used thicker, reusable wax cylinders and a jewel-tipped recording stylus that did not need to be replaced after every recording. Emile Berliner further improved the phonograph by using a flat disk and a system for duplicating records from a steel master. These various phonographs were very popular, and after 1895, hundreds of companies appeared, yet quickly failed. Only a few companies survived into the twentieth century. Have students research later technological developments that affected phonographs and record players.
Logical

Audio cassettes, a compact version of reel-to-reel magnetic tapes, are soon in demand.

CASSETTE TAPE RECORDER

MP3 PLAYER

VINYL LONG PLAYING

1948 Columbia introduces the first 12-inch vinyl records. Relatively cheap to make, these allow for a longer playing time.

1962 Philips, based in the Netherlands, demonstrates its first compact audio cassette. It is sold the following year with dictation machines. A stereo version is introduced in 1967.

1982 The first digital audio compact discs (CDs) are sold in Japan.

1998 MP3 technology becomes popular. This format allows music to be compressed, stored, and transferred digitally over computer networks.

1950   1975   2000

Mechanical Waves and Sound   **519**

HOW It Works

The Piano   L2

Several keyboard instruments predated the piano. The most popular was the harpsichord. When a key is pressed on a harpsichord, a corresponding string is plucked. Consequently, it is difficult to control the loudness of the instrument. In a piano, however, the string is struck by a felt-covered hammer. Pressing the key with more force causes the string to be struck harder, producing a louder sound. Because of this, these instruments were called fortepianos (literally "loud-soft") for their ability to change dynamics. As the instrument evolved, the name was shortened to piano.

When a piano key is pressed, two things happen. The hammer strikes the string and rebounds, while the damper pad moves away. Therefore, the string will continue to vibrate as long as the key is held down.

The use of cast-iron frames allows heavier strings to be strung with greater tension. Greater tension in the string produces a better, cleaner sound and allows the string to vibrate much longer.

Interpreting Photos When a piano key is struck, a series of levers causes the hammer to strike a string. The vibration of the string is amplified by the soundboard.
Visual, Musical

For Enrichment   L3

The piano and its family of instruments probably originated with the hammered dulcimer, which is played by striking the strings with small "hammers." Interested students can research the origin of plucked and struck stringed instruments such as dulcimers and harps.
Verbal, Portfolio

HOW It Works

The Piano

The piano is a highly versatile musical instrument. Usually there are 88 separate keys, which produce a range of notes and volume. The sounds are made by wire strings that vibrate against a soundboard inside the piano.

Interpreting Photos *What causes the strings in a piano to vibrate?*

Grand piano
Pianos can be upright or, like this grand, horizontal. A grand piano makes a rich and powerful sound.

Bridge *Each string passes over a curved piece of wood called a bridge, which transmits the string's vibrations to the soundboard.*

Cast iron frame *This rigid frame is strong enough to allow huge force to be exerted on the strings.*

Bass bridge

Key

Damper

Treble strings *Short, thin strings produce higher pitches.*

Bass strings *Long, thick strings produce lower pitches. The bass strings cross over the mid-range strings to use space efficiently.*

Pins for tuning

Wire string   Damper   Felt-tipped hammer

Soundboard *Made from a large, thin piece of wood (usually spruce), the soundboard resonates and amplifies the sound from the vibrating wires.*

Keyboard action
As a key is pressed down, the section beyond the pivot moves up. This activates a series of levers that flick a hammer upward to strike the string and make it vibrate. The damper is released, which allows the string to continue vibrating.

Interconnected levers

Key

Damper lever   Pivot

Music

Musical instruments can produce a wide variety of sounds. In a wind instrument, such as a flute or trumpet, holes are closed using fingers or valves. This changes the length of the column of air in which a standing sound wave is produced. For some stringed instruments, such as a violin, musicians change the length of the strings by pressing down with their fingers. For other instruments, such as a piano, they use a fixed set of strings of different lengths. ⊙ **Most musical instruments vary pitch by changing the frequency of standing waves.**

Musical instruments often use resonance to amplify sound. **Resonance** (REZ uh nuhns) is the response of a standing wave to another wave of the same frequency. Think of a child being pushed on a swing. If the pushes are timed at the right frequency, the child can swing higher and higher. In the same way, one wave can "push" another wave to a higher amplitude. Resonance can produce a dramatic increase in amplitude. A piano, for example, amplifies sound with a soundboard. The soundboard resonates in response to the vibrating strings.

Once sound waves leave an instrument, they can take several routes to a listener. In a large concert hall, interference with reflected sound waves can be a problem. Theaters such as the one in Figure 20 are designed with reflecting panels and sound-absorbing tiles. These are located with great care to prevent "dead spots" where the volume is reduced by destructive interference of reflected sound waves.

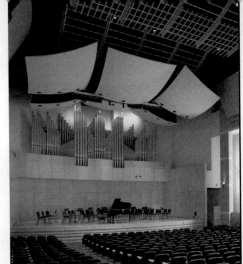

Figure 20 The Central Michigan University Music Building, like many concert halls, was designed by acoustic engineers. Sound-absorbing tiles (on the sides and rear) reduce unwanted reflections. The curved reflecting panels above the stage help gather and direct sound waves toward the audience.

Section 17.4 Assessment

Reviewing Concepts

1. ⊙ List five properties used to explain the behavior of sound waves.
2. ⊙ Name two uses for ultrasound.
3. ⊙ What is the Doppler effect?
4. ⊙ What are the ear's three main regions? Describe the function of each region.
5. ⊙ How is sound recorded?
6. ⊙ How does a musical instrument produce notes at different pitches?

Critical Thinking

7. **Applying Concepts** If workers in a distant stone quarry are blasting, why can you feel the explosion in your feet before you hear it?

8. **Comparing and Contrasting** How does the intensity of a 40-decibel sound compare to the intensity of a 20-decibel sound?

9. **Applying Concepts** How could a bat use reflections of sound waves to determine distance to an insect?

Connecting ⊂ Concepts

Frames of Reference Review what you learned about combining velocities in Section 11.2. Then explain why the Doppler effect depends on the velocity of the sound source in the observer's frame of reference.

Mechanical Waves and Sound **521**

Music
Integrate Language Arts L2

The folk musician Greg Brown has set several of William Blake's poems to music. Many other performers have found musical inspiration in poetry. Choose a recording, such as Greg Brown's setting of Blake's poem "The Chimney Sweeper," and allow students to listen. Ask, **How did the performer use rhythm or pitch to enhance the meaning of the poem?** *(Possible answers: A simple melody can heighten the drama of powerful images, such as those in "The Chimney Sweeper." The rhythm of the music can enhance the sense of rhythm in the poem.)*
Verbal, Musical

❸ ASSESS
Evaluate Understanding L2

Have students outline and summarize the section. Then, divide the class into groups and have students exchange papers and edit each other's outlines. Exchange the papers again, and have students edit the edits. Then, return the papers to the original owners to rewrite.

Reteach L1

Write the vocabulary words for this section. Have students review the section and create definitions for the vocabulary words in their own words.

Connecting ⊂ Concepts

Choosing a particular frame of reference does not change the sound heard by the observer. In physics, one often chooses a frame of reference that makes it easier to understand or solve a problem. With the Doppler effect, one simple choice is to use the observer's frame of reference. The shift in frequency can then be determined from the speed of the sound source in this frame of reference.

Interactive Textbook If your class subscribes to the Interactive Textbook, use it to review key concepts in Section 17.4.

Section 17.4 Assessment

1. Speed, intensity, loudness, frequency, pitch
2. Medical imaging, sonar
3. The Doppler effect occurs when an observer hears a higher frequency as a sound source approaches. When a sound source moves away, the observer hears a lower frequency.
4. The outer ear gathers and focuses sound into the middle ear, which amplifies the vibrations. The inner ear has nerve endings that sense vibrations and transmit signals to the brain.
5. Sound is recorded by converting sound waves into other forms of energy.
6. By changing the frequency of standing waves
7. The speed of sound in solids is generally faster than the speed of sound in air, so the sound wave reaches your feet first through the ground.
8. The intensity of a 40-dB sound is 100 times greater than the intensity of a 20-dB sound.
9. A bat can determine distance based on the amount of time it takes for ultrasound waves the bat emits to reach the insect and bounce back to the bat's ears.

Mechanical Waves and Sound 521

CONCEPTS in Action

Now Hear This L2

Background

There are many ways to reduce noise. Barriers are the most common. The idea of creating "anti-noise" was first developed in the 1970s. Because noise is chaotic and unpredictable, the only way to cancel a noise is by continuously monitoring the noise and generating an appropriate anti-noise signal. Only recently has technology become available that allows real-time, active noise cancellation. An active noise-cancellation system uses a high-speed digital signal processor to sample the noise thousands of times a second. It then is able to create the anti-noise wave. Applications for noise-cancellation technology include active mufflers that reduce exhaust noise; quiet zones in automobiles, airplanes, trucks, and locomotives; and active headsets that provide better hearing protection while still allowing communication.

Build Science Skills L2

Using Models

Purpose Students observe destructive interference of sound waves.

Materials tuning fork hammer, 2 tuning forks with the same frequency (about 400 Hz), stethoscope

Safety Make sure that students handle the tuning forks carefully.

Procedure One student carefully strikes the tuning forks with the tuning fork hammer and holds the tuning forks about 10 cm apart. A second student listens with the stethoscope's listening end placed about 20 cm from the tuning forks. The listener moves the stethoscope's end to find a node where the volume is greatly reduced. This may require several trials. Ask, **What is causing the sound to become inaudible in certain places?** (Destructive interference between the two sound waves) Ask, **How is this different from noise-cancellation technology?** (In noise-cancellation technology, the signal is much more complicated.)

Expected Outcome Students will find regions where the sound is not audible.
Musical, Logical

Now Hear This

Imagine eliminating all unwanted noise and only hearing the sounds you need to hear. That is the goal of noise-cancellation technology.

Noise-cancelling headset *This headset removes noise but allows communication with co-workers.*

In the modern world, there is plenty of unwanted noise from jet aircraft engines, construction equipment, and factory machinery. Traditionally, the way to deal with noise has been to put a barrier, such as an ear plug or ear muffler, between the source of the noise and your ears. This type of ear protection has the drawback, however, that it blocks out most sound, not just unwanted noise. That makes communication with co-workers difficult. Now, new technology is available that selectively removes unwanted noise, but transmits the sounds you need to hear.

Sound Control
Airport workers, jet pilots, rock musicians, and some factory workers all have a need for noise reduction.

Noise-cancellation technology

In noise-cancellation technology, a headset is fitted with a tiny microphone. This microphone is linked to an electronic device that can analyze the amplitude and frequency of sounds. When an undesirable noise is picked up by the microphone, a tiny speaker generates an anti-noise wave. The two waves cancel each other in destructive interference.

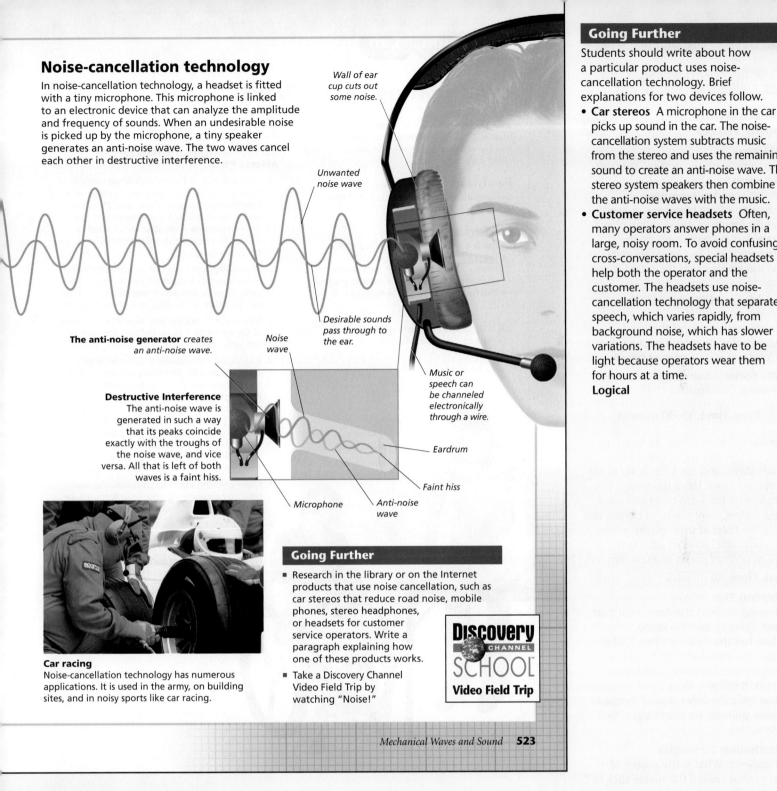

Wall of ear cup cuts out some noise.

Unwanted noise wave

Desirable sounds pass through to the ear.

The anti-noise generator *creates an anti-noise wave.*

Noise wave

Destructive Interference
The anti-noise wave is generated in such a way that its peaks coincide exactly with the troughs of the noise wave, and vice versa. All that is left of both waves is a faint hiss.

Microphone

Anti-noise wave

Music or speech can be channeled electronically through a wire.

Eardrum

Faint hiss

Car racing
Noise-cancellation technology has numerous applications. It is used in the army, on building sites, and in noisy sports like car racing.

Going Further

- Research in the library or on the Internet products that use noise cancellation, such as car stereos that reduce road noise, mobile phones, stereo headphones, or headsets for customer service operators. Write a paragraph explaining how one of these products works.
- Take a Discovery Channel Video Field Trip by watching "Noise!"

DISCOVERY CHANNEL SCHOOL
Video Field Trip

Mechanical Waves and Sound **523**

Investigating Sound Waves

L2

Objective
After completing this activity, students will be able to
• define sound as a mechanical vibration whose frequency depends on the length of the vibrating object.
• state that pitch depends on the frequency and that loudness depends on the amplitude of the sound wave.

 Address Misconceptions

This lab can help dispel the misconception that high-pitched sounds are louder than low-pitched sounds.

Skills Focus Observing, Inferring, Drawing Conclusions

Prep Time 15–30 minutes

Advance Preparation To save class time, cut the wax paper into 10-cm square sheets and cut 1-cm holes in the cardboard tubes. Use a thumbtack as a template for the 1-cm holes and use a sharp scalpel, razor blade, or electric drill to cut the holes. If small plastic mirrors are unavailable, you can substitute sequins or small pieces of aluminum foil.

Class Time 40 minutes

Teaching Tips
• Remind students that they must hum, and not sing, into the kazoo.
• Have half the class start Part A while the other half starts Part B. This will require fewer flashlights and meter sticks. It will also allow the students to hear the differences in pitch because fewer students are humming at the same time.

Questioning Strategies
Ask students: **What is the source of energy that caused the meter stick to vibrate?** *(The mechanical energy or muscle power used to pluck the meter stick)* **What happened to the sound waves when you changed the length of the vibrating object?** *(The pitch changed.)* **How does the pitch affect the frequency of the reflected light's vibration?** *(The higher the pitch, the greater the frequency is.)* **How does loudness affect the amplitude of the reflected light's vibration?** *(The greater the loudness, the greater the amplitude is.)*

Investigating Sound Waves

Sound is produced when a vibrating source causes a medium to vibrate. In this lab, you will investigate how the vibrating source affects characteristics of the sound produced.

Problem What determines the frequency and amplitude of the sound produced by a vibrating object?

Materials
• meter stick
• two cardboard tubes
• scissors or scalpel
• two rubber bands
• wax paper
• balloon
• small mirror
• transparent tape
• flashlight

Skills Observing, Inferring, Drawing Conclusions, Controlling Variables

Procedure

Part A: Investigating How Length Affects Pitch

1. Hold one end of a meter stick down firmly on a table so that 20 centimeters of the meter stick extends past the edge of the table. Pluck the end of the meter stick that extends past the table to produce a vibration and a sound as shown. Observe the vibration and sound of the meter stick.

2. Repeat Step 1, but this time allow 40 centimeters of the meter stick to extend past the edge of the table. Observe and record how the length of the vibrating part of the meter stick affects the pitch.

3. Repeat Step 1, but this time allow 60 centimeters of the meter stick to extend past the edge of the table. Record your observations.

4. Investigate the relationship between length and frequency for a vibrating column of air, as you did with the vibrating meter stick. Make a kazoo by cutting a hole in the middle of one of the cardboard tubes. Make the hole approximately 1 centimeter in diameter. Use a rubber band to fasten the piece of wax paper over one end of the tube. **CAUTION** *Be careful when cutting with sharp instruments; always cut away from yourself and away from nearby people.*

5. Make a second kazoo by cutting the second tube 10 centimeters shorter than the first tube. Using the short tube, repeat Step 4.

6. Hold the shorter kazoo in front of your mouth and hum into the open end, keeping your pitch steady. Repeat this action with the longer kazoo, making sure to hum exactly as you did before. Observe and record how the length of the kazoo affects the pitch of the sound.

Part B: Investigating How Frequency Affects Pitch and How Amplitude Affects Loudness

7. Cut the neck off of the balloon. Replace the wax paper on the longer kazoo with the cut-open balloon. Wrap the rubber band several times around the end of the cardboard tube. The rubber band should hold the balloon tightly stretched over the end of the tube. Use tape to attach the small mirror onto the balloon on the end of the tube.

8. Have a classmate shine a flashlight on the mirror as shown while you hum into the kazoo. Your classmate should position the flashlight so that a spot of light is reflected on the wall. It may be necessary to darken the room. Observe how the spot of light moves when you hum into the kazoo. Make a note of your position and the position and angle of the kazoo and the flashlight.

9. Without changing how loudly you hum, use your voice to raise the pitch of your humming. Observe and record how the movement of the spot of light differs from your observations in Step 8. Make sure you do not change your distance from the wall or the angle at which the light from the flashlight strikes the mirror attached to the kazoo.

10. Repeat Step 9, but this time hum at a lower pitch than you did in Step 8.

11. Repeat Steps 9 and 10, but this time vary the loudness of your humming while keeping the pitch constant.

Analyze and Conclude

1. **Observing** What happened to the frequency of the meter stick's vibration when you made the overhanging part longer?

2. **Inferring** How did the frequency of the meter stick's vibration affect the pitch of its sound?

3. **Inferring** How did the kazoo's length affect its pitch?

4. **Analyzing Data** When you changed the pitch of your humming, how did it affect the frequency of vibration of the mirror?

5. **Analyzing Data** How is the amplitude of the kazoo's vibration related to its loudness?

6. **Controlling Variables** Explain why it was important to keep loudness constant when you changed the pitch of your humming in Step 9.

Go Further Design an experiment to investigate what variables affect the pitch and loudness of vibrating strings. Use an instrument such as a guitar or violin. After your teacher approves your plan, carry out your experiment.

Expected Outcome The pitch becomes lower as the length of the vibrating part of the meter stick and the air column inside the kazoo are lengthened. An increase in the sound's loudness increases the amplitude of the vibration of the reflected light. An increase of the sound's pitch increases the frequency of the vibration of the reflected light.

Go Further

The frequency and amplitude of a vibrating string are easily varied by adjusting the length of the vibrating portion of the string, or the force with which it is plucked, respectively.
Kinesthetic, Logical

Analyze and Conclude
1. The frequency was reduced.
2. The pitch became lower as the frequency was reduced.
3. The longer kazoo had the lower pitch.
4. Humming at a higher pitch increased the frequency of the mirror's vibration.

5. Increasing the loudness increased the amplitude of the kazoo's vibration.
6. Keeping the loudness constant ensured that any change in the frequency of the mirror's vibration was due to the change in pitch.
Logical

Study Guide

Study Tip

Organize New Information
This chapter contains many new words and much new information. Tell students to create outlines, charts, flashcards, time lines, and concept maps to help them visualize relationships. Have them create a vocabulary list with definitions for all of the vocabulary terms in their own words.

Thinking Visually

a. Reflection
b. Refraction
c. Diffraction

Assessment

Interactive Textbook If your class subscribes to the Interactive Textbook, your students can go online to access an interactive version of the Student Edition and a self-test.

Reviewing Content

1. b   2. a   3. c
4. b   5. d   6. c
7. b   8. a   9. c
10. b

Understanding Concepts

11. A wave in a spring and a P wave are longitudinal waves. Both waves have compressions and rarefactions.
12. A surface wave combines the motion of a transverse wave, (perpendicular to the direction of travel) and the motion of a longitudinal wave (back-and-forth parallel to the direction of travel).
13. See Wave B on the diagram below.
14. See Wave C on the diagram below.

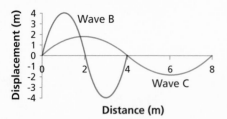

17.1 Mechanical Waves

Key Concepts

- A wave is created when a source of energy causes a vibration to move through a medium.
- The three main types of mechanical waves are transverse, longitudinal, and surface waves.

Vocabulary

mechanical wave, *p. 500;* medium, *p. 500;* crest, *p. 501;* trough, *p. 501;* transverse wave, *p. 501;* compression, *p. 502;* rarefaction, *p. 502;* longitudinal wave, *p. 502;* surface wave, *p. 503*

17.2 Properties of Mechanical Waves

Key Concepts

- A wave's frequency equals the frequency of the vibrating source producing the wave.
- For waves traveling at a constant speed, wavelength is inversely proportional to frequency.
- As energy of a wave increases, amplitude increases.

Vocabulary

periodic motion, *p. 504;* period, *p. 504;* frequency, *p. 504;* hertz, *p. 504;* wavelength, *p. 505;* amplitude, *p. 507*

17.3 Behavior of Waves

Key Concepts

- Reflection does not change the speed or frequency of a wave, but the wave can be flipped upside down.
- Refraction occurs because one side of a wave moves more slowly than the other side.
- A wave diffracts more if its wavelength is large compared to the size of an opening or obstacle.
- Interference can be constructive or destructive.
- A standing wave forms only if the length of a vibrating cord is a multiple of one half wavelength.

Vocabulary

reflection, *p. 508;* refraction, *p. 509;* diffraction, *p. 510;* interference, *p. 510;* constructive interference, *p. 511;* destructive interference, *p. 511;* standing wave, *p. 512;* node, *p. 512;* antinode, *p. 512*

17.4 Sound and Hearing

Key Concepts

- Many behaviors of sound can be explained using a few properties—speed, intensity and loudness, and frequency and pitch.
- Ultrasound is used in a variety of applications, including sonar and ultrasound imaging.
- As a source of sound approaches, an observer hears a higher frequency. When the sound source moves away, the observer hears a lower frequency.
- The outer ear gathers and focuses sound into the middle ear, which receives and amplifies the vibrations. The inner ear uses nerve endings to sense vibrations and send signals to the brain.
- Sound is recorded by converting sound waves into electronic signals that can be processed and stored. Sound is reproduced by converting electronic signals back into sound waves.
- Most instruments vary pitch by changing the frequency of standing waves.

Vocabulary

sound waves, *p. 514;* intensity, *p. 515;* decibel, *p. 515;* loudness, *p. 515;* pitch, *p. 515;* sonar, *p. 516;* Doppler effect, *p. 516;* resonance, *p. 521*

Thinking Visually

Web Diagram Copy the web diagram below onto a sheet of paper. Use information from the chapter to complete the diagram.

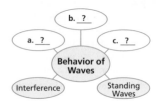

Chapter Resources

Print
- ***Chapter and Unit Tests,*** Chapter 17 Test A and Test B
- ***Test Prep Resources,*** Chapter 17

Technology
- ***Computer Test Bank,*** Chapter Test 17
- ***Interactive Textbook,*** Chapter 17
- ***Go Online,*** PHschool.com, Chapter 17

Assessment

Reviewing Content

Choose the letter that best answers the question or completes the statement.

1. Which of the following is NOT true about mechanical waves?
   a. They carry energy.
   b. They transfer matter.
   c. They can be longitudinal.
   d. They require a medium.

2. In a transverse wave, the medium vibrates
   a. at right angles to the wave direction.
   b. in the same direction as the wave.
   c. in a direction opposite that of the wave.
   d. at a 45° angle to the wave direction.

3. The height of a wave crest is called
   a. wavelength.   b. frequency.
   c. amplitude.   d. energy.

4. For waves moving at a constant speed, if wavelength is doubled, then frequency is
   a. doubled.   b. halved.
   c. unchanged.   d. quadrupled.

5. When a wave is reflected, its speed
   a. increases.   b. increases or decreases.
   c. decreases.   d. is unchanged.

6. When a wave bends around an obstacle, it is called
   a. reflection.   b. refraction.
   c. diffraction.   d. interference.

7. When two waves interfere, the displacement where two troughs meet is
   a. positive.   b. negative.
   c. zero.   d. a crest.

8. A large speaker is better than a small speaker for producing sounds with
   a. low frequency.   b. high frequency.
   c. low intensity.   d. high intensity.

9. The highest-frequency sound human ears can usually hear is about
   a. 20 Hz.   b. 10,000 Hz.
   c. 20,000 Hz.   d. 30,000 Hz.

10. Sonar can make use of
    a. the Doppler effect.   b. ultrasound.
    c. infrasound.   d. resonance.

Understanding Concepts

11. Name two kinds of longitudinal waves and explain how you know they are longitudinal.

12. How are some surface waves similar to both transverse and longitudinal waves?

Copy the diagram below on a separate piece of paper and use it to answer Questions 13–15.

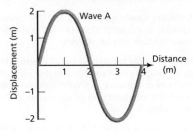

13. On your diagram, draw wave B with the same wavelength as wave A, but twice the amplitude.

14. On your diagram, draw wave C with the same amplitude as wave A, but twice the wavelength.

15. How does the frequency of wave C compare with the frequency of wave A, assuming they travel at the same speed?

16. What causes refraction of a wave as it enters a new medium at an angle?

17. Regardless of the direction of waves far from an island, waves close to the island move toward the shore on all sides. Explain.

18. Why does a node in a standing wave have zero displacement?

19. How is intensity different from loudness?

20. Explain why a fire engine's siren sounds lower in pitch after the fire engine passes you.

21. What is the function of the eardrum?

22. What are the names of the three small bones in the middle ear, and what is their purpose?

23. Why are the materials used in construction of a concert hall important?

Mechanical Waves and Sound **527**

Assessment (continued)

15. The frequency of Wave C is half the frequency of Wave A.

16. A wave refracts because one side of the wave front moves faster than the other side.

17. As waves move into shallower water surrounding the island, they refract or bend toward the land because the shallower water acts as a new medium.

18. At a node, there is complete destructive interference at all times, so the displacement is zero.

19. Intensity is the rate at which a wave's energy flows through a given area. Loudness is a physical response to the intensity of sound.

20. As the siren moves away, each wave front produced by the siren is farther from the previous wave front than if the siren were standing still. The actual frequency does not change but the frequency or pitch heard by the observer is lower.

21. The eardrum is located between the middle ear and outer ear. Sound waves cause it to vibrate and convert the energy of the sound waves into mechanical energy.

22. The bones of the inner ear are the hammer, the anvil, and the stirrup. The vibration of the eardrum causes the hammer to vibrate. It strikes the anvil, which causes the stirrup to move back and forth. Together the three bones amplify the motion of the eardrum.

23. Reflection and interference can affect sound quality. Materials should be used that absorb sound to minimize reflection. The overall design of the interior of the concert hall can minimize the dead spots where destructive interference can occur.

Homework Guide

Section	Questions
17.1	1–2, 11–15, 24, 36
17.2	3–4, 16–17, 25, 30–33
17.3	5–8, 18, 26
17.4	9–10, 19–23, 27–29, 34–35

Critical Thinking

24. The energy of a mechanical wave causes the medium to vibrate. As vibrating particles in the medium collide, most of the energy can be passed on to the next particle, but fluid friction will cause some energy to be converted into thermal energy.

25. The speed of a wave in a medium is measured under a particular set of conditions. The speed can change if the conditions change or if the density of the medium changes. Otherwise, the speed in the medium is a constant.

26. To form a standing wave, two waves must pass through each other and interfere in a regular way. This cannot happen if the waves are traveling in the same direction.

27. The mosquito's wings must be vibrating faster than the bee's. The higher-frequency vibration produces a higher-frequency sound.

28. Intensity depends upon the distance from the source. If the kitten is close and the thunder far away, the kitten's purr could have a greater intensity.

29. The intensity of the 25-dB sound is 10 times greater. A sound 100 times louder than a 25-dB sound has an intensity of 45 dB.

Math Skills

30. The wavelength is 0.69 m.
31. The frequency is 3 cycles/2 s = 1.5 Hz.
32. Speed = frequency × wavelength = 1.5 Hz × 0.69 m = 1.0 m/s
33. Period = wavelength/speed = (10.0 m)/(3.9 m/s) = 2.6 s

Concepts in Action

34. The device uses ultrasound frequencies that are above the range of human hearing, but are in a frequency range that animals can hear.
35. As a machine operates at higher speed, the vibrational frequency increases. The pitch of the noise should increase as well.
36. Students should describe the periodic circular motion of the lily pad. If the waves are not breaking waves, then the lily pad should have no net motion toward shore, regardless of whether the roots are attached to the pond floor.

Critical Thinking

24. Making Generalizations A friend says that all mechanical waves must lose energy as they move through a medium because some energy is lost due to friction. Explain why this is true.

25. Forming Operational Definitions Two sound waves with different frequencies travel through a steel rod at the same speed. Explain by giving an operational definition of wave speed.

26. Relating Cause and Effect Can two waves traveling in the same direction form a standing wave? Explain why or why not.

27. Inferring The buzzing sound of a mosquito flying around your head has a higher pitch than the buzz of a bumblebee. What can you infer about the mosquito's wings compared to the bee's wings?

28. Relating Cause and Effect At the same time, you hear a kitten's purr and a clap of thunder. The kitten's purr is louder. Explain how this is possible.

29. Applying Concepts How much greater is the intensity of a 25-dB sound than a 15-dB sound? What would be the intensity in dB for a sound that is 100 times louder than the 25-dB sound?

Math Skills

Use the illustration below to answer Questions 30–32.

Ocean wave

30. Interpreting Diagrams What is the wavelength of the ocean wave shown in the figure?

31. Evaluating Expressions Three complete wavelengths pass a fixed point once every 2 seconds. What is the frequency of the wave?

32. Calculating What is the speed of the ocean wave in Question 31?

33. Calculating A deep-water wave has a wavelength of 10.0 meters. If it travels at 3.9 m/s, what is the wave's period?

Concepts in Action

34. Applying Concepts Some gardeners protect their gardens from animals by using sound that animals find irritating. Explain how the gardeners can tolerate the sound, while the animals cannot.

35. Formulating Hypotheses Generate a hypothesis about how the frequency of noise made by a machine changes as the machine operates at higher speeds.

36. Writing in Science Write a paragraph describing the motion of a lily pad as several waves from a boat pass by. Explain why the motion would be the same or different if the lily pad were floating free instead of attached by roots to the pond floor. (*Hint:* Before you write, draw a series of diagrams to show the motion.)

Performance-Based Assessment

Using Models Try blowing across the top of a bottle to produce a tone. Experiment to see how adding water of different heights affects the pitch. See if you can arrange a series of eight bottles to produce a musical scale. Learn to play a simple tune on your musical bottles. Summarize your results in a computer presentation that explains the relationship between the height of the air column and the pitch produced.

For: Self-grading assessment
Visit: PHSchool.com
Web Code: cca-2170

Performance-Based Assessment

Encourage students to critique presentations in small groups before making whole-class presentations. The frequency of the tone increases as the water level (depth) in a bottle increases. Students may be curious to try different bottle shapes to see if this affects the tone produced most easily. Students will discover that to play a scale, the series of bottles needs to be arranged in order of lowest water depth to greatest water depth.

Your students can independently test their knowledge of the chapter and print out their test results for your files.

Standardized Test Prep for Indiana

Test-Taking Tip

Controlling Variables

Some test questions ask which variables must be controlled in an experiment. It helps to start by writing an equation for the variables you are given. For the question below, write an equation that includes wavelength and frequency.

Speed = Wavelength × Frequency

This equation gives you one variable to control: the wave speed. Next, think of any conditions that might affect this variable. You know that wave speed changes in a different medium, so the medium must be controlled. Other conditions that are often controlled include conditions in the lab, such as temperature and pressure, or quantities of matter, such as mass or volume.

Which variables must be held constant in an experiment to determine how the frequency of a sound wave affects wavelength?
  I.   time
  II. wave speed
  III. temperature

(A) I only
(B) II only
(C) I and II only
(D) II and III only
(E) I, II, and III

(Answer: D)

Choose the letter that best answers the question or completes the statement.

1. Which of the following is required to transmit energy using mechanical waves?
  (A) medium   (B) crest
  (C) trough   (D) reflection
  (E) period

2. How are wavelength and frequency related for a wave moving at constant speed?
  (A) Wavelength equals frequency.
  (B) Wavelength is greater than frequency.
  (C) Frequency is greater than wavelength.
  (D) Wavelength is proportional to frequency.
  (E) Wavelength is inversely proportional to frequency.

3. Which of the following statements is generally true for the musical instrument (panpipes) below?

  (A) The longest pipe has the highest pitch.
  (B) The shortest pipe has the highest pitch.
  (C) The pipe in the middle has the highest pitch.
  (D) The pitch cannot be changed.
  (E) Any of the pipes could produce the highest pitch.

4. Which conditions best describe what happens when a transverse wave is reflected?
  (A) Some of a wave does not pass through a boundary or surface.
  (B) A wave enters a new medium at an angle.
  (C) A wave becomes longitudinal.
  (D) A wave combines with another wave.
  (E) A wave interferes with another wave.

5. Which of the following variables can affect the wavelength of a sound wave?
  I.   the medium
  II. the frequency of the wave
  III. the amplitude of the wave

  (A) I only   (B) II only
  (C) I and II only   (D) II and III only
  (E) I, II, and III

6. Ocean waves flow past a concrete support for a bridge. The support is 30 meters wide and it sits in very deep water. Which of the following is LEAST likely to occur?
  (A) The waves will reflect.
  (B) The waves will diffract.
  (C) The waves will lose some energy.
  (D) The waves will continue past the support.
  (E) The waves will refract.

Question	Standards
1	ICP.2.3
2	ICP.2.2
3	ICP.2.3
4	ICP.2.4
5	ICP.2.4
6	ICP.2.4

Planning Guide

SECTION OBJECTIVES	STANDARDS		ACTIVITIES and LABS
	NATIONAL	STATE	
18.1 Electromagnetic Waves, pp. 532–538 ⏱ 1 block or 2 periods **18.1.1 Describe** the characteristics of electromagnetic waves in a vacuum and how Michelson measured the speed of light. **18.1.2 Calculate** the wavelength and frequency of an electromagnetic wave given its speed. **18.1.3 Describe** the evidence for the dual nature of electromagnetic radiation. **18.1.4 Describe** how the intensity of light changes with distance from a light source.	A-1, B-5, B-6, G-1, G-2, G-3	ICP.4.4	**SE** Inquiry Activity: How Do Color Filters Work? p. 531 L2 **TE** Teacher Demo: The Photoelectric Effect, p. 537 L2 **TE** Build Science Skills: Observing, p. 538 L2
18.2 The Electromagnetic Spectrum, pp. 539–545 ⏱ 1 block or 2 periods **18.2.1 Rank** and **classify** electromagnetic waves based on their frequencies and wavelengths. **18.2.2 Describe** the uses for different waves of the electromagnetic spectrum.	A-1, A-2, B-5, B-6, E-1, E-2, F-1, F-5, G-1, G-2, G-3	ICP.4.4	**SE** Quick Lab: Evaluating Sunscreen, p. 544 L2 **TE** Teacher Demo: Radio Reception, p. 541 L2
18.3 Behavior of Light, pp. 546–549 ⏱ 1 block or 2 periods **18.3.1 Classify** materials as transparent, translucent, or opaque to visible light. **18.3.2 Describe** what happens when light is reflected, refracted, polarized, or scattered.	A-1, A-2, B-5, B-6	ICP.4.1, ICP.4.4	**TE** Teacher Demo: Reflected Light and Vision, p. 547 L2 **TE** Build Science Skills: Observing, p. 548 L2 **LM** Investigation 18B: Using Polarized Light to Measure Sugar Concentration L1
18.4 Color, pp. 550–557 ⏱ 1 block or 2 periods **18.4.1 Explain** how a prism disperses white light into different colors. **18.4.2 Analyze** factors that determine the color of an object. **18.4.3 Distinguish** among primary, secondary, and complementary colors of light and of pigments.	A-1, B-5, B-6, E-1, E-2, G-1, G-2, G-3	ICP.4.4	**SE** Exploration Lab: Mixing Colored Lights, p. 563 L2 **TE** Teacher Demo: Overlapping Filters, p. 553 L2 **LM** Investigation 18A: Predicting Spectra L2
18.5 Sources of Light, pp. 558–562 ⏱ 1 block or 2 periods **18.5.1 Explain** how light is produced by common sources of light. **18.5.2 Describe** the uses of different light sources. **18.5.3 Distinguish** lasers from other light sources.	A-1, A-2, B-5, B-6, C-6, E-1, E-2, F-1, F-5, F-6, G-1, G-2, G-3		**SE** Quick Lab: Comparing Fluorescent and Incandescent Light, p. 559 L2 **TE** Build Science Skills: Inferring, p. 561 L2

RESOURCES

PRINT and TECHNOLOGY

RSW Section 18.1 **L1**
RSW Math Skill **L2**
MSPS Section 18.1 **L2**
🖳 **T** Chapter 18 Pretest **L2**
    Section 18.1 **L2**
💿 **P** Chapter 18 Pretest **L2**
    Section 18.1 **L2**
SCiLINKS GO Waves **L2**

RSW Section 18.2 **L1**
MSPS Section 18.2 **L2**
🖳 **T** Section 18.2 **L2**
💿 **P** Section 18.2 **L2**
SCiLINKS GO Electromagnetic spectrum **L2**

RSW Section 18.3 **L1**
🖳 **T** Section 18.3 **L2**
💿 **P** Section 18.3 **L2**

RSW Section 18.4 **L1**
DC Finding the Fakes **L2**
🖳 **T** Section 18.4 **L2**
💿 **P** Section 18.4 **L2**
SCiLINKS GO Color **L2**

RSW Section 18.5 **L1**
🖳 **T** Section 18.5 **L2**
💿 **P** Section 18.5 **L2**
SCIENCE NEWS GO Light and optics **L2**

SECTION ASSESSMENT

SE Section 18.1 Assessment, p. 538
iT Section 18.1

SE Section 18.2 Assessment, p. 545
iT Section 18.2

SE Section 18.3 Assessment, p. 549
iT Section 18.3

SE Section 18.4 Assessment, p. 553
iT Section 18.4

SE Section 18.5 Assessment, p. 562
iT Section 18.5

Go Online

Go online for these Internet resources.

PHSchool.com
  Web Code: cca-2180

SCIENCE NEWS
  Web Code: cce-2185

NSTA SCiLINKS
  Web Code: ccn-2181
  Web Code: ccn-2182
  Web Code: ccn-2184

Materials for Activities and Labs

Quantities for each group

STUDENT EDITION

Inquiry Activity, p. 531
cardboard with slit, light source, prism, white paper, filters (red, green, blue), colored markers

Quick Lab, p. 544
2 black paper strips, 2 petri dishes, 12 ultraviolet-detecting beads, sunscreen, clock/watch with second hand

Quick Lab, p. 559
spectroscope, clear incandescent bulb, fluorescent bulb, colored pencils

Exploration Lab, p. 563
light source (red, blue, green), tape, large sheet of white paper

TEACHER'S EDITION

Teacher Demo, p. 537
electroscope, zinc strip, rubber rod, wool, incandescent and UV light sources

Build Science Skills, p. 538
low-wattage bulb, light source

Teacher Demo, p. 541
portable radio with antenna, cardboard or wooden box, chicken wire

Teacher Demo, p. 547
wooden or cardboard box with removable top, white paper

Build Science Skills, p. 548
2 polarizing filters, light source

Teacher Demo, p. 553
2 overhead projectors; red, green, and blue acetate filters

Build Science Skills, p. 556
paints (acrylic, watercolor, oil), artist brushes, watercolor paper, hand lens, flat, wooden sticks

Build Science Skills, p. 561
spectroscope, neon lights

Chapter Assessment

CHAPTER ASSESSMENT

SE Chapter Assessment, pp. 565–566
CUT Chapter 18 Test A, B
CTB Chapter 18
iT Chapter 18
PHSchool.com GO
Web Code: cca-2180

STANDARDIZED TEST PREP

SE Chapter 18, p. 567
TP Diagnose and Prescribe

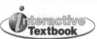

Interactive Textbook with assessment at PHSchool.com

Before you teach

From the Author

Sophia Yancopoulos
Manhattan College

Big Ideas

In studying light and electromagnetic waves, students must first understand that the electromagnetic spectrum extends far beyond the visible light seen by the unaided eye.

Space and Time Because it travels so fast, light is used as a "yardstick" to measure distances to the stars. We map our universe using light, probing the beginnings of time by using the entire electromagnetic spectrum. The afterglow of the big bang can be detected as background radiation of microwaves.

The challenge in measuring the speed of light is that it travels large distances in times too short to be easily measured. Using lanterns, Galileo tried to measure the speed of light from one mountaintop to another, and failed because light traveled back and forth in less time than it took to cover and uncover his lantern.

Forces and Motion Light in the form of electromagnetic waves behaves in many different ways: It can be reflected, refracted, polarized, scattered, and even interfere with itself. For the most part, however, light moves in a straight line at a constant speed, believed to be the ultimate speed in our universe. Uninterrupted, light can travel billions of years through space. However, as Einstein proved in his theory of general relativity, gravity affects light. The sun, neutron stars, and other concentrated matter can bend light from its straight path.

Matter and Energy Some students think of the world as entirely made up of matter. The world is made of both matter and energy, however, and the two interact. Photons can either be absorbed or emitted when interacting with matter. Light's interaction with matter in the photoelectric effect helped Einstein understand the particle nature of light.

Due to its dual particle-wave nature, we all experience difficulty in understanding the nature of light. Reassure students that this discomfort is part of the process of learning science.

Physics Refresher

Electromagnetic Waves 18.1

Isaac Newton analyzed light in terms of mechanical particles, not photons. Einstein showed that the photoelectric effect could be explained if light consisted of photons, each with energy

$$E = hf$$

where h is Planck's constant (6.61×10^{-34} J·s) and f is frequency. Higher-frequency photons have more energy. In the photoelectric effect, there is a threshold frequency below which photons do not have enough energy to eject electrons. But the rate at which electrons are emitted also depends on intensity.

Electromagnetic Spectrum 18.2

All electromagnetic waves travel at the same speed, c, in empty space. However, their speed through a medium depends on the medium and on the frequency of the wave.

An accelerating charge produces time-varying electric and magnetic fields. For radio waves, the accelerating charge can be a current oscillating back and forth in an antenna. The vibrations of atoms and molecules in heated matter result in the emission of infrared waves. Visible light and ultraviolet light generally result from transitions between different excited states of atoms and molecules. The energy of the photon emitted from an atomic or molecular electronic transition equals the difference in the energy levels.

> **Address Misconceptions**
>
> *All electromagnetic waves travel at the same speed in all media.* If true, then light would not refract when passed through a prism. For a strategy to overcome this misconception, see **Address Misconceptions** on **page 543**.

Behavior of Light 18.3

Reflection is a complex process that depends on the frequency of light and on the surface characteristics of a material.

The ratio of the speed of light in a vacuum to the speed of light in a medium is the medium's index of refraction, $n = c/v$.

For: Teaching methods for the electromagnetic spectrum and light
Visit: www.SciLinks.org/PDLinks
Web Code: ccn-1899

The index of refraction is used in Snell's law to relate the angle of incidence, θ_1, to the angle of refraction, θ_2.

$$n_1 \sin \theta_1 = n_2 \sin \theta_2$$

In this equation, n_1 is the first medium's index of refraction and n_2 is the second medium's index of refraction. If $n_1 < n_2$, the light beam refracts toward the normal, as shown in the figure below.

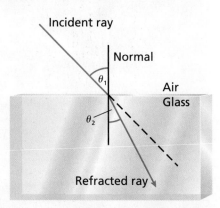

Students may wonder how an electromagnetic wave can be polarized in one plane if the electric and magnetic fields are at right angles to each other. The answer is that physicists determine the polarization of an electromagnetic wave by looking only at its electric field, as shown in the figure below.

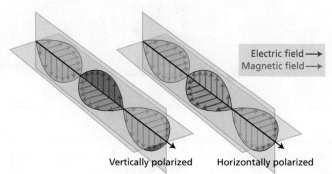

Color 18.4 and 18.5

Each frequency of light is perceived by the human eye as a particular color, but what the human eye perceives as a color may consist of many different combinations of frequencies. An example is the light from a fluorescent light bulb, which consists of a mixture of

distinct emission lines. Different sources of light differ in the mixture of frequencies they produce. A tungsten filament, the sun, and a heated object all emit electromagnetic radiation. The peak emission frequency increases as the temperature increases. For hot objects on Earth, the emitted radiation is mostly red and infrared. A tungsten filament at 2800 K also emits light from the entire visible spectrum, and so the light appears white.

Build Reading Literacy

SQ3R

Survey, Question, Read, Recite, and Review

Strategy Help students read material that contains technical information, diagrams, and figures. This strategy helps students focus on the main points in a section, making it easier for them to remember what they have read. Before students begin, assign a section in the textbook for them to read such as The Waves of the Spectrum, pp. 539–540.

Example

1. S Have students **survey** the entire assignment and look at the headings, material in boldface and italics, and chapter summary. Have them write a short explanation of what they see in each diagram, photo, graph, or chart.

2. Q Have students write **questions** they will answer when they complete their survey. They should turn each heading into a question and leave room below it for the answer.

3. R Have students **read** the section and look for the answers to their questions.

4. R When students finish reading, tell them to think about what they read. They should **recite** the questions they wrote and—using their own words—give the answers they found. If students can't answer a question, have them reread the material for the related heading, looking more carefully to find the answer.

5. R Have students **review** the section by writing the answers they recited. Finally, refer students to the key concepts questions on the first page of the section. Have students answer each of these questions.

See p. 560 for a script on how to use the SQ3R strategy with students. For additional Build Reading Literacy strategies, see pp. 534, 539, 546, and 552.

CHAPTER **18** **The Electromagnetic Spectrum and Light**

ASSESS PRIOR KNOWLEDGE

Use the Chapter Pretest below to assess students' prior knowledge. As needed, review these Science Concepts and Math Skills with students.

Review Science Concepts

Section 18.1 Review electric and magnetic forces. Remind students that mechanical waves require a medium. Review wavelength, frequency, and the wave equation. Remind students how the intensity of sound waves varies with distance from the source.

Section 18.2 Encourage students to recall what they have learned about radiation, thermal energy, and infrared rays. Ask students to think of other electromagnetic waves they have encountered in earlier chapters.

Section 18.3 Encourage students to review behaviors of mechanical waves.

Sections 18.4 and 18.5 Review atomic models if chemistry has been taught. Review conservation of energy and remind students that the colors produced in emission spectra are related to energy transitions in atoms.

Review Math Skills

Scientific Notation, Exponents, Formulas and Equations
Students will need to multiply and divide exponents to solve equations with wavelength and frequency.

Direct students to the **Math Skills** in the **Skills and Reference Handbook** at the end of the student text.

21st Century Learning
Health Literacy

What are the health risks of radiation?

As you read this page, you are being bombarded by radiation from the sun and distant stars, as well as from rocks deep in the ground beneath your feet. Although radiation is a natural part of your world, too much exposure to certain types of radiation can be harmful. Visit the Web site of the Environmental Protection Agency and search for information on radiation exposure. Create a short video or digital presentation to explain radiation risks to someone without a background in science.

Indiana's Academic Standards for Science

ENERGY TRANSPORT
ICP.4.4: Describe the relationships between velocity, frequency, wavelength, and energy in electromagnetic waves. Describe the regions of the electromagnetic spectrum.

MECHANICAL ENERGY AND PROPAGATION OF ENERGY BY WAVES
ICP.2.4: Apply the properties of waves to wave phenomena including reflection, and refraction, as well as the transmission and loss of energy.

Colorful neon lights brighten up a walkway in Chicago's O'Hare Airport.

530 Chapter 18

Chapter Pretest

1. How are electric and magnetic forces related? *(They are two aspects of the same force.)*
2. Can a mechanical wave move through a vacuum? Explain. *(No, a mechanical wave is transmitted by matter.)*
3. What is the equation that relates wave speed, wavelength, and frequency? *(Wave speed = Wavelength × Frequency)*

4. If 3.0×10^7 people share a tax refund of 2.0×10^6 dollars, how much money does each person get? *($0.07 per person)*
5. True or False: An object radiates more energy at higher temperatures. *(True)*
6. If intensity equals x at 10 meters from an ambulance siren, what is the intensity at 20 meters from an ambulance siren? *(b)*
    a. $4x$ **b.** $0.25x$
    c. $2x$ **d.** $0.5x$

7. A refracted wave can do which of the following? *(d)*
    a. Slow down   **b.** Speed up
    c. Bend   **d.** All of the above
8. Electromagnetic energy can be converted into which of the following? *(d)*
    a. Chemical energy
    b. Mechanical energy
    c. Thermal energy
    d. All of the above

Chapter Preview

Discovery CHANNEL SCHOOL

Video Field Trip

Finding the Fakes

Inquiry Activity

How Do Color Filters Work?

Procedure

1. Place a piece of cardboard that has a slit cut into it in sunlight so that a beam of light passes through the slit. **CAUTION** *Never look directly at the sun.*

2. Create a rainbow by positioning a prism in the beam of light that has passed through the slit. Project the rainbow onto white paper.

3. Use colored markers to draw the colors in the order in which they appear on the paper.

4. Replace the paper. Place a red filter between the slit and the prism and draw the colors you see projected onto the paper.

5. Repeat Step 4 with a blue filter and then with a green filter.

Think About It

1. **Inferring** What happens to sunlight when it passes through a prism?

2. **Observing** Which colors did you see projected onto the paper while using each filter? Which colors didn't you see while using each filter?

3. **Drawing Conclusions** What can you conclude about what happens to sunlight as it passes through a filter?

The Electromagnetic Spectrum and Light **531**

Discovery CHANNEL SCHOOL

Video Field Trip

Finding the Fakes

Encourage students to view the Video Field Trip "Finding the Fakes."

ENGAGE/EXPLORE

Inquiry Activity

How Do Color Filters Work?

Purpose In this activity, students begin to determine that white light contains other colors of light.

 Address Misconceptions

Students may think that colored filters change white light into colored light or that white light is a single color. Challenge these misconceptions by asking students to explain their observations in this activity.

Skills Focus Observing, Inferring

Prep Time 10 minutes

Materials cardboard with slit, light source, prism, white paper, filters (red, green, blue), colored markers

Advance Prep Cut narrow slits (about 0.5×7.0 cm) in sheets of cardboard (one per group).

Class Time 10 minutes

Safety Students should never look at the sun through a prism. Do not use prisms that have sharp or chipped edges. Advise students to handle prisms carefully and review safety procedures for broken glass.

Teaching Tips
- If sunlight is not available, use an overhead or slide projector.
- Each group can use one filter at a time and then trade filters.
- For best results, fold colored cellophane several times.

Expected Outcome Primary-color filters will block all other colors in the rainbow. Non-primary color filters allow two or more colors to pass through.

Think About It

1. Students may infer that sunlight contains other colors. A prism makes the colors visible by separating them.

2. Red filters subtract all colors except red. Blue filters block all colors except blue. Only green light passes through a green filter. Secondary-color filters allow more than one color to pass through.

3. A filter allows some colors to pass through and blocks all other colors.

Visual, Group

1 FOCUS

Objectives

18.1.1 Describe the characteristics of electromagnetic waves in a vacuum and how Michelson measured the speed of light.

18.1.2 Calculate the wavelength and frequency of an electromagnetic wave given its speed.

18.1.3 Describe the evidence for the dual nature of electromagnetic radiation.

18.1.4 Describe how the intensity of light changes with distance from a light source.

Reading Focus

Build Vocabulary   L2

Word-Part Analysis Ask students what words they know that have the key word parts *electro, magnet,* and *photo.* (*electricity, magnet,* and *photograph*) Give a definition of each word part. (*Electro* means *"shining," magnet* means *"attracting like material,"* and *photo* means *"light."*) Give additional examples that share the word parts in question (*electron, magnetism, photocopy*).

Reading Strategy   L2

a. B **b.** E **c.** B **d.** M

18.1 Electromagnetic Waves

 Standard: ICP.4.4

Reading Focus

Key Concepts

- How are electromagnetic waves different from mechanical waves?
- What is the maximum speed of light?
- How do electromagnetic waves differ from one another?
- What is the dual nature of electromagnetic radiation?
- What happens as light travels farther from its source?

Vocabulary

- electromagnetic waves
- electric field
- magnetic field
- electromagnetic radiation
- photoelectric effect
- photons
- intensity

Reading Strategy

Comparing and Contrasting Copy the table below. As you read about electromagnetic waves, fill in the table to compare them with mechanical waves. Use E for properties of electromagnetic waves, M for mechanical waves, and B for both.

Travels through vacuum	E
Travels through medium	a. ?
Fits wave model	B
Fits particle model	b. ?
Transverse wave	c. ?
Longitudinal wave	d. ?

What do X-ray machines, microwave ovens, and heat lamps have in common with police radar, television, and radiation therapy? They all use waves. You are surrounded by such waves all the time. But you may not realize it, because most waves are invisible.

With X-rays, you can take pictures of your bones. Your dentist uses X-rays to examine the inner structure of your teeth. Microwaves cook or reheat your meals and carry cell phone conversations between you and your friends. Radio waves bring your favorite music to your radio from the radio station. Ultraviolet rays can give you a sunburn. Without waves, the girl in Figure 1 wouldn't be able to talk with her friends on a cell phone. Without waves, you wouldn't be able to watch your favorite TV show. You wouldn't be able to see colors. In fact, without waves you wouldn't be able to see anything at all.

Figure 1 The waves that carry this girl's cell phone conversation are not visible. The girl may not even know they exist. But their existence is what makes cell phone technology possible.

 532 *Chapter 18*

Section Resources

Print

- **Reading and Study Workbook With Math Support,** Section 18.1 and **Math Skill:** Calculating Wavelength and Frequency
- **Math Skills and Problem Solving Workbook,** Section 18.1
- **Transparencies,** Chapter Pretest and Section 18.1

Technology

- **Interactive Textbook,** Section 18.1
- **Presentation Pro CD-ROM,** Chapter Pretest and Section 18.1
- **Go Online,** NSTA SciLinks, Waves

Electric field

Magnetic field

Direction of wave

Figure 2 Electromagnetic waves consist of changing electric fields and magnetic fields. The fields are at right angles to each other and to the direction of the wave. **Interpreting Diagrams** *How can you tell that electromagnetic waves are transverse waves?*

What Are Electromagnetic Waves?

The visible and invisible waves you will learn about in this chapter exhibit some of the same behaviors as mechanical waves. Other behaviors are unique to electromagnetic waves. **Electromagnetic waves** are transverse waves consisting of changing electric fields and changing magnetic fields. Like mechanical waves, electromagnetic waves carry energy from place to place. Electromagnetic waves differ from mechanical waves in how they are produced and how they travel.

How They Are Produced Electromagnetic waves are produced by constantly changing fields. An **electric field** in a region of space exerts electric forces on charged particles. Electric fields are produced by electrically charged particles and by changing magnetic fields. A **magnetic field** in a region of space produces magnetic forces. Magnetic fields are produced by magnets, by changing electric fields, and by vibrating charges. ◉ **Electromagnetic waves are produced when an electric charge vibrates or accelerates.** Figure 2 shows that the fields are at right angles to each other. You can tell this is a transverse wave because the fields are also at right angles to the direction in which the wave travels.

How They Travel Because changing electric fields produce changing magnetic fields, and changing magnetic fields produce changing electric fields, the fields regenerate each other. As the fields regenerate, their energy travels in the form of a wave. Unlike mechanical waves, electromagnetic waves do not need a medium. ◉ **Electromagnetic waves can travel through a vacuum, or empty space, as well as through matter.** The transfer of energy by electromagnetic waves traveling through matter or across space is called **electromagnetic radiation**.

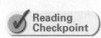

Reading Checkpoint   *What are electromagnetic waves?*

For: Links on waves
Visit: www.SciLinks.org
Web Code: ccn-2181

The Electromagnetic Spectrum and Light **533**

2 INSTRUCT

What Are Electromagnetic Waves?
Use Visuals   L1

Figure 2 Emphasize that an electromagnetic (EM) wave consists of both an electric field and a magnetic field. Have students note that the electric field and magnetic field vibrate in planes that are perpendicular to each other (shown by the yellow areas). Ask, **In which direction is the EM wave in the figure traveling?** *(To the right)* **In which direction are the disturbances in the electric and magnetic fields traveling?** *(Perpendicular to the direction of the EM wave)* **Why can't the electric field wave exist without the magnetic field wave?** *(Each field produces the other—if one is present so must be the other.)* **How is the EM wave different from a wave traveling along a rope? How are they the same?** *(The EM wave does not need a medium to travel through, whereas the wave in the rope could not exist if the rope were not present. Also, the EM wave is made up of electric and magnetic waves, whereas the wave in the rope has a single component. Both waves are transverse waves.)*
Visual

Download a worksheet on waves for students to complete, and find additional teacher support from NSTA SciLinks.

Customize for English Language Learners

Simplify the Presentation
The large number of vocabulary words in this section is a challenge to an English language learner. Help ease the challenge by tailoring your teaching presentation of the section content to the less-proficient English skills of your students. Do this by speaking directly and simplifying the words and sentence structures used to explain the material. Use body language when appropriate to emphasize important words. Restate complicated sentences into shorter phrases that make use of more common words.

Answer to . . .

Figure 2 *They are transverse because their fields are at right angles to the direction in which they are traveling.*

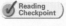 Reading Checkpoint   *Electromagnetic waves are transverse waves consisting of changing electric fields and changing magnetic fields.*

The Speed of Electromagnetic Waves

Build Reading Literacy L1

Sequence Refer to page **290D** in **Chapter 10**, which provides the guidelines for a sequence.

Have students read the text on page 534 related to Michelson's experiment. Then, have students do the following:

1. Create a sketch of Michelson's experimental setup as shown in Figure 3. The sketch should include all labels shown in Figure 3.
2. Number and describe the steps the light follows on its path through the experimental setup. Students should start with the light emitted by the light source as Step 1.
3. Student sketches should include as much detail as they can find in the text, Figure 3, and its caption.

Visual, Portfolio

FYI

Michelson's work earned him a Nobel Prize in Physics, the first ever awarded to an American.

The Speed of Electromagnetic Waves

A thunderstorm is approaching. The sky is dark, and lightning flashes in the distance. Within a few seconds, you hear thunder's low rumble. As the storm approaches, the lightning gets brighter and the thunder louder. The lightning flashes and the sound of thunder come closer in time. Still, you see the lightning before you hear the thunder, because light travels faster than sound. But how much faster is light?

Michelson's Experiment In ancient times, people tried to measure the speed of light but no instrument was accurate enough. Light moves so fast that people thought its speed was infinite. Several experiments in the 1800s proved it was not infinite and gave approximate values. Then, in 1926, the American physicist Albert Michelson (1852–1931) measured the speed of light more accurately than ever before.

Figure 3 shows an experimental setup similar to Michelson's. On top of Mount Wilson in California, Michelson placed an eight-sided rotating mirror. He placed another mirror, this one stationary, on Mount San Antonio, 35.4 kilometers away. Michelson shined a bright light at one face of the rotating mirror. The light reflected to the stationary mirror on the other mountain and then back to Mount Wilson, where it struck another face of the rotating mirror. Michelson knew how fast the eight-sided mirror was rotating and how far the light traveled from mountain to mountain and back again. With those values he was able to calculate the speed of light quite accurately. His findings were similar to modern measurements.

The Speed of Light Since Michelson, many other scientists have measured the speed of light. Their experiments have confirmed that light and all electromagnetic waves travel at the same speed when in a vacuum, regardless of the observer's motion. 🌐 **The speed of light in a vacuum, c, is 3.00×10^8 meters per second.**

Figure 3 Michelson timed a light beam as it traveled from one mountain to another and back again. His experiment measured the speed of light more accurately than it had been measured before. **Inferring** *Why must the light beam travel so far for its speed to be measurable?*

Mt. San Antonio

Mirror

35.4 km

Light source

Octagonal rotating mirror

Telescope

Mt. Wilson

534 *Chapter 18*

Facts and Figures

Speed of Light Due to the definition of the meter, the speed of light has an exact value. The meter is defined as the distance light travels in a vacuum in $\frac{1}{299,752,458}$ of a second. Thus, the speed of light has an exact value of 299,792,458 m/s.

To imagine the speed of light, consider driving non-stop at 60 miles per hour from New York City to San Francisco. This trip would take you about 50 hours (a little more than two days). Light travels this distance in less than two-hundredths of a second (0.02 second).

Wavelength and Frequency

In a vacuum, all electromagnetic waves travel at the same speed. But not all electromagnetic waves are the same. ◉ **Electromagnetic waves vary in wavelength and frequency.**

The speed of an electromagnetic wave is the product of its wavelength and its frequency. Because the speed of electromagnetic waves in a vacuum is constant, the wavelength is inversely proportional to the frequency. As the wavelength increases, the frequency decreases. If you know the wavelength of an electromagnetic wave, you can calculate its frequency.

 Math Skills

Calculating Wave Speed
A radio station broadcasts a radio wave with a wavelength of 3.0 meters. What is the frequency of the wave?

❶ Read and Understand
What information are you given?

$$\text{Speed} = c = 3.00 \times 10^8 \text{ m/s}$$

$$\text{Wavelength} = 3.0 \text{ m}$$

❷ Plan and Solve
What unknown are you trying to calculate?

$$\text{Frequency} = ?$$

What formula contains the given quantities and the unknown?

$$\text{Speed} = \text{Wavelength} \times \text{Frequency}$$

$$or, \ \text{Frequency} = \frac{\text{Speed}}{\text{Wavelength}}$$

Replace each variable with its known value.

$$\text{Frequency} = \frac{3.00 \times 10^8 \text{ m/s}}{3.0 \text{ m}}$$

$$= 1.0 \times 10^8 \text{ Hz}$$

❸ Look Back and Check
Is your answer reasonable?

Check that product of wavelength and frequency gives a speed of 3.0×10^8 m/s.

$$\text{Speed} = 3.0 \text{ m} \times (1.0 \times 10^8 \text{ Hz}) = 3.0 \times 10^8 \text{ m/s}$$

 Math Practice

1. A global positioning satellite transmits a radio wave with a wavelength of 19 cm. What is the frequency of the radio wave? (*Hint:* Convert the wavelength to meters before calculating the frequency.)

2. The radio waves of a particular AM radio station vibrate 680,000 times per second. What is the wavelength of the wave?

3. Radio waves that vibrate 160,000,000 times per second are used on some train lines for communications. If radio waves that vibrate half as many times per second were used instead, how would the wavelength change?

The Electromagnetic Spectrum and Light **535**

Wave or Particle?
Use Visuals L1

Figure 5 Have students observe the pattern the light makes on each of the three cards shown. Ask, **Why are there no interference patterns on the card with two slits?** *(For interference patterns to occur, there must be at least two overlapping wave sources. The vertical slit in the first card provides only a single light source to illuminate the second card.)* **Why does the double-slit card produce an interference pattern?** *(Each slit acts as a source of light waves. As the light waves spread from each source, they overlap and create interference.)* **What occurs between the areas of maximum brightness and maximum darkness?** *(Partial interference occurs, resulting in areas of brightness between the two extremes.)*
Visual, Logical

FYI

A diffraction grating uses diffraction and interference to create a rainbow. At each angle of transmission, only certain frequencies interfere constructively.

Figure 4 The fact that light casts a shadow has been used as evidence for both the wave model of light and the particle model of light.

Figure 5 This diagram illustrates Young's experiment, which showed that light behaves like a wave. When light passes through a single slit and then a double slit, it produces an interference pattern. Constructive interference produces bright bands of light. Destructive interference produces dark bands.
Predicting *What would you expect to see on the screen if light behaved like a stream of particles?*

Wave or Particle?

Scientists know that electromagnetic radiation travels as a wave. Scientists also have evidence that electromagnetic radiation behaves like a stream of particles. In the late 1600s, the English physicist Isaac Newton was the first to propose a particle explanation. He based this hypothesis on two pieces of evidence: light travels in a straight line and it casts a shadow, as shown in Figure 4. But not all evidence supports Newton's hypothesis. So which is light, wave or particle? It is both. ⬤ **Electromagnetic radiation behaves sometimes like a wave and sometimes like a stream of particles.**

Evidence for the Wave Model In 1801, the English physicist Thomas Young (1773–1829) showed that light behaves like a wave. Look at Figure 5. Young passed a beam of light first through a single slit and then through a double slit. Where light from the two slits reached a darkened screen, Young observed alternating bright and dark bands. The bands were evidence that the light had produced an interference pattern. Bright bands indicated constructive interference, and dark bands indicated destructive interference. Interference occurs only when two or more waves overlap. Therefore, Young's experiment showed that light behaves like a wave.

Reading Checkpoint *What is the evidence that light travels like a wave?*

Interference pattern appears on screen.

Card with two slits

Dark bands show destructive interference.

Bright bands show constructive interference.

Card with one slit

Light source

Light from single slit produces coherent light at second card.

A No electrons are emitted.

Bright
red light
or
infrared rays

Metal
plate

B Electrons are emitted.

Dim blue light
or
ultraviolet
rays

Metal
plate

Figure 6 The emissions of electrons from a metal caused by light striking the metal is called the photoelectric effect. **A** Red light or infrared rays, no matter how bright, does not cause electrons to be emitted from this metal surface. **B** When blue light or ultraviolet rays strike the metal surface, electrons are emitted, even if the light is dim.

Evidence for the Particle Model When dim blue light hits the surface of a metal such as cesium, an electron is emitted. A brighter blue light causes even more electrons to be emitted, as you can see in Figure 6. But red light, no matter how bright it is, does not cause the emission of any electrons in this particular metal.

The emission of electrons from a metal caused by light striking the metal is called the **photoelectric effect.** Discovered in 1887, the photoelectric effect was puzzling. Scientists did not understand why dim blue light caused electrons to be emitted from metal but even bright red light did not.

In 1905, Albert Einstein (1879–1955) proposed that light, and all electromagnetic radiation, consists of packets of energy. These packets of electromagnetic energy are now called **photons** (FOH tawnz). Each photon's energy is proportional to the frequency of the light. The greater the frequency of an electromagnetic wave, the more energy each of its photons has.

Blue light has a higher frequency than red light, so photons of blue light have more energy than photons of red light. Blue light consists of photons that have enough energy to cause electrons to be emitted from a metal surface. So blue light can cause emission of electrons.

Red light has a lower frequency than blue light, so photons of red light have less energy than photons of blue light. Red light consists of photons that have too little energy to cause any electrons to be emitted from a metal surface. So red light does not cause emission of electrons.

 What is the photoelectric effect?

FYI

Photons, which are electrically neutral, have a "rest mass" of zero. Technically, however, all photons have energy, and thus all photons have mass. The energy of an individual photon is given by the equation

$$E = hf$$

In this equation, h is Planck's constant (6.6×10^{-34} J•s), and f is the frequency of the photon. The equation shows that as the frequency of the photon increases, so does its energy. This is why higher-frequency, higher-energy blue light is able to produce the photoelectric effect shown in Figure 6B, whereas the lower-frequency, lower-energy red light is not.

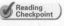

Intensity
Build Science Skills

L2

Observing

Purpose Students observe light intensity.

Materials low-wattage incandescent bulb, light source

Class Time 10 minutes

Procedure Darken the room and turn on the bulb. Ask for several volunteers to walk around the room and observe if the light coming from the bulb can be seen in all parts of the room. Also, have them note the brightness of the bulb at various distances from the bulb.

Expected Outcome Students will observe that the light from the bulb will radiate out in all directions. They also will observe that the brightness of the light decreases as students move farther from the bulb. **Visual, Kinesthetic, Group**

3 ASSESS

Evaluate Understanding

L2

Have students write three math problems (with solutions) based on the frequency-wavelength formula. Have them analyze and solve the problems in class.

Reteach

L1

Use Figure 2 to summarize the key features of an electromagnetic wave.

 Math **Practice**

Solutions

9. Wavelength = Speed/Frequency = $(3.00 \times 10^8$ m/s)/(810,000 Hz) = 370 m

10. Wavelength = Speed/Frequency = $(3.00 \times 10^8$ m/s)/(1.575×10^9 Hz) = 0.190 m

 If your class subscribes to the Interactive Textbook, use it to review key concepts in Section 18.1.

Answer to . . .

Figure 7 *As the can moves farther from the surface, the area the paint covers becomes larger, but less intense. The same happens when light shines on a surface.*

Figure 7 The closer you are to a surface when you spray paint it, the smaller the area the paint covers and the more intense the paint color looks. **Using Models** *How does a can of spray paint help you model a change in light intensity?*

Intensity

The closer you are to a source of light, the brighter the light appears. If you want to read at night, you must sit near a lamp. At night, as you walk away from a street light, the area around you becomes darker. A street light doesn't give off less light when you move farther from it. It just provides you with less light the farther away you are. Photons travel outward from a light source in all directions. Near the light source, the photons spread through a small area, so the light is intense. **Intensity** is the rate at which a wave's energy flows through a given unit of area. You can think of intensity as brightness. Farther from the source, the photons spread over a larger area. ⊙ **The intensity of light decreases as photons travel farther from the source.**

A can of spray paint can help you model a change in light intensity. Look at Figure 7. When the nozzle is close to a piece of paper, the paint forms a small, dense spot. When the nozzle is farther from the paper, the paint forms a larger, fainter spot because the paint is sprayed over a larger area. Like paint on paper, light intensity decreases as distance from the light source increases.

A wave model for light also explains how intensity decreases with distance from a source. As waves travel away from the source, they pass through a larger and larger area. Because the total energy does not change, the wave's intensity decreases.

Section 18.1 Assessment

Reviewing Concepts

1. ⊙ What produces electromagnetic waves?
2. ⊙ How fast does light travel in a vacuum?
3. ⊙ What makes electromagnetic waves different from one another?
4. ⊙ Explain how light behaves like a stream of particles.
5. ⊙ What happens to the intensity of light as photons move away from the light source?
6. How does photon energy relate to frequency?

Critical Thinking

7. **Applying Concepts** Why does blue light cause emission of electrons from metal while red light does not?

8. **Observing** Describe what happens as you get closer to a light source. Explain this observation.

 Math **Practice**

9. What is the wavelength of an AM radio wave in a vacuum if its frequency is 810 kilohertz?
10. A global positioning satellite (GPS) transmits a signal at a frequency of 1575 megahertz. What is the wavelength? (*Hint:* Assume the wave speed is the same as in a vacuum.)

Section 18.1   Assessment

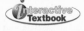

1. The acceleration or vibration of an electric charge produces EM waves.
2. 3.00×10^8 m/s.
3. They vary in wavelength and frequency.
4. Red light photons do not cause electrons to be ejected from a particular metal as blue light photons can.
5. As photons move away from the light source, the intensity decreases.

6. The greater the frequency of an electromagnetic wave, the more energy each of its photons has.
7. Photons of blue light have more energy than photons of red light.
8. The closer you get to a light source, the brighter the light appears because its photons have not spread out as much.

18.2 The Electromagnetic Spectrum

Standard: ICP.4.4

Reading Focus

Key Concepts
- What waves are included in the electromagnetic spectrum?
- How is each type of electromagnetic wave used?

Vocabulary
- electromagnetic spectrum
- amplitude modulation
- frequency modulation
- thermograms

Reading Strategy
Summarizing Copy the chart below and add four more rows to complete the table for the electromagnetic spectrum. After you read, list at least two uses for each kind of wave.

Type of Waves	Uses	
Radio Waves	Communications	a. ?
Infrared Rays	b. ?	Keeping food warm

How do you investigate something that is invisible? First you have to suspect that it exists. Then you have to figure out a way to detect what is invisible and collect data about it. Such was the way the German-born astronomer William Herschel (1738–1822) discovered infrared radiation.

The Waves of the Spectrum

In England in 1800, with a technique discovered earlier, Herschel used a prism to separate the wavelengths present in sunlight. He produced a band of colors: red, orange, yellow, green, blue, and violet. He wondered if the temperature of each color of light was different from the temperature of the other colors of light. As you can see in Figure 8, Herschel placed thermometers at various places along the color band and measured the temperatures. Herschel observed that the temperature was lower at the blue end and higher toward the red end.

This discovery made Herschel pose a new question: Would the temperature increase even more beyond the red end, in an area that showed no color? He measured the temperature just beyond the red end of the color band. This area recorded an even higher temperature than the red area. Herschel concluded there must be invisible radiation beyond the red end of the color band.

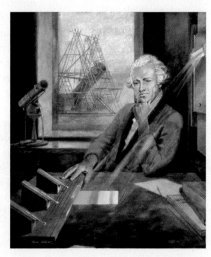

Figure 8 Herschel measured the temperature of different colors of light. The temperature was lowest at the blue end and highest at the red end. Curiosity led Herschel to discover evidence of radiation past the red end of the band of visible light.

The Electromagnetic Spectrum and Light **539**

Section Resources

Print
- **Reading and Study Workbook With Math Support,** Section 18.2
- **Math Skills and Problem Solving Workbook,** Section 18.2
- **Transparencies,** Section 18.2

Technology
- **Interactive Textbook,** Section 18.2
- **Presentation Pro CD-ROM,** Section 18.2
- **Go Online,** NSTA SciLinks, Electromagnetic spectrum

---

1 FOCUS

Objectives
18.2.1 Rank and **classify** electromagnetic waves based on their frequencies and wavelengths.
18.2.2 Describe the uses for different waves of the electromagnetic spectrum.

Reading Focus

Build Vocabulary

LINCS Have students: **L**ist the parts that they know (for example, define *thermogram*). **I**magine a picture (create a mental picture of a thermogram). **N**ote a sound-alike word *(thermometer)*. **C**onnect the terms (make up a short story about thermograms that uses the sound-alike word, *thermometer*). **S**elf-test (quiz themselves).

Reading Strategy
a. Cooking and radar detection systems
b. Detecting heat differences
Additional rows Visible Light: aids in vision and communication; Ultraviolet Rays: health (kill microorganisms in heating and cooling systems), agriculture (energy source to promote plant growth); X-rays: medicine, transportation (inspection tool); Gamma Rays: medicine (kill cancer cells, form images of the brain), industry (inspection tool)

2 INSTRUCT

The Waves of the Spectrum
Build Reading Literacy

Outline Refer to page **156D** in **Chapter 6**, which provides the guidelines for an outline.

Have students outline pp. 539–545. Outlines should follow the heading structure used in the section. Major headings are in green, and subheadings are in blue. Ask, **Based on your outline, what are television waves, microwaves, and radar waves classified as?** *(Types of radio waves)*
Verbal, Logical

FYI

In the Herschel experiment, in theory, waves at the blue end of the spectrum should have more energy than waves at the red end because blue light has a higher frequency than red light. The reason the red is warmer is that a prism does not separate the colors equally. The red light is concentrated into a smaller area than the blue light.

Radio Waves

Use Visuals L1

Figure 9 Emphasize that although the EM waves shown all have different frequencies and wavelengths, they all travel at 3.00×10^8 m/s when in a vacuum. Ask, **In the electromagnetic spectrum, as wavelength decreases, what happens to frequency?** *(Frequency increases.)* **What is the product of any EM wave's frequency and its wavelength in a vacuum?** *(The speed of light, c, or 3.00×10^8 m/s.)* **Which color in the visible spectrum has the highest frequency?** *(Violet light)* **The longest wavelength?** *(Red light)* **Visual, Logical**

Build Science Skills L3

Observing Assign groups of students to carry small AM/FM radios around to various parts of their community and listen to the reception quality of both AM and FM signals. Select specific AM and FM radio stations for students to listen to. Ask students to rate the quality of the reception on a scale from 1 to 10, where 1 is very poor reception and 10 is excellent reception. Also have students describe the physical surroundings where each observation is made. Ask, **Which type of radio signal is more affected by the location of the radio?** *(FM)* **What can you infer from your observations about the relative abilities of AM and FM waves to bend around obstacles?** *(AM radio waves are better at moving around obstacles.)* **Visual, Kinesthetic, Group**

Download a worksheet on the electromagnetic spectrum for students to complete, and find additional teacher support from NSTA SciLinks.

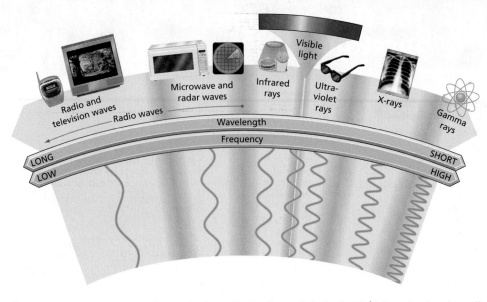

Figure 9 The electromagnetic spectrum consists of radio waves, infrared rays, visible light, ultraviolet rays, X-rays, and gamma rays.
Interpreting Diagrams *Which waves of the electromagnetic spectrum have the longest wavelengths?*

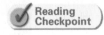

For: Links on the electromagnetic spectrum
Visit: www.SciLinks.org
Web Code: ccn-2182

Today, radiation beyond the red end of the color band is called infrared radiation. Herschel experimented with infrared radiation and found it had many of the same properties as visible light. With these experiments, Herschel opened the door to the study of invisible types of electromagnetic radiation.

The full range of frequencies of electromagnetic radiation is called the **electromagnetic spectrum.** Figure 9 shows the spectrum of electromagnetic radiation in order of increasing frequency from left to right. Visible light is the only part of the electromagnetic spectrum that you can see, but it is just a small part. ➧ **The electromagnetic spectrum includes radio waves, infrared rays, visible light, ultraviolet rays, X-rays, and gamma rays.** Each kind of wave is characterized by a range of wavelengths and frequencies. All of these waves have many useful applications.

Reading Checkpoint *What is the full range of frequencies of electromagnetic radiation called?*

Radio Waves

Radio waves have the longest wavelengths in the electromagnetic spectrum, from 1 millimeter to as much as thousands of kilometers or longer. Because they are the longest waves, radio waves also have the lowest frequencies in the spectrum—300,000 megahertz (MHz) or less. ➧ **Radio waves are used in radio and television technologies, as well as in microwave ovens and radar.**

Customize for Inclusion Students

Visually Impaired
Remind students of the basic wave characteristics and properties of crests, troughs, wavelength, and wave speed. Then, have students imagine a wave that has a wavelength as long as a small house (~10 m). Tell them this length describes a radio wave. Next, have them imagine a wave that has a wavelength equal to about the width of a hand (~12 cm). This describes a microwave. Then, tell students that these electromagnetic waves travel so fast that in one second they can go around Earth several times.

Radio In a radio studio such as the one in Figure 10, music and voices that have been changed into electronic signals are coded onto radio waves and then broadcast. There are two ways that radio stations code and transmit information on radio waves. Both ways are based on a wave of constant frequency and amplitude. To code the information onto this wave so that it can be broadcast, one of two characteristics of the wave must be varied, or modulated.

In **amplitude modulation,** the amplitude of the wave is varied. The frequency remains the same. AM radio stations broadcast by amplitude modulation. In **frequency modulation,** the frequency of the wave is varied. The amplitude remains the same. FM stations broadcast by frequency modulation. Whichever way the radio wave is transmitted, your radio receives it, decodes it, and changes it back into sound waves you can hear.

Have you ever traveled a long distance in a car and "lost" a station on the radio? A station is lost when its signal becomes too weak to detect. An FM radio station is more likely to be lost than an AM station because FM radio signals do not travel as far as AM signals along Earth's curved surface. AM radio stations use frequencies between 535 kilohertz and 1605 kilohertz. FM stations use frequencies between 88 megahertz and 108 megahertz. Particles in Earth's upper atmosphere reflect the lower-frequency AM radio waves much better than the higher-frequency FM radio waves. The reflection helps transmit AM signals farther.

Television Radio waves also carry signals for television programming. The process is like transmitting radio signals. But one difference is that the radio waves carry information for pictures as well as for sound. Once they have been broadcast, the signals are received by an antenna, and sent to the TV set.

Location and weather can affect the reception of television signals by an antenna. For that reason, many people prefer to receive television signals that have been transmitted by satellite. With this type of transmission, TV broadcasts are sent to satellites, which then retransmit the signals back to Earth.

If you have a satellite dish, you can receive the signals directly. If not, a cable service can receive the signals and resend them to your home.

Radio Broadcasting

Figure 10 The announcer's voice and the music on CD leave the radio studio as electronic signals. Those signals are used to produce a wave with either a varying amplitude or a varying frequency.
A AM waves have a varying amplitude.
B FM waves have a varying frequency.

A Amplitude modulation

B Frequency modulation

The Electromagnetic Spectrum and Light **541**

Use Community Resources L2

Arrange for your class to visit a local radio station. Have students observe the equipment used to transmit live and prerecorded programs. Encourage students to ask questions regarding the strength and type of signal the station broadcasts, the range of the signal, and the role the surrounding landscape has in a listener's ability to pick up the signal. Inquire if the station also broadcasts the signal over the Internet, and if so, how this is done.
Interpersonal, Portfolio

Teacher > Demo

Radio Reception L2

Purpose Students observe factors that affect radio signal reception.

Materials small portable radio with an antenna, cardboard or wooden box large enough to contain the radio, boxlike enclosure made of metal chicken wire

Procedure Turn on the radio, extend its antenna, and tune it to a radio station. Have students listen to the radio signal as the radio is first inside the box, next inside the wire enclosure with the antenna inside the enclosure, and finally inside the wire enclosure, but with the antenna sticking out through the enclosure. If possible, repeat these steps for both AM and FM signals.

Expected Outcome The box should have very little, if any, effect on reception. The signal will be lost when the radio and its antenna are enclosed in the wire enclosure. The signal will return when the antenna is extended outside the wire enclosure.
Visual, Group

Answer to . . .

Figure 9 *Radio waves have the longest wavelengths.*

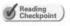 Reading Checkpoint *The full range of frequencies of electromagnetic radiation is called the electromagnetic spectrum.*

The Electromagnetic Spectrum and Light **541**

Section 18.2 (continued)

Data Analysis

How Long Does an Antenna Need to Be? L2

Answers

1. The wavelength is about 435 mm. Thus, frequency = $(3.00 \times 10^8$ m/s$)/(0.435$ m$) = 6.9 \times 10^8$ Hz = 690 MHz.

2. There is an approximately linear relationship between antenna length and wavelength. The wavelength is about four or five times the antenna length.

3. The restaurant transmissions are about the same wavelength as the singer's, about 105 MHz, because the antenna is picking up both transmissions.

4. The transmitted wavelength is about $(3.00 \times 10^8$ m/s$)/(6.0 \times 10^8$ Hz$) = 0.50$ m, or 500 mm. On the graph, this is about halfway between the wavelengths used by antennas C and D. Therefore, the antenna length used should be about 115 mm (about halfway between the lengths of antennas C and D).

For Extra Help L1

Discuss the basic features of a line graph. Point out the relationship between the antenna-length variable (plotted on the vertical axis) and the wavelength variable (plotted on the horizontal axis). Reinforce that each data point (A through E) corresponds to a unique set of horizontal-axis and vertical-axis values. Remind students that the wavelength shown on the graph is related to a unique frequency by the following equation: Speed = Wavelength × Frequency. Tell students that for this exercise, it is acceptable to use 3.00×10^8 m/s as the speed of an electromagnetic wave.
Visual

Data Analysis

How Long Does an Antenna Need to Be?

Have you ever noticed how the lengths of antennas vary from quite short (cell phones) to very long (radio transmitters)? The length of an antenna depends in part on the length of the waves it transmits. Each letter in the graph (A–E) represents an antenna of a different length. The graph shows the wavelengths that can be transmitted by antennas of a few different lengths.

1. **Calculating** What is the frequency of the wave that antenna B transmits? (*Hint:* Assume the wave travels at the speed of light.)

2. **Drawing Conclusions** What relationship is there between antenna length and wavelength?

Antenna Length vs. Wavelength

3. **Inferring** At an outdoor concert, a singer is using a wireless microphone with antenna C. Speakers broadcast her performance. Now and then the speakers also broadcast an employee taking an order at a fast food restaurant nearby. What is the approximate wavelength of the transmissions from the restaurant? How do you know?

4. **Predicting** If you used a microphone that transmitted waves at 600 MHz, approximately how long would its antenna need to be?

Figure 11 A speed-monitoring trailer uses radar to measure the speed of an approaching car. It reminds motorists of the posted speed limit and makes them aware of their actual speed.

Microwaves The shortest-wavelength radio waves are called microwaves. Microwaves have wavelengths from about 1 meter to about 1 millimeter. Their frequencies vary from about 300 megahertz to about 300,000 megahertz.

Microwaves cook and reheat food. When water or fat molecules in the food absorb microwaves, the thermal energy of these molecules increases. But microwaves generally penetrate foods only a few centimeters, so heating occurs only near the surface of the food. That is why instructions tell you to let the food stand for a few minutes—so thermal energy can reach the center by conduction. Microwaves also carry cell phone conversations. The process works much like the radio broadcast.

Radar The word *radar* is an acronym for *ra*dio *d*etection *a*nd *r*anging. Radar technology uses a radio transmitter to send out short bursts of radio waves. The waves reflect off the objects they encounter, and bounce back toward where they came from. The returning waves are then picked up and interpreted by a radio receiver.

Recall that the Doppler effect is an apparent change in the frequency of a wave. The Doppler effect can be used to find the speed of a moving car. Radio waves are sent from a stationary source, such as the radar trailer in Figure 11, toward a moving car. The faster a car is moving toward the source, the higher is the frequency of the radio waves returning to the source.

Facts and Figures

Microwave Cooking Most microwave ovens have a clear door lined with a perforated metal grid. Typically, the holes in the grid are about 2 mm in diameter. The holes are large enough to allow you to see into the microwave oven, but small enough to prevent microwaves from escaping. Microwaves used in cooking have wavelengths between 12 cm and 33 cm.

The reason many microwaves have platforms that rotate the food during cooking has to do with interference. Microwaves inside the oven interfere constructively and destructively, creating hot and cold areas. By rotating the food while it cooks, the uneven cooking effect of these areas is minimized.

Figure 12 A thermogram can be used to diagnose problems in a utility line. A When viewed in visible light, the wires all look the same. B The colors in the thermogram image show that the electric current in the center wire is not flowing as it should.

Infrared Rays

Infrared rays have higher frequencies than radio waves and lower frequencies than red light. Infrared wavelengths vary from about 1 millimeter to about 750 nanometers. (A nanometer is 10^{-9} meters, or one millionth of a millimeter.) ⊙ **Infrared rays are used as a source of heat and to discover areas of heat differences.**

You cannot see infrared radiation, but your skin senses it as warmth. Reptile habitats at zoos are often kept warm with infrared lamps. Restaurants use infrared lamps to keep buffet-style foods at a safe temperature for consumption.

Warmer objects give off more infrared radiation than cooler objects. A device called a thermograph uses infrared sensors to create thermograms. **Thermograms** (THUR moh gramz) are color-coded pictures that show variations in temperature. They are used to find places where a building loses heat to the environment. Thermograms can also locate problems in the path of electric current, as shown in Figure 12.

The human body is usually warmer than its surroundings. After a natural disaster such as an earthquake, search-and-rescue teams use infrared cameras to locate victims quickly—even underground.

Visible Light

The visible part of the electromagnetic spectrum is light that the human eye can see. Each wavelength in the visible spectrum corresponds to a specific frequency and has a particular color. Figure 13 shows the wavelength and frequency ranges of different colors of light in a vacuum.

⊙ **People use visible light to see, to help keep them safe, and to communicate with one another.** Light enables people to read. It is what makes flowers, boxes, signs, and all other objects visible. Automobiles have headlights and taillights that make night driving safer. Traffic lights communicate information to drivers about what is expected of them—to stop, for example, when the light is red.

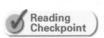
What is the visible part of the electromagnetic spectrum?

For: Activity on the greenhouse effect
Visit: PHSchool.com
Web Code: ccc-2182

Figure 13 Each color of light corresponds to a different range of wavelengths. The wavelengths of visible light are quite small. Wavelengths of red light, for example, are about one hundredth the thickness of a human hair. **Using Tables** *As the wavelength decreases from the red end of the spectrum to the violet end, what happens to the frequency?*

The Visible Spectrum

Color	Wavelength (nm)	Frequency (× 10¹⁴ Hz)
Red	610–750	4.9–4.0
Orange	590–610	5.1–4.9
Yellow	570–590	5.3–5.1
Green	500–570	6.0–5.3
Blue	450–500	6.7–6.0
Violet	400–450	7.5–6.7

The Electromagnetic Spectrum and Light **543**

Infrared Rays
Use Visuals L1

Figure 12 Reinforce the idea that infrared rays are associated with heat and that they are not part of the visible spectrum. Tell students that electric charge dissipates energy in the form of heat as it flows through a conductor such as a wire. Tell students that electrical power transmission lines in good condition do not dissipate a lot of heat. Ask, **What can you infer from the colors of the pole and the top and bottom wires shown in the thermogram in Figure 12B?** *(The wires and the pole are at about the same temperature, and they are not dissipating a lot of heat.)* **What are some possible reasons why the middle wire and its insulating resistor are hot?** *(Student answers may include that excessive current is flowing through the wire, or that there is damage to the wire causing it to have a much higher resistance than the other wires.)* **Visual, Logical**

FYI

A thermogram usually has a key to indicate what temperature each color corresponds to.

Visible Light

Address Misconceptions L2

Because the speed of light in a vacuum is usually given early in any discussion of light, many students fail to realize that light has different speeds in different materials. Furthermore, students often don't understand that different colors of light have different speeds in materials such as glass. Explain that EM waves, which include many other types of waves besides visible light, travel at the speed of light only when in a vacuum. When EM waves travel through any medium other than a vacuum, they travel at speeds less than the speed of light. You may want to use this information to preview Section 18.3, which covers how light interacts with matter. **Verbal**

Answer to . . .

Figure 13 *As wavelength decreases, frequency increases.*

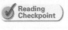 *The visible part of the electromagnetic spectrum is light that people can see.*

For: Activity on electromagnetic waves
Visit: PHSchool.com
Web Code: ccp-2182

Students can learn more about electromagnetic waves online.

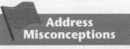

Find links to additional activities and have students monitor phenomena that affect Earth and its residents.

Ultraviolet Rays

Evaluating Sunscreen L2

Objective
After completing this activity, students will be able to
• use the SPF of a sunscreen to predict its effectiveness in blocking ultraviolet radiation.

Skills Focus Observing, Measuring

 Prep Time 10 minutes

Materials 2 black paper strips, 2 petri dishes, 12 ultraviolet-detecting beads, sunscreen, clock or watch with second hand

Advance Prep Provide each lab group with a small vial of the sunscreen labeled with its SPF.

Class Time 15 minutes

Safety Make sure that students wear plastic gloves and safety goggles when applying sunscreen and clean up when they are finished.

Teaching Tips
• Make sure that students spread the sunscreens uniformly.

Expected Outcome The unprotected beads change color within five seconds in the presence of sunlight. Depending on the SPF, sunscreen will delay this change by as much as two minutes.

Analyze and Conclude
1. The beads in the sunscreen-covered petri dish took longer to change color.
2. The color change represents absorption of ultraviolet light, which causes tanning or burning of skin. Sunscreen absorbs most ultraviolet light before it can affect skin or the beads.
3. A sunscreen with a higher SPF would delay the color change for a longer time.
Visual, Group

For Enrichment L3

Have students use the beads to compare the ultraviolet-protection value of different types of plexiglass, sunglasses, and window glass. Students will discover that plexiglass transmits the most ultraviolet light. High-quality sunglasses transmit the least.
Kinesthetic, Visual

Quick Lab

Evaluating Sunscreen

Procedure
1. Insert a black paper strip inside each of two plastic petri dishes to cover the sides. Place six ultraviolet-detecting beads in each dish. Cover each dish with its lid.
2. On one of the lids, spread a thin layer of sunscreen.
3. Place the dishes in direct sunlight. Record the time it takes for the beads in each dish to change color.

Analyze and Conclude
1. **Comparing and Contrasting** Compare the times the beads in the two dishes took to change color.
2. **Using Models** Explain how this lab models the use of sunscreen. What does the color change of the beads represent?
3. **Predicting** How might a sunscreen with a higher SPF (sun protection factor) affect the time needed for the beads to change color?

Go Online
active art

For: Activity on electromagnetic waves
Visit: PHSchool.com
Web Code: ccp-2182

Figure 14 Airport security screeners use X-rays to search baggage for potentially dangerous objects. **Inferring** *Why are there dark areas in this X-ray image?*

Ultraviolet Rays

The wavelengths of ultraviolet rays vary from about 400 nanometers to about 4 nanometers. Ultraviolet radiation has higher frequencies than violet light. **Ultraviolet rays have applications in health and medicine, and in agriculture.**

In moderation, exposure to ultraviolet rays helps your skin produce vitamin D. Vitamin D helps the body absorb calcium from foods to produce healthy bones and teeth. Excessive exposure can cause sunburn, wrinkles, and eventually skin cancer. It can also damage your eyes.

Ultraviolet rays are used to kill microorganisms. In heating and cooling systems of large buildings, ultraviolet rays disinfect the air that flows through the systems. In winter, plant nurseries use ultraviolet lights to help plants grow.

X-Rays

X-rays have very short wavelengths, from about 12 nanometers to about 0.005 nanometers. They have higher frequencies than ultraviolet rays. X-rays have high energy and can penetrate matter that light cannot. **X-rays are used in medicine, industry, and transportation to make pictures of the inside of solid objects.**

Your teeth and bones absorb X-rays. X-ray photographs show softer tissue as dark, highly exposed areas. Bones and teeth appear white. Too much exposure to X-rays can kill or damage living tissue.

The lids on aluminum cans are sometimes inspected with X-rays to make sure they are sealed properly. X-rays can be used to identify the contents of entire truck trailers. Packages and suitcases, such as the one in Figure 14, are X-rayed in search of dangerous contents.

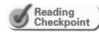 **Reading Checkpoint** *What are X-rays used for?*

Section 18.2 Assessment

1. Radio waves, infrared rays, visible light, ultraviolet rays, X-rays, gamma rays
2. Radio waves: radio and television, microwave ovens, radar; Infrared rays: source of heat, indicator of heat differences, rescue missions; Visible light: sight, safety, and communication; Ultraviolet rays: health, medicine, and agriculture; X-rays: imaging interiors of solid objects in medicine, industry, and transportation; Gamma rays: cancer treatment, imaging the brain, industrial inspection tool
3. Radar sends out radio waves and uses the change in frequency of the reflected waves to calculate the speed of an object, as determined by the Doppler effect.
4. Soft materials show up as dark, highly exposed areas, while white areas are where X-rays are absorbed.

Looking

Listening

Speaking

Thinking and Speaking

Gamma Rays

Gamma rays have the shortest wavelengths in the electromagnetic spectrum, about 0.005 nanometer or less. They have the highest frequencies and therefore the most energy and the greatest penetrating ability of all the electromagnetic waves. Exposure to tiny amounts of gamma rays are tolerable, but overexposure can be deadly. ➣ **Gamma rays are used in the medical field to kill cancer cells and make pictures of the brain, and in industrial situations as an inspection tool.**

Gamma rays are used in radiation therapy to kill cancer cells without harming nearby healthy cells. Gamma rays are also used to make pictures of the human brain, with different levels of brain activity represented by different colors. Four brain scans are shown in Figure 15.

Pipelines are checked with machines that travel on the inside of a pipe, taking gamma ray pictures along the entire length. Technicians examine the pictures for rusting, cracks, or other signs of damage.

Figure 15 Gamma rays emitted by radioactive tracers in the brain are used to produce color-coded images. Areas of high activity show up in red. These images show where the brain is active when the patient is (from left to right) looking at something, listening, speaking, and thinking and speaking. The more involved the task, the more parts of the brain are activated.

Section 18.2 Assessment

Reviewing Concepts

1. ➣ List the kinds of waves included in the electromagnetic spectrum, from longest to shortest wavelength.
2. ➣ Name three uses for each type of wave.
3. How is radar used to determine the speed of a car?
4. How can X-rays make pictures of the inside of solid objects?

Critical Thinking

5. **Comparing and Contrasting** How are AM radio waves similar to FM radio waves? How are they different?

6. **Classifying** What type of electromagnetic wave are microwaves and radar?
7. **Predicting** Which do you think will penetrate farther into a block of lead, X-rays or gamma rays? Explain your reasoning.

Writing in Science

Explanatory Writing Write one paragraph each about three different kinds of electromagnetic waves that you will encounter today. Use a single characteristic, such as wavelength or frequency, to describe each wave. Explain how life might be different without each kind of wave.

The Electromagnetic Spectrum and Light **545**

X-Rays
Integrate Biology   L2

To determine the structures of proteins, biologists at the Argonne National Laboratory Structural Biology Center are shining X-rays onto frozen crystals of proteins. The X-ray images are captured by a quick, electronic camera. With the help of advanced software this information is converted into three-dimensional images that biologists can study to determine how the proteins work. Have students find out the role that proteins play in living cells and have them write a short report.
Verbal, Portfolio

Gamma Rays
Integrate Space Science   L2

Some deep-space objects emit bursts of gamma rays. These rays travel through the empty vacuum of space for millions of years before reaching Earth. However, Earth's atmosphere blocks the gamma rays and keeps them from reaching the surface. Because the rays are blocked, astronomers who want to detect and monitor gamma ray emissions use instruments that orbit above Earth's atmosphere. Ask students to research the cause of deep space gamma emissions and to summarize their findings in a short paragraph.
Logical, Portfolio

3 ASSESS
Evaluate
Understanding   L2

Ask students chosen at random to list the general properties of and one application for each electromagnetic wave type discussed in the section.

Reteach   L1

Use Figure 9 to review the section's key concepts, emphasizing the relationship between the frequency and the wavelength of all electromagnetic waves.

Interactive Textbook If your class subscribes to the Interactive Textbook, use it to review key concepts in Section 18.2.

---

5. AM and FM are similar in that they are a means of coding and transmitting information on radio waves. They are different because AM signals modulate amplitude while FM signals modulate frequency. AM signals travel farther because they reflect off particles in the upper atmosphere.
6. Radio waves
7. Gamma rays should penetrate farther into lead because they have higher-energy photons.

Writing in Science

Sample answer: Today I will encounter microwaves when I cook, infrared rays when I use a TV remote control, and ultraviolet light from the sun. These vary in wavelength, with microwaves the longest wavelength and ultraviolet rays the shortest. If these waves did not exist, I would have to cook differently, use a different kind of remote control, and perhaps need to use sunscreen less often.

Answer to . . .

Figure 14 *Dark areas are regions through which X-rays easily pass.*

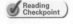
Reading Checkpoint *In medicine, industry, and transportation to image the inside of solid objects*

The Electromagnetic Spectrum and Light   **545**

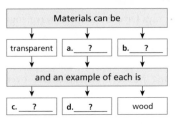

1 FOCUS

Objectives

18.3.1 Classify materials as transparent, translucent, or opaque to visible light.

18.3.2 Describe what happens when light is reflected, refracted, polarized, or scattered.

Reading Focus

Build Vocabulary **L2**

Concept Map Have students construct a concept map of the vocabulary terms used in this section. Instruct students to place the vocabulary terms in ovals and connect the ovals with lines on which linking words are placed. Students should place the main concept (Behavior of Light) at the top or the center. As they move away from the main concept, the topics should become more specific.

Reading Strategy **L2**

a. translucent b. opaque c. glass or water d. frosted glass

2 INSTRUCT

Light and Materials

Build Reading Literacy **L2**

Anticipation Guide Refer to page **388D** in **Chapter 13**, which provides the guidelines for an anticipation guide.

Ask students which statements are true: **1.** All of the light striking an object is absorbed by that object. *(False)* **2.** It is possible to see an object in a room that is completely dark using only your eyes. *(False)* **3.** The cover of your book does not reflect light. *(False)*

Have students read the text on pp. 546 and 547, then revisit the three questions. **Verbal**

FYI

A material need not be transparent or opaque to all forms of electromagnetic radiation. For example, wood is opaque to visible light, but not to all electromagnetic waves. Microwaves and radio waves can pass through wood.

18.3 Behavior of Light

Standards: ICP.2.4, ICP.4.4

Reading Focus

Key Concepts

- What three types of materials affect the behavior of light?
- How does light behave when it enters a new medium?

Vocabulary

- transparent
- translucent
- opaque
- image
- regular reflection
- diffuse reflection
- mirage
- polarized light
- scattering

Reading Strategy

Monitoring Your Understanding Copy the flowchart below. As you read, complete it to show how different materials affect light.

Materials can be		
transparent	a. _?_	b. _?_

and an example of each is		
c. _?_	d. _?_	wood

Figure 16 Water is transparent. You can see through it. That characteristic makes it possible to photograph these fish and other animals living in the ocean.

What would you see if you were snorkeling in warm ocean waters over a coral reef? You might see fish of bright colors, clown fish, sea stars, sponges, and clams. You might see sharks or turtles, and of course, coral. But why can you see these animals so clearly? Why can you see the reef through the water but not, for example, through the bottom of the boat that brought you to the reef?

Light and Materials

Without light, nothing is visible. When you look at the reef animals, what you are really seeing is light. You can see the reef through the water, because light passes through the water between the reef and your eyes. But you can't see the reef through the bottom of the boat because light doesn't pass through the boat.

How light behaves when it strikes an object depends on many factors, including the material the object is made of. **Materials can be transparent, translucent, or opaque.** Each type of material affects the behavior of light in different ways.

A material through which you can see clearly is transparent. A **transparent** material transmits light, which means it allows most of the light that strikes it to pass through it. For example, the water where the fish and coral in Figure 16 live is transparent. While riding on a bus, you can see buildings and trees outside because the bus windows are transparent.

546 *Chapter 18*

Section Resources

Print
- *Laboratory Manual,* Investigation 18B
- *Reading and Study Workbook With Math Support,* Section 18.3
- *Transparencies,* Section 18.3

Technology
- *Interactive Textbook,* Section 18.3
- *Presentation Pro CD-ROM,* Section 18.3

If you can see through a material, but the objects you see through it do not look clear or distinct, then the material is translucent (trans LOO sunt). A **translucent** material scatters light. The soaps in Figure 17A are translucent. When you look into a room through a frosted glass door, you can make out shapes of people and objects, but the shapes are fuzzy and lack detail.

Most materials are opaque (oh PAYK). An **opaque** material either absorbs or reflects all of the light that strikes it. The fruit in Figure 17B is opaque. An opaque object does not allow any light to pass through it. You can't see through a wooden table or a metal desk. Wood and metal are examples of opaque materials.

Interactions of Light

When light encounters matter, some or all of the energy in the light can be transferred to the matter. And just as light can affect matter, matter can affect light. 🔵 **When light strikes a new medium, the light can be reflected, absorbed, or transmitted. When light is transmitted, it can be refracted, polarized, or scattered.**

Reflection When you look in a mirror, you see a clear image of yourself. An **image** is a copy of an object formed by reflected (or refracted) waves of light. Similarly, when you look at a still lake, you can see a sharp reflected image of the far shore. But what happens to the reflected image in the lake if the wind suddenly gusts, causing ripples in the surface of the water? The image is blurred, or fuzzy-looking. When light reflects from a smooth surface, you see a clear, sharp image. When light reflects from a rough surface, you see a blurred reflected image or no image at all.

Regular reflection occurs when parallel light waves strike a surface and reflect all in the same direction. Regular reflection happens when light hits a smooth, polished surface, like a mirror or the surface of a still body of water such as in Figure 18.

Diffuse reflection occurs when parallel light waves strike a rough, uneven surface, and reflect in many different directions. If you could look at this page of your book through a microscope, you would see that the paper has a rough surface. The rough surface causes diffuse reflection of the light that shines on it.

Figure 17 When light strikes a new medium, it can be reflected, absorbed, refracted, polarized, or scattered. **A** The translucent bars of soap scatter light, making the soaps and what you can see through them appear fuzzy. **B** You cannot see through the fruit because opaque materials do not transmit any light.

Figure 18 Almost all objects reflect light. **A** In regular reflection, a smooth surface reflects a clear image because parallel light waves reflect all in the same direction. **B** In diffuse reflection, parallel light waves reflect in many directions.

A Regular reflection

B Diffuse reflection

The Electromagnetic Spectrum and Light **547**

Address Misconceptions L2

Although most students accept that mirrors reflect light, some students reject the idea that ordinary objects also reflect light. This misconception is related to another one that many students have, namely that their eyes do not receive light when observing an object. Probe student misconceptions about vision by asking them to explain what makes it possible for people to see. You may discover a range of misconceptions, including the idea that light fills space (as expressed by saying, "the room is full of light") and the idea that it is the action of people's eyes that makes objects observable. Counter misconceptions using a careful explanation of the connections among reflected light, emitted light, and vision.
Verbal

Teacher > Demo

Reflected Light and Vision L2

Purpose Students observe the role of reflected light in vision perception.

Materials medium-sized wooden or cardboard box with its interior lined with white paper or painted bright white. Box top must be removable or hinged, and have a small hole in its center.

Procedure Show students the box with its top on under normal room lighting conditions. Have students use their observations of the box (and the hole) to predict the box's interior color.

Expected Outcome Most students will not predict that the box's interior is white. Show students the white interior of the box. Explain that whatever amount of light enters the box, it is eventually absorbed after numerous reflections off the white interior surfaces. Because no light escapes the box and travels to the students' eyes, it is not possible to discern the interior color of the box.
Visual, Logical

Build Science Skills `L2`

Observing

Purpose Students observe the effect of polarizing filters.

Materials 2 polarizing filters, light source

Class Time 10 minutes

Procedure Have students work in a group. One group member should hold one filter up to light coming through a window and observe the result. Ask, **Why is the light dimmer after passing through one of the filters?** *(The filter has absorbed some of the light.)* Have another group member align both filters in the same direction and then view the light from the window. Ask, **How does the brightness compare with what you saw when the light passed through a single filter?** *(The light is dimmer after passing through both filters.)* Have a third group member try to arrange the filters in such a way that no light is transmitted through the filters.

Safety Caution students to not look directly at the sun.

Expected Outcome Students will observe how the orientation of the two filters determines the amount of light that passes through. They will see that when the two filters are oriented at 90° to one another, no light is transmitted. **Kinesthetic, Group**

Use Visuals `L1`

Figure 20 Point out to students that Figure 20 represents how a vertical polarizing filter blocks light that is horizontally polarized. Tell students that the glare from horizontal surfaces such as roads and automobile hoods tends to be horizontally polarized. Then ask, **In what direction should the polarizing lenses in a pair of polarizing sunglasses be aligned?** *(To block the horizontally polarized glare, the lenses should be positioned with their polarizing slits aligned vertically.)*

FYI

An actual Polaroid polarizing filter consists of long chain molecules that are stretched preferentially in one direction. Light with an electric field parallel to the chain molecules is absorbed.

Figure 19 Light refracts, or bends, when it moves from one medium to another. Because the light bends, the image you see appears to be bent as well. **Relating Cause and Effect** *Why does the underwater part of the pencil appear to be closer to you than the part above water?*

Refraction A light wave can refract, or bend, when it passes at an angle from one medium into another. You can easily observe two common effects of refraction when light travels from air into water. Refraction makes underwater objects appear closer and larger than they really are. Refraction can also make an object, such as a pencil, appear to break at the surface of the water, as shown in Figure 19.

Refraction can also sometimes cause a mirage. A **mirage** is a false or distorted image. Mirages occur because light travels faster in hot air than in cooler, denser air. On a sunny day, air tends to be hotter just above the surface of a road than higher up. Normally, light travels from the sun all the way to the ground before being reflected. But on a hot day, light is gradually refracted as it moves into layers of hotter and hotter air. This gradual refraction causes some of the light to follow a curved path, rather than a straight path to the ground. Light that reaches your eyes after traveling in this manner can look as if it was reflected from a layer of water. Mirages also form this way above the hot sand in deserts.

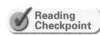
Reading Checkpoint *What is a mirage?*

Polarization Light with waves that vibrate in only one plane is **polarized light**. Polarizing filters transmit light waves that vibrate in this way. Look at Figure 20. Unpolarized light vibrates in all directions. A vertical polarizing filter stops waves vibrating on a horizontal plane. Waves vibrating on a vertical plane pass through. A horizontal polarizing filter then blocks the waves vibrating on a vertical plane. To understand how a polarizing filter works, think of a light wave as being like a postcard that you push through a mail slot in a door. If you hold the postcard so that it lines up with the mail slot, then you can easily push it through. But if the postcard is at an angle to the mail slot, it has trouble passing through. In the same way, a polarizing filter blocks waves with electric fields vibrating in one direction.

Figure 20 This simplified model shows how polarizing filters behave. A vertical polarizing filter blocks light that is horizontally polarized. **Applying Concepts** *What would happen if you looked at light through a horizontally polarizing filter and a vertically polarizing filter at the same time?*

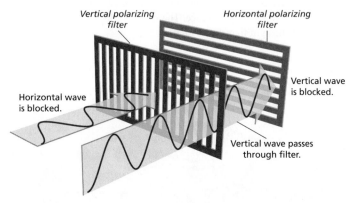

Vertical polarizing filter

Horizontal polarizing filter

Horizontal wave is blocked.

Vertical wave is blocked.

Vertical wave passes through filter.

Facts and Figures

Rainbows A rainbow is a series of concentric colored arcs that form when light from the sun passes through air containing water drops, usually from rain or fog. The rainbow is visible in the direction opposite to that of the sun. The different colors are caused by the refraction and internal reflection of light rays that enter the water drop. Because sunlight is made of light of varying frequencies, these different frequencies refract at different angles in the water drop. The different frequencies (and colors) emerge from the drop and form bands of color in the sky. One edge of the rainbow is red (the wavelength that refracts the least in the water drop) and the other edge is violet (the wavelength that refracts the most in the water drop). The other colors of the visible spectrum fill in the region between red and violet.

Light reflecting from a nonmetallic flat surface, such as a window or the surface of a lake, can become polarized. When sunlight reflects from a horizontal surface, horizontally polarized light reflects more strongly than the rest of the sunlight. This reflection produces glare. To block the glare, polarized sunglasses have vertically polarized filters, which block the horizontally polarized light.

Scattering Earth's atmosphere contains many molecules and other tiny particles. These particles can scatter sunlight. **Scattering** means that light is redirected as it passes through a medium. Look at Figure 21. A scattering effect reddens the sun at sunset and sunrise. Most of the particles in the atmosphere are very small. Small particles scatter shorter-wavelength blue light more than light of longer wavelengths. The sunlight encounters more of the molecules and tiny particles that scatter the shorter-wavelength colors. By the time the sunlight reaches your eyes, most of the blue and even some of the green and yellow have been scattered. Most of what remains for your eyes to detect are the longer wavelengths of light, orange and red.

When the sun is high in the sky, its light travels a shorter distance through Earth's atmosphere. It scatters blue light in all directions much more than other colors of light. Scattering explains why the sky appears blue on a sunny day, even though air itself is colorless.

Figure 21 The lower the sun is on the horizon, the more of the atmosphere the light travels through before it reaches Earth's surface. In certain weather conditions, the blue, green, and yellow wavelengths of sunlight are heavily scattered. What's left to enjoy are the beautiful reds and oranges of sunrise and sunset.

Section 18.3 Assessment

Reviewing Concepts

1. ⬤ Explain the differences among opaque, transparent, and translucent materials. Name two objects made from each type of material.

2. ⬤ List and explain three things that can happen to a light wave when it enters a new medium.

3. What is the difference between diffuse reflection and regular reflection?

4. What happens to light that passes through a horizontal polarizing filter?

Critical Thinking

5. **Predicting** A black car reflects much less light than a white car. Which car's surface will be warmer after 1 hour of sunshine? Explain.

6. **Formulating Hypotheses** A mountain climber finds that her sunglasses are not blocking glare from a vertical rock wall. What can you hypothesize about the polarizing filters in her sunglasses?

7. **Applying Concepts** On a foggy night, you can see a car's headlight beams but you may not be able to see the car itself. Explain why.

Connecting ⬡ Concepts

Mechanical Waves Review the behaviors of mechanical waves discussed in Section 17.2, such as reflection and refraction. Compare them with the behaviors of light.

The Electromagnetic Spectrum and Light **549**

Ask students to identify objects or locations in the classroom that are examples of transparency, translucency, opaqueness, regular reflection, and diffuse reflection. Have students explain why their example is correct.

Reteach L1

Use Figures 16 to 21 as examples that illustrate the key concepts of the section.

Connecting ⬡ Concepts

Reflection: In mechanical waves, the energy of the reflected wave is less than the energy of the original wave. The same is true of light waves because some light will be absorbed or transmitted. Refraction: In mechanical waves, refraction occurs because one side of a wave front moves more slowly than the other side when the wave enters a medium at an angle. Light waves also are refracted because they change speed as they move from one medium into another.

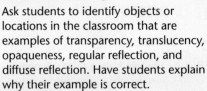 If your class subscribes to the Interactive Textbook, use it to review key concepts in Section 18.3.

Answer to . . .

Figure 19 *Refraction of light from the pencil makes it appear larger than it really is.*

Figure 20 *The two filters would block all of the light.*

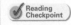 *A mirage is a false or distorted image.*

Section 18.3 Assessment

1. Transparent materials (glass window, water) transmit light. Translucent materials (soaps, frosted glass) scatter light that passes through. Opaque materials (wood table, metal desk) absorb or reflect all incident light.

2. The light can be reflected (bounce off), be absorbed (enter but not exit), or be transmitted (pass through).

3. Diffuse reflection: parallel light waves are reflected in many directions; Regular reflection: reflected parallel light waves are still parallel.

4. Only horizontally polarized light comes out the other side of the filter; all of the rest of the light is blocked by the filter.

5. The black car absorbs much more of the light striking it, so it will be warmer than the white car.

6. The sunglasses have vertically polarized filters that transmit vertically polarized glare reflected from the vertical rock wall.

7. Particles of water in the fog scatter the light from the car's headlights, creating an illuminated "beam" of light that is visible in front of a car. If the car is coming around a corner, the headlight beam is visible before the car is seen.

1 FOCUS

Objectives

18.4.1 Explain how a prism disperses white light into different colors.

18.4.2 Analyze factors that determine the color of an object.

18.4.3 Distinguish among primary, secondary, and complementary colors of light and of pigments.

Reading Focus

Build Vocabulary **L2**

Vocabulary Knowledge Rating Chart Have students construct a chart with four columns labeled Term, Can Define or Use It, Have Heard or Seen It, and Don't Know. Have students copy the six terms into the first column and rate their term knowledge by putting a check in one of the other columns. Ask how many students actually know each term. Have them share their knowledge. Ask focused questions to help students predict text content based on the term, thus giving students a purpose for reading. After students have read the section, have them re-rate themselves.

Reading Strategy **L2**

a. Blue **b.** Magenta **c.** Cyan **d.** Yellow
For primary colors of pigments:

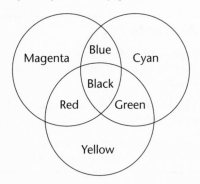

18.4 Color

Standard: ICP.4.4

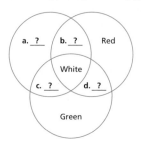

Reading Focus

Key Concepts

- How does a prism separate white light?
- What determines the color of an object?
- What are the primary colors of light?
- What are the primary colors of pigments?

Vocabulary

- dispersion
- primary colors
- secondary color
- complementary colors of light
- pigment
- complementary colors of pigments

Reading Strategy

Venn Diagram Copy the Venn diagram below. After you read, label the diagram for mixing primary colors of light. Make a similar diagram for mixing primary colors of pigments.

Have you ever zoomed in on a color photograph displayed on a computer screen? If you have, you've seen that the photograph is made up of many tiny squares, called *pixels*, as shown in Figure 22. Your computer screen might be set to display 256 colors, thousands of colors, or even millions of colors. All of these colors are generated using various combinations of only three colors of light. If you were to print the same photograph, your printer would also use only three colors, plus black, to create the image out of tiny dots of ink. The three colors the computer uses are different from the three the printer uses. How can that be?

Figure 22 This student is looking at many colors on his computer screen. What he is actually seeing, however, are combinations of only three colors of light.

550 *Chapter 18*

Section Resources

Print
- *Laboratory Manual,* Investigation 18A
- *Reading and Study Workbook With Math Support,* Section 18.4
- *Transparencies,* Section 18.4

Technology
- *Interactive Textbook,* Section 18.4
- *Presentation Pro CD-ROM,* Section 18.4
- *Go Online,* NSTA SciLinks, Color

A

Separating White Light Into Colors

In 1666, the English physicist Isaac Newton investigated the visible spectrum. First, he used a glass prism to produce a visible spectrum from sunlight. With screens, he then blocked all colors of light except blue. Next, he placed a second prism where the blue light was visible. The second prism refracted the blue light but had no further effect on the color. Newton's experiments showed that white sunlight is made up of all the colors of the visible spectrum.

How does a prism separate white light into a visible spectrum? As white light passes through a prism, shorter wavelengths refract more than longer wavelengths, and the colors separate. Look at Figure 23A. When red light, with its longer wavelength, enters a glass prism, it slows down the least of all the colors, and so is bent the least. Violet light is bent the most. The process in which white light separates into colors is called **dispersion.**

A rainbow gives a beautiful example of dispersion. Droplets of water in the air act like prisms. They separate sunlight into the spectrum. When light enters a raindrop, it slows down and refracts. Then it reflects off the far inner surface of the raindrop. It refracts again as it exits the raindrop, speeds up, and travels back toward the source of the light.

Reading Checkpoint *What process causes a rainbow?*

The Colors of Objects

Would it surprise you to learn that an object of any color does not have a definite color? An object's color is the color of light that reaches your eye when you look at the object. The color of any object depends on what the object is made of and on the color of light that strikes the object. Sunlight contains all the colors of the visible spectrum. But when you look, for example, at a red car in sunlight, the red paint reflects mostly red light. Most of the other colors in white light are absorbed at the surface of the paint.

Figure 23 White light is dispersed by prisms and water droplets. **A** When white light passes through a prism, the shorter wavelengths are bent more than the longer wavelengths. The colors are separated. When red light enters the second prism, it is refracted but the color does not change. **B** Water droplets separate the colors of sunlight, producing a rainbow.

B

For: Links on color
Visit: www.SciLinks.org
Web Code: ccn-2184

The Electromagnetic Spectrum and Light **551**

The Electromagnetic Spectrum and Light **551**

Customize for English Language Learners

Think-Pair-Share
Have students work in pairs to think of situations in which the color of an object changes because of the light shining on it. Examples include a building at sunset or a shirt viewed under colored lights at a dance.

Strengthen discussion skills by having students share their examples with the class. Encourage students to refer to Figure 24 for help in explaining the colors seen under different lighting conditions.

---

2 INSTRUCT

Separating White Light Into Colors
Use Visuals   L1

Figure 23 Review refraction with students. Ask, **After leaving the prism, how does the path of red light compare to the path of blue light?** *(Both colors travel in a straight line. The red light travels at a different angle because it refracts less when passing through the prism.)* **If red and blue light refracted the same amount, would they be separated by the prism?** *(No)* **What is the purpose of the white card with the hole?** *(It blocks all of the colors except red.)* **What happens to the red light at the second prism?** *(The red light changes direction but is not separated into new colors).* **What can you conclude about the nature of red light and white light?** *(Red light is more fundamental than white light because it cannot be separated into other colors.)*
Visual, Logical

The Colors of Objects
Build Science Skills   L2

Controlling Variables Help students see the importance of changing one variable at a time. If you look at a red object in white light and then look at a blue object in green light, two variables change, so you cannot draw valid conclusions. By comparing an object (with one color) under two different colors of light, only one variable changes, so valid conclusions can be drawn.
Logical, Visual

Download a worksheet on color for students to complete, and find additional teacher support from NSTA SciLinks.

Answer to . . .

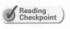

A rainbow is caused by dispersion.

Mixing Colors of Light

Address Misconceptions L2

Many students do not understand the difference between mixing colored lights and mixing pigments. Point out that when two beams of differently colored light overlap, colors are added. This result is in contrast to the more familiar experience of subtracting colors of light by mixing paints or inks that contain different light-absorbing pigments.
Visual

Build Reading Literacy L1

Compare and Contrast Refer to page **226D** in **Chapter 8**, which provides the guidelines for comparing and contrasting.

Students can avoid confusing light and pigments by studying similarities and differences in Figure 25 and Figure 26. Have students complete a compare-contrast table. Ask, **How are the figures similar?** *(Both have primary colors, secondary colors, and include red, green, blue, cyan, yellow, and magenta.)* **How are the figures different?** *(The three primary colors form white in one figure and black in the other. Red, blue, and green are primary colors of light but secondary colors of pigment. Cyan, yellow, and magenta are secondary colors of light but primary colors of pigment.)*
Visual

Figure 24 Under white light, the pots appear white, green, yellow, red, and blue. **Observing** *How does the red pot appear under red, green, and blue light?*

What happens if you change the color of the light shining on an object? Look at Figure 24, which shows the same stack of flower pots in several different colors of light. The pots appear to be different colors when viewed in different colors of light. For example, the red pot looks black when viewed in blue light because the red plastic absorbs all of the light striking it. No red light reaches the object, so none can be reflected from it.

Mixing Colors of Light

Figure 25 shows how equal amounts of three colors of light—red, green, and blue—combine to produce white light. **Primary colors** are three specific colors that can be combined in varying amounts to create all possible colors. **The primary colors of light are red, green, and blue.**

When red light strikes a white surface, red light is reflected. Similarly, when blue light strikes a white surface, blue light is reflected. What happens if both red light and blue light strike a white surface? Both colors are reflected and the two colors add together to make a third color, magenta. When colors of light are mixed together, the colors add together to form a new color.

The secondary colors of light are cyan, yellow, and magenta. Each **secondary color** of light is a combination of two primary colors. Therefore, if you add a primary color to the proper secondary color, you will get white light. Any two colors of light that combine to form white light are **complementary colors of light.** A complementary color pair is a combination of one primary color and one secondary color. Blue and yellow are complementary colors of light, as are red and cyan, and green and magenta.

Figure 25 The three primary colors of light are red, green, and blue. When any two primary colors combine, a secondary color is formed. **Observing** *What color of light is produced when all three primary colors combine in equal amounts?*

Reading Checkpoint *How is a secondary color of light formed?*

Facts and Figures

Wavelength, Frequency, and Color It is better to think of color in terms of frequency than in terms of wavelength. The frequency of a wave is determined by the frequency of the source of the wave. When a light wave enters a new medium, the wavelength and speed of the wave change, but the frequency stays the same.

From an energy standpoint, a photon has a specific energy equal to Planck's constant multiplied by the frequency of the wave. Thus, a photon is defined by frequency, not by wavelength. When a photon enters a new medium, it slows down and its wavelength changes, but its energy (and therefore its frequency) remains unchanged.

Mixing Pigments

Paints, inks, photographs, and dyes get their colors from pigments. A **pigment** is a material that absorbs some colors of light and reflects other colors. Stone Age cave paintings were made with natural pigments from colored earth and clay. Over the centuries, natural pigments have been obtained from many sources, including metal oxide compounds, minerals, plants, and animals. Today's artists use paints made from natural pigments as well as from synthetic, or manufactured, pigments.

The primary colors of pigments are cyan, yellow, and magenta. Perhaps you have noticed that color printers and photocopiers use these three colors, plus black. You can mix varying amounts of these primary pigment colors to make almost any other color. Each pigment reflects one or more colors. As pigments are mixed together, more colors are absorbed and fewer colors are reflected. When two or more pigments are mixed together, the colors absorbed by each pigment are subtracted out of the light that strikes the mixture.

Look at Figure 26. The light filters absorb light in much the same way pigments do. When cyan and magenta are combined, blue is formed. Cyan and yellow combine to form green. Yellow and magenta combine to form red. The secondary colors of pigments are red, green, and blue. Any two colors of pigments that combine to make black pigment are **complementary colors of pigments.**

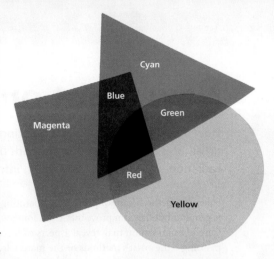

Figure 26 The three primary colors of pigments are cyan, yellow, and magenta. When the three primary colors of pigments are combined, the secondary colors of pigments are formed. **Interpreting Diagrams** *Which colors of pigments combine to make black?*

Section 18.4 Assessment

Reviewing Concepts

1. Explain how a prism separates white light into the colors of the spectrum.
2. What determines the color of an object?
3. What three colors of light can combine to form any other color?
4. What three colors of pigments can combine to form any other color?
5. Explain how the process of dispersion of light forms a rainbow.
6. What are pigments? Explain how different pigments affect light.

Critical Thinking

7. **Predicting** What color would a blue wall appear under green light?
8. **Applying Concepts** Why does combining equal amounts of cyan, yellow, and magenta paints form black?

Explain a Concept Write a letter to a friend who is not in class with you. Explain how an object gets its color. Give evidence and use examples to support your explanation.

Overlapping Filters `L2`

Purpose Students investigate how colors combine by addition and subtraction.

Materials 2 overhead projectors; red, green, and blue acetate filters

Procedure On the surface of an overhead projector, overlap red and green filters. Have students describe what they see projected on the screen. Ask them to predict what will happen when red and blue or green and blue filters overlap.

Expected Outcome Each filter subtracts all colors except one, so two overlapping filters subtract all colors to produce black. **Visual, Group**

---

3 ASSESS

Evaluate Understanding `L2`

Have students invent stage-lighting scenarios in which they describe clothing seen under a particular color of light. Encourage students to brainstorm what the clothing colors might be when viewed in white light.

Reteach `L1`

Compare Figures 25 and 26 to review how colors of light are different from colors of pigments.

Student letters should discuss how color is reflected by an object and how the color depends on the color(s) of light shining on the object.

 If your class subscribes to the Interactive Textbook, use it to review key concepts in Section 18.4.

Answer to . . .

Figure 24 *In red light, the red pot is red; in blue light or green light, the red pot looks black.*

Figure 25 *White light*

Figure 26 *Cyan + magenta + yellow; cyan + red; yellow + blue; magenta + green*

 It is formed when two primary colors combine.

Section 18.4 Assessment

1. Each wavelength refracts a different amount, separating the colors in white light.
2. The color depends on what the object is made of and the color(s) shining on the object.
3. Red, green, and blue
4. Cyan, yellow, magenta
5. Light refracts as it passes in and out of water droplets, separating the colors of the rainbow.

6. A pigment is a material that absorbs some colors and reflects others; each pigment reflects different colors.
7. A blue wall reflects blue light, so under green light the blue wall will appear black.
8. Cyan, yellow, and magenta paints combine in equal amounts to form black paint because these are the three primary colors of pigments.

CONCEPTS
— in Action —

New Light on Old Art

Background `L2`

When a painting is suspected of being a forgery, scientists analyze it using a variety of noninvasive techniques such as optical microscopy, scanning electron microscopy (SEM), X-ray radiography, X-ray fluorescence (XRF), and infrared photography. In optical microscopy, light from the painting passes through a series of lenses in a microscope to produce a magnified image of the painting's surface. In X-ray radiography, the painting is bombarded with X-ray radiation. Areas that contain high-atomic-weight pigments such as white lead and lead-tin yellow appear light in the resulting image. Cracks and areas of low-atomic-weight pigments absorb fewer X-rays and appear dark.

X-ray fluorescence (XRF) is able to determine the types of elements present by bombarding the painting with X-rays. Instead of being scattered, the X-rays are absorbed. The energy that is absorbed results in the emission of X-rays from the paint. The frequency of the emitted X-ray identifies the elements in the paint.

Infrared photography is used to reveal the presence of charcoal or graphite drawings beneath the paint layers. The drawings are revealed because the infrared radiation is absorbed by carbon in the drawing, but not by other substances in the paint.

New Light on Old Art

How does an expert know if a painting is by a famous artist, or is a fake? Scientific methods use electromagnetic radiation—visible light, ultraviolet, infrared, and X-rays.

Scientific methods cannot prove that a painting is genuine, but they can prove that it is a forgery. Careful examination may reveal aspects of the painting—the artist's methods or the materials used—that come from a time period later than the supposed date of the painting.

The simplest techniques used to examine paintings are those involving visible light. Looking at a cross section of a paint sample with a microscope or hand lens shows how the artist built up the layers of paint.

Scientists are able to examine the structure of the paint pigment in detail using high-powered microscopes. The structure can reveal whether the pigment is natural or has been made synthetically. Because synthetic paint pigments were not developed until the 1800s, the presence of synthetic pigment indicates the earliest date for the painting.

VISIBLE LIGHT

Interpreting visible light
This is the part of the electromagnetic spectrum to which human eyes are sensitive. Paint pigments reflect some parts of the visible spectrum and absorb others, so the eye perceives them as colored.

Examining samples
Using scalpels and tweezers, experts take tiny samples from a painting to examine the painted surface.

Paint pigment

Fibers

Microscope

Scalpel

Tweezers

Examining the Paint Surface

Identifying the pigments used in a painting usually requires taking one or more tiny samples from the painting. This sampling must be done with extreme care.

Carmine pigment

COCHINEAL BEETLES

Natural materials
Before the 1800s, most pigments used by artists were from natural sources. Many, including yellow lake, were obtained from plants. Some, such as carmine or cochineal, were of animal origin. Others, like ultramarine, came from minerals.

Yellow lake pigment

BUCKTHORN BERRIES

Lapis lazuli *was ground to a powder to make ultramarine pigment.*

Powdered pigment

Ultramarine pigment

Synthetic pigment has round, fine particles

Natural pigment has rough, crystalline particles

Under the microscope
High magnifications (100 to 500 times) show the physical structure of pigment particles. Here, the particles in the sample of synthetic ultramarine are different from those in the natural sample. Synthetic ultramarine was introduced in 1828, so paintings using this pigment could not have been made earlier than that year.

(continued)

Build Science Skills   L2

Comparing and Contrasting

Purpose Students compare and contrast the properties of paints.

Materials acrylic, watercolor, and oil paints of the same or similar color; several small artist paint brushes; watercolor paper; hand lens; several flat, wooden sticks

Class Time 10 minutes, then 10 minutes after one week

Procedure Have students paint a strip of each type of paint on both the watercolor paper and the flat, wooden stick. Make sure that students label each strip with the type of paint used. Place the strips in an area where they will remain undisturbed. After one week, have students observe all of the paint strips and record their observations.

Safety Have students wear lab aprons and disposable gloves.

Expected Outcome Students will be able to observe the characteristics of each paint type.
Kinesthetic, Group

Looking Beneath the Paint Surface

Rather than removing samples of the paint layer, non-invasive methods examine an intact painting by using the nonvisible regions of the electromagnetic spectrum. Ultraviolet, infrared, and X-rays can reveal many secrets that are invisible to the human eye.

Ultraviolet rays are best at showing surface features. The varnish that is the top layer of most paintings will fluoresce when exposed to ultraviolet. This fluorescence shows whether the original varnish has been disturbed.

Infrared rays can penetrate the layers of paint, so infrared imaging can be used to detect charcoal sketches and other images that are often hidden beneath the painted surface.

X-rays are used to look through a painting. X-rays are absorbed by dense materials and pass through others. Pigments that include metal atoms, such as white lead, show up clearly, as do metal objects used in the painting's construction. One forger was caught when X-rays revealed a machine-made nail in the wooden panel under a painting that was supposedly painted in the 1500s! Machine-made nails were not manufactured until the 1800s.

ULTRAVIOLET RAYS

Interpreting ultraviolet radiation
Although transparent to visible light, the varnish layer on the surface of most paintings can be seen using ultraviolet rays. In this copy of Cranach's painting, the ultraviolet makes the varnish layer fluoresce. Dark regions show areas that have been retouched or painted over.

Darker areas have been retouched or painted over.

Art forgery detection
A technician operates an infrared scanner. He is examining a copy of a painting by the German painter Lucas Cranach the Elder (1472–1553).

556 *Chapter 18*

INFRARED RAYS

Interpreting infrared imaging

The penetrating power of infrared most often uncovers preliminary sketches. But infrared imaging can also reveal surprising changes in the development of a work of art. In this self-portrait by Judith Leyster about 1630, the infrared image reveals that the artist originally included a portrait of herself on the easel. But later she changed the portrait to a musician.

Merry musician in the final painting

Infrared rays penetrate layers of paint, revealing an underlying self-portrait.

Part of the overpainted pattern of crossed keys

Horizontal wooden battens used to strengthen the panel

X-RAYS

Interpreting X-rays

X-rays can reveal the creative process at work. In this portrait of Pope Julius II, painted by Raphael in 1511–1512, the X-ray image shows a pattern of crossed keys on the wall behind the seated figure. The keys do not appear in visible light. Because oil paints are opaque to visible light, the artist probably simply painted over the keys.

Going Further

- Choose one of these painting styles to research: impressionism, surrealism, pointillism, or op art. Prepare an oral report to share with the class, including an explanation of the painting style, how light and color are used in the style, and three samples of the painting style.

- Take a Discovery Channel Video Field Trip by watching "Finding the Fakes."

Discovery CHANNEL SCHOOL
Video Field Trip

Going Further

Student reports should contain relevant examples of the selected style. Brief explanations of each style follow.

- **Perspective** The art of picturing objects or a scene in such a way as to show them as they appear to the eye with reference to relative distance or depth.
- **Impressionism** A theory and school of painting exemplified by Claude Monet, Camille Pissarro, and Alfred Sisley, whose aim was to capture a momentary glimpse of a subject, especially by reproducing the changing effects of light. They applied paint to a canvas in short strokes of pure color.
- **Surrealism** A movement in art and literature in which an attempt is made to portray or interrupt the workings of the unconscious mind as manifested in dreams.
- **Pointillism** The method of painting of certain French impressionists in which a white background is systematically covered with tiny points of pure color that blend together when seen from a distance, producing a luminous effect.
- **Op Art** A style of abstract painting utilizing geometric patterns or figures to create various optical effects, such as the illusion of movement.
Visual, Verbal

Discovery CHANNEL SCHOOL

Video Field Trip

Finding the Fakes

After students have viewed the Video Field Trip, ask them the following questions: **Why are pigment particles in older paintings different from the pigment particles in modern paintings?** *(Pigments ground by hand contained larger particles that varied in size. Today, machines use rollers that produce smaller, more uniform particles.)* **What sources were used for pigments in old paintings?** *(Rocks, minerals, and plants)* **How can forensic scientists tell if an old painting is a forgery?** *(Student answers may include, pigments found in the painting were not used in the artist's lifetime; brush strokes were not typical of the artist; or the canvas was not made of material used in that time period.)* **Why is it easier to prove that a painting is a forgery than to prove it is authentic?** *(Even if the pigments, style of brush strokes, and canvas material all match, the painting could still be the work of someone of the artist's own time or the work of a skilled forger.)*

18.5 Sources of Light

① FOCUS

Objectives

18.5.1 Explain how light is produced by common sources of light.

18.5.2 Describe the uses of different light sources.

18.5.3 Distinguish lasers from other light sources.

Build Vocabulary   L2

Word-Part Analysis Ask students what words they know other than those in the vocabulary list that have the key word parts *lum-, in-, fluor-,* and *co-. (illuminate, inactive, fluoride,* and *cooperate)* Give a definition of each word part. *(Lum-* means "light," *in-* means "not," *fluor-* means "to flow," and *co-* means "together.")* Give additional examples that share these word parts. *(Lumen, inactive, fluorine,* and *co-author)*

Reading Strategy   L2

a. Filament gets hot. Sample answer: Fluorescent—electric current heats electrodes, which emit electrons; electrons strike mercury vapor atoms; mercury atoms emit ultraviolet rays; ultraviolet rays strike phosphor coating; phosphors emit visible light.

② INSTRUCT

Incandescent Light

Use Visuals   L1

Figure 27 Have students carefully examine the photograph. Ask, **How many filaments can you see in this bulb?** *(Possible answer: It looks like there are two filaments on top and one more filament lower down that is not glowing as brightly.)* **How could a bulb use more than one filament?** *(Several filaments could be used to vary the brightness of the bulb, as in a three-way bulb.)*
Logical, Visual

Reading Focus

Key Concepts

- What are the six common sources of light?
- How does each type of light source generate light?

Vocabulary

- luminous
- incandescent
- fluorescence
- phosphor
- laser
- coherent light

Reading Strategy

Sequencing Copy and complete the flowchart below. As you read, pick two other light sources and complete a similar flowchart showing how each source generates light.

Incandescent Bulb

> Electrons flow through filament.
>
> ↓
>
> a. ___?___
>
> ↓
>
> Filament radiates light.

Figure 27 An incandescent bulb contains a filament. As electrons flow through the filament, the filament gets hot and emits light. **Formulating Hypotheses** *Why is a 100-watt bulb generally brighter than a 75-watt bulb?*

As sunlight fades toward the end of the day, objects around you become less and less visible. When the sun has completely set, you can no longer see your surroundings. Objects are invisible in the dark because no light is available to reflect off them. But some things, such as flashlights and fireflies, produce their own light. Objects that give off their own light are **luminous.** The sun is luminous, as are all light sources.

➤ **Common light sources include incandescent, fluorescent, laser, neon, tungsten-halogen, and sodium-vapor bulbs.** Each type of bulb produces light in a different way.

Incandescent Light

The light produced when an object gets hot enough to glow is **incandescent.** Figure 27 shows an incandescent light bulb. Inside, you can see the filament, a thin coil of wire stretched between two thicker wires. ➤ **When electrons flow through the filament of an incandescent bulb, the filament gets hot and emits light.**

The filaments in incandescent light bulbs are made of a substance called tungsten. Incandescent light bulbs are filled with a mixture of nitrogen gas and argon gas at very low pressure. These gases do not react with the filament as oxygen would, and so the filament lasts longer. Incandescent bulbs give off most of their energy as heat, not light.

 ## Section Resources

Print
- **Reading and Study Workbook With Math Support,** Section 18.5
- **Transparencies,** Section 18.5

Technology
- **Interactive Textbook,** Section 18.5
- **Presentation Pro CD-ROM,** Section 18.4
- **Go Online,** Science News, Light and optics

Fluorescent Light

In a process called **fluorescence** (floo uh RES uns), a material absorbs light at one wavelength and then emits light at a longer wavelength. A **phosphor** is a solid material that can emit light by fluorescence. ⊙ **Fluorescent light bulbs emit light by causing a phosphor to steadily emit photons.** A fluorescent bulb, such as the one in Figure 28, is a glass tube that contains mercury vapor. Inside, the glass is coated with phosphors.

When electric current flows through a fluorescent bulb, small pieces of metal called electrodes heat up and emit electrons. The electrons hit atoms of the mercury vapor, causing the mercury atoms to emit ultraviolet rays. The ultraviolet rays strike the phosphor coating on the inside of the tube and the atoms emit visible light.

You may have noticed that office buildings and schools use mostly fluorescent lights. Fluorescent tubes do not get as hot as incandescent bulbs because they emit most of their energy as light. This means that they use energy very efficiently. One 18-watt fluorescent tube provides the same amount of light as a 75-watt incandescent bulb, and the fluorescent tube lasts ten times longer.

Glass tube filled with mercury vapor

Electrode

Electrical contacts

Figure 28 The electrodes in a fluorescent bulb emit electrons that cause the mercury atoms to emit ultraviolet rays. These rays cause the phosphor coating to emit light.

 What happens during fluorescence?

Comparing Fluorescent and Incandescent Light

Materials

spectroscope, clear incandescent bulb, fluorescent bulb, colored pencils

Procedure 🔲 🔲

1. Turn on a clear, incandescent bulb. **CAUTION** *Incandescent bulbs get quite hot after they have been on for some time.* Observe the spectrum of the light coming from the incandescent bulb through a spectroscope.
2. Use colored pencils to draw this spectrum. Label the source of the spectrum.
3. Repeat Steps 1 and 2 with a fluorescent bulb.

Analyze and Conclude

1. **Comparing and Contrasting** How do the spectra produced by incandescent and fluorescent lights compare?
2. **Drawing Conclusions** During fluorescence, electrons absorb energy and move to specific higher energy levels. As they move back to a lower energy level, they release energy in the form of light. How does this fact help explain the appearance of the spectrum of fluorescent light?

The Electromagnetic Spectrum and Light **559**

Fluorescent Light
FYI

In fluorescent light, the phosphors are usually zinc sulfide with traces of copper.

Comparing Fluorescent and Incandescent Light ▮L2▮

Objective
After completing this activity, students will be able to
• explain the difference in spectra of incandescent and fluorescent lights.

 Address Misconceptions

Students may think that all white light is similar and consists of a continuous distribution of frequencies that includes the entire visible spectrum. Use the observations in this activity to help students overcome this misconception.

Skills Focus Observing, Inferring

🕐 **Prep Time** 15 minutes

Class Time 20 minutes

Safety Caution students that they should never directly observe the spectrum of the sun or any other intense light source because it can cause immediate, permanent eye damage. Caution students to avoid touching bulbs, which may become hot.

Expected Outcome Students will observe that incandescent bulbs produce continuous spectra, while the spectra of fluorescent light sources include narrow lines of various colors.

Analyze and Conclude
1. Incandescent light has a continuous spectrum. The spectrum of fluorescent light consists of a number of colored lines.

2. The lines are produced by photons with specific energies emitted by electrons returning from higher energy levels to the ground state.
Visual, Group

Customize for Inclusion Students

Behaviorally Disordered
Divide the class into six groups. Each group will be assigned a light source. Explain that the goal of each group is to find out details about each kind of light source. Foster self-esteem by encouraging groups to give individuals ownership of particular research topics such as

historical details or specialized uses. Give groups choices for presenting their results to minimize pressure related to this project. Options include written reports, posters, multimedia presentations, a Web site, or a mock science museum exhibit.

Answer to . . .

Figure 27 *Hypothesis: A 100-watt bulb is generally brighter because it emits more energy per second.*

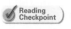 *A material converts UV rays into visible light.*

Laser Light
Build Reading Literacy L2

SQ3R Refer to page 530D in this chapter, which provides guidelines for SQ3R (Study, Question, Read, Recite, Review).

Teach this independent-study skill as a whole-class exercise. Direct students to survey the section and write headings such as Laser Light. As they survey, ask students to write one question for each heading, such as "How does a laser emit light?" Then, have students write answers to the questions as they read the section. After students finish reading, demonstrate how to recite the questions and answers, explaining that vocalizing in your own words helps you retain what you learned. Finally, have students review their notes the next day.
Auditory, Group

📖 HOW It Works

Gas Laser L2

Material excited in a laser is called lasing material. Lasing material can be a gas (CO_2), a gas mixture (helium-neon), a liquid (liquid crystals or organic dyes in a liquid solution or suspension), or a solid crystal (ruby). The lasing material determines the frequency of the light produced. Lasers do not have to produce visible light—there are infrared, ultraviolet, and X-ray lasers.

Interpreting Photographs The waves in the laser beam all have the same wavelength and direction of travel, and their peaks coincide.
Visual

For Enrichment L3

Interested students can make a multimedia presentation for the class explaining an application such as CD players, fiber optic networks, and laser eye surgery.
Verbal, Portfolio

Laser Light

A **laser** is a device that generates a beam of coherent light. The word *laser* stands for *l*ight *a*mplification by *s*timulated *e*mission of *r*adiation. 🔵 **Laser light is emitted when excited atoms of a solid, liquid, or gas emit photons.** Light in which waves have the same wavelength, and the crests and troughs are lined up, is **coherent light**. A beam of coherent light doesn't spread out significantly from its source, so the light has a relatively constant intensity. The energy it carries may be focused on a small area.

Lasers can cut through metals and make computer chips. Surgeons use lasers to cut or repair damaged tissue. Lasers carry information through optical fibers. Laser light is used to measure distances precisely.

📖 HOW It Works

Gas Laser

Laser light is produced by exciting the atoms of a solid, liquid, or gas so that they emit photons. Some of these photons collide with other excited atoms and stimulate the emission of more photons. Eventually some photons are released as an intense beam of light. The gas laser shown here uses a mixture of helium and neon gases. **Interpreting Photographs** *How does a laser produce coherent light?*

A **Gas mixture** Helium and neon gases are held in a sealed glass tube. Additional tubes, containing electrodes, are attached at the sides.

Fully reflective mirror *Photons bounce between this and a second, semi-reflective mirror.*

Using lasers Hand-held devices incorporating lasers are used in stores for reading bar codes. In the home, they are at the heart of many devices such as DVD and CD players.

Laser beam scans the label.

560 *Chapter 18*

⌐ Facts and Figures

Diverging Laser Beams Lasers do not necessarily produce parallel rays of light. A typical pocket diode laser produces red light that would diverge like a point source. A lens inside the laser collimates the beam (makes the rays nearly parallel).

The Lunar Laser Ranging Experiment began in 1969 when Apollo 11 astronauts left reflectors on the moon. Scientists send a laser beam from Earth and measure the time it takes to detect a return signal. The time delay gives the distance to the moon to an accuracy of about 3 cm. The experiment has been used to precisely measure the moon's orbit and movement of tectonic plates on Earth. To hit the reflectors, a laser beam is fired in the reverse direction through a telescope pointing toward the moon. The beam starts out with the same width as the telescope mirror (a few meters). When the beam reaches the moon, it has diverged to a width of more than 6 km.

Neon Light

A big city at night is likely aglow in neon lights. ⊕ **Neon lights emit light when electrons move through a gas or a mixture of gases inside glass tubing.** Many lights called neon lights contain gases other than neon. Often, other gases including helium, argon, and krypton are used in neon lights. Helium gas gives off a pink light. A mixture of argon gas and mercury vapor produces greenish-blue light. Krypton gas produces a pale violet light. Pure neon emits red light when electrons flow through the gas. Each kind of gas emits photons of different energies, and therefore different colors. The different photons emitted combine to give each glowing gas a distinctive color. The color of glass used to make the tube can also affect the color of the light.

Go Online
SCIENCE NEWS

For: Articles on light and optics
Visit: PHSchool.com
Web Code: cce-2185

B **Electrode** An electric current passes between this electrode and its twin on the other side of the tube, raising gas atoms to an excited state. This causes the atoms to release photons.

C **Photon multiplication** The photons begin to bounce back and forth off the mirrors at either end. Some hit other excited atoms, stimulating the emission of additional photons.

D **Semi-reflective mirror** Because it is only semi-reflective, this mirror reflects most of the photons but lets a few of them through.

Neon atom   Tube wall   Mirror

Mirror   Helium atom   Coherent waves

Laser beam

E **Laser beam** A straight, narrow, intense beam of coherent light emerges at this end.

Coherent light
The waves in laser light all have the same wavelength and direction of travel, and their peaks coincide. Light with these properties is called coherent light.

The Electromagnetic Spectrum and Light **561**

Inferring

Purpose Students observe and compare the spectra of different neon lights.

Materials spectroscope, neon lights

Safety Caution students never to view the sun or other intense light sources with a spectroscope because irreversible eye damage could result. Advise students to avoid touching neon lights, which can get quite hot.

Advance Prep To construct an inexpensive spectroscope, tape a 1-cm square of diffraction grating over a hole punched in an index card. Attach the card to cover one end of a small cardboard or plastic tube. Cover the other end of the tube with a card containing a narrow slit. Students will view spectra through the end of the tube with the diffraction grating.

Procedure Have students take home spectroscopes to observe spectra of neon signs near their homes. The lights of neon signs have fairly simple line spectra. Ask students to compare these spectra to determine which signs contain mixtures of gases or are made of colored glass that filters out certain colors.

Expected Outcome If the spectrum of a neon light appears to be a combination of two simpler spectra that students have observed, it probably contains a mixture of the gases responsible for the simpler spectra. If two spectra appear identical except for a specific region of one spectrum that is absent in the other, one of the signs may be made of colored glass that filters out a range of light frequencies.
Visual, Kinesthetic

Go Online
SCIENCE NEWS

Science News provides students with current information on light and optics.

Sodium-Vapor Light
Build Science Skills   L2

Inferring Ask, **Why do sodium-vapor lights have less glare than incandescent lights?** *(In sodium-vapor lights, light comes from vapor filling the entire tube, rather than from a small filament. The light is emitted from a larger area and is easier to look at directly.)* **Logical, Visual**

Tungsten-Halogen Light
Integrate Health   L2

Free, protective metal mesh covers have been offered to owners of tungsten-halogen lights because the bulbs get so hot. Have students find out how these covers can prevent fires. **Verbal**

3 ASSESS
Evaluate Understanding   L2

Invite students to write quiz questions with answers. Announce that good questions will be used on the next test.

Reteach   L1

Make a flowchart showing how each light source emits light. Cut each chart into pieces and shuffle and distribute them to students. Ask students to put the pieces back in the correct order.

Connecting ⊂ Concepts

Sample answer: Incandescent—Electrons flow in wire (electrical energy); moving electrons heat the filament (thermal energy); filament glows (electromagnetic energy).

Interactive Textbook If your class subscribes to the Interactive Textbook, use it to review key concepts in Section 18.5.

Sodium-Vapor Light

Sodium-vapor lights contain a small amount of solid sodium, as well as a mixture of neon and argon gases. **As electric current passes through a sodium-vapor bulb, it ionizes the gas mixture. The mixture warms up and the heat causes the sodium to change from a solid into a gas.** The current of electrons knocks electrons in sodium to higher energy levels. When the electrons move back to lower energy levels, the sodium atoms emit light. Sodium-vapor lights are energy efficient and give off very bright light. Many streets and parking lots are illuminated with sodium-vapor lights. Figure 29 shows how sodium-vapor light produced with neon and argon can alter the color of the objects it illuminates.

Tungsten-Halogen Light

Tungsten-halogen light is produced in much the same way as incandescent light. But unlike incandescent lights, a tungsten-halogen's bulb has a small amount of a halogen gas, such as iodine, bromine, or fluorine. **Inside a tungsten-halogen bulb, electrons flow through a tungsten filament. The filament gets hot and emits light.** The halogen gas reduces wear on the filament, so tungsten-halogen bulbs last longer than incandescent bulbs. The bulb of a tungsten-halogen light is made of quartz, because quartz has a high melting point. If glass were used, it would start to melt when the bulb got hot.

Figure 29 The yellow color of sodium-vapor light makes objects look different than they look in sunlight.

Section 18.5 Assessment

Reviewing Concepts
1. Name six common sources of light.
2. Describe how each type of bulb produces visible light.
3. Why are fluorescent light bulbs often used in office buildings and schools?
4. List three uses for lasers.
5. How are tungsten-halogen bulbs different from incandescent bulbs?

Critical Thinking
6. **Comparing and Contrasting** How are the six main types of lights similar? How are they different?

7. **Applying Concepts** Why do some bulbs heat up more than others?
8. **Formulating Hypotheses** A friend rubs a compact fluorescent bulb on her shirt on a dry day, and the bulb lights up for a moment. Propose a hypothesis to explain why.

Connecting ⊂ Concepts

Energy Review the types of energy in Section 15.1: mechanical, chemical, thermal, electrical, electromagnetic, and nuclear. Then pick two light sources and describe the energy changes in each after you turn on the light.

---

1. Incandescent, fluorescent, lasers, neon lights, sodium-vapor, tungsten-halogen
2. Incandescent: filament gets hot and emits light; Fluorescent: UV rays cause phosphors to emit visible light; Laser: excited atoms of a solid, liquid, or gas emit photons of coherent light; Neon: excited gas atoms emit light when they drop back down to a lower energy level; Sodium-vapor: a gas mixture ionizes, vaporizing sodium and producing excited atoms that emit light when they drop back down to a lower energy level; Tungsten-halogen: filament gets hot and emits light.
3. Fluorescent bulbs are very efficient.
4. Cut through metals; make computer chips; cut or repair tissue in surgery; transmit signals in fiber-optic cables
5. Tungsten-halogen bulbs are hotter and use a mixture of inert and halogen gases.
6. Incandescent and tungsten-halogen lights use a glowing filament. Fluorescent lights cause phosphors to fluoresce. Lasers emit coherent light. Neon lights and sodium vapor lights emit light when excited atoms return to a lower energy level. Refer to pp. 558–562 for differences.
7. Bulbs that heat a gas or a filament will heat up more than other light sources.
8. Hypothesis: The shirt acquires a net charge. The shirt's electric field excites mercury atoms in the bulb.

Mixing Colored Lights

What is color? How many different colors can be formed from a combination of only three colors? In this exploration, you will examine what happens when lights of three different colors are mixed.

Problem
How can you produce a range of colors from three lights of different colors?

Materials
- sources of red, blue, and green light
- tape
- large sheet of white paper

Skills
Observing

Procedure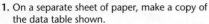

1. On a separate sheet of paper, make a copy of the data table shown.

Data Table		
Light Sources	Colors of Lights	Colors of Shadows
Red only		
Blue only		
Green only		
Red and blue		
Red and green		
Blue and green		
Red, blue, and green		

2. Dim the room lights. Turn on the red light source and shine it on a large sheet of white paper. In your data table, record the colors you observe on the paper. **CAUTION** *Do not touch lamps when they are on. They may be hot.*

3. Place your hand between the light source and the paper as shown. Record the color of your hand's shadow.

4. Repeat Steps 2 and 3 with the blue and then with the green light source.

5. Now turn on the red and blue light sources and allow their beams to partially overlap. Record your observations in your data table.

6. Place your hand in the overlapping beams of light. Note the colors of any shadows that your hand makes. Record your observations.

7. Repeat Steps 5 and 6 with the red and green light sources. Then repeat Steps 5 and 6 with the blue and green light sources.

8. Turn on all three light sources and allow their beams to overlap. Record your observations.

9. Place your hand in the overlapping red, green, and blue beams. Note the colors of any shadows that your hand makes on the white paper. Record your observations.

Analyze and Conclude

1. **Observing** What happened when two colored lights overlapped?

2. **Analyzing Data** How did the combination of two colored lights produce the shadows you observed?

3. **Applying Concepts** Explain how combining three colored lights produced the colors you observed.

4. **Drawing Conclusions** From the shadows you observed when using three colored lights, what can you conclude about how colors of light combine? Explain your answer.

Go Further Examine the effects of red, green, and blue lights on the appearance of familiar objects, such as red apples and green grass. Prepare a report explaining your observations and present the report to the class.

Mixing Colored Lights   L2

Objective
After completing this activity, students will be able to
- describe how colors of light combine by addition.

Skills Focus
Observing, Formulating Hypotheses

 Prep Time 10 minutes

Advance Preparation The red, blue, and green light sources can be floodlights, slide projectors, overhead projectors, or flashlights with filters. The light sources should provide a distinct colored spot of light whose position on the paper can be adjusted.

Class Time 40 minutes

Safety Take care that all electrical equipment is handled properly and plugged only into GFCI-protected receptacles. Do not allow students to handle the light sources because they will be extremely hot. Warn students not to look directly at the light sources or into the sun. Make sure there are no objects that create stumbling hazards, as students work in dim light.

Expected Outcome Overlapping two beams of primary colors of light produces secondary colors and two shadows, one of each primary color of light. Overlapping equal intensities of all three primary colors produces white light and three shadows that are secondary colors.

Sample Data

Red light only: Red light, dark shadow; Blue light only: Blue light, dark shadow; Green light only: Green light, dark shadow; Red and blue light: Magenta light, red and blue shadows; Red and green light: Yellow light, red and blue shadows; Blue and green light: Cyan light, red and blue shadows; Red, blue, and green light: White light, green, red, and blue shadows

Go Further

A colored object will reflect light of its own color and absorb light of other colors. For example, a red apple lit only by green light looks black.
Verbal, Visual

Analyze and Conclude

1. Two colors combined to make a new color.
2. Because there were two light sources, there were two overlapping shadows. In areas on the paper where the hand blocked only one beam of light, the other areas were lit by the other beam of light. Therefore, each shadow was the color of one beam of light.
3. Overlapping two beams produced secondary colors. Combining all three primary colors in equal intensity produced white light.
4. The colors of the shadows show how colors of light combine. In areas where the hand blocked one beam, the shadow was lit by the two other lights. Therefore, these areas were secondary colors of light. For example, where the hand blocked only the blue beam, the shadow was lit by red and green light, producing a yellow shadow. Similarly, red and blue light combined to produce a magenta shadow, and blue and green light combined to produce a cyan shadow.

Study Guide

Study Tip

Review Regularly
Tell students to make reviewing their notes part of their homework plan. They shouldn't just review homework that is assigned every night. Tell students that by reviewing their work for a few minutes each day they will spend less time studying for tests.

Thinking Visually

a. Infrared rays
b. Visible light
c. Ultraviolet rays
d. X-rays

Assessment

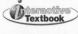 If your class subscribes to the Interactive Textbook, your students can go online to access an interactive version of the Student Edition and a self-test.

Reviewing Content

1. c   2. a   3. b
4. c   5. d   6. b
7. d   8. b   9. a
10. d

Understanding Concepts

11. The electric and magnetic fields regenerate each other.
12. Constructive and destructive interference
13. Infrared cameras are used to find victims because the human body is usually warmer than its surroundings.
14. Excessive exposure to ultraviolet rays can cause sunburn, wrinkles, skin cancer, and damage to eyes. In moderation, ultraviolet rays help the skin to produce vitamin D; they are also used to kill microorganisms in ventilation systems and to help plants grow in nurseries.

18.1 Electromagnetic Waves

Key Concepts

- Electromagnetic waves are produced when an electric charge vibrates or accelerates.
- Electromagnetic waves can travel through a vacuum as well as through matter. The speed of light in a vacuum, c, is 3.00×10^8 m/s.
- Electromagnetic waves vary in wavelength and frequency.
- Electromagnetic radiation behaves sometimes like a wave and sometimes like a stream of particles.
- Light spreads out as it moves away from its source.

Vocabulary

electromagnetic waves, p. 533; electric field, p. 533; magnetic field, p. 533; electromagnetic radiation, p. 533; photoelectric effect, p. 537; photons, p. 537; intensity, p. 538

18.2 The Electromagnetic Spectrum

Key Concepts

- The electromagnetic spectrum includes radio waves, infrared waves, visible light, ultraviolet rays, X-rays, and gamma rays.
- Electromagnetic waves are used in communications, medicine, and industry.

Vocabulary

electromagnetic spectrum, p. 540; amplitude modulation, p. 541; frequency modulation, p. 541; thermograms, p. 543

18.3 Behavior of Light

Key Concepts

- Materials can be transparent, translucent, or opaque.
- When light strikes a new medium, it can be reflected, absorbed, or transmitted.

Vocabulary

transparent, p. 546; translucent, p. 547; opaque, p. 547; image, p. 547; regular reflection, p. 547; diffuse reflection, p. 547; mirage, p. 548; polarized light, p. 548; scattering, p. 549

18.4 Color

Key Concepts

- As white light passes through a prism, shorter wavelengths refract more than longer wavelengths, and the colors separate.
- The color of any object depends on what the object is made of and on the color of light that strikes the object.
- The primary colors of light are red, green, and blue.
- The primary colors of pigments are cyan, yellow, and magenta.

Vocabulary

dispersion, p. 551; primary colors, p. 552; secondary color, p. 552; complementary colors of light, p. 552; pigment, p. 553; complementary colors of pigments, p. 553

18.5 Sources of Light

Key Concepts

- Common light sources include incandescent, fluorescent, laser, neon, tungsten-halogen, and sodium-vapor bulbs.
- Each light source produces light in a different way.

Vocabulary

luminous, p. 558; incandescent, p. 558; fluorescence, p. 559; phosphor, p. 559; laser, p. 560; coherent light, p. 560

Thinking Visually

Web Diagram Copy the web diagram below onto a sheet of paper. Use information from the chapter to complete the diagram.

Chapter Resources

Print
- *Chapter and Unit Tests,* Chapter 18 Test A and Test B
- *Test Prep Resources,* Chapter 18

Technology
- *Computer Test Bank,* Chapter Test 18
- *Interactive Textbook,* Chapter 18
- *Go Online,* PHSchool.com, Chapter 18

Assessment

Interactive Textbook with assessment at PHSchool.com

Reviewing Content

Choose the letter that best answers the question or completes the statement.

1. Electromagnetic waves
   a. all have the same wavelength.
   b. do not carry energy.
   c. can travel through empty space.
   d. all have the same frequency.

2. The particle model describes light as
   a. a stream of photons.
   b. an interference pattern.
   c. a wave.
   d. an electric field.

3. The electromagnetic waves with the highest frequency are
   a. infrared rays.   b. gamma rays.
   c. ultraviolet rays.   d. radio waves.

4. Microwaves and radar are
   a. infrared rays.   b. X-rays.
   c. radio waves.   d. ultraviolet rays.

5. Light that vibrates in only one direction is
   a. scattered.   b. reflected.
   c. refracted.   d. polarized.

6. Objects appear fuzzy through a material that is
   a. polarized.   b. translucent.
   c. transparent.   d. opaque.

7. Combining equal intensities of red light, green light, and blue light makes
   a. a secondary color.
   b. a complementary color.
   c. black light.
   d. white light.

8. A green object
   a. absorbs green light.
   b. reflects green light.
   c. absorbs yellow and blue light.
   d. reflects red and blue light.

9. An object that produces its own light is
   a. luminous.   b. coherent.
   c. opaque.   d. translucent.

10. Which type of light bulb uses phosphors?
    a. neon   b. incandescent
    c. tungsten-halogen   d. fluorescent

Understanding Concepts

11. How do electric and magnetic fields interact in an electromagnetic wave?

12. What behavior of light is evidence for a wave model of light?

13. Why are infrared rays useful in search-and-rescue operations?

14. How are ultraviolet rays harmful? How can they be helpful?

15. X-rays can take pictures of your bones but visible light cannot. Explain why.

16. Explain why you can see through the glass walls of the terrarium below.

17. How do polarized sunglasses work?

18. What does a prism do to white light?

19. How are the secondary colors of light related to the primary colors?

20. What are complementary colors of pigments?

21. When mixing colors of light, why does combining a secondary color with its complementary color give white light?

22. Explain why fluorescent lights are more efficient than incandescent lights.

23. Explain how laser light is different from ordinary visible light.

24. What is the purpose of halogen gas in a tungsten-halogen lamp?

The Electromagnetic Spectrum and Light **565**

Assessment (continued)

15. X-rays have high energy and can penetrate matter, such as muscle, that light cannot. But X-rays are absorbed by teeth and bones, so these areas appear as white on an X-ray photograph.

16. The glass is transparent.

17. Polarized sunglasses block glare with vertically polarized filters, which block the horizontally polarized light reflected from horizontal surfaces.

18. A prism spreads out the colors in white light, separating the colors into a spectrum.

19. Each secondary color of light is produced by the combination of two primary colors.

20. Complementary colors of pigments are two colors that combine to make black pigment, such as blue and yellow, green and magenta, or red and cyan.

21. A secondary color is a combination of two primary colors; when added to its complementary color (the third primary color), white light results.

22. Fluorescent lights do not get as hot as incandescent lights. They are more efficient because they emit most of their energy as visible light.

23. Laser light is coherent light, which means all of the waves have the same wavelength and the crests and troughs are lined up. Laser light can form a beam that can be focused on a small area.

24. The halogen gas reduces wear on the filament, so the bulb lasts longer than an incandescent bulb.

Homework Guide

Section	Questions
18.1	1–2, 11–12, 33–35
18.2	3–4, 13–15, 25–26, 36, 39
18.3	5–6, 16–18, 27, 37
18.4	7–8, 19–21, 28–31, 38
18.5	9–10, 22–24, 32

Critical Thinking

25. Similarities: Microwaves and infrared photons have less energy than invisible light photons. They both travel in a vacuum at the speed of light. Both have applications in communications. Differences: Microwaves are used for cooking and reheating food. Infrared photons have more energy than microwaves.

26. The frequency of the reflected radio waves is reduced because the car is moving away from a stationary radar source.

27. The sunset would be yellow because there would be no scattering if there is no atmosphere.

28. Light: The primary colors red, green, and blue mix to form white light. Pigment: The primary colors cyan, yellow, and magenta mix to form black pigment.

29. In all three cases, two primary colors of pigments combine to form a secondary color of pigment.

30. Only one color, magenta, is needed to produce black.

31. Students might predict that black will result because all three primary colors are being mixed. But the colors are not mixed in equal amounts. Two parts yellow plus two parts magenta plus one part cyan should result in black plus yellow and magenta, which is the same as black plus red. The result should be a dark red.

32. Laser light is very high intensity light that does not spread out, so it can damage tissue in the eye.

Math Skills

33. 3.3 m
34. 6.0×10^9 Hz
35. 40,260,000,000 mi/s; 670,000,000 mi/h

Concepts in Action

36. Rotating the food in a microwave oven will help the food to heat evenly. It works because areas of destructive interference, where little heating occurs, do not stay in one position within the food.

37. Mirages occur when light is gradually refracted through layers of hot air. At 32°C, a mirage is more likely because refraction will be greater than at 23°C.

38. The stage lights shining on the main character must be red. The green pants look black because there is no green light to reflect from them. Using white stage light will allow both the jacket and the pants to look their true colors.

Critical Thinking

25. Comparing and Contrasting How are microwaves and infrared rays similar? How are they different?

26. Applying Concepts How does the frequency of a car's returning radar signal change if the car moves away from the radar source?

27. Applying Concepts What color would the sunset be if you observed it on the moon? (*Hint:* the moon has no atmosphere.)

28. Comparing and Contrasting List the three primary colors of light and the three primary colors of pigments. What is the result if the three primary colors of light are mixed? What is the result if the three primary colors of pigments are mixed?

Use the illustration below to answer Questions 29–31.

29. Interpreting Photos Describe each combination of colors in A, B, and C.

30. Applying Concepts If you had green paint, such as produced in mixture A in the illustration, what is the fewest number of colors you could mix with it to get black? What would the color or colors be?

31. Predicting What color would you expect to make if you combined cyan and yellow from A, magenta and yellow from B, and only the magenta from C? Explain why.

32. Inferring Why might it be unsafe to look directly at laser light?

Math Skills

33. Calculating An FM radio station broadcasts on a frequency of 91 MHz. What is the wavelength of the wave that carries the coded information?

34. Calculating What is the frequency of a microwave that has a wavelength of 0.050 m?

35. Converting Units Convert the speed of light to miles per second and miles per hour. (*Hint:* 1 mile = 1610 meters)

Concepts in Action

36. Problem Solving What can you do to ensure even heating of microwaved food? Why does that work?

37. Predicting Are you more likely to see a mirage in the desert when the temperature is 32°C or 23°C? Explain why.

38. Relating Cause and Effect You are working the lights for a school play. The red jacket on the main character looks red, but her green pants look black. What is happening? How can you make both her jacket and her pants look their true color?

39. Writing in Science Write an advertisement for a sunscreen product. Make sure to explain to consumers why ultraviolet rays are dangerous.

Performance-Based Assessment

Comparing and Contrasting Visit a store that sells a variety of light bulbs including incandescent bulbs, tungsten-halogen bulbs, and fluorescent bulbs. Gather information from the packages on price and expected hours of service and display the data in a table. Conclude from your data which kind of bulb provides the most economical lighting for a particular purpose. Write your conclusions in a paragraph and share it with your family and classmates.

For: Self-grading assessment
Visit: PHSchool.com
Web Code: cca-2180

39. Student answers should mention that lengthy exposure to the sun's ultraviolet rays causes both short-term and long-term damage to the skin. Sunscreens absorb ultraviolet rays before they reach the skin. If students have done the Quick Lab Evaluating Sunscreen, they may use their results to support the claims in the advertisement.

Standardized Test Prep for Indiana

Standards Guide

Question	Standards
1	ICP.4.4
2	ICP.2.4
3	ICP.4.4
4	ICP.4.3
5	ICP.4.3

Test-Taking Tip

Analyzing Data
Some test questions are based on graphs. Take about 20 seconds to scan the graph. Read the labels. Describe the graph to yourself. *The graph gives information on wavelength, from shorter to longer, and frequency, from lower to higher.* Use the information to select which choice best answers the question.

What relationship is represented by the graph?
(A) Frequency is directly proportional to wavelength.
(B) Frequency is inversely proportional to wavelength.
(C) Comparing wavelength and frequency shows photon energy.
(D) Waves with lower frequencies and longer wavelengths exhibit the photoelectric effect.
(E) Wavelength is greater than frequency.

(Answer: B)

Choose the letter that best answers the question or completes the statement.

1. In order of increasing frequency, the electromagnetic waves are radio waves, infrared rays,
   (A) microwaves, visible light, X-rays, and gamma rays.
   (B) visible light, ultraviolet rays, X-rays, and gamma rays.
   (C) ultraviolet rays, X-rays, visible light, and radar.
   (D) gamma rays, X-rays, ultraviolet rays, and visible light.
   (E) gamma rays, X-rays, visible light, and ultraviolet rays.

2. A light source that emits light partly because of its phosphor coating is
   (A) an incandescent bulb.
   (B) a tungsten-halogen lamp.
   (C) a neon tube.
   (D) a fluorescent tube.
   (E) a laser.

3. A material that reflects or absorbs all of the light that strikes it is
   (A) translucent.   (B) opaque.
   (C) black.   (D) transparent.
   (E) incandescent.

4. An electromagnetic wave in space has a frequency of 0.5×10^8 Hz. Its wavelength is
   (A) 0.6 m.   (B) 6 m.
   (C) 60 m.   (D) 600 m.
   (E) 6000 m.

Both a source of red light and a source of blue light shine on a metal, as shown in the diagram below.

5. What scientific concept does the diagram represent?
   (A) interference
   (B) the photoelectric effect
   (C) polarization
   (D) diffuse reflection
   (E) refraction

6. Why was no electron emitted when the red light hit the metal?
   (A) Photons of red light have too little energy.
   (B) There were not enough photons available.
   (C) All electrons had already been emitted when the blue light hit the metal.
   (D) Red light is absorbed by metal.
   (E) Red light is reflected by metal.

The Electromagnetic Spectrum and Light **567**

Performance-Based Assessment

Student answers must include a data table, and their conclusions need to take into consideration a particular lighting purpose. The data table should be organized with types of bulbs versus cost, lifespan, and other criteria such as brightness in lumens. Sample data for comparable bulbs that can be used in a tabletop desk lamp:

Sample Data Table

Type	Cost	Lumens	Lifespan
100-W long-life incandescent	$0.60	1710	5000 h
100-W tungsten-halogen	$4.50	1800	2000 h
26-W compact fluorescent	$7.50	1900	10,000 h

Your students can independently test their knowledge of the chapter and print out their test results for your files.

Planning Guide

SECTION OBJECTIVES	STANDARDS		ACTIVITIES and LABS
	NATIONAL	STATE	
19.1 Mirrors, pp. 570–573 🕐 1 block or 2 periods **19.1.1 Describe** the law of reflection. **19.1.2 Describe** how a plane mirror produces an image. **19.1.3 Describe** real and virtual images and relate them to converging and diverging light rays. **19.1.4 Describe** the physical characteristics of plane, concave, and convex mirrors and **distinguish** between the types of images they form.	A-1, A-2, C-6		**SE** Inquiry Activity: How Can You Make Glass Disappear? p. 569 **L2** **SE** Quick Lab: Measuring the Height of Your Mirror Image, p. 571 **L2** **SE** Consumer Lab: Selecting Mirrors, p. 593 **L2** **TE** Build Science Skills: Observing, p. 570 **L2** **TE** Teacher Demo: Flashlight Mirrors, p. 572 **L2**
19.2 Lenses, pp. 574–578 🕐 1 block or 2 periods **19.2.1 Explain** what causes light to refract. **19.2.2 Define** index of refraction. **19.2.3 Describe** the physical characteristics of concave and convex lenses and **distinguish** between the types of images they form. **19.2.4 Describe** total internal reflection and **explain** its relationship to the critical angle.	A-1, B-6	ICP.2.4	**TE** Teacher Demo: Combining Lenses, p. 576 **L2** **TE** Build Science Skills: Observing, p. 577 **L2** **LM** Investigation 19A: Investigating Reflection and Refraction **L2**
19.3 Optical Instruments, pp. 580–585 🕐 1 block or 2 periods **19.3.1 Distinguish** between how reflecting and refracting telescopes form images. **19.3.2 Explain** how cameras regulate and focus light to form images. **19.3.3 Describe** how light travels in a compound microscope to produce an enlarged image.	A-1, A-2, B-6, C-6, E-2, F-1, G-1, G-2, G-3	ICP.2.4	**SE** Quick Lab: Building a Pinhole Viewer, p. 585 **L2** **TE** Teacher Demo: Making a Telescope, p. 581 **L2** **TE** Teacher Demo: Two Types of Microscopes, p. 584 **L2** **LM** Investigation 19B: Testing a Solar Furnace **L1**
19.4 The Eye and Vision, pp. 588–592 🕐 1 block or 2 periods **19.4.1 Name** the main parts of the eye and **describe** their functions. **19.4.2 Name** common vision problems, **identify** their causes, and **explain** how they can be corrected.	B-6, C-6, E-2, F-1, G-3		

RESOURCES PRINT and TECHNOLOGY	SECTION ASSESSMENT
RSW Section 19.1 **L1**	**SE** Section 19.1 Assessment, p. 573
T Chapter 19 Pretest **L2**	**iT** Section 19.1
Section 19.1 **L2**	
P Chapter 19 Pretest **L2**	
Section 19.1 **L2**	
SCLINKS **GO** Mirrors **L2**	
RSW Section 19.2 **L1**	**SE** Section 19.2 Assessment, p. 578
RSW Math Skill **L2**	**iT** Section 19.2
MSPS Section 19.2 **L2**	
T Section 19.2 **L2**	
P Section 19.2 **L2**	
RSW Section 19.3 **L1**	**SE** Section 19.3 Assessment, p. 585
DC Traveling Light **L2**	**iT** Section 19.3
T Section 19.3 **L2**	
P Section 19.3 **L2**	
SCIENCE NEWS **GO** Light and optics **L2**	
RSW Section 19.4 **L1**	**SE** Section 19.4 Assessment, p. 592
T Section 19.4 **L2**	**iT** Section 19.4
P Section 19.4 **L2**	

Go Online

Go online for these Internet resources.

PHSchool.com
Web Code: cch-2193
Web Code: cca-2190

NSTA SCLINKS
Web Code: ccn-2191

SCIENCE NEWS
Web Code: cce-2193

Materials for Activities and Labs

Quantities for each group

STUDENT EDITION

Inquiry Activity, p. 569
vegetable oil, water, 2 clear plastic or glass containers, 2 equal lengths of borosilicate glass tubing

Quick Lab, p. 571
plane mirror, meter stick, newspaper, masking tape

Quick Lab, p. 585
aluminum foil, black construction paper, cardboard tube, pin, wax paper, 4 rubber bands

Consumer Lab, p. 593
plane, convex, and concave mirrors; 2 metric rulers; roll of string; protractor

TEACHER'S EDITION

Build Science Skills, p. 570
graph paper, metric ruler, pencil, plane mirror

Teacher Demo, p. 572
flashlight with a beam that can be focused

Teacher Demo, p. 576
modeling clay, 2 convex lenses, 2 concave lenses, 2 index cards

Build Science Skills, p. 577
5-cm diameter double-convex lens, pencil

Teacher Demo, p. 581
2 convex lenses (one with a focal length of 10 cm and the other with a focal length of 30 cm), 1 stick of modeling clay

Teacher Demo, p. 584
compound microscope, stereo microscope

Build Science Skills, p. 587
flashlight, fiber optic bundle

Chapter Assessment

CHAPTER ASSESSMENT

SE Chapter Assessment, pp. 595–596
CUT Chapter 19 Test A, B
CTB Chapter 19
iT Chapter 19
PHSchool.com GO Web Code: cca-2190

STANDARDIZED TEST PREP

SE Chapter 19, p. 597
TP Diagnose and Prescribe

Interactive Textbook with assessment at PHSchool.com

Before you teach

From the Author

Sophia Yancopoulos
Manhattan College

Big Ideas

Optics is the science of how mirrors and lenses form images. Light travels in a straight line— except when it doesn't. The laws of optics at this level are straightforward and their applications to telescopes, cameras, fiber optics, and corrective eye gear have an immediate interest.

Forces and Motion Whether reflection or refraction, the bending of light rays depends on the substance the ray is traveling through. It can be tricky to distinguish the different kinds of images formed by concave and convex mirrors and lenses; it will help students if they actually reproduce the ray diagrams themselves, instead of simply looking at them. For a real image, the rays of light actually converge. For a virtual image, the eye and mind assume that light rays are coming in straight lines from the extrapolated point of origin. Students may understand the concept of a virtual image better if they remember that a plane mirror's virtual image is a copy of an object, formed as though the light rays came from behind the mirror. Obviously the rays do not really come from behind the mirror, however, and a virtual image cannot be projected.

The eye is like a self-focusing camera, but the eye's ability to see depends on its shape. Thanks to optics, if a person's cornea or eyeball is the wrong shape for perfect vision, corrective lenses can be used to change the path of the light rays and focus them into a clear image on the retina.

Physics Refresher

Mirrors 19.1

When a light ray reflects from any mirror, the angle of incidence equals the angle of reflection. To see this for a concave mirror, draw a tangent to the surface at the point where the ray is reflected. Then draw a normal line perpendicular to the tangent where the tangent line touches the surface. The angles of incidence and reflection can then be measured from the normal line.

Ray diagrams are useful for determining the locations of images formed by concave mirrors. To draw a diagram, first sketch the object, the mirror, the center of curvature C, the focal point F, and the principal axis. Next, draw three rays, each starting at the topmost point of the object: (1) parallel to the principal axis, reflected through F, (2) through F, reflected parallel to the principal axis, and (3) through C, reflected back along the same line. The point of intersection of the lines is the location of the tip of the image.

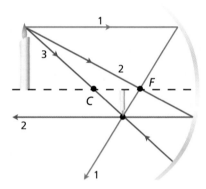

Lenses 19.2

A lens is a curved piece of transparent material used to focus light. A diverging lens is curved inward at the center and is thicker at the outer edges. A converging lens is curved outward at the center and is thinner at the outer edges. The focal length of a lens depends on the refractive index n of the lens as well as the shape of the lens (its radius of curvature). The refractive index depends on the material of which the lens is made. A higher refractive index causes a light ray to be bent more. For simplicity, the text refers to converging lenses as convex, and diverging lenses as concave.

Address Misconceptions

Students may mistakenly think that blocking part of a convex lens would block part of the image it forms. However, light rays reflect off an object through all parts of the lens. Blocking part of the lens produces a dimmer, but complete, image. For a strategy to overcome this misconception, see **Address Misconceptions** *on* **page 576.**

The fraction of a lens is described by the distance from the object to the lens (p), the distance from the image to the lens (q), and the focal length (f). These distances are related by the lens equation:

$$\frac{1}{p} + \frac{1}{q} = \frac{1}{f}$$

The image distance q is always negative for a virtual image because the image is on the same side of the lens as the object. A real image is on the side opposite that of the object, and it has positive q. For a concave lens, the focal length f is negative because the image is virtual. The image distance q is always negative for a concave lens.

As with concave mirrors, ray diagrams are useful for determining the image formed by convex lenses. The rules used to draw the diagrams are similar to those used for concave mirrors. However, a lens has two focal points equidistant on either side of the lens. The primary focal point is on the side of the object, and the secondary focal point is on the other side of the lens. To sketch the image, first draw the object, the lens, the axis of the lens, the two focal points F_1 and F_2, and the principal axis. Next, draw three rays, each starting at the topmost point of the object: (1) parallel to the principal axis and refracting through F_2, (2) through the center point of the lens, passing undisturbed through to the other side, (3) through F_1 and refracting parallel to the principal axis.

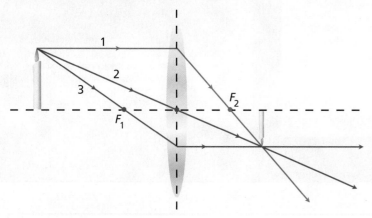

The Eye and Vision 19.4

Eyes are optical instruments that gather and focus light reflected and emitted from objects. Light enters the eye through the cornea. It then passes through the pupil and the lens and (ideally) is focused onto the retina. The cornea and the lens are responsible for focusing the light. The eyes' focus can be changed by tightening or relaxing the muscles around the lens. This slightly changes the shape of the lens so that the amount of refraction changes.

The image that is projected onto the retina is inverted and reversed. The brain translates signals from the retina so that it seems upright. However, there is no way that the brain can adapt to an image that is out of focus. The problems of nearsightedness and farsightedness must be corrected before the light enters the eye.

Build Reading Literacy

Using Context Clues

Understanding the Meanings of Words

Strategy Help students determine the meaning of unfamiliar words. This strategy helps students use clues from the surrounding text to help them infer an unfamiliar word's meaning. Before students begin, assign a section in Chapter 19 for them to read, such as The Law of Reflection, pp. 570–571.

Example
• When students encounter a word they are unfamiliar with have them read the rest of the sentence to determine clues other words in the sentence may give as to the meaning of the unfamiliar word.
• Have students read the surrounding sentences looking for hints to the word's meaning.
• Have students synthesize the meaning from a reading of the whole passage.
• Have students scan the text for a possible definition of the word highlighted in bold or an illustration of it in a diagram.
• Once students think they have determined the word's meaning they should verify it by checking in a dictionary.

See p. 580 for a script on how to use the using context clues strategy with students. For additional Build Reading Literacy strategies, see pp. 573, 574, and 590.

Go Online
NSTA PD LINKS
For: Teaching methods for optics
Visit: www.SciLinks.org/PDLinks
Web Code: ccn-1999

ASSESS PRIOR KNOWLEDGE

Use the Chapter Pretest below to assess students' prior knowledge. As needed, review these Science Concepts with students.

Review Science Concepts

Section 19.1 Review the behavior of light from Chapter 18. Remind students that light waves can be reflected when they strike a new medium. Review the definition of *image*.

Section 19.2 Students should recall that a transparent material transmits light. Review how light rays change as they pass from one medium to another. Remind students that when light passes at an angle from one medium to another, the speed and direction of travel can change.

Section 19.3 Encourage students to review the behaviors of light waves known as reflection and refraction.

Section 19.4 Ask students to recall what they know about the human eye. They should understand that they can see because light reflects from objects into their eyes.

CHAPTER
19 Optics

Each of these small water droplets acts like a lens and forms an image of the flowers in the background.

21st Century Learning

Interpersonal and Collaborative Skills

How do fiber optics work?

Everything that you say over the phone or send over the Internet at some point travels as pulses of light through strands of glass called fiber optic cables. Collaborate with a team to research the field of fiber optics. Create a multimedia presentation that explains the role of total internal reflection in fiber optic transmissions. Review and comment on other presentations by your classmates.

 Indiana's Academic Standards for Science

MECHANICAL ENERGY AND PROPAGATION OF ENERGY BY WAVES
ICP.2.4: Apply the properties of waves to wave phenomena including reflection and refraction.

568 *Chapter 19*

Chapter Pretest

1. What five things can happen to light that strikes a new medium? *(It can be reflected, absorbed, refracted, polarized, scattered)*
2. Define *image*. *(An image is a copy of an object formed by reflected or refracted waves of light.)*
3. True or False: Parallel light rays reflect in many different directions off a smooth surface. *(False)*

4. Which of the following makes an underwater object appear closer and larger than it really is? *(c)*
   a. Reflection   **b.** Absorption
   c. Refraction   **d.** Transmission
5. Which of the following types of material transmits almost all of the light that strikes it? *(c)*
   a. Translucent   **b.** Opaque
   c. Transparent   **d.** Mirror

6. Which of the following occurs to a light ray when it passes from one transparent medium into another at an angle other than 90°? *(d)*
   a. Bent
   b. Changed speed
   c. Refracted
   d. All of these
7. True or False: It is impossible to see unless light enters the eye. *(True)*

Chapter Preview

19.1 Mirrors   19.3 Optical Instruments
19.2 Lenses   19.4 The Eye and Vision

Video Field Trip
Traveling Light

Inquiry Activity

How Can You Make Glass Disappear?

Procedure

1. Pour vegetable oil into a container until it is half full. Repeat this procedure using water in a second container.

2. Insert a section of glass tubing into each container.

3. Look at the glass tubing through the side of the container with vegetable oil. Then look at the glass tubing through the side of the container with water.

Think About It

1. **Observing** What did you see when you looked at the glass tubing through the container with the vegetable oil? Through the container with the water?

2. **Inferring** Based on your observations, what can you infer about how light travels through the vegetable oil and the glass tubing? Through the water and the glass tubing?

Optics **569**

ENGAGE/EXPLORE

Inquiry Activity

How Can You Make Glass Disappear? L2

Purpose In this activity, students begin to recognize that the change in the path of light as it passes from one material to another depends on differences between the two materials.

Skills Focus Observing

Prep Time 10 minutes

Materials 2 clear plastic or glass containers, vegetable oil, water, 2 equal lengths of borosilicate glass tubing

Advance Prep Use borosilicate glass tubing, which is sold as heat-resistant glass under various brand names. If necessary, you can substitute rods for tubing.

Class Time 15 minutes

Safety Students should use care with breakable glass and wear safety goggles. Quickly wipe up any spilled liquid to avoid slips and falls.

Expected Outcome The glass tubing will seem to disappear when it is placed in the vegetable oil, but the tubing will be visible in the water.

Think About It

1. When the tubing is placed in the vegetable oil, the tubing appears almost invisible. When the tubing is placed in the water, the tubing can be seen clearly.
2. Students may infer that the glass tubing appears invisible in vegetable oil because the light is bent at the water–glass interface, but not at the oil–glass interface.
Visual

Video Field Trip
Traveling Light

Encourage students to view the Video Field Trip "Traveling Light."

1 FOCUS

Objectives

19.1.1 Describe the law of reflection.
19.1.2 Describe how a plane mirror produces an image.
19.1.3 Define real and virtual images and relate them to converging and diverging light rays.
19.1.4 Describe the physical characteristics of plane, concave, and convex mirrors and **distinguish** between the types of images they form.

Reading Focus

Build Vocabulary `L2`

Vocabulary Knowledge Rating Chart
Have students construct a chart with four columns: Term, Can Define or Use It, Have Heard or Seen It, Don't Know. Students should copy the vocabulary terms for this section under column 1. They should then place a checkmark under one of the other columns for each term.

Reading Strategy `L2`

a. Inside curved surface b. Both
c. Outside curved surface d. Virtual

2 INSTRUCT

The Law of Reflection
Build Science Skills `L2`

Observing

Purpose Students compare object and image distance in a plane mirror.

Materials graph paper, metric ruler, pencil, plane mirror

Class Time 15 minutes

Procedure Use lumps of clay to mount a mirror vertically on a sheet of graph paper. Hold a pencil in front of the mirror and observe its image. Place the pencil point down on one of the squares. Look into the mirror to observe the image of the pencil point. Count the number of squares from the object to the mirror and from the image to the mirror.

Expected Outcome The image distance behind the mirror appears to be the same as the distance from the mirror to the object.
Visual, Kinesthetic

19.1 Mirrors

Reading Focus

Key Concepts

- What is the law of reflection?
- What type of image is produced by each of the three types of mirrors?

Vocabulary

- ray diagram
- angle of incidence
- angle of reflection
- plane mirror
- virtual image
- concave mirror
- focal point
- real image
- convex mirror

Reading Strategy

Comparing and Contrasting After reading this section, compare mirror types by copying and completing the table.

Mirror	Shape of Surface	Image (virtual, real, or both)
Plane	Flat	Virtual
Concave	a. ___?___	b. ___?___
Convex	c. ___?___	d. ___?___

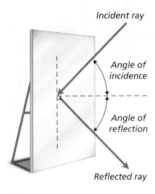

Figure 1 The flat (plane) mirror and the mirror-like lake surface both obey the law of reflection. According to the law of reflection, the angle of an incident ray equals the angle of the reflected ray.

Incident ray

Angle of incidence

Angle of reflection

Reflected ray

It is a bright, sunny day and you are enjoying a peaceful afternoon by a lake. The air is still and the surface of the lake looks just like a sheet of glass. In fact, it is so smooth that you can see your reflection in it.

The Law of Reflection

Optics includes the study of how mirrors and lenses form images. In your study of optics, assume that light is made up of rays that travel in straight lines. A **ray diagram** shows how rays change direction when they strike mirrors and pass through lenses.

Figure 1 shows a simple ray diagram of the law of reflection. The incoming ray, called the incident ray, approaches the mirror. The **angle of incidence** is the angle the incident ray makes with a line drawn perpendicular to the surface of the mirror. The mirror reflects the incident ray. The **angle of reflection** is the angle the reflected ray makes with the perpendicular line. **The law of reflection states that the angle of reflection is equal to the angle of incidence.**

 ## Section Resources

Print
- *Reading and Study Workbook With Math Support,* Section 19.1
- *Transparencies,* Chapter Pretest and Section 19.1

Technology
- *Interactive Textbook,* Section 19.1
- *Presentation Pro CD-ROM,* Section 19.1
- *Go Online,* NSTA SciLinks, Mirrors

Next time you are in a car behind a large truck, look for a sign that reads, "If you can't see my mirror, then I can't see you." Light travels from you to the mirror to the driver's eyes and also from the driver to the mirror to your eyes. If you do not have a line of vision to the truck's side-view mirror, then the truck driver does not have a line of vision to you. It can be dangerous to drive too close to large trucks!

Plane Mirrors

Mirrors are usually made of a sheet of glass that is coated with a thin layer of shiny metal on one surface. A mirror with a flat surface is a **plane mirror.** The large mirror in your bathroom is a plane mirror. When you look into a plane mirror, you see your reversed reflection—a right-left reversed image of yourself. An image is a copy of an object formed by rays of light.

Figure 2 shows how a plane mirror forms an image. To produce your image in a mirror, rays of light strike you and reflect. These reflected rays then strike the mirror and are reflected into your eyes. The dashed lines show how your brain interprets where the rays are coming from. The rays appear to come from behind the mirror. Your image appears the same distance behind the mirror as you are in front, and the image is right side up. If you walk toward the mirror, you'll see your image also move toward the mirror. A plane mirror always produces a virtual image. Although you can see a virtual image, this type of image cannot be projected onto any surface. A **virtual image** is a copy of an object formed at the location from which the light rays appear to come. It is important, however, to realize that the rays do not really come from behind the mirror.

Figure 2 The girl sees a virtual image of herself in the plane mirror. Virtual images such as this cannot be projected onto a screen. Note also how light rays from the object (the girl) reflect from the mirror's surface and obey the law of reflection. *Interpreting Photos* **What do the dashed lines represent?**

Quick Lab

Measuring the Height of Your Mirror Image

Materials

plane mirror, meter stick, newspaper, masking tape

Procedure

1. Have a classmate measure and record your height in centimeters.

2. Stand directly in front of the mirror, 1 m away from it.

3. Look at your image in the mirror. Have a classmate tape newspaper over those parts of the mirror (above and below your image) where you do not see any part of yourself.

4. Measure and record the height of your image by measuring the uncovered part of the mirror.

5. Repeat Steps 3 and 4 for distances of 2 m, 3 m, and 4 m.

Analyze and Conclude

1. **Analyzing Data** How did the height of your image change as you moved farther away from the mirror?

2. **Drawing Conclusions** What is the relationship between your height and the height of your image in the plane mirror?

Optics **571**

Quick Lab

Measuring the Height of Your Mirror Image **L2**

Objective
After completing this lab, students will be able to

• describe how the size of a mirror limits the size of the area that it reflects.

🚩 **Address Misconceptions**

Completing this lab can help students overcome the misconception that it is possible to see an image of one's full height in a mirror of any size, if the mirror is sufficiently far away.

Skills Focus Drawing Conclusions

⏱ **Prep Time** 10 minutes

Advance Prep Full length mirrors can be framed with black construction paper to provide mirror surfaces of different heights. One mirror should be longer than one-half the average height of the students. Another should be shorter than most of the students. The mirrors should be mounted on the wall and perpendicular to the floor. You can mark off distances of 1 to 4 m from each mirror on the floor with masking tape.

Class Time 20 minutes

Safety Framed mirrors should be used. If the mirrors aren't framed, cover the edges with duct tape to reduce the risk of breakage and injury. Students should use caution and wear safety goggles when working with breakable glass mirrors.

Expected Outcome A mirror must be at least half the height of a student to produce a full-length image of the student.

Analyze and Conclude
1. The image became smaller.
2. The image is never more than half the student's height.
Logical

Answer to . . .

Figure 2 *The dashed lines show the point of origin of the virtual image that is formed behind the mirror.*

Concave and Convex Mirrors

Address Misconceptions L2

Students may incorrectly think that concave mirrors form only real images. Challenge this misconception by having students look carefully at Figure 3C. Point out that when the object is very close to the mirror, the curvature of the mirror has less effect. The object's image is similar to the virtual image produced by a plane mirror. Also point out that the reflected rays in Figure 3C don't converge. The rays must converge to form a real image. Finally, explain that a real image produced by a mirror is always inverted. Have students hold a convex mirror very close to their eyes (closer than focal point) and then farther away. **Visual**

Flashlight Mirrors L2

Purpose Students observe how a small flashlight can focus a beam.

Materials flashlight with a beam that can be focused

Procedure Unscrew the head of the flashlight to show students the small bulb. Draw a diagram on the board showing the placement of the bulb at the focal point of the parabolic lens. Replace the head and show how the beam changes size as the head moves back and forth. Have students draw ray diagrams showing the pattern of reflection at different positions.

Expected Outcome The concave mirror in the flashlight focuses the light into a narrow bright beam when the bulb is placed at the focal point of the concave mirror. When the bulb is in front of or behind the focal point, the rays diverge. **Visual, Logical**

Download a worksheet on mirrors for students to complete, and find additional teacher support from NSTA SciLinks.

For: Links on mirrors
Visit: www.SciLinks.org
Web Code: ccn-2191

Figure 3 Concave mirrors can form either real or virtual images. **A** When parallel incoming rays strike a concave mirror, they are reflected through the focal point. **B** Concave mirrors form real images when the reflected light rays converge. **C** Concave mirrors form virtual images when the reflected rays appear to come from a point behind the mirror. **Interpreting Diagrams** *What determines the type of the image formed by a concave mirror?*

Concave and Convex Mirrors

Sometimes you see images that are very distorted. Look into both sides of a polished metal spoon. The images you see are quite different from the image formed by a plane mirror. Each side of the spoon produces a different image because each side is curved differently. The curved surface of the spoon changes the way light is reflected.

Concave Mirrors When the inside surface of a curved mirror is the reflecting surface, the mirror is a **concave mirror.** Figure 3A shows how a concave mirror reflects light rays that are parallel to the optical axis. The curvature of the reflecting surface causes the rays to come together. The point at which the light rays meet is called the **focal point.**

Look again at your reflection in the bowl of a spoon. The upside-down image you see is a real image. A **real image** is a copy of an object formed at the point where light rays actually meet. Unlike a virtual image, a real image can be viewed on a surface such as a screen.

Concave mirrors can form either real or virtual images. The type of image formed depends upon where the object is in relation to the mirror. Figure 3B shows how a concave mirror forms a real image. When the object is farther from the mirror than the focal point, the reflected rays meet in front of the mirror. Figure 3C shows how a concave mirror forms a virtual image. When the object is closer to the mirror than the focal point is the reflected rays spread out and appear to come from behind the mirror.

Concave mirrors are often used in automobile headlights and flashlights to direct the illumination from a single light bulb into a beam. If the bulb is placed at the focal point of a concave mirror, the reflected light rays will be parallel to one another. This results in a brighter beam of light.

Reading Checkpoint *At what location does a real image form?*

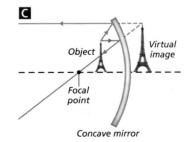

Facts and Figures

Concave Mirror Images There are five general types of images formed by a concave mirror. Consider the distance from the focal point to the mirror as *f*. The image types are: (1) If the object is between the focal point and the mirror, the image is virtual, upright, and enlarged. (2) If the object is located exactly at the focal point, no image is produced.

(3) If the object is located between a distance *f* and a distance 2*f* from the mirror, the image is real, inverted, and enlarged. (4) If the object is located at exactly a distance 2*f* from the mirror, the image is real, inverted, and the same size as the object. (5) If the object is located at a distance greater than 2*f*, the image is real, inverted, and smaller than the object.

Figure 4 Convex mirrors can only form virtual images. **A** When parallel incoming rays strike a convex mirror, they are reflected away from one another. **B** Convex mirrors always form virtual images that are upright and smaller than the object. Because of their reduced image size, convex mirrors on automobiles warn that "Objects are closer than they appear."

Convex Mirrors When the outside surface of a curved mirror is the reflecting surface, the mirror is a **convex mirror.** Figure 4A shows how a convex mirror reflects parallel light rays. Note how the curvature of the convex mirror causes the reflected rays to spread out.

Convex mirrors always cause light rays to spread out and can only form virtual images. Figure 4B shows how a convex mirror forms a virtual image. As the rays from the object reflect from the mirror, the rays spread out. Because they appear to be coming from a point behind the mirror, that is where the image appears. The image formed by a convex mirror is always upright and smaller than the object. This allows the mirror to show a wide angle of view. Because of their wide angle of view, round, convex mirrors are often used in store aisles, at hazardous traffic intersections, and for side mirrors on automobiles.

Go Online
active art

For: Activity on mirrors
Visit: PHSchool.com
Web Code: ccp-2191

Section 19.1 Assessment

Reviewing Concepts

1. How is the angle of incidence of a light ray related to the angle of reflection?
2. What type of image does a plane mirror form?
3. What types of image can be produced by a concave mirror? A convex mirror?
4. How are real images different from virtual images?
5. Why can convex mirrors form only one type of image?

Critical Thinking

6. **Applying Concepts** Explain why a plane mirror cannot form a real image.

7. **Inferring** If you place an object 10 cm from a particular concave mirror, a virtual image forms behind the mirror. What can you infer about the focal point of the mirror?
8. **Applying Concepts** If you look inside the bowl of a shiny metal spoon, your image is upside down. If you look at the outside of the bowl, your image is right side up. Explain.

Writing in Science

Compare-Contrast Paragraph Write a paragraph comparing convex mirrors and concave mirrors. (*Hint:* Use the information from your completed Reading Strategy on page 570.)

Optics **573**

Section 19.1 Assessment

1. The law of reflection states that the angle of reflection is equal to the angle of incidence.
2. A plane mirror always produces a virtual image.
3. Concave mirror: virtual and real; convex mirror: virtual
4. Real images can be projected onto a screen and form at the point where light rays actually converge, whereas virtual images cannot be projected and are formed at the point from which the light rays appear to be coming.

5. Convex lenses always cause light rays to diverge, therefore, they can form only virtual images.
6. For a real image to form, light rays must converge. Because a plane mirror cannot cause light rays to converge, it cannot form a real image.
7. The focal point of the mirror must be farther than 10 cm from the mirror.
8. Light rays from the convex side diverge forming an upright image. Light rays from the concave side converge forming an inverted image.

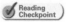

① FOCUS

Objectives

19.2.1 Explain what causes light to refract.

19.2.2 Define index of refraction.

19.2.3 Describe the physical characteristics of concave and convex lenses and **distinguish** between the types of images they form.

19.2.4 Describe total internal reflection and **explain** its relationship to the critical angle.

Reading Focus

Build Vocabulary `L2`

Concept Maps Creating concept maps can help students understand the convex and concave lenses studied in this section. Have students include the following topics: lens shape, images formed, applications, diverging rays, and converging rays. Advanced students could incorporate sketches showing how the images are formed.

Reading Strategy `L2`

a. Ratio of the speed of light in a vacuum to the speed of light in the material.
b. Angle of incidence that produces an angle of refraction of 90 degrees.
c. The complete reflection of a light ray back into its original medium.

② INSTRUCT

Index of Refraction of Light

Build Reading Literacy `L1`

Outline Refer to page **156D** in **Chapter 6,** which provides the guidelines for using an outline.

Have students create an outline of the section (pp. 574–578). Ask, **Based on your outline, what is an index of refraction, and what is total internal reflection?** *(An index of refraction is a measure of how much light changes speed as it enters a new medium. Total internal reflection is the complete reflection of a light ray back into its original medium. The angle depends on the index of refraction.)*
Verbal, Logical

19.2 Lenses

  Standard: ICP.2.4

Reading Focus

Key Concepts

- What causes light to refract?
- What type of images do concave and convex lenses form?
- In what types of materials is total internal reflection likely to occur?

Vocabulary

- index of refraction
- lens
- concave lens
- convex lens
- critical angle
- total internal reflection

Reading Strategy

Building Vocabulary Copy the table below. As you read the section, define in your own words each vocabulary word listed in the table.

Vocabulary Term	Definition
Index of refraction	a. _____?_____
Critical angle of refraction	b. _____?_____
Total internal reflection	c. _____?_____

You may wear eyeglasses or contact lenses and you have probably used a hand lens like the one shown in Figure 5. If so, you have seen how the bending, or refracting, of light can change the way you see something. The enlarged image seen through the lens in Figure 5 is due to refraction. The lens material changes the path of the light rays passing through it. The amount the light rays change direction determines the appearance of the image you see.

Index of Refraction of Light

Light usually travels in straight lines. In a vacuum, light travels at a speed of 3.00×10^8 meters per second. Once light passes from a vacuum into any other medium, it slows down. The speed of light in the new medium depends on the material of the new medium.

Some media, such as air, allow light to pass through almost as fast as it would through a vacuum. In fact, air slows the speed of light only by about three ten-thousandths of one percent (0.0003%). Other media cause light to slow down much more. For instance, the speed of light in water and in glass slows to 2.25×10^8 meters per second and 2.00×10^8 meters per second respectively.

Figure 5 Light rays slow and bend as they pass through the curved glass lens. In this case, the result is a magnified image.

Section Resources

Print

- *Laboratory Manual,* Investigation 19A
- *Reading and Study Workbook With Math Support,* Section 19.2 and **Math Skill:** Calculating Index of Refraction
- *Math Skills and Problem Solving Workbook,* Section 19.2
- *Transparencies,* Section 19.2

Technology

- *Interactive Textbook,* Section 19.2
- *Presentation Pro CD-ROM,* Section 19.2

When light enters a new medium at an angle, the change in speed causes the light to bend, or refract. For example, when light passes from air into glass or water, it slows down. When light passes from glass or water into air, it speeds up. The amount by which the light refracts as it passes from one medium to another depends upon the difference between the speeds of light in the two media.

Figure 6 shows how the path of a light ray changes as it passes from one medium into another. The incident ray of light, traveling through air, first strikes the boundary between the air and the water. As the light ray enters the water, it is refracted. You can see in Figure 6 that the light ray is now traveling in a new direction. As the ray enters the glass, it is refracted even more. Finally, when the ray reenters air, its path is bent again, but back to its original direction. Note that regardless of the refraction that occurs in the water and glass layers, the ray again travels in its original direction when it reenters the air.

How much the speed of a light ray slows as it enters a new material depends on the material's index of refraction. The **index of refraction** for a material is the ratio of the speed of light in a vacuum to the speed of the light in the material. A material with a low index of refraction (near 1) causes light to slow and refract very little. Air, with an index of refraction of 1.0003, is such a material. Diamond, however, with an index of refraction of 2.42, causes light to slow and refract significantly.

Air

Water

Glass

Air

Figure 6 A light ray bends (refracts) as it passes through media with different indices of refraction. **Inferring** *Based on the path of the light ray, which medium has the greatest index of refraction?*

Properties of Gemstones

Gemstones used in jewelry are known for several of their physical properties—primarily luster and optical brilliance. Luster is a measure of the amount of light that strikes a gemstone's surface and is reflected. Flat and smooth surfaces increase a gemstone's luster.

Like luster, the brilliance of a gemstone involves reflected light. Light that is not reflected by a gem's lustrous surface passes into the stone. The brilliance of a gemstone is a measure of the amount of light entering the gem that is reflected back to the viewer. Precise techniques are used to cut gemstones into shapes that produce maximum brilliance. The combination of a specialized shape and the gemstone's inherent high index of refraction gives gems their brilliance.

The table summarizes the index of refraction and luster of several common gemstones. Note that moissanite is a manufactured material used to simulate diamond.

Properties of Natural and Synthetic Gemstones

Material	Index of Refraction	Luster
Diamond	2.42	17.2%
Moissanite	2.65	20.4%
Ruby	1.77	7.4%
Sapphire	1.77	7.4%
Emerald	1.58	4.8%

1. **Interpreting Tables** Which material is the most lustrous? The least lustrous?

2. **Calculating** What percentage of light striking a sapphire gemstone enters it?

3. **Applying Concepts** If a light ray strikes each material at an angle, in which material would the light ray bend the most?

4. **Applying Concepts** The speed of light through an unknown gemstone is 1.69×10^8 m/s. Identify the gemstone.

Optics **575**

Customize for Inclusion Students

Concave and Convex Lenses

Use Community Resources `L2`

Invite a person who repairs cameras to come to your class and demonstrate how a camera operates and forms images. Encourage students to prepare and ask questions related to optical design. Check the phone book to find camera shops that are authorized repair centers.
Interpersonal, Visual

Address Misconceptions `L2`

A common misconception is that blocking part of the surface of a convex lens will block the corresponding part of the image. Address this misconception by holding a convex lens between a lamp and a flat surface (such as a wall or book). Adjust the distances so students see an inverted image of the lamp on the surface. Next, cover part of the lens with your hand. Students will see that the lamp's image on the flat surface is dimmer, but because the light rays bend, the image is complete. Draw a ray diagram on the board to explain this effect.
Visual

Teacher Demo

Combining Lenses `L2`

Purpose Students see the effects of combining lenses.

Materials modeling clay, 2 convex lenses, 2 concave lenses, 2 index cards

Procedure Prior to class, use balls of modeling clay to support each lens vertically. Sketch an object, such as a tree, on the index cards and use clay to support them vertically also. Set up a display with an index card about 10 cm behind a convex lens, and a concave lens about 1 cm in front of a concave lens. Set up a similar display, but now have the concave lens about 10 cm in front of the concave lens. Allow students to look through both setups.

Expected Outcome Students will observe that the effect of a concave lens cancels the effect of a convex lens, as long as the lenses are close together.
Visual

Figure 7 Concave lenses can only form virtual images. **A** When parallel incoming rays strike a concave lens, they are refracted away from one another. **B** As the light rays diverge after passing through the concave lens, they form a virtual image of the object.

Figure 8 A housefly has two large compound eyes. Each eye is made up of thousands of tiny individual eyes called facets. The outer surface of each facet is convex in shape. The eyes give the fly a nearly 360-degree field of view.

Concave and Convex Lenses

Lenses are used to change the path of light rays before they enter your eyes. A **lens** is an object made of transparent material that has one or two curved surfaces that can refract light. The curvature and thickness of a lens affect the way it refracts light.

Concave Lenses A **concave lens** is curved inward at the center and is thickest at the outside edges. Figure 7A shows how a concave lens refracts light rays. As the rays pass through the lens, each one is refracted due to the change of medium. The rays enter the lens at different angles and so they emerge from the lens at different angles. Concave lenses cause incoming parallel rays to spread out, or diverge. (Concave lenses are a type of diverging lens.) The diverging rays appear to come from a single point, the focal point, on the same side of the lens as the object.

 Concave lenses always cause light rays to spread out and can only form virtual images. Figure 7B shows how a concave lens forms a virtual image. The image is formed at the point from which the refracted rays appear to come. The image formed by a concave lens is always smaller than the object.

Concave lenses are often used in the viewfinders of cameras. The small virtual image you see through the viewfinder lens is similar to what the photograph will show. Concave lenses are also combined with mirrors or other lenses to form images in optical instruments such as telescopes.

Convex Lenses Note how the shape of each of the fly's eyes in Figure 8 resembles the exterior surface of a sphere. A shape like this is known as convex. Figure 9A shows that a **convex lens** is curved outward at the center and is thinnest at the outer edges. Figure 9A also shows how light is refracted by a convex lens. As the rays pass through the lens, each one is refracted, and they emerge at different angles. Convex lenses cause incoming parallel rays to come together, or converge. (Convex lenses are also called converging lens.) The converging rays meet at a single point, the focal point, on the side of the lens opposite to the object.

Facts and Figures

Eyeglass Scientists at Lawrence Livermore National Laboratory in California are working on a new type of space telescope known as "Eyeglass." An Eyeglass is different from other space telescopes because it does not use mirrors or traditional glass lenses, but diffractive optics (or Fresnel lenses). The advantages of using an Eyeglass telescope would include its flexibility, lightness, and ability to be folded. The Livermore team has currently constructed the world's largest such lens. It has a diameter of 5 meters and is made of 72 glass panels that can be folded. Although the lens is larger than the Hubble Space telescope, it weighs ten times less.

A

B

C

Figure 9 Convex lenses can form either real or virtual images. **A** When parallel incoming rays strike a convex lens, they are refracted toward each other and pass through the focal point. **B** When an object is located beyond the focal point of a convex lens, a real image is formed. **C** A magnified, virtual image is formed when the object is located between the focal point and the lens.

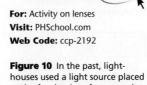

Go Online
active art

For: Activity on lenses
Visit: PHSchool.com
Web Code: ccp-2192

Figure 10 In the past, light-houses used a light source placed at the focal point of a convex lens or series of convex lenses to form a beam of parallel light rays.
Comparing and Contrasting *How does the setup shown in Figure 9A compare with that used in old lighthouses?*

Optics **577**

⬤ **Convex lenses form either real or virtual images.** Whether an image is real or virtual depends upon how far the object is from the lens. Figures 9B and 9C show a convex lens forming real and virtual images.

Convex lenses are used in slide and movie projectors, cameras, and lighthouses like the one in Figure 10. Of course, you don't see an upside-down real image at the movie theatre because the film is placed upside down in the projector. When the rays of light from the upside-down film pass through the projector's convex lens, the real image is projected onto the screen right side up.

Reading Checkpoint *How is a convex lens shaped?*

FYI

The distance from a lens or a mirror to its focal point is known as the focal length, *f*. Notice that Figures 6 and 7 show double concave and double convex lenses, insofar as both surfaces are concave, or convex, respectively. Note that the text uses convex for any converging lens, and concave for any diverging lens. Converging lenses have a positive focal length, and diverging lenses have a negative focal length.

Go Online
active art

For: Activity on mirrors and lenses
Visit: PHSchool.com
Web Code: ccp-2192

Students can interact with simulations of how mirrors and lenses form images.

Total Internal Reflection
Integrate Social Studies [L2]

Alhazen, an eleventh-century Arabian scientist, was an early pioneer in the field of optics. He challenged a common belief that rays emanating from the eyes enabled vision. Alhazen's theory was that light originated from the sun and other luminous objects. The eye saw the light that was reflected from objects. Alhazen also studied the refraction of light and the focusing of light by lenses. He constructed a pinhole camera, magnifying lenses, and parabolic mirrors. Have students research other early scientists who studied optics, such as Archimedes, Galileo, and Kepler.
Verbal, Logical

FYI

Note in Figures 11A and 11B that there are two rays emanating from the glass-air boundary where the incident ray strikes. The size of these rays are approximately representative of the amount of light from the incident ray that is reflected and refracted.

3 ASSESS
Evaluate Understanding [L2]

Randomly ask students to list the general properties of a convex or concave lens. Also, have them name at least one application for the lens.

Reteach [L1]

Have students draw sketches of the different types of image formation by lenses. They may need to refer to Figures 7 and 9.

Connecting ⊂ Concepts

Student answers should demonstrate an understanding that, because the frequency does not change, the only way for the speed to decrease is if the wavelength decreases.

Interactive Textbook If your class subscribes to the Interactive Textbook, use it to review key concepts in Section 19.2

Total Internal Reflection

A relatively new and very important application of refraction is fiber optics. Light rays are generally unable to exit through the sides of the curving fiber optic strands. Because of this, fiber optics are very useful for carrying information in the form of light. Figures 11A through 11C explain how fiber optics work.

As shown in Figure 11A, a light ray exiting from glass into air is refracted. Figure 11B shows that as the angle of incidence of the exiting ray increases, an angle known as the critical angle of refraction is reached. The **critical angle** is the angle of incidence that produces an angle of refraction of 90 degrees. At the critical angle the light ray bends so much that it takes a path along the glass-air boundary. Figure 11C shows that at angles larger than the critical angle, the light ray bends so much that it is reflected back into the glass. This situation is known as total internal reflection. **Total internal reflection** is the complete reflection of a light ray back into its original medium.

⊙ Materials that have small critical angles are likely to cause most of the light entering them to be totally internally reflected. Such materials include diamond and the type of glass used in fiber optic strands. By making use of total internal reflection, fiber optics are able to transmit data in the form of light pulses over large distances with little loss in signal strength. To learn more about fiber optics, see page 586.

Figure 11 Fiber optics make use of total internal reflection. **A** When a ray hits the glass-air boundary at an angle less than the critical angle, it is partly refracted and partly reflected. **B** At the critical angle, the angle of refraction is 90 degrees. **C** When the critical angle is exceeded, all of the light is reflected—total internal reflection occurs.

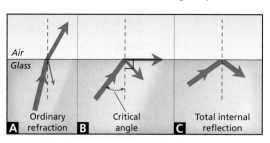

Air / Glass

A Ordinary refraction **B** Critical angle **C** Total internal reflection

Section 19.2 Assessment

Reviewing Concepts
1. ⊙ What causes light rays to bend?
2. ⊙ Why can concave lenses form only one type of image?
3. ⊙ What type of images are formed by concave lenses? By convex lenses?
4. ⊙ Most of the light entering what type of material is likely to be totally internally reflected?

Critical Thinking
5. **Comparing and Contrasting** How is a convex lens different from a concave lens? How are they the same?

6. **Applying Concepts** Explain how a convex lens is similar to a concave mirror.

Connecting ⊂ Concepts

Speed of Light In Chapter 18, you learned that light travels at 3.00×10^8 m/s through the air. This speed is the product of frequency and wavelength (Speed = Frequency × Wavelength). Use this equation to show that the wavelength of the light changes when it passes from air to water. (*Hint:* The speed decreases and the frequency does not change.)

Section 19.2 Assessment

1. When light enters a new medium at an angle, the change in speed causes the light to bend, or refract. The part of the wavefront in the new medium moves at a different speed, causing the wave's direction to change (bend).
2. Because concave lenses always cause light rays to spread out, they can form only virtual images.
3. Concave lenses form only virtual images, whereas convex lenses can form either real or virtual images.

4. Materials that have small critical angles of refraction cause most of the light entering them to be totally internally reflected.
5. Similarities: Both lenses have curved surfaces, refract light rays, and can form images. Differences: Concave lenses make light rays diverge and can only form virtual images, whereas convex lens can make light rays converge or diverge and can form both real and virtual images.
6. Both cause light rays to diverge and can form virtual images.

issues in SCIENCE

Is Video Surveillance an Invasion of Privacy?

Not long ago, video cameras were cumbersome pieces of equipment. They required long cables and stored images on bulky magnetic tape cassettes. Recent advances in optics, digital imaging, and electronic technology have revolutionized video equipment. High-quality digital video cameras that are able to store their images in a variety of convenient formats are now very affordable. Extremely small, battery-powered video cameras are also available to the public.

However, not everyone is excited about the spread of affordable video technology. The explosion in the number of cameras being used for surveillance purposes is a huge concern to many Americans. Is your right to privacy being violated?

The Viewpoints

Video Surveillance Is Not an Invasion of Privacy

Video surveillance is an existing and proven technology that is very effective for many purposes. Traffic cameras on highways help motorists avoid accidents and traffic jams. Video cameras in stores have been used for years to deter and help capture shoplifters. Many major cities have installed cameras at large intersections, to photograph drivers who run red lights. Citations from such systems have cut down on traffic violations and on pedestrian accidents. Sophisticated video systems at some airports can identify known criminals before they board an airplane. The common thing in all of these examples is that the general public is safer because of the use of video surveillance cameras. Having some of our actions recorded on video is a small price to pay for our greatly increased safety.

Video Surveillance Violates a Person's Right to Privacy

Video surveillance comes at a very high price—the loss of personal privacy. Our society is quickly heading toward the day when any individual can be tracked throughout an entire day. Do you want the government and private companies to know every aspect of your life? The United States Supreme Court has stated that some acts that violate a person's reasonable expectation of privacy constitute an illegal search. Yet these actions are going on every day! Video surveillance, which is currently out of control, is just one of many threats to a person's right to a private life. Strict laws designed to protect a person's right to privacy need to be enacted as soon as possible.

Research and Decide

1. **Defining the Issue** Use your own words to describe at least two of the major issues involved in the use of video surveillance cameras.

2. **Analyzing the Viewpoints** List the arguments for and against the use of video surveillance cameras. What are the advantages? What are the disadvantages or risks?

3. **Forming Your Opinion** Is video surveillance an invasion of your right to privacy? If so, in what situations, if any, is it acceptable?

4. **Going Further** Research a recent court case involving video surveillance and privacy. Write a short report summarizing the case. Explain why you agree or disagree with the decision.

For: More on this issue
Visit: PHSchool.com
Web Code: cch-2193

Optics **579**

Is Video Surveillance an Invasion of Privacy? L2

Background
An important issue of video surveillance is whether it is legal. The courts, including the United States Supreme Court, have repeatedly ruled that video surveillance is legal under certain circumstances. A primary requirement is that the surveillance must be done with high regard for a person's right to privacy. It should only be done if other methods for restricting crime are impossible or ineffective. Surveillance cannot be performed in areas such as restrooms or locker rooms, where a person can reasonably expect privacy.

Answers
1. Student answers will vary but should include the issues of safety and privacy.
2. Arguments "for" center around increased safety and the general idea of freedom, whereas "against" arguments center around the right to live your life in privacy. Advantages and disadvantages are closely related to these arguments.
3. Student answers will vary but should clearly state a position and detail situations when video surveillance is acceptable and when it is not.
4. Reports will vary, but should contain a concise summary of the key points in the case and an explanation as to why the student agrees or disagrees with the decision.

Have students further research the issues related to this topic.

1 FOCUS

Objectives

19.3.1 Distinguish between how reflecting and refracting telescopes form images.

19.3.2 Explain how cameras regulate and focus light to form images.

19.3.3 Describe how light travels in a compound microscope to produce an enlarged image.

Reading Focus

Build Vocabulary L2

Flowchart As students read about reflecting telescopes, have them make a flowchart showing the steps in the image formation process. Ask students to provide definitions for any scientific words used in their flowcharts.

Reading Strategy L2

Acceptable answers for **a.** and **b.** include any optical instruments, such as microscopes and cameras. After completing the section, revised diagrams should include refracting and reflecting telescopes, cameras (pinhole, and modern or SLR), and microscopes.

2 INSTRUCT

Telescopes

Build Reading Literacy L1

Using Context Clues Refer to page 568D in this chapter, which provides guidelines for using context clues.

As students read Section 19.3 (pp. 580–585), have them look for unfamiliar words. For example, students may not know definitions for the words *specimen, elements,* and *platform.* Encourage them to use surrounding sentences and figures to help them understand the word. Demonstrate this procedure with the word *shutter* on p. 584. **Verbal**

Use Community Resources L2

Invite a member of the local astronomical society to discuss how different types of telescopes form images and demonstrate their use. **Interpersonal, Visual**

19.3 Optical Instruments

Standard: ICP.2.4

Reading Focus

Key Concepts

- What are the two main types of telescopes?
- How does a camera form an image on film?
- What type of lenses does a compound microscope use to form an image?

Vocabulary

- telescope
- reflecting telescope
- refracting telescope
- camera
- microscope

Reading Strategy

Using Prior Knowledge Copy the diagram below and add to it the names and descriptions of other optical instruments you know. Revise the diagram after reading the section.

Telescopes — Optical Instruments — a. ? — b. ?

Figure 12 Shown below is one of the two Keck telescopes located on the summit of Hawaii's dormant Mauna Kea volcano. The telescopes, one optical and one infrared, are the largest in the United States. **Inferring** *What might be a reason for the telescopes being located on a mountain top?*

580 Chapter 19

Your view of the world is not shaped solely by what you can see with the unaided eye. From the most distant star in the galaxy to the tiniest cell of your skin, optical instruments improve your ability to see objects. With telescopes, you can see images of astronomical, far-away objects—some of which may no longer exist. With microscopes, you can see detailed images of objects too tiny to otherwise be seen. With cameras, you can fill your photo album with images of your family and friends, or places you have visited.

Telescopes, microscopes, and cameras are all examples of optical instruments that enhance your ability to see. All of these optical instruments have something in common—they all use lenses or mirrors, or a combination of the two, to reflect and refract light.

Telescopes

The universe is so vast that the light coming from the farthest stars has traveled billions of years before it reaches Earth. Some of the light takes so long to reach Earth that by the time it gets here, the source of the light—the star—has long since burned out. With a telescope you can see images of the star even though it no longer exists. A **telescope** is an instrument that uses lenses or mirrors to collect and focus light from distant objects. In Greek, the word *teleskopos* means "seeing from a distance."

 Section Resources

Print
- *Laboratory Manual,* Investigation 19B
- *Reading and Study Workbook With Math Support,* Section 19.3
- *Transparencies,* Section 19.3

Technology
- *Interactive Textbook,* Section 19.3
- *Presentation Pro CD-ROM,* Section 19.3
- *Go Online, Science News,* Light and optics

Most historians credit Dutch eyeglass maker Hans Lippershey with inventing the first telescope in 1608. In 1671, Isaac Newton invented a telescope that formed images by reflecting light with a curved mirror. By the end of the 1800s, scientists were looking farther and farther into the universe. Today's telescopes map the universe past and present, helping astronomers figure out its history and its future. There are two main types of telescopes, reflecting telescopes and refracting telescopes.

Reflecting Telescopes The **reflecting telescope** uses mirrors and convex lenses to collect and focus light. Figure 13A shows the path of light through a reflecting telescope. Light from a distant object strikes a large concave mirror and is brought to a focus. This focused light is reflected by an angled mirror and forms a real image. The convex lens of the eyepiece then enlarges the image.

Refracting Telescopes The **refracting telescope** uses convex lenses to collect and focus light. Light from a distant object enters the telescope by passing through a convex lens called the objective lens. The convex lens forms a real image at its focal point inside the telescope. A convex lens in the eyepiece then magnifies this real image. As you look through the eyepiece, you see an enlarged, upside-down, virtual image of the real image. Figure 13B shows the path of light through a refracting telescope.

Go Online
SCIENCE NEWS

For: Articles on light and optics
Visit: PHSchool.com
Web Code: cce-2193

Figure 13 The two main types of telescopes use combinations of mirrors and lenses to magnify images of distant objects. **A** The reflecting telescope uses a large concave mirror to focus the incoming light rays. **B** The refracting telescope uses a series of lenses to focus light from distant objects.

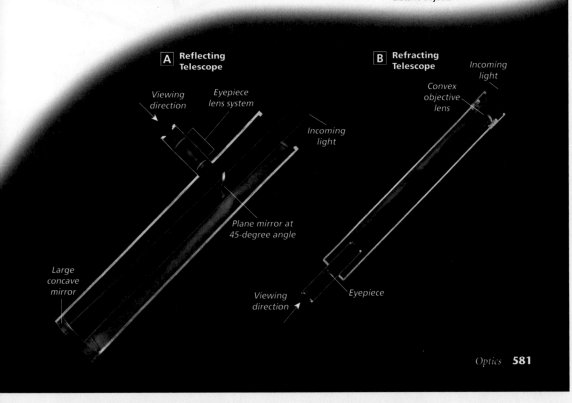

A **Reflecting Telescope**

Viewing direction

Eyepiece lens system

Incoming light

Plane mirror at 45-degree angle

Large concave mirror

Viewing direction

B **Refracting Telescope**

Incoming light

Convex objective lens

Eyepiece

Optics **581**

Use Visuals [L1]

Figure 13 Have students trace the path of the incoming light ray in each kind of telescope. Ask, **What is the purpose of the objective lens or mirror?** *(To gather and focus the light rays)* **What is the purpose of the convex eyepiece lens?** *(To magnify the image produced by the mirror or objective lens)* **Visual, Logical**

Teacher **Demo** [L2]

Making a Telescope

Purpose Students observe the basic requirements for a telescope.

Materials 2 convex lenses (one with a focal length of 10 cm and the other with a focal length of 30 cm), 1 stick of modeling clay

Procedure Use a lump of clay on a desk to hold the 10-cm focal length lens vertically. Place the other lens vertically in clay a few centimeters away. Align the lenses so that you can look through both, with your eyes a few centimeters from the 10-cm focal length lens. Move the 30-cm focal length lens until you see a sharp image in the lens. This image will be upside down and enlarged. Allow students to look through the lenses.

Expected Outcome Students will recognize that one lens gathers light and the other forms a magnified image. **Visual, Logical**

Go Online
SCIENCE NEWS

Science News provides students with current information on light and optics.

Answer to . . .

Figure 12 *The high elevation means the telescope looks through less of Earth's atmosphere, resulting in better images.*

Customize for English Language Learners

Building a Science Glossary
Allow students to work in pairs. Post the section's vocabulary terms on the board. Model how to divide each word into parts, determine the meaning of the word, pronounce the word, and use the word in a sentence. Point out that four of the five vocabulary terms contain the word part *-scope*. Tell students that *-scope* means "an instrument for seeing or observing." Ask students how knowing this word part might help them learn the meaning of the vocabulary words. Students can add the words and definitions to their science glossaries. Make frequent references to the words and assign them in homework or another activity to emphasize their importance.

Cameras
Build Science Skills   L2

Comparing and Contrasting
Have students carefully examine the first camera (1826) and the modern digital camera (2000). Ask, **What features are common to both cameras?** (*Both cameras are dark containers that gather light through a small hole.*) **What are some improvements that the modern digital camera has over the first camera?** (*The digital camera is smaller, lighter, easier to use, has a low-light indicator, automatic flash, auto-focus zoom lens, and camera dock for image transfer to a computer.*)
Visual

DK SCIENCE and History

Photography   L2

Divide the class into groups of two or three students, and assign each group a date from the time line on p. 583. Have each group discuss how the events they're investigating helped spread the use of photography. (*Each advancement made taking photographs easier for the average person.*) Ask them also to relate the advancements in materials to changes in camera design. (*Lightweight plastics replaced metal bodies and glass lenses.*)
Interpersonal, Verbal

Writing in Science

Light enters each camera by passing through a lens that focuses the light into an image at the back of the camera. The Kine-Exakta forms an image on film that must be removed from the camera and developed. The Land camera records the image on film that develops itself in just a minute or two. The digital camera records the image as an electronic file that is later output to a computer or a printer.

Cameras

A **camera** is an optical instrument that records an image of an object. No matter the type of camera, it uses the same basic principle of focusing light rays to form real images. ● **Light rays enter a camera through an opening, are focused by the opening or lens, and form an image that is recorded on film or by a sensor.**

Pinhole Camera Did you know that the word *camera* is Latin for "room?" The earliest cameras were in fact the size of an entire room, and were known as *camera obscura*, or "dark room." One of the earliest uses of a camera obscura is credited to Leonardo da Vinci.

DK SCIENCE and History

Photography

Photography has come a long way since the 1800s, although the basic apparatus is still the same—a box with a hole to let in light.

THREE-COLOR PROJECTOR SYSTEM

Simple wooden box

Hole for lens

FIRST CAMERA

Holders for black-and-white slides

Holders for red, blue, and green color filters

ORIGINAL KODAK CAMERA

1826 Nicéphore Niepce makes the first permanent positive photograph of a landscape.

1840 William Fox Talbot develops the first negative-to-positive process, making multiple black-and-white prints possible.

1861 Scottish physicist James Clerk Maxwell exhibits a color photographic system involving three black-and-white photos, taken through red, blue, and green filters. When the photos are turned into slides, projected on a screen using the same filters, and superimposed, the original scene is recreated, in color.

1888 George Eastman launches the Kodak camera, the first successful roll-film camera. It is preloaded with a 6-meter roll of film at the factory.

1913 German inventor Oscar Barnack develops the UR Leica camera, the first 35 mm camera. It uses the 24 mm x 36 mm frame format.

1820   1855   1890

582   Chapter 19

Facts and Figures

Lenses A variety of lenses can be used with cameras. The standard lens used on cameras is a fixed focal length lens. The magnification of images taken with this lens cannot be changed. In general, this type of lens is the lightest, most compact, and most useful for everyday photography. A variable zoom lens permits the photographer to choose the magnification of the image. These lenses are useful for taking up-close pictures of faraway objects. A wide-angle lens captures a wider field of view. You can take photographs of large objects, such as buildings, with this type of lens. Modern cameras may have retractable zoom lenses. These lenses slide back into the camera when not in use. Cameras may also have interchangeable lenses. The entire lens may be removed from the camera and replaced with another type of lens. Point out to students that, although there are many types of camera lenses, they are all converging lenses that focus light to form an image at the back of the camera.

Da Vinci, an Italian scientist, constructed his camera by making a pinhole opening in the shutter of a window of a darkened room. Images of the outside scenery were projected onto the wall opposite the window. Pinhole cameras do not have to be the size of a room. A simple pinhole camera can consist of a cardboard box with a small hole in one side. Light rays from the top and bottom of an object pass through the pinhole and cross paths. The rays form an upside-down, real image on the back wall of the box. For firsthand experience with a pinhole optical device, build and use the pinhole viewer in the QuickLab later in this section.

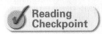 **Reading Checkpoint** *What type of image does a pinhole camera form?*

Writing in Science

Compare-Contrast Paragraph Write a paragraph summarizing how all of the cameras shown are similar. Also describe how the Kine-Exakta camera (1936), the Land camera (1947), and the digital camera (2000) differ in the way in which they record images.

Focusing magnifier

Focusing ring

Standard lens (one of five options)

LED indicator (indicates low light conditions to activate flash)

MODERN COMPACT DIGITAL CAMERA

KINE-EXAKTA CAMERA

INSTANT PICTURES

Camera dock connects to computer for image transfer.

Auto-focus zoom lens

1936 German company Ihagee launches the Kine-Exakta, the first single-lens reflex (SLR) camera for 35 mm film.

1942 Kodak announces a film for color prints, Koda-color, the world's first true color negative film.

1947 American inventor Edwin H. Land demonstrates a new one-step photographic system. It develops and produces finished pictures in a few seconds.

1986 Pentax produces the first fully automatic compact camera with a built-in zoom lens.

2000 High resolution, compact, multi-featured, affordable digital cameras are available and popular.

1925   1960   1995

Optics **583**

Build Science Skills

Applying Concepts Point out to students that the first camera shown on the time line had no lens. This is also true for the pinhole camera described in the text. Instead, light enters through a small hole, and the image is formed on the back wall of the camera. Ask, **Why is it sufficient to have light enter through a hole rather than a lens?** *(Light rays entering the camera travel in a straight line through the pinhole and therefore form an image at the back of the camera.)* **Why is the image inverted, even without a lens?** *(Light entering near the top of the hole goes downward through the pinhole, and light entering near the bottom of the hole goes upward through the pinhole.)* **What advantage does a lens offer over a pinhole?** *(More light can be collected, while still providing a focused image)* **Verbal, Logical**

Facts and Figures

Autofocus Most cameras today contain an electronic system for autofocusing the image. The camera may do this by emitting an infrared signal that reflects off the object that is being photographed. By measuring the intensity of the reflected light, the camera can determine the object's distance. It then adjusts the lens to optimize the focus. Autofocusing may also be done using electronics that examine the amount of contrast in an image. A blurry image has less contrast than a well-focused image. The camera's electronics adjust the lens placement to maximize the image contrast.

Answer to . . .

 Reading Checkpoint *A pinhole camera forms an upside-down, real image.*

Figure 14 Encourage students to discuss how the camera in the figure works. Point out the lenses located both before and after the diaphragm. Explain that together these form the lens elements. Tell students that adjusting the size of the diaphragm's opening (the aperture) controls the amount of light. Ask, **What is the purpose of the prism in the camera?** *(The prism redirects the light from the mirror to the viewfinder.)* **What is the purpose of the shutter?** *(The shutter is usually closed to protect the film. It briefly opens to expose the film to light.)* **Visual, Logical**

Microscopes

 Teacher Demo **L2**

Two Types of Microscopes

Purpose Students will learn about compound and stereo microscopes.

Materials compound microscope, stereo microscope

Procedure Show students the two types of microscopes. Draw simple sketches on the chalkboard of their optical paths. Explain that the compound and stereo microscopes are the two basic types of microscopes. Point out that a compound microscope has high magnification (often 10X, 100X, and 400X) and gives an inverted image of the object. A stereo microscope has low magnification and an erect, three-dimensional image.

Expected Outcome Students will learn about compound and stereo microscopes.
Visual, Logical

Figure 14 Shown here is a typical single lens reflex (SLR) camera. The mirror reflects the image through the viewfinder so the photographer can bring it into focus. When the shutter release button is pushed, the mirror flips up. This allows the focused light rays to pass straight through the lens system and onto the film.

Viewfinder · Prism · Shutter release button · Shutter · Mirror · Lens elements · Film · Diaphragm · Incoming light

Figure 15 This compound microscope uses a mirror to reflect light up and into the microscope.
Comparing and Contrasting *How is the way in which a focused image is formed the same in both a camera and a microscope?*

Eyepiece lens · Objective lens · Slide with specimen · Mirror

584

Modern Film Camera
Figure 14 shows a typical modern film camera. The lens elements focus the incoming light rays. The focused rays then pass through the diaphragm, a device that controls the amount of light passing through the lens. When the shutter release button is pressed, the mirror flips up and the shutter briefly opens to let the focused light rays strike the film.

To bring an object into focus, the lens must be moved toward or away from the film. This focusing, which can be done manually or automatically, is needed to form a sharp image. The focused light reacts with a light-sensitive chemical coating on the film that records the real image. The image is upside down and smaller than the object. After the film is developed and printed, you have photographs for your album.

Microscopes

A **microscope** is an optical instrument that uses lenses to provide enlarged images of very small, near objects. One common type of microscope is called a compound microscope. **The compound microscope uses two convex lenses to magnify small objects.**

Figure 15 shows the structure of a compound microscope. To view an enlarged image of an object, you place the object on a glass slide. You then place the slide on a platform located above a light source. Light rays from below pass up through the object and then pass through a convex lens called the objective. The lens produces an enlarged, upside-down, real image. This image then becomes the "object" for a second convex lens called the eyepiece. The eyepiece enlarges the image. When you look through the eyepiece, you see an enlarged, virtual image of the object. Under the best conditions, modern light microscopes can magnify images more than 1000 times.

Facts and Figures

Microscope Objectives A typical school microscope has three objectives. The shortest objective is low power, with a magnification of 10X. The intermediate objective may have a multiplication of 40X. The longest objective may have a magnification of 100X. The convex lens in the eyepiece, however, typically provides an additional multiplication of 10X. This means the total magnification of the three objectives is 100X, 400X, and 1000X. To obtain enough light with the 1000X magnification, you must place a drop of immersion oil on the lens. When the objective is lowered, the oil eliminates the space between the lens and the coverslip over the specimen. The oil has the same index of refraction as glass. Light, therefore, is not refracted, and you obtain sufficient light to view the object.

Building a Pinhole Viewer

Cardboard tube
Wax paper
Rubber bands
Aluminum foil
Pinhole
Rolled tube of black construction paper

Materials

- cardboard tube
- black construction paper
- aluminum foil
- wax paper
- 4 rubber bands
- pin

Procedure

1. Place aluminum foil over one end of the cardboard tube and use a rubber band to hold the foil in place.

2. Place wax paper over the other end of the tube and hold the paper in place with a rubber band. There should be no wrinkles in the wax paper covering the opening of the tube.

3. Roll a piece of black construction paper lengthwise around the tube. The foil end should be flush with one end of the construction paper as shown. Use two more rubber bands to hold the construction paper in place.

4. Verify that the wax paper end is now in the middle of the black construction paper tube.

5. Use a pin to make a hole in the center of the aluminum foil. You may have to enlarge the hole slightly to see an image clearly.

6. Point the pinhole toward a light source and look through the other end of the viewer. Observe several objects inside your classroom (chairs, tables, and books) and outside of your classroom (houses, trees, and cars). **CAUTION** *Do not use the viewer to look at the sun, as you may injure your eyes.*

Analyze and Conclude

1. **Observing** Describe the images that appeared on the wax paper.

2. **Relating Cause and Effect** What caused the images to appear on the wax paper the way they did?

Section 19.3 Assessment

Reviewing Concepts

1. Name the two main types of telescopes.
2. How does a film camera work?
3. Describe the system of lenses in a compound microscope.
4. What is the purpose of the lens in a camera?

Critical Thinking

5. **Inferring** High-speed film is very sensitive to light. Explain how this could be useful for dim-light photography.

6. **Applying Concepts** Can the image seen in the eyepiece of a compound microscope be projected on a screen?

Connecting Concepts

Speed of Light From Chapter 18 you know that light travels at an extremely high speed. Explain how the images of deep-space objects you see through telescopes are images of the past.

Optics **585**

Building a Pinhole Viewer L2

Objective
After completing this activity, students will be able to
- describe the formation of an inverted image by a pinhole camera.

Skills Focus Observing

 Prep Time 20 minutes

Class Time 25 minutes

Safety Caution students not to look directly into the sun.

Expected Outcome Students will observe an inverted image on the wax paper.

Analyze and Conclude

1. The images produced on the wax paper are reversed left to right, and top to bottom.

2. The rays are reversed left-right and top-bottom as they pass through the opening. **Logical**

---

3 ASSESS

Evaluate Understanding L2

Ask students to name some optical instruments they use. Have students describe what kind of lens or mirror they think is used in the device.

Reteach L1

Have students write several sentences that briefly explain how telescopes, cameras, and microscopes form images.

Connecting Concepts

Because deep-space objects are so far away, it takes thousands of years or more for light emanating from them to reach Earth. Thus, images we currently see in telescopes are actually images of how those deep-space objects appeared thousands or more years ago.

Interactive Textbook If your class subscribes to the Interactive Textbook, use it to review key concepts in Section 19.3

Answer to . . .

Figure 15 *Both use a movable lens or series of lenses to focus the image.*

Optics 585

Section 19.3 Assessment

1. The refracting telescope and the reflecting telescope

2. Light rays enter the camera through an opening, are focused by the lens, and form an image on the film.

3. A compound microscope uses two convex lenses to magnify small objects.

4. Camera lenses focus the incoming light rays to form a sharp image.

5. High-speed film is useful in situations where there are very low light levels because it requires less time to form an image.

6. Yes, the light could be projected onto a screen, but it would not form an image. The enlarged virtual image formed by a microscope cannot be projected onto a screen.

Fiber Optics L2
Background

Optical fibers are usually made of a highly transparent glass. The glass must be extremely pure. Even small amounts of impurities would absorb too much of the light.

To enable light transmission, the refractive index of the core must be greater than the refractive index of the cladding, or layer just outside the core. Ideally, the difference in the refractive indices should be as great as possible. However, consideration must also be given to whether or not the cladding material is able to adhere to the core fiber.

Light propagates through a fiber by total internal reflection. When light inside the fiber optic reaches the interface of the core and the outer layer, it reflects off the outer layer back into the core provided that the angle of incidence is greater than or equal to the critical angle. The light continues to totally internally reflect down the length of the fiber.

Fiber Optics

Optical fibers have caused a revolution in information technology by making it possible to transmit huge amounts of information along slender strands of glass.

Strengthening steel core

Optical fiber

Inside a fiber optic cable
One cable contains several fibers. Each fiber consists of a core and an outer layer made from glass of a lower refractive index. The light is kept within the fiber by total internal reflection.

Protective layer for cable

Optical fiber core

Outer layer

Protective sheath

Internal reflection
Total internal reflection carries light around sharp bends.

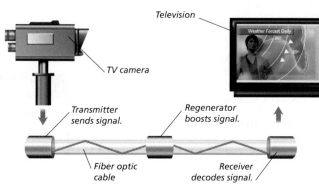

Transmitting a TV signal
TV signals can be sent along optical cables in the form of light. The electrical signal produced by the camera is turned into a digital code by the transmitter, and sent along the cable as rapid pulses of light. The receiver then converts this signal back into an electrical signal, which in turn forms a picture on the TV screen.

Television

TV camera

Transmitter sends signal.

Regenerator boosts signal.

Fiber optic cable

Receiver decodes signal.

586 *Chapter 19*

Optical fibers in medicine

As well as carrying digital information, optical fibers are useful in medicine. This is because they can bend around corners, allowing otherwise inaccessible parts of the body to be viewed.

Tip of the endoscope is inserted first into the body.

A light source is attached here.

Depth scale shows how far the endoscope is inserted into the body.

Eyepiece

ENDOSCOPE

Internal organ is viewed on a computer screen.

Endoscope
Endoscopes are used to view the interior of the body. They are often used for investigations—such as checking for a stomach ulcer—and during surgery, to guide the surgeon.

Surgeons use an endoscope to look at internal organs.

Eye of a sewing needle

Single optical fiber

Strand of glass
Optical fibers are made from ultra-pure glass. Each fiber is thin enough to pass through the eye of a needle. Some top-quality fibers can carry a light beam with just a 10 percent loss of intensity over a kilometer.

Going Further

- Research how fiber optic strands are manufactured. Prepare a poster to present your findings to your class. Include a detailed description of the manufacturing process and the materials used.
- Take a Discovery Channel Video Field Trip by watching "Traveling Light."

DISCOVERY CHANNEL SCHOOL Video Field Trip

Optics **587**

Build Science Skills

Observing

Purpose Students observe properties of optical fibers.

Materials flashlight, fiber optic bundle

Class Time 10 minutes

Procedure In a darkened room, shine a bright light at the end of a straight bundle of optical fibers. Students will notice that the light exits the fibers only at the ends. Now bend the bundle of fibers while continuing to shine the light on the ends of the fibers. Students will observe that the light still only exits the fibers at the ends. Ask, **Why does the light travel through the length of the fibers, even though the fibers are bent?** *(Internal reflection causes the light to bounce off the outer layer of the fibers.)*

Expected Outcome Light enters one end of the fiber bundle and exits the other end, even if the fibers are bent. **Visual, Logical**

Going Further

Student posters and research findings will vary but should include a description of the materials used and the manufacturing process. Optical fiber manufacturing is basically a two-step process involving the fabrication of a specially constructed glass rod called a preform, followed by the melting of the preform, which is then drawn into a thin fiber. Commercial producers use a variety of processes to fabricate the preform, all of which are based on a thermal chemical vapor reaction that forms mixed oxides which are deposited as layers of glass soot onto a rotating high-purity glass rod or tube. **Visual**

DISCOVERY CHANNEL SCHOOL **Video Field Trip**

Traveling Light

After students have viewed the Video Field Trip, ask them the following questions: **Name one advantage of using light signals through glass fibers to transmit information.** *(The information is transmitted at very high speeds through the fiber.)*

Who was the first person to use light to transmit telephone conversations? *(Alexander Graham Bell)* **Describe the process of making a glass fiber for sending signals using light.** *(Pure silica is used to make a fine glass rod. The rod is heated. Molten glass from the end of the rod drips down to form a long thin fiber.)* **Name a practical advantage that glass fibers have over copper wire.** *(The glass is less expensive than copper.)*

1 FOCUS

Objectives

19.4.1 **Name** the main parts of the eye and **describe** their functions.

19.4.2 **Name** common vision problems, **identify** their causes, and **explain** how they can be corrected.

Reading Focus

Build Vocabulary   L2

Word-Part Analysis Tell students that the vocabulary terms *nearsightedness* and *farsightedness* are compound words with a suffix. Explain that the suffix *-ness* means "the state of being." Have students tell each word's word parts and tell what the words mean based on their word parts. *(The word parts of nearsightedness are near, sighted, and -ness. The word parts of farsightedness are far, sighted, and -ness. Nearsightedness means the state of being able to see near. Farsightedness means the state of being able to see far.)*

Reading Strategy   L2

I. The Eye and Vision
  A. Structure of the Eye
    1. Cornea
    2. Pupil and Iris
    3. Lens
    4. Retina
    5. Rods and Cones
  B. Correcting Vision Problems
    1. Nearsightedness
    2. Farsightedness
    3. Astigmatism

2 INSTRUCT

Structure of the Eye

Address Misconceptions   L2

Many people incorrectly assume that the lens of the eye is the primary focusing element. Explain to students that light entering the eye encounters the greatest difference in optical density (indices of refraction) when it passes from the air to the cornea. Therefore, light is focused most by the cornea.
Visual, Logical

19.4 The Eye and Vision

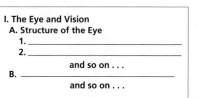

Reading Focus

Key Concepts

- What are the main parts of the eye?
- What are some common vision problems?

Vocabulary

- cornea
- pupil
- iris
- retina
- rods
- cones
- nearsightedness
- farsightedness
- astigmatism

Reading Strategy

Outlining As you read, make an outline of the important ideas in this section. Use the green headings as the main topics and the blue headings as subtopics.

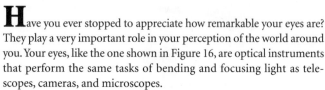

I. The Eye and Vision
  A. Structure of the Eye
    1. _____
    2. _____
          and so on . . .
  B. _____
          and so on . . .

Have you ever stopped to appreciate how remarkable your eyes are? They play a very important role in your perception of the world around you. Your eyes, like the one shown in Figure 16, are optical instruments that perform the same tasks of bending and focusing light as telescopes, cameras, and microscopes.

Your eyes form images every moment they are exposed to light. They receive and focus visible light from objects near and far. Your brain then interprets the images of the objects formed by your eyes.

Figure 16 The lens of the eye focuses incoming light rays onto light-sensitive nerve endings located inside and at the back of your eye.

Structure of the Eye

You can read this page because light reflected from the page enters your eye. But how does this light get transformed into images of objects you recognize? Various parts of the eye, each one having its own specific function, work to make your sense of vision possible. Figure 17 shows the structure of the human eye. **The main parts of the eye are the cornea, the pupil and iris, the lens, and the retina.**

Cornea Light rays enter your eyes through the transparent outer coating of the eye, called the **cornea.** The cornea's curved surface helps to focus light entering your eye.

588 *Chapter 19*

Section Resources

Print
- *Reading and Study Workbook With Math Support,* Section 19.4
- *Transparencies,* Section 19.4

Technology
- *Interactive Textbook,* Section 19.4
- *Presentation Pro CD-ROM,* Section 19.4

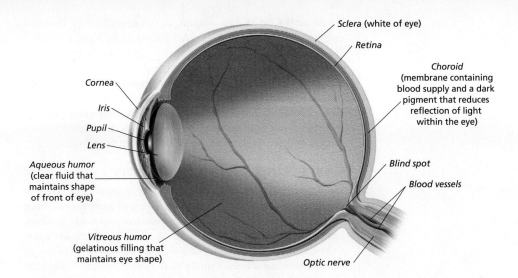

Sclera (white of eye)

Retina

Choroid
(membrane containing
blood supply and a dark
pigment that reduces
reflection of light
within the eye)

Cornea

Iris

Pupil

Lens

Aqueous humor
(clear fluid that
maintains shape
of front of eye)

Blind spot

Blood vessels

Vitreous humor
(gelatinous filling that
maintains eye shape)

Optic nerve

Pupil and Iris After the cornea, light rays pass through the pupil, the part of your eye that looks black. The **pupil** is the opening that allows light rays to enter your eye. The colored part of your eye, the **iris,** contracts and expands to control the amount of light that enters your eye. The controlled movement of the iris is regulated by signals from your brain.

Lens After passing through the pupil, light enters the convex lens in your eye. The lens is a sealed capsule containing a clear fluid. This lens focuses the light onto the light sensor cells at the back of the eye. As you change your focus from near to distant objects, muscles inside the eye change the shape of the flexible lens. The muscles relax and the lens becomes thinner and flatter. If you read for a long time, you'll notice that your eyes become tired and feel strained. This is because the muscles have been contracting for a long time. The best way to relax your eyes is to look far away.

Retina The focused, refracted light is collected at the retina. The **retina** is the inner surface of the eye. Its surface is covered by light-sensitive nerve endings called **rods** and **cones.** The rods and cones convert the light into electrical signals that are sent to the brain through the optic nerve. The area of the retina where the nerve endings come together to form the optic nerve creates a blind spot. This blind spot has no rods or cones and cannot sense light.

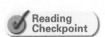 **Reading Checkpoint** *Which part of the eye controls how much light enters?*

Figure 17 The eye is the organ that provides you with sight. Light passes through the cornea, pupil, and lens before striking the retina. Signals from light-sensitive nerves on the retina are sent through the optic nerve to the brain. **Predicting** *What may result if the eyeball has an elongated (too long) shape?*

Optics **589**

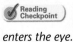

Relate Cause and Effect Refer to page **260D** in **Chapter 9**, which provides the guidelines for relating cause and effect.

Cause-and-effect relationships are the basis of scientific discovery. However, some students may not fully understand the nature of the cause-and-effect relationship. Ask, **When you enter a dark theatre from bright sunlight, the pupil opens very quickly. However it may be a few minutes before your eye fully adjusts to the low light conditions. Why?** (Although the iris opens quickly, a few minutes are required for the rods and cones to adjust to the low light conditions.)
Visual

Correcting Vision Problems

Integrate Health **L2**

Explain that both optometrists and ophthalmologists are trained to diagnose vision defects and prescribe corrective lenses. Tell students that ophthalmologists also treat diseases of the eye. Encourage students to research eye diseases such as glaucoma, cataracts, and conjunctivitis. Have students describe methods of treatment used by ophthalmologists for these diseases, and any means of preventing the diseases.
Visual

Rods and Cones Low-intensity light is sensed by rods. The brain uses signals from rods to distinguish among white, black, and different shades of gray. Cones are sensitive to color, but are less sensitive than rods; that is, they need more light than rods in order to function. The decreased light sensitivity of cones explains why you can't make out the colors of objects in very dim light. There are three different types of cones. Each type of cone is able to sense only a single color—red light, green light, or blue light. People who are colorblind have missing or defective cones of one or more of the three kinds.

Correcting Vision Problems

You have probably heard the expression "20/20 vision." Having 20/20 vision means that you can clearly see things of a certain size from 20 feet. 20/20 vision is considered normal. Not everybody, however, has 20/20 vision. ⬤ **Several common vision problems are nearsightedness, farsightedness, and astigmatism.** They result in people having vision that is worse than 20/20. In many cases, less-than-perfect vision can be corrected with eyeglasses or contact lenses. Corrective eyeware is not new—eyeglasses were used in China and Italy as early as the 1200s.

> ✓ **Reading Checkpoint** *What does it mean to have 20/20 vision?*

Problem: Nearsightedness (Eyeball is too long.)

Image forms in front of retina.

Correction: Eyeglasses with concave lenses

Concave lens

Image forms on retina.

Figure 18 When the eyeball is too long, the focused image forms in front of the retina. By the time the image reaches the retina, it is no longer in focus. This common condition, called nearsightedness, can be corrected with a diverging (concave) lens.

Nearsightedness If you have normal vision, the images you see are clear and undistorted. The light rays that enter your eyes are focused on your retinas. However, for approximately one out of four people, the rays focus before they reach the retina. This condition, called **nearsightedness,** causes distant objects to appear blurry. Nearsightedness occurs either because the cornea is too curved or the eyeball is too long. In either case, the rays of light focus too close to the lens. A nearsighted person can see nearby objects clearly, but distant objects seem blurred. Nearsightedness can be corrected by placing a diverging (concave) lens in front of the eye. The lens spreads the rays out a little before they enter the eye. This causes the image to form farther back, at the retina, instead of in front of it. Some cases of nearsightedness can now be treated with surgery. Figure 18 shows a diagram of a nearsighted eye and how it can be corrected with a diverging (concave) lens.

Facts and Figures

Interfaces in the Eye Light entering the eye encounters four interfaces: (1) air to cornea, (2) cornea to aqueous humor, (3) aqueous humor to lens, and (4) lens to vitreous humor. The indices of refraction are 1.00 for air, approximately 1.376 for the cornea, 1.336 for aqueous humor, and 1.337 for vitreous humor. The index of refraction for the lens ranges from 1.386 to 1.406. Light that enters the eye is bent most when it passes from air into the cornea, because this is where the largest change in index of refraction occurs.

Laser Eye Surgery

The laser has become a sight-saving tool. In laser eye surgery, a laser beam makes small incisions, half the thickness of a human hair, in the eye. Surgeons correct and control different types of vision problems by careful positioning of the laser incisions. As shown below, a laser can be used to destroy abnormal blood vessels that cause failing vision in patients with diabetes. **Interpreting Diagrams** *On what part of the eye do the abnormal blood vessels form?*

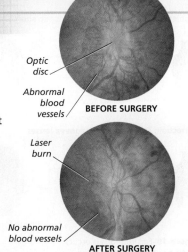

Optic disc

Abnormal blood vessels

BEFORE SURGERY

Laser burn

No abnormal blood vessels

AFTER SURGERY

Results of surgery
Taken through the pupil of the eye, these pictures show how abnormal blood vessels on the retina are burned away by laser treatment. After surgery, the retina appears paler.

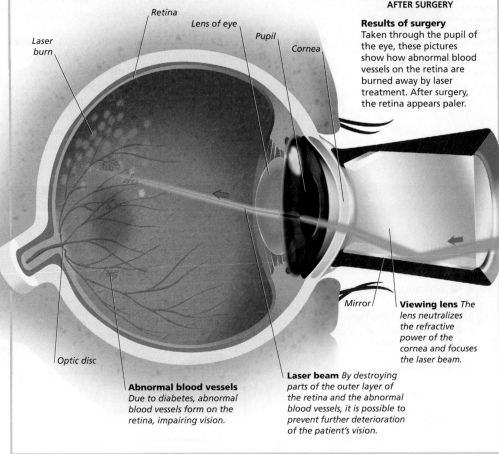

Retina

Lens of eye

Pupil

Cornea

Laser burn

Optic disc

Abnormal blood vessels
Due to diabetes, abnormal blood vessels form on the retina, impairing vision.

Laser beam *By destroying parts of the outer layer of the retina and the abnormal blood vessels, it is possible to prevent further deterioration of the patient's vision.*

Mirror

Viewing lens *The lens neutralizes the refractive power of the cornea and focuses the laser beam.*

Laser Eye Surgery L2

Most people who undergo laser eye surgery have a significant improvement in their vision. This is especially true for those who previously had moderate vision problems. However, not everyone with vision problems is eligible for the surgery. Patients must be over 18 years old with stable vision for at least two years. Their corneas must be sufficiently thick to allow the physician to safely perform the incision. People with severe eye problems should not have the surgery. In addition, certain eye disorders, such as cataracts and glaucoma, as well as eye injuries may prevent a person from having laser eye surgery. Patients should realize that the surgery does not guarantee 20/20 vision, and, as with all surgery, there are risks involved.

Interpreting Diagrams The abnormal blood vessels form on the retina. **Visual**

For Enrichment L3

Have interested students interview a physician who performs laser eye surgery or a person who has undergone the procedure. Students might ask about the requirements, risks, and benefits of the surgery, as well as any drawbacks. Afterwards, students can report to the class about what they learn. **Interpersonal**

Answer to . . .

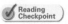

Reading Checkpoint *20/20 vision means that you can recognize objects of a certain size at a distance of 20 feet.*

3 ASSESS

Evaluate Understanding L2

Randomly quiz students about the parts of the eye and their function. Have students draw diagrams showing vision correction for nearsightedness and farsightedness using convex and concave lenses.

Reteach L1

Review the structure of the eye using Figure 17. Have students review Figures 18 and 19 and discuss how the shape of the eyeball affects the eye's ability to focus.

Writing in Science

Student paragraphs will vary but must include all of the parts of the eye (at least the cornea, iris, pupil, lens, and retina) and their functions. More detailed descriptions may include the aqueous humor, vitreous humor, rods, cones, and optic nerve.

Interactive Textbook If your class subscribes to the Interactive Textbook, use it to review key concepts in Section 19.4.

Problem: Farsightedness (Eyeball is too short.)

Image forms behind retina.

Correction: Eyeglasses with convex lenses

Convex lens

Image forms on retina.

Figure 19 Farsightedness occurs when an image is not focused before it reaches the retina. Farsightedness can be corrected by using a converging (convex) lens in front of the eye. **Comparing and Contrasting** *In what ways are farsightedness and nearsightedness similar?*

Farsightedness Blurred images can also be a result of farsightedness. **Farsightedness** is a condition that causes nearby objects to appear blurry. Common causes of farsightedness are either a cornea that is not curved enough or an eyeball that is too short. In either case, the rays of light focus too far from the lens. As a result, the image focuses beyond the retina. A farsighted person can see distant objects clearly, but nearby objects seem blurred. Farsightedness is usually corrected by placing a converging (convex) lens in front of the eye. The lens bends the light rays toward each other before they enter the eye. Because the rays entering the eye are converging, the image is formed on the retina instead of behind the retina. Figure 19 shows a diagram of a farsighted eye and how it can be corrected.

Astigmatism For clear vision, the lens of the eye and the cornea must be properly shaped. When the cornea or lens is misshapen, a defect in vision called astigmatism results. **Astigmatism** is a condition in which objects at any distance appear blurry because the cornea or lens is misshapen. Just as with an eyeball that is too long or too short, this irregularity can prevent light from focusing properly on the retina. The result is that the lens has two different focal points, causing distortion or blurring of the image. Specialized eyeglass lens shapes are used to correct astigmatism.

Section 19.4 Assessment

Reviewing Concepts

1. List, in order, the parts of the eye that light encounters.
2. What are three common problems that affect vision?
3. What is the eye's blind spot?
4. Which kind of lens can correct nearsightedness? Farsightedness?

Critical Thinking

5. **Inferring** Why is the cornea transparent?
6. **Comparing and Contrasting** How is the structure of the eye similar to that of a simple camera?

7. **Making Judgments** Suppose that when you sit at the back of the room, you can't read the chalkboard. What vision problem might you have?
8. **Connecting Concepts** The index of refraction of the cornea is about the same as that of water. Use this fact to explain why you cannot see as well in water as in air.

Steps in a Process Write a paragraph describing how a light ray passes through the eye and results in vision.

Section 19.4   Assessment

1. Cornea, aqueous humor, iris, lens, vitreous humor
2. Nearsightedness, farsightedness, astigmatism
3. The eye's blind spot is the area of the retina where nerve endings come together to form the optic nerve.
4. Nearsightedness: concave lens; farsightedness: convex lens
5. The cornea must be transparent in order for light to pass through it into the rest of the eye.

6. Light enters through an opening and is focused by a lens onto a surface where an image is formed.
7. You are probably nearsighted, that is, unable to see objects far away.
8. Light passing from water into your eye is not bent as much as it passes through the cornea as it is when light passes from air into your eye. This difference in the bending of the light results in the image not being in focus when it strikes the retina.

Answer to . . .

Figure 19 *Both conditions result from length of the eyeball or the curvature of the lens.*

Selecting Mirrors

In this lab, you will compare several mirrors and select the type that is best for a specific use.

Problem
What mirror shape is best for magnifying images? For providing a wide view?

Materials
plane, convex, and concave mirrors; 2 metric rulers; roll of string; protractor

Skills
Observing, Measuring

Procedure

Part A: Comparing Magnification

1. Construct a data table with three rows and four columns. Label the columns Mirror, Size of Image, Magnification, and Field of View. In the column labeled Mirror, label the three rows Plane, Concave, and Convex.

2. Place the plane mirror on a tabletop with its mirror side facing up. Position a metric ruler horizontally across the center of the mirror.

3. Hold the other metric ruler horizontally against your nose, just below your eyes, as shown below. Make sure the ruler's markings face away from you. Look down at the mirror.

4. Use the ruler resting on the mirror to measure the actual length of the image of a 3-cm-long portion of the ruler you are holding. Record the size of the image in your data table.

5. Repeat Steps 2 through 4 using concave and convex mirrors. Observe each image from the same distance.

6. Divide each image size you measured by 3 cm to determine its magnification. Record the magnification in your data table.

Part B: Comparing Fields of View

7. Tie a string to a ruler. Hold the protractor, mirror, and free end of the string. Have a classmate hold the ruler vertically off to one side of the mirror. Position a third classmate (the observer) directly in front of and about 2 meters away from the mirror as shown.

8. Have the classmate holding the ruler slowly move toward the observer while keeping the string tight. The observer should look directly into the mirror and say "Stop!" as soon as the reflection of the ruler can be seen.

9. Measure the angle the string makes with the protractor. Multiply this angle by 2 and record it as the field of view in your data table.

10. Repeat Steps 7 through 9 using concave and convex mirrors. Observe each mirror from the same distance.

Analyze and Conclude

1. **Observing** Which mirror provided the greatest magnification? The widest view?

2. **Applying Concepts** Which mirror shape would work best for a dentist who needs to see a slightly magnified image of a tooth? Explain your answer.

3. **Drawing Conclusions** Could one of the mirrors be used both to view a wide area and to magnify? Explain your answer.

Selecting Mirrors L2

Objective
After completing this activity, students will be able to describe differences between the images formed by plane, concave, and convex mirrors.

Address Misconceptions

This lab may help to correct the misconception that the field of view and magnification are independent of one another.

Skills Focus Observing, Measuring

Prep Time 10 minutes

Class Time 40 minutes

Safety Caution students to be careful with breakable glass mirrors.

Teaching Tips
- Do not provide transparent rulers for this lab. They are difficult to see in the mirror.
- Students who wear glasses or contact lenses will need to experiment to find a comfortable viewing distance in Step 4.
- You may need to show students how to hold the protractor in Step 7. It should be positioned so that the 0° mark is pointing directly toward the observer and the 90° mark is parallel to the surface of the mirror.

Expected Outcome The plane mirror produces an image that is slightly smaller than the actual ruler. The concave mirror magnifies the image and reduces the field of view, and the convex mirror produces the smallest image and the widest field of view.

Sample Data A typical concave hand mirror magnifies by a factor of 2 to 3, and a plane mirror produces an image that is reduced by approximately one-third. Typical fields of view for concave, plane, and convex mirrors are 70°, 80°, and 140°, respectively.

Analyze and Conclude
1. The concave mirror provided the greatest magnification, and the convex mirror produced the widest field of view.
2. A concave mirror is best for a dentist because it magnifies the most.
3. None of these mirrors could be used to observe both a wide area and a magnified view of small details because increasing the magnification reduces the width of the field of view, and increasing the width of the field of view reduces the magnification. **Logical**

Study Guide

Study Tip

Flashcards
Making flashcards is a good way to organize new or hard-to-learn information. Encourage students to review their notes every evening and make flash cards for the material covered that day. Students can review the flash cards alone or with a study partner.

Thinking Visually

a. real
b. virtual
c. converge

CHAPTER
19 Study Guide

19.1 Mirrors

Key Concepts

- The law of reflection states that the angle of reflection is equal to the angle of incidence.
- A plane mirror always produces a virtual image.
- Concave mirrors can form either real or virtual images.
- Convex mirrors always cause light rays to spread out and can only form virtual images.

Vocabulary

ray diagram, *p. 570*

angle of incidence, *p. 570*

angle of reflection, *p. 570*

plane mirror, *p. 571*

virtual image, *p. 571*

concave mirror, *p. 572*

focal point, *p. 572*

real image, *p. 572*

convex mirror, *p. 573*

19.2 Lenses

Key Concepts

- When light enters a new medium at an angle, the change in speed causes the light to bend, or refract.
- Concave lenses always cause light rays to spread out and can only form virtual images.
- Convex lenses can form either real or virtual images.
- Materials that have small critical angles of refraction are likely to cause most of the light entering them to be totally internally reflected.

Vocabulary

index of refraction, *p. 575*

lens, *p. 576*

concave lens, *p. 576*

convex lens, *p. 576*

critical angle, *p. 578*

total internal reflection, *p. 578*

19.3 Optical Instruments

Key Concepts

- There are two main types of telescopes, reflecting telescopes and refracting telescopes.

- Light rays enter a camera through an opening, are focused by the opening or lens, and form an image that is recorded on film or by a sensor.
- The compound microscope uses two convex lenses to magnify small objects.

Vocabulary

telescope, *p. 580*

reflecting telescope, *p. 581*

refracting telescope, *p. 581*

camera, *p. 582*

microscope, *p. 584*

19.4 The Eye and Vision

Key Concepts

- The main parts of the eye are the cornea, the pupil and iris, the lens, and the retina.
- Some common vision problems are nearsightedness, farsightedness, and astigmatism.

Vocabulary

cornea, *p. 588*

pupil, *p. 589*

iris, *p. 589*

retina, *p. 589*

rods, *p. 589*

cones, *p. 589*

nearsightedness, *p. 590*

farsightedness, *p. 592*

astigmatism, *p. 592*

Thinking Visually

Concept Map Use the information from the chapter to complete the concept map below.

 ## Chapter Resources

Print
- *Chapter and Unit Tests,* Chapter 19 Test A and Test B
- *Test Prep Resources,* Chapter 19

Technology
- *Computer Test Bank,* Chapter Test 19
- *Interactive Textbook,* Chapter 19
- *Go Online,* PHSchool.com, Chapter 19

Assessment

Reviewing Content

Choose the letter that best answers the question or completes the statement.

1. A reflected ray of light is one that
   a. bends as it enters a new medium.
   b. bounces off a surface.
   c. always forms an image.
   d. travels faster after it is reflected.

2. Which law states that the angle of incidence equals the angle of reflection?
   a. law of refraction   b. law of diffraction
   c. law of reflection   d. law of images

3. A plane mirror is
   a. curved outward.   b. flat.
   c. curved inward.   d. always round.

4. A virtual image
   a. can never be seen.
   b. cannot be projected.
   c. is always enlarged.
   d. is formed in front of a plane mirror.

5. Concave lenses cause rays to
   a. come together.   b. spread apart.
   c. reflect.   d. form real images.

6. Which forms where light rays converge?
   a. imaginary image   b. real image
   c. virtual image   d. blind image

7. A ray is incident on a material at the material's critical angle. At what angle does the ray refract?
   a. 0 degrees   b. 45 degrees
   c. 90 degrees   d. 180 degrees

8. Which optical device uses mirrors and lenses to magnify images of distant objects?
   a. reflecting telescope b. pinhole camera
   c. microscope   d. refracting telescope

9. The two areas in the eye in which light rays are refracted are
   a. the cornea and the lens.
   b. the pupil and the lens.
   c. the retina and the lens.
   d. the rods and the cones.

10. Which corrects nearsightedness?
    a. concave lens   b. converging lens
    c. diverging mirror   d. astigmatism

Understanding Concepts

11. According to the law of reflection, the angle of incidence is equal to what other angle?

12. Describe the image formed by a plane mirror.

13. Why can convex mirrors produce only virtual images?

14. Under what conditions does light bend when it enters a new medium?

15. How is the index of refraction of a medium related to the speed of light in the medium?

16. Explain why a concave lens cannot form a real image.

17. What occurs when the critical angle is exceeded?

18. A student-drawn ray diagram for a lens is shown below. Identify the errors the student made in the diagram.

19. Which part of the camera shown in Figure 14 controls the amount of light that strikes the film?

20. Explain how the human eye changes focus from near objects to faraway objects.

21. Explain why rods are more effective than cones for seeing objects at night.

22. Explain how diverging and converging lenses are effective for treating nearsightedness and farsightedness.

Optics **595**

Assessment

 If your class subscribes to the Interactive Textbook, your students can go online to access an interactive version of the Student Edition and a self-test.

Reviewing Content

1. b	**2.** c	**3.** b
4. b	**5.** b	**6.** b
7. c	**8.** a	**9.** a
10. a		

Understanding Concepts

11. The angle of reflection
12. The image formed by a plane mirror is virtual, upright, and is located the same distance behind the mirror as the object is in front of the mirror.
13. Convex mirrors always cause light rays to diverge, therefore they can form only virtual images.
14. Light bends when it enters a new medium (with a different index of refraction) at an angle.
15. The greater the index of refraction, the slower the speed of light in the medium.
16. Concave lenses always cause light rays to diverge, therefore they are not able to form real images.
17. Total internal reflection
18. The concave lens produces a reduced, virtual image in front of the lens, not a reduced, real image in back of the lens. The rays should diverge as they exit the lens.
19. The diaphragm and the shutter
20. Ciliary muscles inside the eye change the shape of the flexible lens.
21. Rods are more sensitive to low-intensity light, thus they are more effective at seeing objects at night.
22. Each lens adjusts the path of the incoming light rays before they enter the eye, thus compensating for the vision problems caused by the curvature of the cornea, curvature of the lens, or the length of the eyeball.

Homework Guide

Section	Questions
19.1	1–4, 11–13, 23, 30
19.2	5–7, 14–18, 24–25, 27–28, 31, 33
19.3	8, 19, 26, 29,
19.4	9–10, 20–22, 32

Critical Thinking

23. A concave mirror

24. No; Student-designed experiments should somehow allow for the determination of the position of a submerged object based upon its apparent position when viewed above the water. This position should then be compared with the actual position of the submerged object.

25. Placing light-sensitive film at the image plane of the pinhole viewer would convert it into a camera.

26. Refracting telescopes use only lenses to form an image, whereas reflecting telescopes use both mirrors and lenses.

27. Student diagrams should show a ray striking the water at a very low angle and being reflected, a ray striking the water at a larger angle and bending toward the normal as it is refracted, and a ray striking the water at a right angle and not being reflected or refracted.

28. The ray bends toward the normal as it is refracted when it enters the water. The ray reflects off of the mirror such that the angle of incidence equals the angle of reflection. The ray then bends away from the normal as it is refracted when exiting the water.

29. Most telescopes produce inverted images.

Concepts in Action

30. Billiard balls often behave the same as light rays that are reflected from flat surfaces, that is, their angle of incidence equals their angle of reflection. Knowing this allows you to plan how a struck billiard ball will travel after it bounces off of a bumper.

31. A convex lens

32. Virtual image; applications will vary but may include use as a magnifying lens.

33. The examples used in student paragraphs will vary but should include the following classifications.

  Plane mirror: virtual image; same size image
  Convex mirror: virtual image; reduced size image
  Concave mirror: virtual or real; reduced, equal, or enlarged size images

---

Critical Thinking

23. Applying Concepts Which type of mirror would you use to view an enlarged image of an object?

24. Designing Experiments Can the position of an object on the bottom of a swimming pool be accurately determined when viewed from above and at an angle to the water? Design an experiment to find out if refraction affects the apparent position of a submerged object.

25. Applying Concepts How could you convert the pinhole viewer used in the Quick Lab on page 585 into a device that could take a permanent picture?

26. Comparing and Contrasting What are the differences between a reflecting telescope and a refracting telescope?

27. Using Models Draw a ray diagram showing three rays of light traveling in air and striking the surface of water. Show one ray being reflected, one being refracted, and one entering the water without bending.

28. Predicting The illustration below shows a flashlight aimed down into a tub of water with a flat mirror lying on the bottom. Copy and complete the illustration by predicting the path of the light beam. (*Hint:* Remember to consider the effects of refraction and reflection.)

29. Inferring Many maps of the moon are printed showing the moon flipped upside down. What can you infer about the optical instruments used to view the moon?

Concepts in Action

30. Using Models How can you use the law of reflection to model a game of billiards?

31. Applying Concepts What kind of lens would you use to help you see a splinter in your finger?

32. Interpreting Diagrams The ray diagram below shows the formation of an image using a lens. Is the image a real or virtual image? What kind of lens is producing the image? Give a possible application for this type of lens.

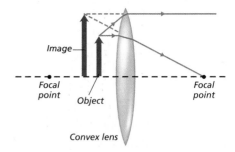

33. Writing in Science Classify plane, convex, and concave mirrors in terms of image type or image size. Write a paragraph citing examples for each classification.

Performance-Based Assessment

Make a telescope using two convex lenses and a cardboard tube from a finished roll of paper towels. Attach the lenses using tape. If possible, get two tubes of slightly different diameters so that one can fit inside the other. Wrap the smaller tube with tape or cardboard to make the smaller tube fit snugly inside the larger tube. How can you focus your telescope?

For: Self-grading assessment
Visit: PHSchool.com
Web Code: cca-2190

Performance-Based Assessment

By sliding the two tubes, you can change the overall length of the telescope and bring the object into focus.

Your students can independently test their knowledge of the chapter and print out their test results for your files.

Standardized Test Prep for Indiana

Standards Guide

Test-Taking Tip

Anticipate the Answer
When answering multiple choice questions, a useful strategy is to cover up the given answers and supply your own answer. Then compare your answer with those listed and select the one that most closely matches.

Practice anticipating the answer in this question.

When the incident angle of a light ray exceeds the critical angle, the ray undergoes
(A) total refraction.
(B) systemic diffraction.
(C) astigmatism.
(D) total internal reflection.
(E) mirror imaging.

(Answer: D)

Choose the letter that best answers the question or completes the statement.

1. Which statement correctly describes a property of mirrors?
   (A) Plane mirrors always form real images.
   (B) Concave mirrors can form real and virtual images.
   (C) The law of reflection only applies to convex mirrors.
   (D) Real images formed by concave mirrors are right side up.
   (E) All mirrors refract light rays to form images.

2. If a light ray slows down as it enters a medium at an angle, the ray is
   (A) totally reflected.
   (B) refracted.
   (C) diffracted.
   (D) evenly dispersed in the new medium.
   (E) travelling faster than 3.0×10^8 m/s.

3. When a ray strikes a plane mirror at an angle,
   (A) the light ray slows down and bends.
   (B) an inverted virtual image is formed.
   (C) the light ray is refracted.
   (D) the angle of incidence of the ray equals the angle of reflection of the ray.
   (E) the image formed is real.

4. Which of the following statements about convex lenses is FALSE?
   (A) They cause light rays to refract.
   (B) They can form real and virtual images.
   (C) They cause incoming parallel rays to converge.
   (D) They are thickest at the outside edges.
   (E) They are used in lighthouses.

5. Which description correctly matches the type of optical instrument?
   (A) Microscope—forms enlarged images of distant objects.
   (B) Camera—focuses incoming light using a series of mirrors.
   (C) Refracting telescope—is made up of two convex lenses.
   (D) Reflecting telescope—is made up of one convex lens and one concave lens.
   (E) Pinhole camera—focuses incoming light using a series of lenses.

Question 6 refers to the ray diagram shown below.

6. Which of the following statements is TRUE?
   (A) The mirror shown is concave.
   (B) The converging light rays form a real image.
   (C) The diverging rays form a real image.
   (D) The diverging rays form a virtual image.
   (E) The reflected light rays are parallel.

Optics **597**

SECTION OBJECTIVES	STANDARDS		ACTIVITIES and LABS
	NATIONAL	STATE	
20.1 Electric Charge and Static Electricity, pp. 600–603 ⏱ 1 block or 2 periods **20.1.1 Analyze** factors that affect the strength and direction of electric forces and fields. **20.1.2 Describe** how electric forces and fields affect electric charges. **20.1.3 Describe** how electric charges are transferred and **explain** why electric discharges occur.	A-1, B-4, B-6, G-1, G-3	ICP.6.1, ICP.6.2	**SE** Inquiry Activity: How Can You Reverse the Battery Direction in a Flashlight? p. 599 **L2** **TE** Teacher Demo: Electric Attraction and Repulsion, p. 601 **L2** **LM** Investigation 20B: Investigating Static Charge **L1**
20.2 Electric Current and Ohm's Law, pp. 604–607 ⏱ 1 block or 2 periods **20.2.1 Describe** electric current and **identify** the two types of current. **20.2.2 Describe** conduction and **classify** materials as good electrical conductors or good electrical insulators. **20.2.3 Describe** the factors that affect resistance. **20.2.4 Explain** how voltage produces electric current. **20.2.5 Calculate** voltage, current, and resistance using Ohm's law.	A-1, A-2, B-4, B-5, B-6, F-6, G-3	ICP.6.4	**SE** Quick Lab: Modeling Resistance in a Wire, p. 606 **L2** **LM** Investigation 20A: Investigating the Telephone **L2**
20.3 Electric Circuits, pp. 609–613 ⏱ 1 block or 2 periods **20.3.1 Analyze** circuit diagrams for series circuits and parallel circuits. **20.3.2 Solve equations** that relate electric power to current, voltage, and electrical energy. **20.3.3 Describe** devices and procedures for maintaining electrical safety.	A-1, A-2, B-4, E-2, F-1, G-3	ICP.6.4, ICP.6.5	**SE** Quick Lab: Modeling a Fuse, p. 612 **L2** **SE** Forensics Lab: Evaluating Electrical Safety, p. 623 **L2** **TE** Teacher Demo: Series and Parallel Circuits, p. 610 **L2**
20.4 Electronic Devices, pp. 618–622 ⏱ 1 block or 2 periods **20.4.1 Explain** how electronics conveys information with analog or digital signals. **20.4.2 Describe** electronic devices used to control electron flow. **20.4.3 Illustrate** how semiconductors are used to make three kinds of solid-state components. **20.4.4 Describe** how solid-state components are used in electronic devices.	A-1, A-2, B-4, B-6, E-2, F-1, G-3		**TE** Teacher Demo: Semiconductors and Current, p. 621 **L2**

RESOURCES PRINT and TECHNOLOGY		SECTION ASSESSMENT
RSW Section 20.1	L1	**SE** Section 20.1 Assessment, p. 603
T Chapter 20 Pretest	L2	**iT** Section 20.1
Section 20.1	L2	
P Chapter 20 Pretest	L2	
Section 20.1	L2	
RSW Section 20.2	L1	**SE** Section 20.2 Assessment, p. 607
MSPS Section 20.2	L2	**iT** Section 20.2
T Section 20.2	L2	
P Section 20.2	L2	
SCLINKS GO Conductors and insulators	L2	
PLM Lab 8: Evaluating Electrical Safety	L2	**SE** Section 20.3 Assessment, p. 613
RSW Section 20.3	L1	**iT** Section 20.3
RSW Math Skill	L2	
MSPS Section 20.3	L2	
DC Current Computers	L2	
T Section 20.3	L2	
P Section 20.3	L2	
SCLINKS GO Electric circuits	L2	
RSW Section 20.4	L1	**SE** Section 20.4 Assessment, p. 622
T Section 20.4	L2	**iT** Section 20.4
P Section 20.4	L2	

Go Online

Go online for these Internet resources.

PHSchool.com
Web Code: cca-2200
Web Code: cch-2203

NSTA SCLINKS
Web Code: ccn-2202
Web Code: ccn-2203

Materials for Activities and Labs

Quantities for each group

STUDENT EDITION

Inquiry Activity, p. 599
flashlight (uses 2 D batteries), 2 D batteries

Quick Lab, p. 606
white paper, metric ruler, number 2 pencil, multimeter

Quick Lab, p. 612
6-volt battery, 2 wires with stripped ends, strip of aluminum foil, scissors, wooden block, unpainted thumbtacks

Forensics Lab, p. 623
9-volt battery, battery clip, multimeter, 3 alligator clips, 4 resistors: 1-ohm, 10-ohm, 100-ohm, 1000-ohm

TEACHER'S EDITION

Teacher Demo, p. 601
pith ball, thread, rubber or ebonite rod, fur

Teacher Demo, p. 610
a 6-volt battery, 3 small light bulbs with sockets, 2 long strands of wire (12 cm), 4 short strands of wire (6 cm)

Build Science Skills, p. 616
several discarded computers, each having its top removed

Teacher Demo, p. 621
a light-emitting diode (LED), an ohmmeter, a DC power source, wires, alligator clips

Chapter Assessment

CHAPTER ASSESSMENT

SE Chapter Assessment, pp. 625–626
CUT Chapter 20 Test A, B
CTB Chapter 20
iT Chapter 20
PHSchool.com GO
Web Code: cca-2200

STANDARDIZED TEST PREP

SE Chapter 20, p. 627
TP Diagnose and Prescribe

Interactive Textbook with

From the Author

Sophia Yancopoulos
Manhattan College

Big Ideas

Electricity is one of the four known universal forces of nature. Electric fields are everywhere. They can produce heat, light, chemical changes, and magnetic fields. They even permeate our bodies.

Matter and Energy Charge is a fundamental property of matter, just as mass is. A net electric charge, positive or negative, usually results from the loss or gain of electrons. Like charges repel, and unlike charges attract, according to the amount of each charge and the distance between them.

Forces and Motion The attraction or repulsion between electrically charged objects is called electric force. Charge can be transferred by friction or by direct contact. The transfer of charge by induction can occur with no contact between objects. Many students will have difficulty with the concept of an electric field. An electric field surrounds any charged particle, whether or not the charge is moving. Because the electric field is defined as the electric force per unit charge, the strength of the field does not depend on the amount of charge acted upon, although field strength does depend on position within the field.

Electric current, the flow of electric charge, is caused by an electrical potential difference, called voltage. Electrical resistance is exactly as it sounds, an opposition to the flow of charge.

Encourage students to create their own mnemonics. For example, in studying electric circuits, students can distinguish between series and parallel more easily if they remember that a series circuit is a single path and serious trouble for the whole circuit if any element in the circuit stops functioning.

Physics Refresher

Electric Charges, Forces, and Fields

20.1 and 20.2

The force between electric charges is described by Coulomb's law: $F = k_C q_1 q_2 / r^2$. This force increases as the charge (q_1 or q_2) increases, and decreases as the square of the distance between the charges (r) increases. Because like charges repel and opposite charges attract, the sign of F indicates a repulsive force (F positive) or an attractive force (F negative). The Coulomb constant, k_C, is 8.99×10^9 N•m^2/C^2.

> **⚑ Address Misconceptions**
>
> *Students may think that most atoms in a charged object contribute to the net charge.* In fact, only a small fraction of the atoms or molecules give up or gain electrons. For a strategy to overcome this misconception, see **Address Misconceptions** on **page 602**.

Like gravitational force, the electric force is a field force: $E = F/q_1 = k_C q_2 / r^2$. The direction of the field lines depends on the charge that produces the field. Positive charges produce a field that points away from the charge. Negative charges produce a field that points toward the charge. The field is stronger where the field lines are closer together. The diagrams below show the electric fields around two unlike charges and around two like charges.

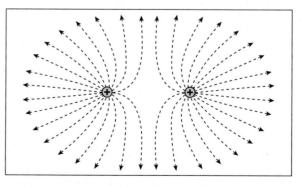

Go Online

PD LINKS
NSTA

For: Teaching methods for electricity
Visit: www.SciLinks.org/PDLinks
Web Code: ccn-2099

Voltage, Current, and Resistance in Circuits 20.2 and 20.3

Address Misconceptions

Students may think that only metals make good conductors. In fact, solutions containing ions and ionized gases are also good conductors. For a strategy to overcome this misconception, see **Address Misconceptions** on **page 605**.

An electrical circuit contains either direct current (flowing in one direction) or alternating current (constantly changing direction). For many materials, the voltage (V), current (I), and resistance (R) in a circuit are related by Ohm's Law: $V = IR$.

In an ideal series circuit, the total current is constant, as it has only one path to follow. The voltage, current, and resistance for each circuit element are:

$$I = I_1 = I_2 = I_3 = \dots$$
$$V = V_1 + V_2 + V_3 + \dots$$
$$R = R_1 + R_2 + R_3 + \dots$$

In an ideal parallel circuit, the voltage across each parallel branch in the circuit is equal in magnitude to the voltage across the power supply (V), but the currents through each element, when added, equal the current through the entire circuit:

$$V = V_1 = V_2 = V_3 = \dots$$
$$I = I_1 + I_2 + I_3 + \dots$$
$$1/R = 1/R_1 + 1/R_2 + 1/R_3 + \dots$$

Electronic Devices 20.4

Both vacuum tubes and diodes can be used to change alternating current to direct current. In a vacuum tube, this is done by a heated filament, which emits electrons, and a metal plate that changes from positive to negative charge with the alternating input current. The emitted electrons are attracted to the plate when it is positively charged, and an output current is produced. The electrons are repelled when the plate is negatively charged, and then there is no output current. In this way, charges in the output current move only in one direction.

The pn junction in a diode works in a similar way, except that the increased resistance in one direction results from the properties of n-type and p-type semiconductors. For charge in the form of positively charged holes and negatively charged electrons to flow through the diode, the p side is connected to the positive battery terminal and the n side is connected to the negative battery terminal. Connected this way, the diode offers very little resistance to current.

Charge Flow in pn Junctions

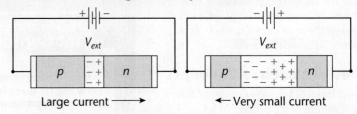

Large current →   ← Very small current

Suppose the battery connections were reversed as shown on the right. Then holes are pulled from the p side toward the negative terminal. Similarly, electrons are pulled from the n side toward the positive terminal. Charges build up quickly in the junction. These charges repel current-carrying charges being pushed through the circuit, and the diode's resistance becomes very large. Almost immediately, the current stops.

Build Reading Literacy

Summarize

Briefly Restating the Main Ideas

Strategy Help students understand a topic by restating the main ideas. Students read a section of the text and then identify main ideas and supporting details. They summarize what they have read by briefly restating the main concepts in a sentence or two. Summarizing can be employed to review brief subsections as well as entire sections and chapters. Have students read the beginning of Section 20.1, pp. 600–601.

Example

1. Ask students to carefully read the selected passage. Then, have them review the passage and identify the main ideas. Demonstrate this process by using the bold headings, Key Concept statements, and vocabulary as aids in determining what the passage is mostly about. List the main ideas on the board.

2. Direct students to write brief summaries of the passage by restating each of the main ideas in one or two sentences, using their own words. Remind students to focus on the most important concepts, omitting details and examples. Students should check to be sure that their summary covers the terms mentioned in the bold headings.

3. Assign the next passage for students to read and summarize. You may want to have students work in small groups to compare their summaries.

4. Have students read and summarize the rest of Section 20.1.

See p. 609 for a script on how to use the summarize strategy with students. For additional Build Reading Literacy strategies, see pp. 600, 606, and 619.

ASSESS PRIOR KNOWLEDGE

Use the Chapter Pretest below to assess students' prior knowledge. As needed, review these Science Concepts and Math Skills with students.

Review Science Concepts

Section 20.1 Review universal forces, magnitude and direction of force, universal gravitation (analogous to $F = kqq/r^2$), electric force, and actions between charged particles.

Section 20.2 Review potential energy and electrical energy as an introduction to voltage. Review work, energy conversions, and conservation of energy.

Section 20.3 Remind students of the definition and units for power. Review thermal energy to prepare for discussion of heating in resistors.

Section 20.4 Review the definition of a vacuum. Review speed, time, and distance (to relate why smaller circuits are faster).

Review Math Skills

Calculating with Significant Figures, Formulas, and Equations
Students will need to calculate with significant figures and use formulas and equations to solve problems dealing with power, voltage, and current.

Direct students to the **Math Skills** in the **Skills and Reference Handbook** at the end of the student text.

CHAPTER
20 Electricity

21st Century Learning
Economic Literacy

How much does it cost to operate common appliances?

After reading Sections 20.2 and 20.3, you should be able to calculate the energy cost of operating electric appliances. Choose an electrical device that you use at home (for example, a computer or hair dryer), and find out its power rating. Estimate how many hours per day you use it, and calculate the energy consumed in kilowatt-hours. Look up the cost of a kilowatt-hour in your area to determine how much the device costs to operate each day. Post your results on a class blog or wiki.

Indiana's Academic Standards for Science

ELECTRICAL ENERGY PROPAGATION AND MAGNETISM
ICP.6.1: Explain that objects that carry a net charge will exert an electric force on other objects that may be attractive or repulsive; **ICP.6.2:** Explain that when charge is transferred from one object to another, the amount lost by one object equals the amount gained by the other, consistent with the principal of conservation of charge; **ICP.6.4:** Define and describe the relationships between voltage, current, resistance and power in open and closed electrical circuits; **ICP.6.5:** Describe the differences in current flow in parallel and in series circuits.

Lightning provides a powerful display of electrical energy.

598 *Chapter 20*

Chapter Pretest

1. Which particles move freely through metals, speeding the transfer of thermal energy? *(b)*
  a. Atoms   **b.** Electrons
  c. Protons   **d.** Molecules
2. Electric forces act between _____. *(charged objects or particles)*
3. True or False: Objects with opposite charges repel one another. *(False)*

4. How will doubling the distance between two masses affect the strength of the gravitational force between them? *(The force of gravity will be only one fourth as strong.)*
5. Energy that is stored and can later be used to move an object is called _____. *(potential energy)*
6. What happens to the kinetic energy of the particles in an object when the thermal

energy of the object is increased? *(The kinetic energy of the particles increases.)*
7. True or False: Power is measured in units of joules. *(False)*
8. If 2.0×10^4 J of energy are produced in 5 s, how much power is generated? *(a)*
  a. 4×10^3 W   **b.** 1×10^5 W
  c. 1×10^4 W   **d.** 4×10^4 W

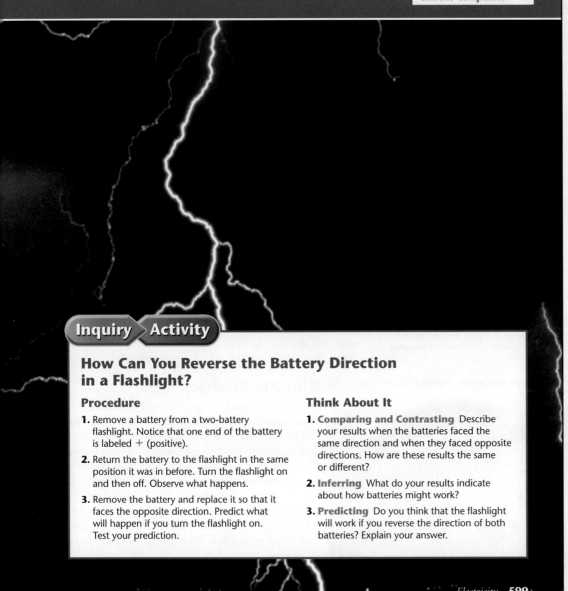

Chapter Preview

20.1 Electric Charge and Static Electricity

20.2 Electric Current and Ohm's Law

20.3 Electric Circuits

20.4 Electronic Devices

Discovery SCHOOL

Video Field Trip

Current Computers

Inquiry › Activity

How Can You Reverse the Battery Direction in a Flashlight?

Procedure

1. Remove a battery from a two-battery flashlight. Notice that one end of the battery is labeled + (positive).

2. Return the battery to the flashlight in the same position it was in before. Turn the flashlight on and then off. Observe what happens.

3. Remove the battery and replace it so that it faces the opposite direction. Predict what will happen if you turn the flashlight on. Test your prediction.

Think About It

1. **Comparing and Contrasting** Describe your results when the batteries faced the same direction and when they faced opposite directions. How are these results the same or different?

2. **Inferring** What do your results indicate about how batteries might work?

3. **Predicting** Do you think that the flashlight will work if you reverse the direction of both batteries? Explain your answer.

Electricity **599**

Discovery SCHOOL

Video Field Trip

Current Computers

Encourage students to view the Video Field Trip "Current Computers."

ENGAGE/EXPLORE

Inquiry › Activity

How Can You Reverse the Battery Direction in a Flashlight? **L2**

Purpose In this activity, students are introduced to the idea that current consists of moving charged particles.

⚑ Address Misconceptions

Some students may mistakenly think that electric current does not move in a specific direction. Therefore, they may be unaware of the significance of having the batteries both pointing in the same direction in a flashlight.

Challenge this misconception by showing students how the needle of an ammeter or galvanometer changes direction when the electrodes connected to a battery's terminals are reversed.

Skills Focus Observing, Inferring

Prep Time 10 minutes

Materials flashlight (uses 2 D-sized batteries), 2 D-sized batteries

Class Time 10 minutes

Safety Students should avoid flashlight breakage, which can produce sharp edges.

Expected Outcome Students will learn that, for a flashlight to work, the batteries in it must be placed so positive and negative ends touch.

Think About It

1. When the batteries faced the same direction, the flashlight worked. When they faced different directions, the flashlight did not work.

2. Students may infer that whatever goes in one end of a battery and out the other end can travel in only one direction.

3. Yes, because the batteries are positioned in the same direction, the flashlight will work, provided good contact exists between the batteries and flashlight terminals. Many flashlights are designed so that the batteries can only make good contact when they point in one direction.
Logical, Group

20.1 Electric Charge and Static Electricity

Standards: ICP.6.1, ICP.6.2

① FOCUS

Objectives

20.1.1 **Analyze** factors that affect the strength and direction of electric forces and fields.

20.1.2 **Describe** how electric forces and fields affect electric charges.

20.1.3 **Describe** how electric charges are transferred and **explain** why electric discharges occur.

Reading Focus

Build Vocabulary **L2**

Word-Part Analysis Ask students, **What word appears in most of the definitions?** *(Electric, electrical, electricity)* Explain that the root word for *electricity* comes from the Greek word for "amber," a substance that is easily charged. Ask, **What can be inferred from this?** *(Electricity deals with charges.)* Explain that the word *static* comes most recently from the Greek word *statikos,* which means "causing to stand." Point out to students that in static electricity, or static discharge, charges jump from one location to another. Thus, charges do move, so the term *static* is unfortunate.

Reading Strategy **L2**

a. The attraction or repulsion between electrically charged objects
b. Field strength depends on the net charge and distance from the charge.
c. Charge can be transferred by friction, contact, or induction.

② INSTRUCT

Electric Charge

Build Reading Literacy **L1**

Outline Refer to page **156D** in **Chapter 6,** which provides the guidelines for an outline.

Have students create an outline of the section (pp. 600–603). Outlines should follow the head structure used in the section. Major headings are shown in green, and subheadings are shown in blue. Ask, **Based on your outline, what are the three ways static electric charges are transferred?** *(Friction, contact, and induction)*
Verbal, Logical

Reading Focus

Key Concepts

- What produces a net electric charge?
- What determines whether an electric force is attractive or repulsive?
- What determines the strength of an electric field?
- What are three ways in which charge is transferred?
- How does a static discharge occur?

Vocabulary

- electric charge
- electric force
- electric field
- static electricity
- law of conservation of charge
- induction

Reading Strategy

Identifying Main Ideas Copy the table below. As you read, write the main idea for each topic.

Topic	Main Idea
Electric Charge	An excess or shortage of electrons produces a net electric charge.
Electric Forces	a._____
Electric Fields	b._____
Static Electricity	c._____

Think back to the last time a thunderstorm swept through your area. A bolt of lightning streaked across the sky, followed moments later by the crash of thunder. Have you ever wondered what causes lightning? Perhaps you've observed something similar on a smaller scale closer to home. When you take clothes out of a dryer, some of them can stick together, like the socks and towel in Figure 1. If you pull the clothes apart in a darkened room, you can see sparks that are like tiny bolts of lightning. This shouldn't be surprising once you realize that lightning and "static cling" have a similar cause—the movement of electric charges.

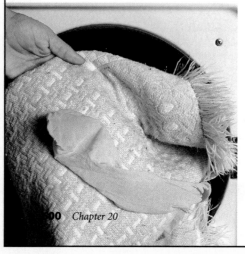

Figure 1 Electric charge is responsible for clothes that stick together when they are removed from a dryer.

Electric Charge

Recall that electrical energy is the energy associated with electric charges. But what exactly is electric charge? **Electric charge** is a property that causes subatomic particles such as protons and electrons to attract or repel each other. There are two types of electric charge, positive and negative. Protons have a positive charge and electrons have a negative charge. Electric charges move in a flash through a lightning bolt. Electric charges attract one another in clothes taken from the dryer. Although charged particles are too small to see, just about everything in your daily life is affected by charge in one way or another.

600 Chapter 20

Section Resources

Print
- *Laboratory Manual,* Investigation 20B
- *Reading and Study Workbook With Math Support,* Section 20.1
- *Transparencies,* Chapter Pretest and Section 20.1

Technology
- *Interactive Textbook,* Section 20.1
- *Presentation Pro CD-ROM,* Chapter Pretest and Section 20.1

Figure 2 shows how charges are arranged in an atom. A cloud of negatively charged electrons surrounds the positively charged nucleus. The atom is neutral because it has an equal number of positive and negative charges. If an atom gains one or more electrons, it becomes a negatively charged ion. If an atom loses electrons, it becomes a positively charged ion. 👄 **An excess or shortage of electrons produces a net electric charge.**

The SI unit of electric charge is the coulomb (C). It takes about 6.24×10^{18} electrons to produce a single coulomb. A lightning bolt is about 10 to 20 coulombs of charge. In comparison, a flash camera uses the energy from 0.025 coulombs of charge to produce each flash.

Electric Forces

Rub an inflated rubber balloon on your clean, dry hair. If it's a dry day, you can use the balloon to pick up bits of paper. The balloon attracts the paper because the balloon is negatively charged and the paper is positively charged. Now rub a second balloon on your hair and bring the two balloons close together. You can feel the balloons repel. The two balloons repel because they are negatively charged. 👄 **Like charges repel, and opposite charges attract.** The force of attraction or repulsion between electrically charged objects is **electric force.**

The French scientist Charles-Augustin de Coulomb (1736–1806) discovered that electric forces obey a law similar to the law of universal gravitation. The electric force between two objects is directly proportional to the net charge on each object and inversely proportional to the square of the distance between them. As you can see in Figure 3, doubling the net charge on one object doubles the electric force. If instead you double the distance between the objects, the electric force is one fourth as strong.

Inside an atom, electric forces are much stronger than gravitational forces. Electric forces form chemical bonds, which must be overcome in chemical changes. Electric forces also cause friction and other contact forces. But on a large scale, matter is mostly neutral and in that case, electric forces are close to zero.

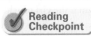
What is electric force?

Figure 2 A neutral atom has equal numbers of protons and electrons.
Drawing Conclusions *What is the overall charge if the atom loses an electron?*

Figure 3 Electric force depends on charge and distance. **A** Opposite charges attract each other. **B** Doubling one charge doubles the force on both charges. **C** Like charges repel. Doubling the distance makes the force one fourth as great.

Electricity **601**

Build Science Skills L2

Using Models Have students apply what they know about force and mass to explain why negative charges are more mobile than positive charges. *(Positive charges are provided by protons, which are much more massive than electrons. Electrons, which carry negative charge, are less massive and therefore more easily moved.)*
Logical

Electric Forces

Teacher Demo

Electric Attraction and Repulsion L2

Purpose To show that attractive forces exist between unlike charges, and repelling forces exist between like charges.

Materials pith ball, thread, rubber or ebonite rod, fur

Procedure Attach the thread to the pith ball. Rub the fur against the rubber rod, and then touch this rod briefly to the pith ball. Bring the rod close to the pith ball. Next, move the fur near the pith ball.

Expected Outcome Friction causes the fur to become positively charged and the rod to become negatively charged. The rod then transfers negative charge to the pith ball. When the rod is brought close to the pith ball, the like charges exert a repelling force on each other, and the ball moves away from the rod. When the fur, which has an opposite charge to the rod, is brought close to the ball, the ball is attracted to the fur.
Visual

Answer to . . .

Figure 2 *Net charge would be +1.*

Reading Checkpoint *An electric force is a force of repulsion or attraction between electrically charged objects.*

Electric Fields

Use Visuals

Figure 4 Stress that the directions of the electric fields for positive and negative charges are a matter of convention, much in the same way that the proton has charge that is called "positive." Emphasize that the field lines show the direction of the force on a positive "test" charge placed in the field. Ask, **In what direction is the force on a proton that is placed in each of these fields?** *(The force is outward [repulsive] in A and inward [attractive] in B.)*
Visual

Static Electricity and Charging

Address Misconceptions L2

Students may think that most or all of the atoms in an object charged by friction contribute to the object's net charge. Emphasize that only a small fraction of the atoms or molecules in a substance give up electrons. For instance, an acrylic rod that has been rubbed with fur may only have a net charge of 10^{-9} C. Explain that, while such a charge is produced by 10 billion electrons, there are about 10^{22} to 10^{24} atoms from which charges could be taken. In other words, only about one in a trillion atoms or molecules donate charges during charging by friction.
Logical

Use Visuals L1

Figure 5 Stress that friction usually separates charges on a pair of electrically neutral objects, whereas charging by contact moves some of the net charge on a charged object to another object. Ask, **What would happen if electrons were conveyed by contact to an object with a positive charge?** *(The electrons would reduce the overall positive charge of the object.)* Ask, **What would happen if the positive and negative charges were equal?** *(The object would become electrically neutral.)*
Visual

Figure 4 The strength of an electric field depends on the amount of charge that produces the field and on the distance from the charge. **A** The electric field around a positive charge points outward. **B** The electric field around a negative charge points inward.

A Field of a positive charge   B Field of a negative charge

Electric Fields

The effect an electric charge has on other charges in the space around it is the charge's **electric field.** Figure 4 shows the fields of positive and negative charges. ◉ **The strength of an electric field depends on the amount of charge that produces the field and on the distance from the charge.** The lines representing the field are closer together near the charge, where the field is stronger.

An electric field exerts forces on any charged object placed in the field. The force depends on the net charge in the object and on the strength and direction of the field at the object's position. The more net charge an object has, the greater is the force on it. The direction of each field line shows the direction of the force on a positive charge.

Static Electricity and Charging

Static electricity is the study of the behavior of electric charges, including how charge is transferred between objects. There are several ways that a net charge can build up on an object or move from one object to another. ◉ **Charge can be transferred by friction, by contact, and by induction.** Keep in mind that whenever there is a charge transfer, the total charge is the same before and after the transfer occurs. This is the **law of conservation of charge**—the total charge in an isolated system is constant.

Charging by Friction The balloon in Figure 5A attracts hair because opposite charges attract. But how do balloons and hair pick up a net charge? Rubbing a balloon on your hair is an example of charging by friction. Electrons move from your hair to the balloon because atoms in rubber have a greater attraction for electrons than atoms in hair. The balloon picks up a net negative charge. Because your hair loses electrons, it becomes positively charged. Even simple everyday activities like walking across a carpet can build up charge this way.

Charging by Contact Why do the girl's hairs repel each other in Figure 5B? In this case, charge is transferred by contact. A Van de Graaff generator has charged the metal sphere. When the girl touches the sphere, she acquires a charge large enough to make her hairs stand on end. The sphere is still charged, but its net charge is reduced.

Figure 5 Charge can be transferred by friction and by contact. **A** Friction transferred electrons from the hair to the balloon. The balloon then attracts the hair because opposite charges attract. **B** A Van de Graaff generator has charged the metal sphere. Touching the sphere transfers charge. The hairs repel each other because like charges repel.

Facts and Figures

Electrical Force and Gravitational Force
Electrical forces are much stronger than the gravitational forces that operate among particles in an atom. For instance, an electron and a proton in a hydrogen atom are 5.3×10^{-11} m apart, on average. The mass of the electron is 9.11×10^{-31} kg and the mass of the proton is 1.67×10^{-27} kg, while both have a charge with magnitude 1.60×10^{-19} C. The gravitational force of attraction between the two particles is 3.6×10^{-47} N, while the electrical force of attraction is 8.2×10^{-8} N, or about 2×10^{39} times greater than the gravitational attraction between them.

Conductors and Insulators

Why is a metal wire usually coated with plastic [...] wire is an electrical conductor. The rubber and [...] insulators. An **electrical conductor** is a material [...] can flow easily. A material through which charge [...] called an **electrical insulator.** The coating aroun[...] trol the current and keep it where it is needed.

A metal is made up of ions in a lattice. Th[...] move. But each ion has one or more electron[...] bound to it. These free electrons can conduct c[...] do not easily conduct charge because they don[...] Metals such as copper and silver are good [...] Wood, plastic, rubber, and air are good electri[...]

Resistance

As electrons move through a conducting wire, [...] trons and ions. These collisions convert som[...] thermal energy. Because less energy is availa[...] through the wire, the current is reduced. **Resis**[...] the flow of charges in a material. The SI unit of [...]

When you drink a milkshake as shown in [...] you use a thicker straw. In the same way, resist[...] make a wire thicker because more electrons can [...] wire. A material's thickness, length, and [...] **resistance.** Resistance is greater in a longer wi[...] travel farther. As temperature increases, a meta[...] because electrons collide more often.

If resistance increases as temperature incr[...] you cool a conductor? Could you reduce the re[...] the idea behind superconductors. A **supercond**[...] has almost zero resistance when it is cooled to [...] best superconductor found thus far must be c[...]

Charging by Induction Suppose you reach for a doorknob after walking across a carpet. You have picked up extra electrons from the carpet, so your hand is negatively charged. The net negative charge in your hand repels electrons in the metal doorknob. Figure 6 shows that electrons move to the base of the doorknob, leaving a net positive charge in the part of the doorknob closest to the hand. Overall, the doorknob is still neutral, but charge has moved within it. This is **induction,** a transfer of charge without contact between materials.

Static Discharge

Why do you get a shock from a doorknob? The spark you feel is a static discharge. **Static discharge occurs when a pathway through which charges can move forms suddenly.** Charges will not travel through air from your hand to the doorknob. But air becomes charged suddenly when the gap between your finger and the doorknob is small. This air provides a path for electrons to flow from your hand to the doorknob. If the room is dark, you can even see this spark.

Lightning is a more dramatic discharge. Charge can build up in a storm cloud from friction between moving air masses. Negative charge in the lower part of the cloud induces a positive charge in the ground below the cloud. As the amount of charge in the cloud increases, the force of attraction between charges in the cloud and charges in the ground increases. Eventually the air becomes charged, forming a pathway for electrons to travel from the cloud to the ground.

Figure 6 Induction occurs when charge is transferred without contact between materials. Negative charges in the hand induce charges to move within the metal doorknob. **Predicting** What would happen if the hand had a net positive charge?

PLANETDIARY

For: Activity on thunder and lightning
Visit: PHSchool.com
Web Code: ccc-2201

Section 20.1 Assessment

Reviewing Concepts

1. How is a net electric charge produced?
2. What determines whether charges attract or repel?
3. Name two factors that affect the strength of an electric field.
4. List three methods of charge transfer.
5. Explain how static discharge occurs.
6. How does electric force depend on the amount of charge and the distance between charges?
7. What is the law of conservation of charge?

Critical Thinking

8. **Forming Hypotheses** Why does plastic food wrap cling better to some materials than to others?

9. **Inferring** When a glass rod is rubbed with neutral silk, the glass becomes positively charged. What charge does the silk now have? Explain.
10. **Relating Cause and Effect** Many lightning strikes occur within a cloud, rather than between clouds and the ground. Explain why. (*Hint:* Assume a cloud has no net charge.)

Writing in Science

Explanatory Paragraph Write a paragraph explaining the series of events that may cause you to receive a shock from a metal doorknob on a dry winter day. (*Hint:* Use a flowchart to organize your ideas before writing your paragraph.)

Electricity **603**

---

1 FOCUS

Objectives

20.2.1 Describe electric current and **identify** the two types of current.

20.2.2 Describe conduction and **classify** materials as good electrical conductors or good electrical insulators.

20.2.3 Describe the factors that affect resistance.

20.2.4 Explain how voltage produces electric current.

20.2.5 Calculate voltage, current, and resistance using Ohm's law.

Reading Focus

Build Vocabulary `L2`

LINCS Have students: List the parts of the vocabulary that they know, such as *potential* and *difference*. Imagine what a *potential difference* might look like and how the terms might fit together. Note a reminding sound-alike word, such as *potential energy*. Connect the terms, perhaps in a long sentence or a short story. Self-test (quiz themselves).

Reading Strategy `L2`

a. Electric current is the flow of electric charge.
b. Electric current is the continuous flow of electric charge.

2 INSTRUCT

Electric Current

Use Visuals `L1`

Figure 7 Emphasize that electric current needs a continuous path through the flashlight. Ask, **How is the direction of current related to the direction of the flow of electrons?** *(Electrons flow from the negative terminal of one battery to the positive terminal of the other; the direction of current is in the opposite direction.)* Then ask, **What is the function of the switch?** *(Flipping the switch to the "on" position completes the path for the flow of charge)*
Visual, Logical

Modeling Resistance in a Wire `L2`

Objective

After completing this activity, students will be able to
• describe how the thickness of a conductor affects its resistance.

Skills Focus Observing, Measuring, Controlling Variables, Using Models

 Prep Time 15 minutes

Materials white paper, metric ruler, number 2 pencil, multimeter

Class Time 25 minutes

Safety Students should wear safety goggles and aprons during the lab. Be sure students wash their hands after completing the lab.

Expected Outcome Students will learn that electrical resistance decreases as the width of the resisting material is increased or the length of the resisting material is decreased.

Analyze and Conclude

1. Resistance is greater in the narrower rectangle; it decreases.
2. There are more available electrons for current within the cross-sectional area of a thick wire than of a thin wire. As wire length decreases, the distance electrons travel decreases, so the number of collisions that cause resistance decreases.
Logical, Group

For Enrichment `L3`

Have students repeat the experiment with different metal strips of identical dimensions and make a table listing the resistances. **Kinesthetic**

Voltage

Build Reading Literacy `L1`

Relate Text and Visuals Refer to page **190D** in **Chapter 7**, which provides the guidelines for relating text and visuals.

Have students read the paragraphs about potential difference while referring to Figure 9. Emphasize that the figure provides an analogy, so that the difficult concept in the text will be easier to visualize. Ask, **How are gravity and an attractive electric field similar?** *(Work must be done against each to increase the potential energy of an object.)*
Logical

Quick Lab

Modeling Resistance in a Wire

Materials

white paper, metric ruler, number 2 pencil, multimeter

Procedure

1. Draw a narrow rectangle 1 cm wide by 5 cm long on the paper. Draw a wide rectangle, 3 cm by 5 cm. Use the pencil to completely fill in both rectangles with graphite.

2. Place the multimeter electrodes at opposite ends of the narrow rectangle. Record the resistance. Keep one electrode in place and slowly drag the other one toward it. Record your observations.

3. Repeat Step 2 using the wide rectangle.

Analyze and Conclude

1. **Observing** In which rectangle is the resistance greater? How does resistance change as the electrodes move together?

2. **Using Models** Explain why a thick wire has lower resistance than a thin wire if all else is equal. Why does resistance decrease as a wire's length decreases?

Voltage

If you remove the batteries from a flashlight, the light will not shine. Why? Because there is resistance in the wires and the bulb, charges do not flow on their own without a source of energy. ⊙ **In order for charge to flow in a conducting wire, the wire must be connected in a complete loop that includes a source of electrical energy.**

Potential Difference Recall that potential energy is related to position. In Figure 9, water at the top of the fountain has more gravitational potential energy than water at the bottom. That is why water falls spontaneously from a higher to a lower height. In the same way, charges flow spontaneously from a higher to a lower potential energy.

The potential energy of a charge depends on its position in an electric field. **Potential difference** is the difference in electrical potential energy between two places in an electric field. Potential difference is measured in joules per coulomb, or volts. Because it is measured in volts, potential difference is also called **voltage.**

Voltage Sources How does water get to the top of the fountain? A pump inside the fountain does work on the water to increase its potential energy. In the same way, a source of voltage such as a battery does work to increase the potential energy of electric charges.

Three common voltage sources are batteries, solar cells, and generators. A **battery** is a device that converts chemical energy to electrical energy. Batteries, like other voltage sources, have terminals that can connect to wires in a circuit. One terminal is positive and the other is negative. A voltage drop, or potential difference, is maintained across the terminals. In a 9-volt battery, for example, the voltage drop is about 9 volts.

Figure 9 A water fountain has a pump inside that lifts water to the top, increasing the gravitational potential energy of the water. In the same way, a voltage source increases the electrical potential energy of electric charges.

Facts and Figures

Diamond As a rule, good conductors of heat are also good conductors of electricity. This is because most conductors are metals, and the electrons in metals can move with ease, transferring energy through the metal, regardless of whether the energy is thermal or electrical. However, one substance that is a good thermal conductor (in fact, the best thermal conductor) is an electrical insulator: diamond. Diamond is a form of carbon in which all carbon atoms are bound to other carbon atoms in a tetrahedral crystal. These strong bonds give diamond its great hardness, and make it possible for kinetic energy to pass easily through the crystal by heat. However, because there are no free electrons to move throughout the crystal, diamond cannot conduct electricity.

Ohm's Law

The unit of resistance, the ohm, is named after the German scientist Georg Ohm (1789–1854). It was Ohm who first determined how resistance and current affect voltage. He discovered that voltage is not the same everywhere in a circuit. Ohm hypothesized that resistance reduces the voltage. He published his research in 1826, but his findings were so controversial that he lost his job. Eventually his work became widely accepted.

Ohm found a mathematical relationship between voltage, current, and resistance. This relationship became known as Ohm's law. According to **Ohm's law,** the voltage (V) in a circuit equals the product of the current (I) and the resistance (R).

Ohm's Law

$$V = I \times R \text{ or } I = \frac{V}{R}$$

When the current is in amperes and the resistance is in ohms, the voltage is in volts. What is the voltage if the resistance is 3 ohms and the current is 3 amps?

$$V = I \times R = 3 \text{ amps} \times 3 \text{ ohms} = 9 \text{ volts}$$

● **Increasing the voltage increases the current. Keeping the same voltage and increasing the resistance decreases the current.** A multimeter, shown in Figure 10, is a device used to measure current, voltage, and resistance.

Figure 10 A multimeter can be used to measure current, voltage, or resistance. Here the voltage of a 9-volt battery is measured.

Ohm's Law
Build Science Skills L2

Calculating Help students use Ohm's law to calculate the voltage when the current is 4.0 amps and the resistance is 3.0 ohms.

$V = I \times R =$
4.0 amps $\times$ 3.0 ohms = 12 volts

Then, help students understand that current is indirectly proportional to resistance by doubling the resistance and calculating the new current while the voltage remains constant:

$I = V/R =$ 12 volts/6.0 ohms = 2.0 amps

Point out that when the resistance is doubled, the current decreases by one half.
Logical

3 ASSESS
Evaluate Understanding L2

Ask students to write two questions each about current, resistance, and voltage. Review the questions for accuracy. Then, have students form groups and ask each other their approved questions.

Reteach L1

Have students use Figure 9 to explain how voltage increases the electrical potential of a charge.

Writing in Science

Paragraphs should describe conductors as materials, such as copper and silver, through which charges move easily. Insulators should be described as materials, such as wood, plastic, or rubber, through which charges do not move easily. Conductors are used in electrical wiring for buildings, and in electrical appliances, while insulators are used to isolate conductors from unwanted contact.

Interactive Textbook If your class subscribes to the Interactive Textbook, use it to review key concepts in Section 20.2.

Section 20.2 Assessment

Reviewing Concepts

1. ● List the two types of current.
2. ● Name two good electrical conductors and two good electrical insulators.
3. ● What variables affect the resistance of a material?
4. ● What causes charge to flow?
5. ● According to Ohm's law, how is voltage related to resistance and current?
6. What is a superconductor?

Critical Thinking

7. **Problem Solving** Suppose you have two wires of equal length made from the same material. How is it possible for the wires to have different resistances?

8. **Applying Concepts** Use Ohm's law to explain how two circuits could have the same current but different resistances.

Writing in Science

Compare-Contrast Paragraph Write a paragraph comparing and contrasting conductors and insulators and the ways in which they might be used. (*Hint:* Identify materials that are good conductors and materials that are good insulators.)

Electricity **607**

Section 20.2 Assessment

1. Direct current, alternating current
2. Good conductors: silver, copper; good insulators: air, plastic
3. Length, thickness, temperature
4. A source of electrical energy causes charge to flow.
5. Voltage equals the product of current and resistance. An increase in voltage increases current. Keeping the same voltage and increasing resistance decreases current.

6. A superconductor is a material that has almost zero resistance when cooled to low temperatures.
7. The two wires may have different thicknesses or different temperatures, which would give them different resistances.
8. If the voltages in the two circuits were such that the ratio of voltage to resistance was the same, both circuits would have the same amount of current.

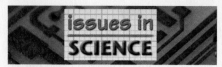

Should Car Companies Be Required to Make Electric Cars? L2

Background

In principle, hydrogen fuel cell technology is safe, clean, and efficient. However, attempts to develop an operable hydrogen-powered vehicle have been scaled back amid concerns about practicality and expense. Proponents of hydrogen fuel vehicles have two main objections to battery electric vehicles. First, BEVs can go only short distances before recharging, which is time-consuming. Second, BEVs don't solve the energy problem but displace it because energy to run them comes from the conventional power grid.

Those who defend BEVs as the more practical option point out that the vast majority of commuters drive only in the daytime, allowing overnight recharging. Also, larger vehicles are being designed with carry larger batteries, which can travel farther before recharging. Moreover, advocates of BEVs claim that the greater expense involved in producing hydrogen gas and the energy inefficiencies in the conversion process are not mere technological obstacles to be overcome with more research, but fundamental scientific roadblocks that make hydrogen an inefficient source of energy.

Answers

1. Answers may include issues related to technology, cost, convenience, and pollution. Answers should reflect the current state of the debate between supporters of these two technologies.
2. Numerous answers are possible; however, good answers may focus upon the contrast between the long-term potential of hydrogen technology and the greater short-term practicality of batteries.
3. Students should develop and state an opinion and provide reasons that are based on facts.
4. The essays should be written in a persuasive style.

Have students further research the issues related to this topic.

Which Technology Should Be Used to Power Electric Cars?

Auto manufacturers have developed technologies for several kinds of alternative-fuel vehicles, including electric cars. Two promising types of electric cars are battery electric vehicles (BEVs) and hydrogen fuel cell cars. However, in both cases, the technology under the hood has some drawbacks.

BEVs are already available. Instead of a fuel tank, a BEV contains a large rechargeable battery pack that powers an electric motor. You can recharge the vehicle's battery pack by using a household electrical outlet. One major problem with BEVs is that they rely on the power grid for energy, and the power plants that generate this energy often burn fossil fuels.

Unlike BEVs, hydrogen fuel cell cars have a fuel tank—but the gas inside is hydrogen, not gasoline. A hydrogen fuel cell is a device that produces electrical energy from a controlled reaction between hydrogen and oxygen. Inside the fuel cell, compressed hydrogen is combined with oxygen from the air. The current generated by the fuel cell is used to power an electric motor. (Fuel cell cars also contain a battery to provide additional power to the motor when needed.) The only by-product of hydrogen fuel cells is water. A major disadvantage of fuel cell cars is that isolating hydrogen is an expensive, energy-intensive process. In order for fuel cell cars to become widely used, engineers will need to find cheaper ways to produce hydrogen and also improve the efficiency of fuel cell technology.

The Viewpoints

Electric Cars Should Use Fuel Cells

Hydrogen fuel cells run on hydrogen, the most abundant element in the universe. Although both hydrogen production and fuel cell technology are very costly, they will become more affordable through technological innovation. Since the only by-product of hydrogen fuel cells is water, the technology is clean and environmentally friendly. In contrast, BEVs are only as "clean" as the power plant used to generate the electricity. Furthermore, BEVs can travel only a limited distance before needing to be recharged (a process that can take several hours). BEVs might seem more practical in the short term, but fuel cell cars offer a better long-term solution.

Electric Cars Should Use Batteries

Batteries are a proven and relatively inexpensive technology that is already being used in electric and hybrid cars. The cost to make a BEV is about one tenth that of a comparable fuel cell car. Although not practical for long road trips, BEVs are well suited for commuters who drive. In addition, many commuters do not use their cars at night; there is plenty of time to recharge the battery of a BEV as long as you remember to plug it in. It is much easier to recharge a BEV than it is to refuel a hydrogen car. For a BEV, you just need an electrical outlet. For hydrogen cars to be practical, we need to build an infrastructure of hydrogen refueling stations from scratch, which would be very time-consuming and costly. In addition, the cost of manufacturing the hydrogen fuel is high.

Research and Decide

1. Defining the Issues List some of the advantages and disadvantages of BEVs. Do the same for hydrogen fuel cell vehicles.

2. Analyzing the Viewpoints Think about the factors you listed in your answer to the first question. Which of those are likely to be most important to a supporter of BEVs? Of hydrogen fuel cell technology? Can you make any generalizations about the difference in their viewpoints?

3. Forming Your Opinion Are BEVs or hydrogen fuel cell vehicles a more promising transportation technology for the future? Explain and defend your position.

4. Writing in Science In 2009, the U.S. Department of Energy announced that it would cut off funding for development of a hydrogen fuel cell vehicle because other technologies can lead to greater reductions in emissions in a shorter time. Write an essay in which you support or criticize this decision.

20.3 Electric Circuits

Standards: ICP.6.4, ICP.6.5

Reading Focus

Key Concepts
- What is included in a circuit diagram?
- How do series and parallel circuits differ?
- How do you calculate electric power and electrical energy use?
- What devices make electricity safe to use?

Vocabulary
- electric circuit
- series circuit
- parallel circuit
- electric power
- fuse
- circuit breaker
- grounding

Reading Strategy
Relating Text and Visuals Copy the table below. As you read, look at Figure 13 on page 610. List three things that the diagram helps you understand about circuits.

What Can Be Seen in the Circuit Diagram?
Wire bringing current from outside
a. ?
b. ?
c. ?

If you've ever seen a house being built, you know that wires hidden inside the walls connect to every electrical outlet and to every light switch. If you were responsible for wiring a house, like the electrician in Figure 11, how would you do it? A good place to start would be the circuit diagrams supplied by the builder or contractor.

Circuit Diagrams

An **electric circuit** is a complete path through which charge can flow. Wires in a house form a complex network of circuits. It may look like a maze of wires, but each connection has a purpose. An electrician uses circuit diagrams to keep track of how elements in a circuit are connected. **Circuit diagrams use symbols to represent parts of a circuit, including a source of electrical energy and devices that are run by the electrical energy.** In a simple circuit, for example, a battery provides the energy to operate a device such as a bell or a light bulb.

A circuit diagram shows one or more complete paths in which charge can flow. Switches show places where the circuit can be opened. If a switch is open, the circuit is not a complete loop, and current stops. This is called an open circuit. When the switch is closed, the circuit is complete and charge can flow. This is called a closed circuit.

Figure 11 To bring electric current into a building, an electrician installs wiring. In a house, all of the wires usually come from one main box.

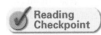 **Reading Checkpoint** *What is an open circuit?*

Electricity **609**

Series Circuits

Series and Parallel Circuits **L2**

Purpose To show how current moves in each kind of circuit.

Materials a 6-volt battery, 3 small light bulbs with sockets, 2 long strands of wire (12 cm), 4 short strands of wire (6 cm)

Procedure Strip the insulation from the ends of the wires and connect the battery and light bulbs in series, similar to the setup shown in Figure 12A. Unscrew one bulb and have students note the results. Rewire the circuit in parallel, similar to Figure 12B. Unscrew one bulb, and have students note the results.

Expected Outcome When one bulb in series is unscrewed, the circuit is broken and all bulbs go out. When the bulb in the parallel circuit is unscrewed, the other lamps are still lit up.
Visual

Parallel Circuits
Use Visuals **L1**

Figure 12 Have students trace the possible paths for current to move through each circuit, starting at the positive terminal of the battery and ending at the negative terminal. Ask, **If there is a break in the part of the circuit containing the outer light bulb in Figure 12B, will there still be a complete circuit?** *(Yes)* **Where will there be a current?** *(In the part of the circuit with the inner bulb)* **Why will the current in the inner bulb be the same as before the outer circuit was broken, but the current in the battery will be less than before?** *(The voltage across and resistance in the inner bulb are unchanged, so the current in the bulb is unchanged. There are fewer bulbs that need current, so the overall current in the battery is less.)*
Visual

Series Circuit **Parallel Circuit**

Direction of current

Battery

Bulb

Figure 12 Circuits can be represented with circuit diagrams. Symbols correspond to each element. **A** A series circuit has one path that each charge can follow. **B** A parallel circuit has more than one path each charge can follow.
Interpreting Diagrams *Which symbol represents a light bulb?*

Figure 13 Most circuits in a house are parallel. This way, even if one device stops working, the others will still work.

Light circuit
Dryer circuit
Fuse box or circuit breaker
Light switch
TV
Meter
Dryer
Ground
Desk with computer
Lamp
Wall socket

610 *Chapter 20*

Figure 12 shows two circuit diagrams. The + and − on the battery symbol indicate the positive and negative terminals. Arrows show the direction of current, from positive to negative. Recall that the direction of current is defined as the direction in which positive charges would flow. Electrons in a wire flow in the opposite direction.

Reading Checkpoint *How is the direction of current defined?*

Series Circuits

In a **series circuit,** charge has only one path through which it can flow. Look at the series circuit in Figure 12A. If one light bulb burns out in a series circuit, it becomes an open circuit. **If one element stops functioning in a series circuit, none of the elements can operate.** The bulbs in a circuit are a source of resistance. Adding bulbs to a series circuit increases the resistance. As a result, the current decreases, and each bulb shines less brightly.

Parallel Circuits

Imagine what would happen if circuits in your home were wired in series. If a light bulb burned out, the television would turn off. To avoid this problem, circuits in the home are mostly wired in parallel. A **parallel circuit** is an electric circuit with two or more paths through which charges can flow. If one bulb in Figure 12B burns out, charge still flows along the other path, and the other bulb stays lit. **If one element stops functioning in a parallel circuit, the rest of the elements still can operate.**

Figure 13 shows a network of circuits connecting electrical devices in a home. These circuits are wired in parallel so they can operate independently.

Customize for English Language Learners

Clarifying Key Concepts
The details of electrical circuits may be confusing to English language learners. To be sure that these students understand circuits, have them keep a Reading/Learning Log. Encourage students to write what they understand in the left column, and what they still have questions about in the right column. Check student logs to determine which, if any, concepts remain unclear.

Power and Energy Calculations

Recall that power is the rate of doing work. The rate at which electrical energy is converted to another form of energy is **electric power.** The unit of electric power is the joule per second, or watt (W). Power often is measured in thousands of watts, or kilowatts (kW). **Electric power can be calculated by multiplying voltage by current.**

For: Links on electric circuits
Visit: www.SciLinks.org
Web Code: ccn-2203

> **Electric Power**
>
> $$P\text{(watts)} = I\text{(amps)} \times V\text{(volts)}$$

Every time you use a 1875-watt hair dryer or turn on a 75-watt light bulb you use electric power. Appliances vary in the amount of power they use.

 Math Skills

Calculating Electric Power

An electric oven is connected to a 240-volt line, and it uses 34 amps of current. What is the power used by the oven?

 Read and Understand

What information are you given?

> **Current** = I = 34 amps
>
> **Voltage** = V = 240 volts

 Plan and Solve

What unknown are you trying to calculate?

> **Power** = P = ?

What formula contains the given quantities and the unknown?

> $P = I \times V$

Replace each variable with its known value.

> $P = 34 \text{ amps} \times 240 \text{ volts}$
>
> $= 8200 \text{ watts}$

 Look Back and Check

Is your answer reasonable?

The answer is reasonable because an electric oven should use much more power than a 1875-watt hair dryer.

Math Practice

1. A clothes dryer uses about 27 amps of current from a 240-volt line. How much power does it use?

2. A camcorder has a power rating of 2.3 watts. If the output voltage from its battery is 7.2 volts, what current does it use?

3. A power tool uses about 12 amps of current and has a power rating of 1440 watts. What voltage does the tool require?

Power and Energy Calculations

 Address Misconceptions **L2**

Students may think that electrical energy is produced or consumed, rather than converted. Stress that electrical energy is conserved in electric circuits. Power is the rate at which electrical energy is used or converted to other forms of energy. Examples include electromagnetic energy emitted by a light bulb, thermal energy provided by the heating element on a stove, and mechanical energy provided by an electric motor. **Logical**

Math Practice

Solutions **L2**

1. $P = I \times V = (240 \text{ V})(27 \text{ A}) = 6500 \text{ W}$
2. $I = P/V = (2.3 \text{ W})/(7.2 \text{ V}) = 0.32 \text{ A}$
3. $V = P/I = (1440 \text{ W})/(12 \text{ A}) = 120 \text{ V}$
Logical

For Extra Help **L1**

Students can write and solve forms of the equation for electric power. **Logical**

Direct students to the **Math Skills** in the **Skills and Reference Handbook** at the end of the student text for additional help.

Additional Problems

1. A lamp has a voltage of 120 V across it and uses a current of 0.5 A. What is the power used by the lamp? *(60 W)*
2. A 1.5 V battery provides 0.067 A of current for a calculator. What is the calculator's power rating? *(0.10 W)*
Logical, Portfolio

Download a worksheet on electric circuits for students to complete, and find additional teacher support from NSTA SciLinks.

Answer to . . .

Figure 12 *A zigzag line in a circle*

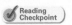 *The direction in which positive charges would flow*

Electrical Safety

Modeling a Fuse L2

Objective
After completing this activity, students will be able to
• describe the principle of an electric fuse.

Skills Focus Observing, Inferring, Using Models

 Prep Time 20 minutes

Materials 6-volt battery, 2 wires with stripped ends, strip of aluminum foil, scissors, wooden block, unpainted thumbtacks

Advance Prep Strip the insulation from the ends of the two pieces of wire and the battery leads.

Class Time 20 minutes

Safety Students should wear safety goggles. Caution students to be careful to avoid injury from splinters in the wood or from the thumbtacks. The wire can become very hot. Caution them to avoid touching it when the ends are connected to the battery.

Expected Outcome The foil fuse will melt, interrupting the circuit. Students will learn that a fuse works by conducting a small amount of electric current and by blocking the flow of a large amount of electric current.

Analyze and Conclude
1. The current caused the aluminum foil to become heated until it melted.
2. The foil, like the metal wire in a fuse, is a conductor that, when too much current passes through it, becomes so hot that it melts.
Logical, Group

For Enrichment L3

Have students repeat the experiment using a multimeter to measure the current and voltage across the foil strip before and after it melts. Ask them to explain their observations. When the foil melts, the current will stop and the voltage will increase to the voltage of the battery.
Kinesthetic, Logical

Quick Lab

Modeling a Fuse
Materials
6-volt battery, two wires with stripped ends, aluminum foil, scissors, wooden block, unpainted metal thumbtacks

Procedure

1. Connect the two wires to the two battery terminals.

2. Cut a strip of aluminum foil about 0.5 cm by 3 cm. In the center, cut the width down to 1 mm. Attach the ends of the foil strip to the wooden block with the thumbtacks.

3. Touch one of the wires to each end of the foil strip to form a circuit.

4. Observe what happens to the foil strip. **CAUTION** *If the wire and the battery become very hot, remove the wires from the foil.*

Analyze and Conclude
1. **Observing** What happened to the foil strip when the wires were attached to it?

2. **Using Models** How is the foil like a fuse? Explain.

Figure 14 Fuses have an internal wire that burns out if a current is too great.

An appliance's power rating lets you know how much power it uses under normal conditions. An electric stove uses about 6000 watts, and a microwave oven uses about 1000 watts. To find the electrical energy used by an appliance, multiply power by time.

> **Electrical Energy**
> $$E = P \times t$$

For example, the power rating of a typical clothes dryer is 5400 watts, or 5.4 kilowatts. If you use the clothes dryer for 2 hours, the energy use is 5.4 kilowatts multiplied by 2 hours, or 10.8 kilowatt-hours. Electric power companies usually determine charges on your electric bill using kilowatt-hours as a unit of energy. A kilowatt-hour equals 3,600,000 joules.

Electrical Safety

Inspectors check all new houses to make sure electrical wiring is installed safely. All wires must be able to carry the maximum expected current. But correct wiring is not enough to prevent electrical accidents. **Correct wiring, fuses, circuit breakers, insulation, and grounded plugs help make electrical energy safe to use.**

In the United States, most household circuits usually have an average voltage of 120 volts. The amount of current in a circuit can vary, depending on the number of devices that are in the circuit. Each device that is turned on increases the current. If the current exceeds the circuit's safety limit, the wire may overheat and start a fire.

Home Safety A **fuse** prevents current overload in a circuit. A wire in the center of the fuse melts if too much current passes through it. This melting is known as "blowing a fuse." After a fuse like one of those shown in Figure 14 blows, it must be replaced with a new fuse before the circuit can carry a current again.

Most houses today use circuit breakers instead of fuses to prevent overloads. A **circuit breaker** is a switch that opens when current in a circuit is too high. The circuit breaker must be reset before the circuit can be used again.

Personal Safety Imagine what could happen if your body became part of an electric circuit. Figure 15 shows some effects that current may have on a person. You might not notice a current of 1 milliamp, but higher currents can be quite dangerous.

Electrical wiring in a home is insulated to protect people. If the insulation is damaged, you may accidentally touch the bare wire and get a shock. Avoid touching electrical devices with wet hands because your hands conduct current more readily when they are wet.

Facts and Figures

Early Fuses Electrical fuses date back almost to the time when electricity itself was first used. Thomas Edison is credited with inventing the first fuse. It is said that platinum wires were used as fuses to protect the submarine telegraph cables that established electrical communication between Europe and North America.

Figure 15 Even a small current in your body can cause a painful shock or injury. **Analyzing Data** *What is the lowest level of current that causes serious injury?*

Effect of Current on Human Body	
Current Level	**Effect**
1 mA	Slight tingling sensation
5 mA	Slight shock
6–30 mA	Painful shock; loss of muscular control
50–150 mA	Extreme pain; severe muscular contractions. Breathing stops; death is possible.
1000–4300 mA	Nerve damage; heart stops, death is likely.
10,000 mA	Severe burns; heart stops, death is probable.

Insulation also prevents short circuits. In a short circuit, current finds a short path through the circuit with less resistance than the full path through the circuit. A three-prong plug can prevent shocks caused by short circuits. In Figure 15 you can see the circular third prong, which connects to ground. These plugs are used on devices with metal exteriors, such as an electric drill. If a short circuit develops, you might get a shock by holding the drill. But instead of entering your body, the current takes an easier path to ground through the grounding wire. The transfer of excess charge through a conductor to Earth is called **grounding.**

A ground-fault circuit interrupter (GFCI) like the one shown in Figure 15 is an electrical safety outlet. It monitors current flowing to and from an outlet or appliance. If these two currents are not equal, it means current is escaping. The GFCI opens the circuit to prevent serious electric shocks.

Ground-fault circuit interrupter (GFCI)

Section 20.3 Assessment

Reviewing Concepts

1. Name two elements included in a circuit diagram.
2. What is the difference between a series circuit and a parallel circuit?
3. Write the equations for calculating electric power and electrical energy.
4. Name five safety devices used with electric current.

Critical Thinking

5. **Problem Solving** Two bulbs connected in parallel shine more brightly than when they are connected to the same voltage source in series. Explain why this doesn't violate the law of conservation of energy.

6. **Applying Concepts** You plug in a string of holiday lights and notice that the entire string turns off when you remove one bulb. Explain why this happens.

 Math Practice

7. A stereo receiver uses a current of 2.2 amps from a 120-volt line. What is its power?
8. A television connected to a 120-volt line uses 102 watts of power. How much current flows through it?

Electricity **613**

Section 20.3 Assessment

1. Sample answers: a source of electrical energy; one or more devices that use electrical energy; conducting wires.
2. A series circuit has only one path for the current. A parallel circuit has two or more paths for the current.
3. The equation for electric power is $P = I \times V$. The equation for electrical energy is $E = P \times t$.
4. Fuses, circuit breakers, insulation, grounded (three-prong) plugs, and ground-fault circuit interrupters (GFCIs)

5. In the parallel circuit, the overall resistance is lower and the voltage across each bulb is the same as the voltage across the power source. Therefore, the current through the bulbs is greater in the parallel circuit than in the series circuit. Energy is still conserved, but it is used at a faster rate by the battery when the bulbs are in a parallel circuit.
6. The bulbs are connected in a series circuit. When one of the holiday lights burns out, current in the entire string is stopped.

Electricity 613

Getting Personal with Computers **L2**

Background

Throughout the 1960s and early 1970s a number of steps were taken toward creating smaller computers. The Altair 8800 came on the market in April, 1975. It was the first affordable microcomputer that was widely available for use. The Altair had 256 bytes of memory, no keyboard or video monitor, and sold for $375. The Alto, which was developed in 1973, more closely resembled modern personal computers. Although the Alto was not marketed commercially, it anticipated some standard features that all personal computers have today, such as a video monitor and a mouse.

In 1969, the first computer network, ARPANET, established a connection among four university computer systems. This network ultimately led to the creation of the Internet. While the early networks did not reach the general public or involve personal computers, the 1970s saw the development of the capability of sending information between computers. This paved the way for e-mail and other features which are now so popular on personal computers.

The personal computer began taking its familiar form in the early 1980s as it became faster, more versatile, and easier to use. These changes were largely due to the higher density of components on microprocessors. As personal computers with increased capability were created, their commercial appeal increased. The World Wide Web was established in 1991. The Internet made it possible to transmit text, pictures, and sound instantly across great distances. Within five years, the Internet was being used commercially by over 50 million people.

Getting Personal with Computers

Millions of people use personal computers every day for activities such as writing letters, browsing the Internet, or playing games.

Monitor or display

Keyboard

Computer

Mouse

Disk drive

Basic Components

A computer system is made up of a monitor or display, a keyboard, a mouse, and a computer. Input devices, such as the mouse and keyboard, feed information into the computer. Output devices, such as the monitor, display information that has been taken in by the input devices and processed by the central processing unit (CPU). The computer contains the CPU, memory chips, hard disk, and motherboard.

Inside a Computer

The CPU and other chips in a computer contain integrated circuits. The circuits consist of millions of miniaturized electronic components deposited onto a thin slice of silicon. Computers use the electric signals and circuits within these chips to represent and process data. A binary number system is used, in which data are stored digitally as strings of 1's and 0's. The digits of a binary number are transmitted as electrical pulses. Each digit is called a bit, with 8 bits making up a byte.

Components formed from layers of silicon

Magnified section of part of the surface of a silicon chip through which data are transmitted

Microprocessor chip

614 *Chapter 20*

Manipulating Bits and Bytes

Computer programs and data, such as word processing files, are stored for the long term on magnetic storage devices such as the hard disk. It is only during actual use of a program and work on data files that they are moved to RAM. Both the hard disk and RAM store data in bytes.

1 Program startup The file to be worked on and the program that allows it to be worked on are stored on the hard disk. Copies of both are moved, via circuits in the motherboard and cables, from hard disk storage to RAM.

2 Work in progress Under the user's control, the CPU works through program instructions. It makes changes to the copy of the data held in RAM.

3 End of session The updated data are saved back to the hard disk, and the program that was being used is erased from RAM.

Hard disk

File and program

CPU

RAM

OPENED COMPUTER

DVD/CD writer

Power supply

Fan housing

Hard disk

Video card houses specially designed graphics chips.

RAM *Random-access memory (RAM) is used to store programs that are being run. Information is temporarily stored in RAM as a series of 1's and 0's. When the computer is switched off, any information stored in RAM is lost.*

Heat Sink *Heat is generated by the flow of electricity inside the computer. A heat sink is needed to dissipate the heat. It draws heat away from the components to protect them.*

CPU *The central processing unit carries out program instructions and controls all the information flowing around the computer.*

Motherboard *This large circuit board houses the CPU, RAM, and ROM (read-only memory). ROM is permanent memory that includes startup instructions.*

Communicating Results Have students research the origins of the various components of the personal computer. Allow time for them to present their findings. Encourage them to include in their presentations some form of visual aid (for example, pictures of the components at various stages of their development, or a time line showing advances). You may want to have two or three students work together to research and create presentations for more complex components, such as the CPU.

Ask, **Was the personal computer invented at one time?** (No. It was the result of several different inventions being developed independently at about the same time.) **What feature of the personal computer has contributed to its becoming smaller, more efficient, and easier to use?** (Although there may be several valid opinions, such as the video monitor, which has made computers more accessible to many nontechnical users, the most important development has been smaller, higher-capacity CPUs.) **Do new inventions become widely used immediately?** (Not as a rule. Many of the features of the personal computer, like the mouse, did not become widely used until many years after their invention.)
Verbal, Portfolio

Build Science Skills **L2**

Applying Concepts

ACTIVITY

Purpose Students become familiar with the inside parts of a personal computer.

Materials several discarded computers, each having its top removed

Class Time 30 minutes

Procedure Have students separate into groups to observe the inside parts of a computer. They should try to locate the computer parts shown on p. 615 of their textbooks.

Expected Outcome Students will be able to point out the different parts of a computer and gain a better understanding of how the parts work together. **Kinesthetic, Visual, Group**

CONCEPTS in Action

Using Computers

Even before there were personal computers, digital computing was put to use in a variety of different ways. Today, computer technology has been miniaturized to create mobile phones, and expanded to allow supercomputers to work at high speed. Virtual reality, a relatively recent development, now allows for realistic simulations in a three-dimensional, computer-generated world.

Mini Computers
Mobile phones and other small electronic devices, such as hand-held computers, use smaller and smaller chips to allow for portability and convenience.

Supercomputers
By cooling the components so that they conduct electricity more efficiently, supercomputers are able to process information at a very fast rate. These computers gain speed by multi-tasking, performing several processes at once. The computer shown here is used in the study of particle physics.

Virtual Reality
Virtual reality is a three-dimensional computer-generated world. Programs such as the NASA flight simulator shown here train students through interactive simulations.

3-D image projector

Instruments and controls

Computer Games
In human-movement tracking technology, computers simulate human movement for realistic computer games. As shown here, markers are placed on a person and used to track his movements. A computer analyzes the path shown by each marker. The computer then recreates the paths for the simulated figures in a computer game, as shown above.

Illuminated markers

Going Further

- Use the library or the Internet to research how making computer circuits smaller allows a computer to operate at a faster speed. Write a paragraph describing one technology that has increased processing speed.

- Take a Discovery Channel Video Field Trip by watching "Current Computers."

DISCOVERY CHANNEL **SCHOOL** Video Field Trip

Going Further

Student research should indicate that smaller computer circuits increase computer speed by shortening the circuit size, and thus the distance electricity must travel. Smaller circuits also allow for more components to be placed in a CPU. The CPU can perform more tasks at once, so less time is required to carry out a series of operations. Also, smaller components provide more space for components to store data. This allows more information to be processed in a given time, and so shortens the overall processing time of a given task. Students' paragraphs on technologies affecting computer speed may include the means of etching smaller circuits on chips, bus design to provide quicker access between the processor and memory, and faster hard drives for reading input faster.
Verbal

 Video Field Trip

Current Computers

After students have viewed the Video Field Trip, ask them the following questions: **Name a device that connects the computer to the outside world in ways that allow information to flow in.** *(Student answers may include keyboard, mouse, modem, high-speed broadband connection, or a connection to a digital camera or scanner.)* **Describe how pressing the key for the letter _p_ on the keyboard gets** translated into information the computer can use. *(Pressing the key sends a signal to the BIOS, or basic input/output system, chip. There it is converted into a number in binary notation using an internally stored table, and the binary number is transferred to the central processing unit.)* **Name one device that connects to the computer and allows useful information to flow out from it.** *(Student answers may include computer screen, printer, modem, broadband connection, and a set of speakers.)* **Which part of the computer controls its operation?** *(The central processing unit, or CPU.)*

1 FOCUS

Objectives

20.4.1 Explain how electronics conveys information with analog or digital signals.

20.4.2 Describe electronic devices used to control electron flow.

20.4.3 Illustrate how semiconductors are used to make three kinds of solid-state components.

20.4.4 Describe how solid-state components are used in electronic devices.

Reading Focus

Build Vocabulary **L2**

Concept Map Have students construct a concept map of the vocabulary terms used in this section. Instruct students to write the vocabulary terms in ovals and connect the ovals with lines on which linking words are placed. Students should place the main concept (Electronics) at the top or the center. Moving away from the main concept, the content should become more specific.

Reading Strategy **L2**

a. Two semiconductors combined so that current moves in one direction but not the other. **b.** Maintains proper voltage level in circuits, controls direction of current **c.** Three semiconductors combined so that current can be switched on or off, or voltage can be amplified. **d.** Amplifies telephone signals **e.** A thin slice of silicon with many tiny solid-state components built up on it **f.** Processes and stores information in computers

2 INSTRUCT

Electronic Signals

Use Community Resources **L2**

Arrange for your class to visit a local telephone company. Have students observe the type of equipment used to transmit telephone calls to anywhere in the world. Encourage students to ask about the relative importance of analog and digital signals in present telephone communication, and have them explain it in their own words in a brief written report. **Interpersonal, Portfolio**

20.4 Electronic Devices

Reading Focus

Key Concepts

- How do electronic signals convey information?
- How do vacuum tubes control electron flow?
- What are two types of semiconductors?
- How are semi-conductors used?
- What are the benefits of using microchips in communication devices?

Vocabulary

- ◆ electronics
- ◆ electronic signal
- ◆ analog signal
- ◆ digital signal
- ◆ semiconductor
- ◆ diode
- ◆ transistor
- ◆ integrated circuit
- ◆ computer

Reading Strategy

Summarizing Copy the table below. As you read, complete the table to summarize what you learn about solid-state components.

Solid-State Component	Description	Uses
Diode	a. ?	b. ?
Transistor	c. ?	d. ?
Integrated circuit	e. ?	f. ?

How do a toaster and a lamp use electric current differently than a computer or a mobile phone? The toaster and lamp are *electrical* devices. They change electrical energy into heat or light. The computer and mobile phone are *electronic* devices, which use electric current to process or send information.

Electronic Signals

The science of using electric current to process or transmit information is **electronics.** The information is carried by an electronic signal. An **electronic signal** is information sent as patterns in the controlled flow of electrons through a circuit.

To understand how this works, think about circuits. If a voltage source is connected to a circuit by a wire, electrons will flow through the wire. Controlling the electron flow—by either altering the voltage or turning the current on and off—produces a coded signal. **Electronics conveys information with electrical patterns called analog and digital signals.**

Figure 16 A computer uses electric current to process information. A toaster uses electric current to change electrical energy into thermal energy.

618 *Chapter 20*

Section Resources

Print
- *Reading and Study Workbook With Math Support,* Section 20.4
- *Transparencies,* Section 20.4

Technology
- *Interactive Textbook,* Section 20.4
- *Presentation Pro CD-ROM,* Section 20.4

Analog Signals An **analog signal** is a smoothly varying signal produced by continuously changing the voltage or current in a circuit. Information is encoded in the strength or frequency of the analog signal. Figure 17A shows one familiar example—a signal used by an AM radio station. The music is encoded as a smoothly changing pattern of the voltage.

Digital Signals A **digital signal** encodes information as a string of 1's and 0's. Figure 17B shows how pulsing a current on and off can produce a digital signal. When the current is off, it represents a "0." When the current is on, it represents a "1." You may be familiar with Morse code, which in a similar way uses two signals. A dot and a dash are all you need to represent the 26 letters of the alphabet and the digits 0 through 9.

Digital signals are more reliable than analog signals. For example, a DVD, or digital video disc, encodes digital signals as a series of pits in the DVD surface. If a pit is damaged, it is often still readable as a 0 or a 1. The quality of video is not affected unless the damage is severe. In comparison, damage to an analog videotape adds noise to the signal.

Vacuum Tubes

To create an electronic signal, you must be able to control the flow of electrons. A vacuum tube was used to control electron flow in early electronic devices. ⬤ **Vacuum tubes can change alternating current into direct current, increase the strength of a signal, or turn a current on or off.**

One useful type of vacuum tube is a cathode-ray tube (CRT) shown in Figure 18. Many computer monitors and televisions contain CRTs. One side of the CRT has three metal plates that emit electron beams. The electrons are emitted at one end of an airless tube and strike a glass surface on the other end. The glass is coated with phosphors that glow red, green, or blue in response to the electron beams. An electronic signal controls the strength and position of the beams to produce images with the light from the phosphors.

Although vacuum tubes have many useful features, some types burn out frequently and need to be replaced. They are also much too large for use in small electronic devices.

 What is a CRT?

Figure 17 Electronic signals convey information by changing voltage or current in a circuit. **A** An analog signal can be produced by smoothly changing voltage. **B** A digital signal can be produced by pulsing a current on and off. **Applying Concepts** *Could a portable radio, in theory, receive and process a digital signal?*

Figure 18 A cathode-ray tube is still used in many computer monitors and television sets.

Electricity **619**

HOW It Works

Digital Camera   L2

Digital photography was initially developed by NASA to transmit images from spacecraft back to Earth. Early cameras on space vehicles were originally television camera units called vidicons, but in the 1970s, charged-coupled devices (CCDs) were developed. Unlike photographic film or vidicon tubes, CCDs have the advantage of detecting most of the light that falls on them. As the technology improved and became more affordable, the number of photosites on a CCD became larger, and the photosites themselves became smaller. This improved the resolution, or sharpness, of the image. The first digital camera for the general public was marketed in 1994.

Interpreting Diagrams The number of photosites on a CCD controls the image sharpness.
Visual

For Enrichment   L3

Interested students or students familiar with digital camera and image technology can make a presentation showing a digital camera and how its images are electronically stored and manipulated. They can obtain additional information on the Internet and in science and engineering periodicals.
Verbal, Portfolio

 HOW It Works

Digital Camera

When light enters an analog camera, it strikes a strip of light-sensitive film behind the lens. In a digital camera, the pattern of light is sensed electronically and turned into digital code.

Interpreting Diagrams *What controls the sharpness of a digital image?*

Miniature digital camera
Digital cameras can be much smaller than traditional cameras because high resolution CCDs do not need to use large lenses.

Lens *The lens focuses light from the scene onto the CCD.*

CCD (charged-coupled device) *The CCD has millions of light-sensitive cells, called photosites. The more photosites per unit area, the sharper the image is.*

Analog-to-digital converter *The analog-to-digital converter turns the output of each photosite into digital code.*

Microprocessor *The microprocessor calculates color values for each part of the image.*

Memory chip *Data about the image are stored on this non-removable chip.*

Memory card *This removable card stores the image as a digital file.*

Light from scene

Digital-to-analog converter *Here the digital data are turned into a form that allows the image to be displayed on the LCD screen.*

Cable to computer

Computer output port *This port allows the digital image to be transferred to a computer.*

How the CCD works
In a CCD, a lens focuses light onto a photosite, which converts the light intensity into an electric current. To create a full color image, the CCD contains a color filter. The filter separates incoming light into one of the three primary colors at each photosite. The microprocessor creates a color image by evaluating the color data for groups of photosites.

Lens   Color filter   Photosite

LCD (liquid crystal display) screen *The LCD screen displays an image of the scene that the camera is aimed at. Images that have been previously saved can also be displayed on the screen.*

Semiconductors

A **semiconductor** is a crystalline solid that conducts current only under certain conditions. Most semiconductors are made with silicon or germanium. In pure form, these elements are poor conductors. But when trace amounts of other elements are added, it becomes possible to control the current inside of the crystals. Figure 19 shows two types of semiconductors. 👁 In n-type semiconductors, the current is a flow of electrons. In p-type semiconductors, it appears as though positive charge flows.

A p-type semiconductor can be made by adding a trace amount of boron to silicon. In Figure 19A, you can see spaces, called holes, at each boron atom. The holes are positively charged. Figure 19B shows an n-type semiconductor made by adding phosphorus to silicon. Phosphorus atoms provide weakly bound electrons that can flow.

By themselves, n-type and p-type semiconductors cannot do much. But when joined together, electrons in the n-type semiconductor are attracted toward the positively charged holes in the p-type semiconductor. As electrons jump from hole to hole, it looks like a flow of positive charge because the locations of the holes change.

Solid-State Components

Semiconductor devices were first used in the late 1940s. These devices were named solid-state components because they used solids rather than vacuum tubes to control current. 👁 **Most modern electronic devices are controlled by solid-state components.** Three of the most useful solid-state components are diodes, transistors, and integrated circuits.

Diodes A **diode** is a solid-state component that combines an n-type and p-type semiconductor. When a voltage is applied across a diode, electrons flow from the n-type to the p-type semiconductor. There is no current if voltage is applied in the opposite direction. Because the current can be in only one direction, a diode can change alternating current to direct current.

Transistors Figure 20B shows a **transistor,** a solid-state component with three layers of semiconductors. A small current flowing through its center layer changes its resistance. A transistor can be used as a switch because the small current can turn another current on or off. It can also be used as an amplifier. A small voltage applied to one side of the transistor produces a large voltage on the other side.

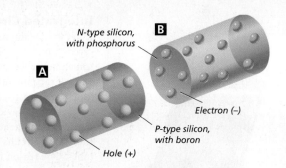

N-type silicon, with phosphorus

Electron (–)

P-type silicon, with boron

Hole (+)

Figure 19 A semiconductor becomes a good conductor of charge if trace amounts of elements are added to it.

A

Direction of hole flow

Direction of electron flow

Exchange of electrons and holes

B

Figure 20 A A diode is two different semiconductors joined in one component. **B** A transistor is three semiconductors with the middle one different from the outer ones. **Applying Concepts** *In addition to the arrangement of the transistor in B, how else might you arrange the transistor?*

Electricity **621**

Semiconductors and Current **L2**

Purpose Students observe how a semiconductor allows and limits current depending on how a voltage is applied across it.

Materials a light-emitting diode (LED), an ohmmeter, a DC power source, wires, alligator clips

Procedure Attach the terminals of the ohmmeter to the LED and have students note the resistance reading. Reverse the positions of the terminals and show students the new resistance. Repeat the test, attaching the wires to the ends of the LED and the DC power source, so that the LED offers minimum resistance. Slowly increase the voltage until the LED glows. Turn off the power supply, reverse the connections, and increase the voltage slowly to the same level as before. Have students note the LED's appearance.

Expected Outcome When the voltage across the LED is positioned one way, the resistance in the LED is high, with little current. When the voltage is reversed, the resistance is low and the current is larger. **Visual**

Solid-State Components

🚩 Address Misconceptions **L2**

Students may think that the positive charges in p-type semiconductors are the result of positive charges moving. While this is the effective result, this is not what is literally happening. The only charges that are actually moving are electrons. The term "holes" suggests the absence of something (in this case, negative charges). Have students think of other ways to consider the motion of an object as the opposite motion of what is left behind. For instance, moving checkers across a board is like moving empty spaces in the opposite direction. Electrons, like checkers, can only move into an empty space. **Logical**

Answer to . . .

Figure 20 *Place two p-type semiconductors on either side of an n-type semiconductor*

Facts and Figures

Smaller Components Over the last 40 years, electronic components have become smaller and more efficient, allowing more computing power to be placed in a smaller space. In 1965, the engineer Gordon Moore stated that the number of transistors on an integrated circuit would double about every two years. This observation is called Moore's law. Over the years, the rate of technological development has met or surpassed Moore's prediction.

In 1972, the leading processing chip held 2500 transistors. By 1974, the number had increased to 5000. In 2003, the largest chip had 410 million transistors, nearly 10 times the number in 2000. There is considerable question as to how small electronic devices can become. Moore himself said that "No physical quantity can continue to change exponentially forever."

Communications Technology

Integrate Language Arts L2

The development of solid-state technology has introduced many new terms into the world's languages. Some are borrowed from other languages. For instance, the term *cybernetics* refers to the study of communication and control in machines. The term comes from the Greek for the steersman of a boat, that is, the one who navigates or controls. Another term, *robot*, comes from the Czech word meaning "worker." Other terms, like *Internet*, are abbreviations, while some terms are initials (such as WWW or Y2K). Have students research and report on several expressions that have appeared because of developments in communications technology.
Verbal

3 ASSESS

Evaluate Understanding L2

Randomly ask students to list the general properties of one electronic device, either a solid-state or vacuum-tube component. Then, have them give examples of applications for these devices.

Reteach L1

Have students use Figure 20 to explain how semiconductors allow electrons to flow in a preferred direction.

Connecting Concepts

All electronic components have some resistance. Their temperature increases when electrons moving through them collide with the atoms in the component. Thus, electrical energy is converted to thermal energy. Heat sinks withdraw this thermal energy from the circuits in various ways. In each energy conversion, energy is conserved, but its form is different.

Interactive Textbook If your class subscribes to the Interactive Textbook, use it to review key concepts in Section 20.4.

Answer to . . .

Figure 21 *No, the vacuum tubes would be too large.*

Figure 21 A mobile phone uses many solid-state components. **Drawing Conclusions** *Would it be possible to make a mobile phone using vacuum tubes rather than solid-state components?*

Integrated Circuits An **integrated circuit** is a thin slice of silicon that contains many solid-state components. The components are carefully built layer by layer on the silicon base. Integrated circuits are sometimes called chips or microchips. They perform as well as a network of vacuum tubes, but they need only a tiny fraction of the space. Mobile phones, pagers, and computers all use microchips.

Electronic devices today are so small because hundreds of millions of components fit on a microchip smaller than your fingertip. Integrated circuits are also blindingly fast compared to vacuum tubes. One reason is that current does not have to travel far to get from point to point in the circuit. So it shouldn't be surprising that as technology improves, and chips get smaller, the chips operate at higher speeds.

Communications Technology

A **computer** is a programmable device that can store and process information. Today you find microchips in all sorts of devices that you wouldn't call computers. **Communication devices use microchips to make them more portable, reliable, and affordable.**

Figure 21 shows the inside a mobile phone, which contains many solid-state components. Transistors amplify the phone's incoming signal. Electronic devices called capacitors store electric charge. They allow a mobile phone to store data such as phone numbers, even if the battery is removed for a short time. Diodes maintain proper voltage levels in the circuits. Without solid-state components, none of this would be possible.

Section 20.4 Assessment

Reviewing Concepts

1. How are electronic devices used to process information?
2. Describe how electron flow is controlled in vacuum tubes.
3. What are two types of semiconductors?
4. How are solid-state components used?
5. How are microchips beneficial for communication devices?

Critical Thinking

6. **Comparing and Contrasting** How are solid-state components like vacuum tubes? How are they different?

622   *Chapter 20*

7. **Applying Concepts** Explain how a diode can be used to change alternating current into direct current.
8. **Using Analogies** Explain how a diode is like a one-way street.

Connecting Concepts

Conservation of Energy Review Section 15.2. How is energy conserved when a heat sink is used to protect electronic components in a computer?

Section 20.4   Assessment

1. Electronic devices process information by using electric current to form patterns called analog and digital signals.
2. Vacuum tubes can control electron flow by changing alternating current into direct current or by turning a current on or off.
3. N-type and p-type
4. Solid-state components are used to control modern electronic devices.
5. Microchips make communications devices more portable, reliable, and affordable.

6. Both control electron flow in electronic devices. Both can convert alternating current to direct current, or amplify a signal. Solid-state components use semiconducting materials to achieve these results instead of the hot wires and charged plates in vacuums.
7. When alternating current enters a diode, only current moving in one direction can pass through. Current moving in the reverse direction is blocked.
8. Charges can only move in one direction through the diode, just as an automobile can only go in one direction on a one-way street.

Evaluating Electrical Safety

Electrical appliances must be safely insulated to protect users from injury. In this lab, you will play the role of a safety engineer determining whether an electric power supply is safely insulated.

Problem
How much resistance is needed in series with a known resistance to reduce the voltage by 99 percent?

Materials
- 9-volt battery
- battery clip
- multimeter
- 3 alligator clips
- 4 resistors:
  1-ohm, 10-ohm, 100-ohm, 1000-ohm

 For the probeware version of this lab, see Probeware Lab Manual, Lab 8.

Skills Calculating, Using Tables

Procedure

1. On a separate sheet of paper, make a copy of the data table shown below.

Data Table

Resistance (ohms)		Voltage difference (volts)	
Current-Carrying	Insulating	Current-Carrying	Insulating
1	1000		
1	100		
10	1000		
10	100		

2. Attach the battery clip to the battery. **CAUTION** *The circuit may become hot.*

3. Use an alligator clip to attach one wire of the 1-ohm resistor to one of the battery clip's wires as shown.

4. Clip one wire of the 1000-ohm resistor to the free end of the 1-ohm resistor. Clip the other wire of the 1000-ohm resistor to the free wire of the battery clip.

5. The 1-ohm resistor represents the current-carrying part of the appliance. The 1000-ohm resistor represents the insulation for the current-carrying part. Place one of the multimeter's electrodes on each wire of the 1-ohm resistor. Record the voltage difference.

6. Place the multimeter's electrodes on the wires of the 1000-ohm resistor. Record the voltage difference.

7. To model a reduction in the resistance of the insulation, repeat Steps 5 and 6, replacing the 1000-ohm resistor with a 100-ohm resistor. Disconnect the resistors from the battery clip.

8. **Predicting** Record your prediction of how increasing the resistance of the current-carrying part of the appliance will affect the voltage difference across the insulating part.

9. To test your prediction, repeat Steps 3 through 7, using a 10-ohm resistor to represent the current-carrying part of the appliance.

Analyze and Conclude

1. **Calculating** When the resistance of the current-carrying part was 1 ohm and the resistance of the insulating part was 100 ohms, what was the ratio of the voltage differences across the current-carrying part and the insulating part?

2. **Drawing Conclusions** In the circuit you built, what is the voltage difference across each resistor proportional to?

3. **Applying Concepts** You know the resistance of the current-carrying part of an appliance. What should the resistance of the insulation be to reduce the voltage by 99 percent?

Evaluating Electrical Safety L2

Objective
After completing this lab, students will be able to
- determine the voltage differences across resistances in series.

Skills Focus Measuring, Calculating, Using Data Tables

Prep Time 20 minutes

Advance Preparation Strip 1–2 cm of insulation from the ends of the wires attached to the battery clips. Label the resistors with their resistances. Each resistor has four colored bands at one end. From the end of the resistor inward, the first three bands for the resistors used in this lab are: 1 ohm brown, black, gold; 10 ohms brown, black, black; 100 ohms brown, black, brown; 1000 ohms brown, black, red. The fourth band indicates the accuracy of the labeled resistance.

Class Time 45 minutes

Safety Caution students to be careful with the sharp tips of the wires when assembling the circuit. Also caution them about handling the circuits when they are carrying current because the circuit parts may become hot.

Teaching Tips
- You may need to show students how to use the multimeters.

Expected Outcome The voltage difference across each resistor in the circuit is proportional to its resistance. The total voltage difference across both resistors is equal to the voltage of the battery, which may decline after the battery has been used for a while.

Analyze and Conclude
1. The ratio of the voltage differences was 0.01 (1/100).
2. The voltage difference across each resistor was proportional to its resistance.
3. The resistance of the insulation should be about 100 times the resistance of the current-carrying part.
Logical, Group

 Probeware Lab Manual Versions of this lab for use with probeware available from Pasco Scientific, Texas Instruments, and Vernier are in the Probeware Manual.

Sample Data Table

Resistance (ohms)		Voltage difference (volts)	
Current-Carrying	Insulating	Current-Carrying	Insulating
1	1000	< 0.01	8.6
1	100	0.09	8.5
10	1000	0.09	8.5
10	100	0.9	7.7 >

Study Guide

Study Tip

Switch Subjects and Take Breaks

When you feel yourself losing focus, switch the type of task you are working on, the subject you are studying, or the environment that you are in. Tell students to organize all of the subjects that they need to study in a night into manageable blocks, based on a single portion of a chapter section. When they have finished one block, suggest that they switch to another block in another part of the subject they are studying, or even another subject altogether. Suggest they take five minute breaks every 30 to 40 minutes to refresh themselves. Taking a 20 minute walk also helps to renew energy and enthusiasm.

Thinking Visually

a. Current
b. Potential difference, or voltage
c. Alternating current

Assessment

Interactive Textbook If your class subscribes to the Interactive Textbook, your students can go online to access an interactive version of the Student Edition and a self-test.

Reviewing Content

1. c   2. d   3. c
4. d   5. c   6. d
7. d   8. c   9. a
10. a

Understanding Concepts

11. The electric force becomes one-fourth as large.

12. The electric field direction depends on whether a positive or negative charge produces the field.

13. If the uncharged object is a conductor, the charged object can attract opposite charges in the uncharged object, causing these charges to move closer to the charged object. The charged object can also transfer charges to the conductor through friction or by contact, and then the charges will move to redistribute charge evenly throughout the conductor.

20.1 Electric Charge and Static Electricity

Key Concepts

- An excess or shortage of electrons produces a net electric charge.
- Like charges repel and opposite charges attract.
- Electric field strength depends on the net charge and distance from the charge.
- Charge can be transferred by friction, by contact, and by induction.
- Static discharge occurs when electric charge is transferred suddenly.

Vocabulary

electric charge, *p. 600;* electric force, *p. 601;* electric field, *p. 602;* static electricity, *p. 602;* law of conservation of charge, *p. 602;* induction, *p. 603*

20.2 Electric Current and Ohm's Law

Key Concepts

- The two types of current are direct current and alternating current.
- Metals such as copper and silver are good conductors. Wood, plastic, rubber, and air are good insulators.
- A material's thickness, length, and temperature affect its resistance.
- In order for charge to flow in a conducting wire, the wire must be connected in a complete loop that includes a source of electrical energy.
- Increasing the voltage increases the current. Keeping the same voltage and increasing the resistance decreases the current.

Vocabulary

electric current, *p. 604;* direct current, *p. 604;* alternating current, *p. 604;* electrical conductor, *p. 605;* electrical insulator, *p. 605;* resistance, *p. 605;* superconductor, *p. 605;* potential difference, *p. 606;* voltage, *p. 606;* battery, *p. 606;* Ohm's law, *p. 607*

20.3 Electric Circuits

Key Concepts

- An electric circuit has a source of electrical energy and devices run by electrical energy.
- If one element stops functioning in a series circuit, none of the elements can operate, but in a parallel circuit, the rest of the elements still can operate.
- Electric power is voltage multiplied by current. Electrical energy is power multiplied by time.
- A variety of devices make electrical energy safe.

Vocabulary

electric circuit, *p. 609;* series circuit, *p. 610;* parallel circuit, *p. 610;* electric power, *p. 611;* fuse, *p. 612;* circuit breaker, *p. 612;* grounding, *p. 613*

20.4 Electronic Devices

Key Concepts

- Electronics convey information with electrical patterns called analog and digital signals.
- Vacuum tubes and solid-state components are two kinds of devices that can control electron flow.
- Solid-state components use semiconductors.

Vocabulary

electronics, *p. 618;* electronic signal, *p. 618;* analog signal, *p. 619;* digital signal, *p. 619;* semiconductor, *p. 621;* diode, *p. 621;* transistor, *p. 621;* integrated circuit, *p. 622;* computer, *p. 622*

Thinking Visually

Web Diagram Copy the web diagram below and use information from the chapter to complete it.

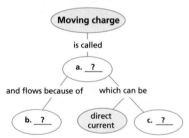

Chapter Resources

Print
- *Chapter and Unit Tests,* Chapter 20 Test A and Test B
- *Test Prep Resources,* Chapter 20

Technology
- *Computer Test Bank,* Chapter Test 20
- *Interactive Textbook,* Chapter 20
- *Go Online,* PHSchool.com, Chapter 20

Interactive Textbook with
assessment at PHSchool.com

Reviewing Content

Choose the letter that best answers the question or completes the statement.

1. A material has a net electric charge because it
   a. discharges.
   b. has an alternating current.
   c. has an excess or shortage of electrons.
   d. has a direct current.

2. Static electricity is the study of
   a. buildup of charge.
   b. electric discharges.
   c. electric fields.
   d. all of the above.

3. A strong electric field is
   a. directed toward a charge.
   b. directed away from a charge.
   c. caused by a large quantity of charge.
   d. caused by a small quantity of charge.

4. What is a material called that easily carries a current?
   a. insulator   **b.** semiconductor
   c. electric potential **d.** conductor

5. A superconducting material
   a. requires very high current.
   b. has no resistance at room temperature.
   c. has no resistance at low temperatures.
   d. has high resistance at low temperatures.

6. What does Ohm's law state?
   a. Current equals voltage times resistance.
   b. Voltage equals resistance divided by current.
   c. Voltage equals current divided by resistance.
   d. Voltage equals current times resistance.

7. Which melts to protect a circuit?
   a. three-prong plug
   b. wiring
   c. diode
   d. fuse

8. What does " *I* " represent in the equation $P = I \times V$?
   a. voltage   **b.** resistance
   c. current   **d.** kilowatts

9. The output of a diode can be
   a. direct current.   **b.** a superconductor.
   c. resistance.   **d.** alternating current.

10. Three layers of semiconductor material can form
    a. a transistor only.
    b. a diode only.
    c. either a transistor or a diode.
    d. neither a transistor nor a diode.

Understanding Concepts

11. How does the electric force between two charged objects change if you double the distance between the objects?

12. What determines the direction of the electric field near a charge?

13. How can a charged object cause charges to move within an uncharged object?

14. If the current in a circuit is clockwise, what is the direction of electron flow?

15. Explain why a wire becomes warmer when charges flow through it.

16. Does voltage flow in a circuit? Explain.

Use the following diagram to answer Questions 17 and 18. The three bulbs are identical.

17. Does the same current pass through each bulb? Explain why or why not.

18. What happens to the other bulbs if bulb A burns out? If bulb B burns out?

19. A battery and a light bulb are connected in a simple circuit. What is the source of electrons that flow through the wire?

20. Explain why a light bulb does not change its brightness when another bulb is added in parallel.

21. What are digital and analog signals?

Electricity **625**

Assessment (continued)

14. Counterclockwise
15. Because of the wire's resistance, some electrical energy is transformed into thermal energy.
16. No. Voltage is applied across a circuit. Only the current is a flow (of charge).
17. No. Together bulbs B and C have twice the resistance that bulb A does, so the current is half as much in bulb B and bulb C as it is in bulb A.
18. If bulb A burns out, bulb B and bulb C stay lit; if bulb B burns out, bulb A stays lit but bulb C doesn't.
19. The electrons come mostly from the atoms in the wire.
20. The current to each bulb is independent of current through other paths in a parallel circuit, so brightness doesn't change when a bulb is added.
21. Digital and analog signals are electronic signals. A digital signal is based on the high and low voltage pattern in a circuit. An analog signal depends only on the varying level of the signal.

 ## Homework Guide

Section	Questions
20.1	1–3, 11–13, 22, 31, 35
20.2	4–6, 14–16, 23, 27–28, 32–33
20.3	7–8, 17–20, 24–25, 29–30, 34
20.4	9–10, 21, 26

Critical Thinking

22. Each hair receives the same type of charge as that on the sphere, so they repel each other.

23. Current will only pass between oppositely charged terminals. The negative terminal is a source of electrons, and the positive terminal accepts electrons.

24. The person has probably overloaded the circuit. He or she should unplug one or two appliances on the circuit and then reset the circuit breaker.

25. Voltage is the same for both settings, but the high-heat setting uses more power. According to $P = IV$, the current must be greater for the high-heat setting. By Ohm's law, then, the resistance for the high-heat setting must be lower.

26. Both n-type and p-type semiconductors are crystalline materials that conduct current only under certain conditions. They differ in that electrons flow in n-type semiconductors, whereas positively charged "holes" flow in p-type semiconductors.

Math Skills

27. On a wet day: $V = I \times R$; $I = V/R =$ (9 V)/(1000 ohms) = 0.009 A
On a dry day: $I = V/R =$ (9 V)/(100,000 ohms) = 0.00009 A

28. The voltage of the battery equals the sum of the potential differences across the bulbs. Each bulb has the same resistance, so the voltage drop across each is the same. Therefore, $V_{bulb} = V_{battery}/6 = (9.0 \text{ V})/6 = 1.5$ V

29. $P = V \times I$; $I = P/V =$ (105 W)/(120 V) = 0.88 A

30. $P = V \times I$; $I = P/V =$ (9300 W)/(240 V) = 39 A
$V = I \times R$; $R = V/I =$ (240 V)/(39 A) = 6.2 ohms

Critical Thinking

22. Applying Concepts In a science museum demonstration, a person on an insulated stand touches a metal sphere. The sphere has a large charge. Explain why the person's hair stands on end.

23. Applying Concepts Explain why a battery is always connected so that one wire goes to the battery's positive terminal and one to the negative terminal.

24. Relating Cause and Effect A person plugs a fan into a wall socket and turns it on. Suddenly, the lights go out in several rooms of the house. Explain what has probably happened and what can be done to fix it.

25. Applying Concepts Explain why a hair dryer has a high-heat setting with a lower resistance than the low-heat setting. (*Hint:* Use the equation $P = IV$.)

26. Comparing and Contrasting How are n-type semiconductors and p-type semiconductors alike. How are they different?

Math Skills

27. Calculating On a wet day, your skin's resistance may be as low as 1000 ohms. On a dry day, it may be as high as 100,000 ohms. How much current moves through your fingers if you touch the terminals of a 9-volt battery on a wet day? On a dry day?

28. Calculating Six light bulbs are connected in series with a 9.0-volt battery. What is the voltage across each bulb?

29. Calculating A freezer has a power rating of 105 watts. How much current does it use if it is plugged into a 120-volt line?

30. Calculating The power rating on an electric oven is 9300 watts. If the oven is plugged into a 240-volt line, how much current does it use? What is the resistance of the oven?

Concepts in Action

31. Relating Cause and Effect You turn a television on and notice a faint crackling sound. If you touch the screen, you get a small shock. What is the source of this electric charge?

32. Inferring Plugs used for connecting an electrical appliance such as a toaster to a wall socket have two prongs. Explain why plugs have two prongs instead of one prong.

33. Inferring The photograph below shows ceramic insulators holding the power lines at each pole. What is the purpose of the insulators?

34. Making Judgments Explain why you think builders should or should not be required to install GFCI (ground-fault circuit interrupter) outlets in all new homes.

35. Writing in Science Write a paragraph explaining in detail why you could be struck by lightning if you stand outside during a thunderstorm. Include a sketch that illustrates the ideas in your paragraph.

Performance-Based Assessment

Designing an Experiment Design and conduct an experiment that uses a light-emitting diode in a simple circuit to demonstrate that current flows only one way through a diode. Before beginning, research the properties and limitations of your diode .

For: Self-grading assessment
Visit: PHschool.com
Web Code: cca-2200

Concepts in Action

31. Electrons build up a static charge on the screen of the CRT.

32. You need a complete circuit. Current moves into the smaller prong of a plug and back through the larger prong. If there is only one prong, the circuit is not complete.

33. The insulators prevent current in the power lines from traveling down the poles to the ground.

34. Students in favor of GFCIs may stress the need for safety. Those opposed may discuss the costs involved.

35. Students should discuss charge buildup on both the person and in the clouds. They should also mention discharge and the attraction between opposite charges.

Standardized Test Prep for Indiana

 Standards Guide

Question	Standards
1	ICP.6.1
2	ICP.6.1
3	ICP.6.4
4	ICP.6.4
5	ICP.6.4
6	ICP.6.4

Test-Taking Tip

When a question refers to a diagram, start by scanning the whole diagram. See if you can remember what each symbol means.

In a circuit diagram, determine if the circuit is series or parallel. Check to make sure that each part of the circuit is complete. In the question below, a wire goes to device #2, but no wire leaves it, so no current enters the device.

The direction of current is from the positive terminal to the negative terminal of the voltage source. Note that the direction of current is opposite the direction of electron flow. In the circuit below, current is in a clockwise direction.

In what order does current flow in the circuit above?

(A) 5 – 6 – 7 – 1 – 5 – 3 – 4
(B) 6 – 7 – 8 – 2 – 5 – 1 – 3 – 4
(C) 4 – 3 – 5 – 7 – 6
(D) 3 – 2 – 5 – 6 – 4 – 7
(E) 4 – 3 – 1 – 5 – 8 – 7 – 6

(Answer: E)

1. In the diagram above, the battery is replaced by an AC voltage source. Which of the following is now true?
   (A) The current enters and leaves device #2.
   (B) The current is always clockwise.
   (C) There is not net movement of charge in the circuit.
   (D) The current is always counterclockwise.
   (E) There is no current in the circuit.

2. If you rub a neutral glass rod with silk, the silk acquires a negative charge. If you rub a neutral glass rod with a rubber rod, the rubber acquires a negative charge. If you rub a neutral rubber rod with silk, the rubber rod acquires a negative charge. Which of the three materials has the strongest attraction for electrons?
   (A) glass
   (B) silk
   (C) rubber
   (D) not enough data to answer
   (E) none, because they have equal attractions for electrons

3. A 1.5-m wire carries a 5.0-A current when a potential difference of 3.7 V is applied. What is the resistance of the wire?
   (A) 0.49 ohms
   (B) 0.74 ohms
   (C) 1.1 ohms
   (D) 1.4 ohms
   (E) 2.0 ohms

4. A space heater is connected to a standard 120-V line. If the resistance of the operating heater is 15 ohms, what power does the heater use? (*Hint*: First calculate the current.)
   (A) 8.0 W
   (B) 64 W
   (C) 960 W
   (D) 1800 W
   (E) 220 kW

5. A 1700-W machine operates at 120 V. What is the resistance in the machine?
   (A) 7.1×10^{22} ohms
   (B) 1.2×10^{21} ohms
   (C) 1.4 ohms
   (D) 8.5 ohms
   (E) 14 ohms

6. A lamp with three 40-W bulbs connected in parallel is plugged into a 120-V outlet. What is the current in the lamp?
   (A) 1 A
   (B) 3 A
   (C) 9 A
   (D) 40 A
   (E) 120 A

Electricity **627**

Performance-Based Assessment

The experiment designs should show that reversing the current through a diode prevents the diode from lighting. The voltage and current limits for an LED should be noted.

Your students can independently test their knowledge of the chapter and print out their test results for your files.

Planning Guide

Use these planning tools

Easy Planner
Teacher Express

SECTION OBJECTIVES	STANDARDS		ACTIVITIES and LABS
	NATIONAL	STATE	
21.1 Magnets and Magnetic Fields, pp. 630–633 ⏱ 1 block or 2 periods **21.1.1 Describe** the effects of magnetic forces and magnetic fields and **explain** how magnetic poles determine the direction of magnetic force. **21.1.2 Interpret diagrams** of magnetic field lines around one or more bar magnets. **21.1.3 Describe** Earth's magnetic field and its effect on compasses. **21.1.4 Explain** the behavior of ferromagnetic materials in terms of magnetic domains.	A-1, A-2, B-1, B-4	ICP.6.6	**SE** Inquiry Activity: How Do Magnets Interact With One Another? p. 629 **L2** **SE** Quick Lab: Observing Magnetic Field Lines, p. 632 **L2** **TE** Build Science Skills: Inferring, p. 631 **L2** **LM** Investigation 21B: Investigating a Compass **L1**
21.2 Electromagnetism, pp. 635–639 ⏱ 1 block or 2 periods **21.2.1 Describe** how a moving electric charge creates a magnetic field and **determine** the direction of the magnetic field based on the type of charge and the direction of its motion. **21.2.2 Relate** the force a magnetic field exerts on a moving electric charge to the type of charge and the direction of its motion. **21.2.3 Explain** how solenoids and electromagnets are constructed and **describe** factors that affect the field strength of both. **21.2.4 Describe** how electromagnetic devices use the interaction between electric currents and magnetic fields.	A-1, A-2, B-4, B-6, E-2, F-1, G-1, G-2, G-3	ICP.6.6, ICP.6.7	**SE** Quick Lab: Making an Electromagnet, p. 637 **L2** **TE** Teacher Demo: Magnetic Field from Electric Current, p. 636 **L2** **TE** Teacher Demo: Electromagnetic Force, p. 638 **L2**
21.3 Electrical Energy Generation and Transmission, pp. 642–647 ⏱ 1 block or 2 periods **21.3.1 Describe** how electric current is generated by electromagnetic induction. **21.3.2 Compare** AC and DC generators and **explain** how they work. **21.3.3 Analyze** factors that determine the output voltage and current produced by a transformer. **21.3.4 Summarize** how electrical energy is produced, transmitted, and converted for use in the home.	A-1, A-2, B-4, E-1, F-1, F-3, G-1, G-2, G-3	ICP.6.6, ICP.6.7, ICP.8.1, ICP.8.6, ICP.8.7	**SE** Application Lab: Investigating an Electric Generator, pp. 648–649 **L2** **TE** Teacher Demo: Generating Alternating Current, p. 643 **L2** **LM** Investigation 21A: Modeling a Computer **L2**

RESOURCES
PRINT and TECHNOLOGY

RSW Section 21.1 **L1**

🖥 **T** Chapter 21 Pretest **L2**

Section 21.1 **L2**

💿 **P** Chapter 21 Pretest **L2**

Section 21.1 **L2**

RSW Section 21.2 **L1**

DC Magnetic Viewpoints **L2**

🖥 **T** Section 21.2 **L2**

💿 **P** Section 21.2 **L2**

SCiLINKS **GO** Electromagnets **L2**

PLM Lab 9: Investigating an Electric Generator **L2**

RSW Section 21.3 **L1**

RSW Math Skill **L2**

🖥 **T** Section 21.3 **L2**

💿 **P** Section 21.3 **L2**

SCiLINKS **GO** Transformers **L2**

PHSchool.com Data sharing **L2**

SECTION
ASSESSMENT

SE Section 21.1 Assessment, p. 633

iT Section 21.1

SE Section 21.2 Assessment, p. 639

iT Section 21.2

SE Section 21.3 Assessment, p. 647

iT Section 21.3

Go Online

Go online for these Internet resources.

PHSchool.com

Web Code: ccd-2210
Web Code: cca-2210

NSTA *SCiLINKS*

Web Code: ccn-2212
Web Code: ccn-2213

Materials for Activities and Labs

Quantities for each group

STUDENT EDITION

Inquiry Activity, p. 629
2 bar magnets

Quick Lab, p. 632
small container of iron filings, 2 bar magnets, paper, 2 textbooks, masking tape

Quick Lab, p. 637
iron nail, 20 small metal paper clips, 20-cm length and 1-m length of insulated wire with stripped ends, 6-volt battery, switch

Application Lab, pp. 648–649
cardboard tube, 5-m length of insulated wire, metric ruler, multimeter, bar magnet, graph paper

TEACHER'S EDITION

Build Science Skills, p. 631
2 bar magnets, a small magnetic compass

Teacher Demo, p. 636
insulated wire, cardboard (10 cm × 10 cm), a burner tripod, a variable DC power supply, 4–6 compasses

Teacher Demo, p. 638
insulated wire, a large horseshoe magnet, a variable DC power supply, 2 ring stands with clamps

Build Science Skills, p. 640
a short pencil (about 5 cm long), a cardboard disk (7 cm wide), a steel thumbtack, a bar magnet, paper

Teacher Demo, p. 643
a hand-operated generator, a galvanometer, insulated wire (2 strands)

Chapter Assessment

CHAPTER ASSESSMENT

SE Chapter Assessment, pp. 651–652
CUT Chapter 21 Test A, B
CTB Chapter 21
iT Chapter 21
PHSchool.com GO
Web Code: cca-2210

STANDARDIZED TEST PREP

SE Chapter 21, p. 653
TP Diagnose and Prescribe

Interactive Textbook with assessment at PHSchool.com

Before you teach

From the Author

Sophia Yancopoulos
Manhattan College

Big Ideas

Like electric fields, magnetic fields are everywhere. Earth has a magnetic field that can be sensed by some migrating birds and fish, bees, and some butterflies. Even humans have vestigial amounts of magnetic material in their noses, which is thought to contribute to a sense of direction. Remind students that electricity and magnetism are different aspects of a single force called electromagnetism.

Forces and Motion Magnetism, like electricity (but unlike gravity), can be either an attractive or repulsive force. A magnet has two poles, labeled north and south. Like poles repel and unlike poles attract, even without touching. This action at a distance is nonintuitive. Once a magnet has been defined by its behavior, however, some surprisingly logical deductions follow. William Gilbert, the seventeenth-century English physician who first recorded and named magnetic polar behavior, did not set out to prove that Earth is a magnet. It was simply the only logical explanation for Earth's behavior. Scattering iron filings around a magnet reveals the magnetic field lines. It is these lines that suggested to English physicist Michael Faraday the concept of the magnetic field. Because it is so easily visualized, the concept of a magnetic field seems deceptively simple. It is in fact extremely subtle. It is important for students to understand that a magnetic field is not a region but a measurement of direction and strength *within* a region.

Matter and Energy Magnetism is caused by moving charged particles. To understand magnetism inside a substance, look at the motion of the electrons inside its atoms. Single electrons act like tiny magnets. Most electrons cancel each other's magnetic effect, but in a ferromagnetic material the fields combine to give the atoms a net magnetic field, and the cluster of atoms behaving like a tiny magnet is called a magnetic domain.

Physics Refresher

Magnetic Materials 21.1

In many substances, the magnetic fields produced by the various electron motions cancel each other out, and the atoms have a net magnetic dipole moment of zero. However, these substances will become strongly magnetic while in an external magnetic field. Such substances are called *paramagnetic*. Substances where the induced atomic magnetic fields align so as to oppose an applied magnetic field are called *diamagnetic*.

> **⚑ Address Misconceptions**
>
> *Students may visualize electrons as spinning particles.* The electron property known as "spin" doesn't refer to a spinning motion. It's a model used to help explain the characteristics of electron behavior. For a strategy to overcome this misconception, see **Address Misconceptions** on **page 633**.

In certain substances, such as iron, nickel, and cobalt, the magnetic fields of the atoms align in an externally applied magnetic field and remain aligned after the field is removed. Such substances are called *ferromagnetic*.

Electromagnetism 21.2

Magnetic fields are produced whenever an electric charge is in motion. Magnetic field lines always form closed loops, never cross each other, and by convention are directed from the "north" magnetic pole to the "south" magnetic pole. The closer the lines are together, the greater the magnetic field strength.

For a current in a wire, the magnetic field strength (B) decreases with radial distance (r) from the wire and increases with current (I).

$$B \propto \frac{I}{r}$$

Go Online

For: Teaching methods for magnetism
Visit: www.SciLinks.org/PDLinks
Web Code: ccn-2199

An applied magnetic field interacts with the magnetic field produced by a moving charge or current. The result of this interaction is a force that is exerted on the charge or current. This force is largest when the direction of the charge motion or current is perpendicular to the magnetic field ($\theta = 90°$), and is zero when the two are parallel ($\theta = 0°$). The equation describing the force on a charge moving with a velocity v or a current moving along a distance L is as follows:

$$F = qvB \sin \theta = ILB \sin \theta$$

Electrical Energy Generation 21.3

Address Misconceptions

Students may think that the changes in voltage and current produced by a transformer violate the principle of energy conservation. For an ideal transformer, the amount of energy that goes into the transformer each second (the input power) is equal to the energy leaving the transformer each second (the output power). For a strategy to overcome this misconception, see **Address Misconceptions** on **page 644.**

When a magnetic field moves through a closed loop of wire, or the loop of wire moves through a magnetic field, a potential difference is induced in the wire, and thus a current is produced. This process is called electromagnetic induction. The induced potential difference and current depend on the rate at which the magnetic field strength changes, or, alternatively, the rate at which the cross-sectional area of the loop changes. This change in the loop's area can take the form of rotating the loop in the magnetic field, which is the basic process for inducing a current in an electrical generator.

A Loop perpendicular to field

B Loop at an angle to field

Because the sides of a rotating coil in a generator move through a magnetic field in an opposite direction after one half turn, the current produced by the generator alternates direction. Another aspect of induction—using a changing current to induce a changing magnetic field—provides the basis for the operation of a transformer.

Build Reading Literacy

Reciprocal Teaching

Modeling Strategies in Combination

Strategy Help students learn to apply the strategies of predict, question, clarify, and summarize. Teaching this strategy should take place over several days, beginning with the teacher modeling and leading students in discussion. The teacher gradually turns leadership over to students and becomes a facilitator, intervening only as needed. Prepare for the reading by choosing a passage of several paragraphs from Chapter 21. Make a copy of the paragraphs and note appropriate places to model the strategies for students.

Example

1. Read a few paragraphs aloud or have one student read aloud as other students follow along silently.
2. Discuss appropriate strategies for clarifying meaning and getting past trouble spots in the passage. Engage the group in discussing ways to apply each of the following strategies:
• Predicting what will come next in the text. Remind students to use what they already know about a topic to make connections that will help them understand what comes next.
• Asking "teacher-like questions" to check understanding and to think about what they need to find out.
• Clarifying the meaning of unfamiliar words or concepts.
• Summarizing what has been read.
3. Reread the paragraphs, modeling all four strategies.
4. Continue reading a few paragraphs at a time, discussing and modeling the strategies.
5. Repeat the process with different passages over a few days, gradually turning over the leadership role to students by having them lead the discussion of portions of the text.
6. When students are comfortable with the strategies, they can lead the entire discussion. Intervene only to get students back on track or to jump-start a discussion.

See p. 645 for a script on how to use the reciprocal teaching strategy with students. For additional Build Reading Literacy strategies, see pp. 630 and 635.

ASSESS PRIOR KNOWLEDGE

Use the Chapter Pretest below to assess students' prior knowledge. As needed, review these Science Concepts and Math Skills with students.

Review Science Concepts

Section 21.1 Review fundamental forces. Review electric charge, repulsive and attractive electric forces between charges, and electric fields. Review electric fields. Remind students of the atomic and molecular structure of solids as a preview to magnetic materials.

Section 21.2 Review direct current. Remind students that current is defined by the direction in which positive charges would flow.

Section 21.3 Review energy conservation and how work or heat can transfer energy. Remind students of how voltage and current determine electric power. Review alternating current, Ohm's law, and electrical safety.

Review Math Skills

Ratios and Proportions Students will use ratios and proportions to calculate voltage changes.

Direct students to the **Math Skills** in the **Skills and Reference Handbook** at the end of the student text.

CHAPTER

21 Magnetism

21st Century Learning

Self Direction

How does an electric motor work?

An electric motor is a device that converts electrical energy into mechanical energy. You will learn how electric motors work in Section 21.2. Use the library or Internet to research how to build a simple kind of electric motor called a stripped-down motor. Document your progress by making a video or photo journal to post on a blog. Explain how each part of the stripped-down motor works.

Indiana's Academic Standards for Science

ELECTRICAL ENERGY PROPAGATION AND MAGNETISM
ICP.6.6: Explain that some objects, called magnets, exert magnetic forces with no direct contact; **ICP.6.7:** Using the examples of motors and generators, explain that electrical energy can be transformed into mechanical energy and vice versa.

SOCIETY (ENERGY PRODUCTION, ENVIRONMENT, ECONOMICS)
ICP.8.1: Describe how energy needs have changed throughout history and how energy needs are met in modern society; **ICP.8.6:** Contrast the dependence on and use of energy and other natural resources in the economies of industrial nations, of developing nations and of undeveloped nations; **ICP.8.7:** Describe the energy needs of a modern urban city, and compare and contrast these needs with those of a modern rural community.

When charged particles from the sun are pulled toward the North or South Pole, they may cause colorful lights in the night sky.

Chapter Pretest

1. True or False: Like charges exert an attractive force on each other. *(False)*
2. True or False: Electric force and magnetic force are two aspects of the same force. *(True)*
3. An electric field tells you *(d)*
   a. force on a charge in the field.
   b. how force varies with position.
   c. direction of force on a positive charge.
   d. All of the above

4. What is the difference between a series circuit and a parallel circuit? *(A series circuit has only one path for current. A parallel circuit has more than one path.)*
5. What is an insulator? *(A material through which charge cannot easily flow)*
6. True or False: The particle in an atom that moves around the nucleus is the electron. *(True)*

7. If current in a circuit increases and power stays the same, what happens to the voltage? *(It decreases.)*
8. True or False: An alternating current is one in which the charges repeatedly change direction. *(True)*

Chapter Preview

21.1 Magnets and Magnetic Fields

21.3 Electrical Energy Generation and Transmission

21.2 Electromagnetism

DISCOVERY
CHANNEL
SCHOOL
Video Field Trip
Magnetic Viewpoints

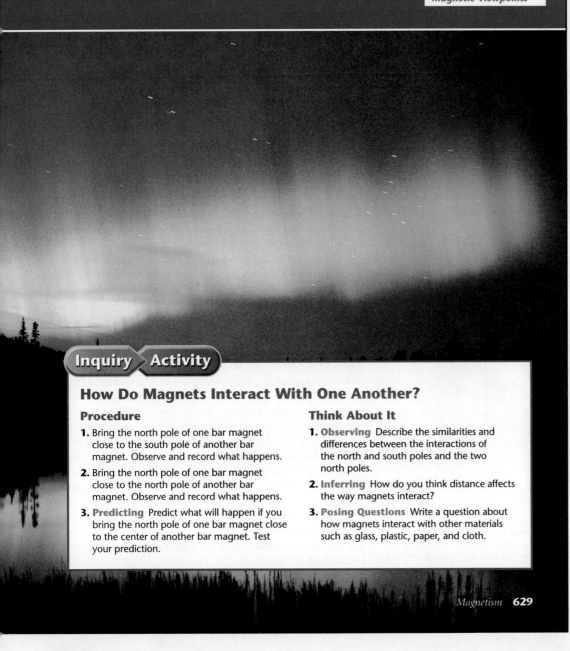

Inquiry > Activity

How Do Magnets Interact With One Another?

Procedure

1. Bring the north pole of one bar magnet close to the south pole of another bar magnet. Observe and record what happens.

2. Bring the north pole of one bar magnet close to the north pole of another bar magnet. Observe and record what happens.

3. **Predicting** Predict what will happen if you bring the north pole of one bar magnet close to the center of another bar magnet. Test your prediction.

Think About It

1. **Observing** Describe the similarities and differences between the interactions of the north and south poles and the two north poles.

2. **Inferring** How do you think distance affects the way magnets interact?

3. **Posing Questions** Write a question about how magnets interact with other materials such as glass, plastic, paper, and cloth.

Magnetism **629**

Video Field Trip

Magnetic Viewpoints

Encourage students to view the Video Field Trip "Magnetic Viewpoints."

ENGAGE/EXPLORE

Inquiry > Activity

How Do Magnets Interact With One Another?   **L2**

Purpose In this activity, students will learn how magnetic fields attract or repel each other, and learn about the direction of magnetic fields.

 Address Misconceptions

Some students may think that magnetic poles are like charges, which can exist in isolation. Challenge this misconception by having students think of magnets as behaving like a pair of opposite charges on opposite ends of a short stick. Ask, **What would the direction of the electric field be between these charges?** *(The electric field lines would spread out from the positive charge and extend toward the negative charge.)* Have students compare their observations of magnetic fields with their conclusions about the fields from pairs of opposite charges. Emphasize that magnetic poles never exist on their own; they always come in pairs.

Skills Focus Observing, Inferring

Prep Time 5 minutes

Materials 2 bar magnets

Class Time 15 minutes

Teaching Tips

• Advise students not to drop or bang the magnets, as this causes the magnets to lose their strength.

Expected Outcome Students will realize that magnets interact differently when like and unlike poles are brought near each other. When a pole of one bar magnet is brought near the middle of another bar magnet, there is a weak attraction, similar to the attraction for nonmagnetized iron.

Think About It

1. The north pole and south pole attracted each other. The north poles repelled each other.

2. Students will probably infer that the magnets will attract or repel each other more strongly the closer they are.

3. Students may ask which materials are attracted to magnets and which are not.

Kinesthetic, Group

1 FOCUS

Objectives

21.1.1 Describe the effects of magnetic forces and magnetic fields and **explain** how magnetic poles determine the direction of magnetic force.

21.1.2 Interpret diagrams of magnetic field lines around one or more bar magnets.

21.1.3 Describe Earth's magnetic field and its effect on compasses.

21.1.4 Explain the behavior of ferromagnetic materials in terms of magnetic domains.

Reading Focus

Build Vocabulary   L2

Word-Part Analysis Have students research the origin of the word *magnet* and write a short paragraph explaining how the word originated. *(The word* magnet *is derived from the name* Magnesia, *a region that was once part of ancient Greece. This area was known for its magnetite ore mines.)*

Reading Strategy   L2

a. Can be temporary or permanent
b. Have north and south poles; like poles repel, unlike poles attract **c.** Only a few materials can be magnets. **d.** Magnets affect objects with iron but don't affect most materials, such as paper, cotton, and so on.

2 INSTRUCT

Magnetic Forces
Build Reading Literacy   L1

KWL (Know/Want to Know/Learned) Refer to page **124D** in **Chapter 5,** which provides the guidelines for a KWL strategy.

Have students label three columns on a sheet of paper K, W, and L. Have them write in the K column what they know about magnetic forces, and in the W column questions they would like answered about the forces exerted by magnets. Then, have students read the paragraphs on this page and record in the L column the answers to as many of their questions as possible.
Verbal, Interpersonal

21.1 Magnets and Magnetic Fields

Standard: ICP.6.6

Reading Focus

Key Concepts

- How do magnetic poles interact?
- How can a magnetic field affect a magnet that enters the field?
- Why are some materials magnetic while others are not?

Vocabulary

- magnetic force
- magnetic pole
- magnetic field
- magnetosphere
- magnetic domain
- ferromagnetic material

Reading Strategy

Using Prior Knowledge Copy the diagram below and add what you already know about magnets. After you read, revise the diagram based on what you learned.

Figure 1 The green magnet and lower red magnet attract each other. The lower red magnet and the yellow magnet repel each other. **Predicting** *What would happen if the upper red magnet on the pencil were flipped over?*

Ancient Greeks observed that magnetite, or lodestone, attracts iron. Some time before 200 A.D., the Chinese sculpted magnetite into spoon-shaped compasses. They called these stones "south pointers." By 1150 A.D., Chinese navigators used compasses with magnetized iron needles. But properties of magnets were not well explained until 1600. In that year, the English physician William Gilbert published *De Magnete.*

Magnetic Forces

You can explore properties of magnets on your own. Either side of a magnet sticks to a refrigerator. Yet if you push two magnets together, they may attract or repel. **Magnetic force** is the force a magnet exerts on another magnet, on iron or a similar metal, or on moving charges. Recall that magnetic force is one aspect of electromagnetic force.

Magnetic forces, like electric forces, act over a distance. Look at the suspended magnets in Figure 1. If you push down on the top two magnets, you can feel the magnets repel. Push harder, and the force increases. Magnetic force, like electric force, varies with distance.

Gilbert used a compass to map forces around a magnetite sphere. He discovered that the force is strongest at the poles. All magnets have two **magnetic poles,** regions where the magnet's force is strongest. One end of a magnet is its north pole; the other end is its south pole. The direction of magnetic force between two magnets depends on how the poles face. **Like magnetic poles repel one another, and opposite magnetic poles attract one another.**

630 *Chapter 21*

Section Resources

Print
- **Laboratory Manual,** Investigation 21B
- **Reading and Study Workbook With Math Support,** Section 21.1
- **Transparencies,** Chapter Pretest and Section 21.1

Technology
- **Interactive Textbook,** Section 21.1
- **Presentation Pro CD-ROM,** Chapter Pretest and Section 21.1

Magnetic Fields

A **magnetic field** surrounds a magnet and can exert magnetic forces. In Figure 2, iron filings are used to show the shape of the magnetic field around a bar magnet. ⊙ **A magnetic field, which is strongest near a magnet's poles, will either attract or repel another magnet that enters the field.** The field lines begin near the magnet's north pole and extend toward its south pole. The arrows on the field lines indicate what direction a compass needle would point at each point in space. Where lines are close together, the field is strong. Where lines are more spread out, the field is weak.

Magnetic Fields Around Magnets You can use iron filings to visualize how magnetic fields of two magnets interact. Figure 3A shows the north pole of one magnet facing the north pole of another magnet. Notice that there are no iron filings in the gap between the magnets. Iron filings are not attracted to this area because the combined magnetic field is very weak. Figure 3B shows the combined field of two magnets with opposite poles facing each other. The field lines start at the north pole of one magnet and extend to the south pole of the other magnet. The field in the gap between the magnets is very strong, as you can see from the dense crowding of iron filings in this area.

Figure 3 Iron filings reveal the combined magnetic field of two interacting magnets. **A** When like poles of two magnets come together, the magnets repel each other. **B** When opposite poles of magnets come together, the magnets attract each other.

Figure 2 A magnetic field surrounds every magnet. Iron filings reveal the field lines, which start near the north pole and extend toward the south pole. *Interpreting Diagrams In which two areas of a bar magnet is the field strongest?*

Magnetism **631**

Earth's magnetic field is produced by the motions of hot, liquefied iron within its core. Induced electric currents in the iron give rise to magnetic fields, which affect the flow of the iron and cause the resulting magnetic fields to become stronger.

Earth's magnetic field undergoes sudden reversals every few hundred thousand years, although the change does not happen at regular intervals. Currently the North Magnetic Pole is a south pole, which explains why "North" on a compass points to the north. Evidence for reversals is found in cooled magma, where iron atoms have aligned with Earth's magnetic field at the time of cooling. Cooled magma in ridges along the ocean floor provides a continuous record of magnetic field reversals over time.
Logical

Build Science Skills L2
Inferring

Purpose Students are helped to an understanding of the shape of the magnetic field around two bar magnets.

Materials 2 bar magnets, a small magnetic compass

Class Time 20 minutes

Procedure Arrange two magnets as shown in either part of Figure 3. Have students place the compass at different positions about 1–2 cm away from the magnets and sketch the direction in which the compass needle points for each position. Ask them how the direction of the needle corresponds to the direction of the field lines in each location. Have them identify any patterns they notice.

Expected Outcome The compass needle will be parallel to the field lines at any location. The needle's south pole points along the field lines toward the north pole of a nearby magnet.
Logical, Visual

Customize for English Language Learners

Reinforce Science Concepts
The various concepts, such as magnetic field, magnetic forces, and magnetic domains, each use the word *magnetic,* but mean and refer to different things. To help English language learners develop a clear understanding of these concepts, have them construct a Word Analysis Chart. Instruct students to write each of the vocabulary words on a separate chart and give a definition of each word. Suggest that they compare and contrast the vocabulary words. Finally, have them draw a picture or diagram to illustrate each concept.

Answer to . . .

Figure 1 *The red magnet would float above the blue magnet.*

Figure 2 *The field is strongest at the poles.*

Observing Magnetic Field Lines **L2**

Objective
After completing this activity, students will be able to
• recognize how the magnetic fields of two magnets combine.

Skill Focus Observing

 Prep Time 10 minutes

Class Time 20 minutes

Safety Students should wear safety goggles, not inhale the iron filings, and wash their hands when finished.

Teaching Tips
• Dropping or banging magnets causes them to lose their strength.
• Suggest that students tape the paper in place, so that the pattern is not accidentally disturbed.

Expected Outcome Students will realize that the interaction of the field lines of two magnets depends on how the magnets are positioned.

Analyze and Conclude
1. The field was strongest in the gap between opposite poles and weakest in the gap between like poles.
2. The field lines of two like poles spread apart and had a gap between the poles with very few field lines. The field lines of two unlike poles extended in lines connecting the north and south pole.
3. No pattern would appear, because sawdust is not magnetic. **Visual, Group**

For Enrichment **L3**

Have students repeat the experiment using different separations between the magnets. Ask, **What happens to the iron filings and to the field strength when two opposite poles are moved apart?** *(The filings are less crowded, indicating the field is weaker.)*
Visual, Logical

Magnetic Materials
FYI

Magnetic domains are quite small and can only be imaged using microscopes. A variety of instruments are used, such as scanning tunneling microscopes, magnetic force microscopes, and light microscopes with polarizing filters.

Figure 4 Earth is surrounded by magnetic field lines. These lines are densest at the poles.

Observing Magnetic Field Lines

Materials

small container of iron filings, 2 bar magnets, paper, 2 textbooks, masking tape

Procedure

1. Place two textbooks side by side, about 7 cm apart.

2. Place the magnets between the books, with north poles facing, about 2 cm apart. Tape the magnets in place.

3. Place the paper over the magnets to form a bridge.

4. Sprinkle iron filings on the paper until you can see the magnetic field lines. Sketch your observations.

5. Carefully return the filings to their container.

6. Repeat Steps 2 through 5 with opposite poles facing.

Analyze and Conclude

1. **Inferring** Where was the magnetic field the strongest? The weakest?

2. **Analyzing Data** How did the fields of like poles facing differ from those of unlike poles facing?

3. **Predicting** What result would you expect if you used sawdust instead of iron filings?

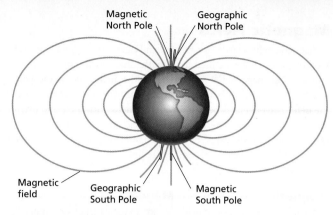

Magnetic Field Around Earth Earth is like a giant magnet surrounded by a magnetic field. The area surrounding Earth that is influenced by this field is the **magnetosphere** (mag NET oh sfeer).

A compass points north because it aligns with Earth's magnetic field. However, as Figure 4 shows, Earth's magnetic poles are not at the geographic poles. The geographic North Pole is at 90° N latitude, but the magnetic North Pole is at about 84° N latitude. Because of this, a compass may point east or west of north. The angle between the direction to true north and to magnetic north is called magnetic declination. Magnetic declination varies with your location on Earth.

 Why does a compass point toward north?

Magnetic Materials

Within an atom, electrons move around the nucleus. This movement, along with a property of electrons called "spin," causes electrons to act like tiny magnets. In many materials, each electron is paired with another having an opposite spin. Magnetic effects mostly cancel each other. As a result, these materials have extremely weak magnetic fields.

Many other materials have one or more unpaired electrons. The unpaired electrons produce magnetic fields. But the fields usually don't combine because the arrangement of the atoms isn't quite right. These materials have weak magnetic fields. In a few materials, such as iron, nickel, and cobalt, the unpaired electrons make a strong magnetic field. Then the fields combine to form magnetic domains. A **magnetic domain** is a region that has a very large number of atoms with aligned magnetic fields. A **ferromagnetic material** (fehr oh mag NET ik), such as iron, can be magnetized because it contains magnetic domains. **When a material is magnetized, most of its magnetic domains are aligned.**

Facts and Figures

Strong and Weak Magnetic Fields Earth has the strongest magnetic field of the rocky inner planets. Earth has an average field strength at its surface of between 30 μT and 60 μT. (A tesla, T, is the unit by which magnetic fields are measured.) This is some 100 times stronger than the magnetic field of Mercury, roughly 1000 to 5000 times stronger than the field of Mars, and about 100,000 times stronger than the field of Venus.

Nonmagnetized Materials The fact that a material is ferromagnetic does not mean it is a magnet. If the domains of a ferromagnetic material are aligned randomly, the magnetization of the domains is cancelled, and it is not a magnet. An iron nail is an example of a nonmagnetized material. It is ferromagnetic, so the domains have the potential to be aligned, but normally they are not. Figure 5A shows the random orientation of domains in nonmagnetized iron.

Magnetized Materials You can easily magnetize a nonmagnetized ferromagnetic material by placing it in a magnetic field. For example, if you put a nonmagnetized iron nail near a magnet, you will turn the nail into a magnet. Figure 5B shows the alignment of magnetic domains in magnetized iron. The applied magnetic field causes magnetic domains aligned with the field to grow larger. This magnetization can be temporary. If the magnet is moved away from the nail, the motion of the atoms in the nail causes the magnetic domains to become randomly oriented again. In some ferromagnetic materials, the domains stay aligned for a long time. These materials are called permanent magnets. They are not truly permanent, because heat or a jarring impact can realign the domains.

If you cut a magnet in half, each half will have its own north pole and south pole because the domains will still be aligned. If you cut the pieces in half again, each half will again have a north pole and a south pole. No matter how many times you cut the magnets, each piece will have two different poles. A magnet can never have just a north pole or just a south pole.

Figure 5 A magnetic field can magnetize ferromagnetic materials. **A** Before magnetization, domains are random. **B** Domains aligned with the field grow during magnetization. Unaligned domains can shrink.

Section 21.1 Assessment

Reviewing Concepts

1. Describe the interaction of magnetic poles.
2. What two things can happen to a magnet entering a magnetic field?
3. What makes a material magnetic?
4. Describe what happens to the fields of two bar magnets when you bring their north poles together.

Critical Thinking

5. **Predicting** What happens if you suspend a bar magnet so that it can swing freely?
6. **Relating Cause and Effect** How are electrons responsible for magnetism?

7. **Predicting** What will happen if you hit a magnet with a hammer? Explain.
8. **Designing Experiments** How could you test the effects of heating and cooling on the magnetization of a bar magnet?

Connecting C **Concepts**

Electric Charge Review electric charge in Section 20.1. Compare the attraction and repulsion of positive and negative charges with the behavior of two bar magnets placed near one another.

Magnetism **633**

Students may be visualizing the motion of the electron as if it were a planet rotating on its axis. Emphasize that the "spin" of an electron is not like the spin of a ball, any more than the orbital motion of an electron around an atom's nucleus is like the motion of a planet around the sun. The term *spin* is applied to electron behavior that mathematically resembles that of a spinning object. Remind students of how electrons in atoms are modeled as "clouds" where they are most likely to be located.
Logical

3 ASSESS

Evaluate Understanding **L2**

Ask students why a refrigerator magnet sticks to the door of a refrigerator. Be sure they explain which material is a permanent magnet, and what happens at the atomic level in the magnetized material. *(The atoms in the refrigerator magnet, which is made of ferromagnetic material, are aligned in the various magnetic domains, and so give the magnet a permanent field. When the magnet is attached to the unmagnetized door of the refrigerator, the atoms of the door are aligned, and so become magnetized temporarily.)*

Reteach **L1**

Use Figure 3 to explain the shape and direction of a magnetic field around a bar magnet.

Connecting C **Concepts**

Like charges and like poles repel, while opposite charges and opposite poles attract. In contrast to electric charges, magnetic poles can't be separated.

Interactive Textbook If your class subscribes to the Interactive Textbook, use it to review key concepts in Section 21.1.

Section 21.1 Assessment

1. Magnetic poles that are alike repel one another, and magnetic poles that are different attract one another.
2. A magnetic field will either attract or repel another magnet that enters the field.
3. For a material to be magnetized, most of its magnetic domains must be aligned.
4. The fields interact, and the field between the magnets becomes very weak.

5. The north end of the magnet will swing toward north, aligning with Earth's magnetic field just as a compass does.
6. The spin and orbital motion of electrons in an atom give the atom a magnetic field.
7. The motion of the atoms can cause the magnetic domains to become randomly aligned. The material loses its magnetization.
8. Students' suggestions for experiments should include some method for testing the magnetization of a bar magnet before and after it is heated and before and after it is cooled.

Answer to . . .

Reading Checkpoint *The north end of a compass points north because a freely suspended bar magnet aligns with Earth's magnetic field.*

HOW It Works

Anti-Theft Security Devices **L2**

Electromagnetic tag systems were first developed in the 1960s, along with other similar RFID (Radio Frequency Identification) technology. This type of system uses electromagnetic waves to identify objects that have been tagged with magnetic material.

Electromagnetic waves consist of changing electric fields and changing magnetic fields that are at right angles to each other and to the direction of the wave. The EM tag system uses the magnetic component of an electromagnetic wave to temporarily magnetize an activated tag as it passes between the pedestals. This change in the tag's magnetic domains produces a small electromagnetic wave with a particular frequency. The wave is detected by a receiver, causing an alarm to sound.

A deactivated tag, however, is fully magnetized, so no change occurs in the magnetic domains when the tag passes between the pedestals. Thus, no electromagnetic wave is produced, and the tag passes through the electromagnetic field undetected.

The magnetic properties of the tag cause it to become temporarily magnetized more easily than ordinary steel objects. This is why a screwdriver or box of paper clips can pass through the system without setting off the alarm.

Other systems make use of thin wire coils in the tags that act as antennas, as well as small circuit elements. Electromagnetic waves emitted from the pedestal at a particular frequency induce a current in the tag's antenna, and this induced current produces an electromagnetic wave with a characteristic frequency. This wave is then detected by the receiver pedestal.

Applying Concepts The deactivated tag is more highly magnetized than the activated tag.
Logical

For Enrichment **L3**

Students can make a multimedia presentation about the EM tag system, as well as other RFID systems. Articles on the subject can be found on the Internet and in science and engineering periodicals.
Verbal, Portfolio

HOW It Works

Anti-Theft Security Devices

Anti-theft security devices are found in stores across the world. One of the best of these devices is the electromagnetic (EM) tag system. This system is based on the interaction between a small piece of magnetic material (a tag) and an EM field created between two pedestals at the store exit. **Applying concepts** *Which is more highly magnetized, an activated or a deactivated tag?*

Library security
Powerful magnets are used to deactivate tags in library books before borrowing. If the tag is not deactivated, the alarm will go off at the library exit.

A **Activated tag** An activated tag is slightly demagnetized. When it passes through the pedestal's EM field, the tag's magnetic domains line up with the field. This change in magnetic domain emits a signal that is picked up by the receiver, which sets off the alarm.

Activated tag (demagnetized)

Magnetic domain

Changing electromagnetic field

B **Deactivated tag** A deactivated tag is fully magnetized. When it passes through the exit, the tag's domains do not change. Because no signal is emitted, the alarm is not set off.

Deactivated tag (fully magnetized)

Receiver pedestal

Flashing alarm light

Transmitter pedestal

Tag signal

Wire loop carrying alternating current

Activated tag attached to item

Changing electromagnetic field

C **The pedestals** The transmitter pedestal contains a wire loop that produces a changing EM field in the region between the pedestals. The receiver pedestal picks up any signal produced by the tag.

21.2 Electromagnetism

Standards: ICP.6.6, ICP.6.7

Reading Focus

Key Concepts
- How can an electric charge create a magnetic field?
- How is an electromagnet controlled?
- How do galvanometers, electric motors, and loudspeakers work?

Vocabulary
- electromagnetic force
- solenoid
- electromagnet
- galvanometer
- electric motor

Reading Strategy

Identifying Main Idea Copy the table below. As you read, write the main idea of the text that follows each topic.

Topic	Main Idea
Electricity and magnetism	a. ?
Direction of magnetic fields	b. ?
Direction of electric currents	c. ?
Solenoids and electromagnets	d. ?
Electromagnetic devices	e. ?

You know that unlike electric charges attract one another and that like electric charges repel one another. It is easy to discover a similar effect with the north and south poles of two magnets. However, it's much more difficult to figure out the relationship between electricity and magnetism. In fact, the connection was discovered accidentally by the Danish scientist Hans Christian Oersted in 1820.

One evening Oersted, pictured in Figure 6, was conducting scientific demonstrations for his friends and students in his home. One demonstration used electric current in a wire, and another used a compass needle attached to a wooden stand. As Oersted turned on the current for the electricity demonstration, he saw the compass needle move. When he turned off the current, the needle moved back to its original position. Further investigation showed that the current in the wire produced a magnetic field. Oersted had discovered a relationship between electricity and magnetism.

Electricity and Magnetism

Electricity and magnetism are different aspects of a single force known as the **electromagnetic force.** The electric force results from charged particles. The magnetic force usually results from the movement of electrons in an atom. Both aspects of the electromagnetic force are caused by electric charges.

Figure 6 In 1820 Hans Oersted discovered how magnetism and electricity are connected. A unit of measure of magnetic field strength, the oersted, is named after him.

Magnetism **635**

Section Resources

Print
- ***Reading and Study Workbook With Math Support,*** Section 21.2
- ***Transparencies,*** Section 21.2

Technology
- ***Interactive Textbook,*** Section 21.2
- ***Presentation Pro CD-ROM,*** Section 21.2
- ***Go Online,*** NSTA SciLinks, Electromagnets

---

1 FOCUS

Objectives

21.2.1 Describe how a moving electric charge creates a magnetic field and **determine** the direction of the magnetic field based on the type of charge and the direction of its motion.

21.2.2 Relate the force a magnetic field exerts on a moving electric charge to the type of charge and the direction of its motion.

21.2.3 Explain how solenoids and electromagnets are constructed and **describe** factors that affect the field strength of both.

21.2.4 Describe how electromagnetic devices use the interaction between electric currents and magnetic fields.

Reading Focus

Build Vocabulary   L2

Concept Map Have students make a concept map comparing the devices in the vocabulary list.

Reading Strategy   L2

a. Electricity and magnetism are different aspects of electromagnetic force.
b. Magnetic fields are produced at right angles to an electric current. **c.** Electric currents are deflected perpendicular to a magnetic field. **d.** Changing the current in an electromagnet controls the strength and direction of its magnetic field.
e. Electromagnetic devices change electrical energy into mechanical energy.

2 INSTRUCT

Electricity and Magnetism
Build Reading Literacy   L1

Predict Refer to page **66D** in Chapter 3, which provides the guidelines for predicting.

Have students read the first two paragraphs on p. 635. Ask them to predict what Oersted discovered about the relationship between electricity and magnetism. (*Predictions should indicate that an electric current produces a magnetic field.*) **Logical**

Teacher › Demo

Magnetic Field from Electric Current **L2**

Purpose Students observe how an electric current produces a magnetic field.

Materials insulated wire, cardboard (10 cm × 10 cm), a burner tripod, a variable DC power supply, 4–6 compasses

Procedure Punch a small hole in the center of the cardboard and thread the wire through the hole. Lay the cardboard flat on the burner tripod's ring support so that the wire passes through the tripod center, perpendicular to the cardboard and extending in a straight line 10 cm on either side. (A ring stand and clamp may be needed to support the upper end of the wire.) Connect both ends of the wire to the terminals of the power supply. Place the compasses on the cardboard at a distance of 3–4 cm from the wire. Turn on the power supply and increase the current until the compass needles begin to deflect. Have students notice how the needles deflect with respect to the wire. Remove the compasses, turn off the power supply, reverse the wire connections, and repeat the demonstration.

Safety Use insulated wire. Follow procedures for electrical safety.

Expected Outcome When the top end of the wire is connected to the positive terminal of the power supply, the magnetic field will be in a counter-clockwise pattern around the wire, according to the right-hand rule. This will cause the poles of the compasses to align themselves along the edge of a circle around the wire. The south poles will form a clockwise pattern. When the connections are reversed, the direction in which the compasses point will reverse.
Visual, Group

Use Visuals **L1**

Figure 8 Explain that the right-hand rule also applies to Figure 8. Ask, **How could you use your hand to determine the deflection of an electron moving through the magnetic poles?** *(Use your right hand with your thumb in the direction of the current, which will be opposite the direction of the electron's travel.)*
Visual

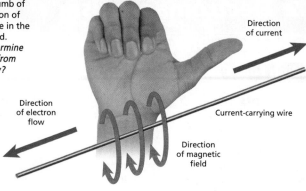

Figure 7 If you point the thumb of your right hand in the direction of the current, your fingers curve in the direction of the magnetic field. **Inferring** *How can you determine the magnetic field direction from the direction of electron flow?*

Direction of current

Direction of electron flow

Current-carrying wire

Direction of magnetic field

Magnetic Fields Around Moving Charges Oersted's discovery about the relationship between a current-carrying wire and a magnet established an important physics principle. **Moving electric charges create a magnetic field.** These moving charges may be the vibrating charges that produce an electromagnetic wave. They may also be, as in Oersted's experiment, the moving charges in a wire. Figure 7 shows how to remember the direction of the magnetic field that is produced. The magnetic field lines form circles around a straight wire carrying a current.

Forces Acting on Moving Charges Recall that an electric field exerts a force on an electric charge. The force is either in the same direction as the electric field or in the opposite direction, depending on whether it is a positive or negative charge.

The effect of a magnetic field on a moving charge is different, as shown in Figure 8. A charge moving in a magnetic field will be deflected in a direction perpendicular to both the magnetic field and to the velocity of the charge. If a current-carrying wire is in a magnetic field, the wire will be pushed in a direction perpendicular to both the field and the direction of the current. Reversing the direction of the current will still cause the wire to be deflected, but in the opposite direction. If the current is parallel to the magnetic field, the force is zero and there is no deflection.

Reading Checkpoint *What are two kinds of moving charges that can create a magnetic field?*

Force deflecting the charge

Velocity of charge

Figure 8 A moving positive charge is deflected at a right angle to its motion by a magnetic field. **Inferring** *In what direction would the particle be deflected if it had a negative charge instead of a positive charge?*

Customize for Inclusion Students

Visually Impaired
The right-hand rule can be used by students with visual impairments to understand magnetic fields and forces. Explain how students can use their right hand to predict the directions of magnetic fields for an electric current in a straight wire and a solenoid. As students may have difficulty using Figure 7, instruct them using a wire, so that they can understand how the right-hand thumb and fingers are oriented for a positive current and its magnetic field. Then, have students adapt the rule for positive charges moving in a magnetic field, as shown in Figure 8 (that is, the thumb points in the direction of the moving charge, the fingers extend in the direction of the magnetic field, and the force on the charge points outward from the palm). Encourage those students who successfully master the rule to explain it to the class.

Making an Electromagnet

Materials
iron nail, 20 small metal paper clips, 20-cm length and 1-m length of insulated wire with stripped ends, 6-volt battery, switch

Procedure

1. Make a circuit using the nail, wire, battery, and switch. Use the shorter wire to connect one terminal of the battery to the switch. Connect the longer wire to the other terminal of the battery. Wrap this wire around the nail 10 times. Then connect the longer wire to the switch.

2. Hold the head of the nail over the pile of paper clips. Close the switch. Record how many paper clips the nail can pick up.

3. Open the switch. **CAUTION** *If the switch is left closed, the wire will become very warm.* Wrap the longer wire 40 more times around the nail in the same direction as before.

4. Close the switch. Record how many paper clips the nail can pick up now.

5. Open the switch and disconnect the circuit.

Analyze and Conclude

1. **Observing** How did your ability to pick up paper clips with the nail change when you increased the number of turns in the coil?

2. **Drawing Conclusions** Why did the nail become a magnet when a current-carrying wire was wrapped around it?

Solenoids and Electromagnets

Before you can use electromagnetic force, you need to be able to control it. Using electromagnetic force requires some simple tools. Figure 9A shows a current-carrying wire with a loop in it. The magnetic field in the center of the loop points right to left through the loop, as shown in Figure 9A.

Suppose you loop the wire many times to make a coil, as shown in Figure 9B. Then the magnetic fields of the loops combine so that the coiled wire acts like a bar magnet. The field through the center of the coil is the sum of the fields from each turn of the wire. A coil of current-carrying wire that produces a magnetic field is called a **solenoid.**

If you place a ferromagnetic material, such as an iron rod, inside the coil of a solenoid, the strength of the magnetic field increases. The magnetic field produced by the current causes the iron rod inside the coil of the solenoid to become a magnet. An **electromagnet** is a solenoid with a ferromagnetic core. 🔵 **Changing the current in an electromagnet controls the strength and direction of its magnetic field.** You can also use the current to turn the magnetic field on and off. People use many devices every day, such as hair dryers, telephones, and doorbells, that utilize electromagnets.

A Loop of wire
Current

B Pole — Pole
Solenoid
Current

Figure 9 The magnetic field lines around a solenoid are like those of a bar magnet. **Applying Concepts** *Which of the poles is north?*

Facts and Figures

Big Magnets Because the magnetic fields produced by electromagnets can be made stronger by properly designing the electromagnet, it is not surprising that the strongest magnetic fields on Earth are produced by specially designed electromagnets. At the National High Magnetic Field Laboratory

(NHMFL) at Florida State University in Tallahassee, electromagnets have been designed that produce continuous magnetic fields with strengths up to 50 teslas. These fields are about a million times stronger than Earth's magnetic field at Earth's surface.

Solenoids and Electromagnets

Making an Electromagnet **L2**

Objective
After completing this activity, students will be able to
- predict how the number of turns of wire affects the strength of the electromagnet.

Skill Focus Observing, Drawing Conclusions

 Prep Time 20 minutes

Advance Prep Cut the wires in advance and use a wire stripper or wire-cutting pliers to remove 2 cm of insulation from each end of the wires.

Class Time 25 minutes

Safety Students should wear safety goggles and be careful handling the coil of wire, as the wire may become hot. Students should open the switch when the electromagnet is not in use.

Expected Outcome Students will learn that the strength of an electromagnet, as indicated by the number of paper clips picked up, is directly related to the number of turns in the coil of wire. More turns make the magnet stronger.

Analyze and Conclude
1. The electromagnet became stronger with more turns in the coil.
2. The current in the coil produced a magnetic field around and through the nail. This caused the magnetic domains in the nail to align, temporarily strengthening the magnetic field of the nail.
Logical, Group

Answer to . . .

Figure 7 *Use the right-hand rule, but point your thumb in the opposite direction of the electron flow (which will be the direction of the current).*

Figure 8 *It would be deflected down.*

Figure 9 *The one on the left because magnetic field lines start at the north pole and end at the south pole.*

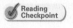 *Vibrating charges, flowing charges in a current*

Students may wonder how the magnetic field of a solenoid can be fairly simple when there are magnetic fields around each segment of wire in the coil. Explain that such fields are present, but that they combine in such a way that the field outside the solenoid is much weaker than inside. The fields combine to effectively form a magnetic field that is similar to that of a bar magnet.
Logical

Electromagnetic Devices

Teacher Demo

Electromagnetic Force L2

Purpose Students observe the magnetic force exerted on a wire carrying an electric current.

Materials insulated wire, a large horseshoe magnet, a variable DC power supply, 2 ring stands with clamps

Procedure Pass the wire through the rings of the ring stands, so that it extends horizontally about 5–10 cm above the table surface. Position the magnet on its side, so that the wire passes between the magnet's poles. Connect the wires to the power supply and turn it on, increasing the current until the wire is deflected. Turn off the power, reverse the connections, and repeat the demonstration.

Safety Use insulated wire. Follow procedures for electrical safety.

Expected Outcome Depending on the orientation of the magnet, the wire will be deflected either in toward the magnet's center or away from it. The deflecting force is proportional to the current in the wire and the strength of the magnetic field.
Visual, Group

Download a worksheet on electromagnets for students to complete, and find additional teacher support from NSTA SciLinks.

For: Links on electromagnets
Visit: www.SciLinks.org
Web Code: ccn-2212

Figure 10 A galvanometer uses an electromagnet to move a pointer. One common application is in an automobile gas gauge. The pointer indicates the amount of current in the wire. The wire is connected to a sensor in the gas tank.

638 Chapter 21

The strength of an electromagnet depends on the current in the solenoid, the number of loops in the coil in the solenoid, and the type of ferromagnetic core. To increase the strength of an electromagnet, increase the current flowing through the solenoid. A greater current produces a stronger magnetic field. Increasing the number of turns, while keeping the same current, will also increase the field strength. Cores that are easily magnetized, such as "soft" iron, make stronger electromagnets.

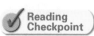 **Reading Checkpoint** *What does the strength of an electromagnet depend on?*

Electromagnetic Devices

Electromagnets can convert electrical energy into motion that can do work. **Electromagnetic devices such as galvanometers, electric motors, and loudspeakers change electrical energy into mechanical energy.** A galvanometer measures current in a wire through the deflection of a solenoid in an external magnetic field. An electric motor uses a rotating electromagnet to turn an axle. A loudspeaker uses a solenoid to convert electrical signals into sound waves you can hear.

Galvanometers Figure 10 shows a **galvanometer,** a device that uses a solenoid to measure small amounts of current. A solenoid is attached to a spring and is free to rotate about an iron core. The solenoid is placed between the poles of two permanent magnets. When there is a current in the solenoid's coils, the resulting magnetic field attempts to align with the field of the permanent magnets. The greater the current, the more the solenoid rotates, as shown by the pointer on the scale. In an automobile fuel gauge, for example, a sensor in the gas tank reduces the current as the gas level decreases. This causes the needle to rotate towards the "empty" mark.

Facts and Figures

Earth's Magnetic Field The magnetic field that is generated within the liquid iron outer core is predominantly dipolar, as shown in Figure 4. Because of this, an analogy is often drawn with the dipolar field from a bar magnet, shown in Figure 2. However, it turns out that a better analogy is with the dipolar field from a solenoid, shown in Figure 9. The combination of convection and Coriolis forces likely causes spiral gyres of flowing liquid iron in the outer core. These spirals are thought by geophysicists to act like the coils of current-carrying wire shown in Figure 9, with the similar result of a dipolar magnetic field passing through them.

Electric Motors An **electric motor** is a device that uses an electromagnet to turn an axle. Figure 11 shows how an electric motor works. In this figure, the wire is connected to a battery. An actual motor has many loops of wire around a central iron core to make the motor stronger. In the motor of an electric appliance, the wire would be connected to an electrical circuit in a building.

What makes a motor turn? When current flows through a loop of wire, one side of the loop is pushed by the field of the permanent magnet. The other side of the loop is pulled. These forces rotate the loop. If there were no commutator ring, the coil would come to rest. But as the loop turns, each C-shaped half of the commutator connects with a different brush, reversing the current. The forces now change direction, so the coil continues to rotate. As long as current flows, rotation continues.

Loudspeakers A loudspeaker contains a solenoid placed around one pole of a permanent magnet. The current in the wires entering the loudspeaker changes direction and increases or decreases to reproduce music, voices, or other sounds. The changing current produces a changing magnetic field in the solenoid coil. The magnetic force exerted by the permanent magnet moves the coil back and forth. As the coil moves, it causes a thin membrane to vibrate, producing sound waves that match the original sound.

Figure 11 A battery supplies current to a loop of wire through the commutator. As the commutator turns, the direction of current switches back and forth. As a result, the coil's magnetic field keeps switching direction, and this turns the coil about an axle.
Predicting *What would happen if you reversed the positive and negative connections on the battery?*

Section 21.2 Assessment

Reviewing Concepts

1. 💬 Besides a magnet, what can create a magnetic field?
2. 💬 How is the magnetic field of an electromagnet controlled?
3. 💬 How are solenoids and electromagnets used in galvanometers, electric motors, and loudspeakers?
4. How does a ferromagnetic rod inside a solenoid affect the strength of an electromagnet?

Critical Thinking

5. **Comparing and Contrasting** What is the effect of a magnetic field on a stationary electric charge? On a moving electric charge?

6. **Applying Concepts** Why is it a good idea to have the coil of a solenoid wound closely with many turns of wire?
7. **Inferring** What is the purpose of the commutator in an electric motor?
8. **Relating Cause and Effect** What causes the membrane in a loudspeaker to vibrate?

Connecting ⊂ **Concepts**

Insulators In Section 20.2 you learned that electric charge doesn't flow easily through electrical insulators. Use this to explain why a solenoid has insulated wires.

Magnetism **639**

Build Science Skills L2

Applying Concepts Have students read the paragraphs on electric motors and help them apply what they already know about work, different forms of energy, and energy conservation. Ask, **What forms of energy are shown for the electric motor in Figure 11?** *(Chemical energy, electrical energy, and mechanical energy)* Ask, **What energy transformations take place when operating the motor?** *(Chemical energy in the battery is converted to electrical energy. Electrical energy interacts with the magnetic field to do work, and so is transformed into the kinetic energy of the rotating wire loop and into any work the motor does.)*
Logical

3 ASSESS

Evaluate Understanding L2

Ask students to list three examples of devices that use electromagnetic forces (at least one of which is not given in the section). Have students explain what each device does and how electricity and magnetism interact in the device. *(Could be an electric bell, relay switch, or microphone)*

Reteach L1

Use Figures 7 and 9 to review the direction of magnetic fields produced by electric currents.

Connecting ⊂ **Concepts**

The strength of the electromagnet depends upon the current in the solenoid. Insulated wires make it possible to direct the current through several tightly wound loops, enhancing the strength of the magnetic field. The insulated wire prevents a short circuit between adjacent coils.

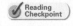 **Interactive Textbook** If your class subscribes to the Interactive Textbook, use it to review key concepts in Section 21.2.

Answer to . . .

Figure 11 *The motor's axle would spin in the opposite direction.*

✓ **Reading Checkpoint** *It depends on the strength of the current, the number of coils of wire, and the type of ferromagnetic core.*

Section 21.2 Assessment

1. A moving electric charge can create a magnetic field.
2. It can be turned on and off. Its strength and direction can be controlled by controlling the current.
3. They change electrical energy into mechanical energy.
4. It makes the magnetic field much stronger. When current flows through the coil, it creates a magnetic field that magnetizes the ferromagnetic rod.

5. A magnetic field doesn't affect a stationary charge. A magnetic field deflects a moving charge in a direction perpendicular to both the field and the velocity.
6. It produces a more uniform field and increases its strength.
7. The commutator reverses the current in the electromagnet, reversing the magnetic field of the electromagnet, and enabling the axle to turn continuously in one direction.
8. The interaction of the magnetic field of the permanent magnet with the changing field of the electromagnet

Peeking Inside the Human Body L2

Background

MRI is an example of a procedure called tomography, where many images of the body are combined to give a composite view. MRI uses nuclear magnetic resonance, or NMR, to obtain information from hydrogen atoms in the body. NMR was discovered in 1946, and was originally used to identify hydrocarbon molecules. In the 1970s, the technique was combined with computers to produce images of tissues in the body.

Build Science Skills L2

Using Analogies

Purpose Students will simulate how applied magnetic fields can disrupt the magnetic fields of atoms.

Materials a short pencil (about 5 cm long), a cardboard disk (7 cm wide), a steel thumbtack, a bar magnet, paper

Class Time 15 minutes

Procedure Insert the thumbtack into the eraser end of the pencil, and punch the pencil through the center of the cardboard disk to make a "top" that can spin. Make sure the cardboard does not slip along the surface of the pencil. Place the top on a piece of paper to prevent marking the table. Spin the top with the thumbtack side upward, making sure that the top is neither too stable or unstable while spinning. Spin the top again, and place one end of the magnet about 2 cm to the side of the thumbtack. Repeat the test, placing the magnet slightly closer, until the spinning top is deflected by the magnet. Make sure that the top is not simply pulled into contact with the magnet. Remove the magnet while the top is still spinning and note its behavior.

Expected Outcome Because the top is fairly stable while spinning, it is analogous to the spinning hydrogen atoms in the body. The alignment and deflection of these atoms by the magnetic fields is analogous to the deflection of the top by the magnet. By observing a large-scale model of an atomic process, students can visualize the atomic process more clearly.
Visual

Peeking Inside the Human Body

Magnetic Resonance Imaging (MRI) is used by doctors to create more detailed images of the human body than are possible with X-rays.

Body tissues vary in their concentration of hydrogen atoms. Fat has a high concentration, as do tissues containing water, because of the hydrogen in H_2O. The concentration of hydrogen atoms in bone is very low. MRI reveals these differences in great detail, with fat and fluids (including blood) showing up as bright areas and bone as dark areas. MRI scans can even depict the brain. It produces images of such detail that they are used by researchers studying how the brain works, as well as by doctors investigating diseases.

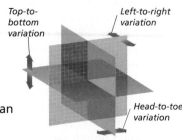

Top-to-bottom variation

Left-to-right variation

Head-to-toe variation

Creating an MRI image
The scanner uses three magnetic fields to read data up and down and along slices of the body. This produces an image that is viewed and interpreted by doctors and radiographers.

Head-to-toe field magnets

Top-to-bottom field magnets

Main magnet *This powerful magnet immerses the patient in a stable, intense magnetic field—the other three magnets create a variable field.*

Radio-frequency source

Motorized bed

Left-to-right field magnets

Inside the scanner
The varying magnetic fields can make images of "slices" through the body in different planes. The main magnet produces a magnetic field as much as 30,000 times stronger than that of Earth.

Each scan can take several minutes, so the patient must lie very still.

640 *Chapter 21*

How MRI works

MRI affects the nuclei of hydrogen atoms in the body. The nuclei are made to absorb and then re-emit energy by a combination of strong magnetic fields and radio wave pulses. The emitted signals are then used to map concentrations of hydrogen in the body.

1. Random axes
The spins of hydrogen nuclei point in random directions. Like tiny magnets, each nucleus has a north pole and a south pole.

Hydrogen nucleus | *Spin axis*

Spin axes line up.

2. Aligning axes
When the main MRI magnet is switched on, the magnetic field makes the spins of hydrogen nuclei mostly point in the same direction.

3. Wobbling axes
A pulse of radio waves from the MRI scanner knocks the hydrogen nuclei out of alignment.

Pulse of radio waves from scanner

Spin axes change direction.

Spin axes realign with magnetic field.

4. Realigning axes
When the pulse stops, hydrogen nuclei emit radio waves as they return to alignment with the main magnetic field. With the lesser magnets switched on as necessary to alter the magnetic field at a local level, these waves are picked up by the scanner, which builds up an image of different tissues.

Radio waves emitted by nuclei.

MRI spinal cord scan
The bright red patch here indicates a tumor on the dark green spinal cord. While bone tissue itself is not visible, the vertebrae can be seen because of the marrow they contain.

Spinal cord tumor highlighted by MRI

Going Further

- Items such as jewelry, watches, coins, keys, and credit cards must be removed before beginning an MRI. Research in the library or on the Internet why these items interfere with the procedure or pose a risk to the patient.

- Take a Discovery Channel Video Field Trip by watching "Magnetic Viewpoints."

DISCOVERY CHANNEL SCHOOL
Video Field Trip

Magnetism **641**

DISCOVERY CHANNEL SCHOOL
Video Field Trip

Magnetic Viewpoints

After students have viewed the Video Field Trip, ask them the following questions: **What is the purpose of magnetic resonance imaging (MRI)?** *(Student answers may include recording images of internal body organs, detecting tumors, and observing how the brain works.)* **How does MRI work?** *(The patient is bathed in a strong magnetic field that causes some nuclei in the body's atoms to line up like spinning tops. A radio pulse knocks the nuclei out of* alignment, and when the pulse stops the nuclei emit a signal as they line up again. A computer analyzes the signal to form an image.)* **What advantage does MRI have over X-rays in the detection of cancers?** *(It can detect some kinds of cancer earlier than X-rays can, and MRI is safer to use than X-rays.)* **Give an example of how MRI is used to study how the brain works.** *(Student answers may include that MRI images show the area of the brain that responds to a sensation such as pain in a particular part of the body. The images can be used to study medical disorders such as epilepsy and schizophrenia.)*

21.3 Electrical Energy Generation and Transmission

1 FOCUS

Objectives

21.3.1 Describe how electric current is generated by electromagnetic induction.

21.3.2 Compare AC and DC generators and **explain** how they work.

21.3.3 Analyze factors that determine the output voltage and current produced by a transformer.

21.3.4 Summarize how electrical energy is produced, transmitted, and converted for use in the home.

Standards: ICP.6.7, ICP.8.1, ICP.8.6, ICP.8.7

Reading Focus

Key Concepts
- How is voltage induced in a conductor?
- Name two types of generators.
- How can a transformer change voltage and current?
- What are some sources of electrical energy in the United States?

Vocabulary
- electromagnetic induction
- generator
- transformer
- turbine

Reading Strategy

Sequencing Copy the flowchart below. As you read, complete it to show how a step-up transformer works. Then make a similar flowchart for a step-down transformer.

Reading Focus

Build Vocabulary L2

Paraphrase Have students explain what the vocabulary terms mean by paraphrasing their definitions. Have them write a sentence in which the word is used, then have the word followed by the phrase *in other words*. This exercise allows students to be certain that they understand the meaning of a given term.

Reading Strategy L2

a. Produces changing magnetic field
b. Induces current in larger coil

2 INSTRUCT

Generating Electric Current

Build Science Skills L2

Classifying Have students recall the process of charge induction from Chapter 20. Ask, **How is electromagnetic induction similar to electric charge induction?** *(Both types of induction involve manipulating charges by using fields, either electric or magnetic, without any other contact with the charges.)* By grouping the processes of using fields to manipulate charges in conductors, the general idea of induction will become more concrete for students.
Verbal, Logical

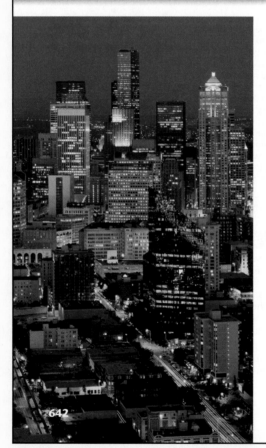

Think about how electrical energy affects a city. Traffic lights change colors to control the flow of cars. Flashing neon lights advertise businesses. Subways use electrical energy to move from place to place. People use electrical energy to warm their homes, cook their suppers, and wash their clothes. At night, lights shine from the windows of tall buildings as shown in Figure 12. Where does all the electrical energy come from?

Generating Electric Current

All of the electrical energy that moves subway trains, lights buildings, and powers factories comes from the two aspects of the electromagnetic force. You already know that an electric current produces a magnetic field. However, you may not know that a magnetic field can be used to produce an electric current. **Electromagnetic induction** is the process of generating a current by moving an electrical conductor relative to a magnetic field. Recall that electrical conductors are materials through which charge can easily flow.

Figure 12 Photographs of large cities, such as Seattle, Washington, are visible reminders of how much people rely on electrical energy.

 Section Resources

Print
- *Laboratory Manual,* Investigation 21A
- *Reading and Study Workbook With Math Support,* Section 21.3 and **Math Skill:** Calculating Voltage
- *Transparencies,* Section 21.3

Technology
- *Probeware Lab Manual,* Lab 9
- *Interactive Textbook,* Section 21.3
- *Presentation Pro CD-ROM,* Section 21.3
- *Go Online,* NSTA SciLinks, Transformers; PHSchool.com, Data sharing

The English scientist Michael Faraday (1791–1867) discovered electromagnetic induction in 1831, opening the way for many practical uses of electromagnetism. 🔵 **According to Faraday's law, a voltage is induced in a conductor by a changing magnetic field.** For example, changing the magnetic field through a coil of wire induces a voltage in the coil. But a current results only if the coil is part of a complete circuit.

You can see this process at work by placing a magnet inside a coil of wire attached to a galvanometer, as shown in Figure 13. If you hold the magnet still, the galvanometer will detect no current in the wire. However, if you quickly move the magnet out of the coil, the current flows briefly, and then immediately drops back to zero. Moving the magnet in and out of the coil causes an electric current first in one direction and then in the other. The same alternating current occurs if you move the coil and keep the magnet still. As long as the magnet and coil are moving relative to one another, the galvanometer will record a current.

Generators

Moving the magnet in the coil shown in Figure 13 produces only a small amount of electric current. Most of the electrical energy used in homes and businesses is produced at large power plants using generators. A **generator** is a device that converts mechanical energy into electrical energy by rotating a coil of wire in a magnetic field. Electric current is generated by the relative motion of a conducting coil in a magnetic field. 🔵 **The two types of generators are AC generators and DC generators.** Although both types have been used, most power plants today use AC generators.

AC Generators Figure 14 shows a simplified AC generator. An actual generator has many loops of wire. The generator produces alternating current, in which charges flow first in one direction and then in the other direction. As you can see, the generator looks very similar to the electric motor you previously studied. While a motor converts electrical energy into mechanical energy, a generator does the opposite.

A wire coil in the generator is attached to metal bands called slip rings. The slip rings are in contact with metal brushes that are in turn attached to a circuit. As the loop of wire is rotated, perhaps by someone turning it, the magnetic field induces a current in the wire. This current is in one direction, and then when the loop turns halfway around, the current reverses direction.

Movement of magnet

Coil

Galvanometer shows that the current is flowing.

Figure 13 According to Faraday's law, the moving magnetic field induces a current in the coil. *Predicting If you increase the number of turns in the coil, and move the magnet at the same speed, will the current increase or decrease?*

Figure 14 In a simple AC generator, an external force rotates the loop of wire in the magnetic field. This induces a current in the wire. *Forming Hypotheses Could you also induce a current if you rotated the magnets instead of the wire loop?*

Wire loop

Slip rings

Brushes

Direction in which the loop is turned

Magnetism **643**

Transformers

Integrate Social Studies

During the early 1880s, electric power in the United States was distributed as direct current. This system was successful at first because electric energy did not have to be transmitted very long distances. However, as demand and the distances between production and consumption increased, direct-current production could only succeed by transmitting electric energy with greater currents. At the same time, the Europeans were developing alternating-current systems for electric power. In 1885, George Westinghouse imported an AC generator and transformers, and installed an electric power system in Pittsburgh, Pennsylvania. Over the next seven years, alternating-current generation became more widespread, despite strong resistance from Thomas Edison and other supporters and producers of direct current.

Verbal

Address Misconceptions **L2**

Students may be confused in thinking that a transformer violates the principle of energy conservation. Explain to students that, for an ideal transformer, the amount of energy that goes into the transformer each second (the input power) is equal to the energy leaving the transformer each second (the output power). Remind students that electrical power equals voltage times current. Because a great deal of electrical energy is lost by heating, which is dependent upon the resistance of the conductor and current, less energy is lost when the voltage is high and the current is low. Thus, while transformers do not create electrical energy, they do help to reduce the loss of electrical energy.

Logical

Download a worksheet on transformers for students to complete, and find additional teacher support from NSTA SciLinks.

Figure 15 Small generators provide power in areas that are not served by power companies. These generators may also be used to provide electrical energy during a power outage.

For: Links on transformers
Visit: www.SciLinks.org
Web Code: ccn-2213

You can buy a small AC generator to power electrical devices during a power outage or to use in areas not served by a power company. Figure 15 shows an AC generator that can produce 3300 watts of power. This is enough for a household or small business to use. Power plants use AC generators that are huge compared to the generator shown here.

DC Generators A DC generator produces a direct current. Its design is very much like the design of an AC generator except that a commutator replaces the slip rings. As the loop rotates, an alternating current is induced in the wire. First, one side of the commutator contacts a brush. When the loop rotates, current is induced in the other direction, but now the other side of the commutator contacts that brush. For this reason, the current that leaves the generator flows in only one direction.

Reading Checkpoint *What kind of current does a DC generator produce?*

Transformers

The electrical energy produced by power plants is transmitted through power lines at very high voltages. These voltages are too high to be used safely in homes. The voltage must first be changed, or transformed. A **transformer** is a device that increases or decreases the voltage and current of two linked AC circuits. A series of transformers changes high-voltage current in power lines into 240-volt current that can be used safely in your home.

A transformer works only with alternating current because only alternating current induces a constantly changing magnetic field. ⊂⊃ **A transformer changes voltage and current by inducing a changing magnetic field in one coil. This changing field then induces an alternating current in a nearby coil with a different number of turns.**

Why Transformers Are Needed Early power plants used DC generators because the power plants were close to the customers. As the demand for electric power increased, power plants had to transmit power much farther. Remember that an electric charge moving through a wire heats the wire. Over long distances, the resistance of the wire causes large losses of power. Power losses can be reduced by using lower current transmitted at a higher voltage. However, voltage and current can be transformed only with alternating current.

Facts and Figures

Uniform Direct Current The direct current produced by a generator with a commutator moves in one direction, but it is not a steady current. As with AC, the induced current from the generator ranges from a maximum value to 0 amps, then increases to the maximum value again. To remedy this, many DC generators use several coils that are mounted on the rotating axle. The commutator consists of many segments, with each coil attached to two oppositely positioned segments. The coils rotate in the magnetic field, and at any given moment they are at different places in their rotation—one may be at a maximum output while another is at a minimum. The different amounts of current are combined and transferred to the output circuit. The coils are oriented in a uniform way to the magnets, so the total output current is nearly the same at all times. In this way, a nearly constant direct current is produced.

Changing Voltage and Current Figure 16 shows two types of transformers. Notice that each transformer has two sets of coils wrapped around a ring-shaped iron core. When there is an alternating current in the primary coil, the current creates a changing magnetic field in the iron core. Because the iron core is also inside the secondary coil, the changing field induces an alternating current in the secondary coil.

The number of turns in the primary and secondary coils determines the voltage and current. To calculate the voltage, divide the number of turns in the secondary coil by the number of turns in the primary coil. The result is the ratio of the output voltage to the input voltage.

Transformers are very efficient because very little energy is lost as heat. Assuming 100% efficiency, the power ($I \times V$) must be the same in the primary and secondary coils. Therefore, if voltage increases in the secondary coil, the current must decrease in the same ratio.

Types of Transformers A step-down transformer decreases voltage and increases current. Notice in Figure 16A that the primary coil has 400 turns, and the secondary coil has 100 turns. If the input voltage in the primary coil is 120 volts, then the output voltage is reduced to 30 volts.

A step-up transformer increases voltage and decreases current. In Figure 16B, the primary coil has 100 turns, and the secondary coil has 400 turns. If the input voltage is 20 volts, the output voltage is 80 volts.

Figure 16 Transformers, such as those at substations of power plants, change voltage. **A** A step-down transformer decreases voltage and increases current. **B** A step-up transformer increases voltage and decreases current.

A Step-down Transformer

Soft iron core — Low voltage

High voltage

400 turns

Secondary coil

100 turns

AC Source

Primary coil

B Step-up Transformer

Low voltage

High voltage

100 turns

Primary coil

400 turns

AC Source

Secondary coil

Magnetism **645**

Build Reading Literacy [L1]

Reciprocal Teaching Refer to page **628D** in this chapter, which provides the guidelines for reciprocal teaching.

To help students understand science concepts, have them apply the strategies of summarize, question, clarify, and predict as they read the section under the heading Transformers. For instance, before students begin to read, ask, **What do you think a transformer is used for?** *(Students may respond that transformers are used to transform, or change, electric current in some way.)* Have students read to verify their predictions. To help students determine what information is important and to check understanding, ask questions such as **Why must voltage from power lines be reduced before entering homes?** *(Voltage is stepped up at power plants so that electric current can be transmitted more efficiently over long distances. Overheating, and therefore loss of power, can be avoided by transmitting lower current at higher voltage. A step-down transformer reduces voltage and increases current to levels that can safely be used to operate appliances in a home.)* Clarify the meanings of unfamiliar words and concepts. Ask students to summarize what has been read. Encourage students to assume the role of leader in these discussions as they become familiar with the use of these strategies. **Verbal, Group**

Use Community Resources [L2]

Suggest that students learn more about different transformers by contacting the Public Information Office of the local electric utility. Have students find out where step-up and step-down transformers are used in your city, how many types of each kind are used, and the number of turns of wire used for the primary and secondary coils of each. Encourage them also to gather information on the efficiency of the transformers. Have them write a short report of their findings. **Intrapersonal, Portfolio**

Answer to . . .

Reading Checkpoint — *Direct current*

Electrical Energy for Your Home

Problem-Solving Activity

Transmitting Electricity to a New School [L2]

Defining the Problem As an engineer, I must first find out what voltage and current are needed for the school, and how this compares with the voltage and current generated at the power plant. If the power plant is very far away from the school, the voltage needs to be stepped up and down more than if the school is close.

Organizing Information Students can find out from the local electric company what the voltage use for schools is, and how far they are from substations. Transformer conversion factors must also be obtained.

Creating a Solution Once a nearby substation has been located and the distance to a power plant determined, connection of power lines can be planned. The voltage changes along the path should ensure that power can travel the necessary distances, and that the final voltage at the school is correct.

Presenting Your Plan Students' posters should include values for the different voltages along the transmission path, and should resemble Figure 18 in layout and content. The school should have some devices with input voltages of 120 V and some that operate at 220–240 V. The generated voltages will depend on how far the power is transmitted. Locally produced electricity may need to be stepped up or down only once, and then only by a factor of about 10. If the school is far from a substation, student designs may include a power substation specifically for the school's use.
Logical, Interpersonal

For Extra Help [L1]

Be sure that the need for transformers is clear to students. Emphasize that stepped-up voltages are necessary to reduce heat loss for long-distance transmissions. Encourage students to examine and understand Figure 18, as the information and presentation given there is similar to what they are to prepare.
Verbal, Visual

Problem-Solving Activity

Transmitting Electricity to a New School

You have been hired as an electrical engineer at your local power plant. Your first task is to plan how electrical energy can be transmitted from the power plant to a school that will soon be built. There are many things you need to investigate. What is the voltage generated at the power plant? How should it be stepped up for transmission? How can it be stepped down for use in the new school?

Defining the Problem Write a few sentences that describe your task and the steps you can take to complete it.

Organizing Information Research the steps that are taken to transmit electrical energy from the power plant to other schools in your area.

Creating a Solution Decide what steps you would take to transmit electrical energy to the new school.

Presenting Your Plan Create a poster showing how electrical energy can be transmitted to the new school. Include descriptions of the types of transformers you could use.

Figure 17 A turbine turns the magnet inside the coil of a generator. **Predicting** *What would happen if a turbine turned faster?*

Electrical Energy for Your Home

A single electric light uses relatively little electrical energy by itself. A massive amount of electrical energy, however, is needed for the lights and other electrical devices that are used by people in an entire city. Consumption on that scale requires equally huge production of electrical energy to meet the demand.

Most of the electrical energy generated in the United States is produced using coal as an energy source. Some other sources are water (hydroelectric), nuclear energy, wind, natural gas, and petroleum. Below each of the generators shown in Figure 17 is a large turbine, which can convert energy from one of these sources into electrical energy. A **turbine** is a device with fanlike blades that turn when pushed, for example, by water or steam. Burning fossil fuels or nuclear reactions can heat water to produce steam that spins a turbine. Water from a reservoir behind a dam can also turn a turbine. To produce electrical energy, the turbine may turn the coils of a generator or it may spin magnets around the coils of wire.

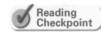 Reading Checkpoint *What can push the blades of a turbine?*

Facts and Figures

Appliance Power Usage Most appliances in the United States are designed to operate between 110 V and 120 V with an alternating-current frequency of 60 Hz. However, some larger appliances, such as electric ranges, clothes dryers, and air conditioners operate at 240 V. Special wiring is needed in the parts of a house where these appliances are used.

Many countries, particularly in Europe, have a household voltage between 220 V and 240 V with a frequency of 50 Hz. Appliances used in these countries are manufactured to operate at these higher voltages. International travelers often carry converters, devices that use a transformer to change voltage and current so that an appliance designed for one system can be used in another system.

Generating plant

240,000 V

11,000 V

High-voltage transmission lines

7200 V

Step-down transformer

Step-up transformer

Step-down transformer (substation)

220–240 V

Follow the steps shown in Figure 18 from the point where electrical energy is generated. The power plant on the left generates electrical energy that is stepped up to hundreds of thousands of volts. Transformers, which are shown in the middle of the diagram, make it possible to bring electrical energy efficiently from the power plant to users. After traveling along the high-voltage transmission lines, the voltage is stepped down at a substation, to a few thousand volts. The electrical energy is then distributed to neighborhoods. Just before the electrical energy reaches people's homes, the voltage is stepped down to between 220 and 240 volts. Heavy duty appliances, like an electric stove, use 240-volt circuits. Most other appliances in the home use 120 volts.

Figure 18 Voltage is increased for long-distance transmission, and then decreased near homes, schools, and businesses.
Interpreting Diagrams *How many step-down transformers are shown in the figure?*

Section 21.3 Assessment

Reviewing Concepts

1. ⬤ How is voltage induced in a conductor?
2. ⬤ Name two types of generators.
3. ⬤ How does a transformer work?
4. ⬤ Name six sources of electrical energy in the United States.

Critical Thinking

5. **Relating Cause and Effect** Explain how water can be used to create electrical energy.
6. **Applying Concepts** What is the connection between Faraday's law and the generation of electrical energy?
7. **Comparing and Contrasting** Describe how AC generators and DC generators are alike and how they are different.

8. **Drawing Conclusions** Why can't you use electrical energy directly from a high-voltage line?
9. **Calculating** An electronic device contains a transformer. Its primary coil has 200 turns, and its secondary coil has 20 turns. If the device is plugged into a 120-volt line, what is the output voltage of the device?

Writing in Science

Compare-Contrast Paragraph Write a paragraph comparing and contrasting what step-up and step-down transformers do. (*Hint:* Use the terms *voltage, primary coil, secondary coil, input,* and *output.*)

Magnetism **647**

Section 21.3 Assessment

1. Voltage is induced in a conductor by a changing magnetic field.
2. AC, which produces alternating current, and DC, which produces direct current
3. A transformer changes voltage and current by generating a changing magnetic field in one coil. This field then induces a current in a nearby coil with a different number of turns.
4. Coal, nuclear power, water (hydroelectric), wind, natural gas, and petroleum

5. Water can turn a turbine that turns the axle of a generator and produces electricity.
6. The relative motion of a magnet and a coil of wire will cause charges to flow in the wire, thus generating an electric current and electrical energy.
7. Both produce an electric current by the rotation of a wire coil in a magnetic field. In a DC generator, current flows in only one direction.
8. High voltages are dangerous. Household devices are designed to use much lower voltages.
9. 12 V

Investigating an Electric Generator

Objective

After completing this activity, students will be able to

• describe how an electric generator works.

Skill Focus Observing, Using Data Tables, Using Graphs

 Prep Time 20 minutes

Advance Prep Cut a 5-m length of wire for each lab group and strip 3 cm of the insulation from the ends of the wires. Provide cardboard tubes from empty paper towel rolls.

Class Time 45 minutes

Safety Students should wear safety goggles and lab aprons.

Teaching Tips

• You may need to show students how to use the multimeters if they have not used them earlier.

• In Step 12 and subsequent steps, make sure that students read the sign or direction of the current correctly; it will be the reverse of the direction observed in the previous steps. If the multimeter does not permit a reading of current flowing in either direction, it may be necessary to reverse the connections of the multimeter wires.

Expected Outcome The induced current is directly proportional to the number of turns. Reversing the poles of the magnet or the direction of the turns reverses the direction of the current.

Investigating an Electric Generator

All generators have two main parts—a magnet and a wire that is wrapped into a coil. The arrangement of these parts varies, depending on the size and power of the generator and whether it produces direct or alternating current. In this lab, you will determine how several variables affect the current produced by a simple generator.

Problem
How do the direction in which the magnet moves and the number and direction of the turns in the coil affect the current that a generator produces?

Materials
• cardboard tube
• 5-m length of insulated wire
• metric ruler
• multimeter
• bar magnet
• graph paper

 For the probeware version of this lab, see the Probeware Lab Manual, Lab 9.

Skills Observing, Using Graphs

Procedure

Part A: Changing the Number of Turns

1. On a separate sheet of paper, make a copy of the data table shown below.

Data Table			
Number of Turns	Direction of Turns	Pole Inserted	Current (mA)
10	Clockwise	North	
20	Clockwise	North	
30	Clockwise	North	
30	Clockwise	South	
30	Counterclockwise	North	

2. Slip the wire between your hand and the cardboard tube so that 15 cm of wire extends from the tube. Use your other hand to wrap the long end of the wire around the tube 10 times in a clockwise direction. Make sure all the turns are within 10 cm of the end of the tube. **CAUTION** *Be careful not to cut yourself on the sharp ends of the wire.*

3. Connect both ends of the wire to the multimeter. Set the multimeter to measure current.

4. Hold the bar magnet by its south pole. Observe the multimeter as you quickly insert the bar magnet into the open end of the cardboard tube that is wrapped with the wire coil. Repeat this step if necessary as you adjust the scale of the multimeter. Record the maximum current in your data table.

5. Disconnect the multimeter from the end of the wire that is farther from the turns.

6. **Predicting** Record your prediction of how increasing the number of turns in the coil will affect the current.

7. To test your prediction, wrap the wire around the end of the tube 10 more times in the same direction as you did previously—clockwise. You should now have a total of 20 turns. Reconnect the wire to the multimeter.

8. Repeat Step 4.

9. Again, disconnect the multimeter from the same end of the wire. Wrap the wire clockwise around the tube 10 more times for a total of 30 turns. Reconnect the wire to the multimeter.

10. Repeat Step 4 and then disconnect the multimeter from the same end of the wire.

Sample Data Table

Number of Turns	Direction of Turns	Pole Inserted	Current (mA)
10	Clockwise	North	0.4
20	Clockwise	North	1.0
30	Clockwise	North	2.5
30	Clockwise	South	−2.4
30	Counterclockwise	North	−2.4

Part B: Changing Other Properties of the Generator

11. **Predicting** Record your prediction of how reversing the direction of the magnet will affect the current.

12. To test your prediction, reconnect the wire to the multimeter exactly as you did before. Repeat Step 4, but this time, hold the magnet by its north pole.

13. **Predicting** Record your prediction of how reversing the direction of the turns in the coil will affect the current if you hold the magnet by its south pole.

14. To test your prediction, remove the wire from the tube. Now wrap 30 turns of wire in the opposite direction—counterclockwise.

15. Repeat Step 4, holding the magnet by its south pole.

16. Construct a graph using the data from the first three rows of your data table. Plot the number of turns on the horizontal axis and the current on the vertical axis.

Analyze and Conclude

1. **Inferring** What caused a current in the wire?

2. **Using Graphs** Based on your graph, what is the relationship between the number of turns and the amount of current?

3. **Analyzing Data** Explain the effect that reversing the direction of the magnet or the direction of the turns had on the direction of the current.

4. **Predicting** Explain whether a generator could be built with a stationary magnet and a coil that moved.

5. **Evaluating and Revising** Did your observations support your predictions? If not, evaluate any flaws in the reasoning you used to make the predictions.

For: Data sharing
Visit: PHSchool.com
Web Code: ccd-2210

Magnetism **649**

Probeware Lab Manual Versions of this lab for use with probeware available from Pasco, Texas Instruments, and Vernier are in the Probeware Lab Manual.

Analyze and Conclude

1. A current flowed in the wire because the moving magnetic field exerted a force on the electrons in the wire, causing them to move.

2. The graph indicates that the number of turns are in direct proportion to the amount of current.

3. Reversing the direction of the magnet or the turns reversed the direction of the force of the magnetic field on the electrons in the wire. This change in direction caused the charges to move in the opposite direction.

4. Yes, it is possible for such a generator to be built. It is only necessary that the magnetic field in the wire coils change. It does not matter which part moves to accomplish this task.

5. Correct predictions should state that an increase in the number of turns in the coil increases the strength of the current, and that reversing the direction of the turns or the magnet will reverse the direction of the current. Errors in reasoning may involve assuming that the direction of the coil or magnet motion does not affect current direction. If a current is too weak to observe, students may fail to realize that the speed of the magnet's motion may account for a weak induced current, and that increasing the number of turns may not provide the right results if the change in the magnetic field is not kept fairly constant throughout the experiment.
Logical

Go Further

Students should easily identify the wire coils and magnets in an actual generator. Generators and motors vary in the placement of the magnets, whether they are permanent or electromagnets, and whether the magnets or the coils rotate.
Logical, Group

Students should see that the current increases in proportion to the number of turns and that it reverses direction when the direction of the magnet or the turns are reversed, but their results will depend on their own data and the data on the site.

Study Tip

Occasionally, Study With a Friend
Tell students to occasionally work together by quizzing each other, comparing notes, and discussing discrepancies in each other's ideas about a subject. This process allows for each student to critically assess accumulated knowledge. Stress that the work should be shared equally between the two students.

Thinking Visually

a. A magnetic field
b. An electric current

21.1 Magnets and Magnetic Fields

Key Concepts
- Like magnetic poles repel one another, and opposite magnetic poles attract one another.
- A magnetic field, which is strongest near a magnet's poles, will either attract or repel another magnet that enters the field.
- When a material is magnetized, most of its magnetic domains are aligned.

Vocabulary
magnetic force, *p. 630*
magnetic pole, *p. 630*
magnetic field, *p. 631*
magnetosphere, *p. 632*
magnetic domain, *p. 632*
ferromagnetic material, *p. 632*

21.2 Electromagnetism

Key Concepts
- Moving electric charges create a magnetic field.
- Changing the current in an electromagnet controls the strength and direction of its magnetic field.
- Electromagnetic devices such as galvanometers, electric motors, and loudspeakers change electrical energy into mechanical energy.

Vocabulary
electromagnetic force, *p. 635*
solenoid, *p. 637*
electromagnet, *p. 637*
galvanometer, *p. 638*
electric motor, *p. 639*

21.3 Electrical Energy Generation and Transmission

Key Concepts
- According to Faraday's law, a voltage is induced in a conductor by a changing magnetic field.
- The two types of generators are AC generators and DC generators.
- A transformer changes voltage and current by inducing a changing magnetic field in one coil. This changing field then induces an alternating current in a nearby coil with a different number of turns.
- Most of the electrical energy generated in the United States is produced using coal as an energy source. Some other sources are water (hydroelectric), nuclear energy, wind, natural gas, and petroleum.

Vocabulary
electromagnetic induction, *p. 642*
generator, *p. 643*
transformer, *p. 644*
turbine, *p. 646*

Thinking Visually

Concept Map Copy the concept map below onto a sheet of paper. Use information from the chapter to complete the chart.

 ## Chapter Resources

Print
- ***Chapter and Unit Tests,*** Chapter 21 Test A and Test B
- ***Test Prep Resources,*** Chapter 21

Technology
- ***Computer Test Bank,*** Chapter Test 21
- ***Interactive Textbook,*** Chapter 21
- ***Go Online,*** PHSchool.com, Chapter 21

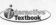
Reviewing Content

Choose the letter that best answers the question or completes the statement.

1. Where is the field of a magnet strongest?
   a. near the north pole
   b. near the south pole
   c. near both poles
   d. near the middle

2. If you cut a magnet in half, you have
   a. no magnets.
   b. two half magnets.
   c. one magnet.
   d. two magnets.

3. A magnet's field lines always start near the magnet's
   a. middle.   b. south pole.
   c. north pole.   d. side.

4. A ferromagnetic material is
   a. always a magnet.
   b. a magnet if its domains are aligned.
   c. a magnet if its domains are not aligned.
   d. never a magnet.

5. An iron bar is placed in a solenoid to
   a. decrease the voltage.
   b. increase the voltage.
   c. increase the magnetic field strength.
   d. decrease the magnetic field strength.

6. Which of these cannot increase the strength of an electromagnet?
   a. making the loops smaller in the coil
   b. placing an iron bar in the coil
   c. winding more loops in the coil
   d. increasing the current in the coil

7. An electric generator converts
   a. electrical energy into mechanical energy.
   b. power into energy.
   c. mechanical energy into electrical energy.
   d. energy into power.

8. What effect does a magnetic field have on a charge moving perpendicular to the field?
   a. It has no effect.
   b. It pulls the charge forward.
   c. It pushes the charge backward.
   d. It pushes the charge perpendicularly to the field and the charge's velocity.

9. A galvanometer is a device used to measure
   a. current.
   b. resistance.
   c. voltage.
   d. magnetic field strength.

10. A transformer increases or decreases
    a. energy.
    b. resistance.
    c. voltage.
    d. direct current.

Understanding Concepts

11. What part of an atom is responsible for producing magnetic fields?

12. Why is iron easy to magnetize when used in an electromagnet?

13. How are magnetic domains in nonmagnetized materials different from the magnetic domains in magnetized materials?

14. Explain how you can determine the direction of a magnetic field produced by a wire if you know the direction of current through the wire.

15. The figure below shows a current-carrying wire between the poles of two magnets. In which direction is charge deflected by the magnetic field?

Current direction

16. How can a change in the voltage of a transformer's primary coil create a change in the secondary coil's voltage, without the coils touching?

17. A transformer is connected to a 9-volt battery. A student tries to use this setup to double the voltage for an experiment. However, the output voltage is zero. Explain why.

Magnetism **651**

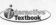 If your class subscribes to the Interactive Textbook, your students can go online to access an interactive version of the Student Edition and a self-test.

Reviewing Content

1. c   2. d   3. c
4. b   5. c   6. a
7. c   8. d   9. a
10. c

Understanding Concepts

11. Moving electrons
12. It is ferromagnetic and can be easily magnetized to become a temporary magnet.
13. The domains in a nonmagnetized material are not aligned. The domains in a magnetized material are aligned.
14. Point your thumb in the direction of the current. Your fingers curl in the direction of the magnetic field.
15. Down
16. The changing voltage in the primary coil creates a changing magnetic field. The secondary coil's voltage is induced by the changing magnetic field that passes through both coils.
17. Transformers only operate with alternating current. The battery provides direct current.

Homework Guide

Section	Questions
21.1	1–4, 11–13, 18, 28
21.2	5–6, 8–9, 14–15, 19–21
21.3	7, 10, 16–17, 22–27, 29–31

Critical Thinking

18. The magnetic domains of the iron nail will align under the influence of the magnet, and so will act temporarily as a magnet. The nail is thus attracted to the magnet. There is no such alignment of the atoms in the button into magnetic domains, and so there is no attraction.

19. The force an electric field exerts is in the direction of the electric field. The force exerted by a magnetic field is perpendicular to both the velocity and the direction of the magnetic field.

20. The left hand could be used for negative charge flow. By pointing the left thumb in the direction of electron flow, the curl of the fingers would indicate the direction of the magnetic field.

21. If you observe the beam traveling horizontally from your left to your right, the beam would be deflected toward you.

22. No. Transformers need a changing magnetic field. The magnetic field of a permanent magnet doesn't change easily.

Math Skills

23. Ratio of secondary turns to primary turns = ratio of output voltage to input voltage
60 turns/20 turns = 3
3 = output voltage/25 V
output voltage = 3 × 25 V = 75 V

24. Ratio of secondary turns to primary turns = ratio of output voltage to input voltage
60 turns/10 turns = 6
6 = output voltage/15 V
output voltage = 6 × 15 V = 90 V

25. Ratio of secondary turns to primary turns = ratio of output voltage to input voltage
50 turns/500 turns = 1/10
1/10 = output voltage/120 V
output voltage = 120 V/10 = 12 V

26. Ratio of secondary turns to primary turns = ratio of input current to output current
60 turns/12 turns = 5
5 = 5 A/output current
output current = 5 A/5 = 1 A

Critical Thinking

18. Inferring Using the concept of magnetic domains, explain why a magnet will attract an iron nail but not a plastic button.

19. Comparing and Contrasting How does the force that an electric field exerts on a moving charged particle differ from the force exerted by a magnetic field? Assume both fields point in the same direction.

20. Inferring You know that if you point the thumb of your right hand in the direction of the current, your fingers curve in the direction of the magnetic field. Could you use your left hand to demonstrate this rule correctly? Explain your answer. (*Hint:* See Figure 7 on page 636.)

21. Applying Concepts A beam of electrons travels from left to right between the poles of a horseshoe magnet. The north pole is on the top, and the south pole is on the bottom. In which direction will the beam be deflected when it passes through the poles of the magnet?

22. Predicting Would a permanent magnet be a good core for a transformer? Explain.

Math Skills

23. Calculating A transformer has 20 turns in its primary coil and 60 turns in its secondary coil. The input voltage for the transformer is 25 volts. What is the output voltage?

24. Calculating A transformer has an input voltage of 10 volts and an output voltage of 60 volts. If the input voltage is changed to 15 volts, what will the output voltage be?

25. Calculating A toy train uses a step-down transformer with 500 turns on its primary coil and 50 turns on its secondary coil. If it is connected to a 120-volt line, what voltage does the toy train use?

26. Calculating A transformer has 12 turns on its primary coil and 60 turns on its secondary coil. If the current in the primary coil is 5 amps, what is the current in the secondary coil?

Concepts in Action

27. Applying Concepts In a tape recorder, the tape is coated with iron oxide that has been magnetized in patterns corresponding to sounds. To play recorded sounds, the tape moves past a tiny coil of wire. Explain how this produces an electrical signal.

28. Problem Solving A child's toy has a magnet hidden inside. How can you determine where the north and south poles of the magnet are, without damaging the toy?

29. Applying Concepts A power plant generates electricity at 1200 volts. The electricity is transmitted at 180,000 volts and then reduced to 2400 volts at a substation. Finally, it is reduced to 120 volts for use in a home. For each transformer, describe the ratio of the number of turns in the primary and secondary coils.

30. Inferring Credit cards have a magnetic strip on them that contains information in a pattern. When a cashier runs the card through a card reader, the magnetic strip passes by a small wire coil. Why is motion necessary for the coil to read the card?

31. Writing in Science Write a paragraph explaining why alternating current is used for power generation and distribution instead of direct current.

Performance-Based Assessment

Creating an Educational Booklet Write a booklet for elementary students describing how electricity is brought from the power plant to their homes. Include simple illustrations and caution statements that young children can understand.

For: Self-grading assessment
Visit: PHschool.com
Web Code: cca-2210

Concepts in Action

27. As the tape moves past the coil, the changing magnetization produces a changing current in the coil, which produces an electrical signal.

28. Move a compass around the toy. The north pole of the compass needle will be attracted to the south pole of the toy's magnet.

29. (1) step-up, ratio 150:1; (2) step-down, ratio 1:75; (3) step-down, ratio 1:20

30. The magnetic field must change to induce a current. The magnetization on the moving card induces a variable current in the coil that corresponds to a pattern of information imprinted on the card.

31. Students' paragraphs should indicate that transformers require alternating current that can be stepped up for long-range transmission. At higher voltages, there is not as much heat loss because the current is low. To make the electrical energy safe to use, it must be stepped down, which again can only be done with transformers and alternating current.

Standardized Test Prep for Indiana

Standards Guide

Question	Standards
1	ICP.6.4
2	ICP.6.4

Test-Taking Tip

Forming Operational Definitions
Some test questions ask you to apply an operational definition. Start by using details in the question as clues to help you recall the definition. The question below describes current direction and asks for the magnetic field direction. Then write what you recall about the definition. How is current defined? *(flow of positive charge)* Which hand do you use? *(right hand)* What points in the direction of the current? *(thumb)* What determines the magnetic field direction? *(curl of fingers)* Lastly, rule out choices that must be wrong. Responses A and B cannot be correct because the magnetic field is at right angles to the current.

Suppose a vertical wire is pushed through a hole in a horizontal tabletop. Current in the wire is directed into the plane of the tabletop from above. What is the magnetic field direction caused by this current, as seen from above?

(A) into the plane of the tabletop
(B) out of the plane of the tabletop
(C) clockwise
(D) counter-clockwise
(E) left to right

(Answer: C)

---

1. Two solenoids are nested one inside the other. The inner solenoid is connected to a 12-V AC voltage source. The outer solenoid is part of a complete circuit. Will the setup function as a transformer?
   (A) No, there is no core.
   (B) No, there needs to be a ring.
   (C) No, both sides need a voltage source.
   (D) It is unclear, because current is not given.
   (E) Yes, AC induces a current in the outer coil.

2. What causes a ferromagnetic material to become magnetic?
   (A) unpaired electrons
   (B) paired electrons
   (C) unpaired protons
   (D) paired protons
   (E) none of the above

3. A transformer has 22 coils in its primary coil and 132 coils in its secondary coil. If the input voltage is 112 V, what is the secondary voltage?

   (A) 6.00 V   (B) 18.7 V
   (C) 222 V   (D) 266 V
   (E) 672 V

4. The figure below is a transformer used in lighting dimmer switches. It has one coil wrapped around an iron core. Three moveable taps (T$_1$, T$_2$, and T$_3$) are connected to the wire. When a tap is moved, the number of coils between that tap and the next tap changes. The coils between T$_1$ and T$_2$ form the primary coil. The coils between T$_2$ and T$_3$ form the secondary coil. To lower the output voltage for this transformer (to dim a light), how should one tap be moved?

   (A) Move T$_1$ closer to T$_2$.
   (B) Move T$_2$ closer to T$_3$.
   (C) Move T$_2$ farther from T$_3$.
   (D) Move T$_3$ farther from T$_2$.
   (E) Move T$_1$ closer to T$_3$.

5. Particle accelerators use electromagnets to change the direction in which charged particles travel. How does a charged particle move within a magnetic field?
   (A) It moves in the same direction as the magnetic field lines.
   (B) It moves in the direction opposite to the magnetic field lines.
   (C) It comes to a stop.
   (D) It moves in a direction perpendicular to the magnetic field lines.
   (E) none of the above

6. Is it possible for a magnetic field to slow down a charged particle moving through the field?
   (A) Yes, if the charge is moving perpendicular to the field at all times.
   (B) Yes, if the charge is moving in the direction of the magnetic field lines.
   (C) Yes, if the charge is moving in the direction opposite to the magnetic field lines.
   (D) Yes, if the charge is moving very slowly.
   (E) No, a magnetic field can only deflect a charged particle.

Magnetism **653**

Performance-Based Assessment

Students' booklets should begin with the process by which some form of energy (falling water, nuclear power, or burning coal, petroleum, or natural gas) is used to drive a turbine. Work used to generate electrical energy, the simple components of a generator, and the use of transformers to increase voltages (to increase transmission distance) and decrease voltages (to make electricity safer to use) must all be included. The text should be simple, with information provided visually through the illustrations.

Your students can independently test their knowledge of the chapter and print out their test results for your files.

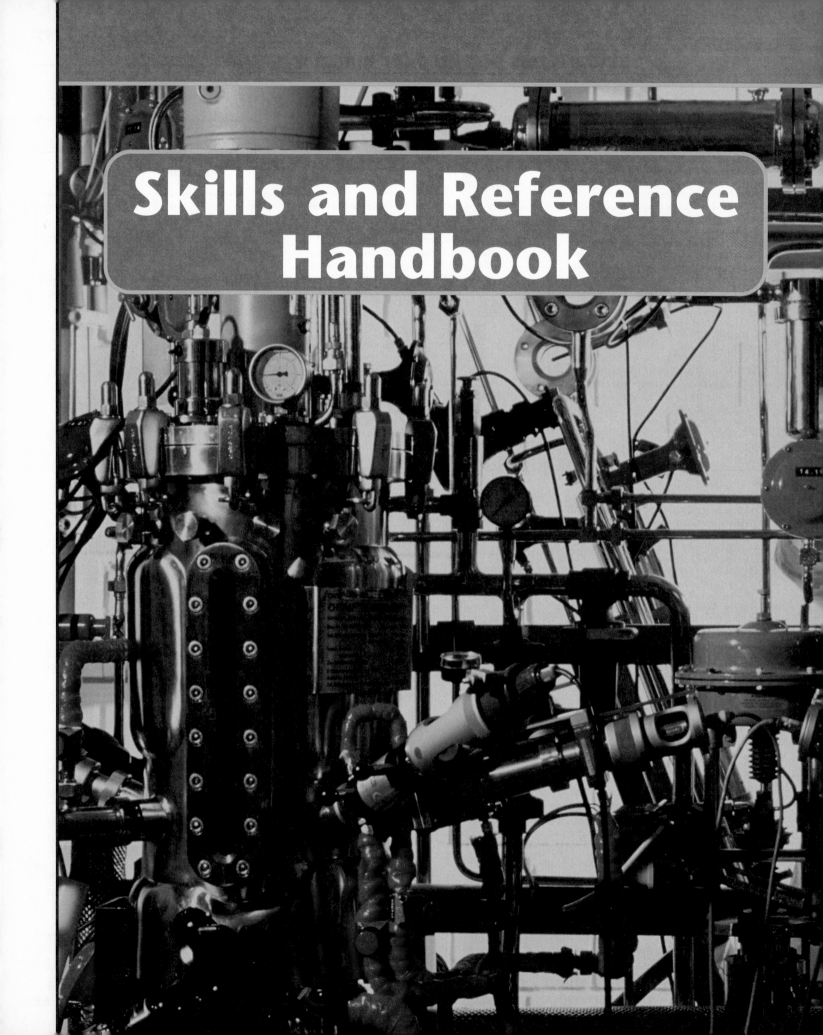

Skills and Reference Handbook

Basic Process Skills

During a physical science course, you often carry out some short lab activities as well as more detailed experiments. Here are some skills that you will use as you work.

Observing

In every science activity, you make a variety of observations. **Observing** is using one or more of the five senses to gather information. Many observations involve the senses of sight, hearing, touch, and smell.

Sometimes you will use tools that increase the power of your senses or make observations more precise. For example, hand lenses enable you to see things in greater detail. Tools may help you eliminate personal opinions or preferences.

In science it is customary to record your observations at the time they are made, usually by writing or drawing in a notebook. You may occasionally make records by using computers, cameras, videotapes, and other tools. As a rule, scientists keep complete accounts of their observations, often using tables to help organize their observations in a regular way.

Inferring

In science as in everyday life, observations are usually followed by inferences. **Inferring** is interpreting an observation or statement based on prior knowledge. For example, you can make several observations using the strobe photograph below. You can observe that the

ball is moving. Based on the motion of the ball, you might infer that the ball was thrown downward at an angle by an experimenter. In making that inference, you would use your knowledge about the motion of projectiles. Someone who knew more about projectile motion might infer that the ball loses energy with each bounce. That is why the height decreases with each bounce.

Notice that an inference is an act of reasoning, not a fact. That means an inference may be logical but not true. It is often necessary to gather further information before you can be confident that an inference is correct. For scientists, that information may come from further observations or from research into the work done by others.

Comparing Observations and Inferences	
Sample Observation	**Sample Inference**
The ball moves less and less vertical distance in the time between each flash of the strobe light.	Gravity is slowing down the ball's upward motion.
The ball moves the same distance to the right in the time between each flash of the strobe light.	Air resistance is so small that it does not slow down the ball's horizontal motion.

Predicting

People often make predictions, but their statements about the future could be either guesses or inferences. In science, a **prediction** is an inference about a future event based on evidence, experience, or knowledge. For example, you can say, *On the first day next month, it will be sunny all day.* If your statement is based on evidence of weather patterns in the area, then the prediction is scientific. If the statement was made without considering any evidence, it's just a guess.

Predictions play a major role in science because they offer scientists a way to test ideas. If scientists understand an event or the properties of a particular object, they should be able to make accurate predictions about that event or object. Some predictions can be tested simply by making observations. For others, carefully designed experiments are needed.

Measuring

Measurements are important in science because they provide specific information and help observers avoid bias. **Measuring** is comparing an object or process to a standard. Scientists use a common set of standards, called the International System of Units, abbreviated as SI (for its French name, *Système International d'Unités*).

What distance does the ball travel in each time interval in the strobe photograph? You can make measurements on the photograph to make more precise statements about the ball's motion.

Calculating

Once scientists have made measurements, calculations are a very important part of analyzing data. How fast is a ball moving? You could directly measure the speed of a ball using probeware such as a motion sensor. But you can also calculate the speed using distance and time measurements. **Calculating** is a process in which a person uses mathematical operations to manipulate numbers and symbols.

Classifying

Classifying is grouping items according to some organizing idea or system. Classifying occurs in every branch of science but it's especially important in chemistry because there are so many different ways that elements can combine to form compounds.

Sometimes you place objects into groups using an established system. Other times you create a system by observing a variety of objects and identifying their properties. For example, you could group household cleaners into those that are abrasive and those that are not. Or you could categorize cleaners as toxic or non-toxic. Ammonia is toxic, whereas vinegar is not.

Using Tables and Graphs

Scientists represent and organize data in tables and graphs as part of experiments and other activities. Organizing data in tables and graphs makes it easier to see patterns in data. Scientists analyze and interpret data tables and graphs to determine the relationship of one variable to another and to make predictions based on the data.

Space-filling model   Electron dot model

Using Models

Some cities refuse to approve new tall buildings if they would cast shadows on existing parks. As architects plan buildings in such locations, they use models to show where a proposed building's shadow will fall at any time of day at any season of the year. A **model** is a mental or physical representation of an object, process, or event. In science, models are usually made to help people understand natural objects and the processes that affect these objects.

Models can be varied. Mental models, such as mathematical equations, can represent some kinds of ideas or processes. For example, the equation for the surface area of a sphere can model the surface of Earth, enabling scientists to determine its size. Models can be two-dimensional (flat) or three-dimensional (having depth). In chemistry, for example, there are several ways to model the arrangement of atoms in a molecule. Two models for a water molecule are shown above. The electron dot model is two-dimensional. It has the advantage of clearly showing how electrons are shared among atoms in the molecule. The space-filling model cannot show the number of electrons inside the atoms or between atoms, but it does show the arrangement of atoms in space.

Experimental Methods

A science experiment is a procedure designed so that there is only one logical explanation for the results. Some types of experiments are fairly simple to design. Others may require ingenious problem solving.

Posing Questions

As a gardener harvested corn in her vegetable garden, she noticed that on one side of the garden the plants produced very few ears of corn. The gardener wondered, *Why didn't the plants on one side of the garden produce as much corn?*

An experiment may begin when someone like the gardener asks a specific question or wants to solve a particular problem. Sometimes the original question leads directly to an experiment, but often researchers need to restate the problem before they can design an appropriate experiment. The gardener's question about the corn, for example, is too broad to be tested by an experiment, since there are so many possible different answers. To narrow the topic, the gardener might think about several related questions: *Were the seeds the same on both sides of the garden? Was the sunlight the same? Is there something different about the soil?*

Formulating Hypotheses

In science, a question about an event is answered by developing a possible explanation called a **hypothesis**. The hypothesis may be developed after long thought and research or come to a scientist "in a flash." To be useful, a hypothesis must lead to predictions that can be tested.

In this case, the gardener decided to focus on the quality of the soil on each side of her garden. She did some tests and discovered that the soil had a lower pH on the side where the plants did not produce well. That led her to propose this hypothesis: *If the pH of the soil is too low, the plants will produce less corn.* The next step is to make a prediction based on the hypothesis, for example, *If the pH of the soil is increased using lime, the plants will yield more corn.* Notice that the prediction suggests the basic idea for an experiment.

Designing Experiments

A carefully designed experiment can test a prediction in a reliable way, ruling out other possible explanations. As scientists plan their experimental procedures, they pay particular attention to the variables that must be controlled and the procedures that must be defined.

The gardener decided to study three groups of plants:
Group 1—20 plants on the side of the garden with a low pH;
Group 2—20 plants on the side of the garden with a low pH, but with lime added; and
Group 3—20 plants on the side of the garden with a high pH.

Controlling Variables

As researchers design an experiment, they identify the **variables**, factors that can change. Some common variables include mass, volume, time, temperature, light, and the presence or absence of specific materials. An experiment involves three categories of variables. The factor that scientists purposely change is called the **manipulated variable**. The factor that may change because of the manipulated variable and that scientists want to observe is called the **responding variable**. And the factors that scientists purposely keep the same are called the **controlled variables**. Controlling variables helps make researchers confident that the observed changes in the responding variable are due to changes in the manipulated variable.

For the gardener, the manipulated variable is the pH of the soil. The responding variable is the number of ears of corn produced by the plants. Among the variables that must be controlled are the amount of sunlight received each day, the time of year when seeds are planted, and the amount of water the plants receive.

Forming Operational Definitions

In an experiment, it is often necessary to define one or more variables explicitly so that any researcher could measure or control the variable in exactly the same way. An **operational definition** describes how a particular variable is to be measured or how a term is to be defined. In this context, the term *operational* means "describing what to do."

The gardener, for example, has to decide exactly how much lime to add to the soil. Can lime be added after the seeds are planted or only before planting? At what pH should no more lime be added to the soil? In this case, the gardener decided to add lime only before planting, and to add enough lime to make the pH equal in Groups 2 and 3.

Analyzing Data

The observations and measurements that are made in an experiment are called **data**. Scientists customarily record data in an orderly way. When an experiment is done, the researcher analyzes the data for trends or patterns, often by doing calculations or making graphs, to determine whether the results support the hypothesis.

For example, the gardener regularly measured and recorded data such as the soil moisture, daily sunlight, and pH of the soil. She found that the soil pH in Groups 2 and 3 started the same, but after two months the soil pH for Group 3 was a little higher than the soil pH for Group 2.

After harvesting the corn, the gardener recorded the numbers of ears of corn produced by each plant. She totaled the number of ears for each group. Her results were the following.

Group 1: 67 ears of corn
Group 2: 102 ears of corn
Group 3: 126 ears of corn

The overall trend was clear: The gardener's prediction was correct.

Drawing Conclusions

Based on whether the results confirm or refute the hypothesis, researchers make a final statement that summarizes the experiment. That final statement is called the **conclusion**. For example, the gardener's conclusion was, *Adding lime to soil with a low pH will improve the production of corn plants.*

Communicating Results

When an experiment has been completed, one or more events may follow. Researchers may repeat the experiment to verify the results. They may publish the experiment so that others can evaluate and replicate their procedures. They may compare their conclusion with the discoveries made by other scientists. And they may raise new questions that lead to new experiments. For example, *Why does the pH level decrease over time when soil is treated with lime?*

Evaluating and Revising

Scientists must be flexible about the conclusions drawn from an experiment. Further research may help confirm the results of the experiment or make it necessary to revise the initial conclusions. For example, a new experiment may show that lime can be effective only when certain microbes are present in the soil. Scientists continuously evaluate and revise experiments based on the findings in new research.

Science Skills

Science Safety

Laboratory work can be exciting, but it can be danger-ous if you don't follow safety rules. Ask your teacher to explain any rules you don't understand. Always pay attention to safety symbols and **CAUTION** statements.

General Safety Rules and First Aid

1. Read all directions for an experiment several times. Follow the directions exactly as they are written. If you are in doubt, ask your teacher for assistance.
2. Never perform unauthorized or unsupervised labs, or handle equipment without specific permission.
3. When you design an experiment, do not start until your teacher has approved your plan.
4. If a lab includes physical activity, use caution to avoid injuring yourself or others. Tell your teacher if there is a reason that you should not participate.
5. Never eat, drink, or bring food into the laboratory.
6. Report all accidents to your teacher immediately.
7. Learn the correct ways to deal with a burn, a cut, and acid splashed in your eyes or on your skin.
8. Be aware of the location of the first-aid kit. Your teacher should administer any required first aid.
9. Report any fire to your teacher immediately. Find out the location of the fire extinguisher, the fire alarm, and the phone where emergency numbers are listed.

Dress Code

10. Always wear safety goggles to protect your eyes when working in the lab. Avoid wearing contact lenses. If you must wear contact lenses, ask your teacher what precautions you should take.
11. Wear a laboratory apron to protect your skin and clothing from harmful chemicals or hot materials.
12. Wear disposable plastic gloves to protect yourself from contact with chemicals that can be harmful. Keep your hands away from your face. Dispose of gloves according to your teacher's instructions.
13. Tie back long hair and loose clothing. Remove any jewelry that could contact chemicals or flames.

Heating and Fire Safety

14. Hot plates, hot water, and hot glassware can cause burns. Never touch hot objects with your bare hands. Use an oven mitt or other hand protection.

15. Use a clamp or tongs to hold hot objects. Test an object by first holding the back of your hand near it. If you feel heat on the back of your hand, the object may be too hot to handle.
16. Tie back long hair and loose clothing, and put on safety goggles before using a burner. Follow instruc-tions from your teacher for lighting and extinguish-ing burners. If the flame leaps out of a burner as you are lighting it, turn the gas off. Never leave a flame unattended or reach across a flame. Make sure your work area is not cluttered with materials.
17. If flammable materials are present, make sure there are no flames, sparks, or exposed sources of heat.
18. Never heat a chemical without your teacher's per-mission. Chemicals that are harmless when cool can be dangerous when heated. When heating a test tube, point the opening away from you and others in case the contents splash or boil out of the test tube.
19. Never heat a closed container. Expanding hot gases may cause the container to explode.

Using Electricity Safely

20. To avoid an electric shock, never use electrical equip-ment near water, or when the equipment or your hands are wet. Use ground fault circuit interrupter (GFCI) outlets if you or your equipment may come into contact with moisture.
21. Use only sockets that accept a three-prong plug. Never use two-prong extension cords or adapters. When removing an electrical plug from a socket or extension cord, grasp the plug, not the cord.
22. Disconnect equipment that is not in use. Be sure cords are untangled and cannot trip anyone.
23. Do not use damaged electrical equipment. Look for dangerous conditions such as bare wires or frayed cords. Report damaged equipment immediately.

Using Glassware Safely

24. Handle fragile glassware, such as thermometers, test tubes, and beakers, with care. Do not touch broken glass. Notify your teacher if glassware breaks. Never use chipped or cracked glassware.
25. Never force glass tubing into a stopper. Your teacher will demonstrate the proper methods.
26. Never heat glassware that is not thoroughly dry. Use a wire screen to protect glassware from flames.
27. Hot glassware may not appear hot. Never pick up glassware without first checking to see if it is hot.
28. Never eat or drink from laboratory glassware.

Using Chemicals Safely

29. Do not let any corrosive or poisonous chemicals get on your skin or clothing, or in your eyes. When working with poisonous or irritating vapors, work in a well-ventilated area and wash your hands thoroughly after completing the activity.
30. Never test for an odor unless instructed by your teacher. Avoid inhaling a vapor directly. Use a wafting motion to direct vapor toward your nose.
31. Never mix chemicals "for the fun of it." You might produce a dangerous, possibly explosive substance.
32. Never touch, taste, or smell a chemical that you do not know for certain to be harmless.
33. Use only those chemicals listed in an investigation. Keep the lids on the containers when chemicals are not being used. To avoid contamination, never return chemicals to their original containers.
34. Take extreme care not to spill any chemicals. If a spill occurs, immediately ask your teacher about the proper cleanup procedure. Dispose of all chemicals as instructed by your teacher.
35. Be careful when working with acids or bases. Pour these chemicals over the sink, not over your workbench. If an acid or base gets on your skin or clothing, rinse it off with plenty of cold water. Immediately notify your teacher about an acid or base spill.
36. When diluting an acid, pour the acid into water. Never pour water into the acid.

Using Sharp Instruments

37. Use sharp instruments only as directed. Scissors, scalpels, pins, and knives are sharp and can cut or puncture your skin. Always direct sharp edges and points away from yourself and others.
38. Notify your teacher immediately if you cut yourself when in the laboratory.

End-of-Experiment Rules

39. All chemicals and any other materials used in the laboratory must be disposed of safely. Follow your teacher's instructions.
40. Clean up your work area and return all equipment to its proper place. Thoroughly clean glassware before putting it away.
41. Wash your hands thoroughly with soap, or detergent, and warm water. Lather both sides of your hands and between your fingers. Rinse well.
42. Check that all burners are off and the gas supply for the burners is turned off.

Safety Symbols

 General Safety Awareness
Follow all safety instructions.

 Physical Safety
Use caution in physical activities.

 Safety Goggles
Always wear goggles in the laboratory.

 Lab Apron
Always wear a lab apron in the laboratory.

 Plastic Gloves
Protect your hands from unsafe chemicals.

 Heating
Be careful using sources of heat.

 Heat-Resistant Gloves
Do not touch hot objects with bare hands.

 Flames
Work carefully around open flames.

 No Flames
Flammable materials may be present.

 Electric Shock
Take precautions to avoid electric shock.

 Fragile Glassware
Handle glassware carefully.

 Corrosive Chemical
Work carefully with corrosive chemicals.

 Poison
Avoid contact with poisonous chemicals.

 Fumes
Avoid inhaling dangerous vapors.

 Sharp Object
Use caution with sharp or pointed tools.

 Disposal
Follow instructions for disposal.

 Hand Washing
Wash your hands before leaving the lab.

Reading and Study Skills

At the beginning of each section, you will find a reading strategy to help you study. Each strategy uses a graphic organizer to help you stay organized. The following strategies and graphic organizers are used throughout the text.

Reading Strategies

Using Prior Knowledge
This strategy helps you think about your own experience before you read a section. Research has shown that you learn new material better if you can relate it to something you already know.

Previewing
Previewing a lesson can give you a sense of how the textbook is organized and what lies ahead. One technique is to look at the section topics (in green and blue type). You also can preview by reading captions. Sometimes previewing helps you simply because you find out a topic isn't as hard as you thought it might be.

Predicting
You can preview a section and then make a prediction. For example, you might predict the meaning of an important concept. Then, as you read, check to see if your prediction was correct. Often you find out that you knew more about a topic than you realized.

Building Vocabulary
Start building new vocabulary by previewing a section and listing boldface terms you don't recognize. Then look for each term as you read. Writing a sentence with a term, and defining a term in your own words are two techniques that will help you remember definitions.

Identifying the Main Idea
The key symbols next to boldface sentences identify the main ideas in a section. You can use topic sentences to find the main idea in a paragraph. Often, a topic sentence is the first or second sentence in a paragraph.

Identifying Cause and Effect
Cause-and-effect relationships are very important in science. A flowchart will help you identify cause-and-effect relationships as you read about a process.

Comparing and Contrasting
Comparing and contrasting can help you understand how concepts are related. Comparing is identifying both similarities and differences, while contrasting focuses on the differences. Compare-and-contrast tables and Venn diagrams work best with this strategy.

Sequencing
When you sequence events, it helps you to visualize the steps in a process and to remember the order in which they occur. Sequences often involve cause-and-effect relationships. Use flowcharts for linear sequences and cycle diagrams for repeating sequences.

Relating Text and Figures
You can use diagrams and photographs to focus on the essential concepts in a section. Then find text that extends the information in the figures. You can also reinforce concepts by comparing different figures.

Summarizing
Summarizing requires you to identify key ideas and state them briefly in your own words. You will remember the content of an entire section better even if you summarize only a portion of the section.

Outlining
You can quickly organize an outline by writing down the green and blue headings in a section. Then add phrases or sentences from the boldface sentences to expand the outline with the most important concepts.

Monitoring Your Understanding
You can evaluate your progress with graphic organizers such as a Know-Write-Learn (KWL) table. To make a KWL table, construct a table with three columns, labeled K, W, and L. Before you read, write what you already know in the first column (K). In the middle column, write what you want to learn (W). After you read, write what you learned (L).

Graphic Organizers

Concept Maps and Web Diagrams

A **concept map** is a diagram that contains concept words in ovals and connects the ovals with linking words. Often the most general concept is placed at the top of the map. The content of the other ovals becomes more specific as you move away from the main concept. Linking words are written on a line between two ovals.

A **web diagram** is a type of concept map that shows how several ideas relate to one central idea. Each subtopic may also link to subtopics, creating the visual effect of a spider web. Linking words are usually not included.

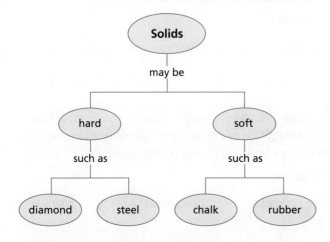

Compare-and-Contrast Tables

A **compare-and-contrast table** is a way of showing the similarities and differences between two or more objects or processes. The table provides an organized framework for making comparisons based on specific characteristics.

The items to be compared are usually column headings across the top of the table. Characteristics for comparison are listed in the first column. You complete the table by filling in information for each item.

Compare-and-Contrast Table		
Contents	Book	CD-ROM
Paper pages	Yes	No
Photographs	Yes	Yes
Videos	No	Yes

Venn Diagrams

A **Venn diagram** consists of two or more ovals that overlap. Each oval represents a particular object or idea. Unique characteristics are shown in the part of each oval that does not overlap. Shared characteristics are shown in the area of overlap.

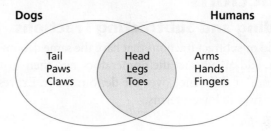

Flowcharts

A **flowchart** is used to represent the order in which a set of events occurs. Each step in the sequence is described in a box. Each box is linked to the next box with an arrow. The flowchart shows a sequence from beginning to end.

Cycle Diagrams

A **cycle diagram** shows boxes representing a cyclical sequence of events. As in a flowchart, boxes are linked with arrows, but the sequence does not have a beginning or end. The boxes are usually arranged in a clockwise circle.

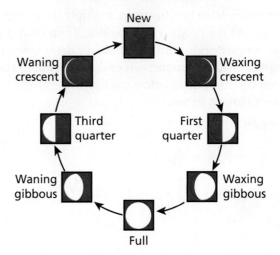

Math Skills

Throughout your study of physical science, you will often need to solve math problems. This appendix is designed to help you quickly review the basic math skills you will use most often.

Fractions

Adding and Subtracting Fractions

To add or subtract fractions that have the same denominator, add or subtract the numerators, and then write the sum or difference over the denominator. Express the answer in lowest terms.

Examples

$$\frac{3}{10} + \frac{1}{10} = \frac{3+1}{10} = \frac{4}{10} = \frac{2}{5}$$

$$\frac{5}{7} - \frac{2}{7} = \frac{5-2}{7} = \frac{3}{7}$$

To add or subtract fractions with different denominators, find the least common denominator. Write an equivalent fraction for each fraction using the least common denominator. Then add or subtract the numerators. Write the sum or difference over the least common denominator and express the answer in lowest terms.

Examples

$$\frac{1}{3} + \frac{3}{5} = \frac{5}{15} + \frac{9}{15} = \frac{5+9}{15} = \frac{14}{15}$$

$$\frac{7}{8} - \frac{1}{4} = \frac{7}{8} - \frac{2}{8} = \frac{7-2}{8} = \frac{5}{8}$$

Multiplying Fractions

When multiplying two fractions, multiply the numerators to find the product's numerator. Then multiply the denominators to find the product's denominator. It helps to divide any numerator or denominator by the greatest common factor before multiplying. Express the answer in lowest terms.

Examples

$$\frac{3}{5} \times \frac{2}{7} = \frac{3 \times 2}{5 \times 7} = \frac{6}{35}$$

$$\frac{4}{14} \times \frac{6}{9} = \frac{2 \times 2}{7 \times 2} \times \frac{2 \times 3}{3 \times 3} = \frac{2 \times 2}{7 \times 3} = \frac{4}{21}$$

Dividing Fractions

To divide one fraction by another, invert and multiply. Express the answer in lowest terms.

Examples

$$\frac{2}{5} \div \frac{3}{4} = \frac{2}{5} \times \frac{4}{3} = \frac{2 \times 4}{5 \times 3} = \frac{8}{15}$$

$$\frac{9}{16} \div \frac{5}{8} = \frac{9}{16} \times \frac{8}{5} = \frac{9 \times 1}{2 \times 5} = \frac{9}{10}$$

Ratios and Proportions

A ratio compares two numbers or quantities. A ratio is often written as a fraction expressed in lowest terms. A ratio also may be written with a colon.

Examples

The ratio of 3 to 4 is written as 3 to 4, $\frac{3}{4}$, or 3 : 4.

The ratio of 10 to 5 is written as $\frac{10}{5} = \frac{2}{1}$, or 2 : 1.

A proportion is a mathematical sentence that states that two ratios are equivalent. To write a proportion, place an equal sign between the two equivalent ratios.

Examples

The ratio of 6 to 9 is the same as the ratio of 8 to 12.

$$\frac{6}{9} = \frac{8}{12}$$

The ratio of 2 to 4 is the same as the ratio of 7 to 14.

$$\frac{2}{4} = \frac{7}{14}$$

You can set up a proportion to determine an unknown quantity. Use x to represent the unknown. To find the value of x, cross multiply and then divide both sides of the equation by the number that comes before x.

Example

Two out of five students have blue notebooks. If this same ratio exists in a class of twenty students, how many students in the class have blue notebooks?

$$\frac{2}{5} = \frac{x}{20} \quad \leftarrow \textbf{Cross multiply.}$$
$$2 \times 20 = 5x \quad \leftarrow \textbf{Divide.}$$
$$8 = x$$

Percents and Decimals

Calculating Percents

A percent is a ratio that compares a number to 100. The word *percent* (%) means "parts of 100" or "per 100 parts." Another way to think of a percent is as a part of a whole expressed in hundredths. Thus, the number 0.41 ("41 hundredths") can also be expressed as 41%, or "41 per 100 parts."

$$0.41 = \frac{41}{100} = 41\%$$

You can calculate a percent by multiplying the ratio of the part to the whole by 100%.

$$\text{Percent} = \frac{\text{Part}}{\text{Whole}} \times 100\%$$

Examples

The fraction $\frac{7}{10}$ is equivalent to 70%.

The fraction $\frac{5}{8}$ is equivalent to 62.5%.

The fraction $\frac{15}{200}$ is equivalent to 7.5%.

You have probably seen data expressed in the form of a percent. For instance, nutrition labels on packaged foods include a column titled "% Daily Value." In this column, the nutrients (such as fat, cholesterol, and fiber) contained in a single serving are compared to the recommended daily intake. You also encounter percents when you go shopping (items on sale might be labeled "20% off") or when you receive test scores.

Example

A student answers 34 questions correctly on a 40-question exam. What is the student's score expressed as a percent?

$$\text{Percent} = \frac{\text{Part}}{\text{Whole}} \times 100\%$$

$$= \frac{\text{Number of correct answers}}{\text{Number of questions asked}} \times 100\%$$

$$= \frac{34}{40} \times 100\%$$

$$= 85\%$$

Converting Between Percents and Decimals

To convert a percent to a decimal value, write the number without the percent sign and move the decimal point two places to the left. Add a zero before the decimal point.

Examples

$$38\% = 0.38$$
$$13.92\% = 0.1392$$

You can convert a decimal value to a percent value by moving the decimal point two places to the right and adding the percent sign.

Examples

$$0.46 = 46\%$$
$$0.8215 = 82.15\%$$

Converting between percents and decimals is often necessary when solving word problems involving composition or concentration.

Example

A nighttime cold medicine is 22% alcohol by volume. How many milliliters of alcohol are in a 250-mL bottle of this medicine?

$22\% = 0.22 \leftarrow$ **Convert percent to a decimal.**

$$\frac{\text{Part}}{\text{Whole}} = \frac{\text{Part}}{250 \text{ mL}} = 0.22$$

$$\text{Part} = 250 \text{ mL} \times 0.22$$

$$\text{Part} = 55 \text{ mL}$$

Example

During a flu epidemic, 28% of the students at a school were absent. If 238 students were absent, what was the school's enrollment?

$28\% = 0.28 \leftarrow$ **Convert percent to a decimal.**

$$\frac{\text{Part}}{\text{Whole}} = \frac{238 \text{ students}}{\text{Whole}} = 0.28$$

$$\text{Whole} = \frac{238 \text{ students}}{0.28}$$

$$\text{Whole} = 850 \text{ students}$$

Math Skills

Exponents

A base is a number that is used as a factor. An exponent is a number that tells how many times the base is to be used as a factor.

Example

$2^5 = 2 \times 2 \times 2 \times 2 \times 2 = 32$

A power is any number that can be expressed as a product in which all of the factors are the same. Any number raised to the zero power is 1. Any number raised to the first power is that number. The only exception is the number 0, which is zero regardless of the power it is raised to.

Exponents	
Powers of 2	**Powers of 10**
$2^4 = 16$	$10^4 = 10{,}000$
$2^3 = 8$	$10^3 = 1000$
$2^2 = 4$	$10^2 = 100$
$2^1 = 2$	$10^1 = 10$
$2^0 = 1$	$10^0 = 1$
$2^{-1} = \frac{1}{2}$	$10^{-1} = \frac{1}{10}$
$2^{-2} = \frac{1}{4}$	$10^{-2} = \frac{1}{100}$
$2^{-3} = \frac{1}{8}$	$10^{-3} = \frac{1}{1000}$
$2^{-4} = \frac{1}{16}$	$10^{-4} = \frac{1}{10{,}000}$

Multiplying With Exponents

To multiply exponential expressions with the same base, add the exponents. The general expression for exponents with the same base is $x^a \times x^b = x^{a+b}$.

Example

$3^2 \times 3^4 = (3 \times 3) \times (3 \times 3 \times 3 \times 3) = 3^6 = 729$

To raise a power to a power, keep the base and multiply the exponents. The general expression is $(x^a)^b = x^{ab}$.

Example

$(3^2)^3 = (3^2) \times (3^2) \times (3^2) = 3^6 = 729$

To raise a product to a power, raise each factor to the power. The general expression is $(xy)^n = x^n y^n$.

Example

$(3 \times 9)^2 = 3^2 \times 9^2 = 9 \times 81 = 729$

Dividing With Exponents

To divide exponential expressions with the same base, keep the base and subtract the exponents. The general expression is

$\frac{x^a}{x^b} = x^{a-b}$

Example

$\frac{5^6}{5^4} = 5^{6-4} = 5^2 = 25$

When the exponent of the denominator is greater than the exponent of the numerator, the exponent of the result is negative. A negative exponent follows the general expression

$x^{-n} = \frac{1}{x^n}$

Example

$2^3 \div 2^5 = 2^{3-5} = 2^{-2} = \frac{1}{2^2} = \frac{1}{4}$

Metric conversions often involve multiplication or division of exponential expressions. Make sure to keep track of the sign of the exponent when performing operations with exponential expressions.

Example

Convert $3.49 \times 10^2 \ \mu m$ to meters. ($1 \ \mu m = 10^{-6} \ m$)

Based on the equivalence $1 \ \mu m = 10^{-6} \ m$, you can write the ratio $1 \ \mu m/10^{-6} \ m$, which equals one.

$3.49 \times 10^2 \ \mu m \times \frac{10^{-6} \ m}{1 \ \mu m} = 3.49 \times 10^2 \times 10^{-6} \ m$

$= 3.49 \times 10^{2-6} \ m$

$= 3.49 \times 10^{-4} \ m$

Scientific Notation

Very large and very small numbers are often expressed in scientific notation. In scientific notation, a number is written as the product of two numbers: a coefficient that is greater than or equal to one and less than ten, and 10 raised to a power. For example, the number 710,000 written in scientific notation is 7.1×10^5. The coefficient in this number is 7.1. The power of ten, or the exponent, is 5. The exponent indicates how many times the coefficient must be multiplied by 10 to equal the number 710,000.

To convert a large number to scientific notation, move the decimal point to the left until it is located just to the right of the first nonzero number. The number of places that you move the decimal point becomes the positive exponent of 10.

Example

$18,930,000 = 1.893 \times 10^7$

To write a number less than 1 in scientific notation, move the decimal point just to the right of the first nonzero number. Use the number of places you moved the decimal point as the negative exponent of 10.

Example

$0.0027 = \dfrac{2.7}{10 \times 10 \times 10} = 2.7 \times 10^{-3}$

When you convert a number to scientific notation, remember that you are not changing the value of the number. You are only changing the way that it is written.

Examples

$500,000 = 5 \times 10^5$

$0.000\ 000\ 042 = 4.2 \times 10^{-8}$

$0.030\ 06 = 3.006 \times 10^{-2}$

$285.2 = 2.852 \times 10^2$

$0.0002 = 2 \times 10^{-4}$

$83,700,000 = 8.37 \times 10^7$

Adding and Subtracting

To add or subtract numbers in scientific notation, the exponents must be the same. If they are different, rewrite one of the numbers to make the exponents the same. Then write the answer so that only one number is to the left of the decimal point.

Examples

$$(3.20 \times 10^3) + (5.1 \times 10^2) = (32.0 \times 10^2) + (5.1 \times 10^2)$$
$$= 37.1 \times 10^2$$
$$= 3.71 \times 10^3$$

$$(3.42 \times 10^{-5}) - (2.5 \times 10^{-6})$$
$$= (34.2 \times 10^{-6}) - (2.5 \times 10^{-6})$$
$$= 31.7 \times 10^{-6}$$
$$= 3.17 \times 10^{-5}$$

Multiplying and Dividing

To multiply or divide numbers in scientific notation, the exponents are added or subtracted.

Examples

$$(1.2 \times 10^3) \times (3.4 \times 10^4) = (4.1 \times 10^{3+4})$$
$$= 4.1 \times 10^7$$

$$(5.0 \times 10^9) \div (2.5 \times 10^6) = (2.0 \times 10^{9-6})$$
$$= 2.0 \times 10^3$$

$$\frac{(1.2 \times 10^{-3})^2}{(10^{-2})^3 \times (2.0 \times 10^{-3})} = \frac{1.2^2 \times (10^{-3})^2}{(10^{-6}) \times (2.0 \times 10^{-3})}$$

$$= \frac{1.44 \times 10^{-6}}{2.0 \times 10^{-6 + 3(-3)}}$$

$$= \frac{1.44 \times 10^{-6}}{2.0 \times 10^{-9}}$$

$$= 0.72 \times 10^{-6 - (-9)}$$

$$= 0.72 \times 10^3$$

$$= 7.2 \times 10^2$$

Math Skills

Significant Figures

When measurements are combined in calculations, the uncertainty of each measurement must be correctly reflected in the final result. The digits that are accurate in the answer are called significant figures. When the result of a calculation has more significant figures than needed, the result must be rounded off. If the first digit after the last significant digit is less than 5, round down. If the first digit after the last significant digit is 5 or more, round up.

Examples

1577 rounded to three significant figures is 1580.
1574 rounded to three significant figures is 1570.
2.458462 rounded to three significant figures is 2.46.
2.458462 rounded to four significant figures is 2.458.

Examples

Each of the measurements listed below has three significant figures. The significant figures are underlined.

<u>456</u> mL
0.<u>305</u> g
<u>70.4</u> mg
0.000<u>457</u> g
<u>5.64</u> × 10³ km
<u>444</u>,000 ng
<u>1.30</u> × 10⁻² m
0.004 <u>06</u> dm

Adding and Subtracting

In addition and subtraction, the number of significant figures in the answer depends on the number with the largest uncertainty.

Example

$$
\begin{array}{r}
25.34 \text{ g} \\
152 \text{ g} \\
+ \quad 4.009 \text{ g} \\
\hline
181 \text{ g}
\end{array}
$$

The measurement with the largest uncertainty is 152 g, and it is measured to the nearest gram. Therefore, the answer is given to the nearest gram.

Example

$189.427 \text{ g} - 19.00 \text{ g} = 170.427 \text{ g} \approx 170.43 \text{ g}$

The measurement with the larger uncertainty is 19.00 g, which is measured to the nearest hundredth of a gram. Therefore, the answer is given to the nearest hundredth of a gram.

Multiplying and Dividing

In multiplication and division, the measurement with the smallest number of significant figures determines the number of significant figures in the answer.

Example

$(5.3 \text{ m}) \times (1.54 \text{ m}) = 8.162 \text{ m}^2 \approx 8.2 \text{ m}^2$

Because 5.3 m has only two significant figures, the answer must be rounded to two significant figures.

Example

$$
\begin{aligned}
\text{Density} &= \frac{\text{Mass}}{\text{Volume}} \\
&= \frac{20.79 \text{ g}}{5.5 \text{ mL}} \\
&= 3.78 \text{ g/mL} \\
&\approx 3.8 \text{ g/mL}
\end{aligned}
$$

Because 5.5 mL has only two significant figures, the answer must be rounded to two significant figures.

Example

Calculate the perimeter [(2 × length) + (2 × width)] and the area (length × width) of a rectangular garden plot that measures 32.8 m by 16 m. Round each answer to the correct number of significant figures.

$$
\begin{aligned}
\text{Perimeter} &= (2 \times 32.8 \text{ m}) + (2 \times 16 \text{ m}) \\
&= 65.6 \text{ m} + 32 \text{ m} \\
&= 97.6 \text{ m} \\
&\approx 98 \text{ m}
\end{aligned}
$$

$\text{Area} = 32.8 \text{ m} \times 16 \text{ m} = 524.8 \text{ m}^2 \approx 5.2 \times 10^2 \text{ m}^2$

Formulas and Equations

An equation is a mathematical sentence that contains one or more variables and one or more mathematical operators (such as $+$, $-$, $\div$, $\times$, and $=$). An equation expresses a relationship between two or more quantities.

A formula is a special kind of equation. A formula such as $V = l \times w \times h$ states the relationship between unknown quantities represented by the variables V, l, w, and h. The formula means that volume (of a rectangular solid) equals length times width times height. Some formulas have numbers that do not vary, such as the formula for the perimeter of a square: $P = 4s$. In this formula, the number 4 is a constant.

To solve an equation or formula for an unknown quantity, first rearrange the equation so that the unknown is on one side of the equation, and all the known quantities are on the other side. Then substitute known values for the variables. Be sure to include units.

Example

An airplane travels in a straight line at a speed of 600 km/h. How far does it fly in 3.5 hours?

Write the formula that relates speed, distance, and time.

$$\text{Speed} = \frac{\text{Distance}}{\text{Time}}$$

$$v = \frac{d}{t}$$

To solve for distance, multiply both sides of the equation by t.

$$v = \frac{d}{t}$$

$$v \times t = \frac{d}{t} \times t$$

$$v \times t = d$$

Substitute in the known values.

$$600 \text{ km/h} \times 3.5 \text{ h} = d$$
$$2100 \text{ km} = d$$

Example

What is the volume of 642 g of gold if the density of gold is 19.3 g/cm³?

Write the formula that relates density, mass, and volume.

$$\text{Density} = \frac{\text{Mass}}{\text{Volume}}$$

$$d = \frac{m}{v}$$

First solve the equation for the unknown quantity, volume (v).

$$d = \frac{m}{v}$$

$$v \times d = m$$

$$v = \frac{m}{d}$$

Then substitute in the known values for m and d.

$$v = \frac{642 \text{ g}}{19.3 \text{ g/cm}^3}$$

$$v = 33.2645 \text{ cm}^3$$

$$v \approx 33.3 \text{ cm}^3$$

Example

A gas has a volume of 5.0 L at a temperature of 200 K. The temperature of the gas is increased under constant pressure until the final volume of the gas is 15 L. What is the final temperature of the gas?

Write the formula that describes how the volume of a gas changes with temperature if the pressure and number of particles are constant.

$$\frac{V_1}{T_1} = \frac{V_2}{T_2}$$

First solve the equation for the unknown quantity, T_2.

$$\frac{V_1}{T_1} = \frac{V_2}{T_2}$$

$$T_2 = \frac{V_2 \times T_1}{V_1}$$

Now substitute the known values for V_1, V_2, and T_1.

$$T_2 = \frac{15 \text{ L} \times 200 \text{ K}}{5 \text{ L}}$$

$$T_2 = 600 \text{ K}$$

Math Skills

Conversion Factors

Many problems involve converting measurements from one unit to another. You can convert units by using an equation that shows how units are related. For example, 1 in. = 2.54 cm relates inches and centimeters.

To write a conversion factor, divide both sides of the equation by 1 in.

$$\frac{1 \text{ in.}}{1 \text{ in.}} = \frac{2.54 \text{ cm}}{1 \text{ in.}}$$

$$1 = 2.54 \text{ cm/in.}$$

Because the conversion factor is equal to 1, you can multiply one side of an equation by it and preserve equality. You can make a second conversion factor by dividing both sides of the equation by 2.54 cm.

$$\frac{1 \text{ in.}}{2.54 \text{ cm}} = \frac{2.54 \text{ cm}}{2.54 \text{ cm}} = 1$$

One conversion factor converts inches to centimeters and the other converts centimeters to inches. Choose the conversion factor that cancels out the unit that you have a measurement for.

Example

Convert 25 inches to centimeters. Use the conversion factor 2.54 cm/in. so that the inches units cancel.

$$25 \text{ in.} \times \frac{2.54 \text{ cm}}{1 \text{ in.}} \approx 64 \text{ cm}$$

Some conversions are more complicated and require multiple steps.

Example

Convert 23°F to a Celsius temperature. The conversion formula is °F = $(\frac{9}{5} \times °C) + 32°F$.

First solve the equation for °C.

$$°F = (\tfrac{9}{5} \times °C) + 32°F$$

$$°F - 32°F = \tfrac{9}{5} \times °C$$

$$\tfrac{5}{9}(°F - 32°F) = °C$$

Now substitute in 23°F.

$$°C = \tfrac{5}{9}(23°F - 32°F) = \tfrac{5}{9}(-9) = -5$$

Thus, 23°F is equivalent to −5°C.

Example

A grocer is selling oranges at a price of 3 for $1.00. How much would 10 oranges cost?

Use the equality 3 oranges = $1.00 to write a conversion factor. The desired conversion factor should have dollars in the numerator so that the oranges units cancel.

$$10 \text{ oranges} \times \frac{\$1.00}{3 \text{ oranges}} = \$3.33$$

Example

Water runs through a hose at a rate of 2.5 gallons per minute. What is the rate of water flow in gallons per day?

To convert gal/min to gal/d, you must use conversion factors based on the following equalities.

$$60 \text{ min} = 1 \text{ h}$$

$$24 \text{ h} = 1 \text{ d}$$

$$\frac{2.5 \text{ gal}}{\text{min}} \times \frac{60 \text{ min}}{1 \text{ h}} \times \frac{24 \text{ h}}{1 \text{ d}} = 3600 \text{ gal/d}$$

Example

The density of nitrogen gas is 1.17 g/L. What is the density of nitrogen expressed in micrograms per deciliter (μg/dL)?

Derive the needed conversion factors from the following equalities.

$$10^6 \ \mu\text{g} = 1 \text{ g}$$

$$10 \text{ dL} = 1 \text{ L}$$

$$\frac{1.17 \text{ g}}{\text{L}} \times \frac{10^6 \ \mu\text{g}}{1 \text{ g}} \times \frac{1 \text{ L}}{10 \text{ dL}} = 1.17 \times 10^5 \ \mu\text{g/dL}$$

Data Tables

Data tables help to organize data and make it easier to see patterns in data. If you plan data tables before doing an experiment, they will help you record observations in an orderly fashion.

The data table below shows United States immigration data for the year 2001. Always include units of measurement so people can understand the data.

Immigration to the United States, 2001	
Place of Origin	**Number of Legal Immigrants**
Africa	53,948
Asia	349,776
Europe	175,371
North America	407,888
South America	68,888

Bar Graphs

To make a bar graph, begin by placing category labels along the bottom axis. Add an overall label for the axis *Place of Origin*. Decide on a scale for the vertical axis. An appropriate scale for the data in the table is 0 to 500,000. Label the vertical axis *Number of People*. For each continent, draw a bar whose height corresponds to the number of immigrants. You will need to round off the values. For example, the bar for Africa should correspond to 54,000 people. Add a graph title to make it clear what the graph shows.

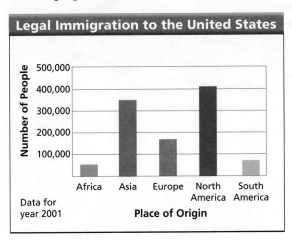

Circle Graphs

Use the total number to calculate percentages. For example, the percentage of immigrants from Africa in 2001 was 53,948 ÷ 1,061,984 = 0.051 ≈ 5%. Multiply each percent by 360° to find the central angle of each wedge. For Africa, the central angle is 18°. Use a protractor to draw each central angle. Color and label the wedges and finish your graph with a title.

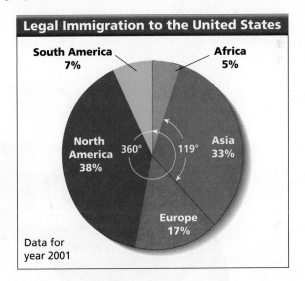

Line Graphs

The slope of a straight-line graph equals the "rise over the run." The rise is the change in the y values and the run is the change in the x values. Using points A and B on the graph below gives

$$\text{Slope} = \frac{\text{Rise}}{\text{Run}} = \frac{5-3}{9-3} = \frac{2}{6} = 0.33$$

21st Century Skills

The Partnership for 21st Century Skills is the leading advocacy organization focused on infusing skills for the 21st century into education. The organization brings together the business community, education leaders, and policy makers to define a powerful vision for 21st century education to ensure every child's success as citizens and workers by providing tools and resources to help facilitate and drive change.

Today's students will spend their adult lives in a multitasking, multifaceted, technology-driven, diverse, vibrant world—and they must arrive equipped to do so. The goal of 21st Century Learning is to bridge the gap between how students live and how they learn. A way to bridge the gap is summarized in the diagram below.

The arches of the rainbow represent student outcomes. These are the skills, knowledge, and expertise students will need to master to succeed in work and life in the 21st century. The pools at the base of the rainbow represent the 21st Century Support Systems that must be present in order for students to master the skills described in the rainbow.

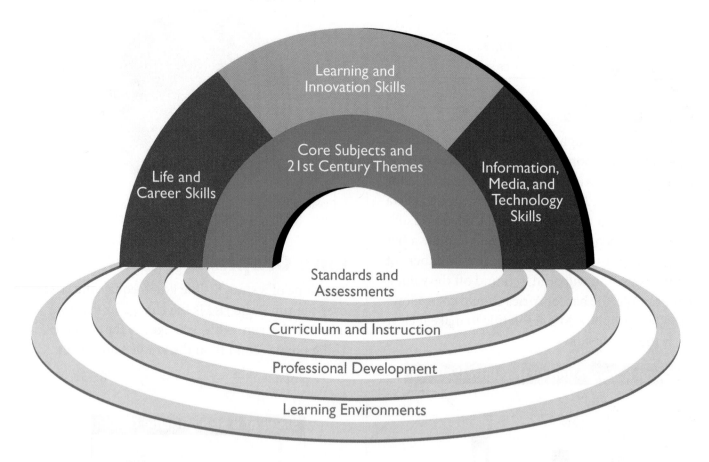

Core Subjects and 21st Century Themes

Let's start with the green section of the rainbow: Core Subjects and 21st Century Themes. Today's students will still need to master core subjects such as English (reading or language arts), world languages, arts, mathematics, economics, sciences, geography, history, government, and civics. However, they can move beyond basic competence to higher levels of understanding if schools weave into those subjects such themes as global awareness; financial, economic, business, and entrepreneurial literacy; civic literacy; and health literacy.

Learning and Innovation Skills

The yellow section, Learning and Innovation Skills, prepares students for increasingly complex life and work environments. Skills such as creativity and innovation allow students to implement, analyze, refine, and evaluate new ideas. Critical thinking and problem-solving skills allow students to make their way through the multistep process required to find solutions—be they conventional or innovative—to non-familiar problems. Communication and collaboration skills will be key to success in today's global, interconnected, multicultural world.

Information, Media, and Technology Skills

The 21st century is a technology- and media-suffused environment that requires mastery of the skills in the blue section—Information, Media, and Technology Skills. These skills include information literacy, media literacy, and ICT (information, communications, and technology) literacy. Students must learn to access, evaluate, and use information from a wide variety of sources. They will need to know how to recognize, understand, and create media messages. In order to function in the new knowledge economy, today's students will need to use digital devices, communication and networking tools, and social networks professionally as well as personally.

Life and Career Skills

The ultimate goal is to prepare students for success beyond the classroom with Life and Career Skills. This is a globally competitive information age with complex life and work environments. These environments require such skills as flexibility and adaptability, initiative and self-direction, social and cross-cultural skills, productivity and accountability, and leadership and responsibility.

Adapted from Partnership for 21st Century Skills, 177 N. Church Avenue, Suite 305, Tucson, AZ 85701, 520-623-2466; www.21stcenturyskills.org.

21st Century Learning
Communication Skills

Why is soil acidity important in gardening?

In order for their plants to thrive, gardeners and farmers need to be mindful of the acidity of the soil. Suppose you are planning a small garden for your neighborhood. Use the library or Internet to find out the typical soil acidity for your area and how this affects the variety of plant life. Talk to a local gardener, farmer, or plant nursery worker to find out how soil acidity is measured and maintained. Then write a paragraph that outlines your plan for the garden, making sure to discuss soil pH considerations.

Using Technology

Prentice Hall provides references in your textbook to a variety of technology options for enhancing your learning experiences. They include the Interactive Textbook, probeware versions of textbook labs, Sci-Links®, PHSchool.com, Science News®, Planet Diary, and Active Art.

The Interactive Textbook is a resource that expands your learning with a variety of interactive opportunities.

- **Entire text online and on CD-ROM**
- **Multimedia activities** With engaging video, audio, and interactive features, the Interactive Textbook makes learning a multimedia experience. All of the interactive features can be accessed with a single click.
- **Additional assessment opportunities with instant feedback** You don't have to wait to receive feedback—you'll know immediately whether you're on track.

 Probeware Labs

Ten of the textbook labs have an alternate probeware version in the Probeware Lab Manual. Probeware labs have several advantages over traditional labs.

- **Instant feedback** Your data are displayed immediately, so you know right away if the lab is working.
- **Graphing and data analysis** Built-in tools let you immediately focus on science concepts instead of getting bogged down in generating graphs and tables.
- **Encourage creativity** With probeware labs, you can ask (and answer) what-if questions.

The National Science Teachers Association manages the SciLinks® Service, a project that blends the best of the two main educational resources—textbooks and the Internet. Under each SciLinks icon that appears in this book, you'll find the SciLinks URL (www. scilinks.org) and a code. Go to the SciLinks Web site, sign in, type the code from the page you are reading, and you'll receive a list of URLs that are selected by science educators.

Go Online opportunities appear throughout the textbook to alert you to interactive opportunities at the Prentice Hall Web site.

- **Data-Sharing Labs** Share and compare data with students from across the country.
- **Background for Issues** Access more detailed information about issues featured in the textbook.
- **Self-Assessments** Take self-tests with instant feedback to monitor your own progress and stay on track.

Stay current with articles from Science News. Use the keyword links to quickly find relevant articles written for a high school audience.

Planet Diary features weekly reports on environmental news and natural phenomena such as earthquakes, tornadoes, and hurricanes.

The Active Art resources feature interactive simulations that help you practice skills and understand content.

Standardized Test Prep

The strategies listed here will help you learn how to apply test-taking skills in a logical fashion. Once you know how to prepare for a test, you can improve your chances for getting the right answer. You'll be able to approach a test with confidence and tell yourself, "I will do well."

Preparing for a Standardized Test

- **Be well rested.** Get plenty of sleep the night before the test. You will perform better if you are not tired.
- **Eat a good breakfast.** The brain works better when it has fuel.
- **Bring a sweater or sweatshirt.** You will want to be comfortable, no matter how warm or cool the testing room is.
- **Wear a watch.** Be aware of how many questions you have to answer and the amount of time you are given.
- **Remember your supplies.** You will likely need several sharp #2 pencils and a good eraser. Bring a calculator if it is permitted.
- **Allow plenty of time to get to the test site.** You will be more relaxed if you arrive early.

Taking a Standardized Test

- **Read the directions first.** Then start answering the questions.
- **Read all of the answers.** Then make your choice.
- **Underline important words and phrases.**
- **Cross out choices you know are wrong.**
- **Do the easy questions first.** Don't get stuck on difficult questions. You can come back to them.
- **Record your answers properly.** Be sure to put your answers in the right place. Fill in the marks completely.
- **Answer every question.**
- **Stay relaxed.** If you get nervous, stop and take a few deep breaths.
- **Change your body position.** Once in a while, shift your position to keep comfortable.
- **Stick with your first choice.** Change an answer only when you are SURE your first choice is wrong.
- **Review your answers if you have time.**

Question Strategies

Multiple Choice

- **Read the question thoroughly and carefully.**
- **Know what the question wants from you.** Are you expected to provide all possible answers, or the best answer? Do you have to find all responses that apply, or one that does not apply?
- **Anticipate the answer.** If you know the answer even before you read the list of responses, look for an answer that is similar to the one you are thinking of.
- **Skip the question if you get stuck.** Don't lose precious time. You can always go back to it later.
- **Read all answers.** Even when you think you have found the correct answer right away, you may find a better answer.
- **If you find two correct answers, keep reading!** You may discover an "All of the above" option. Or the question may ask for the "best" answer.
- **Eliminate responses you know are wrong.** If you have fewer options to choose from, you are more likely to choose the correct response.

Constructed Response (Short Answer)

- **Know which question(s) to answer.** Do you have to answer all of them or only some? If you can choose, answer the ones you are most familiar with.
- **Notice action words.** Do you have to "draw" a diagram? "Create" a list? "Write" a paragraph?
- **Make notes.** Write down names, dates, facts, and figures that come to mind. Don't waste time; write only as much as you need to jog your memory.
- **Make a brief outline.** Plan how to approach the response. Then stick to it; don't get sidetracked.
- **Write legibly.** Neatness counts. Don't lose points just because the evaluator couldn't read your response.
- **Use key terms and vocabulary.** Your answer will be more precise and sound more credible.
- **Be thorough.** But don't waste time on unnecessary details or long explanations.
- **Always provide an answer.** Partial credit is better than no credit. If time is short, outline or list the remaining information.
- **Leave space.** You can add information you may think of later.

SI *(Système International d'Unités)* is a revised version of the metric system, which was originally developed in France in 1791. SI units of measurement are used by scientists throughout the world. The system is based on multiples of ten. Each unit is ten times larger or ten times smaller than the next unit. The most commonly used SI units are given below.

You can use conversion factors to convert between SI and non-SI units. Try the following conversions. How tall are you in meters? What is your weight in newtons? What is your normal body temperature in degrees Celsius?

Metric ruler

Commonly Used Metric Units

Length	The distance from one point to another
meter (m)	A meter is slightly longer than a yard. 1 meter = 1000 millimeters (mm) 1 meter = 100 centimeters (cm) 1000 meters = 1 kilometer (km)

Volume	The amount of space an object takes up
liter (L)	A liter is slightly more than a quart. 1 liter = 1000 milliliters (mL)

Mass	The amount of matter in an object
gram (g)	A gram has a mass equal to about one paper clip. 1000 grams = 1 kilogram (kg)

Temperature	The measure of hotness or coldness
degrees Celsius (°C)	0°C = freezing point of water at sea level 100°C = boiling point of water at sea level

Triple-Beam Balance

Metric–Customary Equivalents

2.54 centimeters (cm) = 1 inch (in.)
1 meter (m) = 39.37 inches (in.)
1 kilometer (km) = 0.62 miles (mi)
1 liter (L) = 1.06 quarts (qt)
250 milliliters (mL) = 1 cup (c)
9.8 newtons (N) = 2.2 pounds (lb)
°C = 5/9 × (°F − 32)

Thermometer   **Graduated cylinder**

The laboratory balance is an important tool in scientific investigations. You can use a balance to determine the masses of materials that you study or experiment with in the laboratory.

Different kinds of balances are used in the laboratory. One kind of balance is the triple-beam balance. The balance that you may use in your science class is probably similar to the balance illustrated. To use the balance properly, you should learn the name, location, and function of each part of the balance you are using.

The Triple-Beam Balance

The triple-beam balance is a single-pan balance with three beams The back, or 100-gram, beam is divided into ten units of 10 grams. The middle, or 500-gram, beam is divided into five units of 100 grams. The front, or 10-gram, beam is divided into ten major units, each of which is 1 gram. Each 1-gram unit is further divided into units of 0.1 gram. What is the largest mass you could measure with a triple-beam balance?

The following procedure can be used to find the mass of an object with a triple-beam balance.
1. When no object is on the pan, and the riders are at zero, make sure the pointer is at zero. If it is not, use the adjustment screw to zero the balance.
2. Place the object on the pan.
3. Move the rider on the middle beam notch by notch until the horizontal pointer drops below zero. Move the rider back one notch.
4. Move the rider on the back beam notch by notch until the pointer again drops below zero. Move the rider back one notch.
5. Slowly slide the rider along the front beam until the pointer stops at zero. The mass of the object is the sum of the readings on the three beams.

Pointer (at zero)

Pan

Riders

Beams

Adjustment screw

Triple-Beam Balance

Element	Symbol	Atomic Number	Atomic Mass[†]	Element	Symbol	Atomic Number	Atomic Mass[†]
Actinium	Ac	89	(277)	Neodymium	Nd	60	144.24
Aluminum	Al	13	26.982	Neon	Ne	10	20.179
Americium	Am	95	(243)	Neptunium	Np	93	(237)
Antimony	Sb	51	121.75	Nickel	Ni	28	58.71
Argon	Ar	18	39.948	Niobium	Nb	41	92.906
Arsenic	As	33	74.922	Nitrogen	N	7	14.007
Astatine	At	85	(210)	Nobelium	No	102	(259)
Barium	Ba	56	137.33	Osmium	Os	76	190.2
Berkelium	Bk	97	(247)	Oxygen	O	8	15.999
Beryllium	Be	4	9.0122	Palladium	Pd	46	106.4
Bismuth	Bi	83	208.98	Phosphorus	P	15	30.974
Bohrium	Bh	107	(264)	Platinum	Pt	78	195.09
Boron	B	5	10.81	Plutonium	Pu	94	(244)
Bromine	Br	35	79.904	Polonium	Po	84	(209)
Cadmium	Cd	48	112.41	Potassium	K	19	39.098
Calcium	Ca	20	40.08	Praseodymium	Pr	59	140.91
Californium	Cf	98	(251)	Promethium	Pm	61	(145)
Carbon	C	6	12.011	Protactinium	Pa	91	231.04
Cerium	Ce	58	140.12	Radium	Ra	88	(226)
Cesium	Cs	55	132.91	Radon	Rn	86	(222)
Chlorine	Cl	17	35.453	Rhenium	Re	75	186.21
Chromium	Cr	24	51.996	Rhodium	Rh	45	102.91
Cobalt	Co	27	58.933	Roentgenium	Rg	111	(272)
Copper	Cu	29	63.546	Rubidium	Rb	37	85.468
Curium	Cm	96	(247)	Ruthenium	Ru	44	101.07
Darmstadtium	Ds	110	(269)	Rutherfordium	Rf	104	(261)
Dubnium	Db	105	(262)	Samarium	Sm	62	150.4
Dysprosium	Dy	66	162.50	Scandium	Sc	21	44.956
Einsteinium	Es	99	(252)	Seaborgium	Sg	106	(263)
Erbium	Er	68	167.26	Selenium	Se	34	78.96
Europium	Eu	63	151.96	Silicon	Si	14	28.086
Fermium	Fm	100	(257)	Silver	Ag	47	107.87
Fluorine	F	9	18.998	Sodium	Na	11	22.990
Francium	Fr	87	(223)	Strontium	Sr	38	87.62
Gadolinium	Gd	64	157.25	Sulfur	S	16	32.06
Gallium	Ga	31	69.72	Tantalum	Ta	73	180.95
Germanium	Ge	32	72.59	Technetium	Tc	43	(98)
Gold	Au	79	196.97	Tellurium	Te	52	127.60
Hafnium	Hf	72	178.49	Terbium	Tb	65	158.93
Hassium	Hs	108	(265)	Thallium	Tl	81	204.37
Helium	He	2	4.0026	Thorium	Th	90	232.04
Holmium	Ho	67	164.93	Thulium	Tm	69	168.93
Hydrogen	H	1	1.0079	Tin	Sn	50	118.69
Indium	In	49	114.82	Titanium	Ti	22	47.90
Iodine	I	53	126.90	Tungsten	W	74	183.85
Iridium	Ir	77	192.22	Ununbium	Uub*	112	(277)
Iron	Fe	26	55.847	Ununquadium	Uuq*	114	—
Krypton	Kr	36	83.80	Uranium	U	92	238.03
Lanthanum	La	57	138.91	Vanadium	V	23	50.941
Lawrencium	Lr	103	(262)	Xenon	Xe	54	131.30
Lead	Pb	82	207.2	Ytterbium	Yb	70	173.04
Lithium	Li	3	6.941	Yttrium	Y	39	88.906
Lutetium	Lu	71	174.97	Zinc	Zn	30	65.38
Magnesium	Mg	12	24.305	Zirconium	Zr	40	91.22
Manganese	Mn	25	54.938				
Meitnerium	Mt	109	(268)				
Mendelevium	Md	101	(258)				
Mercury	Hg	80	200.59				
Molybdenum	Mo	42	95.94				

[†] Number in parentheses gives the mass number of the most stable isotope

*Name not officially assigned

The following problems provide additional practice for solving equations and word problems. If you need help, look at the Math Skills Boxes on the referenced pages, where you will find solutions to similar problems.

Using Scientific Notation
(See Math Skills, page 15.)
1. The floor of a room measures 7.5 m by 6.0 m.
   a. What area of carpeting (in m^2) would you need to cover the entire floor? Express your answer in scientific notation.
   b. What would the area be in cm^2? (*Hint:* 10^4 cm^2 = 1 m^2).
   c. Suppose you want to tile the floor with square tiles that measure 30.5 cm on a side. How many tiles would you need? (*Hint:* Divide the total floor area by the area of a single tile.)
2. A mercury thermometer exchange program collected 1045 mercury thermometers in a month.
   a. If each thermometer contains 0.70 g of mercury, what is the total mass of mercury? Express your answer in scientific notation.
   b. A hazardous waste container holds 100.0 cm^3. Can this container hold all of the mercury? (*Hint:* Find the volume by dividing the mass by the density of mercury, 11.3 g/cm^3.)

The Combined Gas Law
(See Math Skills, page 80.)
1. The air in a bicycle tire is at a temperature of 11.0°C and a pressure of 542 kPa. What is the pressure in the tire if the temperature increases to 29.0°C while you ride the bicycle? Assume the volume of the tire does not change.

2. A helium tank holds 20.0 L of helium at a pressure of 3050 kPa. How many balloons can the tank fill if each balloon holds 2.0 L of gas at a pressure of 105 kPa? The balloons and the tank are both at room temperature. (*Hint:* Find the volume the helium in the tank would expand to if its pressure were reduced to 105 kPa. Then divide by the volume of one balloon.)

Formulas and Names for Compounds
(See Math Skills, page 174.)
1. Write the formulas for the ionic compounds lead(II) sulfide and lithium nitrate.
2. Name the molecular compounds with these formulas: NBr_3, SCl_2, and CCl_4.
3. Write the names for the ionic compounds $FeCl_2$ and $FeCl_3$.

Balancing Chemical Equations
(See Math Skills, page 195.)
Balance the following equations.
1. $H_2 + Cl_2 \rightarrow HCl$
2. $Ca(OH)_2 + HCl \rightarrow CaCl_2 + H_2O$
3. $Fe + O_2 \rightarrow Fe_3O_2$
4. $C_2H_4 + O_2 \rightarrow CO_2 + H_2O$

Balancing Nuclear Equations
(See Math Skills, page 295.)
1. Write a balanced nuclear equation for the beta decay of bismuth-210.
2. Write a balanced nuclear equation for the alpha decay of polonium-214.
3. Determine the product for the alpha decay of uranium-234.
4. What is the product of the beta decay of phosphorus-30?

Measuring Speed
(See Math Skills, page 333.)
1. A runner travels 3.0 kilometers in 24 minutes, then another 2.5 kilometers in 27 minutes, and finally 1.2 kilometers in 15 minutes. What is the runner's average speed?
2. A bus travels 140 km in 3.0 hours and then stops for a 30-minute rest stop. The bus then travels 120 km in 2.0 hours. What is the average speed for the entire trip?
3. A plane's average speed for a 300.0-km trip is 550 km/h. How long did the flight take?

Measuring Acceleration
(See Math Skills, page 346.)
1. During a crash, a bicycle racer moving at 17 m/s comes to a complete stop in 1.5 seconds. Calculate the bicycle's deceleration.
2. A ball is thrown straight up into the air. It comes to a rest at the highest point after 2.0 seconds. How fast was it going when it was thrown upward?

Newton's Second Law
(See Math Skills, page 367.)
1. A truck with a mass of 2200 kg accelerates when the traffic light turns green. If the net force on the truck is 3500 N in the forward direction, what is the truck's acceleration?
2. A bicycle with its rider has a total mass of 95 kg. If the bicycle accelerates at a rate of 2.0 m/s^2, what is the net force acting on the bicycle?
3. What net force is needed to accelerate a 9000-kg truck at the rate of 2.0 m/s^2?

Appendix D PROBLEM BANK

Calculating Power
(See Math Skills, page 415.)

1. While lifting a box 0.75 m straight up, you exert an upward force of 320 N on the box. How much work do you do on the box? What is the power if you take 2.0 s to lift the box?

2. A dog sled is pulled at a constant horizontal speed of 8.0 m/s by a team of dogs. What is the power of the dogs if they are applying a constant horizontal force of 200.0 N to the sled? (*Hint:* Calculate the work done in one second).

3. How much work can a 500-watt engine do in 1.0 hour?

Calculating IMA and AMA
(See Math Skills, page 425.)

1. A crowbar is 0.75 m long and the fulcrum is located 10.0 cm from the end of the bar. What is the ideal mechanical advantage of the crowbar?

2. A person changing a tire exerts a force of 520 N on a car jack to apply a lifting force of 12,000 N. What is the actual mechanical advantage of the car jack?

3. A pair of pliers has an actual mechanical advantage of 3.5. If you were to squeeze the handles together with a force of 3.0 N, how much force would the jaws of the pliers exert?

4. If a machine has an efficiency of 35%, and you do 1500 J of work on the machine, what will be the work output of the machine?

Kinetic Energy
(See Math Skills, page 448.)

1. A 13,000-kg automobile moves at 28 m/s. What is the automobile's kinetic energy?

2. Two birds fly at the same speed, 4.0 m/s. One bird has a mass of 0.25 kg and the other has a mass of 0.75 kg. What is the kinetic energy of each bird?

Conservation of Energy
(See Math Skills, page 458.)

1. An 80.0-kg diver climbs a ladder up to a high-dive platform 10.0 meters above the ground.

a. How much gravitational potential energy does the diver gain?

b. After diving, what is the diver's speed at the water? Assume all of the potential energy has been converted to kinetic energy.

2. A 4.0-kg bowling ball returns to a bowler along a horizontal track at a speed of 5.0 m/s. At the end of the track, the ball must rise up an incline to a height of 1.0 m. Show that the ball has enough energy to make it to the top of the ramp. Assume friction can be ignored.

Specific Heat
(See Math Skills, page 477.)

1. How much heat is needed to raise the temperature of a plastic beaker by 10.0°C? The beaker's mass is 24.4 g and the specific heat of the plastic is 1.90 J/g•°C.

2. Tin has a specific heat of 0.23 J/g•°C. How much heat is needed to raise the temperature of 550 g of tin from 65°C to 125°C?

3. What mass of water will change its temperature by 10.0°C when 500.0 J of heat is added to it?

Speed of Mechanical Waves
(See Math Skills, page 506.)

1. A wave on a rope has a wavelength of 1.5 m and a frequency of 3.0 Hz. What is the speed of the wave?

2. A motorboat in a lake makes a surface wave with a frequency of 13 Hz and a wavelength of 0.15 m. What is the speed of the wave?

3. Seven ocean wave crests pass by a pier in 28.0 s. If the wave speed is 11 m/s, what is the wavelength of the waves?

Calculating Wave Speed
(See Math Skills, page 535.)

1. A cell phone transmits a carrier wave at a frequency 1900 MHz. What is the wavelength of the wave? (Assume the wave moves at the speed of light in a vacuum.)

2. A carrier wave from an FM station has a frequency 94.5 MHz. What is the wavelength?

3. A light-emitting diode (LED) emits light with a wavelength of 630 nanometers. What is the frequency of the light and what color is the LED?

Power, Voltage, and Current
(See Math Skills, page 611.)

1. A flashlight uses a 6.0-W light bulb connected to 3.6-V nickel-cadmium battery. How much current does the bulb use?

2. A hair dryer has a power rating of 1600 W. If it is connected to a 120-volt line, how much current does it draw?

Answers to even-numbered Math Practice and Section Assessment questions that involve calculations are given below. Use these answers to check your work.

Chapter 1

Math Practice, page 15
2. Distance = 2.6×10^{13} m
Section 1.3 Assessment, page 21
8. 1.5×10^{-4} cm^3

Chapter 3

Math Practice, page 80
2. $T_2 = 580$ K
Section 3.2 Assessment, page 81
10. $P_2 = 281$ kPa

Chapter 6

Math Practice, page 174
2. Cu_2S
4. sodium hydroxide
Section 6.3 Assessment, page 175
8. lithium chloride, barium oxide, sodium nitride, lead sulfate
10. K_2S

Chapter 7

Math Practice, page 195
2. a. $2H_2O_2 \rightarrow 2H_2O + O_2$
   b. $Mg + 2HCl \rightarrow H_2 + MgCl_2$
Section 7.1 Assessment, page 198
10. $2Mg + O_2 \rightarrow 2MgO$

Chapter 10

Math Practice, page 295
2. $^{14}_{6}C \rightarrow ^{14}_{7}N + ^{0}_{-1}e$
4. $^{90}_{38}Sr \rightarrow ^{90}_{39}Y + ^{0}_{-1}e$
Section 10.1 Assessment, page 297
10. $^{226}_{88}Ra \rightarrow ^{222}_{86}Rn + ^{4}_{2}He$

Chapter 11

Math Practice, page 333
2. $v = 62$ km/h
Math Practice, page 346
2. $(v_f - v_i) = 36$ m/s
4. $v_i = -25$ m/s
Section 11.3 Assessment, page 348
8. $a = 0.83$ m/s^2

Chapter 12

Math Practice, page 367
2. $a = 2$ m/s^2
4. $m = 50$ kg
Section 12.2 Assessment, page 369
6. Deceleration = 11 m/s^2

Chapter 14

Math Practice, page 415
2. Power = 7.5 W
Section 14.1 Assessment, page 416
8. Power = 50 W
Math Practice, page 425
2. IMA = 10
Section 14.3 Assessment, page 426
8. Efficiency = 80%

Chapter 15

Math Practice, page 448
2. 440 kJ
Section 15.1 Assessment, page 452
8. PE = 44 kJ
Math Practice, page 458
2. PE = 2100 J; $v = 7.7$ m/s
Section 15.2 Assessment, page 459
10. $h = 0.20$ m

Chapter 16

Math Practice, page 477
2. $Q = 34$ kJ
4. $\Delta T = 10.0°C$
Section 16.1 Assessment, page 478
10. $Q = 7.8$ kJ

Chapter 17

Math Practice, page 506
2. Speed = 0.4 m/s
4. Wavelength = 0.5 km
Section 17.2 Assessment, page 507
10. Period = 0.5 s

Chapter 18

Math Practice, page 535
2. Wavelength = 440 m
Section 18.1 Assessment, page 538
10. Wavelength = 0.190 m

Chapter 20

Math Practice, page 611
2. $I = 0.32$ amps
Section 20.3 Assessment, page 613
8. $I = 0.85$ amps

Glossary

A

absolute zero a temperature of 0 kelvins (pp. 78, 475)

acceleration the rate at which velocity changes (p. 342)

accuracy the closeness of a measurement to the true value of what is measured (p. 19)

acid a compound that produces hydronium ions (H_3O^+) when dissolved in water; a proton donor (p. 241)

actual mechanical advantage the ratio of the output force to the input force in a machine (p. 422)

air resistance fluid friction acting on an object moving through the air (p. 360)

alkali metals the elements in Group 1A of the periodic table, not including hydrogen (p. 140)

alkaline earth metals the elements in Group 2A of the periodic table (p. 141)

alloy a mixture of two or more elements, at least one of which is a metal, that has the characteristic properties of a metal (p. 178)

alpha particle a positively charged particle, emitted by certain radioactive nuclei, made up of two protons and two neutrons; a helium nucleus (p. 293)

alternating current (AC) a flow of electric charge that regularly reverses its direction (p. 604)

amino acids compounds that contain both carboxyl and amino functional groups (p. 280)

amplitude the maximum displacement of a medium from the rest position (p. 507)

amplitude modulation (AM) a method of transmitting a radio signal in which the amplitude of the carrier wave varies while its frequency remains the same (p. 541)

analog signal a smoothly varying signal produced by continuously changing the voltage or current in a circuit (p. 619)

angle of incidence the angle an incident ray makes with a line perpendicular to a surface it strikes (p. 570)

angle of reflection the angle a reflected ray makes with a line perpendicular to a surface it strikes (p. 570)

angle of refraction the angle a light ray makes with the normal after it enters a new medium at an angle (p. 575)

anion an ion with a negative charge (p. 160)

antinode a point of maximum displacement midway between two nodes in a standing wave (p. 512)

Archimedes' principle the equivalence of the buoyant force on an object and the weight of the fluid displaced by the object (p. 401)

aromatic hydrocarbons hydrocarbons that contain a ring structure similar to benzene (p. 266)

astigmatism an eye condition in which objects at any distance appear blurry because of the distorted shape of the cornea (p. 592)

astronomy the study of the universe beyond Earth (p. 4)

atom the smallest particle of an element (p. 39)

atomic mass unit (amu) one twelfth the mass of a carbon-12 atom (p. 134)

atomic number a unique number for each element that equals the number of protons in an atom of that element (p. 110)

average speed the total distance traveled divided by the time it takes to travel that distance (p. 333)

B

background radiation nuclear radiation that occurs naturally in the environment (p. 296)

base a compound that produces hydroxide ions (OH^-) when dissolved in water; a proton acceptor (p. 242)

battery a device that converts chemical energy into electrical energy (p. 606)

beta particle an electron emitted by an unstable nucleus (p. 294)

biology the study of life and life processes (p. 4)

biomass energy the chemical energy stored in living things (p. 464)

boiling point the temperature at which a substance boils; the temperature at which vapor pressure is equal to atmospheric pressure (p. 47)

Boyle's law the inverse variation of the volume of a gas with its pressure if the temperature and the number of particles are constant (p. 79)

buffer a solution that is resistant to large changes in pH (p. 248)

buoyancy the ability of a fluid to exert an upward force on an object placed in it (p. 400)

buoyant force an upward force acting on an object in a fluid (p. 400)

C

calorimeter instrument used to measure thermal energy released or absorbed during a chemical or physical change (p. 478)

camera an optical instrument that records an image of an object (p. 582)

carbohydrate a compound composed of carbon, hydrogen, and oxygen in which the ratio of hydrogen to oxygen atoms is 2 : 1 (p. 278)

catalyst a substance that affects the rate of a chemical reaction without being used up in the reaction (p. 215)

cation an ion with a positive charge (p. 160)

central heating system a heating system that heats many rooms from one central location (p. 489)

centripetal force a force that continuously changes the direction of an object to make it move in a circle (p. 381)

chain reaction a series of fission reactions triggered by neutrons released during the fission of a nucleus (p. 311)

Charles's law the direct proportion of the volume of a gas to its temperature (in kelvins) if the pressure and the number of particles of the gas are constant (p. 78)

chemical bond the force that holds atoms or ions together as a unit (p. 160)

chemical change change that occurs when a substance reacts and forms one or more new substances (p. 56)

chemical energy the energy stored in chemical bonds (pp. 206, 451)

chemical equation a representation of a chemical reaction in which the reactants and products are expressed as formulas (p. 193)

chemical formula notation that shows what elements a compound contains and the ratio of the atoms or ions of these elements in the compound (p. 161)

chemical property any property that produces a change in the composition of matter (p. 54)

chemistry the study of the composition, structure, properties, and reactions of matter (p. 4)

circuit breaker a switch that opens when the current in a circuit is too high (p. 612)

coefficients numbers that appear before a formula in a chemical equation to show the relative proportions of each reactant and product (p. 194)

coherent light light waves having the same wavelength, with the crests and troughs lined up (p. 560)

colloid a mixture that contains some particles that are intermediate in size between the small particles in a solution and the larger particles in a suspension (p. 44)

combustion reaction a chemical reaction in which a substance reacts rapidly with oxygen, often producing heat and light (p. 204)

complementary colors of light any two colors of light that combine to form white light (p. 552)

complementary colors of pigments any two colors of pigments that combine to make black pigment (p. 553)

compound a substance that is made from two or more simpler substances and can be broken down into those simpler substances (p. 40)

compound machine a combination of two or more simple machines that operate together (p. 435)

compression an area of a longitudinal wave where the particles of the medium are close together (p. 502)

computer a programmable device that can store and process information (p. 622)

concave lens a lens that is curved inward at the center and is thickest at the outside edges (p. 576)

concave mirror a mirror that is curved inward (p. 572)

concentration the amount of solute dissolved in a certain amount of solvent (p. 238)

condensation the phase change in which a substance changes from a gas or vapor to a liquid (p. 90)

conduction the transfer of thermal with no overall transfer of matter, within a material or between materials that are touching (p. 479); the transfer of electric charge by direct contact with a conductor (p. 602)

conductivity a material's ability to allow heat or electric charges to flow (p. 46)

cones light-sensitive neurons in the retina that detect color (p. 589)

constant acceleration a steady change in velocity (p. 345)

constructive interference the interaction among two or more waves in which displacements combine to produce a wave with a larger displacement (p. 511)

controlled experiment an experiment in which only one variable, the manipulated variable, is deliberately changed at a time (p. 8)

convection the transfer of thermal energy when particles of a fluid move from one place to another (p. 480)

convection current circulation of a fluid in a loop as the fluid alternately heats up and cools down (p. 481)

conversion factor a ratio of equivalent measurements that is used to convert a quantity from one unit to another (p. 18)

convex lens a lens that is curved outward at the center and is thinnest at the outside edges (p. 576)

convex mirror a mirror that is curved outward (p. 573)

cornea the transparent outer coating of the eye (p. 588)

covalent bond a chemical bond in which two atoms share a pair of valence electrons (p. 166)

crest the highest point of a transverse wave (p. 501)

critical angle the angle of incidence that produces an angle of refraction equal to 90 degrees (p. 578)

critical mass the smallest possible mass of a fissionable material that can sustain a chain reaction (p. 311)

crystals solids whose particles are arranged in a lattice structure (p. 162)

D

decibel a unit that compares the intensities of different sounds (p. 515)

decomposition reaction a chemical reaction in which a compound breaks down into two or more simpler substances (p. 200)

density the ratio of a material's mass to its volume (p. 17)

deposition the phase change in which a gas or vapor changes directly into a solid without first changing into a liquid (p. 91)

Glossary

destructive interference the interaction among two or more waves in which displacements combine to produce a wave with a smaller displacement (p. 511)

diffraction the bending of a wave as it moves around an obstacle or passes through a narrow opening (p. 510)

diffuse reflection reflection that occurs when parallel light waves strike a rough, uneven surface and reflect in many different directions (p. 547)

digital signal a signal that encodes information as a string of 1's and 0's (p. 619)

diode a solid-state component with an n-type semiconductor joined to a p-type semiconductor (p. 621)

direct current (DC) a flow of electric charge in only one direction (p. 604)

direct proportion a relationship between two variables in which their ratio is constant (p. 23)

dispersion the process of dissolving by breaking into smaller pieces (p. 230), the process in which white light separates into colors (p. 551)

dissociation the separation of ions in an ionic compound as the compound dissolves (p. 229)

distance the length of the path between two points (p. 329)

distillation a process that separates the substances in a solution based on their boiling points (p. 50)

Doppler effect a change in sound frequency caused by motion of the sound source, motion of the listener, or both (p. 516)

double-replacement reaction a chemical reaction in which two compounds exchange positive ions and form two new compounds (p. 203)

E

efficiency the percentage of the work input that becomes work output in a machine (p. 425)

elastic potential energy the potential energy of an object that is stretched or compressed (p. 450)

electric charge a property that causes subatomic particles such as protons and electrons to attract or repel one another (p. 600)

electric circuit a complete path through which electric charge can flow (p. 609)

electric current a continuous flow of electric charge (p. 604)

electric field a field in a region of space that exerts electric forces on charged particles; a field produced by electric charges or by changing magnetic fields (pp. 533, 602)

electric force the attraction or repulsion between electrically charged objects (p. 601)

electric motor a device that uses an electromagnet to turn an axle (p. 639)

electric power the rate at which electrical energy is converted to another form of energy (p. 611)

electrical conductor a material through which electric charge can flow easily (p. 605)

electrical energy the energy associated with electric charges (p. 452)

electrical insulator a material through which charge cannot flow easily (p. 605)

electrolyte a compound that produces ions when it dissolves (p. 249)

electromagnet a solenoid with a ferromagnetic core (p. 637)

electromagnetic energy a form of energy consisting of changing electric and magnetic fields (p. 452)

electromagnetic force a force associated with charged particles, which has two aspects, electric force and magnetic force (pp. 378, 635)

electromagnetic induction the process of generating a current by moving an electrical conductor relative to a magnetic field (p. 642)

electromagnetic radiation the transfer of energy by electromagnetic waves (p. 533)

electromagnetic spectrum the full range of electromagnetic radiation (p. 540)

electromagnetic wave a transverse wave consisting of changing electric and changing magnetic fields (p. 533)

electron a negatively charged subatomic particle that is found in the space outside the nucleus of an atom (p. 108)

electron cloud a visual model of the most likely locations for the electrons in an atom (p. 116)

electron configuration the arrangement of electrons in the orbitals of an atom (p. 118)

electron dot diagram a diagram of an atom, ion or molecule in which each dot represents a valence electron (p. 158)

electronics the science of using electric currents to process or transmit information (p. 618)

electronic signal information sent as patterns in the controlled flow of electrons through a circuit (p. 618)

element a substance that cannot be broken down into simpler substances (p. 39)

endothermic a description of a change in which a system absorbs engergy from its surroundings (p. 86)

endothermic reaction a chemical reaction that absorbs energy from its surroundings (p. 209)

energy the ability to do work (p. 447)

energy conservation the practice of finding ways to use less energy or to use energy more efficiently (p. 466)

energy conversion the process of changing energy from one form to another (p. 454)

energy levels the possible energies that electrons in an atom can have (p. 114)

enzyme a protein that acts as a catalyst for reactions in cells (p. 284)

equilibrium a state in which the forward and reverse paths of a physical or chemical change take place at the same rate (p. 216)

evaporation the process that changes a substance from a liquid to a gas at temperatures below the substance's boiling point (p. 89)

exothermic a description of a change in which a system releases energy to its surroundings (p. 86)

exothermic reaction a chemical reaction that releases energy to its surroundings (p. 208)

external combustion engine a heat engine in which the fuel burns outside the engine (p. 486)

F

farsightedness an eye condition that causes nearby objects to be blurry (p. 592)

ferromagnetic material a material that can be magnetized because it contains magnetic domains (p. 632)

filtration a process that separates materials based on the size of their particles (p. 50)

fission a nuclear reaction in which an atomic nucleus is split into two smaller parts (p. 309)

flammability a material's ability to burn in the presence of oxygen (p. 54)

fluid a substance or mixture that flows and has no shape of its own (p. 391)

fluid friction a friction force that opposes the motion of an object through a fluid (p. 360)

fluorescence a process in which phosphorescent material converts radiation into visible light (p. 559)

focal point the point at which light rays parallel to the axis of a mirror or lens meet or appear to meet (p. 572)

force a push or a pull that acts on an object (p. 356)

fossil fuels rich deposits of hydrocarbon mixtures that formed from the remains of organisms (p. 267, p. 462)

frame of reference a system of objects that are not moving with respect to one another (p. 328)

free fall the movement of an object toward Earth because of gravity (p. 343)

frequency the number of complete cycles per unit time for a periodic motion (p. 504)

frequency modulation (FM) a method of transmitting a radio signal in which the frequency of the carrier wave varies while its amplitude remains the same (p. 541)

friction a force that opposes the motion of objects that touch as they move past each other (p. 359)

fulcrum the fixed point a lever rotates around (p. 428)

functional group an atom or group of atoms that determines the properties of an organic compound. (p. 272)

fuse a device that prevents overheating due to current overload in a circuit (p. 612)

fusion a nuclear reaction in which the nuclei of two atoms combine to form a larger nucleus (p. 315)

G

galvanometer a device that uses an electromagnet to measure small amounts of current (p. 638)

gamma ray a penetrating form of radiation emitted by an unstable nucleus (p. 294)

gas the state of matter in which a material has neither a definite shape nor a definite volume (p. 70)

generator a device that converts mechanical energy into electrical energy by the relative motion of a coil of wire with respect to a magnetic field (p. 643)

geology the study of the origin, history, and structure of Earth (p. 4)

geothermal energy thermal energy beneath Earth's surface (p. 464)

gravitational force an attractive force that acts between any two objects (p. 380)

gravitational potential energy potential energy that depends upon an object's height above a reference point (p. 449)

gravity the attraction between any two objects because of their masses (p. 361)

ground state a state in which all the electrons in an atom have the lowest possible energies (p. 118)

grounding the transfer of excess charge through a conductor to Earth (p. 613)

group a column of elements in a periodic table (p. 131)

H

half-life the time required for one half of a sample of a radioactive isotope to decay (p. 299)

halogens the elements in Group 7A of the periodic table (p. 144)

heat the transfer of thermal energy from one object to another because of a difference in temperature (p. 474)

heat engine any device that converts thermal energy into work (p. 483)

heat of fusion the energy a substance must absorb in order to change from a solid to a liquid (p. 86)

heat of vaporization the energy a substance must absorb in order to change from a liquid to a gas (p. 88)

heat pump a device that uses work to transfer thermal energy from a colder area to a warmer area (p. 490)

hertz (Hz) the unit of measure for frequency, equal to one cycle per second (p. 504)

Glossary

heterogeneous mixture a type of mixture in which the parts of the mixture are noticeably different from one another (p. 41)

homogeneous mixture a type of mixture in which the substances are so evenly distributed that it is difficult to distinguish one substance in the mixture from another (p. 42)

horsepower (hp) a common unit of power, equal to about 746 watts (p. 416)

hydraulic system a device that uses a pressurized fluid acting on pistons of different sizes to increase force (p. 395)

hydrocarbon an organic compound that contains only the elements hydrogen and carbon (p. 264)

hydroelectric energy energy obtained from flowing water (p. 463)

hydrogen fuel cell a cell that generates electricity from a controlled reaction between hydrogen and oxygen (p. 608)

hypothesis a proposed answer to a question (p. 8)

I

ideal mechanical advantage (IMA) the mechanical advantage of a machine in the absence of friction (p. 423)

image a copy of an object formed by reflected or refracted rays of light (p. 547)

incandescent a description of an object hot enough to glow (p. 558)

inclined plane a slanted surface along which a force moves an object to a different elevation (p. 431)

index of refraction the ratio of the speed of light in a vacuum to the speed of light in a medium (p. 575)

indicator a substance that changes color in the presence of an acid or a base (p. 241)

induction the transfer of charge without contact between materials (p. 603)

inertia the tendency of an object to resist a change in its motion (p. 364)

input arm the distance between the fulcrum in a lever and the input force (p. 428)

input distance the distance through which the input force acts in a machine (p. 419)

input force the force exerted on a machine (p. 419)

instantaneous speed the rate at which an object is moving at a given moment in time (p. 334)

integrated circuit a thin slice of silicon that contains many solid-state components; a microchip (p. 622)

intensity the rate at which a wave's energy flows through a given unit of area (pp. 515, 538)

interference the interaction of two or more waves that combine in a region of overlap (p. 510)

internal combustion engine a heat engine in which the fuel burns inside the engine (p. 487)

inverse proportion a relationship in which the product of two variables is a constant when all other variables are held constant (p. 23)

ion an atom or group of atoms that has a positive or negative charge (p. 159)

ionic bond the force that holds cations and anions together (p. 160)

ionization the process by which neutral molecules gain or lose electrons (p. 230)

iris the colored part at the front of the eye, which expands and contracts to control the amount of light entering the eye (p. 589)

isomers organic compounds with the same molecular formula but with different structural formulas (p. 265)

isotopes atoms of a given element that have different numbers of neutrons and different mass numbers (p. 112)

J

joule (J) the SI unit of work, equal to 1 newton-meter (p. 414)

K

kinetic energy the energy an object has due to its motion (pp. 71, 447)

L

laser a device that generates a beam of coherent light (p. 560)

law of conservation of charge law stating that the total electric charge in an isolated system is constant; electric charge is never created or destroyed (p. 602)

law of conservation of momentum law stating that the total momentum of a system does not change if no net force acts on the system (p. 376)

length the straight-line distance between two points (p. 16)

lens an object made of any thin, transparent material that has one or two curved surfaces that can refract light (p. 576)

lever a rigid bar that is free to move around a fixed point (p. 428)

lift an upward force due to a pressure difference between the top and bottom of a wing (p. 396)

linear graph a graph in which the displayed data form a straight line (p. 347)

liquid the state of matter in which a material has a definite volume but not a definite shape (p. 69)

longitudinal wave a wave in which the vibration of the medium is parallel to the direction the wave travels (p. 502)

loudness a physical response to the intensity of sound, modified by physical factors (p. 515)

luminous a description of an object that gives off its own light (p. 558)

M

machine a device that changes a force (p. 417)

magnetic domain a region that has a large number of atoms with aligned magnetic fields (p. 632)

magnetic field a field in a region of space that exerts magnetic forces; a field produced by magnets, by changing electric fields, or by moving charges (pp. 533, 631)

magnetic force the force a magnetic field exerts on a magnet, on a ferromagnetic material, or on a moving electric charge (p. 630)

magnetic pole a region on a magnet where the force produced by the magnet is strongest (p. 630)

magnetosphere the area surrounding Earth that is influenced by Earth's magnetic field (p. 632)

malleability the ability of a solid to be hammered without shattering (p. 46)

manipulated variable the variable that causes a change in another variable (p. 8)

mass the amount of matter in an object (p. 16); a measure of the inertia of an object, which depends on the amount of matter the object contains (p. 365)

mass number the sum of the number of protons and neutrons in the nucleus of an atom (p. 110)

mechanical advantage the number of times that a machine increases an input force (p. 421)

mechanical energy the energy associated with the motion and position of everyday objects (p. 450)

mechanical wave a disturbance in matter that carries energy from one place to another (p. 500)

medium the material through which a wave travels (p. 500)

melting point the temperature at which a substance changes from solid to liquid (p. 47)

metals elements that are good conductors of heat and electric current (p. 135)

metallic bond the attraction between a metal cation and the shared electrons that surround it (p. 176)

metalloids elements with properties that fall between those of metals and nonmetals (p. 136)

microscope an optical instrument that uses lenses to provide enlarged images of very small, near objects (p. 584)

mirage a false or distorted image (p. 548)

model a representation of an object or event (p. 10)

molarity the number of moles of a dissolved solute per liter of solution (p. 239)

molar mass the mass of one mole of a substance (p. 196)

mole an amount of a substance that contains approximately 6.02×10^{23} particles of the substance (p. 195)

molecule a neutral group of atoms that are joined together by one or more covalent bonds (p. 166)

momentum the product of an object's mass and its velocity (p. 374)

monomer a small organic molecule that joins with other monomers to form a polymer (p. 275)

N

nearsightedness an eye condition in which distant objects are blurry (p. 590)

net force the overall force acting on an object after all the forces are combined (p. 357)

network solid a solid in which all the atoms are linked by covalent bonds (p. 263)

neutralization a chemical reaction between an acid and a base (p. 244)

neutron a neutral subatomic particle that is found in the nucleus of an atom (p. 109)

newton (N) the SI unit for force, equal to the force that causes a 1-kilogram mass to accelerate at a rate of 1 meter per second squared ($1 \text{ N} = 1 \text{ kg·m/s}^2$) (p. 357)

noble gases the elements in Group 8A of the periodic table (p. 145)

node a point on a standing wave that has no displacement from the rest position (p. 512)

nonlinear graph a graph in which the displayed data form a curved line (p. 348)

nonmetals elements that are poor conductors of heat and electric current (p. 136)

nonrenewable energy resource a source of energy that exists in limited quantities and, once used, cannot be replaced except over the course of millions of years (p. 462)

nuclear energy the energy stored in atomic nuclei (p. 452)

nuclear radiation charged particles and electromagnetic waves that are emitted from the nuclei of radioisotopes (p. 293)

nucleic acid a large, nitrogen-containing polymer, found mainly in the nuclei of cells (p. 279)

nucleus the dense, positively charged mass located in the center of an atom (p. 105)

Glossary

O

observation information obtained through the senses (p. 8)

Ohm's law the relationship of voltage, current, and resistance: $V = IR$ (p. 607)

opaque a description of a material that either absorbs or reflects all of the light that strikes it so nothing can be seen through it (p. 547)

orbital a region of space around the nucleus where an electron is likely to be found (p. 117)

organic compounds compounds that contain carbon and hydrogen, often combined with a few other elements such as oxygen or nitrogen (p. 262)

output arm the distance between the fulcrum in a lever and the output force (p. 428)

output distance the distance an output force acts through in a machine (p. 420)

output force the force exerted by a machine (p. 420)

oxidation-reduction (redox) reaction a chemical reaction in which electrons are transferred from one reactant to another (p. 204)

P

parallel circuit an electric circuit with two or more paths through which charge can flow (p. 610)

pascal (Pa) the SI unit of pressure, equal to 1 newton per square meter (N/m^2) (p. 391)

period a row in a periodic table of elements (p. 131); the time required for one complete cycle of a periodic motion (p. 504)

periodic law the pattern of repeating properties displayed by elements in the periodic table (p. 131)

periodic motion any motion that repeats at regular time intervals (p. 504)

periodic table an arrangement of elements in columns, based on a set of properties that repeat from row to row (p. 127)

pH a measure of the hydronium ion concentration of a solution (p. 247)

phase change a reversible physical change that occurs when a substance changes from one state of matter to another (p. 84)

phosphor a solid material that emits light by fluorescence (p. 559)

photoelectric effect the emission of electrons from a metal caused by light striking the metal (p. 537)

photon a packet of electromagnetic energy (p. 537)

photosynthesis a process in which plants chemically combine carbon dioxide and water into carbohydrates, a process requiring light and chlorophyll (p. 282)

physical change a change that occurs when some properties of a material change, but the substances in the material stay the same (p. 51)

physical property any characteristic of a material that can be observed or measured without changing the composition of the substances in the material (p. 45)

physics the study of matter and energy and the interactions between the two through forces and motion (p. 4)

pigment a material that selectively absorbs certain colors of light and reflects other colors (p. 553)

pitch the frequency of a sound as a listener perceives it (p. 515)

plane mirror a mirror with a flat surface (p. 571)

plasma a state of matter in which atoms have been stripped of their electrons (p. 315)

polar covalent bond a covalent bond in which electrons are not shared equally (p. 168)

polarized light a type of light including light with waves that vibrate in only one plane (p. 548)

polyatomic ion a covalently bonded group of atoms that has a positive or negative charge and acts as a unit (p. 172)

polymer a large molecule formed when many smaller molecules are linked together by covalent bonds (p. 275)

potential difference voltage, or the difference in electrical potential energy between two places in an electric field (p. 606)

potential energy energy that is stored as a result of position or shape (p. 448)

power the rate of doing work (p. 414)

precipitate a solid that forms and separates from a liquid mixture (p. 57)

precision a gauge of how exact a measurement is (p. 19)

pressure the result of a force distributed over an area (pp. 75, 390)

primary colors three specific colors that can be combined in varying intensities to create millions of colors (p. 552)

products new substances formed as a result of a chemical reaction (p. 192)

projectile motion the curved path of an object in free fall after it is given an initial forward velocity (p. 362)

protein a long polymer that forms when amino acids bond together (p. 280)

proton a positively charged subatomic particle that is found in the nucleus of an atom (p. 108)

pulley a simple machine that consists of a rope that fits into a groove in a wheel (p. 432)

pupil the opening that allows light to enter the eye (p. 589)

pure substance matter that always has exactly the same composition; an element or compound (p. 39)

Q

quark a subatomic particle theorized to be among the basic units of matter (p. 305)

R

radiation the transfer of energy by waves moving through space (p. 481)

radioactivity the process in which an unstable atomic nucleus emits charged particles and energy (p. 292)

radioisotope an isotope with an unstable nucleus (p. 292)

rarefaction an area of a longitudinal wave where the particles of the medium are spread out (p. 502)

ray diagram a diagram that shows how light rays change direction when they strike mirrors and pass through lenses (p. 570)

reactant a substance that undergoes change in a chemical reaction (p. 192)

reaction rate the rate at which reactants change into products over time (p. 212)

reactivity the property that describes how readily a substance combines chemically with other substances (p. 55)

real image a copy of an object formed at the point where light rays actually meet (p. 572)

reflecting telescope a telescope that uses mirrors and convex lenses to collect and focus light (p. 581)

reflection the interaction that occurs when a wave bounces off a surface that it cannot pass through (p. 508)

refracting telescope a telescope that uses only lenses to collect and focus light (p. 581)

refraction the bending of a wave as it enters a new medium at an angle (p. 509)

refrigerant a fluid that vaporizes and condenses inside the tubing of a heat pump (p. 490)

regular reflection a reflection that occurs when parallel light waves strike a surface and all reflect in the same direction (p. 547)

relative motion movement in relation to a frame of reference (p. 329)

renewable energy resource a source of energy that can be replaced in a relatively short period of time (p. 463)

resistance the opposition to the flow of electric charges in a material (p. 605)

resonance the response of a standing wave to another wave of the same frequency, with dramatic increase in amplitude of the standing wave (p. 521)

responding variable a variable that changes in response to a change in the manipulated variable (p. 8)

resultant vector the vector sum of two or more vectors (p. 331)

retina the inner surface of the back of the eye, containing light-sensitive nerve endings (p. 589)

reversible reaction a chemical reaction in which the conversion of reactants into products and the conversion of products into reactants happens at the same time (p. 217)

rods light-sensitive neurons in the retina that detect low-intensity light and distinguish black, white, and gray (p. 589)

rolling friction a friction force that acts on rolling objects, caused by the change in shape at the point of rolling contact (p. 360)

S

salt an ionic compound formed when an acid reacts with a base (p. 244)

saturated hydrocarbon a hydrocarbon in which all of the bonds are single bonds (p. 264)

saturated solution a solution that contains as much solute as the solvent can normally hold at a given temperature (p. 236)

scattering a process by which light is redirected as it passes through a medium (p. 549)

science a system of knowledge about the natural world and the methods used to find that knowledge (p. 3)

scientific law a statement that summarizes a pattern found in nature (p. 9)

scientific method an organized plan used for gathering, organizing, and communicating information (p. 7)

scientific notation a way of expressing a value as the product of a number between 1 and 10 and a power of 10 (p. 14)

scientific theory a well-tested explanation for a set of observations or experimental results (p. 9)

screw an inclined plane wrapped around a cylinder (p. 431)

secondary color new color that results when any two of the primary colors are combined (p. 552)

semiconductor a crystalline solid that conducts electric current only under certain conditions (p. 621)

series circuit an electric circuit with only one path through which charge can flow (p. 610)

significant figures all the digits in a measurement that are directly measured, plus the last digit, which is estimated (p. 19)

single-replacement reaction a chemical reaction in which one element takes the place of another element in a compound (p. 202)

sliding friction a friction force that opposes the motion of an object as it slides over a surface (p. 359)

Glossary

slope the steepness of a line, equal to the ratio of a vertical change to the corresponding horizontal change (pp. 23, 334)

solar energy sunlight that is converted into usable energy (p. 464)

solenoid a coil of current-carrying wire that produces a magnetic field (p. 637)

solid the state of matter in which materials have a definite shape and a definite volume (p. 69)

solubility the maximum amount of solute that normally dissolves in a given amount of solvent at a certain temperature (p. 235)

solute a substance whose particles are dissolved in a solution (p. 229)

solution a mixture that forms when substances dissolve and form a homogeneous mixture (p. 42)

solvent a substance in which a solute dissolves (p. 229)

sonar a technique for determining the distance to an object under water (p. 516)

sound wave a longitudinal wave consisting of compressions and rarefactions, which travels through a medium (p. 514)

specific heat the amount of heat needed to raise the temperature of one gram of a material by one degree Celsius (p. 476)

speed the ratio of the distance an object moves to the amount of time the object moves (p. 332)

standing wave a wave that appears to stay in one place and does not seem to move through a medium (p. 512)

static electricity the study of the behavior of electric charges, including how charge is transferred between objects (p. 602)

static friction a friction force that acts on objects that are not moving (p. 359)

strong nuclear force the powerful attractive force that binds protons and neutrons together in the nucleus (pp. 308, 379)

sublimation the phase change in which a substance changes from a solid to a gas or vapor without changing to a liquid first (p. 91)

substance matter that always has exactly the same composition; an element or compound (p. 39)

substituted hydrocarbon a hydrocarbon in which one or more hydrogen atoms have been replaced, or substituted (p. 272)

superconductor a material that has almost zero resistance when it is cooled to low temperatures (p. 605)

supersaturated solution a solution that contains more solute than the solvent can normally hold at a given temperature (p. 236)

surface wave a wave that travels along a surface separating two media (p. 503)

suspension a heterogeneous mixture that separates into layers over time (p. 43)

synthesis reaction a chemical reaction in which two or more substances react to form a single substance (p. 200)

T

technology the use of scientific knowledge to solve practical problems (p. 3)

telescope an optical instrument that uses lenses (or lenses and mirrors) to collect and focus light from distant objects (p. 580)

temperature a measure of how hot or cold an object is compared to a reference point (p. 475)

terminal velocity the constant velocity of a falling object when the force of air resistance equals the force of gravity (p. 361)

thermal conductor a material that conducts thermal energy well (p. 480)

thermal energy the total potential and kinetic energy related to the motion of all the particles in an object (p. 451)

thermal expansion the increase in volume of a material when its temperature increases (p. 476)

thermal insulator a material that conducts thermal energy poorly (p. 480)

thermodynamics the study of conversions between thermal energy and other forms of energy (p. 482)

thermogram a color-coded picture using variations in infrared radiation to show variations in temperature (p. 543)

thermometer an instrument that measures temperature (p. 20)

total internal reflection the complete reflection of a light ray back into its original medium when the angle of incidence is greater than the critical angle of refraction (p. 578)

transformer a device that increases or decreases the voltage of two linked AC circuits (p. 644)

transistor a solid-state component with three layers of semiconductor material, used to turn current on or off or to increase the strength of electronic signals (p. 621)

transition metals elements that form a bridge between elements on the left and right sides of the periodic table (p. 136)

translucent a description of a material that scatters light that passes through it (p. 547)

transmutation the conversion of one element to another through a nuclear reaction (p. 303)

transparent a description of a material that allows most of the light that strikes it to pass through (p. 546)

transuranium elements elements with atomic numbers greater than 92 (p. 304)

transverse wave a wave that causes a medium to vibrate at right angles to the direction in which the wave travels (p. 501)

trough the lowest point of a transverse wave (p. 501)

turbine a device with fanlike blades that turn when pushed, for example, by water or steam (p. 646)

U

unsaturated hydrocarbon a hydrocarbon that contains one or more double or triple bonds (p. 265)

unsaturated solution a solution in which more solute can be dissolved at a given temperature (p. 236)

V

valence electron an electron that is in the highest occupied energy level of an atom (p. 139)

vaporization the phase change in which a substance changes from a liquid into a gas (p. 88)

vapor pressure the pressure caused by the collisions of particles in a vapor with the walls of a container (p. 89)

vector a quantity that has a direction associated with it (p. 330)

velocity the speed and direction an object is moving, measured relative to a reference point (p. 336)

virtual image a copy of an object formed at the point from which light appears to be coming (p. 571)

viscosity the tendency of a liquid to keep from flowing; resistance to flowing (p. 45)

vitamin an organic compound that organisms need in small amounts, but cannot produce (p. 284)

voltage potential difference, the difference in electrical potential energy between two places in an electric field (p. 606)

volume the amount of space taken up by an object (p. 16)

W

waste heat thermal energy discharged into an area at a lower temperature without being converted into useful work (p. 483)

watt (W) the SI unit of power, equal to one joule per second (p. 415)

wavelength the distance between a point on a wave and the same point on the next cycle of the wave (p. 505)

weak nuclear force a powerful attractive force that acts over a short range (p. 380)

wedge a V-shaped object whose sides are two inclined planes sloped toward each other (p. 431)

weight the force of gravity acting on an object (p. 367)

wheel and axle a simple machine that consists of two rigidly attached disks or cylinders, each one with a different radius (p. 430)

work the product of distance and the force in the direction an object moves (p. 412)

work input the work done on a machine as the input force acts through the input distance (p. 419)

work output the work done by a machine as the output force acts through the output distance (p. 420)

Spanish Glossary

A

absolute zero / cero absoluto una temperatura de 0 kelvin (págs. 78, 475)

acceleration / aceleración la tasa a la cual cambia la velocidad (pág. 342)

accuracy / exactitud la cercanía de una medida al valor real de lo que se mide (pág. 19)

acid / ácido un compuesto que produce iones hidronios (H_3O^+) cuando se disuelve en agua; un donante de protones (pág. 241)

actual mechanical advantage / ventaja mecánica real la relación de la fuerza desarrollada con respecto a la fuerza aplicada en una máquina (pág. 422)

air resistance / resistencia del aire fricción de un fluido que actúa sobre un objeto que se mueve a través del aire (pág. 360)

alkali metals / metales alcalinos los elementos del Grupo 1A de la tabla periódica, sin incluir el hidrógeno (pág. 10)

alkaline earth metals / metales terreo-alcalinos los elementos del Grupo 2A de la tabla periódica (pág. 141)

alloy / aleación una mezcla de dos o más elementos, de los cuales al menos uno es un metal, que tiene las propiedades características de un metal (pág. 178)

alpha particle / partícula alfa una partícula de carga positiva que es emitida por algunos núcleos radiactivos y está formada por dos protones y dos neutrones; un núcleo de helio (pág. 293)

alternating current (AC) / corriente alterna (CA) un flujo de energía eléctrica que cambia de positiva a negativa a intervalos regulares (pág. 604)

amino acids / aminoácidos compuestos que contienen los grupos funcionales carboxilo y amino (pág. 280)

amplitude / amplitud el máximo desplazamiento de un determinado medio desde su posición de reposo (pág. 507)

amplitude modulation (AM) / amplitud modulada (AM) un método para la transmisión de señales de radio en el que la amplitud de la onda transmisora varía mientras que la frecuencia permanece estable (pág. 541)

analog signal / señal análoga una señal de variación gradual que se produce al cambiar continuamente el voltaje o corriente en un circuito (pág. 619)

angle of incidence / ángulo de incidencia el ángulo que forma un rayo incidente con una línea perpendicular a la superficie sobre la que impacta (pág. 570)

angle of reflection / ángulo de reflexión el ángulo que forma un rayo reflejado con una línea perpendicular a la superficie sobre la que impacta (pág. 570)

angle of refraction / ángulo de refracción el ángulo que forma un rayo de luz con el normal después de ingresar a un nuevo medio a un ángulo determinado (pág. 575)

anion / anión un ión de carga negativa (pág. 160)

antinode / antinodo un punto de máximo desplazamiento a mitad de camino entre dos nodos y una onda estacionaria (pág. 512)

Archimedes' principle / principio de Arquímedes la equivalencia de la fuerza de flotación de un objeto y el peso del fluido desplazado por el objeto (pág. 401)

aromatic hydrocarbons / hidrocarburos aromáticos hidrocarburos que contienen una estructura de anillos similar al benceno (pág. 26)

astigmatism / astigmatismo condición de los ojos en la que los objetos situados a cualquier distancia aparecen borrosos debido a la forma distorsionada de la córnea (pág. 592)

astronomy / astronomía el estudio del Universo más allá de la Tierra (pág. 4)

atom / átomo la partícula más pequeña de un elemento (pág. 39)

atomic mass unit (amu) / unidad de masa atómica (uma) una doceava parte de la masa que tiene un átomo de carbono-12 (pág. 134)

atomic number / número atómico un único número por cada elemento que equivale al número de protones en un átomo de ese elemento (pág. 110)

average speed / rapidez media la distancia total recorrida dividida por el tiempo que se necesita para recorrer esa distancia (pág. 333)

B

background radiation / radiación de fondo radiación nuclear que se produce naturalmente en el ambiente (pág. 296)

base / base un compuesto que produce iones hidróxidos (OH^-) cuando se disuelve en agua; un receptor de protones (pág. 242)

battery / batería un artefacto que convierte la energía química en energía eléctrica (pág. 606)

beta particle / partícula beta un electrón emitido por un núcleo inestable (pág. 294)

biology / biología el estudio de la vida y los procesos vitales (pág. 4)

biomass energy / energía de la biomasa la energía química que se almacena en las cosas vivas (pág. 464)

boiling point / punto de ebullición la temperatura a la cual hierve una sustancia; la temperatura a la cual la presión del vapor es igual a la presión atmosférica (pág. 47)

Boyle's law / ley de Boyle la variación inversa del volumen de un gas y su presión si la temperatura y el número de partículas son constantes (pág. 79)

buffer / búfer una solución que es resistente a grandes cambios en su pH (pág. 248)

buoyancy / flotación la capacidad que tiene un fluido de ejercer una fuerza ascendente en los objetos colocados en él (pág. 400)

buoyant force / fuerza de flotación una fuerza ascendente que actúa sobre un objeto colocado en un fluido (pág. 400)

C

calorimeter / calorímetro instrumento que sirve para medir la energía térmica que se libera o absorbe durante un cambio químico o físico (pág. 478)

camera / cámara fotográfica un instrumento óptico que registra la imagen de un objeto (pág. 582)

carbohydrate / carbohidrato un compuesto de carbono, hidrógeno y oxígeno en el cual la relación de los átomos de hidrógeno respecto de los átomos de oxígeno es de 2:1 (pág. 278)

catalyst / catalizador una sustancia que afecta la velocidad de una reacción química sin que sea usada en la reacción (pág. 215)

cation / catión un ión con carga positiva (pág. 160)

central heating system / sistema de calefacción central un sistema de calefacción que calienta varias habitaciones desde una ubicación central (pág. 489)

centripetal force / fuerza centrípeta una fuerza que cambia continuamente la dirección de un objeto para hacerlo moverse en un círculo (pág. 381)

chain reaction / reacción en cadena una serie de reacciones de fisión disparadas por neutrones liberados durante la fisión de un núcleo (pág. 311)

Charles's law / ley de Charles la proporción directa del volumen de un gas con respecto a su temperatura (en kelvins), si la presión y el número de partículas del gas son constantes (pág. 78)

chemical bond / enlace químico la fuerza que mantiene los átomos e iones juntos como una unidad (pág. 160)

chemical change / cambio químico cambio que se produce cuando una sustancia reacciona y forma una o más sustancias nuevas (pág. 56)

chemical energy / energía química la energía almacenada en los enlaces químicos (págs. 206, 451)

chemical equation / ecuación química una representación de una reacción química en la cual los reactantes y los productos se expresan como fórmulas (pág. 193)

chemical formula / fórmula química notación que muestra los elementos que contienen un compuesto y la relación de los átomos o iones de estos elementos en el compuesto (pág. 161)

chemical property / propiedad química toda propiedad que produce un cambio en la composición de la materia (pág. 54)

chemistry / química el estudio de la composición, estructura, propiedades y reacciones de la materia (pág. 4)

circuit breaker / interruptor de circuito un interruptor que se abre cuando la corriente en un circuito es demasiado alta (pág. 612)

coefficients / coeficientes los números que aparecen antes de una fórmula en una ecuación química para mostrar las proporciones relativas de cada reactante y producto (pág. 194)

coherent light / luz coherente ondas de luz que tienen la misma longitud de onda, con sus crestas y valles alineados (pág. 560)

colloid / coloide una mezcla que contiene algunas partículas que son de tamaño intermedio entre las partículas pequeñas de una solución y las partículas grandes de una suspensión (pág. 44)

combustion reaction / reacción de combustión una reacción química en la que una sustancia reacciona rápidamente con el oxígeno, produciendo a menudo calor y luz (pág. 204)

complementary colors of light / colores complementarios de la luz dos colores cualesquiera de luz que se combinan para formar luz blanca (pág. 552)

complementary colors of pigments / colores complementarios de pigmentos dos colores cualesquiera de pigmentos que se combinan para formar un pigmento negro (pág. 553)

compound / compuesto una sustancia que está formada por dos o más sustancias más simples y que se puede descomponer en esas sustancias más simples (pág. 40)

compound machine / máquina compuesta una combinación de dos o más máquinas simples que operan juntas (pág. 435)

compression / compresión un área en una onda longitudinal en la cual las partículas de ese medio están juntas entre sí (pág. 502)

computer / computadora un artefacto programable que puede almacenar y procesar información (pág. 622)

concave lens / lente cóncava lente curvada hacia dentro en el centro y que tiene mayor grosor en los bordes exteriores (pág. 576)

concave mirror / espejo cóncavo un espejo que se curva hacia dentro (pág. 572)

concentration / concentración la cantidad de soluto disuelto en una determinada cantidad de solvente (pág. 238)

Spanish Glossary

condensation / condensación el cambio de fase en el que una sustancia cambia de gas o vapor a líquido (pág. 90)

conduction / conducción la transferencia de energía térmica sin transferencia significativa de materia, dentro de un material o entre materiales en contacto (pág. 479); la transferencia de carga eléctrica por contacto directo con un conductor (pág. 602)

conductivity / conductividad la capacidad que tiene un material de permitir que fluyan el calor o las cargas eléctricas (pág. 46)

cones / conos las neuronas sensibles a la luz de la retina que detectan el color (pág. 589)

constant acceleration / aceleración constante un cambio continuo en la velocidad (pág. 345)

constructive interference / interferencia constructiva la interacción entre dos o más ondas en las que los desplazamientos se combinan para formar una onda con un desplazamiento más amplio (pág. 511)

controlled experiment / experimento controlado experimento en el que una sola variable, la variable manipulada, se cambia deliberadamente en un momento determinado (pág. 8)

convection / convección transferencia de energía térmica cuando las partículas de un fluido se mueven de un lugar a otro (pág. 480)

convection current / corriente de convección circulación de un fluido en un circuito cuando el fluido se calienta y se enfría alternativamente (pág. 481)

conversion factor / factor de conversión una razón de medidas equivalentes que se usan para convertir una determinada cantidad de una unidad a otra (pág. 18)

convex lens / lente convexa lente curvada hacia fuera en el centro y más delgada en los bordes exteriores (pág. 576)

convex mirror / espejo convexo espejo curvado hacia afuera (pág. 573)

cornea / córnea capa externa y transparente del ojo (pág. 588)

covalent bond / enlace covalente enlace químico en el que dos átomos comparten un par de electrones de valencia (pág. 166)

crest / cresta el punto más alto de una onda transversal (pág. 501)

critical angle / ángulo crítico el ángulo de incidencia que produce un ángulo de refracción igual a 90 grados (pág. 578)

critical mass / masa crítica la masa más pequeña posible de un material fisionable que puede generar una reacción en cadena (pág. 311)

crystals / cristales sólidos cuyas partículas se encuentran dispuestas en una estructura reticular (pág. 162)

D

decibel / decibelio una unidad que compara las intensidades de diferentes sonidos (pág. 515)

decomposition reaction / reacción de descomposición una reacción química en la que un compuesto se separa en dos o más sustancias más simples (pág. 200)

density / densidad la relación entre el volumen y la masa de un material (pág. 17)

deposition / deposición cambio de fase en el que un gas o vapor cambia directamente al estado sólido sin pasar primero por el estado líquido (pág. 91)

destructive interference / interferencia destructiva la interacción entre dos o más ondas cuyos desplazamientos se combinan para producir una onda con un desplazamiento menor (pág. 511)

diffraction / difracción la curvatura de una onda que se mueve alrededor de un obstáculo o pasa a través de una abertura estrecha (pág. 510)

diffuse reflection / reflexión difusa la reflexión que se produce cuando ondas de luz paralelas chocan contra una superficie áspera y desigual, y se reflejan en muchas direcciones diferentes (pág. 547)

digital signal / señal digital una señal que codifica la información como una secuencia de unos y ceros (pág. 619)

diode / diodo un componente de estado sólido con un semiconductor de tipo n unido a un semiconductor de tipo p (pág. 621)

direct current (DC) / corriente directa (CD) el flujo de carga eléctrica que corre en una sola dirección (pág. 604)

direct proportion / proporción directa una relación entre dos variables cuya proporción es constante (pág. 23)

dispersion / dispersión el proceso de disolución por rotura en partes pequeñas (pág. 230); proceso en el que la luz blanca se separa en colores (pág. 551)

dissociation / disociación separación de iones en un compuesto iónico a medida que éste se disuelve (pág. 229)

distance / distancia longitud de la trayectoria entre dos puntos (pág. 329)

distillation / destilación el proceso que separa las sustancias en una solución según sus puntos de ebullición (pág. 50)

Doppler effect / efecto Doppler un cambio en la frecuencia de sonido provocada por el movimiento de la fuente de sonido, movimiento de la persona que escucha o de ambos (pág. 516)

double-replacement reaction / reacción de sustitución doble una reacción química en la que dos componentes intercambian iones positivos y forman otros dos nuevos compuestos (pág. 203)

E

efficiency / eficiencia porcentaje de trabajo de entrada que se transforma en trabajo de salida en una máquina (pág. 425)

elastic potencial energy / energía elástica potencial energía potencial de un objeto al ser estirado o comprimido (pág. 450)

electric charge / carga eléctrica una propiedad que provoca atracción o rechazo entre partículas subatómicas como los protones y electrones (pág. 600)

electric circuit / circuito eléctrico recorrido completo a través del cual puede fluir la carga eléctrica (pág. 609)

electric current / corriente eléctrica un flujo continuo de carga eléctrica (pág. 604)

electric field / campo eléctrico campo en una región del espacio que ejerce fuerzas eléctricas sobre partículas cargadas; campo generado por cargas eléctricas o por campos magnéticos variables (págs. 533, 602)

electric force / fuerza eléctrica la atracción o rechazo entre objetos con carga eléctrica (pág. 601)

electric motor / motor eléctrico un aparato que utiliza un electroimán para mover o rotar un eje (pág. 639)

electric power / potencia eléctrica la velocidad a la que la energía eléctrica se convierte en otro tipo de energía (pág. 611)

electrical conductor / conductor eléctrico un material a través del cual la carga eléctrica puede fluir fácilmente (pág. 605)

electrical energy / energía eléctrica energía asociada con las cargas eléctricas (pág. 452)

electrical insulator / aislante eléctrico un material a través del cual la carga eléctrica no puede fluir fácilmente (pág. 605)

electrolyte / electrolito un compuesto que produce iones al ser disuelto (pág. 249)

electromagnet / electroimán un solenoide con núcleo ferromagnético (pág. 637)

electromagnetic energy / energía electromagnética una forma de energía que consiste en campos eléctricos y magnéticos variables (pág. 452)

electromagnetic force / fuerza electromagnética una fuerza asociada con las partículas cargadas, la cual tiene dos aspectos, fuerza eléctrica y fuerza magnética (págs. 378, 635)

electromagnetic induction / inducción electromagnética el proceso de generación de corriente en el que un conductor eléctrico se mueve en relación a un campo magnético (pág. 642)

electromagnetic radiation / radiación electromagnética la transferencia de energía por medio de ondas electromagnéticas (pág. 533)

electromagnetic spectrum / espectro electromagnético rango completo de radiación electromagnética (pág. 540)

electromagnetic wave / onda electromagnética onda transversal formada por campos eléctricos y campos magnéticos variables (pág. 533)

electron / electrón una partícula subatómica con carga negativa que se encuentra en el espacio fuera del núcleo de un átomo (pág. 108)

electron cloud / nube de electrones modelo visual de las ubicaciones más probables de los electrones en un átomo (pág. 116)

electron configuration / configuración de electrones la disposición de los electrones en las órbitas de un átomo (pág. 118)

electron dot diagram / diagrama de puntos de electrones diagrama de un átomo, ión o molécula en el que cada punto representa la valencia de un electrón (pág. 158)

electronics / electrónica la ciencia que utiliza corrientes eléctricas para procesar o transmitir información (pág. 618)

electronic signal / señal electrónica información enviada en forma de patrones en el flujo controlado de electrones a través de un circuito (pág. 618)

element / elemento sustancia que no puede ser descompuesta en sustancias más simples (pág. 39)

endothermic / endotérmico la descripción de un cambio en el que un sistema absorbe energía de su entorno (pág. 86)

endothermic reaction / reacción endotérmica una reacción química que absorbe energía del entorno (pág. 209)

energy / energía capacidad de realizar un trabajo (pág. 447)

energy conservation / conservación de la energía práctica para encontrar formas de utilizar menos energía o de utilizarla en forma más eficiente (pág. 466)

energy conversion / conversión de la energía el proceso de cambiar energía de una forma a otra (pág. 454)

energy levels / niveles energéticos energías posibles que pueden tener los electrones de un átomo (pág. 114)

enzyme / enzima una proteína que actúa como catalítico para las reacciones en las células (pág. 284)

equilibrium / equilibrio estado en el que las trayectorias hacia delante y hacia atrás de un cambio físico o químico se realizan a la misma velocidad (pág. 216)

evaporation / evaporación el proceso por el cual una sustancia en estado líquido se transforma en gas a temperaturas por debajo del punto de ebullición de esa sustancia (pág. 89)

exothermic / exotérmico descripción de un cambio en el que el sistema libera energía hacia su entorno (pág. 86)

exothermic reaction / reacción exotérmica una reacción química que libera energía hacia el entorno (pág. 208)

external combustion engine / motor de combustión externa un motor térmico en el que el combustible se quema fuera de él (pág. 486)

F

farsightedness / hipermetropía condición de los ojos que provoca una visión borrosa de los objetos cercanos (pág. 592)

ferromagnetic material / material ferromagnético un material que puede ser magnetizado por su contenido de dominios magnéticos (pág. 632)

filtration / filtración proceso que separa los materiales de acuerdo al tamaño de sus partículas (pág. 50)

fission / fisión una reacción nuclear en que el núcleo de un átomo se separa en dos partes pequeñas (pág. 309)

flammability / flamabilidad capacidad que tiene un material de quemarse en presencia de oxígeno (pág. 54)

fluid / fluido sustancia o mezcla que fluye y que no tiene forma definida (pág. 391)

fluid friction / fricción de fluido una fuerza de fricción que se opone al movimiento de un objeto dentro de un fluido (pág. 360)

fluorescence / fluorescencia proceso en el que un material fosforescente convierte la radiación en luz visible (pág. 559)

focal point / punto de enfoque punto en el que se encuentran o parecen encontrarse los rayos de luz paralelos al eje de un espejo o lente (pág. 572)

force / fuerza la atracción o rechazo que actúa sobre un objeto (pág. 356)

fossil fuels / combustibles fósiles mezclas de depósitos ricos en hidrocarburos que se formaron a partir de restos de organismos (pág. 267)

frame of reference / marco de referencia un sistema de objetos que no se mueve con respecto a otro (pág. 328)

free fall / caída libre movimiento de un objeto hacia la Tierra por causa de la gravedad (pág. 343)

frequency / frecuencia cantidad de ciclos completos en una unidad de tiempo para producir un movimiento periódico (pág. 504)

frequency modulation (FM) / frecuencia modulada (FM) método de transmisión de una señal de radio en el que varía la frecuencia de la onda portadora mientras su amplitud permanece igual (pág. 541)

friction / fricción fuerza que se opone al movimiento de los objetos que se tocan a medida que cada uno de ellos se mueve con respecto al otro (pág. 359)

fulcrum / fulcro punto fijo alrededor del cual gira una palanca (pág. 428)

functional group / grupo funcional átomo o grupo de átomos que determina las propiedades de un compuesto orgánico (pág. 272)

fuse / fusible dispositivo que evita el sobrecalentamiento de un circuito por sobrecarga (pág. 612)

fusion / fusión una reacción nuclear en la que se combinan los núcleos de dos átomos para formar un núcleo más grande (pág. 315)

G

galvanometer / galvanómetro un aparato que utiliza un electroimán para medir pequeñas cantidades de corriente (pág. 638)

gamma ray / rayo gamma una forma penetrante de radiación que emite un núcleo inestable (pág. 294)

gas / gas estado de la materia en el que un material no tiene forma ni volumen definidos (pág. 70)

generator / generador un aparato que convierte la energía mecánica en energía eléctrica por el movimiento relativo de una bobina de alambre respecto de un campo magnético (pág. 643)

geology / geología estudio del origen, historia y estructura de la Tierra (pág. 4)

geothermal energy / energía geotérmica energía térmica existente debajo de la superficie de la Tierra (pág. 464)

gravitational force / fuerza gravitatoria una fuerza de atracción que actúa entre dos objetos cualesquiera (pág. 380)

gravitational potential energy / energía potencial gravitacional energía potencial que depende de la altura de un objeto por encima de un punto de referencia (pág. 449)

gravity / gravedad atracción entre dos objetos cualesquiera por efecto de sus masas (pág. 361)

ground state / estado basal estado en el que todos los electrones de un átomo tienen la mínima energía posible (pág. 118)

grounding / conexión a tierra la transferencia del exceso de carga a través de un conductor a Tierra (pág. 613)

group / grupo columna de elementos en una tabla periódica (pág. 131)

H

half-life / vida media tiempo que requiere la mitad de una muestra de un isótopo radiactivo para descomponerse (pág. 299)

halogens / halógenos los elementos del Grupo 7A de la tabla periódica (pág. 144)

heat / calor transferencia de energía térmica de un objeto a otro debido a la diferencia de temperatura (pág. 474)

heat engine / motor térmico todo artefacto que transforma la energía térmica en trabajo (pág. 483)

heat of fusion / calor de fusión la energía que debe absorber una sustancia para pasar del estado sólido al líquido (pág. 86)

heat of vaporization / calor de vaporización la energía que debe absorber una sustancia para pasar del estado líquido al gaseoso (pág. 88)

heat pump / bomba térmica dispositivo que utiliza el trabajo para transferir energía térmica de un área más fría a un área más cálida (pág. 490)

hertz (Hz) / hercios (Hz) unidad para medir la frecuencia que equivale a un ciclo por segundo (pág. 504)

heterogeneous mixture / mezcla heterogénea tipo de mezcla en la que sus partes son notoriamente diferentes unas de otras (pág. 41)

homogeneous mixture / mezcla homogénea tipo de mezcla en la que las sustancias están distribuidas en forma tan pareja que es difícil distinguir una de otra (pág. 42)

horsepower (hp) / caballo de potencia (hp) unidad de potencia que equivale aproximadamente a 746 vatios (pág. 416)

hydraulic system / sistema hidráulico dispositivo que utiliza la acción de un fluido presurizado sobre pistones de diferentes tamaños para aumentar la fuerza (pág. 395)

hydrocarbon / hidrocarburo compuesto orgánico que solamente contiene hidrógeno y carbono (pág. 264)

hydroelectric energy / energía hidroeléctrica energía que se obtiene a partir del agua en movimiento (pág. 463)

hydrogen fuel cell / pila de combustible de hidrógeno pila que genera electricidad a partir de una reacción controlada entre hidrógeno y oxígeno (pág. 608)

hypothesis / hipótesis una respuesta propuesta ante una pregunta (pág. 8)

I

ideal mechanical advantage (IMA) / ventaja mecánica ideal (VMI) ventaja mecánica de una máquina en ausencia de fricción (pág. 423)

image / imagen copia de un objeto formada por rayos de luz que se reflejan o refractan (pág. 547)

incandescent / incandescente descripción de un objeto lo suficientemente caliente como para brillar (pág. 558)

inclined plane / plano inclinado superficie inclinada a lo largo de la cual una fuerza mueve un objeto hacia una elevación diferente (pág. 431)

index of refraction / índice de refracción la relación entre la velocidad de la luz en un vacío y la velocidad de la luz en un medio (pág. 575)

indicator / indicador una sustancia que cambia de color en presencia de un ácido o una base (pág. 241)

induction / inducción transferencia de carga entre materiales, sin entrar en contacto (pág. 603)

inertia / inercia la tendencia de un objeto a resistir un cambio en su movimiento (pág. 364)

input arm / brazo de entrada distancia entre el fulcro en una palanca y la fuerza aplicada (pág. 428)

input distance / distancia de entrada distancia a través de la cual la fuerza aplicada actúa en una máquina (pág. 419)

input force / fuerza aplicada fuerza que se ejerce sobre una máquina (pág. 419)

instantaneous speed / rapidez instantánea velocidad a la que se mueve un objeto en un momento dado en el tiempo (pág. 334)

integrated circuit / circuito integrado delgada capa de silicio que contiene muchos componentes; microchip (pág. 622)

intensity / intensidad velocidad a la que fluye la energía de una onda a través de una determinada unidad de espacio (págs. 515, 538)

interference / interferencia la interacción de dos o más ondas que se combinan en una zona en común (pág. 510)

internal combustion engine / motor de combustión interna máquina térmica en la que el combustible se quema dentro de la máquina (pág. 487)

inverse proportion / proporción inversa la relación en la que el producto de dos variables es una constante cuando todas las demás variables permanecen constantes (pág. 23)

ion / ión un átomo o grupo de átomos que tiene carga positiva o negativa (pág. 159)

ionic bond / enlace iónico fuerza que mantiene unidos a cationes y aniones (pág. 160)

ionization / ionización proceso por el cual las moléculas neutrales ganan o pierden electrones (pág. 230)

iris / iris parte coloreada del frente del ojo que se expande y contrae para controlar la cantidad de luz que penetra en él (pág. 589)

isomers / isómeros compuestos orgánicos con la misma fórmula molecular pero con diferente fórmula estructural (pág. 265)

isotopes / isótopos átomos de un determinado elemento que posee diferentes cantidades de neutrones y diferentes cantidades de masa (pág. 112)

J

joule (J) / julio (J) unidad del trabajo de SI que equivale a 1 newton por metro (pág. 414)

Spanish Glossary

K

kinetic energy / energía cinética la energía que tiene un objeto debido a su movimiento (págs. 71, 447)

L

laser / láser un dispositivo que genera un haz de luz coherente (pág. 560)

law of conservation of charge / ley de la conservación de la carga ley que establece que la carga eléctrica total en un sistema aislado se mantiene constante; la carga eléctrica nunca se crea ni se destruye (pág. 602)

law of conservation of momentum / ley de la conservación del momento ley que establece que el momento total de un sistema no cambia si no hay fuerza neta que actúe sobre el sistema (pág. 376)

length / longitud la distancia en línea recta entre dos puntos (pág. 16)

lens / lente un objeto hecho con material transparente y delgado que tiene una o dos superficies curvas que pueden refractar luz (pág. 576)

lever / palanca una barra rígida que puede moverse libremente alrededor de un punto fijo (pág. 428)

lift / fuerza de elevación una fuerza hacia arriba creada por la diferencia de presión entre la parte superior y la parte inferior de un ala (pág. 396)

linear graph / gráfica lineal una gráfica en la que los datos mostrados forman una línea recta (pág. 347)

liquid / líquido el estado de la materia en el que un material tiene un volumen definido pero no una forma definida (pág. 69)

longitudinal wave / onda longitudinal una onda en la que la vibración del medio es paralela a la dirección en que viaja la onda (pág. 502)

loudness / volumen una respuesta física a la intensidad del sonido, modificada por factores físicos (pág. 515)

luminous / luminoso la descripción de un objeto que emite su propia luz (pág. 558)

M

machine / máquina un dispositivo que cambia una fuerza (pág. 417)

magnetic domain / dominio magnético una región que tiene muchos átomos con campos magnéticos alineados (pág. 632)

magnetic field / campo magnético un campo en una región del espacio que ejerce fuerzas magnéticas; un campo producido por imanes, por campos eléctricos variables o por cargas en movimiento (págs. 533, 631)

magnetic force / fuerza magnética la fuerza que un campo magnético ejerce sobre un imán, sobre un material ferromagnético o sobre una carga eléctrica en movimiento (pág. 630)

magnetic pole / polo magnético una región de un imán en donde la fuerza es mayor (pág. 630)

magnetosphere / magnetosfera el área que rodea la Tierra y que está bajo la influencia del campo magnético (pág. 632)

malleability / maleabilidad la capacidad que tiene un sólido de ser golpeado sin quebrarse (pág. 46)

manipulated variable / variable manipulada la variable que causa un cambio en otra variable (pág. 8)

mass / masa la cantidad de materia que tiene un objeto (pág. 16); medida de la inercia de un objeto que depende de la cantidad de materia que contiene el mismo (pág. 365)

mass number / número de masa la suma del número de protones y neutrones del núcleo de un átomo (pág. 110)

mechanical advantage / ventaja mecánica la cantidad de veces que una máquina aumenta la fuerza aplicada (pág. 421)

mechanical energy / energía mecánica la energía relacionada con el movimiento y la posición de objetos cotidianos (pág. 450)

mechanical wave / onda mecánica la perturbación en la materia que lleva energía de un lugar a otro (pág. 500)

medium / medio el material a través del cual viajan las ondas (pág. 500)

melting point / punto de fusión temperatura a la cual una sustancia cambia de sólida a líquida (pág. 47)

metals / metales elementos que son buenos conductores de calor y corriente eléctrica (pág. 135)

metallic bond / enlace metálico la atracción existente entre un catión metálico y los electrones compartidos que lo rodean (pág. 176)

metalloids / metaloides elementos con propiedades que están entre las de los metales y los no metales (pág. 136)

microscope / microscopio instrumento óptico que usa lentes para agrandar la imagen de objetos cercanos y muy pequeños (pág. 584)

mirage / espejismo imagen falsa o distorsionada (pág. 548)

model / modelo representación de un objeto o evento (pág. 10)

molarity / molaridad el número de moles de un soluto disuelto por litro de solución (pág. 239)

molar mass / masa molar masa de un mol de una sustancia (pág. 196)

mole / mol cantidad de una sustancia que contiene aproximadamente 6.02×10^{23} partículas de la sustancia (pág. 195)

molecule / molécula un grupo neutro de átomos, unidos entre sí por uno o más enlaces covalentes (pág. 166)

momentum / momento producto de la masa de un objeto y su velocidad (pág. 374)

monomer / monómero una pequeña molécula orgánica que se une con otros monómeros para formar un polímero (pág. 275)

N

nearsightedness / miopía una condición ocular que hace que los objetos distantes aparezcan borrosos (pág. 590)

net force / fuerza neta la fuerza total que actúa sobre un objeto después que todas las fuerzas se combinan (pág. 357)

network solid / sólido reticulado un sólido que tiene todos sus átomos unidos por enlaces covalentes (pág. 263)

neutralization / neutralización la reacción química entre un ácido y una base (pág. 244)

neutron / neutrón una partícula subatómica neutra que se encuentra en el núcleo de un átomo (pág. 109)

newton (N) / newton (N) la unidad de fuerza del SI que equivale a la fuerza que hace que 1 kilogramo de masa se acelere a razón de 1 metro por segundo cuadrado ($1 \text{ N} = 1 \text{ kg·m/s}^2$) (pág. 357)

noble gases / gases nobles elementos en el Grupo 8A de la tabla periódica (pág. 145)

node / nodo un punto de una onda que no presenta desplazamiento con respecto a la posición de reposo (pág. 512)

nonlinear graph / gráfica no lineal una gráfica en que los datos trazados o mostrados forman una línea curva (pág. 348)

nonmetals / no metales elementos que son malos conductores del calor y la corriente eléctrica (pág. 136)

nonrenewable energy resource / recurso energético no renovable una fuente de energía que existe en cantidades limitadas y que una vez utilizada no puede ser reemplazada salvo con el transcurso de millones de años (pág. 462)

nuclear energy / energía nuclear la energía que se encuentra almacenada en los núcleos atómicos (pág. 452)

nuclear radiation / radiación nuclear partículas y ondas electromagnéticas con carga emitidas desde el núcleo de los radioisótopos (pág. 293)

nucleic acid / ácido nucleico un polímero grande con nitrógeno que se encuentra principalmente en el núcleo de las células (pág. 279)

nucleus / núcleo masa densa con carga positiva que se encuentra ubicada en el centro de un átomo (pág. 105)

O

observation / observación información que se obtiene a través de los sentidos (pág. 8)

Ohm's law / ley de Ohm la relación entre voltaje, corriente y resistencia $V = IR$ (pág. 607)

opaque / opaco la descripción de un material que absorbe o refleja toda la luz que incide sobre él de modo que no puede verse nada a través del mismo (pág. 547)

orbital / orbital región de espacio alrededor del núcleo en donde es posible encontrar un electrón (pág. 117)

organic compounds / compuestos orgánicos compuestos que contienen carbón e hidrógeno, a menudo se combinan con algunos otros elementos tales como el oxígeno o nitrógeno (pág. 262)

output arm / brazo de salida la distancia entre el fulcro en una palanca y la fuerza desarrollada (pág. 428)

output distance / distancia de salida distancia a través de la cual actúa una fuerza desarrollada de una máquina (pág. 420)

output force / fuerza desarrollada fuerza que ejerce una máquina (pág. 420)

oxidation-reduction (redox) reaction / reacción de oxidación-reducción (redox) una reacción química en la que hay transferencia de electrones entre los reactantes (pág. 204)

P

parallel circuit / circuito en paralelo un circuito eléctrico con dos o más pasos a través de los que puede fluir carga (pág. 610)

pascal (Pa) / pascal (Pa) unidad de presión del SI que equivale a 1 newton por metro cuadrado (N/m^2) (pág. 391)

period / período hilera en una tabla periódica de elementos (pág. 131); el tiempo que se necesita para tener un ciclo completo de movimiento periódico (pág. 504)

periodic law / ley periódica el patrón de repetición de propiedades que muestran los elementos en la tabla periódica (pág. 131)

periodic motion / movimiento periódico todo movimiento que se repite a intervalos regulares (pág. 504)

periodic table / tabla periódica una organización de elementos en columnas basada en una serie de propiedades que se repiten de hilera en hilera (pág. 127)

pH / pH una medida de la concentración del ión de hidronio que tiene una solución (pág. 247)

Spanish Glossary

phase change / cambio de fase un cambio físico reversible que ocurre cuando una sustancia cambia de un estado de materia a otro (pág. 84)

phosphor / fósforo material sólido que emite luz por fluorescencia (pág. 559)

photoelectric effect / efecto fotoeléctrico la emisión de electrones de un metal causada por la luz que llega hasta un metal (pág. 537)

photon / fotón paquete de energía electromagnética (pág. 537)

photosynthesis / fotosíntesis proceso en que las plantas combinan químicamente dióxido de carbono y agua para formar carbohidratos, proceso que requiere luz y clorofila (pág. 282)

physical change / cambio físico un cambio que ocurre cuando algunas propiedades de un material cambian, pero las sustancias del material permanecen constantes (pág. 51)

physical property / propiedad física toda característica de un material que se puede observar o medir sin cambiar la composición de las sustancias del material (pág. 45)

physics / física el estudio de materia y energía y las interacciones entre las dos a través de fuerzas y movimiento (pág. 4)

pigment / pigmento un material que absorbe selectivamente ciertos colores de luz y refleja otros colores (pág. 553)

pitch / tono frecuencia de un sonido como lo percibe quien lo escucha (pág. 515)

plane mirror / espejo plano espejo con superficie plana (pág. 571)

plasma / plasma el estado de la materia en el que los átomos han sido despojados de sus electrones (pág. 315)

polar covalent bond / enlace polar covalente enlace covalente en el que los electrones no se comparten por igual (pág. 168)

polarized light / luz polarizada tipo de luz que tiene luz con ondas que vibran en un solo plano (pág. 548)

polyatomic ion / ión poliatómico un grupo de átomos con enlaces covalentes de átomos que tiene carga positiva o negativa y actúa como unidad (pág. 172)

polymer / polímero una molécula de gran tamaño que se forma cuando muchas moléculas pequeñas están unidas entre sí por enlaces covalentes (pág. 275)

potential difference / diferencia potencial voltaje, es decir, la diferencia de energía eléctrica potencial entre dos puntos de un campo eléctrico (pág. 606)

potential energy / energía potencial energía que se almacena como consecuencia de la posición o forma (pág. 448)

power / potencia tasa de realizar trabajo (pág. 414)

precipitate / precipitado un sólido que se forma y se separa de una mezcla líquida (pág. 57)

precision / precisión medida de cuán exacta es una medición (pág. 19)

pressure / presión resultado de una fuerza distribuida sobre un área (págs. 75, 390)

primary colors / colores primarios tres colores específicos que se pueden combinar en intensidades variadas para crear millones de colores (pág. 552)

products / productos sustancias nuevas que se forman como consecuencia de una reacción química (pág. 192)

projectile motion / movimiento de proyectil la trayectoria curvada de un objeto en caída libre después de haber recibido una velocidad horizontal inicial (pág. 362)

protein / proteína polímero grande que se forma cuando los aminoácidos se unen entre sí (pág. 280)

proton / protón una partícula subatómica con carga positiva que se encuentra en el núcleo de un átomo (pág. 108)

pulley / polea una máquina simple con una cuerda que pasa por el canal de una rueda (pág. 432)

pupil / pupila abertura que permite la entrada de luz en el ojo (pág. 589)

pure substance / sustancia pura material que siempre tiene exactamente la misma composición; elemento o compuesto (pág. 39)

Q

quark / quark partícula subatómica que según las teorías se encuentra entre las unidades básicas de la materia (pág. 305)

R

radiation / radiación transferencia de energía por ondas que se mueven en el espacio (pág. 481)

radioactivity / radiactividad proceso en el que un núcleo atómico inestable emite partículas con carga y energía (pág. 292)

radioisotope / radioisótopo isótopo con núcleo inestable (pág. 292)

rarefaction / rarefacción área de una onda longitudinal en que las partículas del medio se esparcen (pág. 502)

ray diagram / diagrama de rayo diagrama que muestra cómo los rayos de luz cambian de dirección cuando chocan contra los espejos y pasan a través de los lentes (pág. 570)

reactant / reactante una sustancia que sufre cambios durante una reacción química (pág. 192)

reaction rate / velocidad de reacción velocidad con que los reactantes se transforman en productos en un tiempo determinado (pág. 212)

reactivity / reactividad propiedad que describe con qué facilidad una sustancia se combina químicamente con otras sustancias (pág. 55)

real image / imagen real copia de un objeto que se forma en el punto en que los rayos de luz se encuentran (pág. 572)

reflecting telescope / telescopio reflector telescopio que utiliza espejos y lentes convexas para reunir y enfocar luz (pág. 581)

reflection / reflexión la interacción que se produce cuando una onda rebota contra una superficie que no puede atravesar (pág. 508)

refracting telescope / telescopio refractor telescopio que usa sólo lentes para reunir y enfocar luz (pág. 581)

refraction / refracción la curva de una onda al entrar en ángulo en un nuevo medio (pág. 508)

refrigerant / refrigerante fluido que se vaporiza y se condensa dentro de la tubería de una bomba de calor (pág. 490)

regular reflection / reflexión regular reflexión que se produce cuando ondas de luz paralelas chocan contra una superficie y todas se reflejan en la misma dirección (pág. 547)

relative motion / movimiento relativo movimiento en relación al marco de referencia (pág. 329)

renewable energy resource / recurso renovable de energía fuente de energía que se puede reemplazar en períodos relativamente cortos (pág. 463)

resistance / resistencia oposición al flujo de cargas eléctricas en un material (pág. 605)

resonance / resonancia la respuesta de una onda estacionaria a otra onda de la misma frecuencia, con gran incremento de amplitud de la onda estacionaria (pág. 521)

responding variable / variable respuesta variable que cambia en respuesta a un cambio en la variable manipulada (pág. 8)

resultant vector / vector resultante la suma vectorial de dos o más vectores (pág. 331)

retina / retina superficie interna de la parte posterior del ojo, que contiene terminales nerviosas sensibles a la luz (pág. 589)

reversible reaction / reacción reversible una reacción química en la que la conversión de reactantes en productos y la conversión de productos en reactantes se produce al mismo tiempo (pág. 217)

rods / bastoncillos neuronas sensibles a la luz en la retina que detectan luz de baja intensidad y distinguen blanco, negro y gris (pág. 589)

rolling friction / fricción de rodamiento fuerza de fricción que actúa sobre objetos rodantes y que se produce debido al cambio de forma en el punto de contacto de rodamiento (pág. 360)

S

salt / sal compuesto iónico que se forma cuando un ácido reacciona con una base (pág. 244)

saturated hydrocarbon / hidrocarburo saturado un hidrocarburo que tiene todos sus enlaces simples (pág. 264)

saturated solution / solución saturada una solución que contiene la cantidad de soluto que el solvente puede contener a una cierta temperatura (pág. 236)

scattering / dispersión proceso en el que la luz cambia de dirección cuando atraviesa un medio (pág. 549)

science / ciencia sistema de conocimientos sobre el mundo natural y los métodos que se usan para encontrar esos conocimientos (pág. 3)

scientific law / ley científica una afirmación que resume un patrón que se encuentra en la naturaleza (pág. 9)

scientific method / método científico un plan organizado que se utiliza para recoger, organizar y transmitir información (pág. 7)

scientific notation / notación científica una forma de expresar un valor como el producto de un número entre 1 y 10 y una potencia de 10 (pág. 14)

scientific theory / teoría científica una explicación bien comprobada que corresponde a un conjunto de observaciones o resultados experimentales (pág. 9)

screw / tornillo plano inclinado envuelto alrededor de un cilindro (pág. 431)

secondary color / color secundario color nuevo que resulta cuando se combinan dos colores primarios (pág. 552)

semiconductor / semiconductor un sólido cristalino que conduce corriente eléctrica sólo bajo ciertas condiciones (pág. 621)

series circuit / circuito en serie circuito eléctrico con un sólo trayecto a través del cual puede fluir la carga (pág. 610)

significant figures / cifras significativas todos los dígitos que se miden directamente en una medición, más el último dígito, que es aproximado (pág. 19)

single-replacement reaction / reacción de sustitución simple una reacción química en la que un elemento toma el lugar de otro en un compuesto (pág. 202)

sliding friction / fricción de deslizamiento una fuerza de fricción que se opone al movimiento de un objeto a medida que se desliza sobre una superficie (pág. 359)

Spanish Glossary

slope / pendiente línea inclinada que equivale a la proporción de un cambio vertical con el correspondiente cambio horizontal (págs. 23, 334)

solar energy / energía solar luz solar que se convierte en energía utilizable (pág. 464)

solenoid / solenoide una bobina de alambre conductor que produce un campo magnético (pág. 637)

solid / sólido estado de la materia en el que los materiales tienen una forma definida y un volumen definido (pág. 69)

solubility / solubilidad cantidad máxima de soluto que se disuelve normalmente en una cierta cantidad de solvente a cierta temperatura (pág. 235)

solute / soluto una sustancia cuyas partículas se disuelven en una solución (pág. 229)

solution / solución una mezcla que se forma cuando se disuelven sustancias y forman una mezcla homogénea (pág. 42)

solvent / solvente una sustancia en la que se disuelve un soluto (pág. 229)

sonar / sonar técnica que sirve para determinar la distancia a un objeto bajo el agua (pág. 516)

sound wave / onda sonora onda longitudinal que consiste en compresiones y rarefacciones y que viaja a través de un medio (pág. 514)

specific heat / calor específico cantidad de calor que se necesita para elevar la temperatura de un gramo de material un grado Celsius (pág. 476)

speed / rapidez proporción de la distancia a que se mueve un objeto con respecto a la cantidad de tiempo en que se mueve el objeto (pág. 332)

standing wave / onda estacionaria onda que parece quedarse en un lugar y no moverse a través de un medio (pág. 512)

static electricity / electricidad estática estudio del comportamiento de las cargas eléctricas y de la manera en que la carga se transfiere entre objetos (pág. 602)

static friction / fricción estática fuerza de fricción que actúa sobre los objetos que no se mueven (pág. 359)

strong nuclear force / fuerza nuclear fuerte una fuerza potente de atracción que une protones y neutrones en el núcleo (págs. 308, 379)

sublimation / sublimación cambio de fase en que una sustancia cambia de estado sólido a gaseoso o vapor sin pasar por el estado líquido primero (pág. 91)

substance / sustancia materia que siempre tiene exactamente la misma composición; elemento o compuesto (pág. 39)

substituted hydrocarbon / hidrocarburo sustituido hidrocarburo en el que uno o más átomos de hidrógeno han sido reemplazados o sustituidos (pág. 272)

superconductor / superconductor un material con resistencia casi cero al ser enfriado a temperaturas bajas (pág. 605)

supersaturated solution / solución supersaturada una solución que contiene más cantidad de soluto que el solvente puede retener normalmente a una determinada temperatura (pág. 236)

surface wave / onda superficial onda que viaja a lo largo de una superficie y que separa dos medios (pág. 503)

suspension / suspensión una mezcla heterogénea que se separa con el tiempo en capas (pág. 43)

synthesis reaction / reacción de síntesis reacción química en la que dos o más sustancias reaccionan para formar una sola sustancia (pág. 200)

T

technology / tecnología uso del conocimiento científico para resolver problemas prácticos (pág. 3)

telescope / telescopio un instrumento óptico que usa lentes (o lentes y espejos) para recoger y enfocar luz desde objetos lejanos (pág. 580)

temperature / temperatura es una medición de cuán caliente o frío está un objeto si se lo compara con un punto de referencia (pág. 475)

terminal velocity / velocidad terminal velocidad constante de un objeto en caída cuando la fuerza de resistencia del aire es igual a la fuerza de gravedad (pág. 361)

thermal conductor / conductor térmico un material que conduce bien la energía térmica (pág. 480)

thermal energy / energía térmica la energía potencial y cinética total relacionada con el movimiento de todas las partículas de un objeto (pág. 451)

thermal expansion / expansión térmica aumento de volumen de un material cuando incrementa su temperatura (pág. 476)

thermal insulator / aislante térmico material que no conduce bien la energía térmica (pág. 480)

thermodynamics / termodinámica estudio de las conversiones entre energía térmica y otras formas de energía (pág. 482)

thermogram / termograma un dibujo o imagen con código de colores que utiliza variaciones en la radiación infrarroja y que sirve para mostrar los cambios en la temperatura (pág. 543)

thermometer / termómetro un instrumento que sirve para medir la temperatura (pág. 20)

total internal reflection / reflexión interna total la reflexión completa de un rayo de luz que regresa a su medio original cuando el ángulo de incidencia es mayor que el ángulo crítico de refracción (pág. 578)

transformer / transformador un dispositivo que aumenta o disminuye el voltaje de dos circuitos CA conectados (pág. 644)

transistor / transistor un componente en estado sólido que tiene tres capas de material semiconductor y que sirve para encender o apagar corriente o para incrementar la fuerza de señales electrónicas (pág. 621)

transition metals / metales de transición elementos que forman un puente entre los elementos que se encuentran en el lado izquierdo y derecho de la tabla periódica (pág. 136)

translucent / translúcido descripción de un material que dispersa luz que pasa a través del mismo (pág. 547)

transmutation / transmutación la conversión de un elemento en otro por medio de una reacción nuclear (pág. 303)

transparent / transparente descripción de un material que deja pasar la mayor parte de la luz que incide sobre él (pág. 546)

transuranium elements / elementos del grupo transuranio elementos que tienen números atómicos mayores que 92 (pág. 304)

transverse wave / onda transversal onda que hace vibrar a un medio en ángulos rectos en la dirección en que viaja la onda (pág. 50)

trough / valle punto más bajo de una onda transversal (pág. 501)

turbine / turbina un dispositivo con paletas en forma de ventilador que giran cuando son impulsadas, por ejemplo, por agua o vapor (pág. 646)

U

unsaturated hydrocarbon / hidrocarburo no saturado hidrocarburo que contiene uno o más enlaces dobles o triples (pág. 265)

unsaturated solution / solución no saturada una solución en que puede disolverse más soluto a una determinada temperatura (pág. 236)

V

valence electron / electrón de valencia electrón que se encuentra en el nivel energético más alto ocupado que tiene un átomo (pág. 139)

vaporization / vaporización cambio de fase en que una sustancia cambia de estado líquido a gaseoso (pág. 88)

vapor pressure / presión de vapor presión que producen las colisiones o choques de partículas en un vapor dentro de las paredes de un contenedor (pág. 89)

vector / vector una cantidad que tiene una dirección asociada con la misma (pág. 330)

velocity / velocidad la rapidez y la dirección en la que se mueve un objeto y se mide según un punto de referencia (pág. 336)

virtual image / imagen virtual una copia de un objeto que se forma en el punto desde donde parece venir la luz (pág. 571)

viscosity / viscosidad la tendencia que tiene un líquido a dejar de fluir; resistencia a fluir (pág. 45)

vitamin / vitamina un compuesto orgánico que no producen los organismos vivos pero lo necesitan en pequeñas cantidades (pág. 284)

voltage / voltaje diferencia potencial, la diferencia de energía eléctrica potencial entre dos puntos en un campo eléctrico (pág. 606)

volume / volumen la cantidad de espacio que ocupa un objeto (pág. 16)

W

waste heat / calor perdido energía térmica descargada en un área a una temperatura más baja que no se convierte en trabajo útil (pág. 483)

watt (W) / vatio (W) unidad de potencia del SI que equivale a un julio por segundo (pág. 415)

wavelength / longitud de onda la distancia entre un punto de la onda y el mismo punto en el siguiente ciclo de la onda (pág. 505)

weak nuclear force / fuerza nuclear débil fuerza de atracción potente que actúa sobre un alcance corto o a corta distancia (pág. 380)

wedge / cuña objeto en forma de V que tiene lados en forma de dos planos inclinados, el uno hacia el otro (pág. 431)

weight / peso fuerza de gravedad que actúa sobre un objeto (pág. 367)

wheel and axle / rueda y eje una máquina simple que está formada por dos discos o cilindros rígidamente unidos y cada uno tiene un radio diferente (pág. 430)

work / trabajo el producto de la distancia y fuerza en la dirección en que se mueve un objeto (pág. 412)

work input / trabajo de entrada trabajo que realiza una máquina cuando la fuerza aplicada actúa a través de la distancia de entrada (pág. 419)

work output / trabajo de salida trabajo que realiza una máquina cuando la fuerza desarrollada actúa a través de la distancia de salida (pág. 420)

Index

Index (continued)

Index (continued)

Index (continued)

isobutane, 265
isomers, **265**
isotopes, **112**
    atomic mass and, 134
    of chlorine, 134
    radioisotopes, 293
Issues in Science, 59, 281, 302, 513, 579, 608

J

Joule, James Prescott, **414,** 482
joule (J), **414,** 476
journals, scientific, 25

K

karats, and purity of gold, 178
Keck telescopes, 580
kelp forests, 726
Kelvin (K) scale, 20, 475
    gas laws and, 78, 80
kilometers (km), 329
kilopascal (kPa), 75
kilowatt-hours, 612
kilowatts, 611
kinetic energy, 6, **71, 447**–448, 456–457
    in crystal lattices, 164
    temperature and, 475
kinetic theory, 71
    of gases, 73
    of matter, 9
knowledge, scientific, 3
krypton, 145, 561

L

L1 *Strategies for students who need additional help, Teacher's Edition pages 3, 5, 6, 7, 11, 14, 15, 19, 20, 22-25, 41–44, 47, 48, 51, 54, 57, 58, 68–72, 74, 76–78, 80, 81, 85, 88, 91, 100, 101, 103, 105, 108–110, 112, 113, 118, 126, 129, 131, 132, 136, 138, 140, 143–145, 160–162, 164, 166, 169, 174, 175, 177, 179, 181, 192, 194, 195, 197, 198, 202, 204, 205, 207–209, 212, 215, 217–219, 229, 230, 234–239, 241, 245–247, 249, 262, 263, 268, 269, 273–276, 279, 280, 282, 284, 293–295, 297, 299, 301, 304, 305, 309, 310, 315, 328, 329, 331, 333, 336, 337, 342, 343, 346–348, 356–358, 361, 362, 364, 367–369, 372, 376–378, 381, 382, 390–393, 397, 400, 404, 414–416, 419–421, 425, 426, 428, 431–433, 435, 446, 448, 449, 452, 455, 457–459, 462–464, 466, 475, 477–480, 483, 486, 489, 491, 492, 501, 503, 504, 506, 507, 510–512, 516, 517, 521, 533–536, 538–540, 542, 543, 545, 548, 549, 551–553, 558, 562, 573–575, 578, 580, 581, 584, 585, 589, 590, 592, 600, 602–604, 606, 607, 609–611, 613, 619, 622, 630, 633, 635, 636, 639, 643, 645, 646, 647*

L3 *Strategies for students who need to be challenged, Teacher's Edition pages 21, 44, 49, 87, 90, 111, 125, 137, 163, 196, 201, 233, 243, 248, 271, 277, 314, 335, 360, 366, 402, 429, 434, 450, 465, 488, 502, 505, 520, 540, 544, 560, 561, 591, 606, 612, 620, 632, 634*

labs. *See* Contents, xii–xv.
Land, Edwin H., 583

Landsteiner, Karl, 252
lanthanide series, 136
lapis lazuli, 555
laser, **560**–561
laser surgery, 591
latitude and longitude system, 339
lattice
    crystal, 162–163, 164
    metal, 177
lauric acid, 92
Lavoisier, Antoine, 126, 196
laws, scientific, 9
lead, 142
    compounds of, 203
    dangers of, 148
Learning disabled, See Inclusion Students
Le Châtelier, Henri-Louis, 218, 266
Le Châtelier's principle, 218–219
LEDs. *See* light-emitting diodes.
length, **16**
lens(es), 574–**576,** 577–578
    concave, 576
    convex, 576–577
    of eye, 589, 591
levers, 427, **428**–429
Leyster, Judith, 557
Libby, W. F., 313
life science, 4
lift, **396**–397, 398–399
light, 546–549. *See also* color.
    bulbs, 145, 176, 558
    coherent, 560
    energy levels and, 116
    fluorescent, 559
    incandescent, 558, 559
    incident ray of, 575
    index of refraction, 574–575
    laser, 560–561
    neon lights, 145, 561
    polarization of, 548–49
    reflection of, 135, 547
    refraction of, 548
    scattering of, 43, 44, 549
    sodium-vapor, 562
    speed of, 14, 15, 310, 459, 534, 574
    tungsten-halogen, 562
    visible, 452, 540, 543
light-emitting diodes (LEDs), 129, 183, 621
lighthouses, 170, 577
light microscopes, 584
lightning, 452, 600, 603
lime (quicklime), 170, 204
    in glass-making, 137
limestone, 141, 270, 673, 711
    reaction with hydrochloric acid, 199
line, slope of, 334
linear graphs, 23, **347**
Lippershey, Hans, 581
liquid(s), **69,** 135
    behavior of, 73
    conduction in, 479
    kinetic theory and, 73
    viscosity of, 45
liquid crystal display (LCD), 620
lithium, 140
    atomic structure and, 118, 131
litmus paper, 241, 243
longitude, 339

---

longitudinal waves, **502,** 505, 507
lost wax casting, 49
loudness, **515**
loudspeakers, 518–519, 639
Lowell, Francis, 422
luminous, 558
lye, 240, 242

M

McCormick, Cyrus, 423
machines, **417**
    compound, 435
    efficiency of, 425–426
    inclined plane, 427, 430
    levers, 427, 428–429
    mechanical advantage, 421–424, 438–439
    pulley, 427, 432–434
    screw, 427, 431
    simple, 427–433
    wedge, 427, 431
    wheel and axle, 427, 430
    work and, 417–420
macula, 591
magnesium, 135, 138, 141
    alloys of, 181
    electron dot diagram, 166
    as essential element, 146
    reaction with oxygen, 101
magnesium chloride, 161, 231
magnetic resonance imaging (MRI), 640–641
magnetic stripes, 679
magnetism, 628–653
    Earth's magnetic field, 632
    electromagnets, 637–638
magnetic domains, **632**–633
magnetic materials, 632–633
magnetic field, **533, 631**–632, 637
magnetic forces, 379, **630**
magnetic poles, **630**
magnetite, 630
magnetophone, 518
magnetosphere, **632**
malleability, **46,** 135–137
manipulated variable, **8,** 23
Marsden, Ernest, 104
Mars, 2
mass, **16, 365**
    compared to weight, 368–369
    conservation of, 191, 193
    conversion between mole and, 196, 197, 198
    conversion to energy, 310
    critical, 311
    energy and, 447, 449, 459
    mass-energy equation, 310, 459
    molar, 196, 197
    percent by, 238
    of reactant, 197
    thermal energy and, 475
mass number, **110**
    isotopes and, 112
mass transportation, 466
Math Practice, Teacher's Edition pages 15, 20, 80, 81, 174, 175, 195, 198, 295, 297, 333, 337, 346, 348, 367, 369, 393, 415, 416, 425, 426, 448, 452, 458, 459, 477, 478, 506, 507, 535, 538, 611, 613
Math problems, See Math Practice

Index (continued)

Index (continued)

Index (continued)

Acknowledgments

Staff Credits

The people who made up the *Prentice Hall Physical Science: Concepts in Action* team—representing design services, editorial, editorial services, market research, marketing services, education technology, production services, project office, and publishing processes—are listed below. Bold type denotes the core team members.

Leann Davis Alspaugh, Neil Benjamin, **Barbara Bertell,** Suzanne Biron, Diane Braff, Kristen Cetrulo Braghi, **Kenneth Chang,** Jonathan D. Cheney, **Todd Christy,** Bob Craton, Kathleen J. Dempsey, **Frederick Fellows,** Jonathan Fisher, Kathryn Fobert, Paul Gagnon, Julia Gecha, Robert Graham, Ellen Welch Granter, Susan Hutchinson, **Judie Jozokos,** Kelly Kelliher, Dotti Marshall, **Tim McDonald,** Terri Mitchell, **Jen Paley, Caroline M. Power,** Siri Schwartzman, Malti Sharma, Emily Soltanoff, Jennifer Teece

Additional Credits

Ann Bekebrede, Frances Jenkins, Matt Walker

The DK Designs team who contributed to *Prentice Hall Physical Science: Concepts in Action* were as follows: Samantha Borland, Marian Broderick, Carole Curcie, Richard Czapnik, Nigel Duffield, Cynthia Frazer, James A. Hall, Rose Horridge, Heather Jones, Anthony Limerick, David Lloyd, Marie Osborn, Leyla Ostovar, Ralph Pitchford, Pamela Shiels, Andrew Szudek

Illustration

Leann Davis Alspaugh: 223; DK Picture Library: 487, 517, 581, 584, 621, 662; Paul Gagnon: 4; Gene Givan: 234, 272, 289; Ellen Welch Granter: 16, 17, 22b, 23, 24b, 92, 134b, 150, 208l, 208r, 215, 221, 469, 470, 542, 543, 558, 559, 563, 564, 566, 567r, 775; Graph/fix: Bruce Cowie: 130b, 358, 361, 396, 413, 418, 431, 480, 481, 482, 491b, 512, 571; J/B Woolsey Associates: 131, 132–133, 134t, 140, 141, 142, 143, 144, 145, 153, 155, 161t; George Kelvin: 259, 343, 601, 605, 606, 609, 632, 633, 636, 638, 639, 643, 647; George Ladas: 336, 337, 343; Matt Mayerchak: 2, 7, 14, 22t, 100t, 108, 113, 126, 130t, 139, 152, 158, 165, 170, 176, 186, 192, 199, 206, 212, 216, 222, 292, 298, 303, 308t, 318, 356, 363, 372, 378, 384, 390, 394, 400t, 406r, 412t, 417, 421t, 427, 440, 446, 453, 462, 468, 474, 479, 486t, 494, 500, 504t, 508, 514t, 526, 570t, 574, 580, 588, 594; Morgan-Cain & Associates: 20, 29, 30, 31, 65, 85b, 88, 97, 123l, 123r, 127, 159t, 159b, 160, 161b, 162, 164, 166t, 166b, 168t, 168b, 169, 171, 172t, 172b, 173, 175, 177, 187, 188l, 188r, 224, 225, 229, 230, 231, 237, 263, 264, 294–295, 296, 299t, 308l, 309, 310, 311, 319, 320, 321, 359, 368, 376, 380, 381, 382, 385, 387, 391, 395b, 397, 400b, 401, 406l, 407, 408, 409, 419, 428, 441, 442, 443l, 471, 475t, 475b, 478, 486b, 489, 490, 492, 496, 497, 501, 502, 503, 504b, 505, 507, 509t, 511, 516, 527, 528, 529, 570l, 572bl, 572br, 573tl, 573tr, 575t, 576l, 576r, 577t, 577m, 577b, 578, 584b, 585, 589, 590, 592, 595, 596l, 596r, 597, 656, 657, 663, 665, 666, 671, 673; Jen Paley: 24t, 26, 28, 38, 41, 42, 45, 47, 54, 60, 62, 64, 68, 71, 72t, 75, 78l, 84, 94, 96, 109, 112, 117, 119, 120, 154, 167, 184, 189, 197, 293, 299b, 357, 377, 383, 386, 392, 395t, 405, 421b, 433, 438, 439, 443r, 463, 476, 479b, 491t, 493, 509b, 514b, 515, 532, 539, 546, 550, 567l, 575b, 663ml, 663tr, 663mr, 668tl, 668bl, 668mr, 668br; Precision Graphics: 44, 46, 69, 70, 72, 77, 78r, 89, 95, 100b, 102, 103, 104, 121, 122, 193, 194, 207, 217, 230, 258, 262, 264, 265, 266, 267, 273, 274, 276, 279, 282, 331, 430, 432, 533, 534, 536, 537, 538, 540, 541, 548; www.TrevorJohnston.com: 8, 85t

Cover design Maria Keogh/Kokopelli Design Studio, Inc.;

Cover photo Tom Sanders/Image State

Photo research Paula Wehde

Dorling Kindersley picture research done in London, England by Cynthia Frazer and Marie Osborn; Dorling Kindersley illustrations done by Richard Bonson, KJA.Artists.com, and Martin Sanders in London, England

Photographs

Every effort has been made to secure permission and provide appropriate credit for photographic material. The publisher deeply regrets any omission and pledges to correct errors called to its attention in subsequent editions.

Unless otherwise acknowledged, all photographs are the property of Pearson Education, Inc.

Photo locators denoted as follows: Top (T), Center (C), Bottom (B), Left (L), Right (R), Background (Bkgd)

Front Cover

(Bkgd) Tom Sanders, (Inset, R) Jello5700/iStockphoto, (Inset, MR) Carroteater/Shutterstock, (Inset, ML) Alexey Stiop/Shutterstock, (Inset, L) Barry Winiker/SuperStock.

Back Cover

(Bkgd) Tom Sanders, (Inset, R) Courtesy of The Round Barn Theatre at Amish Acres Historic Farm and Heritage Resort, Nappanee, Indiana, (Inset, MR) SuperStock, (Inset, ML) Ablestock/Getty Images/Thinkstock, **(Inset, L) SuperStock**

Front Matter

i, ii, Tom Sanders; **iv** (B) ©Fukuhara Inc./Corbis; **vi** (TL) Photo Researchers, Inc.; **vii** (B) Alain Nogues/Corbis; **viii** (B) Donald Miralle/Staff/Getty Images; **x** (B) ©Galen Rowell/Corbis; **xi** (TR) Roger Ressmeyer/Corbis; **xiii** (B) Breck P. Kent Natural History Photography; **xv** (B) Colin Keates/DK Images; **xviii** (C) Rosenfeld Images Ltd./Photo Researchers, Inc.

2 Jeff Gentner/©AP Images, (BC,) Photo Researchers, Inc., (TR) Rosenfeld Images Ltd./Photo Researchers, Inc., (BL) Science Photo Library/Photo Researchers, Inc.; **3** (B) ©AP Images, (TL) Courtesy of AT&T Archives and History Center, Warren, NJ, (TR, C) Ryan McVay/Getty Images; **4** (BCL) ©Paul Seheult/Corbis, (TCR) AGStockUSA, (TR) John W. Bova/Photo Researchers, Inc., (L) Kevin Fleming/Corbis, (BR) Leland Bobbé/Corbis, (C) NASA; **5** (B) Richard Berenholtz/Corbis; **6** Dennis MacDonald/PhotoEdit, Inc.; **7** (BR, B) Dennis MacDonald/PhotoEdit, Inc., (TR) Rosenfeld Images Ltd./Photo Researchers, Inc.; **9** (BR) Colin Cuthbert / Newcastle University/Photo Researchers, Inc.; **10** (T) ©The Boeing Company; **11** (TR) Steve Chenn/Corbis; **12** (BL) Jeremy Sutton Hibbert/Rex Features, Limited; **13** (CR, BR) ©DK Images, (CC) Anna Clopet/Corbis; **14** (BL) Frank Zullo/Photo Researchers, Inc., (TR) Rosenfeld Images Ltd./Photo Researchers, Inc.; **16** (TL) Will Hart/PhotoEdit, Inc.; **17** (TR) ©Don Farrall /Getty Images, (B) C Squared Studios /Getty Images; **18** Jonathan Nourok/PhotoEdit, Inc.; **19** (CR) ©DK Images, (B) Tom Pantages; **21** (TR) Sally and Richard Greenhill Photo Library; **22** (TR) Rosenfeld Images Ltd./Photo Researchers, Inc.; **25** (TR) ©AP Images, (TL) Layne Kennedy/Corbis; **34** (TR) Gabe Palmer/Corbis, (CL) Mark Richards/PhotoEdit, Inc., (BR) Scott Speakes/Corbis, (BR) Tom Stack & Associates, Inc.; **35** (BR) Bill Aron/PhotoEdit, Inc., (TR) Peter Beck/Corbis, (BL) Reuters/Corbis, (TL) The Image Works, Inc.; **36** Peter Menzel/Stock Boston; **38** (T) Peter Menzel/Stock Boston, (B) Phil Banko/Corbis; **39** (BR) ©Lester V. Bergman/Corbis, (R, BC) Charles D. Winters/Photo Researchers, Inc.; **40** (CL) Bill Aron/PhotoEdit, Inc., (TL) Dave King/Courtesy of The Science Museum, London/©DK Images, (BL) Mark A. Schneider/Photo Researchers, Inc.; **42** (CL) Fukuhara, Inc./Corbis; **43** (TC) Dennis MacDonald/PhotoEdit, Inc., (BL) Grafton Marshall Smith/Corbis; **44** (TL) Rachel Epstein/PhotoEdit, Inc.; **45** (TBR) E. J. Tarbuck, (T) Peter Menzel/Stock Boston, (B) Ross Durant Photography/Getty Images; **46** (B) Araldo de Luca/Corbis; **47** (TR) Jeffrey Greenberg/Photo Researchers, Inc.; **48** (B) Ric Ergenbright/Corbis; **50** (T) Eda Rogers; **51** (TR) Nancy Ney/Corbis, (C) Paul A. Souders/Corbis; **54** (BL) Michelle Garrett/Corbis, (T) Peter Menzel/Stock Boston; **55** (B) Chinch Gryniewicz; Ecoscene/Corbis; **57** (TL) Grant Smith/Corbis, (TR) Pat Bruno/Positive Images, (BR) Souders Studios/Getty Images; **58** (T) ©Mike Rex/Alamy Images; **59** ©Richard Schultz/Corbis; **63** (CR) C.C. Lockwood/Photoshot; **66** Charles Mauzy/Corbis; **68** (T) Charles Mauzy/Corbis; **69** (BR) Charles D. Winters/Photo Researchers, Inc., (TR) Clive Streeter/DK Images; **71** (BR) Chris Mooney/Getty Images; **72** (TR) Charles Thatcher/Getty Images; **73** (BR) Photo(s) by Jim Whitmer; **74** (TR, TC) Michael Cogliantry/Getty Images; **75** (T) Charles Mauzy/Corbis; **76** Tony Freeman/PhotoEdit, Inc.; **81** (T) Pat Lanza/Photoshot; **84** (T) Charles Mauzy/Corbis; **86** (BL) AGStockUSA, (TR) Galen Rowell/Corbis; **89** (BR) Dave King/Courtesy of The Science Museum, London/©DK Images, (TR) Steve & Dave Maslowski/Photo Researchers, Inc.; **91** Margo Wright/Courtesty Tinker Take-Off; **98** News & Media Relations, Rice University; **100** (T) News & Media Relations, Rice University; **101** (BR) Clive Streeter/©DK Images, (T) Stephen Frisch/Stock Boston; **102** (BL) Clive Streeter/DK Images; **103** (B) Mary Kate Denny/PhotoEdit, Inc.; **105** (TR) Bettmann/Corbis; **108** (BL) Michael Powers/Stock Boston, (T) News & Media Relations, Rice University; **110** (B) ©Dr. R. Legeckis/Photo Researchers, Inc., (TL) Charles D. Winters/Photo Researchers, Inc., (C) Russell Lappa/Photo Researchers, Inc.; **111** (TR) Science Museum/Science & Society Picture Library; **113** (B) Bohdan Hrynewych/Stock Boston, (T) News & Media Relations, Rice University; **118** (TL) William Sallaz/Duoma/Corbis; **119** (TR) Jerry Mason/Photo Researchers, Inc.; **124** Wolfgang Kaehler/Corbis; **126** (BL) Michael Newman/PhotoEdit, Inc., (TR) Wolfgang Kaehler/Corbis; **129** (TR) Alan Schein Photography/Corbis; **130** (TR) Wolfgang Kaehler/Corbis; **135** (BL) Science Photo Library/Photo Researchers, Inc.; **136** (B) Jonathan Nourok/PhotoEdit, Inc.; **138** (TL) ©sciencephotos/Alamy Images, (CR, CL) Charles D. Winters/Photo Researchers, Inc., (TC) Dave King/Courtesy of The Science Museum, London/©DK Images, (CR) Fundamental Photographs, (TRL)

Richard Megna/Fundamental Photographs, (TCL) Science Photo Library/Photo Researchers, Inc.; **139** (B) Mike Fiala/Getty Images, (TR) Wolfgang Kaehler/Corbis; **140** (TR) Richard Megna/Fundamental Photographs; **141** (L) ©inga spence/Alamy Images, (C) ©Stefano Scata /Getty Images; **142** (TR) ©Michael Ventura/Alamy Images, (BL) Dana White/PhotoEdit, Inc.; **143** (TR) David Nunuk/Science Photo Library/Photo Researchers, Inc.; **144** (TR) Elena Rooraid/PhotoEdit, Inc., (B) Pearson Education/Prentice Hall College; **145** (T) Raymond Gendreau/Getty Images; **147** (TR) ©DK Images, (BR) Martin Brigdale/©DK Images, (BL) Philip Dowell/©DK Images, (CC) Roger Phillips/©DK Images, (CL) Stephen Hayward/©DK Images, (CR) Steve Gorton/©DK Images; **156** George D. Lepp/Corbis; **158** (TR) George D. Lepp/Corbis; **161** (BR) Galen Rowell/Corbis; **162** (TR) ©M. Claye/Jacana Scientific Control/Photo Researchers, Inc.; **163** (TCR) Colin Keates/©DK Images, (TR) Colin Keates/The Natural History Museum, London/©DK Images; **165** (B) Charles Gupton/Stock Boston, (TR) George D. Lepp/Corbis; **166** (TL) Mark M. Lawrence/Corbis; **170** (T) George D. Lepp/Corbis, (BL) Jennifer Cheung; **171** (TR, TL) Thomas Markusen/Markusen Metal Studios Ltd.; **172** (TL) ©Matthias Kulka/Corbis; **176** (BL) Andrew Syred/Photo Researchers, Inc., (T) George D. Lepp/Corbis; **178** (BC) ©Dave King/Motoring Picture Library. National Motor Museum, Beaulieu/DK Images, (CR) Hulton Archive/Getty Images; **179** (CR) George Hall/Corbis; **180** (TL) ©SuperStock/AGE Fotostock, (TR) Paul Conklin/PhotoEdit, Inc.; **182** (BL) ©DK Images, (BC) Colin Keates/©DK Images; **183** (TC) ©Clive Streeter/Courtesy of The Science Museum, London/DK Images, (TR) Clive Streeter/©DK Images, (TR) Jan Hinsch/Science Photo Library/Photo Researchers, Inc., (C) Matthew Ward/©DK Images, (BL) Tony Craddock/Photo Researchers, Inc.; **192** (BL) ©Charles O'Rear/Corbis; **194** (TL) Stock Connection; **197** John E. Kelly/Getty Images; **199** (BR) David Bartruff/Stock Boston; **200** (TL) Tom Pantages; **201** (TR) Don Johnston/Getty Images; **202** (TR) Clive Steeter/©DK Images, (TC, BL) Clive Streeter/©DK Images; **203** (TR) Richard Megna/Fundamental Photographs; **204** (TL) Charles D. Winter/Photo Researchers, Inc., (B) Richard Megna/Fundamental Photographs; **206** (BL) Bill Bachmann/PhotoEdit, Inc.; **209** (TR) Richard Megna/Fundamental Photographs; **211** (BC) Mike Stewart/Corbis, (CR) Paul A. Souders/Corbis; **212** (BL) Will Hart; **213** (BR) Steven Martine/©AP Images; **214** (BL) ©DK Images; **216** (B) David Sailors Photography, (B) David Sailors/Corbis; **218** (B) Edgar Fahs Smith Collection/Rare Book and Manuscript Library, University of Pennsylvania, (T) Getty Images; **219** (TR) Ken Graham/Accent Alaska; **226** Claus Meyer/Minden Pictures; **228** (T) Claus Meyer/Minden Pictures, (B) Sea Images/PhotoLibrary Group, Inc.; **229** (TR) Chris Collins/Corbis; **230** (TL) Eric Kamp/PhotoLibrary Group, Inc.; **231** (TR) Annie Griffiths Belt/Corbis; **233** (TR) Dick Makin Imaging; **235** (T) Claus Meyer/Minden Pictures; **236** (R) Fundamental Photographs, (TL) Jules Frazier/Getty Images, (C, BL) Richard Megna/Fundamental Photographs; **237** (BR) Mark Hanauer/Corbis; **238** (BR) Steve Gorton/©DK Images; **239** (TR) Bill Varie/Corbis; **240** (T) Claus Meyer/Minden Pictures, (B) Russ Lappa; **241** (BR) Paul Silverman/Fundamental Photographs; **243** (B) Bob Krist/Corbis, (T) PictureNet/Corbis; **244** (BL) James L. Amos/Corbis; **246** (T) Claus Meyer/Minden Pictures, (B) The Image Works, Inc.; **249** (TR) David Young-Wolff/Getty Images; **256** (R) Fundamental Photographs, (L, C) Richard Megna/Fundamental Photographs; **260** Arnulf Husmo/Getty Images; **262** (T) Arnulf Husmo/Getty Images, (B) Mark A. Johnson/Corbis; **264** (TL) Javier Larrea Roa/AGE Fotostock; **266** (BL) C. Marvin Lang/University of Wisconsin at Stevens Point; **267** (B) ©David Lyons/Alamy Images, (T) Davis Muench/Corbis; **268** (T) Barry Rowland/AGE Fotostock; **269** (T) Spencer Platt/Getty Images; **272** (T) Arnulf Husmo/Getty Images; **274** (TR) Hisham Ibrahim/Getty Images; **275** (T) Arnulf Husmo/Getty Images, (B) Digital Vision/Getty Images; **276** (TC) Andy Crawford/©DK Images, (TL) Michael Pole/Corbis; **277** (B) ©DK Images, (TR) The Advertising Archive; **278** ©Bichon/photocuisine/Corbis; **279** (BL) Stephen Simpson/Getty Images; **280** (L) Andrew Whittuck/DK Images; **281** Scott Camazine/Photo Researchers, Inc., (TL) Yogi, Inc./Corbis; **282** (B) Aldo Torelli/Getty Images, (T) Arnulf Husmo/Getty Images; **284** (TL) Michael P. Gadomski/Photo Researchers, Inc.; **287** (CR) Shannon Fagan/Corbis; **290** CERN/Photo Researchers, Inc.; **292** (BL) ©The Granger Collection, NY, (TR) CERN/Photo Researchers, Inc., (BC) Jean-Loup Charmet/Science Photo Library/Photo Researchers, Inc.; **293** (TR) Francois Gohier/Photo Researchers, Inc.; **296** (TL) Roberto de Gugliemo/Photo Researchers, Inc.; **297** (TR) Alain Nogues/Corbis; **298** (TR) CERN/Photo Researchers, Inc., (BL) Kenneth Garrett; **301** ©The Trustees of The British Museum; **302** (T) Creatas/©Punchstock; **303** (TR) CERN/Photo Researchers, Inc., (BR) David Lees/Corbis; **304** NASA; **305** (TR) David Parker/Science Photo Library/Photo Researchers, Inc.; **306** (TL, R) Roger Ressmeyer/Corbis; **308** (TR) CERN/Photo Researchers, Inc.; **309** (BR) ©AP Images;

311 (BR) Matthew McVay/Getty Images; **312** (BR) Hulton Archive/Getty Images, (BL) Photo Researchers, Inc., (BC) Physics Today Collection / American Institute of Physics/Photo Researchers, Inc.; **313** (BL) Science Source/Photo Researchers, Inc.; **315** (TR) Roger Ressmeyer/Corbis; **322** Jon Arnold/Getty Images; **324** (TR) Michael J. Doolittle/The Image Works, Inc., (L) Reuters/Corbis, (BR) Robert Brenner/PhotoEdit, Inc.; **325** (TR) ©Syracuse Newspapers / Suzanne Dunn/The Image Works, Inc., (BL) Adam Woolfitt/Corbis, (C) Jonathan Hillyer/Esto, (BR) Lou Jones/Getty Images; **326** ©Duomo/Corbis; **328** (T) ©Duomo/Corbis, (BL) Tony Freeman/PhotoEdit, Inc.; **329** (T) Pedro Coll/AGE Fotostock; **332** (T) ©Duomo/Corbis, (B) Dennis O'Clair/Getty Images; **334** (TR) Leonard Lessin/Peter Arnold, Inc., (T) Steve Krongard/Getty Images; **336** (T) ©Randy Wells/Corbis, (BL) Sharon Green/Corbis; **338** (CR) ©DK Images, (R) Joel W. Rogers/Corbis, (BL) Stephen Oliver/©DK Images; **340** (TR) ESA / CE / EURO-CONTROL/Photo Researchers, Inc.; **341** (TR) Stephen Oliver/©DK Images; **342** (T) ©Duomo/Corbis, (BL) David Young-Wolff/PhotoEdit, Inc.; **344** (TL) Barnabas Kindersley/©DK Images, (B) Lester Lefkowitz/Corbis; **345** (TR) Benjamin Rondel/Corbis; **347** (T) Karl Weatherly/Getty Images, (B) Michael Newman/PhotoEdit, Inc.; **355** Bob Martin/Getty Images; **356** (BL) ©AP Images, (TR) Bob Martin/Getty Images; **357** (R, L) David Young-Wolff/PhotoEdit, Inc.; **358** (T) David Young-Wolff/PhotoEdit, Inc.; **361** (TR) James Steinberg/Photo Researchers, Inc., (BR) Nicholas Bergkessel, Jr./Photo Researchers, Inc.; **362** (R) Fundamental Photographs, (TC) Peticolas/Megna/Fundamental Photographs; **363** (C) ©Bettmann/Corbis, (B) ©The Granger Collection, NY, (TR) Bob Martin/Getty Images; **364** (TL) Bettmann/Corbis, (BR, BL) Insurance Institute for Highway Safety, (CL) Sheila Terry/Science Photo Library/Photo Researchers, Inc.; **365** (BR, BL) Insurance Institute for Highway Safety; **366** (C) ©Mercedes Benz/©DK Images; **369** (TR) ©AP Images, (TL) Bettmann/Corbis; **370** (R) Steve Fitchett/Getty Images; **371** (TR, CR, BL) David Wootton Photography; **372** (TR) Bob Martin/Getty Images, (BL) Joe McBride/Getty Images; **373** (R) Duomo/Corbis; **374** (C) ©Doug Martin/Photo Researchers, Inc., (CR) Corbis; **375** (BL) Bettmann/Corbis, (BR) Joyrides/Joe Schwartz, (CC) Macduff Everton/Corbis; **378** (TR) Bob Martin/Getty Images, (BL) Ludek Press/Science Photo Library/Photo Researchers, Inc.; **379** (BR) Michelle D. Bridwell/PhotoEdit, Inc., (TR) Tony Anderson/Getty Images; **388** ©Guy Grenier/Masterfile Corporation; **390** (T) ©Guy Grenier/Masterfile Corporation, (B) Aaron Haupt/Stock Boston, (CL) Jonathan Nourok/PhotoEdit, Inc.; **391** (BR) Charles D. Winter/Photo Researchers, Inc.; **392** ©sciencephotos/Alamy Images; **394** (T) ©Guy Grenier/Masterfile Corporation; **396** (T) Firefly Productions/Corbis; **398** (R) Cameron Heryet/Getty Images; **400** (T) ©Guy Grenier/Masterfile Corporation; **402** (BL) Steve Kaufman/Corbis; **404** (T) Layne Kennedy/Corbis; **406** (TL) ©sciencephotos/Alamy Images; **410** Paul Chesley/Getty Images; **412** (TR) Paul Chesley/Getty Images, (BL) Reuters/Corbis; **414** (B) ©David Grossman/The Image Works, Inc., (TL) Dennis MacDonald/PhotoEdit, Inc.; **416** (T) Kevin Fleming/Corbis, (CL) Tony Freeman/PhotoEdit, Inc.; **417** (TR) Paul Chesley/Getty Images; **418** (T) Tony Freeman/PhotoEdit, Inc.; **420** (TL) Kevin Fleming/Corbis; **421** (TR) Paul Chesley/Getty Images; **422** (BL) ©Bettmann/Corbis, (BC) North Wind Picture Archives, (BR) Science & Society Picture Library; **423** (BR) Lambert/Stone/Getty Images, (CL, CC) Science & Society Picture Library; **424** (BL) Wolfgang Deuter/Corbis; **426** (TL) Michael Rosenfeld/Getty Images; **427** (B) ©Rube Goldberg Inc., (TR) Paul Chesley/Getty Images; **428** (C) Richard Hutchings/PhotoEdit, Inc., (TR) Rob Crandall/The Image Works, Inc.; **430** (BL) Neil Beer/Corbis; **431** (TR) Michael Thompson/Animals Animals/Earth Scenes; **432** (TL) H. David Seawell/Corbis; **435** (TR) ©Fukuhara Inc./Corbis; **436** (T) DK Images; **437** (CR) John Kelly/Getty Images; **439** (T) Getty Images; **444** David A. Northcott/Corbis; **446** (TR) David A. Northcott/Corbis, (BL) Galen Rowell/Corbis; **447** (TR) David R. Frazier/Photo Researchers, Inc., (C) Michael Pohuski/Getty Images, (B) Mike Powell/Getty Images; **448** (BL) Adamsmith/Getty Images; **450** (TR) CSA Images, (TL) Mark Thompson/Getty Images; **451** (R) Dawson Jones/Stock Boston, (B) Tom Stewart/Corbis; **452** (B) ©Myron Jay Dorf/Corbis, (T) ©Warren Faidley/Corbis; **453** (B) American Museum of Natural History , (TR) David A. Northcott/Corbis; **454** (T) Myron Jay Dorf/Corbis; **455** (T) Donald Miralle/Staff/Getty Images; **456** (TL) John W. Bova/Photo Researchers, Inc., (B) Phil Degginger/Getty Images; **457** (TR) Gilbert Iundt/TempSport//Corbis; **459** (T) Topham/The Image Works, Inc.; **460** (R) ©Robin Smith/Getty Images; **462** (TR) David A. Northcott/Corbis, (B) George Hunter/Getty Images; **463** (TR) David Parker/Science Photo Library/Photo Researchers, Inc.; **464** (B) ©Visions of America/Joe Sohm/Getty Images, (TL) Charles Krebs/Corbis; **465** (TR) Dave King/©DK Images; **466** John Elk/Stock Boston; **472** ©W.A. Sharman; Milepost 92 ?/Corbis; **474** (BL) ©The Granger Collection, NY, (TR) ©W.A. Sharman; Milepost 92 ?/Corbis; **475** (B) Duncan Smith/Corbis, (TR) Jonelle Weaver/Getty Images; **479** (TR) ©W.A. Sharman; Milepost

718 *Acknowledgments*

92 ?/Corbis, (BR) Alfred Pasieka/Photo Researchers, Inc.; **480** (BL) Eastcott/Momatiuk/Stock Boston, (T) Penina/Getty Images, (BR) Steve Cohen/Getty Images; **483** Geoffrey Wheeler/National Institute of Standards and Technology; **486** (T) ©W.A. Sharman; Milepost 92 ?/Corbis; **491** (B) David Young-Wolff/PhotoEdit, Inc.; **498** Peter Sterling/Getty Images; **500** (B) M. Timothy O'Keefe/Photoshot, (T) Peter Sterling/Getty Images; **504** (T) Peter Sterling/Getty Images; **508** (T) Peter Sterling/Getty Images; **509** (BL) Tom Stack & Associates, Inc.; **510** (TL) Fundamental Photographs, (TR) Richard Megna/Fundamental Photographs; **512** (TL, CL) Richard Megna/Fundamental Photographs; **513** (TL) ©Stephen Frink ; **514** (T) Peter Sterling/Getty Images; **515** (B) C Squared Studios/Getty Images, (T) Martin Fox/PhotoLibrary Group, Inc.; **516** (TL) Darryl Torckler/Getty Images; **518** (BR) Clive Streeter/©DK Images, (BC) Dave King/DK Images, (BL) The Science Museum, London/DK Images; **519** (BL) Bettmann/Corbis, (CC) Corbis; **520** (TR) ©DK Images, (CC) DK Images; **521** (TR) Talaske, Inc.; **522** (B) Randy Jolly/Corbis; **523** (BL) Alan Thornton/Getty Images; **532** (B) Rob Bartee/SuperStock; **536** (TL) Dave King/©DK Images; **541** (B) David Young-Wolff/Getty Images, (T) Robert E. Daemmrich/Getty Images; **542** Spencer Grant/PhotoEdit, Inc.; **543** (TR, TL) FLIR Systems, Inc; **544** (BL) David Arky/Corbis; **545** (T) WDCN / Univ. College London/Photo Researchers, Inc.; **546** (B) ©Stephen Frink ; **547** (B) Arthur Morris/Corbis, (TL) C Squared Studios/Getty Images, (TR) Stockbyte/Getty Images; **550** (BR) B Busco/The Image Bank/Getty Images, (BL) Jerome Wexler/Photo Researchers, Inc.; **551** (TL) Dave King/Courtesy of The Science Museum, London/©DK Images; **552** (BL) Leonard Lessin/Photo Researchers, Inc.; **554** (B) ©DK Images; **555** (T) ©DK Images; **556** (CR, BL) Volker Steger/Photo Researchers, Inc.; **557** (CL) ©National Gallery, London, (CC) RAPHAEL/©National Gallery, London; **558** ©David R. Frazier/Photo Researchers, Inc.; **559** (TR) David Young-Wolff/PhotoEdit, Inc.; **560** (BC) ©DK Images, (C) Dave King/©DK Images; **562** (TL, CL) Tony Freeman/PhotoEdit, Inc.; **565** PhotoEdit, Inc.; **568** David Frates/Positive Images; **570** (TR) David Frates/Positive Images; **571** (TR) Ariel Skelley/Corbis; **574** (TR) David Frates/Positive Images; **576** (BL) Darwin Dale/Photo Researchers, Inc.; **577** (BR) Peter Finger/Corbis; **579** (TL) Stockbyte/Getty Images; **580** (BL) ©Roger Ressmeyer/Corbis, (TR) David Frates/Positive Images; **582** (BR) Corbis, (CR) Science & Society Picture Library; **583** (CL) ©DK Images, (BC) Corbis; **587** (TR) BSIP, Edwige/Photo Researchers, Inc., (TCR) Dave King/DK Images; **588** (BL) Dave Greenwood/Getty Images, (T) David Frates/Positive Images; **591** (B) ©DK Images, (TR, TCR) Paul Parker/Photo Researchers, Inc.; **600** (BL) Michael Newman/PhotoEdit, Inc.; **602** (BL) ©DK Images, (CL) Andy Crawford/©DK Images; **607** (R) Fundamental Photographs; **608** (TL) Grantpix/Photo Researchers, Inc.; **609** (B) Dennis MacDonald/PhotoEdit, Inc.; **612** (B) Russ Lappa; **613** (R) Fundamental Photographs, (T) Stockbyte/Getty Images; **616** (TR) Lawrence Migdale/Photo Researchers, Inc., (BL) NASA; **618** (BL) Ephraim Ben-Shimon/Corbis, (BR) Michael Matisse/Getty Images; **619** (TR) ©DK Images, (CR) DK Images, (B) Science & Society Picture Library; **622** (T) Digital Vision/Getty Images; **626** (CR) Getty Images; **628** Photoshot; **630** (TR) Photoshot, (BL) Reprinted by permission of Houghton Mifflin Company. All rights reserved.; **631** (CR, BR) Spencer Grant/Photo Researchers, Inc.; **634** (TR) Jose Luis Pelaez, Inc./Corbis; **635** (BR) Bettmann/Corbis, (TR) Photoshot; **638** (BR) Harvey Schwartz/PhotoLibrary Group, Inc.; **640** (B) ©DK Images; **641** (BL) Sovereign, ISM/Photo Researchers, Inc.; **642** (TR) Photoshot; **644** (T) SuperStock; **645** (BR) Lloyd Cluff/Corbis; **646** (BL) A & C Wiley/Wales/PhotoLibrary Group, Inc., (TR) David Papazian/Corbis; **654** (C) David Nunuk/Science Photo Library/Photo Researchers, Inc.; **656** (BC) David Frazier/Photo Researchers, Inc., (TR) Photo Researchers, Inc., (CL) Reuters/Corbis; **657** (CR) Bojan Brecelj/Corbis, (BR) James King-Holmes/Science Photo Library/Photo Researchers, Inc., (TC) Pat Lanza/Photoshot, (TL) Stock Boston, (BL) Tom Stack & Associates, Inc.; **658** Pete Turner/Getty Images; **660** (BL) Gary Kazanjan/©AP Images, (TR) Pete Turner/Getty Images; **661** (TR) Martin & Marli Miller; **664** (TR) Pete Turner/Getty Images; **665** (BR) Phillip Hayson/Photo Researchers, Inc., (T) Tom Bean; **666** (TL, B) Breck P. Kent Natural History Photography, (CL) Roberto De Gugliemo/Science Photo Library/Photo Researchers, Inc.; **667** (L) Breck P. Kent Natural History Photography; **668** (T) Colin Keates/DK Images; **669** ©Chip Clark/Smithsonian Institution, (TL) Breck P. Kent Natural History Photography; **670** (TR) Pete Turner/Getty Images; **671** (TR) Simon Fraser/Science Photo Library/Photo Researchers, Inc.; **672** (BL) Breck P. Kent Natural History Photography, (TL) Tom Bean; **673** (T) Francois Gohier/Photo Researchers, Inc., (B) Lynn McLaren/Photo Researchers, Inc.; **674** (B) ©Dirk Wiersma/Photo Researchers, Inc., (BM) Breck P. Kent Natural History Photography; **675** (TR) Breck P. Kent Natural History Photography, (TL) Jan Butchofsky/Corbis, (CL) Jim Sugar/Corbis, (TC) Tom Bean; **676** (TR) Pete Turner/Getty Images, (BL) Science Source/Photo Researchers, Inc.; **677** (TL) Martin Land/Science Photo Library/Photo Researchers, Inc.; **680** (BL) Harry Taylor/©DK Images, (CR) Time & Life Pictures/Getty Images; **681** (CC) NASA, (CR) Roger Harris/Photo Researchers, Inc., (BL) Science Museum, London/DK Images; **683** (TR) Galen Rowell/Corbis; **684** (TR) Pete Turner/Getty Images; **685** (TR) David Parker/Science Photo Library/Photo Researchers, Inc., (B) Tom Bean; **688** (TR) Joseph Sohm/Visions of America/Photo Researchers, Inc.; **690** (B) David Weintraub/Photo Researchers, Inc., (TR) Pete Turner/Getty Images; **692** (T) Breck P. Kent Natural History Photography, (B) G. Brad Lewis/Getty Images; **694** (BC) Francesca Yorke/©DK Images, (BR) Mike Severns/©DK Images, (BL) Rob Reichenfeld/©DK Images; **695** (TR) Colin Keates/©DK Images, (TC) Dave King/©DK Images, (T) DK Images; **696** (T) ©Thomas Wiewandt; **702** ©Thomas Wiewandt; **704** (T) ©Thomas Wiewandt, (B) Planetary Visions Ltd/Photo Researchers, Inc.; **707** (TR) Samuel R. Maglione/Photo Researchers, Inc.; **708** (T) ©Eberhard Hummel/AGE Fotostock; **709** (T) ©Thomas Wiewandt, (B) Breck P. Kent Natural History Photography; **711** (T) ©Egmont Strigl /PhotoLibrary Group, Inc., (BC) David Lyons/©DK Images, (CR) Martin Miller/Photo Researchers, Inc.; **713** (T) ©Thomas Wiewandt, (B) Larry Miller/Photo Researchers, Inc.; **716** (B) blickwinkel/Alamy Images, (CL) Martin & Marli Miller, (T) Tom Bean; **717** (B) Animals Animals/Earth Scenes, (TR) Bruce Roberts/Photo Researchers, Inc.; **719** (T) ©Thomas Wiewandt, (BR) Bernhard Edmaier/Photo Researchers, Inc.; **720** (B) John Buttenkant/Photo Researchers, Inc.; **721** ©MERVYN REES/Alamy Images; **723** (B) ©Radius Images/Alamy; **724** (T) Mark J. Terril/©AP Images; **725** (B) ©Jim Corwin/Photo Researchers, Inc., (T) ©Thomas Wiewandt; **727** (B) ©Dr. R. Legeckis/Photo Researchers, Inc.; **728** (BL) Christophe Boisvieux/Corbis, (BR) George Gerster/Photo Researchers, Inc., (BC) Jason Hawkes/Corbis; **730** (B) Mike Dunning/©DK Images; **731** (TL) Amos Nachoum/Corbis; **732** (T) ©Thomas Wiewandt, (B) Tom Bean; **735** (R) ©The Natural History Museum, London; **738** (TR) ©The Natural History Museum, London, (TL) John Sibbick; **744** Stocktrek/Corbis; **746** (CL) ©AP Images, (B) ©Galen Rowell/Corbis, (TR) Stocktrek/Corbis; **749** (L) ©Paul Seheult/Corbis, (TR) Karl Shone/©DK Images; **752** (TR) Stocktrek/Corbis; **755** (BR) Corbis, (TR) Stocktrek/Corbis; **756** (TR) NASA; **760** (BL) Karl Shone/©DK Images, (TR) Stocktrek/Corbis; **761** (B) ©Ashway/Alamy Images, (T) ©John Warburton-Lee Photography/Alamy Images; **762** (TL) ©Martin Cameron/Alamy Images, (CL) Adam Jones/Photo Researchers, Inc., (BL) David R. Frazier/Photo Researchers, Inc.; **763** (TR) ©blickwinkel/Alamy Images, (B) ©Chris Cheadle/Alamy Images, (TL) Trevor McDonald/Photo Researchers, Inc.; **764** (TL) Kennan Ward/Corbis; **765** (BR) Carl Roessler/Getty Images, (TR) Stocktrek/Corbis; **769** (TR) Science Source/Photo Researchers, Inc.; **770** (L) Tom Sanders/Aerial Focus; **772** (BC, B) NOAA; **773** (BL) ©Matthew Cavanaugh/epa/Corbis; **774** ©Mark A. Schneider/Photo Researchers, Inc., (TR) Stocktrek/Corbis; **775** (TR) Simon Fraser/Photo Researchers, Inc.; **778** (TR) Stocktrek/Corbis; **780** (TL) Daryl Balfour/Getty Images; **781** (TR) Martin & Marli Miller; **782** Deborah Davis /Getty Images; **788** Science Photo Library/Photo Researchers, Inc.; **790** (TR) Science Photo Library/Photo Researchers, Inc., (B) Tom Stack & Associates, Inc.; **791** (TR) Bettmann/Corbis, (TL) Stapleton Collection/Corbis; **794** (TL) NASA Jet Propulsion Laboratory/©AP Images, (BL) Science Source/Photo Researchers, Inc.; **795** (C) ©DK Images, (TR) GRIN/NASA; **796** (B) ©AP Images, (TR) Science Photo Library/Photo Researchers, Inc.; **797** (B) Corbis, (T) Roger Ressmeyer/Corbis; **800** (BR) Frank Zullo/Photo Researchers, Inc., (T) Science Photo Library/Photo Researchers, Inc.; **802** (T) NASA; **803** (TR) Science Photo Library/Photo Researchers, Inc.; **804** (BL) USGS/Science Photo Library/Photo Researchers, Inc.; **805** (B) ©Science Source/Photo Researchers, Inc., (T, C) Tom Stack & Associates, Inc.; **806** (BC) ©Bettmann/Corbis, (CR, BL) NASA, (BL) Ria Novosti/Science Photo Library/Photo Researchers, Inc.; **807** (C) ©DK Images, (BR) Marshall Space Flight Center/NASA Image Exchange, (CR) NASA; **808** (BL) JPL-Caltech/Cornell/NMMNH/NASA, (TR) Photo Researchers, Inc., (TL, TC) Tom Stack & Associates, Inc.; **809** (B) ©JPL/TSADO/Tom Stack & Associates, Inc., (T) Tom Stack & Associates, Inc.; **810** (BL) Photo Researchers, Inc., (TR) Science Photo Library/Photo Researchers, Inc.; **811** (BR) James Stevenson/©DK Images; **812** (B) D. Ducros/Photo Researchers, Inc., (C) NASA, (TL) NASA/Science Photo Library/Photo Researchers, Inc.; **814** (TL) Bettmann/Corbis, (BL) NASA; **815** (CR) DK Images; **816** (BL) ©DK Images, (T) Raymond Turvey /©DK Images; **817** (BL) ©Charles O'Rear/Corbis, (CR) Alan Keohane/©DK Images, (TCL) Getty Images; **818** (TR) Science Photo Library/Photo Researchers, Inc.; **820** (TL) Corbis; **826** (C) David Malin/Anglo-Australian Observatory; **828** (TR) David Malin/Anglo-Australian Observatory, (B) Reed Kaestner/Corbis; **829** (B) Courtesy of SOHO. SOHO is a project of international cooperation between ESA and NASA/NASA; **831** (TR) David Nunuk/Science Photo Library/Photo Researchers, Inc.; **833** (T) ©Roger